FROGGER™

ELEMENTS OF CALCULUS
AND ANALYTIC GEOMETRY

The Addison-Wesley Mathematics Series

Elements of Calculus and Analytic Geometry

George B. Thomas, Jr.
Massachusetts Institute of Technology

Ross L. Finney
Massachusetts Institute of Technology

Addison-Wesley Publishing Company

Menlo Park, California · Reading, Massachusetts
London · Amsterdam · Don Mills, Ontario · Sydney

Books in the *Addison-Wesley Mathematics Series*

ALGEBRA
R. Johnson, L. Lendsey, W. Slesnick

GEOMETRY
E. Moise, F. Downs

ALGEBRA AND TRIGONOMETRY
R. Johnson, L. Lendsey, W. Slesnick, G. Bates

PRE-CALCULUS MATHEMATICS
M. Shanks, C. Fleenor, C. Brumfiel

**ELEMENTS OF CALCULUS AND
ANALYTIC GEOMETRY**
G. Thomas, R. Finney

Cover photo by © Manfred P. Kage/Peter Arnold

ISBN 0-201-07664-0
DEFGHIJKL-DO-88765432

PREFACE

Calculus is a subject in which much can be learned by doing problems. In this text special attention has been given to selecting an unusually ample supply, including some new applications from engineering, the physical sciences, business, economics, and the life sciences. Hand-held calculator exercises are also included.

This book closely follows the recommendations of the Committee on Mathematics of the Advanced Placement Program. It contains the material on analytic geometry and all the material on functions of one variable from the authors' *Calculus and Analytic Geometry*, Fifth Edition. There is also an expanded chapter on infinite series (Chapter 12) and a chapter on differential equations (Chapter 13). This selection of topics meets the requirements set forth in the syllabus of the College Entrance Examination Board for both the AB and BC examinations.

At the request of many users, we have moved several topics toward the front of the book. Trigonometric functions are introduced briefly in Chapter 1. The review of trigonometry and the presentation of differentiation of sines and cosines that used to be in Chapter 6 now appear in Chapter 2. L'Hôpital's rule is presented in Chapter 3, and Newton's method has been moved to Chapter 2. Simpson's rule is now included with the trapezoidal rule in Chapter 4.

The level of rigor is about the same as in earlier editions of *Elements of Calculus and Analytic Geometry*. For example, we do not prove that a function that is continuous on a closed and bounded interval has a maximum on the interval, but we state that theorem and use it in proving the Mean Value Theorem.

The first three chapters present a comprehensive treatment of derivatives of functions of one variable: development of the definition, formulas, and applications. Chapters 4 and 5 are on integration, with applications. Among the new applications are: estimating cardiac output, calculating light output from flashbulbs, determining the average daily inventory of a business, and using Delesse's rule to analyze tissue composition.

Chapter 6 deals with the derivatives of the remaining trigonometric functions, and with the logarithmic and exponential functions. If one wished to include some of the material on hyperbolic functions immediately after

Chapter 6, then the material on methods of integration in Chapter 7 could be expanded to include the six integration formulas that come from the differential formulas XXVII′ to XXXII′ in Article 9–5. Otherwise, it is possible to skip Chapter 9 if one also omits the subsequent problems that involve hyperbolic functions.

Chapter 8 (Plane Analytic Geometry) and Chapter 10 (Polar Coordinates) treat properties of the conic sections, cardioids, and other standard topics, including areas and arc length.

Chapter 11 (Vectors and Parametric Equations) introduces vector geometry, and vector functions and their derivatives. The material in the chapter has been reordered so that the introduction to components and the algebra of vector addition precedes the application of vectors to parametric equations in kinematics. There is a new article on derivatives of vector functions. The chapter concludes with a derivation of the fact from astronomy that the line joining a planet with its sun sweeps over equal areas in equal times (Kepler's second law of planetary motion in a central force field).

Chapter 12 (Infinite Series) has been completely rewritten, and now contains twice the number of examples and exercises. Sequences are treated first, and separately from series. More attention is paid to estimation. The chapter also introduces a new and surprisingly simple algorithm (Salamin's algorithm) for estimating pi. The treatment of differentiation and integration of power series with which the chapter concludes gives students access to a useful technique for estimating the values of a number of definite integrals that cannot be evaluated with standard formulas.

Chapter 13 (Differential Equations) now includes an introduction to the method of undetermined coefficients. New examples and applications are provided, such as electric circuits, vibrations, carbon-14 dating, growth of bacteria, and the determination of blood sugar.

The basic formulas from the prerequisite subjects—algebra, geometry, and trigonometry—are collected for reference in an appendix at the end of the book. In general, however, the more difficult formulas are reviewed in the text at the time they are needed. The authors' experience, both as students and teachers, indicates that one by-product of a good calculus course is likely to be a much firmer grasp of the fundamental skills of high-school mathematics. This is particularly true when the student supplies the missing steps in illustrative exercises and examples.

Answers for most of the problems are given and are keyed to the text by page, as well as by problem number, article, and chapter. The answers that are new to this edition were provided by Paul H. Siegel and Daniel W. Litwhiler. We are grateful to them for this valuable help, and we continue to be grateful to our friends and colleagues who contributed solutions and problems to earlier editions.

Many students, colleagues, and friends have given us the benefit of their criticism and suggestions. We would especially like to mention the valuable contributions of Carl W. R. de Boor, Felicia De May, Fred A. Franklin, William A. Ferguson, Solomon Garfunkel, Andrew D. Jorgensen, William Ted Martin, Arthur P. Mattuck, Eric Reissner, J. Barkley Rosser, Oliver G. Selfridge, Donald R. Sherbert, Norton Starr, William U. Walton, and Martha Zelinka. But even with the addition of the reviewers mentioned separately, this list is far from complete. To each and every person who has at any time contributed helpful suggestions, comments, or criticisms, whether or not we have been able to incorporate these into the books, we say "Thank you very much."

It is a pleasure to acknowledge the superb assistance in illustration, editing, design, and composition that the staff of Addison-Wesley Publishing Company has given to the preparation of this edition. The senior author also acknowledges with gratitude the special talent and productivity beyond his expectation that his co-author has brought to this new edition.

Any errors that may appear are the responsibility of the authors. We will appreciate having these brought to our attention.

May 1980   G. B. T., Jr.
                                                                   R. L. F.

ACKNOWLEDGMENTS

The authors would like to thank the following reviewers for the quality of their attention and for their many thoughtful suggestions.

Kenneth C. Abernethy	Virginia Military Institute
Fred G. Brauer	University of Wisconsin at Madison
William R. Fuller	Purdue University
Douglas Hall	Michigan State University
Roger B. Hooper	University of Maine
William Perry	Texas A & M University
David Rearick	University of Colorado
Robert D. Stalley	Oregon State University
Virginia Skinner	El Camino College
G. Wayne Sullivan	Volunteer State Community College
Dwann Veroda	El Camino College
Martha Zelinka	Weston High School

AVAILABLE SUPPLEMENTS

The following supplementary materials are available for student use:

Pocket Calculator Supplement by J. Barkley Rosser and Carl W. R. de Boor (University of Wisconsin at Madison)

This text has two goals: to use the calculator to carry out numerical experiments that illuminate points made in the calculus course, and to show how calculus techniques can make the calculator a more efficient tool. The various chapters are concerned with particular calculator topics such as Root Finding, Sources of Error, etc., rather than specific chapters of the Calculus text. **Order Code: 6502**

Self-Study Manual for *Elements of Calculus and Analytic Geometry* by Maurice D. Weir (Naval Postgraduate School, Monterey, CA)

This manual is designed to assist students in mastering the basic ideas of calculus by presenting the objectives, theorems, concepts, and techniques of each section of "Elements" in a semi-programmed format with complete answers. Key problems for each objective are identified, and a self-test on each chapter completes the material. **Order Code: 7667**

You may order these materials directly from the publisher. Write to

Addison-Wesley Publishing Company
2725 Sand Hill Road
Menlo Park, CA 94025

CONTENTS

THE RATE OF
CHANGE OF A FUNCTION

⊢—⊐
INTRODUCTION

Calculus is the mathematics of change and motion. Where there is motion or growth, where forces are at work producing acceleration, calculus is the right mathematical tool. This was true in the beginnings of the subject, and it is true today. Calculus is used to predict the orbits of earth satellites; to design inertial navigation systems, cyclotrons, and radar systems; to explore problems of space travel; to test scientific theories about ocean currents and the dynamics of the atmosphere; and to model economic, social, and psychological behavior. Calculus is used increasingly to model problems in the fields of business, biology, medicine, animal husbandry, and political science. Of course, a scientist needs a great deal more than mathematical competence, and needs more mathematics than calculus. But calculus is a tool of great importance and usefulness and is a prerequisite for further study in nearly all branches of higher mathematics.

One of the great mathematicians of the twentieth century, John von Neumann (1903–57), wrote: "The calculus was the first achievement of modern mathematics, and it is difficult to overestimate its importance. I think it defines more unequivocally than anything else the inception of modern mathematics; and the system of mathematical analysis, which is its logical development, still constitutes the greatest technical advance in exact thinking."*

Calculus provides methods for solving two large classes of problems. The first of these involves finding the rate at which a variable quantity is changing. When a body travels in a straight line, its distance from its starting point changes with time and we may ask *how fast* it is moving at any given instant. *Differential calculus* is the branch of calculus that treats such problems.

On the other hand, if we are given the *velocity* of a moving body at every instant of time, we may seek to find the distance it has moved as a function of time. This second type of problem, that of finding a function when its rate of change is known, belongs to the domain of *integral calculus*.

Modern science and engineering use both branches of calculus to express physical laws in precise mathematical terms, and to study the consequences of those laws. It was with calculus that Sir Isaac Newton (1642–1727) was able to explain the motion of the planets about the sun as a consequence of the physical assumption known today as the law of gravitational attraction. Kepler (1571–1630) spent some twenty years studying observational data and using empirical methods to discover the three laws now known as Kepler's laws:

a) Each planet traces an orbit about the sun which is an ellipse with the sun at one focus.

b) The line joining the planet and the sun sweeps over equal areas in equal intervals of time.

c) The squares of the periods of revolution of the planets about the sun are proportional to the cubes of their mean distances from the sun.

---

* World of Mathematics, Vol. 4, "The Mathematician," by John von Neumann, pp. 2053–2063.

With the calculus as the main mathematical tool, all three of these laws can be derived from Newton's laws of gravitation and motion.

German mathematician and philosopher Gottfried Wilhelm Leibniz (1646–1716) independently developed a large part of the calculus. His notation has been widely adopted in preference to Newton's.

Analytic geometry, which forms a third division of the subject matter of this book, was the creation of several mathematicians.* Two French mathematicians, René Descartes (1596–1650) and Pierre de Fermat (1601–1665), are the chief inventors of analytic geometry as we now know it. The idea of locating a point in the plane by means of its directed distances from two perpendicular axes is Descartes', and his name is commemorated in the terminology "Cartesian coordinates." We discuss coordinates in Article 1–2. The distinguishing characteristic of analytic geometry is that it uses algebraic methods and equations to gain information about geometric problems. Conversely, it lets us portray algebraic equations as geometric curves, and thus bring the tools of geometry to bear on algebraic problems. Most of the theory of calculus can be presented in geometrical terms, and calculus and analytic geometry may be profitably united and studied as a whole.

The connection between algebra and geometry in analytic geometry is made by setting up a one-to-one correspondence between the points of a plane and ordered pairs of numbers (x, y). There are many ways to establish such a correspondence. The one most commonly used is the one described here.

A line in the plane, extending indefinitely to the left and to the right, is chosen, defined to be horizontal, and called the *x-axis* or *axis of abscissas*. (See Fig. 1–1.) A point of origin O on this line and a unit of length are then chosen. The axis is scaled off in terms of this unit. The number zero is attached to O, the number $+a$ is attached to the point which is a units to the right of O, and the number $-a$ is attached to the point located symmetrically to the left of O. This establishes a one-to-one correspondence between the points of the x-axis and the set of all *real numbers* (numbers which may be represented by terminating or nonterminating decimals).

Now through O take a second, vertical line in the plane, extending indefinitely up and down. This line is to be the *y-axis*, or *axis of ordinates*. The unit of length used to represent $+1$ on the y-axis need not be the one used to represent $+1$ on the x-axis. The y-axis is scaled off in terms of the unit of length adopted for it, with the positive number $+b$ attached to the point b units above O and the negative number $-b$ attached to the point located symmetrically b units below O.

We are now ready to assign number pairs to points. If a line perpendicular to the x-axis is drawn through the point marked a, and another line is

1-2
COORDINATES

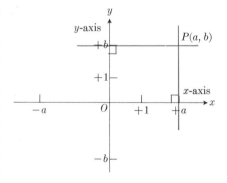

1–1 The line perpendicular to the x-axis at a and the line perpendicular to the y-axis at b cross at $P(a, b)$.

---

* See *World of Mathematics*, Vol. 1, "Commentary on Descartes and Analytical Geometry," pp. 235–37. Also the article "The Invention of Analytic Geometry," by Carl B. Boyer, *Scientific American*, January, 1949.

drawn perpendicular to the y-axis at b, their point of intersection is labeled $P(a, b)$. The number a is the *x-coordinate* of P, and the number b is the *y-coordinate* of P. The pair (a, b) is called the *coordinate pair* of the point P. Note that (a, b) is an *ordered pair*; we list the x-coordinate first and the y-coordinate second.

To be sure that none of the points in the plane has been missed, we can start with any point P and draw lines through it perpendicular to the two axes. If these perpendiculars cross the x- and y-axes at a and b, then P has already been assigned the coordinate pair (a, b).

Points can never be assigned more than one coordinate pair; when we drop perpendiculars from $P(a, b)$ to the axes the perpendiculars must meet the axes at a and b. Only one perpendicular can be drawn from a point to a line.

The two axes divide the plane into four quadrants, called the first quadrant, second quadrant, and so on, as in Fig. 1–2.

There are times when there is no physical relation between the units used to measure x and y. For example, if y is the maximum number of minutes that a diver can stay at a depth of x meters without having to stop to decompress on the way up, then the "1" on the x-axis stands for one meter, while the "1" on the y-axis stands for one minute. Clearly, there is no need to mark the two 1's the same number of millimeters, or whatever, from the origin.

In surveying, on the other hand, one foot measured north-and-south should be the same as one foot measured east-and-west. For this reason, it is usually assumed in trigonometry that the units of length on the two axes are the same. We make this assumption in analytic geometry also.

In this book, if coordinates of points are given without any physical units attached, it is to be assumed that the scales on the two axes are the same. In particular, this assumption is made wherever our work involves angles between lines or lengths of line segments that are not parallel to the axes.

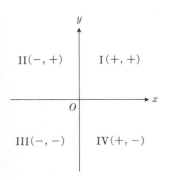

1–2   The four quadrants.

PROBLEMS

In each of the following problems (1–12), first draw a pair of coordinate axes. Then plot the given point $P(a, b)$ and plot:

a) The point Q such that PQ is perpendicular to the x-axis and is bisected by it. Give the coordinates of Q. (P and Q are symmetric with respect to the x-axis.)

b) The point R such that PR is perpendicular to and is bisected by the y-axis. Give the coordinates of R. (P and R are symmetric with respect to the y-axis.)

c) The point S such that PS is bisected by the origin. Give the coordinates of S. (P and S are symmetric with respect to the origin.)

d) The point T such that PT is perpendicular to and is bisected by the 45° line L through the origin bisecting the first quadrant and the third. Give the coordinates of T,

assuming equal units on the axes. (P and T are symmetric with respect to L.)

1. $(1, -2)$	**2.** $(2, -1)$	**3.** $(-2, 2)$
4. $(-2, 1)$	**5.** $(0, 1)$	**6.** $(1, 0)$
7. $(-2, 0)$	**8.** $(0, -3)$	**9.** $(-1, -3)$
10. $(\sqrt{2}, -\sqrt{2})$	**11.** $(-\pi, -\pi)$	**12.** $(-1.5, 2.3)$

13. If $P = P(x, y)$, then the coordinates of the point Q described in (a) above can be expressed in terms of x and y as $(x, -y)$. Express the coordinates of R, S, and T in terms of x and y.

In Problems 14–17, take the units of length on the two axes to be equal.

14. A line is drawn through the point $(0, 0)$ and the point $(1, 1)$. What acute angle does it make with the positive x-axis? Sketch.

15. There are three parallelograms with vertices at $(-1, 1)$, $(2, 0)$, and $(2, 3)$. Sketch them and give the coordinate pairs of the missing vertices.

16. A circle in quadrant II is tangent to both axes. It touches the y-axis at $(0, 3)$.

a) At what point does it meet the x-axis? Sketch.

b) What are the coordinates of the center of the circle?

17. The line through the points $(1, 1)$ and $(2, 0)$ cuts the y-axis at the point $(0, b)$. Find b by using similar triangles.

If a particle starts at a point $P_1(x_1, y_1)$ and goes to a new position $P_2(x_2, y_2)$, we say that its coordinates have changed by increments Δx (read *delta x*) and Δy (read *delta y*). For example, if the particle moves from $A(1, -2)$ to $B(6, 7)$, as in Fig. 1–3, then these increments are

$$\Delta x = 5, \qquad \Delta y = 9.$$

1–3
INCREMENTS

Observe that the *increment* in a coordinate is the *net change*, given by

$$\Delta x = (x \text{ of terminal point}) - (x \text{ of initial point})$$

and

$$\Delta y = (y \text{ of terminal point}) - (y \text{ of initial point}).$$

The positions the particle occupies between its initial and terminal locations do not affect these net changes.

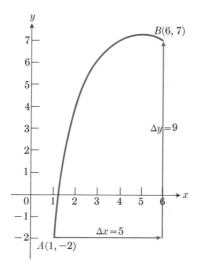

1–3   When a particle moves from one point to another, Δx and Δy are computed from the coordinates of the initial and terminal positions:

$$\Delta x = 6 - 1 = 5, \qquad \Delta y = 7 - (-2) = 9.$$

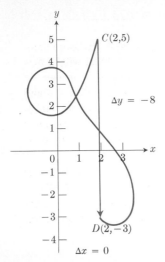

1–4 The net change in the x-coordinate in moving from $C(2, 5)$ to $D(2, -3)$ is zero.

If the initial position of a particle is $P_1(x_1, y_1)$ and its terminal position is $P_2(x_2, y_2)$, then we compute the increments Δx and Δy by the formulas

$$\Delta x = x_2 - x_1, \qquad \Delta y = y_2 - y_1.$$

Either increment can be any real number: positive, negative, or zero. The increments from $C(2, 5)$ to $D(2, -3)$ in Fig. 1–4, for example, are

$$\Delta x = 2 - 2 = 0, \qquad \Delta y = -3 - 5 = -8.$$

The net change in x from C to D is zero. The y-coordinate decreases by 8 as we move from C to D.

If the same unit of measurement is used on both coordinate axes, we can express all distances in the plane in terms of this common unit. We use the Pythagorean theorem, as shown in Fig. 1–5. The distance d between two points $P_1(x_1, y_1)$ and $P_2(x_2, y_2)$ is the length of the hypotenuse. It can be computed as:

$$d = \sqrt{(\Delta x)^2 + (\Delta y)^2} = \sqrt{(x_2 - x_1)^2 + (y_2 - y_1)^2}.$$

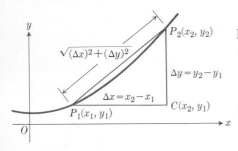

1–5 Distance is calculated with the Pythagorean theorem.

EXAMPLE 1. If a particle starts from $P_1(-1, 2)$ and goes straight to $P_2(2, -2)$, then its x-coordinate changes by

$$\Delta x = x_2 - x_1 = 2 - (-1) = 3.$$

Its y-coordinate changes by

$$\Delta y = y_2 - y_1 = -2 - 2 = -4.$$

The distance between P_1 and P_2 is

$$d = \sqrt{(\Delta x)^2 + (\Delta y)^2} = \sqrt{(3)^2 + (-4)^2} = \sqrt{9 + 16} = 5.$$

EXAMPLE 2. The set of all points whose distance from the origin is a positive number r is a circle whose radius is r and whose center is the origin. The coordinates of any point $P(x, y)$ on this circle satisfy the equation

$$\sqrt{(x - 0)^2 + (y - 0)^2} = r,$$

or

$$\sqrt{x^2 + y^2} = r,$$

or

$$x^2 + y^2 = r^2.$$

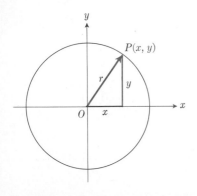

1–6 $x^2 + y^2 = r^2$, for points on the circle of radius r centered at $(0, 0)$.

(See Fig. 1–6.)

PROBLEMS

In Problems 1 through 6, a particle moves in the plane from A to B. Point C is to be found at the intersection of the horizontal line through A and the vertical line through B. Sketch, and find

a) the coordinates of C **b)** Δx **c)** Δy

d) the length of AB under the assumption that the x-axis and y-axis have the same units.

  1. $A(-1, 1)$, $B(1, 2)$ **2.** $A(1, 2)$, $B(-1, -1)$

  3. $A(-3, 2)$, $B(-1, -2)$ **4.** $A(-1, -2)$, $B(-3, 2)$

  5. $A(-3, 1)$, $B(-8, 1)$ **6.** $A(0, 4)$, $B(0, -2)$

In Problems 7 through 10, write an equation that must be satisfied by the coordinates of a point $P(x, y)$ if P is to lie on the circle of radius 5 whose center is at the given point. It may help to sketch the circle first.

  7. $(0, 0)$ **8.** $(5, 0)$ **9.** $(-3, 4)$ **10.** (h, k)

11. If a particle starts at $A(-2, 3)$ and its coordinates change by increments $\Delta x = 5$, $\Delta y = -6$, what will its new position be?

12. The coordinates of a particle change by $\Delta x = 5$ and $\Delta y = 6$ in moving from $A(x, y)$ to $B(3, -3)$. Find x and y.

13. Find the starting position of a particle whose terminal position is $B(u, v)$ after its coordinates have changed by increments $\Delta x = h$, and $\Delta y = k$.

14. A particle moves from the point $A(-2, 5)$ to the y-axis in such a way that $\Delta y = 3\Delta x$. What are its new coordinates?

15. A particle moves along the parabola $y = x^2$ from the point $A(1, 1)$ to the point $B(x, y)$. Sketch the parabola and show that

$$\frac{\Delta y}{\Delta x} = x + 1 \quad \text{if } \Delta x \neq 0.$$

SLOPE OF A STRAIGHT LINE

Lines in the coordinate plane rise or fall at a steady rate as we move along them from left to right, unless, of course, they are horizontal or vertical. Horizontal lines do not rise or fall at all, and on a vertical line one cannot move from left to right. The rate of rise or fall as we move from left to right along a line is called the *slope* of the line. We measure slopes in such a way that rising lines have positive slopes, falling lines have negative slopes, and horizontal lines slope 0. Vertical lines are not assigned any slope.

    To begin, let L be a line in the plane that is not parallel to the y-axis, and let $P_1(x_1, y_1)$ and $P_2(x_2, y_2)$ be any two distinct points on L (see Fig. 1-7). As we move along L from P_1 to P_2, the increment $\Delta y = y_2 - y_1$ is called the *rise* from P_1 to P_2. The increment $\Delta x = x_2 - x_1$ is called the *run* from P_1 to P_2. Since L is not vertical, $\Delta x \neq 0$, and we define the *slope* of L to be

$$\frac{\text{rise}}{\text{run}} = \frac{\Delta y}{\Delta x} = \frac{y_2 - y_1}{x_2 - x_1} = m. \tag{1}$$

It is traditional to use the letter m to denote slope.

    Figure 1-7 shows both Δx and Δy to be positive, but either one, or both, could be negative, depending on the inclination of L and on the choice of P_1 and P_2. However, the ratio $\Delta y/\Delta x$ of these two quantities does not depend on how we choose P_1 and P_2 from L. It depends only on the inclination of L. There are two reasons for this:

1. When we choose the two points P_1 and P_2 from L it does not matter which we call P_1 and which we call P_2. If we interchange the labels P_1 and

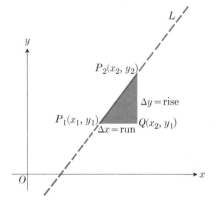

1-7 The slope of this line is $\Delta y/\Delta x = m$.

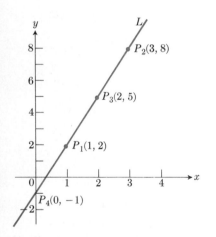

1–8 $\Delta y/\Delta x = \Delta y'/\Delta x'$ because the ratios of corresponding sides of similar triangles are equal.

P_2 the number we calculate as m is the same as before, because

$$\frac{y_1 - y_2}{x_1 - x_2} = \frac{y_2 - y_1}{x_2 - x_1}. \qquad (2)$$

2. If we start with any other two points from L, say $P'_1(x'_1, y'_1)$ and $P'_2(x'_2, y'_2)$, the number m' we get for the slope is the same as m. Why? Because the triangles $P_1 Q P_2$ and $P'_1 Q' P'_2$ in Fig. 1–8 are similar. Thus,

$$m' = \frac{\Delta y'}{\Delta x'} = \frac{\Delta y}{\Delta x} = m. \qquad (3)$$

EXAMPLE 1. The slope of the line through the points $P_1(1, 2)$ and $P_2(3, 8)$ in Fig. 1–9 is

$$m = \frac{8 - 2}{3 - 1} = 3.$$

If we take P_2 first and P_1 second, we obtain

$$m = \frac{2 - 8}{1 - 3} = \frac{-6}{-2} = 3,$$

the same as before.

REMARK. If we multiply both sides of the equation $\Delta y/\Delta x = m$ by Δx, we obtain

$$\Delta y = m\, \Delta x. \qquad (4)$$

This means that as a particle moves along L, the change in y is proportional to the change in x. The slope m is the proportionality factor. The slope is the rate of rise per unit of run. To compute the amount of rise, multiply the slope by the amount of run.

EXAMPLE 2. If (x, y) and $(x + \Delta x, y + \Delta y)$ are any two points on the line L in Fig. 1–9, then

$$\Delta y = 3\, \Delta x.$$

Starting from $P_1(1, 2)$, if we increase x by 1 unit we increase y by 3 units, bringing us to the point $P_3(2, 5)$. Or, if we decrease x by 1 unit, we *decrease y* by 3 units, taking us to $P_4(0, -1)$.

1–9 $\Delta y = 3 \Delta x$ for every change of position on this line.

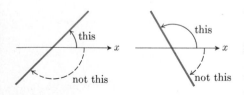

1–10 Angles of inclination.

The *angle of inclination* of a line that crosses the x-axis is the smallest positive angle that the line makes with the positively directed x-axis (Fig. 1–10). (Positive angles are measured counterclockwise.) The angle of inclination of a line that does not cross the x-axis is 0. Thus, angles of inclination may have any measure from $0°$ up to but not including $180°$.

Slopes and angles of inclination are related in the following way. The slope of a nonvertical line is the tangent of its angle of inclination:

$$m = \tan \phi. \tag{5}$$

(See Fig. 1–11.)

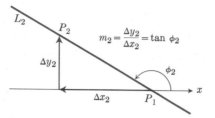

Both Δx_1 and Δy_1 are positive, so m_1 is positive.

Here, Δx_2 is negative but Δy_2 is positive. Therefore, m_2 is negative.

1–11　In each picture m is $\tan \phi$.

EXAMPLE 3.　Figures 1–12 and 1–13 give numerical examples of Eq. (5).

Lines whose inclination angles are near 90° have slopes that are numerically very large.

$$\phi_1 = 89°59' \qquad m_1 = \tan \phi_1 \approx 3437.7$$

$$\phi_2 = 90°01' \qquad m_2 = \tan \phi_2 \approx -3437.7$$

In fact we can make the slope numerically larger than any preassigned number N by taking ϕ still closer to 90°. This point is sometimes summarized by saying that "a vertical line has infinite slope," or "the slope of a line becomes infinite as its angle of inclination approaches 90°." But, strictly speaking, we do not assign *any* real number to be the slope of a *vertical* line.

The symbol ∞ is used to represent "infinity." However, we do not use this symbol in arithmetic in the ordinary way. Infinity is not a real number. We used the phrase "becomes infinite" in the preceding paragraph only as a way to say "outgrows every preassigned real number."

Parallel lines have equal angles of inclination. Hence, in general, they have equal slopes (Fig. 1–14). The only exception is when the parallel lines are vertical, for then they have no slope at all (Fig. 1–15). [*Caution.* This does not mean that they have zero slope.]

Two lines that have equal slopes $m_1 = \tan \phi_1$ and $m_2 = \tan \phi_2$ also have equal angles of inclination. The reason is this: If

$$\tan \phi_1 = \tan \phi_2 \tag{6}$$

and

$$0 \leq \phi_1 < 180°, \qquad 0 \leq \phi_2 < 180°, \tag{7}$$

then $\phi_1 = \phi_2$.

When two nonvertical lines are *perpendicular*, their slopes m_1 and m_2 are related by the equation

$$m_1 = -\frac{1}{m_2} \qquad \text{or} \qquad m_1 m_2 = -1. \tag{8}$$

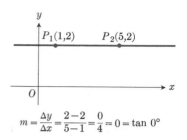

$$m = \frac{\Delta y}{\Delta x} = \frac{2-2}{5-1} = \frac{0}{4} = 0 = \tan 0°$$

Figure 1–12

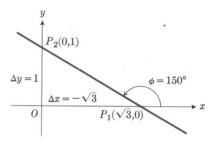

$$m = \frac{\Delta y}{\Delta x} = \frac{1-0}{0-\sqrt{3}} = \frac{1}{-\sqrt{3}} = \tan 150°$$

Figure 1–13

1–14　When parallel lines are not vertical, they have the same slope, $\tan \phi$.

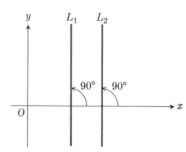

1–15　Parallel vertical lines have equal angles of inclination, but no slope. Note that $\tan \phi$ is not defined when $\phi = 90°$.

To see why, note that the angles of inclination of the lines differ by 90°, so that

$$\phi_2 = 90° + \phi_1,$$

as shown in Fig. 1–16. (If not, just renumber the lines.) This lets us write m_2 as

$$m_2 = \tan \phi_2 = \tan (90° + \phi_1) = -\cot \phi_1 = -\frac{1}{\tan \phi_1} = -\frac{1}{m_1}.$$

The argument can be reversed to show that two lines whose slopes satisfy Eq. (8) have angles of inclination that differ by 90°.

1–16 The exterior angle theorem of geometry says that $\phi_2 = 90° + \phi_1$ in this figure. This in turn means that $m_1m_2 = -1$, as explained in the text.

PROBLEMS

Plot the given points A and B, and find the slope (if any) of the line determined by them. Find the slope of a line perpendicular to AB, in each case.

1. $A(1, -2)$, $B(2, 1)$ 2. $A(-2, -1)$, $B(1, -2)$
3. $A(1, 0)$, $B(0, 1)$ 4. $A(-1, 0)$, $B(1, 0)$
5. $A(2, 3)$, $B(-1, 3)$ 6. $A(1, 2)$, $B(1, -3)$
7. $A(0, 0)$, $B(-2, -4)$ 8. $A(\frac{1}{2}, 0)$, $B(0, -\frac{1}{3})$
9. $A(0, 0)$, $B(x, y)$ $(x \neq 0, y \neq 0)$
10. $A(0, 0)$, $B(x, 0)$ $(x \neq 0)$
11. $A(0, 0)$, $B(0, y)$ $(y \neq 0)$
12. $A(a, 0)$, $B(0, b)$ $(a \neq 0, b \neq 0)$

In Problems 13–16, plot the points A, B, C, and D. Then determine whether or not $ABCD$ is a parallelogram. Say which parallelograms are rectangles.

13. $A(0, 1)$, $B(1, 2)$, $C(2, 1)$, $D(1, 0)$
14. $A(-2, 2)$, $B(1, 3)$, $C(2, 0)$, $D(-1, -1)$
15. $A(-1, -2)$, $B(2, -1)$, $C(2, 1)$, $D(1, 0)$
16. $A(-1, 0)$, $B(0, -1)$, $C(2, 0)$, $D(0, 2)$

Answer the next two questions by measuring slopes in Fig. 1–17.

17. Find the rate of change of temperature in degrees per inch for:

a) gypsum wall board   b) fiberglass insulation

c) wood sheathing

18. Which of the materials just listed is the best insulator? the poorest? Explain.

19. The line through the origin and $P(x, y)$ has slope $+2$, and the line through $(-1, 0)$ and $P(x, y)$ has slope $+1$. Find x and y.

20. Sketch the line L that passes through the origin with slope $-\frac{1}{2}$. Show that if $P(x, y)$ lies on L, then $y = -(x/2)$.

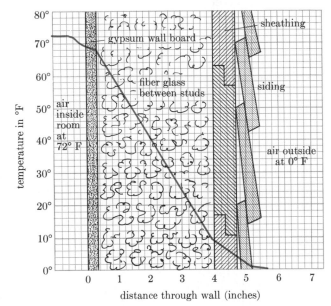

1–17 Temperature gradients in a wall. (*Source: Differentiation*, by W. U. Walton *et al.*, Project CALC, Education Development Center, Inc., Newton, Mass. (1975); p. 25.)

In Problems 21–23, use slopes to determine whether the given points are collinear (lie on a common straight line).

21. $A(1, 0)$, $B(0, 1)$, $C(2, -1)$
22. $A(-2, 1)$, $B(0, 5)$, $C(-1, 2)$
23. $A(-2, 1)$, $B(-1, 1)$, $C(1, 5)$, $D(2, 7)$
24. Let $P_1(x_1, y_1)$ and $P_2(x_2, y_2)$ be two points. Find the coordinates of the midpoint of the segment $P_1 P_2$.

We continue the development of analytic geometry in this article by finding equations for lines in the coordinate plane. An *equation for a line* is an equation that is satisfied by the coordinates of the points that lie on the line and is not satisfied by the coordinates of the points that lie elsewhere. Lines that have slopes and lines that do not have slopes will be treated separately.

We start with a line L that is perpendicular to the x-axis at $(x_1, 0)$. Every point on L has its first coordinate equal to x_1. Its second coordinate can be any number. In other words, the coordinates of the points (x, y) that lie on L all satisfy the equation

$$x = x_1. \tag{1}$$

(See Fig. 1–18.) To check that $x = x_1$ is an equation for L, it remains to show that the points of the plane that are not on L have first coordinates different from x_1. They all do, because the perpendiculars from these points to the x-axis do not cross the axis at x_1.

To write an equation for a line L that is not vertical, we may start with its slope m, together with the coordinates of a point $P_1(x_1, y_1)$ on L. If $P(x, y)$ is any other point of L, then we can write the slope of L as

$$\frac{y - y_1}{x - x_1} = m, \tag{2}$$

or

$$y - y_1 = m(x - x_1). \tag{3}$$

(See Fig. 1–19.) If $P(x, y)$ coincides with $P_1(x_1, y_1)$ then its coordinates still satisfy Eq. (3). Thus the coordinates of all the points that lie on L satisfy Eq. (3). If $P(x, y)$ is a point not on L, then the slope of PP_1 is different from m. This means that the coordinates x and y of P do not satisfy Eq. (2), and therefore do not satisfy Eq. (3). It follows that Eq. (3) is an equation for L.

EXAMPLE 1. Write an equation for the line through $(-2, -1)$ and $(3, 4)$.

Solution. The slope of the line is

$$\frac{4 - (-1)}{3 - (-2)} = \frac{5}{5} = 1.$$

Either of the given points $(-2, -1)$ or $(3, 4)$ will serve as the point (x_1, y_1) in Eq. (3), as shown below:

Using $(3, 4)$ we obtain

$$y - 4 = 1 \cdot (x - 3),$$
$$y - 4 = x - 3$$
$$y = x + 1.$$

Using $(-2, -1)$ we obtain

$$y - (-1) = 1 \cdot (x - (-2)),$$
$$y + 1 = x + 2,$$
$$y = x + 1.$$

EQUATIONS OF STRAIGHT LINES

1–18 $x = x_1$ is an equation for the vertical line through the point $(x_1, 0)$.

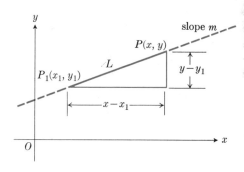

1–19 L is the line through $P_1(x_1, y_1)$ whose slope is m. A point $P(x, y)$ lies on L if and only if $P = P_1$ or slope $PP_1 = m$.

We get the same equation no matter which point we use. The line is shown in Fig. 1–20.

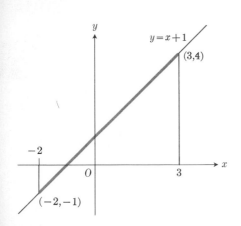

1–20   The line $y = x + 1$. The segment corresponding to $-2 \le x \le 3$ is shaded.

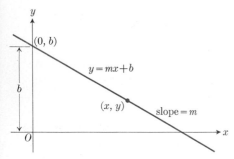

1–21   The line $y = mx + b$ has slope m and y-intercept b.

Equation (3) is called the *point–slope* form of the equation of the line, since it gives the equation in terms of one point $P_1(x_1, y_1)$ on the line and the slope m. The three numbers x_1, y_1, and m are constants, while x and y are variables. By a *variable* we mean a symbol, such as x, which may take any value in some set of numbers. In Eq. (3), x may take any real value whatever. As x varies continuously from a negative value $-N$ to a positive value $+M$, the corresponding point $P(x, y)$ traces an unbroken portion of the line from left to right.

When we solve Eq. (3) for y we find that

$$y = mx + b, \tag{4}$$

where m is the slope of the line and b is $y_1 - mx_1$, which is a constant. In fact, $(0, b)$ is the point where the line crosses the y-axis (Fig. 1–21). The number b is called the *y-intercept* of the line, and Eq. (4) is called the *slope–intercept equation* of the line.

EXAMPLE 2.   The slope–intercept equation of the line

$$y - 7 = 5(x + 4)$$

is

$$y = 5x + 27.$$

The slope is $m = 5$ and the intercept is $b = 27$.

For a horizontal line, the equation $y = mx + b$ reduces to $y = 0 \cdot x + b$, or

$$y = b.$$

EXAMPLE 3.   The equation $y = -5$ is the slope–intercept equation of the line that passes through $(0, -5)$ with slope $m = 0$.

More generally, an equation

$$Ax + By + C = 0, \tag{5}$$

where A, B, and C are constants with at least one of A and B different from zero, represents a *straight line*.

$$\text{If } B = 0, \quad \text{then } Ax + C = 0 \quad \text{and } x = -\frac{C}{A},$$

and the line is a vertical line, as in Eq. (1). On the other hand,

$$\text{if } B \ne 0, \quad \text{then } y = -\frac{A}{B}x - \frac{C}{B},$$

and this represents a straight line with

$$m = -\frac{A}{B}, \quad b = -\frac{C}{B}.$$

An equation like (5) that contains only first powers of x and y is said to be "linear in x and in y." Thus we may summarize our discussion by saying that every straight line in the plane is represented by a linear equation and, conversely, every linear equation represents a straight line.

EXAMPLE 4. Find the slope of the line $2x + 3y = 5$.

Solution. By solving $2x + 3y = 5$ for y, we obtain the slope–intercept form $y = -\frac{2}{3}x + \frac{5}{3}$. The slope is $m = -\frac{2}{3}$.

Lines that cross both axes have nonzero slopes, and, if they do not pass through the origin, so that $b \neq 0$, dividing both sides of $y = mx + b$ by b leads to an equation of the form

$$\frac{x}{a} + \frac{y}{b} = 1, \tag{6}$$

where $a = -b/m$. When $x = 0$, Eq. (6) simplifies to $y = b$, the y-intercept. When $y = 0$, Eq. (6) simplifies to $x = a$, the x-intercept. We call Eq. (6) the *two-intercept equation* of the line.

EXAMPLE 5. The line through $(-3, 0)$ and $(0, 4)$ has x-intercept $a = -3$ and y-intercept $b = 4$. The two-intercept equation of the line is

$$\frac{x}{-3} + \frac{y}{4} = 1.$$

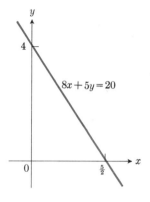

1–22 To draw this graph, the intercepts were located first.

A quick way to graph a line that crosses both axes is this: Find the intercepts, mark them on the axes, and sketch the line through the marked points.

EXAMPLE 6. Graph the line $8x + 5y = 20$.

Solution. Find the x-intercept: Set $y = 0$ in the equation to obtain $8x = 20$, or $x = \frac{5}{2}$. Find the y-intercept: Set $x = 0$ in the equation to obtain $5y = 20$, or $y = 4$. Then mark the intercepts on a pair of axes and sketch the line (Fig. 1–22).

EXAMPLE 7. (*Demand*) The demand for a product, x (number of units sold), and the price p per unit of the product are sometimes related by a linear equation of the form

$$\frac{x}{x_0} + \frac{p}{p_0} = 1, \tag{7}$$

where x_0 and p_0 are constants. The equation is the *demand law* for the product. The graph of the equation, in this case the line in Fig. 1–23, is called the *demand curve.*

The quantities x and p are never negative in their economic context. Therefore, only the points from $(x_0, 0)$ to $(0, p_0)$ on the graph of Eq. (7) have coordinates with economic meaning. The intercepts x_0 and p_0 can have the following interpretations. The demand x_0 is the demand for a "free" product,

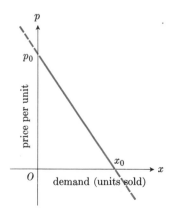

1–23 The graph of a demand law shows how consumer demand responds to different prices of a product.

because it corresponds to $p = 0$. The demand disappears at the price p_0. (See Problem 19.)

Table 1–1 summarizes the representative equations for straight lines, including vertical and horizontal lines.

Table 1–1   Equations of lines

$Ax + By + C = 0$	Linear equation (general form)
$y - y_1 = m(x - x_1)$	Point–slope equation
$y = mx + b$	Slope–intercept equation
$\dfrac{x}{a} + \dfrac{y}{b} = 1$	Two-intercept equation
$x = a$	Vertical line
$y = b$	Horizontal line

PROBLEMS

In each of the following problems (1 through 10), plot the given pair of points and find an equation for the line determined by them.

1. $(0, 0)$, $(2, 3)$ **2.** $(1, 1)$, $(2, 1)$

3. $(1, 1)$, $(1, 2)$ **4.** $(-2, 1)$, $(2, -2)$

5. $(-2, 0)$, $(-2, -2)$ **6.** $(1, 3)$, $(3, 1)$

7. $(a, 0)$, $(0, b)$ $(a \neq 0, b \neq 0)$

8. $(0, 0)$, $(1, 0)$ **9.** $(0, 0)$, $(0, 1)$

10. $(2, -1)$, $(-2, 3)$

In each of the following problems (11 through 18), find the slope and intercepts of the line. Then graph the line.

11. $y = 3x + 5$ **12.** $2y = 3x + 5$

13. $x + y = 2$ **14.** $2x - y = 4$

15. $x - 2y = 4$ **16.** $3x + 4y = 12$

17. $4x - 3y = 12$ **18.** $x = 2y - 5$

19. The demand law $x + 6p = 20$ gives the relation between the wholesale price p of coffee (dollars per pound) and the number of pounds x consumed per person in the United States from 1960 through 1974.* [See Example 7.]

a) Write the law in two-intercept form and sketch the demand curve.

b) At what price does the demand law predict that the demand for coffee will disappear? What would the consumption be if coffee were free?

c) In 1974, U.S. coffee consumption was 12.8 pounds per person. What was the wholesale price?

d) What consumption does the law predict for a wholesale price of $1.30 per pound? (This was the U.S. consumption at that price in 1975.)

20. Find the line that passes through the point $(1, 2)$ and is parallel to the line $x + 2y = 3$.

21. a) Find the line L through $A(-2, 2)$ and perpendicular to the line

$$L'\colon 2x + y = 4.$$

b) Find the point B where the lines L and L' of part (a) intersect.

c) Using the result of part (b), find the distance from the point A to the line L' of part (a).

22. Find the line through $(1, 4)$ and having angle of inclination $\phi = 60°$.

23. Find the angle of inclination of the line $2x + y = 4$.

24. The pressure p experienced by a diver under water is proportional to the depth d. In sea water the pressure at $d = 100$ meters is approximately 10.42 atmospheres.

a) Write an equation for p in terms of d.

b) What is the pressure 50 meters below the surface?

25. A ray of light comes in along the line $x + y = 1$ above the x-axis and reflects off the x-axis. Write an equation for its new path.

26. The carbon steel used in railroad track expands when heated. For the temperatures normally encountered in use, the length ℓ of a piece of track is related to the temperature t by a linear equation. To express ℓ in terms of t, two mea-

---

*   Based on U.S. Department of Commerce figures. See *The U.S. Fact Book*, an unabridged edition of *The Statistical Abstract of the United States*, Grosset and Dunlap, Publishers, New York (1977), pp. 95 and 437.

surements are taken:

$$\ell_1 = 35 \text{ ft}, \qquad t_1 = 65°\text{F}$$

$$\ell_2 = 35.16 \text{ ft}, \qquad t_2 = 135°\text{F}$$

Write a linear equation for ℓ and t.

27. The perpendicular distance ON between the origin and the line L is p, and ON makes an angle α with the positive x-axis. Show that L has equation $x \cos \alpha + y \sin \alpha = p$.

28. If A, B, C, C' are constants, and not both A and B are zero, show that (a) the lines

$$Ax + By + C = 0, \qquad Ax + By + C' = 0,$$

either coincide or are parallel, and that (b) the lines

$$Ax + By + C = 0, \qquad Bx - Ay + C' = 0,$$

are perpendicular.

We begin this article by describing sets of values that are typical of those taken on by variables in calculus.

Intervals

The set of values that a variable x may take on is called the *domain* of x. The domains of the variables in many applications of calculus are intervals like those shown in Fig. 1–24. An *open* interval is the set of all real numbers that lie *strictly between* two fixed numbers a and b:

1–6
FUNCTIONS AND GRAPHS

In symbols		In words
$a < x < b$	or $\quad(a, b)$	"The open interval a b"

Closed intervals contain both endpoints:

In symbols		In words
$a \leq x \leq b$	or $\quad[a, b]$	"The closed interval a b"

Half-open intervals contain one but not both endpoints:

In symbols		In words
$a \leq x < b$	or $\quad[a, b)$	"The interval a less than or equal to x less than b"
$a < x \leq b$	or $\quad(a, b]$	"The interval a less than x less than or equal to b"

Figure 1–24

EXAMPLE 1. If both x and y are to be real variables in the expression

$$y = \sqrt{1 - x^2},$$

then x^2 must not be greater than 1, because the square root of a negative number is not a real number. The appropriate domain for x is the closed interval $-1 \leq x \leq 1$.

EXAMPLE 2. If x and y are to be real variables in the expression

$$y = \frac{1}{\sqrt{1 - x^2}},$$

then x must be further restricted to the open interval $-1 < x < 1$ because $1/0$ is not a number.

EXAMPLE 3. If x and y are to be real variables and

$$y = \sqrt{\frac{1}{x} - 1},$$

then $(1/x) - 1 \geq 0$ or $(1/x) \geq 1$. That is, x must be positive and less than or equal to 1. Therefore, the largest possible domain for x is the half-open interval $0 < x \leq 1$.

The domains of variables are sometimes unbounded sets, like the set of real numbers, or the set of nonnegative numbers, or the set of numbers less than 3. We can describe these sets with inequalities too, as in the next example.

EXAMPLE 4

Equation	Largest possible domain if x and y are to be real variables
$y = x^2$	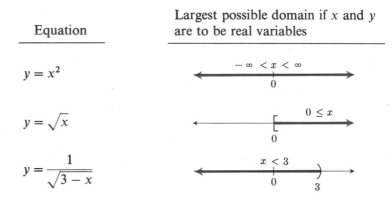 $-\infty < x < \infty$
$y = \sqrt{x}$	$0 \leq x$
$y = \dfrac{1}{\sqrt{3-x}}$	$x < 3$

Sets like these are sometimes called "infinite" intervals.

Some domains are unions of intervals.

EXAMPLE 5. The value of $y = \sqrt{x/(x-1)}$ is real if x takes on any value in the union of the infinite intervals $x \leq 0$ and $x > 1$, as we shall now show.

The fraction under the square-root sign is zero when $x = 0$, and it is undefined when $x = 1$. An easy way to determine the sign of the fraction for the other values of x is shown at the left.

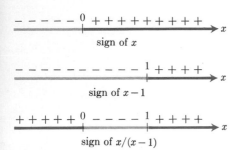

Functions

In calculus we are interested in how variables are related. We want to know, for example, how the distance an object travels is related to its speed; or how the concentration of a medicine in the bloodstream is related to the length of time between doses; or how the number of rabbits in an arctic predator–prey food chain depends on the number of foxes. There is an especially important kind of relation between two variables that we call a *function*. The key idea of a function is that as soon as we choose a value for the first variable, the corresponding value of the second variable is then determined. In other words, a function pairs the values of the variables together in such a way that each value of the first variable is paired with *exactly one* value of the second variable.

Definition. *A function is a set of ordered pairs of numbers* (x, y) *with the following property: To each value of the first variable* (x) *there corresponds a unique value of the second variable* (y).

EXAMPLE 6. Let the domain of x be the set $\{0, 1, 2, 3, 4\}$. Assign to each value of x the number $y = x^2$. The function so defined is the set of pairs

$$\{(0, 0), \quad (1, 1), \quad (2, 4), \quad (3, 9), \quad (4, 16)\}.$$

EXAMPLE 7. Let the domain of x be the closed interval $-2 \le x \le 2$. Assign to each value of x the number $y = x^2$. The set of ordered pairs (x, y) such that $-2 \le x \le 2$ and $y = x^2$ is a function. We can also describe the function with set-builder notation:

$$\{(x, y) \mid -2 \le x \le 2, y = x^2\}. \tag{1}$$

The outside braces denote "set," (x, y) denotes the typical element of the set, and the vertical bar is read "such that." The statement after the bar is the condition or rule the typical element must satisfy to qualify for membership in the set. We often use this notation when the elements in a set are too numerous to list individually. The basic idea is still present: When a value is assigned to the first variable x, the corresponding value of the second variable y is then determined. In this case, $y = x^2$. If x is $\frac{1}{3}$, then $y = \frac{1}{9}$. The pair $(\frac{1}{3}, \frac{1}{9})$ belongs to the function.

The next example shows how to describe functions without set-builder notation. Every function is determined by two things: (1) *the domain* of the first variable x and (2) *the rule* or condition that the pairs (x, y) must satisfy to belong to the function. We can therefore describe a function completely by giving its domain and rule.

EXAMPLE 8

Function	Name
The function whose domain is the set $-2 \le x \le 2$ and that pairs with each value of x the number $y = x^2$.	The function $y = x^2, \quad -2 \le x \le 2$
The function that pairs with each value of x different from 2 the number $x/(x - 2)$.	The function $y = \dfrac{x}{x - 2}, \quad x \ne 2$

Graphs

The set of points in the plane whose coordinate pairs are also the ordered pairs of a function is called the *graph* of the function. The next example shows how to sketch such a graph. The process of sketching the graph of a function is called *graphing* the function.

EXAMPLE 9. Graph the function $y = x^2$, $-2 \le x \le 2$.

Solution. To graph a function we carry out three steps.

1. Make a table of pairs from the function, as in Table 1–2.

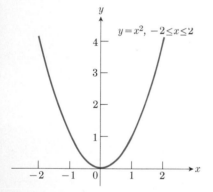

Figure 1–25

Figure 1–26

Table 1–2.

x	y
-2.0	4.0
-1.75	3.06
-1.5	2.25
-1.0	1.0
-0.5	0.25
0	0
0.5	0.25
1.0	1.0
1.5	2.25
1.75	3.06
2.0	4.0

2. Plot enough of the corresponding points to learn the shape of the graph. Add more pairs to the table if necessary (Fig. 1–25).

3. Complete the sketch by connecting the points (Fig. 1–26).

Here is some more terminology associated with functions. The variable x which generates the first of the two numbers in the ordered pairs (x, y) of a function is called the *independent variable* or *argument* of the function. The second variable y is called the *dependent variable*. The y-value that corresponds to a particular x-value is called the *image* of that x-value. We say that the function *maps* the x-value to its image. The domain of the independent variable x is called the *domain* of the function. The set of values taken on by the dependent variable y is the *range* of the function. The range is the image of the domain.

EXAMPLE 10. *The function $y = 1/x$, $x \ne 0$.* The domain of this function is the set of all real numbers different from 0. The image of each number in the domain is the reciprocal of the number. The pairs of the function all have the form $(x, 1/x)$. Table 1–3 shows some of the pairs. The range of the function is also the set of all numbers different from 0. Because the domain and range are infinite we cannot show the entire graph. We sketch just enough to show the behavior of the function. We refer to the sketch as the graph of the function, even though it is incomplete. It is conventional to do that (Fig. 1–27).

Table 1–3. Values of $y = 1/x$ for selected values of x

x	$\pm\frac{1}{10}$	$\pm\frac{1}{3}$	$\pm\sqrt{2}$	± 2
$y = \dfrac{1}{x}$	± 10	± 3	$\pm\dfrac{1}{\sqrt{2}}$	$\pm\frac{1}{2}$

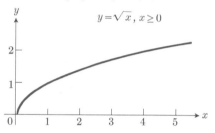

1–27   The graph of $y = 1/x$, $x \neq 0$.

EXAMPLE 11. *The function* $y = \sqrt{x}$, $x \geq 0$. This function maps every nonnegative number x to the number $\sqrt{x}$.

Pairs:	$(x, \sqrt{x})$	Graph:	Fig. 1–28
Domain:	$x \geq 0$	Range:	$y \geq 0$

Obsidian dating has led to estimates of glacial events as old as 179,000 years, well beyond the reliable 40,000-year range of carbon-14 dating. Obsidian (volcanic glass) absorbs water from the atmosphere, which seeps into the glass to form a layer called a *hydration* layer that can be seen under a microscope. The depth of the layer beneath a given surface (with some variation) is proportional to the square root of the time elapsed since the surface was created. Thus, measuring the depths of hydration layers in artifacts and stones allows us to estimate the dates of past events, like the shaping of a prehistoric axe or the chipping of a pebble by a glacier. A typical formula relating a layer's depth d to elapsed time t is

$$d = \sqrt{5t} \text{ } \mu m \text{ (millionths of a meter)},$$

where t is measured in thousands of years. The layer is $\sqrt{5} \approx 2.24$ μm thick after 1000 years, $\sqrt{10} \approx 3.16$ μm thick after 2000 years, and so on. For more about this relatively recent dating technique, read Friedman and Trembour, "Obsidian: The Dating Stone," *American Scientist*, Jan.–Feb., 1978, pp. 44–51.

1–28   The graph of $y = \sqrt{x}$, $x \geq 0$.

1–29   The graph of $y = \sqrt{1 - x^2}$, $-1 \leq x \leq 1$.

EXAMPLE 12. *The function* $y = \sqrt{1 - x^2}$, $-1 \leq x \leq 1$.

Pairs:	$(x, \sqrt{1 - x^2})$	Graph:	The semicircle shown in Fig. 1–29.
Domain:	$-1 \leq x \leq 1$	Range:	$0 \leq y \leq 1$

EXAMPLE 13. *The function* $y = 1/\sqrt{3 - x}$, $x < 3$.

Pairs:	$(x, 1/\sqrt{3 - x})$	Graph:	Fig. 1–30.
Domain:	The set of real numbers less than 3 (see Table 1–4).	Range:	$y > 0$

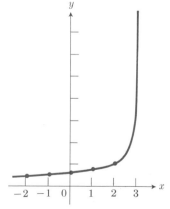

1–30   The graph of $y = 1/\sqrt{3 - x}$, $x < 3$.

Table 1–4. Values of $y = 1/\sqrt{3-x}$
for selected values of x

x	-2	-1	0	1	2	2.9
y	0.45	0.50	0.58	0.71	1.00	3.16

We always keep two restrictions in mind when we define functions. First, we **never divide by zero.** When we see $y = x/(x-2)$, we must think "$x \neq 2$." We must do so even if this restriction is not stated explicitly. Second, we deal with real-valued functions exclusively. We must restrict our domains when we have square roots, or fourth roots, or other even roots. If $y = \sqrt{1-x^2}$, we should think "x^2 must not be greater than 1. The domain must not extend beyond the interval $-1 \leq x \leq 1$."

EXAMPLE 14. *The absolute value function,* $y = |x|$. This function assigns to each number x the nonnegative number $\sqrt{x^2}$. We call this number the *absolute value* of x. The symbol for the absolute value of x is $|x|$:

$$|x| = \sqrt{x^2} = \begin{cases} x, & \text{if } x \geq 0, \\ -x, & \text{if } x < 0. \end{cases}$$

The absolute value function maps every positive number to itself. It maps every negative number to its negative, which is the corresponding positive number. Thus, $|x|$ is never negative. The absolute value function works like an electric current rectifier that converts either positive or negative current to positive current.

Pairs:	$(x, |x|)$	Graph:	Fig. 1–31
Domain:	$-\infty < x < \infty$	Range:	$y \geq 0$

1–32 The absolute value of a number is its distance from 0.

Absolute Value

The absolute value function of Example 14 has an important geometric interpretation. The number $|x|$ measures the distance between the origin 0 and the point that represents x on the scale of real numbers. It does so regardless of whether x is positive or negative. (See Fig. 1–32.)

EXAMPLE 15. A number x that lies between -1 and $+1$ is less than one unit away from zero. That is, $|x| < 1$. Conversely, if $|x| < 1$, then x lies between -1 and $+1$. For this reason we often write $|x| < 1$ as a shorthand way of describing the interval $-1 < x < 1$ (Fig. 1–33).

EXAMPLE 16. Describe the domain $|x| \geq 1$ without absolute values. Sketch the domain.

Solution. $|x| \geq 1$ means that the distance between x and the origin is one

1–33 The domain $|x| < 1$.

1–31 The absolute value function.

unit or more. That is, either $x \leq -1$ or $x \geq 1$. The domain is the union of the intervals sketched in Fig. 1–34.

The equality

$$|ab| = |a||b| \qquad\qquad (2)$$

holds for all real numbers a and b. The steps from left to right are

$$|ab| = \sqrt{(ab)^2} = \sqrt{a^2b^2} = \sqrt{a^2}\sqrt{b^2} = |a||b|.$$

The *triangle inequality*

$$|a + b| \leq |a| + |b| \qquad\qquad (3)$$

is true for all real numbers a and b. If the numbers a and b have the same sign, then $|a + b| = |a| + |b|$. If they have opposite signs, then $|a + b| < |a| + |b|$.

When we subtract one of the numbers a and b from the other, the sign of the result depends on which way we subtract. But $a - b$ and $b - a$ differ from each other only in sign. That is,

$$|a - b| = |b - a|. \qquad\qquad (4)$$

The number $|a - b| = |b - a|$ measures the distance between a and b on the real number line.

EXAMPLE 17. Describe the domain $|x - 4| < 5$ without absolute values.

1–35 $|x - 4| < 5$ and $-1 < x < 9$ both describe the open interval $(-1, 9)$.

Solution 1. $|x - 4| < 5$ says the distance between x and 4 is less than 5. This lets x vary between $4 - 5 = -1$ and $4 + 5 = 9$. The domain is the interval $-1 < x < 9$. See Fig. 1–35.

Solution 2. $|x - 4| < 5$ says $(x - 4)$ lies between -5 and $+5$, or

$$-5 < x - 4 < 5.$$

To find out what this inequality says about x, as opposed to $x - 4$, we can add 4 to each quantity in the inequality. The addition preserves the inequality, and shows that $-1 < x < 9$. Moreover, these algebraic steps are reversible.

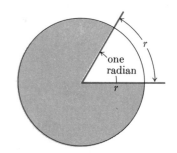

Figure 1–36

Radian Measure

The measure of an angle at the center of a circle that is subtended by an arc of the circle one radius long is said to be one *radian* (Fig. 1–36). More generally, the number of radians in an angle that is subtended by an arc s units long is

$$\theta = \frac{s}{r}. \qquad\qquad (5)$$

(See Fig. 1–37.) To see how radians correspond to degrees we can look at a semicircle. The length of the semicircle is π radii. Therefore a 180° angle has

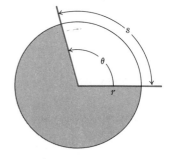

1–37 $\theta = (s/r)$ radians.

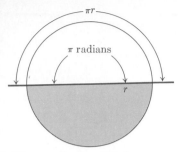

1–38 π radians = 180 degrees.

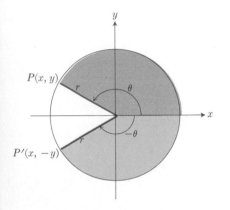

1–39 Angles of opposite sign.

a measure of π radians (Fig. 1–38). An angle of 1° then measures $\pi/180 \approx$ 0.01745 radians, or about two hundredths of a radian. One radian measures $180/\pi \approx 57.3$ degrees. As with degree measure, counterclockwise rotations have positive radian measures and clockwise rotations have negative radian measures (Fig. 1–39).

A radian is normally too large a unit to be convenient in the daily practice of navigation and civil engineering, but radians play a special role in the calculus of trigonometric functions, as we shall see in Article 2–10. We therefore include radian measure in the tables of values of the functions $\sin \theta$, $\cos \theta$, and $\tan \theta$ in the following example.

EXAMPLE 18. *The sine, cosine and tangent functions.* When an angle of measure θ is placed in standard position at the center of a circle of radius r as in Fig. 1–40, then

$$\sin \theta = \frac{y}{r}, \qquad \cos \theta = \frac{x}{r}, \qquad \tan \theta = \frac{y}{x}. \qquad (6)$$

Note that $\tan \theta = y/x$ is not defined for values of θ for which $x = 0$. In radian measure this means that $\pi/2, 3\pi/2, \ldots, -\pi/2, -3\pi/2, \ldots$ are excluded from the domain of the tangent function.

Table 1–5. Values of $\sin \theta$, $\cos \theta$, and $\tan \theta$ for selected values of θ

Degrees	−180	−135	−90	−45	0	45	90	135	180
θ (radians)	$-\pi$	$-\dfrac{3\pi}{4}$	$-\dfrac{\pi}{2}$	$-\dfrac{\pi}{4}$	0	$\dfrac{\pi}{4}$	$\dfrac{\pi}{2}$	$\dfrac{3\pi}{4}$	π
$\sin \theta$	0	−0.71	−1	−0.71	0	0.71	1	0.71	0
$\cos \theta$	−1	−0.71	0	0.71	1	0.71	0	−0.71	−1
$\tan \theta$	0	1		−1	0	1		−1	0

In Table 1–5,

$$\tan \theta = \frac{\sin \theta}{\cos \theta}, \qquad \text{except when } \cos \theta = 0,$$

which can also be seen by dividing the formulas at the beginning of the example. Note also that the values of the sine, cosine, and tangent repeat. This regular repetition, or *periodicity*, can be seen even more clearly in the graphs in Fig. 1–41. The values of the sine and cosine repeat every 2π units. The values of the tangent repeat every π units. In symbols, we write

$$\sin (\theta + 2\pi) = \sin \theta; \qquad \cos (\theta + 2\pi) = \cos \theta; \qquad \tan (\theta + \pi) = \tan \theta. \qquad (7)$$

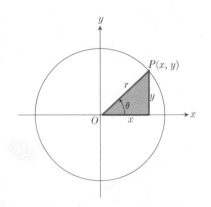

1–40 Angle θ in standard position.

Functional Notation

We often name functions with a single letter like f. This lets us use the simple notation $f(x)$, read "f of x," for the number y that corresponds to x. The number $f(x)$ is called *the value of f at x*, or *the image of x under f*. If f is the function that squares each number in its domain, then the rule that defines f is $f(x) = x^2$. This gives us another name for the function: "the function $f(x) = x^2$."

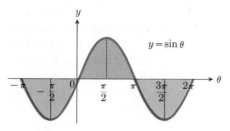

a) Domain: $-\infty < \theta < \infty$
   Range: $-1 \le y \le 1$

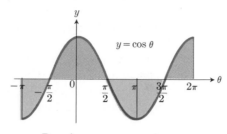

b) Domain: $-\infty < \theta < \infty$
   Range: $-1 \le y \le 1$

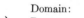

c) Domain: All real numbers except odd integer multiples of $\pi/2$.
   Range: $-\infty < y < \infty$

1–41   Graphs of the sine, cosine, and tangent functions.

1–42   Diagram for the function f.

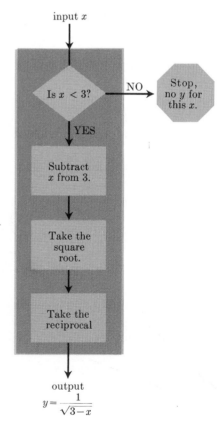

1–43   Diagram for the function $y = 1/\sqrt{3-x}$.

EXAMPLE 19.   If $f(x) = (2 - x)/(1 + x)$, then the value of f at $x = -5$ is

$$f(-5) = \frac{2 - (-5)}{1 + (-5)} = \frac{7}{-4} = -\frac{7}{4}.$$

Functions are like Machines

It is sometimes useful to think of a function as a machine with an input x and output $y = f(x)$. (See Fig. 1–42.) The machine may be offered any real number as input, but the first thing it asks is "Are you in my domain?" If the answer is "No", the machine politely flashes a signal that says, "Sorry, I can't accept you." But if the answer is "Yes", then the machine proceeds to calculate the value of $f(x)$ and displays the answer, or prints it out. In this way, a table of pairs (x, y) such that $y = f(x)$ is produced.

EXAMPLE 20.   The machine shown in Fig. 1–43 calculates values of the function $y = 1/\sqrt{3 - x}$. Table 1–4 in Example 13 is a table of input–output pairs (x, y) from this machine.

1–44 Two functions can be composed when the range of the first lies in the domain of the second.

Composition

Think of making a new function machine by hooking two machines together so that the outputs of the first are the inputs of the second. The new machine is the *composite* of the ones of which it is made, and its output function is *composed* of the functions of the two machines. If the first machine is f, and the second is g, as in Fig. 1–44, then the output of the composite that corresponds to the input x is $g(f(x))$, read "g of f of x."

EXAMPLE 21. If $f(x) = \sin x$ and $g(x) = -(x/2)$, then $g(f(x)) = -(\sin x)/2$.

EXAMPLE 22. If $f(x) = x^2$ and $g(x) = x - 7$, find a formula for $g(f(x))$. Then find $g(f(2))$.

Solution

$$g(f(x)) = f(x) - 7 = x^2 - 7;$$

$$g(f(2)) = f(2) - 7 = 2^2 - 7 = -3.$$

The order in which functions are composed can affect the result. Watch what happens when we compose the functions of Example 22 in the reverse order, first g, then f.

EXAMPLE 23. If $f(x) = x^2$ and $g(x) = x - 7$, find a formula for $f(g(x))$. Then find $f(g(2))$.

Solution

$$f(g(x)) = (g(x))^2 = (x - 7)^2,$$

$$f(g(2)) = (2 - 7)^2 = 25.$$

The functions $g(f(x)) = x^2 - 7$ and $f(g(x)) = (x - 7)^2$ are not the same. In fact, the only value of x for which their values are equal is $x = 4$. We can check this by solving the equation $x^2 - 7 = (x - 7)^2$ for x:

$$x^2 - 7 = x^2 - 14x + 49,$$

$$14x = 56,$$

$$x = 4.$$

Functions of More than One Independent Variable

The values of some functions are calculated from the values of more than one independent variable.

EXAMPLE 24. *Economic order quantity* (EOQ). Items that are sold regularly by a retail store have to be reordered when they begin to run low. The question that always arises is how many of the items, radios, shoes, or what have you, to reorder. To answer this question, a store manager has to think about two kinds of costs. There are the costs of holding the items between the time they arrive and the time they are sold—costs of insurance and storage space, and of capital tied up. There is also a setup cost incurred each time an order is placed, associated with secretarial time and communications. If we assume that the setup cost is the same for each order, no matter how large or small, then the problem of determining the size of an order comes down to the following. Large orders have a low setup cost per item, but a high holding cost. Small orders have a high setup cost per item, but a low holding cost. How can one find an order quantity Q that strikes an economical balance between the cost of ordering and the cost of holding inventory?

One of the simplest estimates for Q is given by the formula

$$Q = \sqrt{\frac{2KM}{h}}, \tag{8}$$

where

$K =$ the setup cost (fixed cost of placing an order),

$M =$ number of items sold per week,

$h =$ holding cost for each item per week.

For example, if $K = \$2.00$, $M = 20$ radios per week, and $h = \$0.05$, then $Q = 40$ radios. The most economical quantity to order is 40 radios. Since weekly sales are 20 radios, this means placing an order every two weeks.

As you can see, the formula for Q ignores a number of real factors that may influence a store manager's decision. Shipping charges may vary with order size, for instance, or prices may be about to change. Nevertheless, the formula is accurate enough in many cases to be of practical importance. We will show how the formula is derived in Article 3–6. (For more information, see *Principles of Operations Research*, Second Edition, by Harvey M. Wagner. Prentice-Hall, Inc., 1975, p. 18.)

EXAMPLE 25. (From "Concorde Sonic Booms as an Atmospheric Probe," N. K. Balachandran, W. L. Donn, and D. H. Rind, *Science*, 1 July 1977; Vol. 197, p. 47.)

The distance y at which the grazing (farthest) ray of sound from an atmospheric source hits the surface of the earth is a function of

$T =$ surface temperature (in degrees Kelvin),

$h =$ elevation (in km) of the source (for example, the Concorde),

$d =$ vertical temperature gradient (in degrees Kelvin per km).

The formula for y is

$$y = 2(Th/d)^{1/2}. \tag{9}$$

Evaluated for $T = 296°K$, $h = 13$ km, and $d = 6° K/km$, the formula yields $y = 50.65$ km.

To calculate the distance at which the Concorde's sonic boom is heard in the preceding example, we need to know the values of the earth's surface temperature T, the plane's elevation h, and the vertical temperature gradient d. But these values are all that we need to know. As soon as they are known, the value of y is determined. The set of all ordered 4-tuples (T, h, d, y) with

$$y = 2(Th/d)^{1/2}, \qquad T \geq 0, \qquad h \geq 0, \qquad d \geq 0, \qquad \textbf{(10)}$$

is a function of the three variables T, h, and d. The physical meanings of the variables keep their values from being negative.

The *domain* of the function $y = 2(Th/d)^{1/2}$ is the set of all ordered triples (T, h, d) with T, h, and d nonnegative. The *range* is the set of numbers $y \geq 0$. The variables T, h, and d are *independent* in the sense that the values assigned to any one variable need not depend on the others. The variable y is the *dependent* variable of the function. Its value is fixed by T, h, and d.

We say that y is a function of T, h, and d. This statement leaves out a lot of detail, but it still says two things:

1. T, h, and d can be assigned values independently;

2. Giving T, h, and d determines y.

More generally, suppose that some quantity y is determined by n other quantities $x_1, x_2, x_3, \ldots, x_n$. Then the set of all ordered $(n + 1)$-tuples $(x_1, x_2, x_3, \ldots, x_n, y)$ obtained by substituting values of $x_1, x_2, x_3, \ldots, x_n$ along with the value of y that corresponds to them, is a function. The domain of the function is the set of allowable n-tuples $(x_1, x_2, x_3, \ldots, x_n)$. The range is the set of corresponding y-values. If values can be assigned independently to each of the x's, we call them independent variables and say that y is a function of the n x's. We write

$$y = f(x_1, x_2, x_3, \ldots, x_n). \qquad \textbf{(11)}$$

The Greatest Integer Function

Most of the information about functions in this book will come from graphs and equations. However, any rule that gives a value y for each value of x expresses y as a function of x. Here is an example of a function that is determined by a verbal statement.

EXAMPLE 26. *The greatest integer function* $y = [x]$. For each real number x, the value of this function is the largest integer less than or equal to x. The symbol for this integer is $[x]$, read "the greatest integer in x." Some sample values are

$$[1.9] = 1, \qquad [2] = 2, \qquad \text{and} \qquad [3.4] = 3.$$

If x is negative, $[x]$ may have a larger absolute value than x does:

$$[-2.7] = -3, \qquad [-0.5] = -1.$$

The range of $y = [x]$ is the set of integers. Figure 1–45 shows the graph.

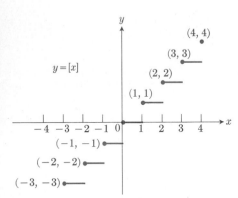

1–45 For each number x, the number $y = [x]$ is the greatest integer less than or equal to x.

The greatest integer function is an example of a *step function*. Phenomena that we can model with step functions are:

1. The price of postage for first-class mail, as a function of weight.

2. The output of a blinking light, as a function of time.

3. The number displayed by a meter or machine that gives digital outputs, as a function of time.

Step functions exhibit points of *discontinuity*, where they suddenly jump from one value to another without taking on any of the intermediate values. In Fig. 1–45, the greatest integer in x jumps from 1 when $x < 2$ to 2 at $x = 2$, without taking on any of the intervening values.

PROBLEMS

Find the largest possible domain of x and the corresponding range of y for each function in Problems 1–6.

1. $y = \sqrt{x + 4}$

2. $y = \sqrt{1 - \sqrt{x}}$

3. $y = \dfrac{x^2}{x^2 + 1}$

4. $y = \sqrt{\dfrac{x}{x + 1}}$

5. $y = x - \dfrac{1}{x}$

6. $y = (\sqrt{x})^2$

In Problems 7–9, graph each function. Use a calculator, if one is available, to calculate the function values.

7. $y = \sqrt{9 - x^2}$

8. $y = \dfrac{1}{x^2}$, $-2 \le x \le 2$, $x \ne 0$

9. $y = \sqrt{x + 1}$, $-1 \le x \le 3$

10. Which of the graphs in Fig. 1–46 could be the graph of $y = x^2 - 1$? Why?

a)   b)

c)   d)

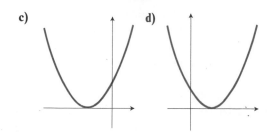

Figure 1–46

11. Which of the graphs in Fig. 1–46 could be the graph of $y = (x - 1)^2$? Why?

12. By solving $x^2 + y^2 = 1$ for y, replace the equation by an equivalent system of two equations each of which determines y as a function of x. Graph these two equations. [*Hint*. See Example 12.]

13. Make a table of values with $x = 0, \frac{1}{2}, 1, \frac{3}{2}$, and 2, and sketch the graph of the function

$$y = \begin{cases} x, & \text{when } 0 \le x \le 1 \\ 2 - x, & \text{when } 1 \le x \le 2. \end{cases}$$

In Problems 14–17, describe the domain of x without the use of absolute values.

14. $|x| < 2$

15. $|x| \ge 2$

16. $|x - 1| \le 5$

17. $\left| \dfrac{x}{2} - 1 \right| \le 1$

In Problems 18–20, use absolute values to describe the domain of x.

18. $-8 \le x \le 8$ **19.** $-3 < x < 5$ **20.** $-5 < x < -1$

21. When does $|1 - x|$ equal $1 - x$, and when does it equal $x - 1$?

Graph the functions in Problems 22 and 23.

22. $y = |4 - x^2|$, $-3 \le x \le 3$

23. $y = |x| + x$, $-2 \le x \le 2$

Convert the following degree measures to radian measure.

24. 45°   **25.** $-60°$ **26.** 90°

27. 120°   **28.** $-30°$ **29.** $-135°$

Convert the following radian measures to degree measure.

30. $\dfrac{\pi}{3}$ **31.** $-\dfrac{\pi}{6}$ **32.** $\dfrac{\pi}{4}$

33. $\dfrac{2\pi}{3}$ **34.** $\dfrac{3\pi}{2}$ **35.** $-\dfrac{\pi}{2}$

A function f is an *even* function of x if $f(-x) = f(x)$ for every value of x, and *odd* if $f(-x) = -f(x)$ instead. The function $f(x) = x^2$ is even, because $(-x)^2$ always equals x^2. The function $f(x) = x^3$ is odd, because $(-x)^3 = -x^3$. Which of the functions in Problems 36–43 are even functions of x, and which are odd?

36. x **37.** $|x|$ **38.** x^4

39. $\sin x$ **40.** $\cos x$ **41.** $\tan x$

42. If $f(x) = 1/x$, find $f(2)$, $f(x + 2)$, and $(f(x + 2) - f(2))/2$.

43. If $F(t) = 4t - 3$, find $(F(t + h) - F(t))/h$.

Copy and complete the following table.

$f(x)$	$g(x)$	$g(f(x))$
44. $x - 7$	$\sqrt{x}$	
45. $x + 2$	$3x$	
46. $x^2 + 2x + 1$		$|x + 1|$
47.	$\sqrt{x - 5}$	$\sqrt{x^2 - 5}$

48. The hydration layer in an obsidian axe is found to be 10 μm thick. Use the formula, $d = \sqrt{5t}$, following Example 11, to estimate how many years ago the axe was shaped.

49. During the summer, Martin Enterprises sells 50 lawnmowers a week. The setup cost for each order of mowers is \$4.50, and the holding cost for each mower is \$1.05 a week. What is the company's economic order quantity? (See Example 24.)

50. If weekly sales double, by what factor does this increase the economic order quantity, Q, of Example 24? By what factor do weekly sales have to increase for Q to double?

51. As a Concorde pilot preparing to land near Washington, D.C., you plan to slow the Concorde to subsonic speeds far enough away so that no one in the city will hear the sonic boom. You will be flying at an altitude of 16 km when you break the sound barrier, and the temperature gradient in the Washington area is 7°K/km. How close to Washington can you break the sound barrier under these circumstances? (See Example 25.) Use $T = 296°K$.

52. For nonnegative numbers, $[x]$ is the integer part of the decimal form of x. What is the corresponding description of $[x]$ when $x < 0$?

Graph the functions in Problems 53 and 54. The number $[x]$ is the greatest integer in x.

53. $y = x - [x]$, $-3 \le x \le 3$

54. $y = \left[\dfrac{x}{2}\right]$, $-3 \le x \le 3$

1–7

SLOPE OF A CURVE

In this article we shall define what we mean by the *slope of a curve* at a point P on the curve. We start with the slope of a secant line through P and a nearby point.

In Fig. 1–47, $P(x_1, y_1)$ is any point on the curve $y = f(x)$. Let $Q(x_2, y_2)$ be another point on the curve, with $\Delta x = x_2 - x_1 \ne 0$. Then the slope of the secant line joining the points P and Q is

$$m_{\text{sec}} = \text{slope of } PQ = \frac{y_2 - y_1}{x_2 - x_1} = \frac{\Delta y}{\Delta x}. \tag{1}$$

Suppose now we hold P fixed and move Q along the curve toward P. As we do so, the slope of the secant line PQ will probably vary. But it may happen (and does for most curves encountered in practice) that as Q moves closer and closer to P along the curve, the slope of the secant line varies by smaller and smaller amounts and, in fact, approaches a constant limiting value. When this happens, as it does in the following example, we call this limiting value the *slope of the tangent to the curve at P*, or more briefly, *the slope of the curve at P*. In Fig. 1–47, Q approaches P from the right. But in attempting to compute the limiting value of the slope of the secant line, we must allow Q to approach P from the left as well.

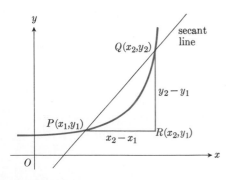

1–47 In many cases the slope $(y_2 - y_1)/(x_2 - x_1)$ of the secant line will approach a constant limiting value as Q moves toward P along the curve.

EXAMPLE 1. Find the slope of the curve

$$y = x^3 - 3x + 3 \tag{2}$$

at the point $P(x_1, y_1)$.

Solution. Since $P(x_1, y_1)$ is a point on the curve, its coordinates satisfy the equation

$$y_1 = x_1^3 - 3x_1 + 3. \tag{3a}$$

If $Q(x_2, y_2)$ is a second point on the curve, and if

$$\Delta x = x_2 - x_1, \qquad \Delta y = y_2 - y_1,$$

then

$$x_2 = x_1 + \Delta x, \qquad y_2 = y_1 + \Delta y$$

must also satisfy Eq. (2). That is,

$$y_1 + \Delta y = (x_1 + \Delta x)^3 - 3(x_1 + \Delta x) + 3$$

$$= x_1^3 + 3x_1^2 \,\Delta x + 3x_1(\Delta x)^2 + (\Delta x)^3 - 3x_1 - 3\,\Delta x + 3. \tag{3b}$$

When we subtract Eq. (3a) from Eq. (3b), we obtain

$$\Delta y = 3x_1^2 \,\Delta x + 3x_1(\Delta x)^2 + (\Delta x)^3 - 3\,\Delta x. \tag{4}$$

We find the slope of the secant line PQ by dividing both sides of Eq. (4) by Δx. (For this, we need $\Delta x \neq 0$, which is why we never let Q coincide with P.) The result is

$$m_{\text{sec}} = \frac{\Delta y}{\Delta x} = 3x_1^2 + 3x_1\,\Delta x + (\Delta x)^2 - 3. \tag{5}$$

Now comes the most important step! When Q approaches P along the curve, Δx and Δy both approach zero. Thus the slope of PQ will be the ratio of two small numbers. This information alone is not helpful, since the ratio of two small numbers may be practically anything. But we have further information here, since we also know from Eq. (5) that

$$m_{\text{sec}} = (3x_1^2 - 3) + (3x_1 + \Delta x)\,\Delta x.$$

The right side of this equation is the sum of two terms, one of which,

$$3x_1^2 - 3,$$

remains constant as Δx approaches zero, while the other,

$$(3x_1 + \Delta x)\,\Delta x,$$

becomes smaller and, in fact, itself approaches zero as Δx does. We summarize this by saying that

the limit of m_{sec} as Δx approaches zero is $3x_1^2 - 3$.

By definition, this limit is the slope of the tangent to the curve, or the slope of the curve at the point (x_1, y_1). Since (x_1, y_1) might have been *any* point on the curve of Eq. (2), we may delete the subscript 1 and say that

$$m = 3x^2 - 3 \tag{6}$$

gives the slope at any point $P(x, y)$ on the curve.

We can use the slope formula for a curve to learn more about its shape than we would discover without this information.

x	y	m
-2	1	9
-1	5	0
0	3	-3
1	1	0
2	5	9

a)

b)

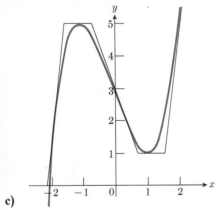

c)

Figure 1–48

EXAMPLE 2. From the slope formula $m = 3x^2 - 3$ for the curve $y = x^3 - 3x + 3$ in Example 1, we can see that $m = 0$ when $x = \pm 1$. We also see that the slope is negative for x between -1 and $+1$, and that elsewhere it is positive. If we substitute values of x between -2 and $+2$, say, into Eq. (2) to find y, and into Eq. (6) to find m, we obtain the table of values shown in Fig. 1–48(a). When the points from this table are plotted, and a tangent is drawn at each point, we obtain Fig. 1–48(b). With the aid of this tangent frame we can now draw a good picture of the curve (Fig. 1–48(c)).

REMARK. We sometimes think of the slope of a secant line as an average rate of change, as in the next example.

EXAMPLE 3. Biologists are interested in average growth rates of populations. The graph in Fig. 1–49 shows how the number of *Drosophila* flies grew in a controlled experiment during a fifty-day interval. The graph was made by counting the flies at regular intervals, plotting a point for each count, and drawing a smooth curve through the plotted points. The slope $\Delta p/\Delta t$ of the secant line PQ in the figure is about nine flies per day. It was computed from the coordinates of P and Q in the following way:

$$\frac{\Delta p}{\Delta t} = \frac{(340 - 150)(\text{flies})}{(45 - 23)(\text{days})} = \frac{190(\text{flies})}{22(\text{days})} \simeq 9 \text{ flies/day}.$$

This is the average rate of change in the number of flies in the twenty-two day interval from $t = 23$ to $t = 45$.

1–49 Growth of a *Drosophila* population in a controlled experiment. (*Source:* A. J. Lotka, *Elements of Mathematical Biology.* Dover, New York (1956); p. 69.)

PROBLEMS

Use the method illustrated in Example 1 to find the slope of each of the following curves at a point (x, y) on the curve. Use the equation of the curve and the equation you get for its slope to make a table of values, as in Example 2. Include in your table all points where the curve has a horizontal tangent. Sketch the curve, making use of all the information in your table of values.

1. $y = x^2 - 2x - 3$

2. $y = 2x^2 - x - 1$

3. $y = 4 - x^2$

4. $y = x^2 - 4x$

5. $y = x^2 - 4x + 4$

6. $y = x^2 + 4x + 4$

7. $y = 6 + x - x^2$

8. $y = 6 + 5x - x^2$

9. $y = x^2 + 3x + 2$

10. $y = 2 - x - x^2$

11. $y = 2x^3 + 3x^2 - 12x + 7$

12. $y = x^3 - 3x$

13. $y = x^3 - 12x$

14. $y = x^2(4x + 3) + 1$

15. $y = x^3 - 3x^2 + 4$

16. From Fig. 1–49, estimate the increase that took place in the *Drosophila* population during the twenty-third day.

We now show how to find the slope of the curve defined by the equation $y = f(x)$. Let $P(x_1, y_1)$ be a fixed point on the curve. The subscript 1 is used to emphasize that x_1 and y_1 are to be held constant throughout the following discussion. If $Q(x_1 + \Delta x, y_1 + \Delta y)$ is another point on the curve, then

$$y_1 + \Delta y = f(x_1 + \Delta x),$$

and from this we subtract

$$y_1 = f(x_1)$$

to obtain

$$\Delta y = f(x_1 + \Delta x) - f(x_1).$$

(See Fig. 1–50.) Then the slope of the secant line PQ is

$$m_{\text{sec}} = \frac{\Delta y}{\Delta x} = \frac{f(x_1 + \Delta x) - f(x_1)}{\Delta x}. \tag{1}$$

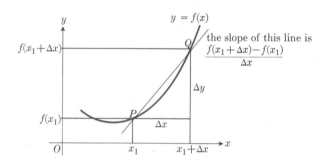

Figure 1–50

The division in Eq. (1) can only be *indicated* when we are talking about a general function $f(x)$, but for any specific equation such as $f(x) = x^3 - 3x + 3$ in Eq. (2) of Article 1–7, this division of Δy by Δx is actually to be carried out *before* we do the next operation, as we did in going from Eq. (4) to Eq. (5) in Article 1–7.

Having performed the division indicated in Eq. (1), we now investigate what happens when we hold x_1 fixed and take Δx to be smaller and smaller, approaching zero. If m_{sec} approaches a constant value, we call this value its *limit* and define this to be the *slope m_{tan} of the tangent to the curve at* $P(x_1, y_1)$. The mathematical symbols which summarize this discussion are

$$m_{\text{tan}} = \lim_{Q \to P} m_{\text{sec}} = \lim_{\Delta x \to 0} \frac{\Delta y}{\Delta x} = \lim_{\Delta x \to 0} \frac{f(x_1 + \Delta x) - f(x_1)}{\Delta x}. \tag{2}$$

The symbol "lim" with "$\Delta x \to 0$" written beneath it is read "the limit, as Δx approaches zero, of ..."

It is customary to indicate that the limit in Eq. (2) (when it exists) is related to the original function f at the point x_1, by writing it as $f'(x_1)$ (read "f-prime at x_1"). Thus $f'(x_1)$ is *defined* by

$$f'(x_1) = \lim_{\Delta x \to 0} \frac{f(x_1 + \Delta x) - f(x_1)}{\Delta x}. \tag{3}$$

The indicated limit may exist for some values of x_1 and fail to exist for other values. (We shall discuss this situation in more detail below.) At each point x_1 where the limit does exist, the function f is said to have a *derivative* (or to be *differentiable*) and the number $f'(x_1)$ is said to be the derivative of f at x_1.

The process of finding the derivative of a function is the fundamental operation of differential calculus. In fact, we may now define *differential calculus* to be that branch of mathematics which deals with the following two general problems.

PROBLEM I.   Given a function f, determine those values of x (in the domain of f) at which the function possesses a derivative.

PROBLEM II.   Given a function f and an x at which the derivative exists, find $f'(x)$.

EXAMPLE 1.   In Article 1–7 we found that the result of applying the operations on the right side of Eq. (3) to the function

$$f(x) = x^3 - 3x + 3 \tag{4}$$

for any x_1, was $3x_1^2 - 3$. That is, the function f in Eq. (4) possesses a derivative whose value at *any* x_1 is

$$f'(x_1) = 3x_1^2 - 3. \tag{5}$$

Thus the answer to Problem I above is: "The function f of Eq. (4) possesses a derivative at every x in the domain $-\infty < x < +\infty$." The answer to Problem II is given by Eq. (5).

Now for most of the functions considered in this book, it will turn out that the answer to Problem I is that the derivative exists at all but a few values of x; that is, the places where the derivative fails to exist will be exceptional. Then the x_1 in Eq. (3) may be *any* of the nonexceptional values of x. Therefore, we might as well write x instead of x_1 in Eq. (3) if we remember that

x is to be held constant,   while Δx varies and approaches zero

in the calculation of the derivative

$$f'(x) = \lim_{\Delta x \to 0} \frac{f(x + \Delta x) - f(x)}{\Delta x}. \tag{6}$$

With this understanding, we shall henceforth omit the subscript 1 in talking about the derivative and shall use Eq. (6) to define the derivative of f, with respect to x, at any x in its domain for which the limit exists.

The Derived Function

Let x be a number in the domain of the function f. If the limit indicated in Eq. (6) exists, then it provides a rule for associating a number $f'(x)$ with the number x. The set of all pairs of numbers $(x, f'(x))$ that can be formed by this process is called the *derived function* f'. The *domain* of f' is a subset of the domain of f. It contains all numbers x in the domain of f at which the limit in

(6) exists, but does not contain those exceptional values where the derivative fails to exist. The derived function f' is also called the *derivative* of f.

EXAMPLE 2.   For every value of x, the derivative of the function $f(x) = mx + b$ is the slope m.

STEP 1.   Write out $f(x + \Delta x)$ and $f(x)$:

$$f(x + \Delta x) = m(x + \Delta x) + b$$
$$= mx + m\,\Delta x + b,$$
$$f(x) = mx + b.$$

STEP 2.   Subtract $f(x)$ from $f(x + \Delta x)$:

$$f(x + \Delta x) - f(x) = m\,\Delta x.$$

STEP 3.   Divide by Δx:

$$\frac{f(x + \Delta x) - f(x)}{\Delta x} = \frac{m\,\Delta x}{\Delta x} = m.$$

STEP 4.   Calculate the limit as Δx approaches zero:

$$f'(x) = \lim_{\Delta x \to 0} \frac{f(x + \Delta x) - f(x)}{\Delta x} = m.$$

The derivative $f'(x)$ is defined at every value of x. It has the constant value m, the slope of the line.

In the next example, the domain of the derived function is not the domain of the function itself.

EXAMPLE 3.   The absolute-value function

$$f(x) = |x|$$

has a derivative at every point except the origin. As shown in Fig. 1–51, the derivative of f is $+1$ when x is positive and -1 when x is negative. To see that f has no derivative at $x = 0$, note that a secant line through the origin and some other point Q on the graph has slope $+1$ if the point is to the right, and slope -1 if the point is to the left. Therefore, there is no unique number that is the limit of the slopes of these secants as Q approaches the origin.

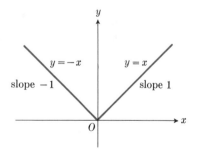

1–51   The graph of $y = |x|$.

The domain of the derivative of $f(x) = |x|$ consists of all real numbers $x \neq 0$. The range consists of the two numbers -1 and $+1$. We summarize this by writing

$$f'(x) = \begin{cases} -1 & \text{if } x < 0, \\ +1 & \text{if } x > 0. \end{cases}$$

(See Problem 21.)

Another way to see why $f(x) = |x|$ has no derivative at $x = 0$ is to write down the difference quotient of Eq. (6) for this function at $x = 0$, namely

$$\frac{f(x + \Delta x) - f(x)}{\Delta x} = \frac{|0 + \Delta x| - |0|}{\Delta x} = \frac{|\Delta x|}{\Delta x}.$$

The limit of this quotient as $\Delta x \to 0$ is $+1$ for positive values of Δx and -1 for negative values of Δx. For the limit in Eq. (6) to exist, we would have to arrive at the same number for both positive and negative values of Δx.

NOTATIONS.   In addition to $f'(x)$, various notations are used to denote the derivative of $y = f(x)$ with respect to x. The ones most commonly used are

$$y', \qquad \frac{dy}{dx}, \qquad \text{and} \qquad D_x y.$$

The last two of these may be interpreted as

$$\frac{dy}{dx} = \frac{d}{dx}(y),$$

where d/dx stands for the operation "derivative with respect to x of" the expression that follows it, and

$$D_x y = D_x(y)$$

with D_x meaning the same thing as d/dx, namely, "derivative with respect to x of" the expression that follows it.

EXAMPLE 4.   Find $f'(x)$ for the function

$$f(x) = x^2 + \frac{1}{x}, \qquad x \neq 0.$$

Solution.   We carry out the operations indicated on the right side of Eq. (6) in the following order:

1. Write out $f(x + \Delta x)$ and $f(x)$:

$$f(x + \Delta x) = (x + \Delta x)^2 + \frac{1}{x + \Delta x}$$

$$= x^2 + 2x\,\Delta x + (\Delta x)^2 + \frac{1}{x + \Delta x},$$

$$f(x) = x^2 + \frac{1}{x}.$$

2. Subtract $f(x)$ from $f(x + \Delta x)$:

$$f(x + \Delta x) - f(x) = 2x\,\Delta x + (\Delta x)^2 + \frac{1}{x + \Delta x} - \frac{1}{x}$$

$$= 2x\,\Delta x + (\Delta x)^2 + \frac{x - (x + \Delta x)}{x(x + \Delta x)}$$

$$= \Delta x\left(2x + \Delta x - \frac{1}{x(x + \Delta x)}\right).$$

3. Divide by Δx:

$$\frac{f(x + \Delta x) - f(x)}{\Delta x} = 2x + \Delta x - \frac{1}{x(x + \Delta x)}.$$

4. Calculate the limit as Δx approaches zero:

$$f'(x) = \lim_{\Delta x \to 0} \frac{f(x + \Delta x) - f(x)}{\Delta x}$$

$$= \lim_{\Delta x \to 0} \left(2x + \Delta x - \frac{1}{x(x + \Delta x)}\right) \qquad \textbf{(a)}$$

$$= 2x + 0 - \frac{1}{x(x + 0)} \qquad \textbf{(b)}$$

$$= 2x - \frac{1}{x^2}.$$

In a later article we shall discuss the validity of the various limit operations involved in going from (a) to (b) in Step 4. If we anticipate these results, we may say that, *after* the division by Δx has been carried out and the expression has been reduced to a form that does not involve division by zero when Δx is set equal to zero, the limit as Δx *approaches* zero does exist and may be found by replacing Δx by 0 in this reduced form.

The replacement of Δx by a single letter makes the expressions that come up when we calculate derivatives somewhat easier to read and write. If we replace Δx by h in Eq. (6) we get

$$f'(x) = \lim_{h \to 0} \frac{f(x + h) - f(x)}{h}. \qquad \textbf{(7)}$$

The next example shows the use of h in place of Δx. It also shows what to do when the steps we would normally follow to calculate a derivative lead to division by 0 when Δx, now h, approaches 0.

EXAMPLE 5.   Find dy/dx if $y = \sqrt{x}$ and $x > 0$.

Solution.   With $f(x) = \sqrt{x}$ and $f(x + h) = \sqrt{x + h}$, we form the quotient

$$\frac{f(x + h) - f(x)}{h} = \frac{\sqrt{x + h} - \sqrt{x}}{h}. \qquad \textbf{(a)}$$

Unfortunately, this will involve division by 0 if we replace h by 0. We therefore look for an equivalent expression in which this difficulty does not arise. If we attempt to rationalize the numerator in (a), we find

$$\frac{\sqrt{x + h} - \sqrt{x}}{h} = \frac{\sqrt{x + h} - \sqrt{x}}{h} \cdot \frac{\sqrt{x + h} + \sqrt{x}}{\sqrt{x + h} + \sqrt{x}}$$

$$= \frac{(x + h) - x}{h(\sqrt{x + h} + \sqrt{x})} = \frac{1}{\sqrt{x + h} + \sqrt{x}}.$$

When we let h approach 0 now, we learn that

$$\frac{dy}{dx} = \lim_{h \to 0} \frac{1}{\sqrt{x + h} + \sqrt{x}} = \frac{1}{\sqrt{x + 0} + \sqrt{x}} = \frac{1}{2\sqrt{x}}.$$

EXAMPLE 6. Find the slope of the curve $y = \sqrt{x}$ at $x = 4$, and write an equation for the tangent to the curve at $x = 4$.

Solution. The slope we seek is the value of the derivative of $y = \sqrt{x}$ at $x = 4$. According to Example 5, this is the value of $1/(2\sqrt{x})$ at $x = 4$, or $\frac{1}{4}$.

The tangent to the curve $y = \sqrt{x}$ at $x = 4$ is the line through the point $(4, 2)$ whose slope is the slope of the curve at $(4, 2)$, or $m = \frac{1}{4}$. The point-slope equation of this line is

$$(y - 2) = \tfrac{1}{4}(x - 4),$$

which simplifies to

$$y = \tfrac{1}{4}x + 1.$$

EXAMPLE 7. The graphs in Fig. 1–52(a) show the number of rabbits and foxes in a small arctic population. They are plotted as functions of time for 200 days. The number of rabbits increases at first, as the rabbits reproduce. But the foxes prey on the rabbits, and as the number of foxes increases, the rabbit population levels off and then drops.

1–52 Rabbits and foxes in an arctic predator–prey food chain. (*Source: Differentiation*, by W. U. Walton *et al.*, Project CALC, Education Development Center, 1975, p. 86.)

The graph in Fig. 1–52(b) is the graph of the derivative of the rabbit population. It was made by estimating the slope of the population curve at frequent intervals. These estimates were plotted as values of the derivative, and a smooth curve was drawn through them. For example, the slope of the rabbit population curve at $t = 20$ is about 40. Figure 1–53 shows how this value was estimated. Accordingly, (20, 40) was plotted as a point on the graph of the derivative. In other words, the slope at the point (20, 1700) on the upper curve is the ordinate of the point (20, 40) on the lower curve.

1–53   Enlarged view of rabbit-population curve near the day $x = 20$. The ratio $\Delta y / \Delta x = 40$ is a good estimate of the slope of the curve at the point (20, 1700) because the short segment of the curve is so close to being straight.

Note that the time when the rabbit population is dropping fastest is not when the fox population is largest. It occurs before the fox population peaks, about when the fox population is growing most rapidly. Rates of increase and decrease, and more generally the interpretation of derivatives as rates of change, are the subject of the next article.

PROBLEMS

For each of the functions f in Problems 1–20, find the derivative $f'(x)$, by means of the definition in Eq. (6) or Eq. (7). Then find the slope of the tangent to the curve $y = f(x)$ at $x = 3$, and write an equation for the tangent line.

1. $f(x) = x^2$

2. $f(x) = x^3$

3. $f(x) = 2x + 3$

4. $f(x) = x^2 - x + 1$

5. $f(x) = \dfrac{1}{x}$

6. $f(x) = \dfrac{1}{x^2}$

7. $f(x) = \dfrac{1}{2x + 1}$

8. $f(x) = \dfrac{x}{x + 1}$

9. $f(x) = 2x^2 - x + 5$

10. $f(x) = x^3 - 12x + 11$

11. $f(x) = x^4$

12. $f(x) = ax^2 + bx + c$ (a, b, c constants)

13. $f(x) = x - \dfrac{1}{x}$

14. $f(x) = ax + \dfrac{b}{x}$ (a, b constants)

15. $f(x) = \sqrt{2x}$

16. $f(x) = \sqrt{x + 1}$

17. $f(x) = \sqrt{2x + 3}$

18. $f(x) = \dfrac{1}{\sqrt{x}}$

19. $f(x) = \dfrac{1}{\sqrt{2x + 3}}$

20. $f(x) = \sqrt{x^2 + 1}$

21. Graph the derivative of $f(x) = |x|$ (Example 3). Then graph the function $y = |x|/x$, $x \neq 0$. What can you conclude?

22. What is the value of the derivative of the rabbit population in Example 7 when the number of rabbits is largest? smallest?

23. What is the size of the rabbit population in Example 7 when its derivative is largest? smallest?

24. Use the graphical technique described in Example 7 to sketch the graph of the derivative of the *Drosophila* population shown in Fig. 1–49.

1-9

VELOCITY AND RATES

When a body moves in a straight line, it is customary to represent the line of motion by a coordinate axis. We select a reference point 0 on the line as origin, adopt a positive direction and a unit of distance on the line, and then describe the motion by an equation which gives the coordinate of the body as a function of the time t that has elapsed since the start of the motion.

EXAMPLE 1.　The equation of motion for a freely falling body is

$$s = \tfrac{1}{2}gt^2, \tag{1}$$

where g is the acceleration due to gravity and is approximately 32 (ft/sec^2), and s is the distance in feet that the body has fallen in t seconds from the start when it was at rest. (See Fig. 1–54.)

More generally, suppose the law of motion is given by a function f,

$$s = f(t), \tag{2}$$

and that we are required to find the *velocity* of the body at some instant of time t. First of all, how shall we *define* the instantaneous velocity of a moving body?

If we assume that *distance* and *time* are the fundamental physical quantities that we can measure, we may be led to reason as follows. At time t, the body is in the position

$$s = f(t), \tag{3}$$

and at time $t + \Delta t$ the body is in the position

$$s + \Delta s = f(t + \Delta t). \tag{4}$$

Hence during the interval of time from t to $t + \Delta t$, the body has undergone a displacement

$$\Delta s = f(t + \Delta t) - f(t). \tag{5}$$

The quantities in Eqs. (3), (4), and (5) are all physical quantities that can be measured (by clocks and tapelines, say).

We now define the *average velocity* of the moving body to be Δs divided by Δt:

$$v_{\text{av}} = \frac{\Delta s}{\Delta t} = \frac{f(t + \Delta t) - f(t)}{\Delta t}. \tag{6}$$

For example, a sprinter who runs 100 meters in 10 seconds has an average velocity of

$$v_{\text{av}} = \frac{\Delta s}{\Delta t} = \frac{100 \text{ m}}{10 \text{ sec}} = 10 \text{ m/sec.}$$

To obtain the *instantaneous velocity* of the moving body at time t, we take its average velocity over shorter and shorter intervals of time Δt. Then the instantaneous velocity, or what we call the *velocity at time t*, is the limit

1–54　Distance fallen by a 3-cm ball bearing released at $t = 0$ seconds.

of the average velocities as Δt approaches zero:

$$v = \lim_{\Delta t \to 0} v_{av} = \lim_{\Delta t \to 0} \frac{\Delta s}{\Delta t} = \lim_{\Delta t \to 0} \frac{f(t + \Delta t) - f(t)}{\Delta t}. \tag{7}$$

Note that Eq. (7) defines v to be the derivative of $s = f(t)$ with respect to t:

$$v = \frac{ds}{dt} = f'(t). \tag{8}$$

EXAMPLE 2. Find the velocity of the freely falling body in Example 1.

Solution. The equation of motion in Example 1 is

$$s = \tfrac{1}{2}gt^2.$$

We apply the method of the previous article to find the derivative of s with respect to t. The result is

$$v = \frac{ds}{dt} = gt.$$

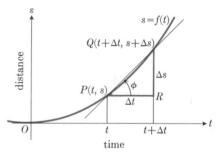

In general, when we graph $s = f(t)$ as a function of t, the average and instantaneous velocities both have geometric interpretations. The average velocity is the slope of a secant line (Fig. 1–55). The instantaneous velocity at time t is the slope of the tangent to the graph at the point $(t, f(t))$. (See Fig. 1–56.) The latter interpretation is sometimes used to estimate the velocity when our information about a motion is given by a graph instead of by an equation.

1–55 Distance vs. time for a moving body. The slope $\Delta s/\Delta t$ of the secant line PQ is the average velocity of the body over the interval from t to $(t + \Delta t)$.

EXAMPLE 3. In the graph of Fig. 1–56, s represents the coordinate of some point of a bicycle being ridden along a straight road. At $t = 8$, the tangent line appears to be rising at the rate of 40 s-units in an interval of two t-units; that is, the velocity at time $t = 8$ is apparently

$$\frac{40 \text{ (ft)}}{2 \text{ (sec)}} = 20 \text{ (ft/sec)}.$$

We say the velocity is "apparently" 20 ft/sec because we cannot be sure that we have accurately constructed the tangent to the curve. Indeed, an accurate construction would require that we know the derivative $f'(t)$ exactly at $t = 8$, and this is the very thing we are trying to estimate. On the other hand, we can make a fair approximation to the tangent line by inspection, and this is what we have done in the graph.

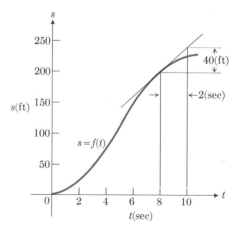

There are many other applications of the notion of average rate and instantaneous rate.

1–56 The motion of a bicyclist. The slope $m = 20$ ft/sec of the tangent line at $t = 8$ is the velocity at that instant. It is the limit of average velocities taken over shorter and shorter intervals.

EXAMPLE 4. The quantity of water Q (gal) in a reservoir at time t (min) is a function of t. Water may flow into or out of the reservoir. As it does so, suppose that Q changes by an amount ΔQ from time t to time $(t + \Delta t)$. Then the average and instantaneous rates of change of Q with respect to t are:

$$\text{Average rate:} \quad \frac{\Delta Q}{\Delta t} \text{ (gal/min)}$$

$$\text{Instantaneous rate:} \quad \frac{dQ}{dt} = \lim_{\Delta x \to 0} \frac{\Delta Q}{\Delta t} \text{ (gal/min)}.$$

EXAMPLE 5. (*Marginal analysis*) Economists often call the derivative of a function the *marginal value* of the function. Suppose, for example, that a company produces x tons of steel per week at a total cost of $y = f(x)$ dollars. This total cost includes such items as a portion of the cost of building and maintaining the company's steel mills, salaries of executives, taxes, office maintenance, cost of raw materials, labor, etc. Suppose that to produce $x + \Delta x$ tons of steel weekly would cost $y + \Delta y$ dollars. The increase in cost per unit increase in output would be $\Delta y/\Delta x$. The limit of this ratio, as Δx tends to zero, is called the *marginal cost*. In other words, if the total cost is y for weekly output x, then the marginal cost is the derivative of y with respect to x. It gives the rate of increase of cost per unit increase of output from the level x. (See Problem 18.)

To sell x tons of steel per week, the company prices its steel at $P = F(x)$ dollars per ton. The company's *revenue* is then the product $xP = xF(x)$. Its *marginal revenue* is the derivative of xP with respect to x, or the rate of change of revenue per unit increase in production. The company's profit, T, is the difference between revenue and cost:

$$T = xP - y.$$

In Chapter 3 we shall see how the company should adjust production to achieve maximum profit. The adjustment involves the *marginal profit*, dT/dx, which is the rate of increase of profit per unit increase of production. (For a further discussion of applications to economics, see Chapter 3 of William J. Baumol's *Economic Theory and Operations Research, Fourth Edition*, Prentice-Hall, Inc., 1977.)

Every derivative may be interpreted as the instantaneous rate of change of one variable per unit change in another. Thus, if the function defined by $y = f(x)$ has a derivative

$$f'(x) = \lim_{\Delta x \to 0} \frac{\Delta y}{\Delta x} = \lim_{\Delta x \to 0} \frac{f(x + \Delta x) - f(x)}{\Delta x},$$

we may interpret $\Delta y/\Delta x$ as *average rate of change* and

$$f'(x) = \lim_{\Delta x \to 0} \frac{\Delta y}{\Delta x}$$

as *instantaneous rate of change* of y with respect to x. Such a rate tells us the amount of change that would be produced in y by a change of one unit in x, provided the rate of change remained constant.

The average rate of change of y per unit change in x, $\Delta y/\Delta x$, when multiplied by the number of units of change in x, Δx, gives the actual change in y:

$$\Delta y = \frac{\Delta y}{\Delta x} \Delta x.$$

The instantaneous rate of change of y per unit change in x, $f'(x)$, multiplied by the number of units change in x, Δx, gives the change that would be produced in y if the point (x, y) were to move along the *tangent line* instead of moving along the curve; that is,

$$\Delta y_{\text{tan}} = f'(x)\, \Delta x.$$

(See Fig. 1–57.)

One reason calculus is important is that it enables us to find quantitatively how a change in one of two related variables affects the other variable.

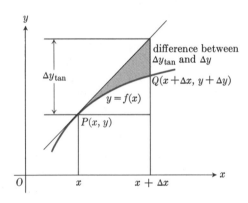

1–57 If f has a derivative at x, the difference between $\Delta y_{\text{tan}} = f'(x)\, \Delta x$ and Δy will be small when Δx is small.

PROBLEMS

1. If a, b, c are constants and

$$f(t) = at^2 + bt + c,$$

show that

$$f'(t) = \lim_{\Delta t \to 0} \frac{f(t + \Delta t) - f(t)}{\Delta t} = 2at + b.$$

In Problems 2 through 10, the law of motion gives s as a function of t. Apply the *result* found in Problem 1 above to write the velocity, $v = ds/dt$, by inspection.

2. $s = 2t^2 + 5t - 3$

3. $s = \frac{1}{2}gt^2 + v_0 t + s_0$ (g, v_0, s_0 constants)

4. $s = 4t + 3$ **5.** $s = t^2 - 3t + 2$

6. $s = 4 - 2t - t^2$ **7.** $s = (2t + 3)^2$

8. $s = (2 - t)^2$ **9.** $s = 3 - 2t^2$

10. $s = 64t - 16t^2$

11. The following data give the coordinates s of a moving body for various values of t. Plot s versus t on coordinate paper and sketch a smooth curve through the given points. Assuming that this smooth curve represents the motion of the body, estimate the velocity (a) at $t = 1.0$, (b) at $t = 2.5$, (c) at $t = 2.0$.

s (in ft)	10	38	58	70	74	70	58	38	10
t (in sec)	0	0.5	1.0	1.5	2.0	2.5	3.0	3.5	4.0

12.* When a certain chemical reaction was allowed to run for t minutes, it produced the amounts of substance $A(t)$ shown in the following table.

t (min)	10	15	20	25	30	35	40
$A(t)$ (moles)	26.5	36.5	44.8	52.1	57.1	61.3	64.4

a) Find the average rate of the reaction for the interval from $t = 20$ to $t = 30$.

b) Plot the data points from the table, draw a smooth curve through them, and estimate the instantaneous rate of the reaction at $t = 25$.

When a model rocket is launched, the propellant burns for a few seconds, accelerating the rocket upwards. After burnout, the rocket coasts upward for a while, then begins a period of free fall back to the ground. A small explosive charge pops out a parachute shortly after the rocket starts down. The parachute slows the rocket's fall enough to keep it from breaking when it lands. Figure 1–58 shows velocity data from the flight of a model rocket. Use the data to answer the questions in Problems 13–17.

1–58 Velocity of a model rocket.

13. How fast was the rocket climbing when the engine stopped?

---

14. For how many seconds did the engine burn?

15. When did the rocket reach its highest point? What was its velocity then?

16. When did the parachute pop out? How fast was the rocket falling then?

17. How long did the rocket fall before the parachute popped out?

18. Suppose that the dollar cost of producing x washing machines is $f(x) = 2000 + 100x - 0.1x^2$.

a) Find the average cost of producing 100 washing machines.

b) Find the marginal cost for 100 washing machines.

c) Show that the marginal cost for 100 washing machines is approximately the cost of producing one more washing machine after the first 100 have been made, by (i) computing the cost directly, (ii) interpreting Fig. 1–57 drawn for $f(x) = 2000 + 100x - 0.1x^2$, with $x = 100$ and $\Delta x = 1$.

19. When a bactericide was added to a nutrient broth in which bacteria were growing, the bacteria population continued to grow for a while, but then stopped growing and began to decline. The size of the population at time t (hours) was $b(t) = 10^6 + 10^4 t - 10^3 t^2$. Use the result of Problem 1 to find the growth rates at

a) $t = 0$,   **b)** $t = 5$, and   **c)** $t = 10$ hours.

d) About how long did it take to kill all the bacteria?

20. A swimming pool is to be drained for cleaning. If Q represents the number of gallons of water in the pool t minutes after the pool has started to drain, and $Q = 200(30 - t)^2$, how fast is the water running out at the end of 10 minutes? What is the *average* rate at which the water flows out during the first 10 minutes?

21. a) If the radius of a circle changes from r to $(r + \Delta r)$, what is the average rate of change of the area of the circle with respect to the radius?

b) Find the instantaneous rate of change of the area with respect to the radius.

22. The volume V (ft³) of a sphere of radius r (ft) is $V = \frac{4}{3}\pi r^3$. Find the rate of change of V with respect to r.

23. The radius r and altitude h of a certain cone are equal at all times. Find the rate of change of the volume $V = \frac{1}{3}\pi r^2 h$ with respect to h.

PROPERTIES OF LIMITS

In this article we look more carefully at what it means to say that something "approaches a limit." The limits we are most concerned with are the ones that come up in the calculation of the derivative

$$f'(x) = \lim_{\Delta x \to 0} \frac{f(x + \Delta x) - f(x)}{\Delta x} \qquad (1)$$

of the function $y = f(x)$. In the next chapter we shall develop rules that will let us calculate the derivatives of a wide variety of functions without having to apply Eq. (1) directly each time, as we have had to do so far. But these rules still rest upon this defining equation, for they are themselves derived from it.

Let us return to the function

$$f(x) = x^3 - 3x + 3 \qquad (2)$$

investigated in Article 1–7. By algebra we find that

$$\frac{f(x + \Delta x) - f(x)}{\Delta x} = 3x^2 - 3 + 3x\,\Delta x + (\Delta x)^2. \qquad (3)$$

The notion of limit has not entered so far. But now we say "hold x fixed and make Δx approach 0." That is, Δx is to vary in Eq. (3) while x is held constant. What is the domain of the variable Δx in this equation? The answer is first that Δx must be such that the function in (2) is defined at $(x + \Delta x)$. That is, $f(x + \Delta x)$ must make sense. In the present case this places no restriction on Δx, since Eq. (2) defines f for the domain of all real numbers. But there is also the second restriction that Δx *must be different from zero*, because we cannot divide by zero. Thus we reach a crucial point. We want to know what happens in Eq. (3) when Δx is taken nearer and nearer to zero, but we cannot take $\Delta x = 0$.

We get past this point by making two observations. First, Eq. (3) holds for every value of Δx different from zero, no matter how small. Second, for each fixed value of x we can make the right side of Eq. (3) as nearly equal to

$$L(x) = 3x^2 - 3 \qquad (4)$$

as we wish, provided we don't wish for exact equality, by taking Δx sufficiently close to zero. Let us write $F(x, \Delta x)$ for the right side of Eq. (3) to acknowledge that it depends on both x and Δx. That is,

$$F(x, \Delta x) = 3x^2 - 3 + 3x\,\Delta x + (\Delta x)^2. \qquad (5)$$

Then our second observation is what we mean when we say that for each x the limit of $F(x, \Delta x)$, as Δx approaches zero, is $L(x)$. We illustrate this idea and develop a more formal statement of it in the course of the next example.

EXAMPLE 1. Suppose that we are manufacturers of the product $F(x, \Delta x)$ in Eq. (5), which, if we could achieve perfection, would be the $L(x)$ of Eq. (4). A buyer comes to us to place an order. The buyer is particular, but does not expect perfection. To satisfy the buyer, we need only produce an $F(x, \Delta x)$ that differs from perfection by an amount less than a certain tolerance limit, which the buyer will specify. In other words, we can sell our $F(x, \Delta x)$ if we can guarantee that it lies between

$$L(x) - \epsilon \qquad \text{and} \qquad L(x) + \epsilon, \qquad (6)$$

where ϵ (epsilon) is a positive number representing the prescribed tolerance limit. For instance, we might contract to grind a shaft to a diameter of 3 ± 10^{-5} inches. The ideal diameter is $L(x) = 3$ in. The tolerance limit is $\epsilon = 10^{-5}$ in. The diameter of the shaft we produce is $F(x, \Delta x)$. We can sell our work provided $F(x, \Delta x)$ lies between $L(x) - 10^{-5}$ and $L(x) + 10^{-5}$ inches.

Now, the way we improve the quality of our product $F(x, \Delta x)$ is to make Δx small. In other words, the amount of imperfection,

$$F(x, \Delta x) - L(x) = 3x\,\Delta x + (\Delta x)^2 \qquad (7)$$

is brought between $-\epsilon$ and $+\epsilon$,

$$-\epsilon < 3x\,\Delta x + (\Delta x)^2 < +\epsilon, \qquad (8a)$$

by making Δx close to zero. By taking pains, we can make Δx as close to zero (either positive or negative) as we wish. Therefore we can always satisfy the most exacting customer.

Here is the order of events. The customer first places an order and specifies an $\epsilon > 0$. Then, for any fixed x, we satisfy the inequalities in (8a) by taking Δx close enough to zero. That is, given the ϵ, there is a positive number δ (Greek letter "delta"), which may be very small, such that (8a) is satisfied when we take Δx so small that $-\delta < \Delta x < \delta$, $\Delta x \neq 0$.

How do we find a δ that will work for the given ϵ?

The inequalities in (8a) are the same as

$$\left| 3x\,\Delta x + (\Delta x)^2 \right| < \epsilon. \qquad (8b)$$

Can we solve (8b) for Δx, in terms of ϵ and x? *Yes*, if we use a bit of strategy! That $(\Delta x)^2$ in (8b) makes the mathematics harder than it has to be. We do not, in fact, have to find the *complete* solution set for (8b): We need only be sure we make $|\Delta x|$ small enough to win. We can take advantage of the fact that powers like $(\Delta x)^2$, $(\Delta x)^3$, and so on are smaller in absolute value than the first power $|\Delta x|$, whenever $|\Delta x| < 1$. Since we plan to make $|\Delta x|$ small anyway, we start by making it less than one. So our first step in "solving" (8b) is to make

i) $$0 < |\Delta x| < 1,$$

and to observe that (i) implies

ii) $$|(\Delta x)|^2 < |\Delta x|.$$

The next step is to apply the triangle inequality $|a + b| \leq |a| + |b|$ to the left side of (8b), and get

iii) $$\left| 3x\,\Delta x + (\Delta x)^2 \right| \leq \left| 3x\,\Delta x \right| + \left| (\Delta x)^2 \right|.$$

Combining (i) through (iii), we get

$$\left| 3x\,\Delta x + (\Delta x)^2 \right| \leq \left| 3x\,\Delta x \right| + \left| (\Delta x)^2 \right|$$
$$< \left| 3x \right|\left| \Delta x \right| + \left| \Delta x \right| = \left(\left| 3x \right| + 1 \right)\left| \Delta x \right|. \qquad (8c)$$

From this we see that any $|\Delta x|$ that is both less than 1 and small enough to make

$$\left(\left| 3x \right| + 1 \right)\left| \Delta x \right| < \epsilon \qquad (8d)$$

will satisfy (8b). To find such a Δx, we divide both sides of (8d) by $(\left| 3x \right| + 1)$:

$$\left| \Delta x \right| < \frac{\epsilon}{\left| 3x \right| + 1}. \qquad (8e)$$

For specific numerical values of ϵ and x we can satisfy (8b) if we let δ be the smaller of the two numbers

$$1 \qquad \text{and} \qquad \frac{\epsilon}{|3x| + 1},$$

and then require that $0 < |\Delta x| < \delta$.

What we have just shown, for the particular functions $L(x)$ and $F(x, \Delta x)$ given by Eqs. (4) and (5), is this: *Given any number x and any positive number ϵ, there exists a positive number δ such that*

$$\big| F(x, \Delta x) - L(x) \big| < \epsilon$$

for all Δx with

$$0 < |\Delta x| < \delta.$$

Because there is such a positive number δ for *each* possible tolerance specification ϵ, we say that $L(x)$ is the *limit* of $F(x, \Delta x)$ as Δx approaches zero.

REMARK 1.   In the foregoing example, if we were interested only in values of x for which $-4 \leq x \leq 4$, say, then $|3x| + 1 \leq 12 + 1 = 13$. In such a situation, for any positive number ϵ, the number $\delta = \min\{1, \epsilon/13\}$ would always be a sufficiently small positive number to guarantee fulfillment of our contract.

REMARK 2.   We sometimes have to impose a further restriction $|\Delta x| \leq h$ on Δx to keep $(x + \Delta x)$ within the domain of f. (This eventuality is taken into account in the first sentence of the definition below.) If $f(x) = \sqrt{9 - x^2}$, then

$$F(x, \Delta x) = \frac{\sqrt{9 - (x + \Delta x)^2} - \sqrt{9 - x^2}}{\Delta x},$$

and we need to require

$$|x + \Delta x| \leq 3 \qquad \text{as well as} \quad |x| \leq 3 \qquad \text{and} \qquad \Delta x \neq 0.$$

For $x = 2.7$, for example, we could take $h = 0.3$ to guarantee $|x + \Delta x| \leq 3$ when $|\Delta x| \leq h$.

These preliminary remarks should now enable us to understand the following definition of a limit.

Definition.   *Let $F(x, \Delta x)$ be defined for some fixed value of x and for all values of Δx (different from zero) in some interval $-h < \Delta x < +h$, that is, for $-h < \Delta x < 0$ and for $0 < \Delta x < +h$. Let there be a number $L(x)$ (which may depend upon x), such that, to any positive number ϵ, there corresponds a positive number δ, $0 < \delta < h$, having the property that $F(x, \Delta x)$ differs from $L(x)$ by less than ϵ for every $|\Delta x|$ that is different from zero and less than δ. That is, if*

$$0 < |\Delta x| < \delta, \tag{9a}$$

then

$$|F(x, \Delta x) - L(x)| < \epsilon. \tag{9b}$$

We then say that $L(x)$ is the limit of $F(x, \Delta x)$ as Δx approaches zero, and abbreviate this by writing

$$L(x) = \lim_{\Delta x \to 0} F(x, \Delta x). \tag{10}$$

The notation in the definition above is complicated by the fact that the function $F(x, \Delta x)$ depends upon both x and Δx, although only Δx varies during the limit process. If we ignore the x completely and use another letter, say t instead of Δx, to stand for the variable, we obtain a simpler definition of limit, as follows.

Definition.   *A function F, which is defined on the domain*

$$t_1 < t < c \qquad and \qquad c < t < t_2,$$

is said to approach the limit L as t approaches c, and we write

$$\lim_{t \to c} F(t) = L$$

if, given any positive number ϵ, there is a positive number δ such that the values of F are within ϵ of L for all t within δ of c, $t \neq c$:

$$|F(t) - L| < \epsilon \qquad when \quad 0 < |t - c| < \delta.$$

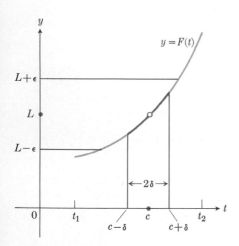

Note that saying "$F(t)$ approaches L" is the same as saying "$F(t) - L$ approaches zero." Also, there is no best value of δ. If one value of δ works for a given ϵ, then every positive number *smaller* than that δ will work, too. (See Fig. 1–59.)

The function F may or may not be defined at $t = c$. We shall illustrate the definition by several examples.

Sometimes, the function F is defined at c and the limit as t approaches c is just $F(c)$. This is the situation when $F(t)$ is a polynomial function of t.

1–59 $F(t)$ can be kept between $L - \epsilon$ and $L + \epsilon$ by keeping t between $c - \delta$ and $c + \delta$.

EXAMPLE 2.   Show that the limit of $F(t) = t^2$, as t approaches 3, is $L = 9$.

Solution.   What we have to show is this: For any positive number ϵ there is a positive number δ such that

$$|t^2 - 9| < \epsilon \qquad when \quad 0 < |t - 3| < \delta.$$

Note that

$$|t^2 - 9| = |(t + 3)(t - 3)| = |t + 3| \, |t - 3|$$

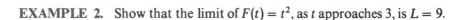

is the product of a factor $|t + 3|$ that is near 6 and a factor $|t - 3|$ that is near 0 when t is near 3. If we first require t to stay within, say, 0.5 of 3, then

$$2.5 < t < 3.5 \qquad and \qquad 5.5 < t + 3 < 6.5.$$

As a result,

$$|t^2 - 9| < 6.5|t - 3|.$$

Now

$$6.5|t - 3| < \epsilon \quad \text{provided} \quad |t - 3| < \frac{\epsilon}{6.5}.$$

Therefore, if $\delta = \min\{0.5, \epsilon/6.5\}$ then

$$|t^2 - 9| < \epsilon \quad \text{when} \quad 0 < |t - 3| < \delta.$$

(See Fig. 1-60.)

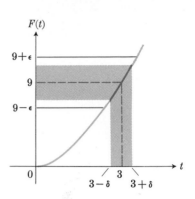

1-60 $F(t) = t^2$ lies between $9 - \epsilon$ and $9 + \epsilon$ for every $t \neq 3$ between $3 - \delta$ and $3 + \delta$.

Sometimes a function $F(t)$ has one limit as t approaches c from the right, but another limit as t approaches c from the left. This is the case in the next example.

EXAMPLE 3. Investigate the limit of the function F defined by

$$F(t) = [t], \text{ the greatest integer in } t,$$

as t approaches 3. (See Fig. 1-61.)

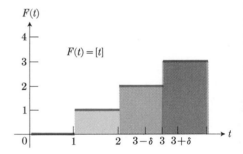

1-61 At each integer the greatest integer function has different right- and lefthand limits.

Solution. Our first guess might be that the required limit is $L = 3$, since certainly the functional values of $F(t) = [t]$ are close to 3 when t is equal to or slightly *greater* than 3. But when t is slightly *less* than 3, say $t = 2.9999$, then $[t] = 2$. That is, if δ is any positive number less than unity, $0 < \delta < 1$, then

$$[t] = 2 \quad \text{if} \quad 3 - \delta < t < 3,$$

while

$$[t] = 3 \quad \text{if} \quad 3 < t < 3 + \delta.$$

Hence, if we are challenged with a small positive ϵ, for example $\epsilon = 0.01$, we cannot find a $\delta > 0$ that makes

$$|[t] - 3| < \epsilon \quad \text{for} \quad 0 < |t - 3| < \delta.$$

In fact, no number L will work as the limit in this case. When t is near 3, *some* of the functional values of $[t]$ are 2 while others are 3. Hence the functional values are not all close to any one number L. Therefore,

$$\lim_{t \to 3} [t] \text{ does not exist.}$$

The so-called "right- and lefthand limits" do, however, exist. As the names imply, the righthand limit L^+ is a number such that the functional values of $F(t)$ are close to L^+ when t is slightly greater than 3 (that is, to the right of 3), and the lefthand limit L^- is a number such that $F(t)$ is close to L^- when t is slightly less than 3. In our example,

$$L^+ = \lim_{t \to 3^+} [t] = 3, \qquad L^- = \lim_{t \to 3^-} [t] = 2.$$

The notation $t \to 3^+$ may be read "t approaches 3 from above" (or "from the right," or "through values larger than 3") with an analogous meaning for $t \to 3^-$.

Sometimes a function $F(t)$ has neither a right- nor a lefthand limit as t approaches c.

EXAMPLE 4.   The function F, $F(t) = \sin(1/t)$, $t \neq 0$, has no limit as $t \to 0$. This is a consequence of the fact that in every neighborhood of $t = 0$ the function F takes all values between -1 and $+1$. Hence there is no single number L such that the functional values $F(t)$ are *all* close to L when t is close to zero. These remarks apply even when we restrict t to positive values or to negative values. In other words, this function does not even have a righthand limit or a lefthand limit as t approaches zero. (See Fig. 1–62.)

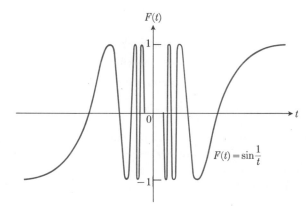

1–62   The function $F(t) = \sin(1/t)$, $t \neq 0$, has neither a right- nor a lefthand limit as t approaches 0.

Sometimes a function $F(t)$ has a limit as $t \to c$ even though the function is not defined at $t = c$. We shall describe such a function in Example 6, but first we state a theorem that gives us information we can use to treat the example easily. The theorem presents four fundamental properties of limits.

***Theorem* 1.**   *If* $L_1 = \lim_{t \to c} F_1(t)$ *and* $L_2 = \lim_{t \to c} F_2(t)$ *both exist and are finite, then*

  i) $\lim [F_1(t) + F_2(t)] = \lim F_1(t) + \lim F_2(t) = L_1 + L_2,$

  ii) $\lim [kF_1(t)] = k \lim F_1(t) = kL_1$ (*k any number*),

  iii) $\lim [F_1(t) \cdot F_2(t)] = \lim F_1(t) \cdot \lim F_2(t) = L_1 L_2,$

  iv) $\lim \dfrac{F_1(t)}{F_2(t)} = \dfrac{\lim F_1(t)}{\lim F_2(t)} = \dfrac{L_1}{L_2},$ *if* $L_2 \neq 0,$

it being understood that all of the limits are to be taken as $t \to c$.

The formal proof of Theorem 1 is given in Article 1–11. You may wish to postpone the details until then. Informally, we can paraphrase the theorem in terms that make it highly reasonable: When t is close to c, $F_1(t)$ is close to L_1 and $F_2(t)$ is close to L_2. Then we naturally think that $F_1(t) + F_2(t)$ is close to $L_1 + L_2$, $kF_1(t)$ is close to kL_1, $F_1(t) \cdot F_2(t)$ is close to $L_1 L_2$, and $F_1(t)/F_2(t)$ is close to L_1/L_2 if L_2 is not zero. We use these ideas when we calculate sums, products, or quotients in which we approximate irrational numbers like π or $\sqrt{3}$ with rational numbers like 3.14159 or 1.732. What keeps this discussion from being a proof is that the word "close" is not precise. The phrases "arbitrarily close to" and "sufficiently close to" might improve things a bit, but the full ϵ and δ treatment of Article 1–11 is the clincher.

The limits must be *finite* in this theorem, and (iv) applies only if the denominator does not tend to zero.

We should add a word about the meaning to be attached to such statements as: "When t approaches zero, $1/t$ approaches infinity" or, in symbols,

$$\lim_{t \to 0} \frac{1}{t} = \infty.$$

(See Fig. 1–63.) The specific meaning of the expression

$$\lim_{t \to c} F(t) = \infty$$

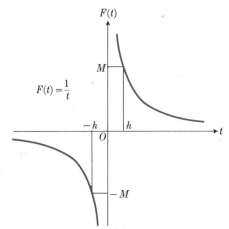

is: "For any M, however large it may be, there is an $h > 0$ such that $|F(t)| > M$ for all t satisfying $0 < |t - c| < h$." Note that this allows $F(t)$ to be either negative or positive, and requires only that the *numerical* or *absolute* value of $F(t)$ can be made indefinitely large by taking t sufficiently close to c. If we may replace $|F(t)| > M$ by $F(t) > M$ in the statement above, we say $\lim F(t) = +\infty$, and if we may replace $|F(t)| > M$ by $F(t) < -M$, we say $\lim F(t) = -\infty$. Thus

$$\lim_{t \to 0} \frac{1}{t} = \infty, \qquad \lim_{t \to 0} \frac{1}{|t|} = +\infty, \qquad \lim_{t \to 0} -\frac{1}{t^2} = -\infty. \qquad \textbf{(11)}$$

When speaking of infinity as the limit of a function f, we do not mean that the difference between $f(t)$ and infinity becomes small, but rather that $f(t)$ is numerically large when t is near c.

1–63 $\lim_{t \to 0^+} (1/t) = +\infty$ and $\lim_{t \to 0^-} (1/t) = -\infty$.

The great virtue of Theorem 1 is this: Once we notice that, for the function $F(t) = t$,

$$\lim_{t \to c} t = c, \qquad \qquad \textbf{(12)}$$

and that, for the constant function $F(t) = k$ (the function whose value is the constant k for every t),

$$\lim_{t \to c} k = k, \qquad \qquad \textbf{(13)}$$

then we immediately have

$$\lim_{t \to c} t^2 = c^2, \qquad \qquad \text{(from (iii))}$$

$$\lim_{t \to c} t^2 - 5 = c^2 - 5, \qquad \qquad \text{(from (i))}$$

$$\lim_{t \to c} 4t^2 = 4c^2, \qquad \qquad \text{(from (ii))}$$

and, if $c \neq 0$,

$$\lim_{t \to c} \frac{t^2 - 5}{4t^2} = \frac{c^2 - 5}{4c^2} \qquad \text{(from (iv))}.$$

In short, if $f(t)$ and $g(t)$ are any polynomials in t whatsoever, then

$$\lim_{t \to c} \frac{f(t)}{g(t)} = \frac{f(c)}{g(c)}, \qquad \text{provided } g(c) \neq 0. \qquad \textbf{(14)}$$

(See Problems 1–6 of Article 1–11.)

EXAMPLE 5. Find

$$\lim_{t \to 2} \frac{t^2 + 2t + 4}{t + 2}.$$

Solution. The function whose limit we are to find is the quotient of two polynomials. The denominator, $t + 2$, is not zero when $t = 2$. Therefore, by Eq. (14),

$$\lim_{t \to 2} \frac{t^2 + 2t + 4}{t + 2} = \frac{(2)^2 + 2 \cdot 2 + 4}{2 + 2} = 3.$$

The condition $L_2 \neq 0$ in part (iv) of Theorem 1 means, of course, that limits like the ones required in the determination of instantaneous velocity and the slope of a curve, that have *both* L_1 and L_2 equal to zero, cannot be evaluated by the direct use of (iv). The next example shows how we can sometimes get around this problem. The key is to replace the offending quotient $f(t)/g(t)$ by an expression that (1) has the same values as the quotient for all values of t near c, and therefore the same limit as $t \to c$ (if there is one), and (2) whose limit as $t \to c$ is found by evaluating the expression at $t = c$. Fortunately, to do all this is often easier than it sounds.

EXAMPLE 6. Does the function

$$F(t) = \frac{t^3 - 8}{t^2 - 4}$$

have a limit as t approaches 2? If so, what is it?

Solution. Both the numerator and the denominator of $F(t)$ approach 0 as $t \to 2$. However, if we factor the numerator and denominator, we find that

$$\frac{t^3 - 8}{t^2 - 4} = \frac{(t - 2)(t^2 + 2t + 4)}{(t - 2)(t + 2)}.$$

Therefore, for all values of t different from 2, $(t - 2)/(t - 2) = 1$ and

$$\frac{t^3 - 8}{t^2 - 4} = \frac{t^2 + 2t + 4}{t + 2}.$$

Hence,

$$\lim_{t \to 2} \frac{t^3 - 8}{t^2 - 4} = \lim_{t \to 2} \frac{t^2 + 2t + 4}{t + 2} = 3.$$

The function $F(t)$ does have a limit as $t \to 2$, and that limit is 3.

The two basic steps in evaluating the limit of the quotient $F(t)$ as t approached 2 were: (1) divide the numerator and denominator by a common factor, and (2) evaluate the simplified expression at $t = 2$.

We conclude this article with a theorem that will be used repeatedly in our later work. The theorem is often called the "sandwich theorem."

Theorem 2 (The Sandwich Theorem).   *Suppose $f(t) \leq g(t) \leq h(t)$ for all values of t near c. Furthermore, suppose that the function values $f(t)$ and $h(t)$ approach a common limit L as t approaches c. Then $g(t)$ also approaches L as limit when t approaches c.*

Proof.   By hypothesis, to any positive number ϵ there corresponds a positive number δ such that both $f(t)$ and $h(t)$ lie between $L - \epsilon$ and $L + \epsilon$ when t is within δ units of c, and $t \neq c$; that is,

$$L - \epsilon < f(t) < L + \epsilon, \qquad L - \epsilon < h(t) < L + \epsilon$$

when

$$0 < |t - c| < \delta.$$

But this also implies

$$L - \epsilon < f(t) \leq g(t) \leq h(t) < L + \epsilon$$

or

$$L - \epsilon < g(t) < L + \epsilon.$$

In other words,

$$|g(t) - L| < \epsilon \qquad \text{when} \quad 0 < |t - c| < \delta.$$

This establishes the conclusion,

$$\lim_{t \to c} g(t) = L. \qquad \text{Q.E.D.}$$

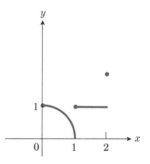

1-64   To define a function like the one graphed here, different formulas may be used for different parts of the domain.

PROBLEMS

Evaluate the limits indicated in Problems 1–8.

1. $\lim\limits_{t \to 2} \dfrac{t + 3}{t + 2}$

2. $\lim\limits_{x \to 1} \dfrac{x^2 - 1}{x - 1}$

3. $\lim\limits_{y \to 2} \dfrac{y^2 + 5y + 6}{y + 2}$

4. $\lim\limits_{y \to 2} \dfrac{y^2 - 5y + 6}{y - 2}$

5. $\lim\limits_{x \to -3} \dfrac{x^2 + 4x + 3}{x + 3}$

6. $\lim\limits_{x \to 1} \dfrac{2x - 1}{8x^3 - 1}$

7. $\lim\limits_{t \to \infty} \dfrac{t + 1}{t^2 + 1}$ [Set $t = 1/h$, simplify, and let $h \to 0$.]

8. $\lim\limits_{t \to \infty} \dfrac{t^2 - 2t + 3}{2t^2 + 5t - 3}$

9. The values of the function graphed in Fig. 1–64 are

given by:

$$f(x) = \begin{cases} \sqrt{1 - x^2}, & \text{if } 0 \leq x < 1, \\ 1, & \text{if } 1 \leq x < 2, \\ 2, & \text{if } x = 2. \end{cases}$$

a) At what points c in the domain of f does $\lim_{x \to c} f(x)$ exist?

b) At what points does only the lefthand limit exist?

c) Only the righthand limit?

10. Suppose that the function f is defined by

$$f(x) = \begin{cases} x & \text{if } -1 \leq x < 0, \text{ or } 0 < x \leq 1, \\ 1 & \text{if } x = 0, \\ 0 & \text{if } x < -1, \text{ or } x > 1. \end{cases}$$

Graph f, and repeat parts (a), (b), and (c) of Problem 9.

11. The attempt to find a derivative for $f(x) = |x|$ at $x = 0$ leads to the consideration of $\lim(|\Delta x|/\Delta x)$. Find $\lim_{\Delta x \to 0^+}(|\Delta x|/\Delta x)$ and $\lim_{\Delta x \to 0^-}(|\Delta x|/\Delta x)$ and conclude that $|x|$ has no derivative at 0.

12. Find some neighborhood of $t = 3$, that is, a domain $0 < |t - 3| < \delta$, such that, when t is restricted to this domain, the difference between $t^2 + t$ and 12 will be numerically smaller than (a) $\frac{1}{10}$, (b) $\frac{1}{100}$, (c) ϵ, where ϵ may be any positive number. [See Example 2.]

13. As $x \to 0^+$, the functions $1/x$, $1/x^2$, $1/\sqrt{x}$ all become infinite. Which one increases most rapidly and which one least rapidly?

14. Find $\lim_{x \to 1}[(x^n - 1)/(x - 1)]$, n a positive integer. Compare your result with the limit in Problem 2.

It is sometimes easy to guess the value of a limit once it is known to exist. Ignoring the question of whether the limits in Problems 15 and 16 exist (they do, and are finite), use a calculator to guess their value. First take $\Delta x = 0.1, 0.01, 0.001, \ldots$, continuing until you are ready to guess the right-hand limit. Then test your guess by using $\Delta x = -0.1, -0.01, \ldots$

15. (*Calculator*) $\displaystyle\lim_{\Delta x \to 0} \frac{\sqrt{4 + \Delta x} - 2}{\Delta x}$

16. (*Calculator*) $\displaystyle\lim_{\Delta x \to 0} \frac{\sin \Delta x}{\Delta x}$

[Use radian measure. Also see Fig. 1–65.]

17. (*Calculator*) To estimate the value of the derivative of

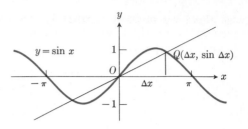

1–65 The slope of the secant OQ is $(\sin \Delta x)/\Delta x$.

$f(x) = \sqrt{9 - x^2}$ at $x = 0$, first write $F(x, \Delta x)$ from *Remark 2* with $x = 0$. Then proceed as in Problems 15 and 16.

18. (*Calculator*) Example 4 shows that the function $F(t) = \sin(1/t)$, $t \neq 0$, has no limit as $t \to 0$. However, the function $F(t) = t \cdot \sin(1/t)$, $t \neq 0$, does have a limit as $t \to 0$. Use a calculator to collect numerical evidence for this.

19. Each of the limits in Problems 15 and 16 is the derivative of a function at $x = 0$. Find the function in each case.

In Problems 20 and 21, each limit is the derivative of a function at some point. Find the function and the point.

20. $\displaystyle\lim_{h \to 0} \frac{(1 + h)^2 - 1}{h}$ **21.** $\displaystyle\lim_{h \to 0} \frac{|-1 + h| - |-1|}{h}$

22. The inequality

$$1 - \frac{t^2}{6} < \frac{\sin t}{t} < 1$$

holds when t is measured in radians and $|t| < 1$. Use this inequality and Theorems 1 and 2 to find $\lim_{t \to 0}(\sin t)/t$.

**A PROOF OF
THE LIMIT THEOREM**

We now prove Theorem 1 of Article 1–10. In all four parts of the theorem we assume that $F_1(t)$ and $F_2(t)$ have finite limits L_1 and L_2 as t approaches c:

$$\lim F_1(t) = L_1, \qquad \lim F_2(t) = L_2. \tag{1}$$

i) $\lim[F_1(t) + F_2(t)] = L_1 + L_2$

To prove that the sum, $F_1(t) + F_2(t)$, has the limit $L_1 + L_2$, as t approaches c we must show that:

To any positive number ϵ, there corresponds a positive number δ such that

$$|F_1(t) + F_2(t) - (L_1 + L_2)| < \epsilon \qquad \text{whenever} \quad 0 < |t - c| < \delta. \tag{2a}$$

To this end, let ϵ be an arbitrary positive number. Then $\epsilon/2$ is also a positive number and, because $F_1(t)$ has L_1 as limit, there is a positive number δ_1 such that

$$|F_1(t) - L_1| < \frac{\epsilon}{2} \qquad \text{when} \quad 0 < |t - c| < \delta_1. \tag{2b}$$

Likewise, there is a positive number δ_2 such that

$$|F_2(t) - L_2| < \frac{\epsilon}{2} \qquad \text{when} \quad 0 < |t - c| < \delta_2. \tag{2c}$$

Now let $\delta = \min\{\delta_1, \delta_2\}$. Then δ is a positive number, and whenever $0 < |t - c| < \delta$, we have

$$|F_1(t) + F_2(t) - (L_1 + L_2)| = |F_1(t) - L_1 + F_2(t) - L_2|$$
$$\leq |F_1(t) - L_1| + |F_2(t) - L_2|$$
$$< \frac{\epsilon}{2} + \frac{\epsilon}{2} = \epsilon.$$

This establishes part (i) of the theorem, because we have shown that the condition required by (2a) is met.

ii) $\lim [kF_1(t)] = kL_1$

For the second part of the theorem, let k be any number and suppose that ϵ is an arbitrary positive number. Then $\epsilon/(1 + |k|)$ is positive, and, because $F_1(t)$ has L_1 as its limit when t approaches c, there is a positive number δ such that

$$|F_1(t) - L_1| < \frac{\epsilon}{1 + |k|} \qquad \text{when} \quad 0 < |t - c| < \delta. \tag{3a}$$

If we multiply both sides of the first inequality (3a) by $|k|$, and use the fact that $|k|/(1 + |k|)$ is less than 1, we see that

$$|kF_1(t) - kL_1| = |k| \cdot |F_1(t) - L_1| < \epsilon \qquad \text{when} \quad 0 < |t - c| < \delta. \tag{3b}$$

This establishes part (ii) of the theorem.

iii) $\lim [F_1(t) \cdot F_2(t)] = L_1 \cdot L_2$

Let ϵ be an arbitrary positive number, and write

$$F_1(t) = L_1 + (F_1(t) - L_1), \qquad F_2(t) = L_2 + (F_2(t) - L_2).$$

When we multiply these expressions and subtract $L_1 L_2$, we get

$$F_1(t) \cdot F_2(t) - L_1 L_2 = L_1(F_2(t) - L_2) + L_2(F_1(t) - L_1)$$
$$+ (F_1(t) - L_1) \cdot (F_2(t) - L_2). \tag{4a}$$

The numbers $\sqrt{\epsilon/3}$, $\epsilon/[3(1 + |L_1|)]$, and $\epsilon/[3(1 + |L_2|)]$ are all positive, and, because $F_1(t)$ has limit L_1 and $F_2(t)$ has limit L_2, there are positive numbers $\delta_1, \delta_2, \delta_3,$ and δ_4 such that

$$|F_1(t) - L_1| < \sqrt{\epsilon/3} \qquad \text{when} \quad 0 < |t - c| < \delta_1,$$
$$|F_2(t) - L_2| < \sqrt{\epsilon/3} \qquad \text{when} \quad 0 < |t - c| < \delta_2,$$
$$|F_1(t) - L_1| < \epsilon/[3(1 + |L_2|)] \qquad \text{when} \quad 0 < |t - c| < \delta_3,$$
$$|F_2(t) - L_2| < \epsilon/[3(1 + |L_1|)] \qquad \text{when} \quad 0 < |t - c| < \delta_4.$$

We now let δ be the minimum of the four positive numbers δ_1, δ_2, δ_3, δ_4. Then δ is a positive number and, by taking absolute values in Eq. (4a) and applying the triangle inequality, we get

$$|F_1(t)F_2(t) - L_1 L_2| \leq |L_1| \cdot |F_2(t) - L_2| + |L_2| \cdot |F_1(t) - L_1|$$
$$+ |F_1(t) - L_1| \cdot |F_2(t) - L_2|$$
$$< \frac{\epsilon}{3} + \frac{\epsilon}{3} + \frac{\epsilon}{3} = \epsilon \quad \text{when} \quad 0 < |t - c| < \delta. \quad \textbf{(4b)}$$

This completes the proof of the third part of the theorem.

iv) $\displaystyle \lim \frac{F_1(t)}{F_2(t)} = \frac{L_1}{L_2} \quad$ if $\quad L_2 \neq 0$

Since L_2 is not zero, $|L_2|$ is a positive number and, because $F_2(t)$ has L_2 as limit when t approaches c, we know that there is a positive number δ_1 such that

$$|F_2(t) - L_2| < \frac{|L_2|}{2} \quad \text{when} \quad 0 < |t - c| < \delta_1. \quad \textbf{(5a)}$$

Now, for any numbers A and B, it can be shown that

$$|A| - |B| \leq |A - B| \quad \text{and} \quad |B| - |A| \leq |A - B|,$$

from which it follows that

$$||A| - |B|| \leq |A - B|. \quad \textbf{(5b)}$$

Taking $A = F_2(t)$ and $B = L_2$ in (5b), we can deduce from (5a) that

$$-\tfrac{1}{2}|L_2| < |F_2(t)| - |L_2| < \tfrac{1}{2}|L_2| \quad \text{when} \quad 0 < |t - c| < \delta_1.$$

By adding $|L_2|$ to the three terms of the foregoing inequality we get

$$\tfrac{1}{2}|L_2| < |F_2(t)| < \tfrac{3}{2}|L_2|,$$

from which it follows that

$$\left| \frac{1}{F_2(t)} - \frac{1}{L_2} \right| = \left| \frac{L_2 - F_2(t)}{L_2 F_2(t)} \right| \leq \frac{2}{|L_2|^2} |L_2 - F_2(t)| \quad \textbf{(5c)}$$

when $0 < |t - c| < \delta_1$. All that we have done so far is to show that the difference between the reciprocals of $F_2(t)$ and L_2, at the left side of the inequality, is no greater in absolute value than a constant times $|L_2 - F_2(t)|$, when t is close enough to c. The fact that L_2 is the limit of $F_2(t)$ has not yet been used with full force. But now let ϵ be an arbitrary positive number. Then $\tfrac{1}{2}|L_2|^2\epsilon$ is also a positive number and there is a positive number δ_2 such that

$$|L_2 - F_2(t)| < \frac{\epsilon}{2} |L_2|^2 \quad \text{when} \quad 0 < |t - c| < \delta_2. \quad \textbf{(5d)}$$

We now let $\delta = \min \{\delta_1, \delta_2\}$ and have a positive number δ such that the inequalities in (5c) and (5d) combine to produce the result

$$\left| \frac{1}{F_2(t)} - \frac{1}{L_2} \right| < \epsilon \quad \text{when} \quad 0 < |t - c| < \delta.$$

What we have just shown is that

If $\lim F_2(t) = L_2$ *as t approaches c, and* $L_2 \neq 0$, *then*

$$\lim \frac{1}{F_2(t)} = \frac{1}{L_2}.$$

Having already proved the product law, we get the final quotient law by applying the product law to $F_1(t)$ and $1/F_2(t)$ as follows:

$$\lim \frac{F_1(t)}{F_2(t)} = \lim \left[F_1(t) \cdot \frac{1}{F_2(t)} \right] = [\lim F_1(t)] \cdot \left[\lim \frac{1}{F_2(t)} \right] = L_1 \cdot \frac{1}{L_2}.$$

PROBLEMS

1. Prove:

a) $\lim_{t \to c} t = c$

b) $\lim_{t \to c} k = k, \quad k$ a constant

2. If $F_1(t)$, $F_2(t)$, and $F_3(t)$ have limits L_1, L_2, and L_3, respectively, as t approaches c, prove that their sum has limit $L_1 + L_2 + L_3$. Generalize the result to the sum of any finite number of functions.

3. If n is any positive integer greater than 1, and $F_1(t)$, $F_2(t)$, ..., $F_n(t)$ have the finite limits L_1, L_2, ..., L_n, respectively, as t approaches c, prove that the product of the n functions has limit $L_1 \cdot L_2 \cdot \cdots \cdot L_n$. [Use part (iii) of Theorem 1, and induction on n.]

4. Use the results of Problems 1(a) and 3 to deduce that

$$\lim_{t \to c} t^n = c^n \quad \text{for any positive integer } n.$$

5. Use Theorem 1 and the results of Problems 1, 2, and 4 to prove that $\lim_{t \to c} f(t) = f(c)$ for any polynomial function

$$f(t) = a_0 t^n + a_1 t^{n-1} + \cdots + a_n.$$

6. Use Theorem 1 and the result of Problem 5 to prove that if $f(t)$ and $g(t)$ are polynomials, and if $g(c) \neq 0$, then

$$\lim_{t \to c} \frac{f(t)}{g(t)} = \frac{f(c)}{g(c)}.$$

REVIEW QUESTIONS AND EXERCISES

1. Define what is meant by the *slope* of a straight line. How would you find the slope of a straight line from its graph? From its equation?

2. In Fig. 1–66, the lines L_1, L_2, and L_3 have slopes m_1, m_2, m_3, respectively. Which slope is algebraically least? Greatest? Write the three slopes in order of increasing size with the symbols for "less than" or "greater than" correctly inserted between them.

3. Describe the family of lines $y - y_1 = m(x - x_1)$:

a) If (x_1, y_1) is fixed and different lines are drawn for different values of m;

b) If m and x_1 are fixed and different lines are drawn for different values of y_1.

4. Define *function*. What is the *domain* of a function? What is its *range*?

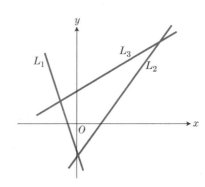

1–66 Lines L_1, L_2, L_3 have slopes m_1, m_2, m_3, respectively.

5. The domain of a certain function is the set $0 \le x \le 2$. The range of the function is the single number $y = 1$.

a) Sketch and describe the graph of the function.

b) Write an expression for the function.

c) If we interchange the axes in part (a), does the new graph so obtained represent a function? Explain.

6. Give an example of a step function different from those mentioned in the text.

7. Write a rule of the form $y = f(x)$ for the function f that is the composite of $y = |x - 10|$ followed by $y = \sqrt{1 - x}$. Find the largest possible domain of f and the corresponding range of y.

8. *Definition.* *A rational number is one that can be expressed in the form p/q, where p and q are integers with no common divisor greater than one, and q > 0. A real number that is not rational is called irrational.*

With these definitions in mind, plot a few points on the graph of the function that maps the rational number p/q (reduced to lowest terms as above) into $1/q$, and maps each irrational number into zero. This function has been described as the "ruler function" because of the resemblance of its graph to the markings on an ordinary ruler showing inches, half-inches, quarters, eighths, and sixteenths by lines of different lengths. The edge of the ruler corresponds to the x-axis. Do you see why this terminology is rather appropriate?

9. Is it appropriate to define a *tangent line* to a curve C at a point P on C as a line that has just the one point P in common with C? Illustrate your discussion with graphs.

10. Define, carefully, the concept of *slope of a tangent* to a curve at a point on the curve.

11. Define the concept of *average velocity*; of *instantaneous velocity*.

12. What more general concept includes both the concept of slope of the tangent to a curve and the concept of instantaneous velocity?

13. Define the derivative of a function at a point in its domain. Illustrate your definition by applying it to the function f defined by $f(x) = x^2$, at $x = 2$.

14. A function f, whose domain is the set of all real numbers, has the property that $f(x + h) = f(x) \cdot f(h)$ for all x and h; and $f(0) \neq 0$.

a) Show that $f(0) = 1$. [*Hint.* Let $h = x = 0$.]

b) If f has a derivative at 0, show that f has a derivative at every real number x, and that

$$f'(x) = f(x) \cdot f'(0).$$

15. Give an example of a function, defined for all real x, that fails to have a derivative (a) at some point, (b) at several points, (c) at infinitely many points.

16. Suppose F is a function whose values are all less than or equal to some constant M; $F(t) \le M$. Prove: If $\lim_{t \to c} F(t) = L$, then $L \le M$. [*Suggestion.* An indirect proof may be used to show that $L > M$ is false. For, if $L > M$, we may take $\frac{1}{2}(L - M)$ as a positive number ϵ, apply the definition of limit, and arrive at a contradiction.]

17. Let $f(x) = mx + b$. Prove that, for any positive number ϵ, the number $\delta = \epsilon/(1 + |m|)$ is a positive number such that

$$|f(x) - f(c)| < \epsilon \quad \text{when} \quad |x - c| < \delta.$$

What conclusion can you now draw about the limit of $f(x)$ as x approaches c?

18. Suppose that $\lim_{t \to c} F(t) = -7$ and $\lim_{t \to c} G(t) = 0$. Find the limit as t approaches c of each of the following functions.

a) $F^2(t)$ **b)** $3 \cdot F(t)$ **c)** $F(t) \cdot G(t)$ **d)** $\dfrac{F(t)}{G(t) + 7}$

MISCELLANEOUS PROBLEMS

1. a) Plot the points $A(8, 1)$, $B(2, 10)$, $C(-4, 6)$, $D(2, -3)$, $E(4\frac{2}{3}, 6)$.

b) Find the slopes of the lines AB, BC, CD, DA, CE, BD.

c) Do four of the five points A, B, C, D, E form a parallelogram? (Why?)

d) Do three of the five points lie on a common straight line? (Why?)

e) Does the origin $(0, 0)$ lie on a straight line through two of the five points? (Why?)

f) Find equations of the lines AB, CD, AD, CE, BD.

g) Find the coordinates of the points in which the lines AB, CD, AD, CE, BD intersect the x- and y-axes.

2. Given the straight line $2y - 3x = 4$ and the point $(1, -3)$.

a) Find the equation of the straight line through the given point and perpendicular to the given line.

b) Find the distance between the given point and the given line.

3. Plot the three points $A(6, 4)$, $B(4, -3)$, and $C(-2, 3)$.

a) Is triangle ABC a right triangle? Why?

b) Is it isosceles? Why?

c) Does the origin lie inside, outside, or on the boundary of the triangle? Why?

d) If C is replaced by a point $C'(-2, y)$ such that angle $C'BA$ is a right angle, find y, the ordinate of C'.

4. Find the equations of the straight lines passing through the origin which are tangent to the circle of center $(2, 1)$ and radius 2.

5. Let $P_1(x_1, y_1)$ and $P_2(x_2, y_2)$ be any two points. Find the coordinates of the midpoint of the line segment $P_1 P_2$.

6. The x- and y-intercepts of a line L are respectively a and b. Show that an equation of L is $(x/a) + (y/b) = 1$.

7. Given the line L: $ax + by + c = 0$. Find (a) its slope, (b) its y-intercept, (c) its x-intercept, (d) the line through the origin perpendicular to L.

8. Show that the distance between a point $P(x_1, y_1)$ and a line $ax + by + c = 0$ is equal to

$$\frac{|ax_1 + by_1 + c|}{\sqrt{a^2 + b^2}}.$$

(There are neat solutions of this problem in Vol. 59, 1952, of the *American Mathematical Monthly*, pp. 242 and 248.)

9. How many circles can you find that are tangent to the three lines

$$L_1: \quad x + y = 1;$$

$$L_2: \quad y = x + 1;$$

$$L_3: \quad x - 3y = 1?$$

Give the center and radius of at least one such circle. You may use the result of Problem 8.

10. Find, in terms of b, b', and m, the perpendicular distance between the parallel lines $y = mx + b$ and $y = mx + b'$.

11. Given the two lines

$$L_1: \quad a_1 x + b_1 y + c_1 = 0; \qquad L_2: \quad a_2 x + b_2 y + c_2 = 0.$$

If k is a constant, describe the set of points whose coordinates satisfy the equation

$$(a_1 x + b_1 y + c_1) + k(a_2 x + b_2 y + c_2) = 0.$$

12. Determine the coordinates of the point on the straight line $y = 3x + 1$ that is equidistant from $(0, 0)$ and $(-3, 4)$.

13. Find an equation of a straight line that is perpendicular to $5x - y = 1$ and is such that the area of the triangle formed by the x-axis, the y-axis, and the straight line is equal to 5.

14. Given the equation $y = (x^2 + 2)/(x^2 - 1)$. Express x in terms of y and determine the values of y for which x is real.

15. Express the area A and the circumference C of a circle as functions of the radius r. Express A as a function of C.

16. In each of the following functions, what is the largest domain of x and the corresponding range of y?

a) $y = \dfrac{1}{1 + x}$

b) $y = \dfrac{1}{1 + x^2}$

c) $y = \dfrac{1}{1 + \sqrt{x}}$

17. Without the use of the absolute-value symbol, describe the domain of x for which $|x + 1| < 4$.

18. If $y = 2x + |2 - x|$, express x in terms of y.

19. For what range of values of y does the equation $y = x + |2 - x|$ determine x as a single-valued function of y? Solve for x in terms of y on this set of values.

20. If $y = x + (1/x)$, express x in terms of y and determine the values of y for which x is real.

21. a) If $f(x) = x^2 + 2x - 3$, find $f(-2)$; $f(-1)$; $f(x_1)$; $f(x_1 + \Delta x)$.

b) If $f(x) = x - (1/x)$, show that $f(1/x) = -f(x) = f(-x)$.

22. Sketch the graph of each of the following equations:

a) $y = |x - 2| + 2$ **b)** $y = x^2 - 1$

c) Find the point on the curve in part (b) where the tangent to the curve makes an angle of $45°$ with the positive x-axis.

23. Sketch a graph of the function $y = |x + 2| + x$ for the domain $-5 \le x \le 2$. What is the range?

24. Show that the expression

$$M(a, b) = \frac{(a + b)}{2} + \frac{|a - b|}{2}$$

is equal to a when $a \ge b$ and is equal to b when $b \ge a$. In other words, $M(a, b)$ gives the larger of the two numbers a and b. Find a similar expression, $m(a, b)$, which gives the smaller of the two numbers.

25. For each of the following expressions $f(x)$, sketch first the graph of $y = f(x)$, then the graph of $y = |f(x)|$, and finally the graph of $y = f(x)/2 + |f(x)|/2$.

a) $f(x) = (x - 2)(x + 1)$ **b)** $f(x) = x^2$

c) $f(x) = -x^2$ **d)** $f(x) = 4 - x^2$

26. *Lagrange interpolation formula.* Let (x_1, y_1), (x_2, y_2), $\ldots$, (x_n, y_n) be n points in the plane, no two of them having the same abscissas. Find a polynomial, $f(x)$, of degree $(n - 1)$, which takes the value y_1 at x_1, y_2 at x_2, $\ldots$, y_n at x_n; that is, $f(x_i) = y_i$ ($i = 1, 2, \ldots, n$). [*Hint:*

$$f(x) = y_1 \phi_1(x) + y_2 \phi_2(x) + \cdots + y_n \phi_n(x),$$

where $\phi_k(x)$ is a polynomial that is zero at x_i ($i \ne k$) and $\phi_k(x_k) = 1$.]

27. Let $f(x) = ax + b$ and $g(x) = cx + d$. What condition must be satisfied by the constants $a, b, c,$ and d in order that $f(g(x))$ and $g(f(x))$ shall be identical?

28. Let $f(x) = (ax + b)/(cx + d)$. If $d = -a$, show that $f(f(x)) = x$, identically.

29. If $f(x) = x/(x - 1)$, find (a) $f(1/x)$, (b) $f(-x)$, (c) $f(f(x))$, (d) $f(1/f(x))$.

30. Using the definition of the derivative, find $f'(x)$ if $f(x)$ is

a) $(x - 1)/(x + 1)$ **b)** $x^{3/2}$ **c)** $x^{1/3}$

31. Use the definition of the derivative to find:

a) $f'(x)$ if $f(x) = x^2 - 3x - 4$,

b) $\dfrac{dy}{dx}$ if $y = \dfrac{1}{3x} + 2x$,

c) $f'(t)$ if $f(t) = \sqrt{t - 4}$.

32. a) By the Δ-method, find the slope of the curve $y = 2x^3 + 2$ at the point $(1, 4)$. (b) At which point of the curve in (a) is the tangent to the curve parallel to the x-axis? Sketch the curve.

33. If $f(x) = 2x/(x - 1)$, find (a) $f(0)$, $f(-1)$, $f(1/x)$; (b) $\Delta f(x)/\Delta x$; (c) $f'(x)$, using the result of part (b).

34. Given $y = 180x - 16x^2$. Using the method of Article 1–7, find the slope of the curve at the point (x_1, y_1). Sketch the curve. At what point does the curve have a horizontal tangent?

35. Find the velocity $v = ds/dt$ if the distance a particle moves in time t is given by $s = 180t - 16t^2$. When does the velocity vanish?

36. If a ball is thrown straight up with a velocity of 32 ft/sec, its height after t sec is given by the equation $s = 32t - 16t^2$. At what instant will the ball be at its highest point, and how high will it rise?

37. If the pressure P and volume V of a certain gas are related by the formula $P = 1/V$, find (a) the average rate of change of P with respect to V, (b) the rate of change of P with respect to V at the instant when $V = 2$.

38. The volume V (in^3) of water remaining in a leaking pail after t sec is $V = 2000 - 40t + 0.2t^2$. How fast is the volume decreasing when $t = 30$?

39. Given $(x - 1)/(2x^2 - 7x + 5) = f(x)$. Find (a) the limit of $f(x)$ as $x \to \infty$, (b) the limit of $f(x)$ as $x \to 1$, (c) $f(-1/x)$, $f(0)$, $1/f(x)$.

40. Compute the coordinates of the point of intersection of the straight lines $3x + 5y = 1$ and $(2 + c)x + 5c^2y = 1$, and determine the limiting position of this point as c tends to 1.

41. Find (a) $\lim_{n\to\infty} (\sqrt{n^2 + 1} - n)$,

   (b) $\lim_{n\to\infty} (\sqrt{n^2 + n} - n)$.

42. Given $\epsilon > 0$, find $\delta > 0$ such that $\sqrt{t^2 - 1} < \epsilon$ when $0 < |t - 1| < \delta$.

43. Given $\epsilon > 0$, find M such that
$$\left| \frac{t^2 + t}{t^2 - 1} - 1 \right| < \epsilon$$
when $t > M$.

44. Show that $\lim_{t\to 0} t \sin (1/t)$ exists and is zero, even though $\sin (1/t)$ has no limit as t approaches zero.

45. Prove that if $f(t)$ is bounded (that is, $|f(t)| < M$ for some constant M) and $g(t)$ approaches zero as t approaches a, then $\lim_{t\to a} f(t)g(t) = 0$.

46. Prove that if $f(t)$ has a finite limit as t approaches a, then there exist numbers m, M, and $h > 0$ such that $m < f(t) < M$ if $0 < |t - a| < h$.

47. *Properties of inequalities.* If a and b are any two real numbers, we say a is less than b and write $a < b$ if (and only if) $b - a$ is positive. If $a < b$ we also say that b is greater than a $(b > a)$. Prove the following properties of inequalities:

a) If $a < b$, then $a + c < b + c$ and $a - c < b - c$ for any real number c.

b) If $a < b$ and $c < d$, then $a + c < b + d$. Is it also true that $a - c < b - d$? If so, prove it; if not, give a counterexample.

c) If a and b are both positive (or both negative) and $a < b$, then $1/b < 1/a$.

d) If $a < 0 < b$, then $1/a < 0 < 1/b$.

e) If $a < b$ and $c > 0$, then $ac < bc$.

f) If $a < b$ and $c < 0$, then $bc < ac$.

48. *Properties of absolute values.*

a) Prove that $|a| < |b|$ if, and only if, $a^2 < b^2$.

b) Prove that $|a + b| \le |a| + |b|$.

c) Prove that $|a - b| \ge ||a| - |b||$.

d) Prove, by mathematical induction, that
$$|a_1 + a_2 + \cdots + a_n| \le |a_1| + |a_2| + \cdots + |a_n|.$$

e) Using the result from part (d), prove that
$$|a_1 + a_2 + \cdots + a_n| \ge |a_1| - |a_2| - \cdots - |a_n|.$$

49. Graph $|x| + |y| = 1$. [*Hint.* For each quadrant write an equivalent equation without absolute values.]

50. Graph $y = \sqrt{|x|}$, $-4 \le x \le 4$. Compare your graph with Fig. 1–28.

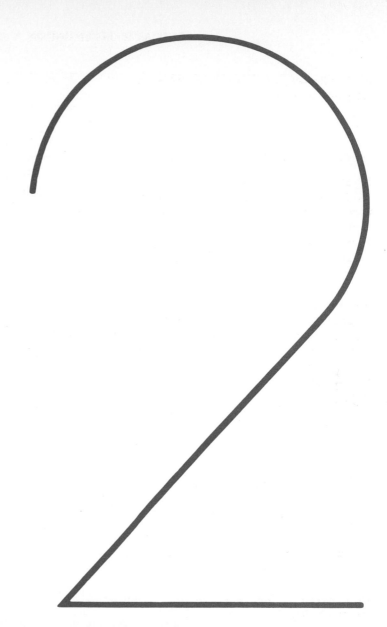

FORMAL DIFFERENTIATION

2–1

INTRODUCTION

In Chapter 1, we learned how to find the rate of change of a function by applying the rule

$$\text{Rate of change of } y \text{ with respect to } x = \lim \frac{\Delta y}{\Delta x}, \tag{1}$$

at any point where the limit $(\Delta y/\Delta x)$ exists. We also saw that this rate of change can be interpreted as the slope of the graph of the function $y = f(x)$. If we want the slope at just one point, say $x = x_1$, $y = y_1$, we can calculate numerically

$$\text{Slope at } P_1(x_1, y_1) = \lim_{h \to 0} \frac{f(x_1 + h) - f(x_1)}{h}. \tag{2}$$

With an electronic calculator and a formula for $f(x)$ that can be evaluated with the calculator, we choose some sequence of values of h, like 0.1, 0.01, 0.001, 0.0001, and so on. With x_1 held fixed, we calculate successive values of the quotient

$$\frac{\Delta y}{\Delta x} = \frac{f(x_1 + h) - f(x_1)}{h}, \tag{3}$$

and from these we deduce what we think the limit would be, if there were a limit. But this does not tell us that the limit exists; and even if it does exist, we may not be able to find its value with sufficient accuracy by straight numerical work.

In addition to the numerical method of finding slope, we were able to go at the job algebraically in some instances. The result of the algebra was a formula that gave useful information about the graph of the function. But each new equation $y = f(x)$ led to heavy algebra if we used the Δ-process of Eq. (1) every time. In one of the exercises, we saw that we could take a general second-degree equation $y = ax^2 + bx + c$, where a, b, and c are constants, apply the Δ-process to this, and get a general formula for the derivative (the slope), $dy/dx = 2ax + b$. Here we have a very simple way of going directly from the equation of the curve to its slope formula, if the equation is a quadratic expression in x. The obvious question to ask is whether there are other simple rules that we can use for general cubic equations, or polynomials of higher degree. The purpose of this chapter is to provide an affirmative answer, and to go beyond that to other types of functions as well. We shall develop a set of easy rules that make it possible to write down the derived function for any polynomial and some other functions as well. The use of these rules is called formal differentiation. When we find the derivative of a function, whether by use of the Δ-process or a standard formula, we say that we differentiate the function. In calculus, the verb "differentiate" means "find the derivative of." Applications of the derivative will be taken up in more detail in Chapter 3. In Chapter 4 we take up the opposite question: Can you find a function $f(x)$ whose derivative is equal to a given expression? That process is called formal integration, or antidifferentiation.

As we go on, we shall learn how to differentiate and integrate the trigonometric functions, logarithmic and exponential functions, and combinations of such functions. We shall also learn some of the many applications of these calculus operations. Theory and applications are interwoven.

A single term of the form cx^n, where c is a constant and n is zero or a positive integer, is called a *monomial* in x. A function that is the sum of a finite number of monomial terms is called a *polynomial* in x. For example,

$$f(x) = x^3 - 5x + 7, \qquad g(x) = (x^2 + 3)^3, \qquad h(x) = 4x, \qquad \phi(x) = 5$$

are polynomials in x, and

$$s(t) = \tfrac{1}{2}gt^2, \qquad v(t) = v_0 + gt$$

are polynomials in t.

We shall now derive some formulas that will enable us to find the derivatives of polynomial functions very easily. In every case we derive the formula from the basic definition:

Let $y = f(x)$ define a function f. If the limit

$$\frac{dy}{dx} = \lim_{\Delta x \to 0} \frac{\Delta y}{\Delta x}, \tag{1a}$$

meaning

$$f'(x) = \lim_{\Delta x \to 0} \frac{f(x + \Delta x) - f(x)}{\Delta x}, \tag{1b}$$

exists and is finite, we call this limit the derivative of y with respect to x and say that f is differentiable at x.

Rule 1. *The derivative of a constant is zero.*

The geometric meaning of this result is that the graph of the equation $y = c$ is everywhere parallel to the x-axis (Fig. 2–1). To prove it analytically, let

$$y = f(x) = c,$$

where c is a constant. Then

$$\Delta y = f(x + \Delta x) - f(x) = c - c = 0.$$

Dividing by Δx gives

$$\frac{\Delta y}{\Delta x} = \frac{0}{\Delta x} = 0$$

and

$$\frac{dy}{dx} = \lim_{\Delta x \to 0} \frac{\Delta y}{\Delta x} = 0.$$

**POLYNOMIAL FUNCTIONS
AND THEIR DERIVATIVES**

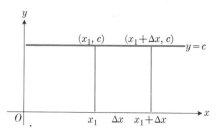

2–1 The slope of the graph of $y = $ constant is zero.

Rule 2. *The derivative, with respect to x, of x^n is nx^{n-1} when n is any positive integer.*

To prove this result, we let

$$y = f(x) = x^n,$$

where n may be any positive integer. Then, by the binomial theorem,

$$y + \Delta y = f(x + \Delta x) = (x + \Delta x)^n$$

$$= \begin{cases} x + \Delta x & \text{if } n = 1, \\ x^2 + 2x\,\Delta x + (\Delta x)^2 & \text{if } n = 2, \\ x^3 + 3x^2\,\Delta x + 3x\,(\Delta x)^2 + (\Delta x)^3 & \text{if } n = 3, \\ x^n + nx^{n-1}\,\Delta x + (\text{terms in } x \text{ and } \Delta x)\cdot(\Delta x)^2 & \text{if } n > 3. \end{cases}$$

From this we subtract $y = x^n$ and obtain

$$\Delta y = \begin{cases} \Delta x & \text{if } n = 1, \\ 2x\,\Delta x + (\Delta x)^2 & \text{if } n = 2, \\ 3x^2\,\Delta x + (3x + \Delta x)\cdot(\Delta x)^2 & \text{if } n = 3, \\ nx^{n-1}\,\Delta x + (\text{terms in } x \text{ and } \Delta x)\cdot(\Delta x)^2 & \text{if } n > 3. \end{cases}$$

Dividing by Δx, we find next that

$$\frac{\Delta y}{\Delta x} = \begin{cases} 1 & \text{if } n = 1, \\ 2x + \Delta x & \text{if } n = 2, \\ 3x^2 + (3x + \Delta x)\cdot\Delta x & \text{if } n = 3, \\ nx^{n-1} + (\text{terms in } x \text{ and } \Delta x)\cdot\Delta x & \text{if } n > 3. \end{cases}$$

Finally, we let Δx approach zero and find

$$\frac{dy}{dx} = \lim_{\Delta x \to 0}\frac{\Delta y}{\Delta x} = \begin{cases} 1 & \text{if } n = 1, \\ 2x & \text{if } n = 2, \\ 3x^2 & \text{if } n = 3, \\ nx^{n-1} & \text{if } n > 3. \end{cases}$$

In particular, the case $n = 1$ tells us that

$$\frac{dx}{dx} = 1.$$

Since the results for $n = 1, 2, 3$ are simply special cases of the general result, we have

$$\frac{dy}{dx} = nx^{n-1} \quad \text{if} \quad y = x^n \text{ and } n = \text{any positive integer.} \tag{2}$$

EXAMPLE 1.   If $y = x^5$, then $dy/dx = 5x^4$.

Rule 3.   *If $u = f(x)$ is a differentiable function of x and c is a constant, then*

$$\frac{d(cu)}{dx} = c\frac{du}{dx}.$$ **(3)**

Proof.   Let

$$y = cu,$$ **(4a)**

where

$$u = f(x).$$

Then if x is replaced by $x + \Delta x$, we have

$$y + \Delta y = c(u + \Delta u),$$ **(4b)**

where

$$u + \Delta u = f(x + \Delta x).$$

Subtracting (4a) from (4b), we obtain

$$\Delta y = c\,\Delta u$$

and dividing this by Δx, we have

$$\frac{\Delta y}{\Delta x} = c\frac{\Delta u}{\Delta x}.$$ **(4c)**

Since u has a derivative

$$\lim_{\Delta x \to 0} \frac{\Delta u}{\Delta x} = \frac{du}{dx}$$

and

$$\frac{dy}{dx} = \lim_{\Delta x \to 0} \frac{\Delta y}{\Delta x} = \lim_{\Delta x \to 0} c\frac{\Delta u}{\Delta x} = c\frac{du}{dx}.$$

Since $y = cu$, this is the same as

$$\frac{d(cu)}{dx} = c\frac{du}{dx},$$

which we wished to show.

EXAMPLE 2. $d(7x^5)/dx = 7 \cdot 5x^4 = 35x^4$. Geometrically this says that if we stretch the graph of $y = x^5$ in the y-direction by multiplying each ordinate by 7, then we multiply each slope by 7 also (Fig. 2–2).

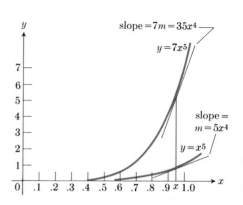

2–2   Graphs of $y = x^5$ and the stretched curve $y = 7x^5$. Multiplying the ordinates by 7 multiplies all the slopes by 7.

In general, if c is a constant and n is a positive integer, Eqs. (2) and (3) together tell us that

$$\frac{d(cx^n)}{dx} = cnx^{n-1}.$$ **(5)**

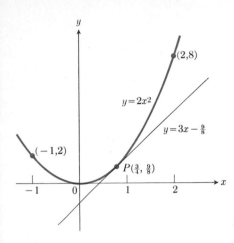

2–3 The line $y = 3x + c$ is tangent to the curve $y = 2x^2$ at $P(0.75, 1.125)$ if $c = -\frac{9}{8} = -1.125$.

EXAMPLE 3. Find the value of the constant c if the line $y = 3x + c$ is tangent to the curve $y = 2x^2$. Also find the point of tangency.

Solution. The slope of the line $y = 3x + c$ is $m = 3$. The slope of the curve at $P(x, y)$ is $dy/dx = 4x$. If P is a point of tangency, the two slopes are equal:

$$\text{At } P(x, y), \qquad m = 3 = 4x, \qquad \text{or} \qquad x = \tfrac{3}{4}.$$

Then $y = 2(\tfrac{3}{4})^2 = \tfrac{18}{16} = \tfrac{9}{8}$ must also equal $3x + c = 3(\tfrac{3}{4}) + c$. Therefore,

$$\tfrac{9}{4} + c = \tfrac{9}{8} \qquad \text{and} \qquad c = \tfrac{9}{8} - \tfrac{9}{4} = -\tfrac{9}{8}.$$

The point of tangency is

$$P(x, y) = P(\tfrac{3}{4}, \tfrac{9}{8}) = P(0.75, 1.125).$$

(See Fig. 2–3.)

Rule 4. *The derivative of the sum of a finite number of differentiable functions is the sum of their derivatives.*

To prove this, we first consider the sum of two terms,

$$y = u + v,$$

where we suppose that u and v are differentiable functions of x. When x is replaced by $x + \Delta x$, the new values of the variables will satisfy the equation

$$y + \Delta y = (u + \Delta u) + (v + \Delta v).$$

We subtract

$$y = u + v$$

from this and obtain

$$\Delta y = \Delta u + \Delta v,$$

and hence

$$\frac{\Delta y}{\Delta x} = \frac{\Delta u}{\Delta x} + \frac{\Delta v}{\Delta x}.$$

When Δx approaches zero, we get

$$\frac{dy}{dx} = \lim_{\Delta x \to 0} \frac{\Delta y}{\Delta x} = \lim_{\Delta x \to 0} \left(\frac{\Delta u}{\Delta x} + \frac{\Delta v}{\Delta x} \right) = \lim_{\Delta x \to 0} \frac{\Delta u}{\Delta x} + \lim_{\Delta x \to 0} \frac{\Delta v}{\Delta x} = \frac{du}{dx} + \frac{dv}{dx}.$$

Therefore,

$$\frac{d(u + v)}{dx} = \frac{du}{dx} + \frac{dv}{dx}.$$

This equation says that the derivative of the sum of two terms is the sum of their derivatives.

We may proceed by induction to establish the result for the sum of any finite number of terms. For example, if

$$y = u_1 + u_2 + u_3,$$

where u_1, u_2, and u_3 are differentiable functions of x, then we may take

$$u = u_1 + u_2, \qquad v = u_3,$$

and apply the result already established for the sum of two terms, namely,

$$\frac{dy}{dx} = \frac{d(u_1 + u_2)}{dx} + \frac{du_3}{dx}.$$

Since the first term is again a sum of two terms, we have

$$\frac{d(u_1 + u_2)}{dx} = \frac{du_1}{dx} + \frac{du_2}{dx},$$

so that

$$\frac{d(u_1 + u_2 + u_3)}{dx} = \frac{du_1}{dx} + \frac{du_2}{dx} + \frac{du_3}{dx}.$$

Finally, if it has been established for some integer n that

$$\frac{d(u_1 + u_2 + \cdots + u_n)}{dx} = \frac{du_1}{dx} + \frac{du_2}{dx} + \cdots + \frac{du_n}{dx},$$

and we let

$$y = u + v,$$

with

$$u = u_1 + u_2 + \cdots + u_n,$$

$$v = u_{n+1},$$

then we find in the same way as above that

$$\frac{d(u_1 + u_2 + \cdots + u_{n+1})}{dx} = \frac{du_1}{dx} + \frac{du_2}{dx} + \cdots + \frac{du_{n+1}}{dx}.$$

This enables us to conclude that if the theorem is true for a sum of n terms it is also true for a sum of $(n + 1)$ terms; and since it is already established for the sum of two terms, we conclude that it is true for the sum of any finite number of terms.

EXAMPLE 4.   Find dy/dx if $y = x^3 + 7x^2 - 5x + 4$.

Solution.   We find the derivatives of the separate terms and add the results:

$$\frac{dy}{dx} = \frac{d(x^3)}{dx} + \frac{d(7x^2)}{dx} + \frac{d(-5x)}{dx} + \frac{d(4)}{dx}$$

$$= 3x^2 + 14x - 5x^0 + 0$$

$$= 3x^2 + 14x - 5.$$

Second Derivatives

The derivative

$$y' = \frac{dy}{dx}$$

is the first derivative of y with respect to x, and its derivative

$$y'' = \frac{dy'}{dx} = \frac{d}{dx}\left(\frac{dy}{dx}\right)$$

is called the *second derivative of y with respect to x*. The operation of taking the derivative of a function twice in succession is denoted by

$$\frac{d}{dx}\left(\frac{d}{dx}\cdots\right), \quad \text{or} \quad \frac{d^2}{dx^2}(\ldots).$$

In this notation, we write the second derivative of y with respect to x as

$$\frac{d^2y}{dx^2}.$$

More generally, the result of differentiating a function $y = f(x)$ n times in succession is denoted by $y^{(n)}$, $f^{(n)}(x)$, or d^ny/dx^n.

EXAMPLE 5. For example, if $y = x^3 - 3x^2 + 2$, then

$$y' = \frac{dy}{dx} = 3x^2 - 6x, \qquad y''' = \frac{d^3y}{dx^3} = 6,$$

$$y'' = \frac{d^2y}{dx^2} = 6x - 6, \qquad y^{(iv)} = \frac{d^4y}{dx^4} = 0.$$

In mechanics, if $s = f(t)$ gives the position of a moving body at time t, then

The first derivative ds/dt gives the *velocity*, and

The second derivative d^2s/dt^2 gives the *acceleration*

of the body at time t.

EXAMPLE 6. A body moves in a straight line according to the law of motion

$$s = t^3 - 4t^2 - 3t.$$

Find its acceleration at each instant when the velocity is zero.

Solution. The velocity v and acceleration a are

$$v = \frac{ds}{dt} = 3t^2 - 8t - 3, \qquad a = \frac{dv}{dt} = 6t - 8.$$

The velocity is zero when

$$3t^2 - 8t - 3 = (3t + 1)(t - 3) = 0,$$

that is, when

$$t = -\tfrac{1}{3} \quad \text{or} \quad t = 3.$$

The corresponding values of the acceleration are

$$t = -\tfrac{1}{3}, \quad a = -10; \qquad t = 3, \quad a = 10.$$

PROBLEMS

In Problems 1–5, s represents the position of a moving body at time t. Find the velocity $v = ds/dt$ and the acceleration $a = dv/dt = d^2s/dt^2$.

1. $s = t^2 - 4t + 3$ **2.** $s = 2t^3 - 5t^2 + 4t - 3$

3. $s = gt^2/2 + v_0 t + s_0$; (g, v_0, s_0 constants)

4. $s = 3 + 4t - t^2$ **5.** $s = (2t + 3)^2$

Find $y' = dy/dx$ and $y'' = dy'/dx$ in Problems 6–15.

6. $y = x^4 - 7x^3 + 2x^2 + 5$ **7.** $y = 5x^3 - 3x^5$

8. $y = 4x^2 - 8x + 1$ **9.** $y = \dfrac{x^4}{4} - \dfrac{x^3}{3} + \dfrac{x^2}{2} - x + 3$

10. $y = 2x^4 - 4x^2 - 8$ **11.** $12y = 6x^4 - 18x^2 - 12x$

12. $y = 3x^7 - 7x^3 + 21x^2$ **13.** $y = x^2(x^3 - 1)$

14. $y = (x - 2)(x + 3)$ **15.** $y = (3x - 1)(2x + 5)$

16. A particle projected vertically upward with a speed of 160 ft/sec reaches an elevation $s = 160t - 16t^2$ at the end of t seconds. (a) How high does it rise? (b) How fast is it traveling when it reaches an elevation of 256 feet going up and again when it reaches this elevation coming down?

17. Find the line tangent to the curve $y = 2x^2 + 4x - 3$ at the point $(1, 3)$.

18. Find the lines tangent to the curve $y = x^3 + x$, where the slope is equal to 4. What is the smallest value the slope of this curve can ever have and where on the curve does the slope equal this smallest value?

19. Find the points on the curve $y = 2x^3 - 3x^2 - 12x + 20$, where the tangent is parallel to the x-axis.

20. Suppose that you have plotted the point $P(x, x^2)$ on the graph of $y = x^2$. To construct the tangent to the graph at P, locate the point $T(x/2, 0)$ on the x-axis and draw the line through T and P. Show that this construction is correct.

21. The tangent to the curve $y = x^n$ at $P(x_1, y_1)$ intersects the x-axis at $T(t, 0)$. Express t in terms of n and x_1, then show how the result can be used to construct the tangent at P.

22. Find the x- and y-intercepts of the line L that is tangent to the curve $y = x^3$ at $A(-2, -8)$.

23. A line L is drawn tangent to the curve $y = x^3 - x$ at the point $A(-1, 0)$. Where else does this line intersect the curve?

24. (*Curvature*) It is shown later in this book that one can define a number that represents the curvature of $y = f(x)$ at $P(x, y)$. The formula is

$$\text{Curvature} = y''/(1 + (y')^2)^{3/2},$$

where $y' = dy/dx$ and y'' is the second derivative. Use this formula to find the curvature of $y = x^2$:

a) at the origin,   **b)** at $(1, 1)$,   and   **c)** as $x \to \infty$.

25. Find the values of the constants a, b, and c if the curve $y = ax^2 + bx + c$ is to pass through the point $(1, 2)$ and is to be tangent to the line $y = x$ at the origin.

26. Find the constants a, b, and c so that the two curves $y = x^2 + ax + b$ and $y = cx - x^2$ shall be tangent to each other at the point $(1, 0)$.

27. Find the constant c if the curve $y = x^2 + c$ is to be tangent to the line $y = x$.

In the preceding article we learned how to find the derivative of a polynomial very quickly by using certain simple formulas. First we found the derivative of a monomial in x,

$$\frac{d}{dx}(cx^n) = cnx^{n-1},$$

and then we proved that the derivative of the sum of a finite number of such terms is the sum of their derivatives.

In this article we shall derive formulas for finding the derivative with respect to x of

Products: $y = uv$,

Quotients: $y = u/v$,

Powers: $y = u^n$,

2–3

RATIONAL FUNCTIONS AND THEIR DERIVATIVES

when u and v are any differentiable functions of x. For the present, this will mean that u and v may be polynomials in x, for example. But after we learn to differentiate functions like sin x and log x, the same basic formulas will apply to combinations of these as well.

The product of two polynomials in x is again a polynomial in x; hence if u and v are polynomials the product uv is also a polynomial. Similarly, if n is a positive integer and u is a polynomial, then u^n is again a polynomial. For example, if

$$u = x^2 + 1, \quad v = x^3 + 3, \qquad \text{then} \qquad uv = x^5 + x^3 + 3x^2 + 3,$$

and if

$$u = x^2 + 1, \quad n = 2, \qquad \text{then} \qquad u^n = x^4 + 2x^2 + 1.$$

But the ratio u/v of two polynomials in x is generally not a polynomial. Such a function is called a *rational* function of x, where the word *ratio* is the key to the real meaning of the word rational.

Rule 5. *The derivative of the product*

$$y = uv$$

of two differentiable functions of x is given by

$$\frac{d(uv)}{dx} = u\frac{dv}{dx} + v\frac{du}{dx}. \tag{1}$$

To prove this result, we let

$$y = uv,$$

where u and v are differentiable functions of x. Let Δx be an increment in x, and let the corresponding increments in y, u, v be denoted by Δy, Δu, Δv. These increments may be either positive, negative, or zero, but $\Delta x \neq 0$. Then

$$y + \Delta y = (u + \Delta u)(v + \Delta v)$$

$$= uv + u\,\Delta v + v\,\Delta u + \Delta u\,\Delta v.$$

When we subtract from this the equation

$$y = uv,$$

we obtain

$$\Delta y = u\,\Delta v + v\,\Delta u + \Delta u\,\Delta v.$$

Next we divide by Δx,

$$\frac{\Delta y}{\Delta x} = u\frac{\Delta v}{\Delta x} + v\frac{\Delta u}{\Delta x} + \Delta u\frac{\Delta v}{\Delta x}.$$

Finally, when Δx approaches zero, so will Δu, since

$$\lim \Delta u = \lim\left(\frac{\Delta u}{\Delta x}\Delta x\right) = \lim\frac{\Delta u}{\Delta x}\lim \Delta x = \frac{du}{dx}\cdot 0.$$

Thus,

$$\lim \frac{\Delta y}{\Delta x} = \lim \left(u \frac{\Delta v}{\Delta x} + v \frac{\Delta u}{\Delta x} + \Delta u \frac{\Delta v}{\Delta x} \right)$$

$$= \lim u \frac{\Delta v}{\Delta x} + \lim v \frac{\Delta u}{\Delta x} + \lim \Delta u \frac{\Delta v}{\Delta x}$$

$$= \lim u \lim \frac{\Delta v}{\Delta x} + \lim v \lim \frac{\Delta u}{\Delta x} + \lim \Delta u \lim \frac{\Delta v}{\Delta x}$$

$$= u \frac{dv}{dx} + v \frac{du}{dx} + 0 \cdot \frac{dv}{dx}.$$

That is,

$$\frac{dy}{dx} = u \frac{dv}{dx} + v \frac{du}{dx},$$

which establishes (1).

EXAMPLE 1. Economists often use the expression "rate of growth" in relative rather than absolute terms. For example, in a given industry, let $u = f(t)$ be the size of the labor force at time t. (This function will be treated as though it were differentiable even though it is an integer-valued step function. We approximate the step function by a smooth curve.) Let $v = g(t)$ be the average production per person in the labor force at time t. Then the total production is $y = uv$. If the labor force is growing at the rate of 4 percent annually and the production per worker is growing at the rate of 5 percent per year, find the rate of growth of the total production, y.

Solution. We are given these data:

$$y = uv, \qquad \frac{du}{dt} = 0.04u, \qquad \frac{dv}{dt} = 0.05v.$$

By the rule for the derivative of a product, we have

$$\frac{dy}{dt} = u \frac{dv}{dt} + v \frac{du}{dt} = u(0.05v) + v(0.04u) = 0.09uv = 0.09y.$$

From the result $dy/dt = 0.09y$ we deduce that the total production is increasing at the rate of 9 percent annually. All of the rates are instantaneous rates, valid at some instant of time t.

Note that the derivative of a product is *not* the product of the derivatives. Instead, we add together two terms $u(dv/dx)$ and $v(du/dx)$. In the first of these we leave u untouched and differentiate v, and in the second we differentiate u and leave v alone. In fact, it is possible to extend the formula, by the method of mathematical induction, to show that the derivative of a product

$$y = u_1 u_2 \ldots u_n$$

of a finite number of differentiable functions is given by

$$\frac{d}{dx}(u_1 u_2 \cdots u_n) = \frac{du_1}{dx} \cdot u_2 \cdots u_n + u_1 \frac{du_2}{dx} \cdots u_n + \cdots + u_1 u_2 \cdots u_{n-1} \frac{du_n}{dx}, \quad (2)$$

where the right side of the equation consists of the sum of the n terms obtained by multiplying the derivative of each one of the factors by the other $(n-1)$ factors undifferentiated.

Rule 6. *At a point where $v \neq 0$, the derivative of the quotient*

$$y = \frac{u}{v}$$

of two differentiable functions u and v is given by

$$\frac{d}{dx}\left(\frac{u}{v}\right) = \frac{v\dfrac{du}{dx} - u\dfrac{dv}{dx}}{v^2}. \quad (3)$$

To prove this, consider a point $x = c$ where $v \neq 0$ and where u and v are differentiable. Let x be given an increment Δx and let Δy, Δu, Δv be the corresponding increments in y, u, v. Then, as $\Delta x \to 0$,

$$\lim (v + \Delta v) = \lim v + \lim \Delta v$$

while

$$\lim \Delta v = \lim \frac{\Delta v}{\Delta x} \cdot \Delta x = \frac{dv}{dx} \cdot 0 = 0.$$

Therefore the value of $v + \Delta v$ is close to the value of v when $x + \Delta x$ is close to c, that is, when Δx is near zero. In particular, since $v \neq 0$ at $x = c$, it follows that $v + \Delta v \neq 0$ when Δx is *near* zero, say when $0 < \lceil \Delta x \rceil < h$. Let Δx be so restricted. Then $v + \Delta v \neq 0$ and

$$y + \Delta y = \frac{u + \Delta u}{v + \Delta v}.$$

From this we subtract

$$y = \frac{u}{v}$$

and obtain

$$\Delta y = \frac{u + \Delta u}{v + \Delta v} - \frac{u}{v}$$

$$= \frac{(vu + v\,\Delta u) - (uv + u\,\Delta v)}{v(v + \Delta v)}$$

$$= \frac{v\,\Delta u - u\,\Delta v}{v(v + \Delta v)}.$$

We divide this by Δx and have

$$\frac{\Delta y}{\Delta x} = \frac{v\dfrac{\Delta u}{\Delta x} - u\dfrac{\Delta v}{\Delta x}}{v(v + \Delta v)}.$$

When Δx approaches zero,

$$\lim \frac{\Delta u}{\Delta x} = \frac{du}{dx},$$

$$\lim \frac{\Delta v}{\Delta x} = \frac{dv}{dx},$$

and

$$\lim v(v + \Delta v) = \lim v \, \lim (v + \Delta v) = v^2 \neq 0.$$

Therefore,

$$\frac{dy}{dx} = \lim \frac{\Delta y}{\Delta x} = \frac{\lim \left(v \dfrac{\Delta u}{\Delta x} - u \dfrac{\Delta v}{\Delta x} \right)}{\lim v(v + \Delta v)} = \frac{v \dfrac{du}{dx} - u \dfrac{dv}{dx}}{v^2},$$

which establishes Eq. (3).

EXAMPLE 2. $y = (x^2 + 1)/(x^2 - 1)$, $x^2 \neq 1$. We apply Rule 6 for the derivative of a fraction, and have

$$\frac{dy}{dx} = \frac{(x^2 - 1) \cdot 2x - (x^2 + 1) \cdot 2x}{(x^2 - 1)^2}$$

$$= \frac{-4x}{(x^2 - 1)^2}.$$

Rule 7. *If $u = g(x)$ is a differentiable function of x and n is a positive integer, then*

$$\frac{d}{dx}(u^n) = nu^{n-1} \frac{du}{dx}. \tag{4}$$

For $n = 1$, we interpret Eq. (4) as

$$\frac{d}{dx}(u) = u^0 \frac{du}{dx} = \frac{du}{dx}$$

which is certainly true provided $u \neq 0$. When $u = 0$, we would get 0^0, which is an indeterminate expression but which we shall interpret as being 1 to be consistent. For n greater than or equal to 2, we let

$$y = u^n,$$

where u and n satisfy the hypotheses, give x an increment Δx, and call the increments of y and u, Δy and Δu. Then

$$y + \Delta y = (u + \Delta u)^n$$

$$= u^n + nu^{n-1} \Delta u + \frac{n(n-1)}{2} u^{n-2} (\Delta u)^2 + \cdots + (\Delta u)^n.$$

From this we subtract the original equation and obtain

$$\Delta y = nu^{n-1} \Delta u + (\text{terms in } u \text{ and } \Delta u)(\Delta u)^2.$$

Next, we divide by Δx:

$$\frac{\Delta y}{\Delta x} = nu^{n-1} \frac{\Delta u}{\Delta x} + (\text{terms in } u \text{ and } \Delta u)\frac{(\Delta u)^2}{\Delta x}.$$

Now when Δx approaches zero,

$$\lim \frac{\Delta u}{\Delta x} = \frac{du}{dx}$$

by the definition of the derivative, while

$$\lim \frac{(\Delta u)^2}{\Delta x} = \lim \left(\frac{\Delta u}{\Delta x} \Delta u \right) = \lim \frac{\Delta u}{\Delta x} \lim \Delta u = \frac{du}{dx} \cdot 0 = 0.$$

Hence,

$$\lim \frac{\Delta y}{\Delta x} = \lim \left[nu^{n-1} \frac{\Delta u}{\Delta x} + (\cdots) \frac{(\Delta u)^2}{\Delta x} \right]$$

$$= \lim nu^{n-1} \frac{\Delta u}{\Delta x} + \lim (\cdots) \frac{(\Delta u)^2}{\Delta x}$$

$$= nu^{n-1} \frac{du}{dx} + 0;$$

that is,

$$\frac{dy}{dx} = nu^{n-1} \frac{du}{dx},$$

which establishes Eq. (4).

EXAMPLE 3. $y = (x^2 + 1)^3 (x^3 - 1)^2$. We could, of course, expand everything here and write y as a polynomial in x, but this is not necessary. Instead, we first use Eq. (1) for the derivative of a product:

$$\frac{dy}{dx} = (x^2 + 1)^3 \frac{d}{dx} (x^3 - 1)^2 + (x^3 - 1)^2 \frac{d}{dx} (x^2 + 1)^3.$$

Then we evaluate the remaining derivatives by Eq. (4):

$$\frac{d}{dx} (x^3 - 1)^2 = 2(x^3 - 1) \frac{d}{dx} (x^3 - 1)$$

$$= 2(x^3 - 1) \cdot 3x^2 = 6x^2 (x^3 - 1),$$

and

$$\frac{d}{dx} (x^2 + 1)^3 = 3(x^2 + 1)^2 \frac{d}{dx} (x^2 + 1)$$

$$= 3(x^2 + 1)^2 \cdot 2x = 6x(x^2 + 1)^2.$$

We substitute these into the earlier equation and have

$$\frac{dy}{dx} = (x^2 + 1)^3 6x^2 (x^3 - 1) + (x^3 - 1)^2 6x(x^2 + 1)^2$$

$$= 6x(x^2 + 1)^2 (x^3 - 1)[x(x^2 + 1) + (x^3 - 1)]$$

$$= 6x(x^2 + 1)^2 (x^3 - 1)(2x^3 + x - 1).$$

EXAMPLE 4. Write the polynomial

$$f(x) = x^3 - 2x + 3 \qquad (5)$$

in the form

$$f(x) = C_0 + C_1(x - 2) + C_2(x - 2)^2 + C_3(x - 2)^3, \qquad (6)$$

where C_0, C_1, C_2, and C_3 are constants.

Solution. We differentiate both expressions for $f(x)$ three times, and substitute $x = 2$ to get

$$f(x) = C_0 + C_1(x - 2) + C_2(x - 2)^2 + C_3(x - 2)^3, \qquad f(2) = C_0;$$

$$f'(x) = C_1 + 2C_2(x - 2) + 3C_3(x - 2)^2, \qquad f'(2) = C_1;$$

$$f''(x) = 2C_2 + 6C_3(x - 2), \qquad f''(2) = 2C_2;$$

$$f'''(x) = 6C_3, \qquad f'''(2) = 6C_3;$$

and

$$f(x) = x^3 - 2x + 3, \qquad f(2) = 8 - 4 + 3 = 7;$$
$$f'(x) = 3x^2 - 2, \qquad f'(2) = 12 - 2 = 10;$$
$$f''(x) = 6x, \qquad f''(2) = 12;$$
$$f'''(x) = 6, \qquad f'''(2) = 6.$$

This gives two expressions for the value of each derivative of f at $x = 2$. Equating them, we find

$$C_0 = f(2) = 7, \quad C_1 = f'(2) = 10, \quad C_2 = \tfrac{1}{2}f''(2) = 6, \quad C_3 = \tfrac{1}{6}f'''(2) = 1.$$

Therefore,

$$f(x) = x^3 - 2x + 3 \;=\; 7 + 10(x - 2) + 6(x - 2)^2 + (x - 2)^3.$$

The first way of writing $f(x)$ is less informative than the second way if we are especially interested in the way $f(x)$ varies for values of x near 2. One of the ways calculus is used is to make approximations. Two things are important in making an approximation: First, the form of the approximation, and second, the size of the error. For the present example we can say that, when x is near 2, the successive powers of $(x - 2)$ are small, and

$$f(x) \approx 7, \quad \text{with an error about } 10(x - 2)$$

$$f(x) \approx 7 + 10(x - 2), \quad \text{with an error about } 6(x - 2)^2$$

$$f(x) \approx 7 + 10(x - 2) + 6(x - 2)^2, \quad \text{with an error exactly } (x - 2)^3$$

$$f(x) = 7 + 10(x - 2) + 6(x - 2)^2 + (x - 2)^3, \quad \text{with no error.}$$

Figure 2–4 shows the first two of these approximations to $f(x)$.

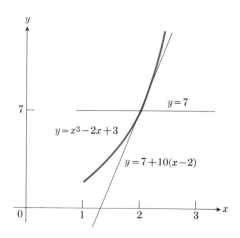

2–4 Graph of $y = x^3 - 2x + 3$ near $x = 2$ with horizontal and tangent line approximations.

Rule 8. *At a point where u = g(x) is differentiable and different from zero, the derivative of*

$$y = u^n$$

is given by

$$\frac{d(u^n)}{dx} = nu^{n-1}\frac{du}{dx} \tag{7}$$

if n is a negative integer.

Rule 8 is the extension of Eq. (4) to the case where *n* is a *negative integer*. To prove it, we combine the results in Eqs. (3) and (4) as follows. Let

$$y = u^{-m} = \frac{1}{u^m},$$

where −*m* is a negative integer, so that *m* is a positive integer. Then, using (3) for the derivative of a quotient, we have

$$\frac{dy}{dx} = \frac{d\left(\frac{1}{u^m}\right)}{dx} = \frac{u^m\frac{d(1)}{dx} - 1\frac{d(u^m)}{dx}}{(u^m)^2} \tag{8}$$

at any point where *u* is differentiable and different from zero. Now the various derivatives on the right side of (8) can be evaluated by formulas already proved, namely,

$$\frac{d(1)}{dx} = 0,$$

since 1 is a constant, and

$$\frac{d(u^m)}{dx} = mu^{m-1}\frac{du}{dx},$$

since *m* is a *positive integer*. Therefore,

$$\frac{dy}{dx} = \frac{u^m \cdot 0 - 1 \cdot mu^{m-1}\frac{du}{dx}}{u^{2m}} = -mu^{-m-1}\frac{du}{dx}.$$

If −*m* is replaced by its equivalent value *n*, this equation reduces to Eq. (7).

EXAMPLE 5. $y = x^2 + 1/x^2$, $x \neq 0$. We may write

$$y = x^2 + x^{-2}.$$

Then

$$\frac{dy}{dx} = 2x^{2-1}\frac{dx}{dx} + (-2)x^{-2-1}\frac{dx}{dx}$$

$$= 2x - 2x^{-3}.$$

PROBLEMS

Find dy/dx in each of the following problems (1 through 8).

1. $y = x^3/3 - x^2/2 + x - 1$ **2.** $y = (x - 1)^3(x + 2)^4$

3. $y = (x^2 + 1)^5$ **4.** $y = (x^3 - 3x)^4$

5. $y = (x + 1)^2(x^2 + 1)^{-3}$ **6.** $y = \dfrac{2x + 1}{x^2 - 1}$

7. $y = \dfrac{2x + 5}{3x - 2}$ **8.** $y = \left(\dfrac{x + 1}{x - 1}\right)^2$

Find ds/dt in each of the following problems (9 through 15).

9. $s = \dfrac{t}{t^2 + 1}$ **10.** $s = (2t + 3)^3$

11. $s = (t^2 - t)^{-2}$ **12.** $s = t^2(t + 1)^{-1}$

13. $s = \dfrac{2t}{3t^2 + 1}$ **14.** $s = (t + t^{-1})^2$

15. $s = (t^2 + 3t)^3$

16. With the book closed, state and prove the formula for the derivative of the product of two differentiable functions u and v.

17. With the book closed, state and prove the formula for the derivative of the quotient u/v of two differentiable functions u and v.

18. With the book closed, state and prove the formula for the derivative with respect to x of u^n, where n is a positive integer and u is a differentiable function of x.

19. In Example 1, suppose that the labor force u is decreasing at the rate of 2 percent per year while the productivity per person is increasing at the rate of 3 percent per year. Is the total productivity increasing or decreasing, and at what rate?

20. In Example 4, $f(x) = x^3 - 2x + 3$ was claimed to be equal to $7 + 10(x - 2) + 6(x - 2)^2 + (x - 2)^3$. Expand the terms in this latter expression, using the binomial theorem, and thus show that the two expressions are identical.

21. Suppose that the function $f(x) = x^3 - 2x + 3$ of Example 4 is put into the form $f(x) = a_0 + a_1(x - 1) + a_2(x - 1)^2 + a_3(x - 1)^3$, where a_0, a_1, a_2, and a_3 are constants. Determine these constants in terms of $f(1)$, $f'(1)$, $f''(1)$, and $f'''(1)$. If the linear expression $L_1(x) = a_0 + a_1(x - 1)$ is used to approximate $f(x)$ for values of x near 1, about how large is the error? What is the limit of

$$\frac{f(x) - L_1(x)}{(x - 1)^2}$$

as x approaches 1?

Let us begin with an example.

EXAMPLE 1. What is the inverse of the function $f(x) = x^3$ and what is its derivative?

Solution. We look at the graph of $y = x^3$, shown in Fig. 2–5, and also at the graph of $x = y^3$ or $y = x^{1/3}$. The function $f(x) = x^3$ corresponds to a mapping from any real number to its cube. The inverse function should take that output and map it back to the original x. The function that does this is $g(x) = x^{1/3}$. Thus,

$$g(f(x)) = (f(x))^{1/3} = (x^3)^{1/3} = x,$$

and also, in the opposite order,

$$f(g(x)) = (g(x))^3 = (x^{1/3})^3 = x.$$

The composite of f with g or of g with f is the *identity mapping* $y = x$ (Fig. 2–6).

2–4

**INVERSE FUNCTIONS
AND THEIR DERIVATIVES**

2–5   Graphs of the inverse functions $f(x) = x^3$ for $0 \le x \le 2$ and $g(x) = x^{1/3}$ for $0 \le x \le 8$. Each curve is the mirror image of the other with respect to the line $y = x$. Both curves should be reflected into the third quadrant for negative x.

2–6   The composite of $f(x) = x^3$ and $g(x) = x^{1/3}$ in both orders is the identity function: $f(g(x)) = g(f(x)) = x$; f is the inverse of g and g is the inverse of f.

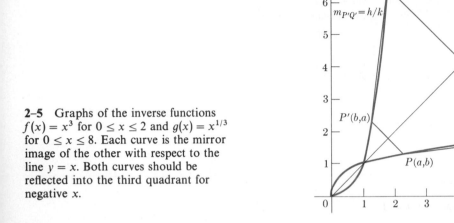

Next, we look at the slopes of the two curves in Fig. 2–5. If we want the derivative of $g(x)$ at $x = a$, we can start with the slope of a secant line PQ through $P(a, b)$ where $b = a^{1/3}$ and $Q(a + h,\ b + k)$ where $b + k = (a + h)^{1/3}$. The slope of PQ is $m_{PQ} = \text{rise/run} = k/h$. The slope of the tangent at P is the limit of m_{PQ} as h approaches zero:

$$m_{\tan P} = \lim_{h \to 0} m_{PQ} = \lim_{h \to 0} \frac{(a + h)^{1/3} - a^{1/3}}{h}. \tag{1}$$

We could rationalize the numerator in the last expression in Eq. (1) by multiplying the numerator and denominator by $(a + h)^{2/3} + (a + h)^{1/3} a^{1/3} + a^{2/3}$. But we prefer to go about the task in a geometric way that can be extended to any two inverse functions. The point $P'(b, a)$ is on the graph of $f(x) = x^3$ because $b^3 = a$. Likewise, the point $Q'(b + k, a + h)$ is on the graph of f. The slope of the secant line through these two points P' and Q' is

$$m_{P'Q'} = \text{rise/run} = h/k = 1/m_{PQ}. \tag{2}$$

When Q approaches P on the g curve, its mirror image Q' approaches P' on the f curve, and vice versa. The slopes of the two secant lines approach the respective slopes of the tangents. For the secant lines, the product of the slopes is 1. The same relation must hold for the limits: The slope of the tangent to one curve is the reciprocal of the slope of the tangent to the other, at mirror-imaged points P and P', provided that neither tangent slope is zero. We have a fast way to find the slope of the curve $f(x) = x^3$ at $x = b$; just take the formal derivative and put $x = b$:

$$f'(x) = 3x^2, \quad \text{so} \quad m_{\text{tan } P'} = f'(b) = 3b^2. \tag{3}$$

Therefore, if $b \neq 0$, we also have a formula for the slope of the curve $g(x) = x^{1/3}$ at $x = a = b^3$:

$$g'(a) = g'(b^3) = \frac{1}{3b^2} = \frac{1}{3a^{2/3}} = \tfrac{1}{3}a^{-2/3}. \tag{4}$$

To summarize:

> The derivative of $g(x) = x^{1/3}$ at $x = a$ is
>
> $$g'(a) = \tfrac{1}{3}a^{-2/3} \qquad \text{for any } a \neq 0. \tag{5}$$

Or, in terms of x, for any $x \neq 0$, the function $g(x) = x^{1/3}$ is differentiable and its derivative is $\tfrac{1}{3}x^{-2/3}$.

We have just shown that, for all $x \neq 0$, the derivative of x^n is nx^{n-1} when $n = \tfrac{1}{3}$. The same argument will apply to x^n for $n = \tfrac{1}{5}, \tfrac{1}{7}, \tfrac{1}{9}$, and so on. And if we keep $x > 0$, so that even roots of x are defined, then the argument will also apply to x^n for $n = \tfrac{1}{2}, \tfrac{1}{4}, \tfrac{1}{6}, \ldots$. We take $n = 1/m$, where m is a positive integer, and consider the two functions $f(x) = x^m$ and $g(x) = x^{1/m}$. Each is the inverse of the other (on suitably restricted domains). Their graphs are mirror images of one another in the line $y = x$. The slope of the tangent to one curve at $P(a, b)$ is the reciprocal of the slope of the other at $P'(b, a)$, provided a and b are both different from zero. That is,

> If $a^{1/m} = b \neq 0$, and $f(x) = x^m$, $g(x) = x^{1/m}$, then
>
> $$g'(a) = \frac{1}{f'(b)} = \frac{1}{mb^{m-1}} = \frac{1}{m}b^{1-m} = \frac{1}{m}(a^{1/m})^{1-m} = \frac{1}{m}a^{(1/m)-1}. \tag{6}$$

In more familiar notation, with $n = 1/m$, we have:

Rule 9. *If* $g(x) = x^n$ *with* $n = 1/m$, *where* m *is a positive integer, then* $g'(x) = nx^{n-1}$ *for any* $x \neq 0$ *if* m *is odd, or for any* $x > 0$ *if* m *is even.*

EXAMPLE 2

a) When $x \neq 0$,

$$\frac{d}{dx}(x^{1/5}) = \tfrac{1}{5}x^{-4/5}.$$

b) When $x > 0$,

$$\frac{d}{dx}(x^{1/2}) = \tfrac{1}{2}x^{-1/2}.$$

REMARK.   We can extend Rule 9 to any rational n in the following way.

If n is any rational number, then there are integers p and q, with q positive, such that $n = p/q$. We put $g(x) = x^n = (x^{1/q})^p = u^p$ with $u = x^{1/q}$. Then, by applying Rules 7 (or 8) and 9, we get

$$g'(x) = pu^{p-1}\frac{du}{dx} = pu^{p-1}(1/q)x^{(1/q)-1}$$

$$= p(x^{1/q})^{p-1}(1/q)x^{(1/q)-1}$$

$$= \frac{p}{q}(x)^{(p/q)-(1/q)+(1/q)-1} = nx^{n-1}.$$

In writing this we assume that, for any given p and q, the domain of x is restricted to avoid division by zero and to avoid even roots of negative numbers.

Let us return now to the two graphs in Fig. 2–5. The mirror-image relations that are shown there apply to any two inverse functions. Hence the slopes of their tangents at corresponding mirrored points are reciprocals, provided neither is zero. We state the result as Rule 10.

Rule 10.   *Let $f(x)$ and $g(x)$ be inverse functions on suitably restricted domains. If $g(a) = b$ and $f(b) = a$, then $g'(a) = 1/f'(b)$ provided the derivatives are defined and $f'(b)g'(a) \neq 0$.*

REMARK.   A function defined by a formula $y = f(x)$ may fail to have a unique inverse. But if it does, we can attempt to find a formula for the inverse function g by interchanging the letters x and y in the original equation and then solving for y. We may not always be able to solve conveniently for y but, when we can, the resulting equation will express the inverse we seek in terms of x.

EXAMPLE 3.   Find the inverse of the function $f(x) = x^3 + 1$.

Solution.   In the original formula, $y = x^3 + 1$, we interchange the letters x and y and get $x = y^3 + 1$. We then solve for y to get

$$y^3 = x - 1 \qquad \text{or} \qquad y = (x - 1)^{1/3}.$$

The inverse function is expressed in terms of x by the formula

$$g(x) = (x - 1)^{1/3}.$$

Formally, we have

$$f(g(x)) = ((x - 1)^{1/3})^3 + 1 = x \qquad \text{and} \qquad g(f(x)) = ((x^3 + 1) - 1)^{1/3} = x.$$

EXAMPLE 4.   Find the inverse of the function $f(x) = 1/x$, for $x \neq 0$.

Solution.   In the original equation $y = 1/x$, interchange the letters x and y and get $x = 1/y$. When we solve this for y we get $y = 1/x$. In this example, $g(x) = 1/x$ is the inverse of $f(x) = 1/x$. That is, f is its own inverse. Formally, we have $f(f(x)) = 1/f(x) = 1/(1/x) = x$.

EXAMPLE 5. Find the inverse of $f(x) = x^2$ on the domain $x \geq 0$.

Solution. In the equation $y = x^2$, interchange x and y and get $x = y^2$. Solve for y to get $y = \pm\sqrt{x}$. Choose the positive square root, $y = \sqrt{x}$, because it is the one whose graph is the mirror image of the graph of f on the domain $x \geq 0$. Thus, the inverse of $f(x) = x^2$ on the domain $x \geq 0$ is $g(x) = \sqrt{x}$. Formally, when $x \geq 0$, we have $\sqrt{x^2} = x$ and $(\sqrt{x})^2 = x$.

PROBLEMS

1. Find the inverse of the function $f(x) = 2x + 3$. Verify that Rule 10 applies to the function f and its inverse function g.

2. Use Rule 10 to find the derivative of the function $g(x) = (x - 1)^{1/3}$ in Example 3.

3. Sketch the curve $y = 1/x$ and observe that it is symmetric about the line $y = x$. What is the slope of the curve at $P(a, 1/a)$? What is its slope at the point $P'(1/a, a)$? Do these slopes satisfy Rule 10?

4. If $b = a^{2/3}$, find db/da. What restrictions, if any, should be put on the domain of a?

5. Find the x- and y-intercepts of the line L that is tangent to the curve $y = x^{1/2}$ at $x = 4$.

6. The function

$$f(x) = x^{1/2} + x^{-1/2}$$

is to be approximated near $x = 4$ by a quadratic function

$$Q(x) = C_0 + C_1(x - 4) + C_2(x - 4)^2$$

by choosing coefficients C_0, C_1, and C_2 in such a way that $f(4) = Q(4)$, $f'(4) = Q'(4)$, and $f''(4) = Q''(4)$. Find the coefficients. Use the result to estimate the difference between $f(x)$ and the tangent-line approximation $L(x) = C_0 + C_1(x - 4)$, and compare this estimate of error with the actual error at $x = 4.41 = (2.1)^2$. (We use "error" to mean $f(x) - L(x)$.)

7. a) Sketch graphs of $y = x^3$ and $y = x^{1/3}$ for $-2 \leq x \leq 2$, and sketch the lines tangent to them at $(1, 1)$ and $(-1, -1)$.

b) Which of these functions fails to have a derivative at one value of x, and what is that x? What is the slope of the other curve at that x? What lines are tangent to the curves at that x?

The functions we have dealt with so far have been of the form $y = f(x)$, which express y explicitly in terms of x. Quite often, however, we encounter equations like

$$x^2 + y^2 = 1, \qquad xy = 1,$$

$$y^2 = x, \qquad x^2 + xy + y^2 = 3,$$

which do not give y explicitly in terms of x. Nevertheless each of the equations listed defines a relation between y and x. When a definite number from some domain is substituted for x, the resulting equation determines one or more values of y to be associated with the given value of x. We therefore say that the equation determines y as one or more *implicit functions* of x. The domain of x is usually restricted to make y real.

It happens that each of the equations given above can be solved to give y explicitly in terms of x, but such is not the case for

$$x^5 + 4xy^3 - 3y^5 = 2.$$

Nevertheless, it is possible to calculate dy/dx from such an equation by the method known as *implicit differentiation*. In this method we simply treat y as an unknown but differentiable function of x and apply the rules for finding

2-5

IMPLICIT RELATIONS AND THEIR DERIVATIVES

derivatives of u^n, uv, u/v, etc., which we have already developed. (For a discussion of the validity of the assumption that the equation does define y as one or more differentiable functions of x, we must refer the reader to more advanced textbooks, such as Olmsted, *Advanced Calculus*, Appleton-Century-Crofts, 1961, p. 289.)

EXAMPLE 1.   Find dy/dx if $x^5 + 4xy^3 - 3y^5 = 2$.

Solution.   We simply differentiate both sides of the given equation with respect to x. Thus,

$$\frac{d}{dx}(x^5) + \frac{d}{dx}(4xy^3) - \frac{d}{dx}(3y^5) = \frac{d}{dx}(2),$$

or

$$5x^4 + 4\left(x\frac{d(y^3)}{dx} + y^3\frac{dx}{dx}\right) - 15y^4\frac{dy}{dx} = 0,$$

$$5x^4 + 4\left(3xy^2\frac{dy}{dx} + y^3\right) - 15y^4\frac{dy}{dx} = 0,$$

$$(12xy^2 - 15y^4)\frac{dy}{dx} = -(5x^4 + 4y^3).$$

Finally, at all points where

$$12xy^2 - 15y^4 \neq 0,$$

we have

$$\frac{dy}{dx} = \frac{5x^4 + 4y^3}{15y^4 - 12xy^2}.$$

Note that the rule

$$\frac{d}{dx}u^n = nu^{n-1}\frac{du}{dx}$$

becomes

$$\frac{dy^5}{dx} = 5y^4\frac{dy}{dx}$$

when applied to y^5.

The result of applying this method to any of the equations listed above will be to give an expression for dy/dx in terms of both x and y. This is no real handicap since, if we want the slope of the tangent to a curve at a point (x_1, y_1), for instance, we need merely substitute x_1 for x and y_1 for y in the final expression for dy/dx.

EXAMPLE 2.   Find the slope of the tangent to the curve $x^2 + xy + y^2 = 7$ at the point $(1, 2)$. (See Fig. 2–7.)

Solution.   We differentiate both sides of the equation with respect to x, noting that xy is a product, uv, and that y^2 has the form u^n, while 7 is a

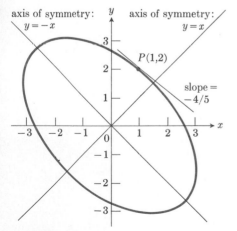

2–7   Graph of $x^2 + xy + y^2 = 7$ with slope of tangent at $P(1, 2)$: $(dy/dx)_{(1,2)} = -\frac{4}{5}$.

constant. Thus

$$2x\frac{dx}{dx} + \left(x\frac{dy}{dx} + y\frac{dx}{dx}\right) + 2y\frac{dy}{dx} = 0,$$

$$(x + 2y)\frac{dy}{dx} = -(2x + y),$$

and wherever $x + 2y \neq 0$, we have

$$\frac{dy}{dx} = -\frac{2x + y}{x + 2y}.$$

In particular, at $(1, 2)$ we have

$$\left(\frac{dy}{dx}\right)_{(1,2)} = -\frac{4}{5}.$$

Note that at those points where $2x + y = 0$, the slope is zero and the tangent is parallel to the x-axis. Where $x + 2y = 0$, the tangent is parallel to the y-axis: At these points we cannot solve for dy/dx but we can solve for dx/dy and it is zero.

The method of implicit differentiation enables us to show also that:

Rule 11.   *If u is a differentiable function of x and*

$$y = u^{p/q},$$

where p and q are integers with $q > 0$, then

$$\frac{dy}{dx} = \frac{p}{q}u^{(p/q)-1}\frac{du}{dx} \qquad (1)$$

provided $u \neq 0$ if $p/q < 1$.

This is the familiar rule for the derivative of u^n, but extended to the case where $n = p/q$ is any rational number.

Restrictions on x

The domain of x in Rule 11 is assumed to be restricted to values for which $u^{p/q}$ and $u^{(p/q)-1}$ are both defined as real numbers. For example, if $u = 1 - x^2$ and $p/q = \frac{1}{2}$, then, in order for

$$y = u^{1/2} = (1 - x^2)^{1/2}$$

to be real, we must have $x^2 \leq 1$. Any larger value of x^2 would make $1 - x^2$ negative. Also, in order for

$$\frac{dy}{dx} = \frac{1}{2}(1 - x^2)^{-1/2}(-2x) = \frac{-x}{\sqrt{1 - x^2}}$$

to be defined as a real number, we need to impose the added restriction that $x^2 \neq 1$, which corresponds to $u \neq 0$, thus avoiding division by zero. Therefore, in applying Eq. (1) to $u = 1 - x^2$ with $p/q = \frac{1}{2}$, we assume that x lies in the interval $-1 < x < 1$.

To establish Rule 11, let

$$y = u^{p/q},$$

which means that

$$y^q = u^p.$$

Then, differentiating both sides of the equation implicitly and using the familiar formulas for the derivatives of y^q and u^p (since p and q are integers, these formulas are valid), we obtain

$$q y^{q-1} \frac{dy}{dx} = p u^{p-1} \frac{du}{dx}.$$

Hence if $y \neq 0$, we have

$$\frac{dy}{dx} = \frac{p u^{p-1}}{q y^{q-1}} \frac{du}{dx}.$$

But

$$y^{q-1} = \left(u^{p/q} \right)^{q-1} = u^{p-(p/q)},$$

so that

$$\frac{dy}{dx} = \frac{p}{q} \frac{u^{p-1}}{u^{p-(p/q)}} \frac{du}{dx} = \frac{p}{q} u^{(p/q)-1} \frac{du}{dx}.$$

This establishes Eq. (1).

REMARK.   The restriction $y \neq 0$ is the same as the restriction $u \neq 0$ but was made without reference to whether p/q was or was not less than one. The restriction is certainly not needed if $p/q = 1$, since then we simply have $y = u$ and

$$\frac{dy}{dx} = \frac{du}{dx}.$$

The case

$$y = x^{3/2}$$

is typical of the case

$$y = u^{p/q}, \qquad p/q > 1,$$

and we shall show that for this case the slope of the curve is 0 at $x = 0$. We may work directly with the definition of the tangent to the curve at $(0, 0)$ as the limiting position of a secant line through $(0, 0)$ and a second point $P_1(x_1, y_1)$ on the curve as P_1 approaches the origin (Fig. 2–8). Then the slope of OP_1 is

$$m = \frac{\text{rise}}{\text{run}} = \frac{y_1 - 0}{x_1 - 0} = \frac{x_1^{3/2}}{x_1} = x_1^{1/2}.$$

Now as P_1 approaches O, we have

$$m_0 = \lim_{x_1 \to 0} m = \lim_{x_1 \to 0} x_1^{1/2} = 0;$$

2–8 Graph of $y = x^{3/2}$. Slope at $x = 0$ is $\lim m_{OP_1} = 0$.

that is, the slope of the tangent to the curve at O is zero. If we use the formula just derived, we obtain

$$y = x^{3/2}, \qquad \frac{dy}{dx} = \frac{3}{2}x^{1/2},$$

and at $x = 0$ this also equals zero.

In the strictest sense, this function has no derivative at $x = 0$, since the function does not exist to the left of the origin. This means that only the righthand limit,

$$\lim_{\Delta x \to 0^+} \frac{f(x + \Delta x) - f(x)}{\Delta x},$$

can be calculated at $x = 0$. Nevertheless, it is customary to say that the curve in Fig. 2–8 has a horizontal tangent at the origin, since the only secant lines that can be drawn from $O(0, 0)$ to points P on the curve tend to a unique limiting position as P approaches O along the curve.

PROBLEMS

In Problems 1–23, find dy/dx.

1. $x^2 + y^2 = 1$

2. $y^2 = \dfrac{x - 1}{x + 1}$

3. $x^2 + xy = 2$

4. $x^2 y + xy^2 = 6$

5. $y^2 = x^3$

6. $x^{2/3} + y^{2/3} = 1$

7. $x^{1/2} + y^{1/2} = 1$

8. $x^3 - xy + y^3 = 1$

9. $x^2 = \dfrac{x - y}{x + y}$

10. $y = \dfrac{x}{\sqrt{x^2 + 1}}$

11. $y = x\sqrt{x^2 + 1}$

12. $y^2 = x^2 + \dfrac{1}{x^2}$

13. $2xy + y^2 = x + y$

14. $y = \sqrt{x} + \sqrt[3]{x} + \sqrt[4]{x}$

15. $y^2 = \dfrac{x^2 - 1}{x^2 + 1}$

16. $(x + y)^3 + (x - y)^3 = x^4 + y^4$

17. $(3x + 7)^5 = 2y^3$

18. $y = (x + 5)^4(x^2 - 2)^3$

19. $\dfrac{1}{y} + \dfrac{1}{x} = 1$

20. $y = (x^2 + 5x)^3$

21. $y^2 = x^2 - x$

22. $x^2 y^2 = x^2 + y^2$

23. $y = \dfrac{\sqrt[3]{x^2 + 3}}{x}$

24. a) By differentiating the equation $x^2 - y^2 = 1$ implicitly, show that $dy/dx = x/y$.

b) By differentiating both sides of the equation $dy/dx = x/y$ implicitly, show that

$$\frac{d^2y}{dx^2} = \frac{y - x\left(\dfrac{dy}{dx}\right)}{y^2} = \frac{y - \dfrac{x^2}{y}}{y^2} = \frac{y^2 - x^2}{y^3},$$

or, since $y^2 - x^2 = -1$ from the original equation,

$$\frac{d^2y}{dx^2} = \frac{-1}{y^3}.$$

Use the method outlined in Problem 24 to find dy/dx and d^2y/dx^2 in each of the following problems (25 through 28).

25. $x^2 + y^2 = 1$

26. $x^3 + y^3 = 1$

27. $x^{2/3} + y^{2/3} = 1$

28. $xy + y^2 = 1$

29. A particle of mass m moves along the x-axis. The velocity $v = dx/dt$ and position x satisfy the equation

$$m(v^2 - v_0^2) = k(x_0^2 - x^2),$$

where k, v_0, and x_0 are constants. Show, by implicitly differentiating this equation with respect to t, that whenever $v \neq 0$,

$$m\frac{dv}{dt} = -kx.$$

Find the lines that are respectively *tangent* and *normal* to the following curves at the points indicated as P_0. (A line is said to be *normal* to a curve at a point P_0 if it is perpendicular to the tangent at P_0.)

30. $x^2 + xy - y^2 = 1,$ $P_0(2, 3)$

31. $x^2 + y^2 = 25,$ $P_0(3, -4)$

32. $x^2 y^2 = 9,$ $P_0(-1, 3)$

33. $\dfrac{x - y}{x - 2y} = 2,$ $P_0(3, 1)$

34. $(y - x)^2 = 2x + 4,$ $P_0(6, 2)$

35. Find the two points where the curve $x^2 + xy + y^2 = 7$

crosses the x-axis, and show that the tangents to the curve at these points are parallel. What is the common slope of these tangents?

36. Find points on the curve $x^2 + xy + y^2 = 7$ (a) where the tangent is parallel to the x-axis; (b) where the tangent is parallel to the y-axis. (In the latter case, dy/dx is not defined, but dx/dy is. What value does dx/dy have at these points?)

37. Use the quadratic equation formula to solve $x^2 + xy + y^2 - 7 = 0$ for y in terms of x. Then find dy/dx at $P(1, 2)$ directly from an expression of the form $y = f(x)$.

2–6

THE INCREMENT OF A FUNCTION

In this article we estimate the change produced in a function $y = f(x)$ when x changes by a small amount Δx. To be precise, let us focus our attention on a portion of the graph of $y = f(x)$ in the neighborhood of a point $P(x, y)$ where the function is differentiable. Then, if $Q(x + \Delta x, y + \Delta y)$ is a second point on the curve, with $\Delta x \neq 0$, we know that

$$\text{The slope of the secant line } PQ = \frac{\Delta y}{\Delta x}$$

approaches the limiting value

$$\frac{dy}{dx} = f'(x)$$

as Δx approaches zero. Therefore, the difference

$$\epsilon = \frac{\Delta y}{\Delta x} - \frac{dy}{dx} \tag{1}$$

is small when $|\Delta x|$ is small.

Now, saying that

$$\lim_{\Delta x \to 0} \frac{\Delta y}{\Delta x} = \frac{dy}{dx} = f'(x) \tag{2}$$

is equivalent to saying that

$$\lim_{\Delta x \to 0} \epsilon = 0. \tag{3}$$

In other words, we may deduce from Eqs. (1), (2), and (3) that

$$\frac{\Delta y}{\Delta x} = \frac{dy}{dx} + \epsilon, \tag{4a}$$

where

$$\epsilon \to 0 \quad \text{as} \quad \Delta x \to 0. \tag{4b}$$

If we multiply both sides of (4a) by Δx, we also have

$$\Delta y = \frac{dy}{dx} \Delta x + \epsilon \, \Delta x. \tag{4c}$$

Although Eq. (4c) was derived with $\Delta x \neq 0$, it is still a true equation even when $\Delta x = 0$. In fact, if we define ϵ by Eq. (1) when $\Delta x \neq 0$, and take $\epsilon = 0$ when $\Delta x = 0$, then Eqs. (4b, c) hold whether $\Delta x = 0$ or not.

Figure 2–9 shows that the first term on the right side of Eq. (4c) is equal to the change Δy_{tan} that would be produced in y by a change Δx along the tangent line. This is called the *principal part* of Δy since, for small values of Δx, it usually is large in comparison with the second term, $\epsilon \, \Delta x$.

The significance of Eqs. (4b, c) is that

$$\Delta y = \Delta y_{\text{tan}} + \epsilon \, \Delta x = \text{change in } y \text{ along the curve}$$

and

$$\Delta y_{\text{tan}} = \frac{dy}{dx} \Delta x = \text{change in } y \text{ along the tangent line}$$

differ by an amount

$$\epsilon \, \Delta x,$$

which tends to zero more rapidly than Δx does when Δx approaches zero.

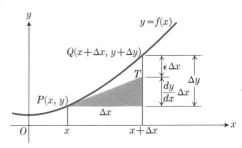

2–9　The increment Δy given by $\Delta y = f(x + \Delta x) - f(x) = (dy/dx)\,\Delta x + \epsilon \cdot \Delta x$.

EXAMPLE.　(See Fig. 2–10.) The area enclosed by a circle of radius r is $A = \pi r^2$. If the radius is increased to $r + h$, find the increase in A and compare with Eqs. (4b) and (4c).

Solution.　$\Delta A = \pi(r + h)^2 - \pi r^2 = 2\pi rh + \pi h^2$. This has the form

$$\Delta A = \frac{dA}{dr} \Delta r + \epsilon(\Delta r)$$

with

$$\frac{dA}{dr} = 2\pi r, \qquad \Delta r = h, \qquad \text{and} \qquad \epsilon = \pi \, \Delta r = \pi h.$$

Geometrically, $2\pi rh$ is the product of the circumference of the original circle and the change in radius $\Delta r = h$. When h is small, this accounts for nearly all of the change in the area. The remaining bit, πh^2, is the product of two numbers, $\epsilon = \pi h$ and $\Delta r = h$, which are both small when h is small.

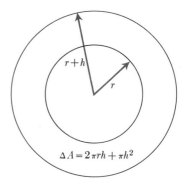

2–10　The area between the circles is $\Delta A = \pi(r + h)^2 - \pi r^2$.

PROBLEMS

For each of the following functions, find (a) Δy; (b) the principal part of Δy, namely, $\Delta y_{\text{tan}} = (dy/dx)\Delta x$; and (c) the difference, $\Delta y - \Delta y_{\text{tan}}$.

1. $y = x^2 + 2x$　　　　　　**2.** $y = 2x^2 + 4x - 3$

3. $y = x^3 - x$　　　　　　**4.** $y = x^4$

5. $y = x^{-1}$

For each of the following functions $y = f(x)$, *estimate* $y + \Delta y = f(x + \Delta x)$ by calculating y plus the principal part of Δy for the given data.

6. $y = \sqrt{x}, \quad x = 4, \quad \Delta x = 0.5$

7. $y = \sqrt[3]{x}, \quad x = 8, \quad \Delta x = -0.5$

8. $y = x^{-1}, \quad x = 2, \quad \Delta x = 0.1$

9. $y = \sqrt{x^2 + 9}, \quad x = -4, \quad \Delta x = -0.2$

10. $y = \dfrac{x}{x + 1}, \quad x = 1, \quad \Delta x = 0.3$

11. The volume $y = x^3$ of a cube of edge x increases by an amount Δy when x increases by an amount Δx. Show that Δy may be represented geometrically as the sum of the volumes of:

a) three slabs of dimensions x by x by Δx,
b) three bars of dimensions x by Δx by Δx,
c) one cube of dimensions Δx by Δx by Δx.

Illustrate by a sketch.

2-7

NEWTON'S METHOD FOR SOLVING EQUATIONS

We know simple formulas for solving linear and quadratic equations. There are somewhat more complicated formulas for cubic and quartic equations. At one time it was hoped that similar formulas might be found for quintic and higher-degree equations, but a young Norwegian mathematician, Niels Henrik Abel (August 5, 1802–April 6, 1829), showed that no formulas like these are possible for quintic or higher-order equations.

There are, however, several numerical techniques for solving equations. One of these is the Newton or, as it is more accurately named, the Newton–Raphson method, which we discuss in this article. If you have access to a computer or a programmable calculator, you can easily write a program to do the arithmetic. If not, you can still see how it can be done. The method is:

1. Guess a first approximation to a root of the equation $f(x) = 0$. A graph of $y = f(x)$ will help.

2. Use the first approximation to get a second, the second to get a third, and so on. To go from the nth approximation x_n to the next approximation x_{n+1}, use the formula

$$x_{n+1} = x_n - \frac{f(x_n)}{f'(x_n)} \tag{1}$$

where $f'(x_n)$ is the derivative of f at x_n. We first show how the method works, and then go to the theory behind it.

EXAMPLE. Use the procedure described above to find where the graph of $y = x^3$ intersects the line $y = x + 1$.

Solution. The curve and line cross when $x^3 = x + 1$. We put this equation into the form $f(x) = 0$ with

$$f(x) = x^3 - x - 1.$$

Then $f'(x) = 3x^2 - 1$. A brief table of values of $f(x)$, $f'(x)$, and $x - f(x)/f'(x)$ was used to construct the graph shown in Fig. 2–11. The curve crosses the x-axis at a root of the equation $f(x) = 0$. We have taken $x_1 = 1$ as our first approximation. We then used Eq. (1) repeatedly to get x_2, x_3, and so on, as shown in Table 2–1.

2–11 Newton's method for finding a root of $f(x) = 0$ uses the tangent to approximate the curve.

Table 2–1. Approximate data for Fig. 2–11.

n	x_n	$f(x_n)$	$f'(x_n)$	$x_{n+1} = x_n - \dfrac{f(x_n)}{f'(x_n)}$
1	1	-1	2	1.5
2	1.5	0.875	5.75	1.347826087
3	1.347826087	0.100682174	4.449905482	1.325200399
4	1.325200399	0.002058363	4.268468293	1.324718174
5	1.324718174	0.000000925	4.264634722	1.324717957
6	1.324717957	-5×10^{-10}	4.264632997	1.324717957

At $n = 6$ we come to the result $x_6 = x_5 = 1.324717957$. When $x_{n+1} = x_n$, Eq. (1) shows that $f(x_n) = 0$. Hence we have found a solution of $f(x) = 0$ to nine decimals, or so it appears. (Our calculator shows only ten figures, and we cannot guarantee the accuracy of the ninth decimal, though we believe it to be correct as given.)

What is the theory behind the method? It is this: We use the tangent to approximate the graph of $y = f(x)$ near the point $P(x_n, y_n)$, where $y_n = f(x_n)$ is small, and we let x_{n+1} be the value of x where that tangent line crosses the x-axis. (We assume that the slope $f'(x_n)$ of the tangent is not zero.) The equation of the tangent is

$$y - y_n = f'(x_n)(x - x_n). \tag{2}$$

We put $y_n = f(x_n)$ and $y = 0$ into Eq. (2) and solve for x:

$$x - x_n = \frac{-f(x_n)}{f'(x_n)},$$

or, as in Eq. (1),

$$x = x_n - \frac{f(x_n)}{f'(x_n)}.$$

REMARK 1.   The method doesn't work if $f'(x_n) = 0$. In that case, choose a new starting place. Of course, it may happen that $f(x) = 0$ and $f'(x) = 0$ have a common root. To detect whether that is so, we could first find the solutions of $f'(x) = 0$, and then check the value of $f(x)$ at such places.

In the example, we started at the point $A(1, -1)$ in Fig. 2–11. The tangent at A crosses the x-axis at $T(1.5, 0)$. We take $x_2 = 1.5$, $y_2 = f(x_2) = 0.875$, and approximate the graph near $A'(1.5, 0.875)$ by the line tangent to the curve at A'. That tangent crosses the x-axis at $x_3 = 1.347\dots$. Each successive approximation becomes the input for the right side of Eq. (1) to get the next approximation. It is clear from Eq. (1) that $x_{n+1} = x_n$ implies that $f(x_n) = 0$, and conversely. Therefore, if the process stops with $x_{n+1} = x_n$, as in the example, we have a zero of $f(x)$.

REMARK 2.   In Fig. 2–11 we have also indicated that the process might have started at the point $B(3, 23)$ on the curve, with $x_1 = 3$. Point B is quite far from the x-axis, but the tangent at B crosses the x-axis at $C(2.11\dots, 0)$, so that x_2 is still an improvement over x_1. If we take $x_1 = 3$ and use Eq. (1) repeatedly as before, with $f(x) = x^3 - x - 1$ and $f'(x) = 3x^2 - 1$, we confirm the nine-place solution $x_7 = x_6 = 1.324717957$ in seven steps.

The curve in Fig. 2–11 has a high turning point at $x = -1/\sqrt{3}$ and a low turning point at $x = +1/\sqrt{3}$. We would not expect good results from Newton's method if we were to start with x_1 between these points, but we can start any place between A and B and get the answer. It would not be very clever to do so, but we could even begin far to the right of B, for example with $x_1 = 10$. It takes a bit longer, but the process still converges to the same answer as before.

REMARK 3.   Newton's method does not always converge. For instance, if

$$f(x) = \begin{cases} \sqrt{x - r} & \text{for } x \geq r, \\ -\sqrt{r - x} & \text{for } x \leq r, \end{cases} \tag{3}$$

the graph will be like that shown in Fig. 2–12. If we begin with $x_1 = r - h$, we get $x_2 = r + h$, and successive approximations go back and forth between these two values. No amount of iteration will bring us any closer to the root r than our first guess.

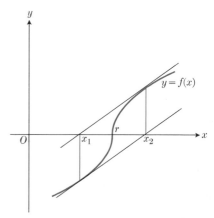

2–12 Graph of a function for which Newton's method fails to converge.

PROBLEMS

Sketch the graph of $y = f(x)$ in each of the following problems (1 through 6). Show that $f(a)$ and $f(b)$ have opposite signs and use Newton's method to estimate the root of the equation $f(x) = 0$ between a and b. One might use $x_1 = (a + b)/2$ as a first approximation.

1. $f(x) = x^2 + x - 1$, $\quad a = 0$, $\quad b = 1$

2. $f(x) = x^3 + x - 1$, $\quad a = 0$, $\quad b = 1$

3. $f(x) = x^4 + x - 3$, $\quad a = 1$, $\quad b = 2$

4. $f(x) = x^4 - 2$, $\quad a = 1$, $\quad b = 2$

5. $f(x) = 2 - x^4$, $\quad a = -1$, $\quad b = -2$

6. $f(x) = \sqrt{2x + 1} - \sqrt{x + 4}$, $\quad a = 2$, $\quad b = 4$

7. Suppose our first guess is lucky, in the sense that x_1 is a root of $f(x) = 0$. What happens to x_2 and later approximations?

8. To find $x = \sqrt[q]{a}$, we apply Newton's method to $f(x) = x^q - a$. Here we assume that a is a positive real number and q is a positive integer. Show that x_2 is a "weighted average" of x_1 and a/x_1^{q-1}, and find the coefficients m_1, m_2 such that

$$x_2 = m_1 x_1 + m_2 \left(\frac{a}{x_1^{q-1}} \right), \quad \begin{matrix} m_1 > 0, \quad m_2 > 0, \\ m_1 + m_2 = 1. \end{matrix}$$

What conclusion would you reach if x_1 and a/x_1^{q-1} were equal? What would be the value of x_2 in that case? (You may also wish to read the article by J. P. Ballantine, "An averaging method of extracting roots," *American Mathematical Monthly*, **63**, 1956, pp. 249–252, where more efficient ways of averaging are discussed. *Also see* J. S. Frame, "The solution of equations by continued fractions," *Ibid.*, **60**, 1953, pp. 293–305.)

9. Show that Newton's method applied to $f(x)$ in Eq. (3) leads to $x_2 = r + h$ if $x_1 = r - h$, and to $x_2 = r - h$ if $x_1 = r + h$, where $h > 0$. Interpret the result geometrically.

10. (See Remark 3.) Is it possible that successive approximations actually get "worse," in that x_{n+1} is farther away from the root r than x_n is? Can you find such a "pathological" example? [*Hint.* Try cube roots in place of square roots in Eq. (3).]

2-8

COMPOSITE FUNCTIONS AND THEIR DERIVATIVES: THE CHAIN RULE

We have already seen that, if u is a differentiable function of x, and $y = u^n$, then

$$\frac{dy}{dx} = nu^{n-1} \frac{du}{dx} \tag{1}$$

for n a rational number. This is a special case of a more general rule. One part of Eq. (1) is

$$nu^{n-1} = \frac{dy}{du},$$

so that the equation can also be written in the form

$$\frac{dy}{dx} = \frac{dy}{du} \cdot \frac{du}{dx}, \tag{2}$$

and the latter form is known as the chain rule for the derivative of a composite function.

Rule 12. The Chain Rule for the Derivative of a Composite Function. *If y is a differentiable function of u and u is a differentiable function of x, then y is a differentiable function of x and*

$$\frac{dy}{dx} = \frac{dy}{du} \cdot \frac{du}{dx}. \tag{3}$$

Before we prove this rule, let us look at a particular example.

EXAMPLE 1. For oscillations of small amplitude, the relation between the period T and the length L of a simple pendulum may be approximated by the equation

$$T = 2\pi \sqrt{\frac{L}{g}}, \tag{4}$$

where $g = 980$ cm/sec^2 is the acceleration due to gravity. When the temperature θ changes, the length L either increases or decreases at a rate that is proportional to L:

$$\frac{dL}{d\theta} = kL, \tag{5}$$

where k is a proportionality constant. What is the rate of change of the period with respect to temperature?

Solution. We assume that g is constant and then

$$T = \left(\frac{2\pi}{\sqrt{g}}\right) L^{1/2}$$

is a function of L. We don't need an explicit formula for the relation between L and θ in order to apply Rule 12, which, for this example takes the form

$$\frac{dT}{d\theta} = \frac{dT}{dL} \cdot \frac{dL}{d\theta} = \left(\frac{2\pi}{\sqrt{g}}\right) \tfrac{1}{2} L^{-1/2} \frac{dL}{d\theta}$$

$$= \left(\frac{2\pi}{\sqrt{g}}\right) \tfrac{1}{2} L^{-1/2}(kL) = \left(\frac{k}{2}\right) \left(2\pi \sqrt{\frac{L}{g}}\right) = \left(\frac{k}{2}\right) T.$$

Thus the rate of change of the period is proportional to the period, with proportionality factor $k/2$.

If θ changes by a small increment $\Delta\theta$, then L and T change by increments

$$\Delta L \approx \Delta L_{\text{tan}} = kL\,\Delta\theta \qquad \text{and} \qquad \Delta T \approx \Delta T_{\text{tan}} = \frac{kT\,\Delta\theta}{2}.$$

Thus,

$$\frac{\Delta T}{T} \approx \frac{1}{2} \frac{\Delta L}{L}.$$

A temperature change that gives a 0.002-percent change in L results in approximately a 0.001-percent change in the period T.

The idea behind the chain rule is this: If $y = f(u)$ is differentiable at $u = u_0$, then an increment Δu produces an increment Δy such that

$$\Delta y = f'(u_0)\,\Delta u + \epsilon_1\,\Delta u, \tag{6a}$$

and if $u = g(x)$ is differentiable at $x = x_0$, then an increment Δx produces an increment Δu such that

$$\Delta u = g'(x_0)\,\Delta x + \epsilon_2\,\Delta x, \tag{6b}$$

where

        ϵ_1 approaches zero when Δu does,

and

        ϵ_2 approaches zero when Δx does.

Combining Eqs. (6a) and (6b) gives

$$\Delta y = [f'(u_0) + \epsilon_1][g'(x_0) + \epsilon_2]\,\Delta x.$$

Dividing through by Δx, we get

$$\frac{\Delta y}{\Delta x} = f'(u_0)g'(x_0)$$

$$+ \text{(terms in } \epsilon_1 \text{ and } \epsilon_2 \text{ that go to zero when } \Delta x \text{ and } \Delta u \text{ do)}.$$

As Δx approaches zero, so does Δu, and we get

$$\lim \frac{\Delta y}{\Delta x} = f'(u_0)g'(x_0),$$

which is the same as

$$\left(\frac{dy}{dx}\right)_{x_0} = \left(\frac{dy}{du}\right)_{u_0}\left(\frac{du}{dx}\right)_{x_0}.$$

EXAMPLE 2. *Snowball melting.* How long does it take a snowball to melt?

Discussion. We start with a mathematical model. Let us assume that the snowball is, approximately, a sphere of radius r and volume $V = (\frac{4}{3})\pi r^3$. (Of course the snowball is not a perfect sphere, but we can apply mathematics only to a mathematical model of the situation, and we choose one that seems reasonable and is not too complex.) In the same way, we choose some hypothesis about the rate at which the volume of the snowball is changing. One model is to assume that the volume decreases at a rate that is proportional to the surface area: In mathematical terms,

$$\frac{dV}{dt} = -k(4\pi r^2).$$

We tacitly assume that k, the proportionality factor, is a constant. (It probably depends upon several things, like the relative humidity of the surrounding air, the air temperature, the incidence of sunlight or its absence, to name a few.) Finally, we need at least one more bit of information: How long has it taken for the snowball to melt some specific percent? We have nothing to guide us unless we make one or more observations, but let us now assume a particular set of conditions in which the snowball melted $\frac{1}{4}$ of its volume in two hours. (You could use letters instead of these precise numbers: say n percent in h hours. Then your answer would be in terms of n and h.) Now to work. Mathematically, we have the following problem.

Given:

$$V = \tfrac{4}{3}\pi r^3 \qquad \text{and} \qquad \frac{dV}{dt} = -k(4\pi r^2),$$

and $V = V_0$ when $t = 0$, and $V = \frac{3}{4}V_0$ when $t = 2$ hr.

To find: The value of t when $V = 0$.

We apply the chain rule to differentiate $V = (\frac{4}{3})\pi r^3$ with respect to t:

$$\frac{dV}{dt} = \frac{4}{3}\pi(3r^2)\frac{dr}{dt} = 4\pi r^2 \frac{dr}{dt}.$$

We set this equal to the given rate, $-k(4\pi r^2)$, and divide by $4\pi r^2$ to get

$$\frac{dr}{dt} = -k.$$

The radius is changing at a *constant rate.*

How long does it take for the radius to go from its initial value

$$r_0 = \left(\frac{3V_0}{4\pi}\right)^{1/3}$$

to $r = 0$? In two hours, r decreases from r_0 to

$$r_2 = \left(\frac{9V_0}{16\pi}\right)^{1/3},$$

because V has decreased to $3V_0/4$. Dividing the second of these equations by the first, we get

$$\frac{r_2}{r_0} = \left(\frac{3}{4}\right)^{1/3} = c \approx 0.91.$$

Thus, $r_2 = cr_0$, where $c \approx 0.91$. Since dr/dt is a constant, $-k$, the constant rate at which r is changing is equal to

$$k = \frac{r_0 - r_2}{2} = \frac{(1-c)r_0}{2}.$$

The time it takes the snowball to melt is

$$\frac{r_0}{k} = \frac{2}{(1-c)} \approx 21.87 \text{ hr.}$$

If $\frac{1}{4}$ of the volume melts in two hours, it takes nearly 20 hours for the rest of it to melt.

REMARK 1.   If we were natural scientists who were really interested in testing our model, we could collect some data and compare them with the results of the mathematics. One practical application may lie in analyzing the proposal to tow large icebergs from polar waters to offshore locations near Southern California to provide fresh water from the melting ice. As a first approximation, we might assume that the iceberg is a large cube, or a pyramid, or a sphere.

Parametric Equations

In many applications a curve traced by a moving particle can be described by expressing the coordinates x and y of a point $P(x, y)$ on the curve as functions of a third variable, say the time t, for a specified domain of that variable. The equations

$$x = f(t), \qquad y = g(t),$$

which express x and y in terms of t, are then called *parametric equations*, and the variable t is called a *parameter*.

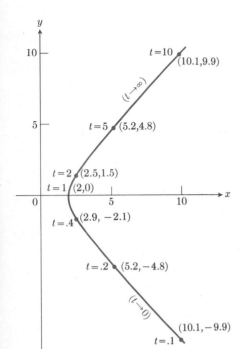

2–13 Graph of $x = t + (1/t)$, $y = t - (1/t)$, $t > 0$. (Part shown is for $0.1 \leq t \leq 10$.)

EXAMPLE 3. Sketch the path traced by the point $P(x, y)$ if

$$x = t + \frac{1}{t}, \qquad y = t - \frac{1}{t} \tag{7}$$

for each positive real number t.

Solution. We make a brief table of values, plot the points, and draw a smooth curve through them (Fig. 2–13). From Table 2–2, or from Eqs. (7), we see that, if t is replaced by $1/t$, the value of x is unchanged and only the sign of y changes. Thus the graph is symmetric with respect to the x-axis. For large values of t, the difference between x and y is small:

$$x - y = \frac{2}{t}, \tag{8a}$$

and if we add the two equations in (7) we get

$$x + y = 2t. \tag{8b}$$

It is now easy to eliminate t between Eqs. (8a) and (8b) by multiplication:

$$(x - y)(x + y) = x^2 - y^2 = 4. \tag{9}$$

The coordinates of all the points described by the parametric equations (7) satisfy Eq. (9), but the converse is not true because Eq. (9) does not require x to be positive. Figure 2–13 shows the part of the graph that corresponds to $0.1 \leq t \leq 10$. For smaller positive values of t, the curve extends downward and to the right, approaching the line $y = -x$. As t tends to $+\infty$, the curve extends up and to the right and approaches the line $y = x$. If we want the slope at any point on the curve, other than at $t = 1$ where the tangent is vertical, we use the chain rule in the form

$$\frac{dy}{dx} = \frac{dy/dt}{dx/dt} = \frac{1 + t^{-2}}{1 - t^{-2}} = \frac{t^2 + 1}{t^2 - 1}. \tag{10}$$

For example, when $t = 5$, $x = 5.2$, $y = 4.8$, and $dy/dx = 26/24$. The line tangent to the graph at this point is

$$y - 4.8 = \tfrac{13}{12}(x - 5.2).$$

Table 2–2. Values of $x = t + (1/t)$ and $y = t - (1/t)$ for selected values of t

t	$1/t$	x	y
0.1	10.0	10.1	-9.9
0.2	5.0	5.2	-4.8
0.4	2.5	2.9	-2.1
1.0	1.0	2.0	0.0
2.0	0.5	2.5	1.5
5.0	0.2	5.2	4.8
10.0	0.1	10.1	9.9

REMARK 2.   In the foregoing example, we can also find dy/dx by differentiating Eq. (9) implicitly:

$$2x - 2y\frac{dy}{dx} = 0, \qquad \frac{dy}{dx} = \frac{x}{y} = \frac{t + t^{-1}}{t - t^{-1}} = \frac{t^2 + 1}{t^2 - 1}.$$

We get a result that is equivalent to Eq. (10). We expect the same result, because the chain rule works that way. The derivative dy/dx does not exist at $t = 1$, where $dx/dt = 0$ and $y = 0$.

PROBLEMS

In Problems 1–4, each pair of equations represents a curve in parametric form. In each case, find the equation of the curve in the form $y = F(x)$ by eliminating t, then calculate dy/dt, dy/dx, and dx/dt, and verify that they satisfy the chain rule, Eq. (3). (See Example 3.)

1. $x = 3t + 1, \quad y = t^2$ **2.** $x = t^2, \quad y = t^3$

3. $x = \dfrac{t}{1 - t}, \quad y = t^2$ **4.** $x = \dfrac{t}{1 + t}, \quad y = \dfrac{t^2}{1 + t}$

5. If a point traces the circle $x^2 + y^2 = 25$ and if $dx/dt = 4$ when the point reaches (3, 4), find dy/dt there.

In each of the following problems (6 through 10), find dy/dx, (a) by using the chain rule, and also (b) by first expressing y directly in terms of x, and then differentiating.

6. $y = u^2 + 3u - 7; \quad u = 2x + 1$

7. $y = \dfrac{u^2}{u^2 + 1}; \quad u = \sqrt{2x + 1}$

8. $y = z^{2/3}; \quad z = x^2 + 1$ **9.** $y = w^2 - w^{-1}; \quad w = 3x$

10. $y = 2v^3 + \dfrac{2}{v^3}; \quad v = (3x + 2)^{2/3}$

Many natural phenomena are periodic; that is, they repeat after definite periods of time. Such phenomena are most readily studied with trigonometric functions, particularly sines and cosines. Our object in this article and the next is to apply the operations of the calculus to these functions, but before we do, we shall review some of their properties.

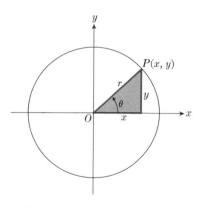

2–9
BRIEF REVIEW OF TRIGONOMETRY

When an angle of measure θ is placed in standard position at the center of a circle of radius r, as in Fig. 2–14, the trigonometric functions of θ are defined by the equations

$$\sin\theta = \frac{y}{r}, \qquad \cos\theta = \frac{x}{r}, \qquad \tan\theta = \frac{y}{x},$$

$$\csc\theta = \frac{r}{y}, \qquad \sec\theta = \frac{r}{x}, \qquad \cot\theta = \frac{x}{y}. \tag{1}$$

Observe that $\tan\theta$ and $\sec\theta$ are not defined for values of θ for which $x = 0$. In radian measure, this means that $\pi/2$, $3\pi/2$, ..., $-\pi/2$, $-3\pi/2$, ... are excluded from the domains of the tangent and the secant functions. Similarly, $\cot\theta$ and $\csc\theta$ are not defined for values of θ corresponding to $y = 0$: that is, for $\theta = 0, \pi, 2\pi, \ldots, -\pi, -2\pi, \ldots$. For those values of θ where the functions are defined, it follows from Eqs. (1) that

$$\csc\theta = \frac{1}{\sin\theta}, \qquad \sec\theta = \frac{1}{\cos\theta}, \qquad \cot\theta = \frac{1}{\tan\theta}.$$

2–14 Angle θ in standard position.

Since, by the theorem of Pythagoras, we have

$$x^2 + y^2 = r^2,$$

it follows that

$$\cos^2 \theta + \sin^2 \theta = 1. \qquad \textbf{(2)}$$

It is also useful to express the coordinates of $P(x, y)$ in terms of r and θ as follows:

$$x = r \cos \theta,$$
$$y = r \sin \theta. \qquad \textbf{(3)}$$

When $\theta = 0$ in Fig. 2–14, we have $y = 0$ and $x = r$; hence, from the definitions (1), we obtain

$$\sin 0 = 0, \qquad \cos 0 = 1.$$

Similarly, for a right angle, $\theta = \pi/2$, we have $x = 0$, $y = r$; hence

$$\sin \frac{\pi}{2} = 1, \qquad \cos \frac{\pi}{2} = 0.$$

Radian Measure

As defined in Article 1–6, the number of radians θ in the angle in Fig. 2–15 is the number of "radius units" contained in the arc s subtended by the central angle θ; that is,

$$\theta \text{ (in radians)} = \frac{s}{r}. \qquad \textbf{(4a)}$$

This also implies that

$$s = r\theta \qquad (\theta \text{ in radians}). \qquad \textbf{(4b)}$$

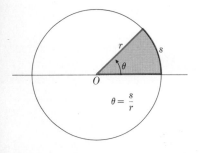

2–15   In radian measure, $\theta = s/r$.

Another useful interpretation of radian measure is easy to get if we take $r = 1$ in (4b). Then the central angle θ, in radians, is just equal to the arc s subtended by θ. We may imagine the circumference of the circle marked off with a scale from which we may read θ. We think of a number scale, like the y-axis shifted one unit to the right, as having been wrapped around the circle. The unit on this number scale is the same as the unit radius. We put the zero of the scale at the place where the initial ray crosses the circle, and then we wrap the positive end of the scale around the circle in the counterclockwise direction, and wrap the negative end around in the opposite direction (see Fig. 2–16). Then θ can be read from this curved s-"axis."

Two points on the s-axis that are exactly 2π units apart will map onto the same point on the unit circle when the wrapping is carried out. For example, if $P_1(x_1, y_1)$ is the point to which an arc of length s_1 reaches, then arcs of length $s_1 + 2\pi$, $s_1 + 4\pi$, and so on, will reach exactly the same point after going completely around the circle one, or two, or more, times. Similarly P_1 will be the image of points on the negative s-axis at $s_1 - 2\pi$, $s_1 - 4\pi$, and so on. Thus, from the wrapped s-axis, we could read

$$\theta_1 = s_1,$$

or

$$\theta_1 + 2\pi, \quad \theta_1 + 4\pi, \quad \ldots, \quad \theta_1 - 2\pi, \quad \theta_1 - 4\pi, \quad \ldots .$$

A unit of arc length $s = 1$ radius subtends a central angle of $57°18'$ (approximately); so

$$1 \text{ radian} \approx 57°18'. \tag{5}$$

We find this, and other relations between degree measure and radian measure, by using the fact that the full circumference has arc length $s = 2\pi r$ and central angle $360°$. Therefore

$$360° = 2\pi \text{ radians}, \tag{6a}$$

$$180° = \pi \text{ radians} = 3.14159\ldots \text{ radians}, \tag{6b}$$

$$\left(\frac{360}{2\pi}\right)° = 1 \text{ radian} \approx 57°17'44.8'', \tag{6c}$$

$$1° = \frac{2\pi}{360} = \frac{\pi}{180} \approx 0.01745 \text{ radians}. \tag{6d}$$

It should be emphasized, however, that the radian measure of an angle is dimensionless, since r and s in Eqs. (4a, b) both represent lengths measured in identical units, for instance feet, inches, centimeters, or light-years. Thus $\theta = 2.7$ is to be interpreted as a pure number. The sine and cosine of 2.7 are the ordinate and abscissa, respectively, of the point $P(x, y)$ on a circle of radius r at the end of an arc of length 2.7 radii. For practical purposes we would convert 2.7 radians to $2.7(360/2\pi)$ degrees and say

$$\sin 2.7 = \sin\left[2.7\left(\frac{360}{2\pi}\right)°\right] \approx \sin\left[154°41'55''\right]$$

$$\approx 0.42738.$$

(See Article 1–6 for a short table of angles, their radian measures, and their sines and cosines.)

Periodicity

The mapping from the real numbers s onto points $P(x, y)$ on the unit circle by the wrapping process described above and illustrated in Fig. 2–16 defines the coordinates as functions of s because Eqs. (1) apply, with $\theta = s$ and $r = 1$:

$$x = \cos \theta = \cos s, \qquad y = \sin \theta = \sin s.$$

Because $s + 2\pi$ maps onto the same point that s does, it follows that

$$\cos (\theta + 2\pi) = \cos \theta,$$
$$\sin (\theta + 2\pi) = \sin \theta. \tag{7}$$

Equations (7) are *identities*; that is, they are true for all real numbers θ. These identities would be true for $\theta' = \theta + 2\pi$:

$$\cos \theta' = \cos (\theta' - 2\pi) \qquad \text{and} \qquad \sin \theta' = \sin (\theta' - 2\pi). \tag{8}$$

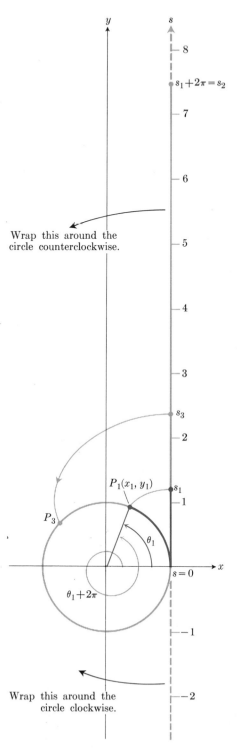

Wrap this around the circle counterclockwise.

Wrap this around the circle clockwise.

2–16 The curved s-"axis" wrapped around the unit circle.

Equations (7) and (8) say that 2π can be added to or subtracted from the domain variable of the sine or cosine functions with no change in the function values. The same process could be repeated any number of times. Consequently

$$\cos(\theta + 2n\pi) = \cos\theta,$$
$$\sin(\theta + 2n\pi) = \sin\theta, \qquad n = 0, \pm 1, \pm 2, \ldots. \tag{9}$$

Figure 2–17(a, b) shows graphs of the curves

$$y = \sin x \qquad \text{and} \qquad y = \cos x.$$

The portion of each curve between 0 and 2π is repeated endlessly to the left and to the right. We also note that the cosine curve is the same as the sine curve shifted to the left an amount $\pi/2$.

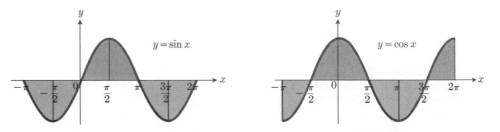

2–17   The value of the sine at x is the value of the cosine at $(x - \pi/2)$. That is, $\sin x = \cos(x - \pi/2)$.

EXAMPLE.* The builders of the Trans-Alaska Pipeline used insulated pads to keep the heat from the hot oil in the pipeline from melting the permanently frozen soil beneath. To design the pads, it was necessary to take into account the variation in temperature throughout the year. The variation was represented in the calculations by a *general sine function* of the form

$$f(x) = A \sin\left[\frac{2\pi}{B}(x - C)\right] + D,$$

where $|A|$ is the *amplitude*, $|B|$ is the *period*, C is the *horizontal shift*, and D is the *vertical shift* (Fig. 2–18). Figure 2–19 shows how such a function can be used to represent temperature data. The data points in the figure are plots of the mean air temperature for Fairbanks, Alaska, based on records of the National Weather Service from 1941 to 1970. The sine function that is used to fit the data is

$$f(x) = 37 \sin\left[\frac{2\pi}{365}(x - 101)\right] + 25,$$

where f is temperature in degrees fahrenheit, and x is the number of the day counting from the beginning of the year.

The fit is remarkably good.

---

* From "Is the curve of temperature variation a sine curve?" by B. M. Lando and C. A. Lando. *The Mathematics Teacher*, September 1977, **7**, 6, pages 534–537.

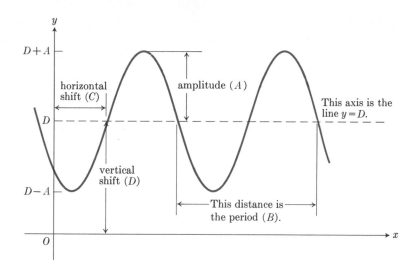

2–18 The general sine curve
$y = A \sin\left[(2\pi/B)(x - C)\right] + D$, shown
for A, B, C and D positive.

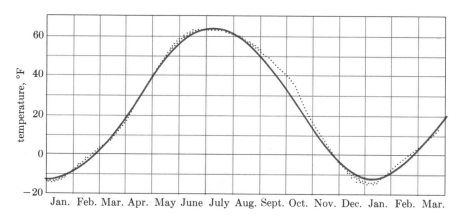

2–19 Normal mean air temperatures at Fairbanks, Alaska, plotted as data points.
The approximating sine function is

$$f(x) = 37 \sin\left[\frac{2\pi}{365}(x - 101)\right] + 25.$$

(From "Is the curve of temperature variation a sine curve?" by B. M. Lando and
C. A. Lando. *The Mathematics Teacher*, September 1977, **7**, 6; Fig. 2, p. 535.)

More Trigonometric Identities

Figure 2–20 shows two angles of opposite sign but of equal magnitude. By
symmetry, the points $P(x, y)$ and $P'(x, -y)$, where the rays of the two angles
θ and $-\theta$ intersect the circle, have equal abscissas, and ordinates that differ
only in sign. Hence we have

$$\sin(-\theta) = -\frac{y}{r} = -\sin\theta, \qquad \textbf{(10a)}$$

$$\cos(-\theta) = \frac{x}{r} = \cos\theta. \qquad \textbf{(10b)}$$

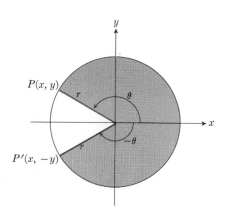

2–20 Angles of opposite sign.

In particular,

$$\sin\left(-\frac{\pi}{2}\right) = -\sin\frac{\pi}{2} = -1,$$

$$\cos\left(-\frac{\pi}{2}\right) = \cos\frac{\pi}{2} = 0.$$

It will be helpful, for reasons which will soon be made apparent, to review the formulas

$$\sin (A + B) = \sin A \cos B + \cos A \sin B, \tag{11a}$$

$$\cos (A + B) = \cos A \cos B - \sin A \sin B, \tag{11b}$$

together with two formulas obtained from these by replacing B by $-B$ and recalling that

$$\sin (-B) = -\sin B, \qquad \cos (-B) = \cos B, \tag{11c}$$

namely,

$$\sin (A - B) = \sin A \cos B - \cos A \sin B, \tag{11d}$$

$$\cos (A - B) = \cos A \cos B + \sin A \sin B. \tag{11e}$$

Equation (11e) may be established for all angles A and B by two applications of the formula for the distance between two points:

$$d = \sqrt{(x_2 - x_1)^2 + (y_2 - y_1)^2}.$$

The first application gives the law of cosines. The second then yields the identity (11e). The other formulas (11a, b, d) can be derived from (11e) as shown below.

Law of cosines. In Fig. 2–21 triangle OAB has been placed with O at the origin and A on the x-axis at $A(b, 0)$. The third vertex B has coordinates

$$x = a \cos \theta, \qquad y = a \sin \theta,$$

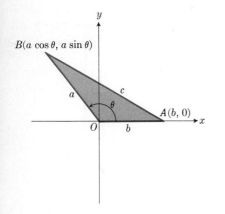

2–21 To derive the law of cosines, compute the distance between A and B, and square.

as given by Eq. (3) with $r = a$. The angle AOB has measure θ. By the formula for the distance between two points,

The square of the distance c between A and B is:

$$c^2 = (a \cos \theta - b)^2 + (a \sin \theta)^2 = a^2 (\cos^2 \theta + \sin^2 \theta) + b^2 - 2ab \cos \theta,$$

or

$$c^2 = a^2 + b^2 - 2ab \cos \theta. \tag{12}$$

Equation (12) is called the *law of cosines*. In words, it says: "The square of any side of a triangle is equal to the sum of the squares of the other two sides minus twice the product of those two sides and the cosine of the angle between them." When the angle θ is a right angle, its cosine is zero, and Eq. (12) reduces to the theorem of Pythagoras. Equation (12) holds for a general angle θ, since it is based solely on the distance formula and on Eqs. (3) for the coordinates of a point. The same equation works with the exterior angle $(2\pi - \theta)$, or the opposite of $(2\pi - \theta)$, in place of θ, because

$$\cos (2\pi - \theta) = \cos (\theta - 2\pi) = \cos \theta.$$

It is still a valid formula when B is on the x-axis and $\theta = \pi$ or $\theta = 0$, as we can easily verify if we remember that $\cos 0 = 1$ and $\cos \pi = -1$. In these special cases, the right side of Eq. (12) becomes $(a - b)^2$ or $(a + b)^2$.

Addition formulas. Equation (11e) follows from the law of cosines applied to the triangle OPQ in Fig. 2–22. We take $OP = OQ = r = 1$. Then the coordinates of P are

$$x_P = \cos A, \qquad y_P = \sin A$$

and of Q,

$$x_Q = \cos B, \qquad y_Q = \sin B.$$

Hence the square of the distance between P and Q is

$$(PQ)^2 = (x_Q - x_P)^2 + (y_Q - y_P)^2$$
$$= (x_Q^2 + y_Q^2) + (x_P^2 + y_P^2) - 2(x_Q x_P + y_Q y_P)$$
$$= 2 - 2 (\cos A \cos B + \sin A \sin B).$$

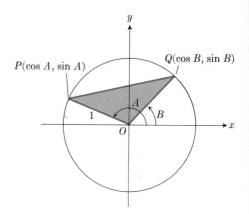

2–22 Diagram for $\cos (A - B)$.

But angle $QOP = A - B$, and the law of cosines gives

$$(PQ)^2 = (OP)^2 + (OQ)^2 - 2(OP)(OQ) \cos (A - B) = 2 - 2 \cos (A - B).$$

When we equate these two expressions for $(PQ)^2$, we obtain

$$\cos (A - B) = \cos A \cos B + \sin A \sin B.$$

We now deduce Eqs. (11a, b, d) from Eq. (11e). We shall also need the results

$$\sin 0 = 0, \qquad \sin (\pi/2) = 1, \qquad \sin (-\pi/2) = -1,$$
$$\cos 0 = 1, \qquad \cos (\pi/2) = 0, \qquad \cos (-\pi/2) = 0. \tag{13}$$

1. In Eq. (11e), we put $A = \pi/2$ and use Eqs. (13) to get

$$\cos \left(\frac{\pi}{2} - B \right) = \sin B. \tag{14a}$$

In this equation, if we replace B by $\pi/2 - B$ and $\pi/2 - B$ by $\pi/2 - (\pi/2 - B)$, we get

$$\cos B = \sin \left(\frac{\pi}{2} - B \right). \tag{14b}$$

Equations (14a, b) express the familiar results that the sine and cosine of an angle are the cosine and sine, respectively, of the complementary angle.

2. We next put $B = -\pi/2$ in Eq. (11e) and use Eq. (13) to get

$$\cos \left(A + \frac{\pi}{2} \right) = -\sin A. \tag{14c}$$

3. We can get the formula for cos $(A + B)$ from Eq. (11e) by substituting $-B$ for B everywhere:

$$\cos (A + B) = \cos [A - (-B)]$$
$$= \cos A \cos (-B) + \sin A \sin (-B)$$
$$= \cos A \cos B - \sin A \sin B, \tag{11b}$$

where the final equality uses Eqs. (11c), established earlier.

4. To derive formulas for sin $(A \pm B)$, we use the identity Eq. (14a) with B replaced by

$$A + B \quad \text{or} \quad A - B.$$

Thus we have

$$\sin (A + B) = \cos [\pi/2 - (A + B)]$$
$$= \cos (\pi/2 - A - B)$$
$$= \cos (\pi/2 - A) \cos B + \sin (\pi/2 - A) \sin B$$
$$= \sin A \cos B + \cos A \sin B. \tag{11a}$$

Equation (11d) follows from this if we replace B by $-B$.

These are the key results of analytic trigonometry, and all have been derived simply from the distance formula and the definitions of sine and cosine. The most important formulas to remember are the following:

$$\sin (A + B) = \sin A \cos B + \cos A \sin B, \tag{11a}$$

$$\cos (A + B) = \cos A \cos B - \sin A \sin B, \tag{11b}$$

$$\sin (-B) = -\sin B, \quad \cos (-B) = \cos B. \tag{11c}$$

If we let

$$\alpha = A + B \quad \text{and} \quad \beta = A - B,$$

so that

$$A = \tfrac{1}{2}(\alpha + \beta), \quad B = \tfrac{1}{2}(\alpha - \beta),$$

and subtract Eq. (11d) from Eq. (11a), we obtain the further useful identity

$$\sin \alpha - \sin \beta = 2 \cos \frac{\alpha + \beta}{2} \sin \frac{\alpha - \beta}{2}. \tag{15}$$

PROBLEMS

In Problems 1 through 9, sketch the graph of the given equation.

1. $y = 2 \sin x$

2. $y = 5 \sin 2x$

3. $y = \sin 2\pi x$

4. $y = 2 \cos 3x$

5. $y = \tan \dfrac{x}{3}$

6. $y = \sin x + \cos x$

7. $y = \sin x - \cos x$

8. $y = \sin (x - 1)$

9. $y = \cos [2\pi(x + 1)]$

10. Find the (a) amplitude, (b) period, (c) horizontal shift, and (d) vertical shift of the general sine function

$$f(x) = 37 \sin \left[\frac{2\pi}{365} (x - 101) \right] + 25.$$

11. Use the equation in Problem 10 to approximate the answers to the following questions about the temperatures in Fairbanks, Alaska, shown in Fig. 2–19. Assume that the year has 365 days.

a) What is the highest mean daily temperature shown?

b) What is the lowest mean daily temperature shown?

c) What is the average of the highest and lowest mean daily temperatures shown? Why is this average the vertical shift of the function?

12. Show that the area of a sector of a circle having central angle θ and radius r is $\frac{1}{2}r^2\theta$, if θ is measured in radians.

13. Let $A(r, 0)$ be the point where the positive x-axis cuts a circle of radius r, center at the origin O. Let $P(r \cos \theta, r \sin \theta)$ be a point on the circle in the first quadrant, with angle $AOP = \theta$ radians. Let AT be tangent to the circle at A and suppose it intersects the line OP at T. By considering the areas of triangle AOP, sector AOP, and triangle AOT, prove the following inequality:

$$\sin \theta < \theta < \tan \theta \qquad \text{if} \quad 0 < \theta < \pi/2.$$

14. In Eq. (11e) take $B = A$. Does the result agree with something else you know?

15. In Eq. (11d) take $B = A$. Does the result agree with something you already know?

16. Derive a formula for $\tan (A - B)$ from Eqs. (11d, e).

17. Derive a formula for $\tan (A + B)$ from Eqs. (11a, b).

18. Express all of the trigonometric functions of a general angle θ in terms of $\sin \theta$ and $\cos \theta$.

19. A function $f(\theta)$ is said to be

an even function of θ if $f(-\theta) = f(\theta)$,

an odd function of θ if $f(-\theta) = -f(\theta)$.

Which of the six trigonometric functions are even, and which are odd?

20. Derive formulas for $\cos 2A$ and $\sin 2A$ from Eqs. (11a, b).

21. Let P and Q be points on a circle with radius $r = 1$, center at the origin O, and such that OP makes an angle $-B$ with the positive x-axis, OQ an angle A. Use the law of cosines to derive a formula for $\cos (A + B)$ directly from this configuration.

(*Problems 22–27 require a calculator.*) Try out the following identities for various values of θ.

22. $\sin (-\theta) = -\sin \theta$ **23.** $\cos (-\theta) = \cos \theta$

24. $\cos \theta = \sin \left(\dfrac{\pi}{2} - \theta\right)$ **25.** $\sin \theta = \cos \left(\dfrac{\pi}{2} - \theta\right)$

The equations in Problems 26 and 27 hold for some values of θ but not for others. Experiment with values of θ until you think you know for which values of θ they hold.

26. $\sin \dfrac{\theta}{2} = \sqrt{\dfrac{1 - \cos \theta}{2}}$ **27.** $\cos \dfrac{\theta}{2} = \sqrt{\dfrac{1 + \cos \theta}{2}}$

We shall now apply the operations of the calculus to the sine and cosine functions. We need the result given by the following theorem.

DIFFERENTIATION OF SINES AND COSINES

Theorem. *If θ is measured in radians, then*

$$\lim_{\theta \to 0} \frac{\sin \theta}{\theta} = 1. \qquad (1)$$

Proof. First we shall suppose that θ is a small positive angle at the center of a circle of radius $r = 1$ (Fig. 2–23). In the figure, OP and OQ are sides of the angle, PT is tangent to the circle at P and intersects the side OQ at T. We observe that

$$\text{Area } \triangle OPQ < \text{Area sector } OPQ < \text{Area } \triangle OPT. \qquad (2)$$

These areas may be expressed in terms of θ as follows:

$$\text{Area } \triangle OPQ = \tfrac{1}{2}\overline{OP} \cdot \overline{OQ} \cdot \sin \theta = \tfrac{1}{2} \sin \theta, \qquad (3a)$$

$$\text{Area sector } OPQ = \tfrac{1}{2}r^2\theta = \tfrac{1}{2}\theta, \qquad (3b)$$

$$\text{Area } \triangle OPT = \tfrac{1}{2}\overline{OP} \cdot \overline{PT} = \tfrac{1}{2} \tan \theta. \qquad (3c)$$

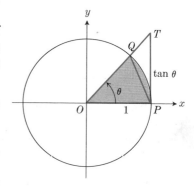

2–23 Area $\triangle OPQ <$ area sector $OPQ <$ area $\triangle OPT$.

We substitute from Eqs. (3a, b, c) into (2) and obtain

$$\tfrac{1}{2}\sin\theta < \tfrac{1}{2}\theta < \tfrac{1}{2}\tan\theta, \qquad \text{when}\quad 0 < \theta < \frac{\pi}{2}. \tag{4}$$

Since $\sin\theta$ is positive in (4), the inequality signs will go the same way if we divide all three terms by $\tfrac{1}{2}\sin\theta$. Therefore,

$$1 < \frac{\theta}{\sin\theta} < \frac{1}{\cos\theta}, \qquad \text{when}\quad 0 < \theta < \frac{\pi}{2}. \tag{5a}$$

We next take reciprocals in (5a), which requires that we reverse the inequality signs:

$$1 > \frac{\sin\theta}{\theta} > \cos\theta, \qquad \text{when}\quad 0 < \theta < \frac{\pi}{2}. \tag{5b}$$

This quickly brings us to our goal. Since $\cos\theta$ approaches 1 as θ approaches zero, the Sandwich Theorem (Theorem 2, Article 1–10) tells us that

$$\lim_{\theta\to 0}\frac{\sin\theta}{\theta} = 1.$$

The geometrical argument leading to Eq. (1) is based on the assumption that θ is positive, but the same limit is obtained if θ approaches zero through negative values. For if $\theta = -\alpha$ and α is positive, then when α approaches zero, we have

$$\frac{\sin\theta}{\theta} = \frac{\sin(-\alpha)}{-\alpha} = \frac{-\sin\alpha}{-\alpha} = \frac{\sin\alpha}{\alpha} \to 1.$$

This concludes the proof.

If θ were not measured in radians but in degrees, the limit that we would obtain in place of Eq. (1) would be

$$\lim_{\theta\to 0}\frac{\sin\theta°}{\theta} = \frac{\pi}{180}. \tag{6}$$

It is to avoid the factor $\pi/180$ in this equation that we use radian measure in all calculus operations with trigonometric functions.

Table 2–3 shows $\sin\theta$ and $(\sin\theta)/\theta$ for a few selected values of θ near zero. To get the effect of $(\sin\theta)/\theta$ approaching 1, we read the last column upward from the bottom.

Table 2–3

Degrees	θ (radians)	$\sin\theta$	$\dfrac{\sin\theta}{\theta}$
0°	0	0	Undefined
1°	0.017453	0.017452	0.99994
2°	0.034907	0.034899	0.9998
5°	0.08727	0.08716	0.9987
10°	0.17453	0.17365	0.995

Derivative of sin u

We now consider a function defined by

$$y = \sin u$$

and calculate the derivative from the definition

$$\frac{dy}{du} = \lim_{\Delta u \to 0} \frac{\Delta y}{\Delta u}.$$

Let u be given an increment Δu and y a corresponding increment Δy. Then

$$y + \Delta y = \sin (u + \Delta u),$$

and hence

$$\Delta y = \sin (u + \Delta u) - \sin u \tag{a}$$

$$= 2 \cos \left(u + \frac{\Delta u}{2}\right) \sin \frac{\Delta u}{2}, \tag{b}$$

where we have used Eq. (15) of Article 2–9, with $\alpha = u + \Delta u$ and $\beta = u$, in going from (a) to (b). If we divide (b) by Δu, we have

$$\frac{\Delta y}{\Delta u} = 2 \cos \left(u + \frac{\Delta u}{2}\right) \frac{\sin (\Delta u/2)}{\Delta u}$$

$$= \cos \left(u + \frac{\Delta u}{2}\right) \frac{\sin (\Delta u/2)}{\Delta u/2},$$

$$= \cos (u + \theta) \frac{\sin \theta}{\theta},$$

where $\theta = \Delta u/2$. We now let θ approach zero and make use of Eq. (1), and obtain

$$\lim_{\Delta u \to 0} \frac{\Delta y}{\Delta u} = \lim_{\theta \to 0} \left[\cos (u + \theta) \frac{\sin \theta}{\theta}\right] = \cos u.$$

But since $y = \sin u$, this means that

$$\frac{dy}{du} = \frac{d (\sin u)}{du} = \cos u.$$

If u is a differentiable function of x, we may apply the chain rule

$$\frac{dy}{dx} = \frac{dy}{du} \frac{du}{dx}$$

to this, with the result that we obtain

$$\frac{d (\sin u)}{dx} = \cos u \cdot \frac{du}{dx}. \tag{7}$$

Thus to find the derivative of the sine of a function, we take the cosine of the same function and multiply it by the derivative of the function.

EXAMPLE 1.   If

$$y = \sin 2x,$$

then

$$\frac{dy}{dx} = \cos 2x \cdot \frac{d(2x)}{dx} = 2 \cos 2x.$$

Derivative of cos u

To obtain a formula for the derivative of cos u, we make use of the identities

$$\cos u = \sin\left(\frac{\pi}{2} - u\right), \qquad \sin u = \cos\left(\frac{\pi}{2} - u\right).$$

Thus

$$\frac{d\,(\cos u)}{dx} = \frac{d\,\sin\,[(\pi/2) - u]}{dx}$$

$$= \cos\left(\frac{\pi}{2} - u\right)\frac{d[(\pi/2) - u]}{dx}$$

$$= \sin u \cdot -\frac{du}{dx},$$

or

$$\frac{d\,(\cos u)}{dx} = -\sin u \frac{du}{dx}. \tag{8}$$

This equation tells us that the derivative of the cosine of a function is minus the sine of the same function, times the derivative of the function.

EXAMPLE 2.   Let

$$y = \cos (x^2).$$

Then

$$\frac{dy}{dx} = -\sin (x^2)\frac{d(x^2)}{dx} = -2x \sin (x^2).$$

The formulas (7) and (8) may be combined with the formulas given previously, as in the following examples.

EXAMPLE 3.   Find dy/dx if

$$y = \sin^2 (3x).$$

Solution.   Let

$$y = \sin^2 (3x) = u^2, \qquad u = \sin 3x.$$

Then,

$$\frac{dy}{dx} = 2u\frac{du}{dx} = 2 \sin 3x \frac{d (\sin 3x)}{dx}$$

$$= 2 \sin 3x \cdot \cos 3x \frac{d(3x)}{dx}$$

$$= 6 \sin 3x \cos 3x$$

$$= 3 \sin 6x.$$

EXAMPLE 4. Find dy/dx if

$$y = \sec^2 5x = (\cos 5x)^{-2}.$$

Solution. We apply the formula for the derivative of a function to a power,

$$\frac{d(u^n)}{dx} = nu^{n-1}\frac{du}{dx}.$$

We then have

$$\frac{dy}{dx} = -2 (\cos 5x)^{-3}\frac{d (\cos 5x)}{dx}$$

$$= (-2 \sec^3 5x)\left(-\sin 5x \frac{d(5x)}{dx}\right)$$

$$= +10 \sec^3 5x \sin 5x.$$

EXAMPLE 5. Find the velocity and acceleration of a particle moving in a circle of radius r with constant angular velocity $\omega = d\theta/dt > 0$.

Solution (See Fig. 2–24a).   If the position of the particle at time t is $P(x, y)$, then

$$x = r \cos \theta, \qquad y = r \sin \theta, \tag{9a}$$

and it is given that the angular velocity

$$\frac{d\theta}{dt} = \omega \tag{9b}$$

is constant. The velocity (Fig. 2–24b) is a vector **v** with components

$$v_x = \frac{dx}{dt} = \frac{dx}{d\theta}\frac{d\theta}{dt}, \qquad v_y = \frac{dy}{dt} = \frac{dy}{d\theta}\frac{d\theta}{dt} \tag{9c}$$

parallel to the x- and y-axes respectively. Also, the acceleration (Fig. 2–24c) is a vector **a** with components

$$a_x = \frac{dv_x}{dt}, \qquad a_y = \frac{dv_y}{dt} \tag{9d}$$

2–24   The velocity and acceleration vectors of a particle moving counterclockwise around a circle at a constant angular velocity.

parallel to the coordinate axes. From (9a) and (9b), we find

$$v_x = \frac{dx}{dt} = -r \sin \theta \frac{d\theta}{dt} = -\omega r \sin \theta = -\omega y,$$

$$v_y = \frac{dy}{dt} = r \cos \theta \frac{d\theta}{dt} = \omega r \cos \theta = \omega x, \tag{9e}$$

and from these we find in turn

$$a_x = \frac{dv_x}{dt} = -\omega \frac{dy}{dt} = -\omega^2 x,$$

$$a_y = \frac{dv_y}{dt} = \omega \frac{dx}{dt} = -\omega^2 y. \tag{9f}$$

The velocity vector has both magnitude and direction. Its magnitude is

$$\sqrt{v_x^2 + v_y^2} = \sqrt{\omega^2 y^2 + \omega^2 x^2} = \omega \sqrt{y^2 + x^2} = \omega r,$$

which is the angular velocity ω times the radius of the circle. Its direction is specified, except for sense, by its slope, which is given by

$$\frac{v_y}{v_x} = \frac{dy/dt}{dx/dt} = \frac{dy}{dx},$$

which is the same as the slope of the tangent to the curve at P. In Fig. 2–24(b), the sense is seen graphically to be in the counterclockwise direction, since from (9e) the x-component has a sign opposite to the sign of y because ω is positive.

Similarly, the acceleration vector has magnitude

$$\sqrt{a_x^2 + a_y^2} = \omega^2 \sqrt{x^2 + y^2} = \omega^2 r,$$

and its direction will be opposite to that of the vector from O to P, since the latter has components x and y, while (9f) shows that the acceleration has its corresponding components just $(-\omega^2)$ times these; that is,

$$\text{The acceleration vector } \mathbf{a} = -\omega^2(\mathbf{OP}).$$

This shows that the acceleration is toward the center of the circle at each instant and has a constant magnitude $\omega^2 r$.

To summarize: If a particle moves in a circle of radius r with constant angular velocity $\omega > 0$, then its velocity vector is tangent to the circle and has magnitude ωr, while its acceleration vector points toward the center of the circle and has magnitude $\omega^2 r$. Hence (by Newton's second law) the force needed to keep a particle of mass m moving at constant speed ωr in a circle of radius r is $m\omega^2 r$, directed toward the center of the circle.

PROBLEMS

Evaluate limits 1–22 by making use of Eq. (1) together with appropriate trigonometric identities and theorems on limits.

1. $\lim\limits_{\theta \to 0} \dfrac{\tan \theta}{\theta}$

2. $\lim\limits_{\theta \to \pi} \dfrac{\sin \theta}{\pi - \theta}$

[*Hint.* Let $x = \pi - \theta$.]

3. $\lim\limits_{\theta \to 0} \dfrac{\sin 2\theta}{\theta}$

4. $\lim\limits_{x \to 0} \dfrac{\sin x}{3x}$

5. $\lim\limits_{t \to 0} \dfrac{t}{\sin t}$

6. $\lim\limits_{x \to 0} \dfrac{x}{\sin 3x}$

7. $\lim\limits_{x \to 0} \dfrac{\sin 5x}{\sin 3x}$

8. $\lim\limits_{x \to 0} \tan 2x \csc 4x$

9. $\lim\limits_{\theta \to 0} \dfrac{\sin^2 \theta}{\theta}$

10. $\lim\limits_{\theta \to 0} \dfrac{1 - \cos \theta}{\theta}$

[*Hint.* If $|\theta| < \pi$, then
$$1 - \cos \theta = \frac{\sin^2 \theta}{1 + \cos \theta}.$$]

11. $\lim\limits_{\theta \to 0} \dfrac{1 - \cos \theta}{\theta^2}$

12. $\lim\limits_{y \to 0} \dfrac{\tan 2y}{3y}$

13. $\lim\limits_{u \to 0} \dfrac{3u}{\sin 5u}$

14. $\lim\limits_{x \to \infty} x \sin \dfrac{1}{x}$

[*Hint.* Let $1/x = u$.]

15. $\lim\limits_{y \to \infty} 2y \tan \dfrac{\pi}{y}$

16. $\lim\limits_{x \to \pi/2} \dfrac{2x - \pi}{\cos x}$

17. $\lim\limits_{\theta \to 0} \theta \cot 2\theta$

18. $\lim\limits_{x \to 0} \dfrac{x^2 + 2x}{\sin 2x}$

19. $\lim\limits_{x \to 0} \dfrac{\sin 2x}{2x^2 + x}$

20. $\lim\limits_{h \to 0} \dfrac{\sin (a + h) - \sin a}{h}$

21. $\lim\limits_{h \to 0} \dfrac{\cos (a + h) - \cos a}{h}$

22. $\lim\limits_{h \to 2} \dfrac{\cos (\pi/h)}{h - 2}$

In Problems 23 through 40, find dy/dx.

23. $y = \sin (3x + 4)$

24. $y = x \sin x$

25. $y = \dfrac{\sin x}{x}$

26. $y = \cos 5x$

27. $y = x^2 \sin 3x$

28. $y = \sqrt{2 + \cos 2x}$

29. $y = \sin^2 x + \cos^2 x$

30. $y = \dfrac{2}{\cos 3x}$

31. $y = 3 \sin 2x - 4 \cos 2x$

32. $y = 3 \cos^2 2x - 3 \sin^2 2x$

33. $y = 2 \sin x \cos x$

34. $y = \dfrac{1}{\sin x}$

35. $y = \cos^2 3x$

36. $y = \cot x$

37. $y = \sin^2 x^2$

38. $y = \cos (\sin \sqrt{x^2 + 1})$

39. $x \sin 2y = y \cos 2x$

40. $y^2 = \sin^4 2x + \cos^4 2x$

41. Find an equation of the tangent to the curve $y = \sin mx$ at $x = 0$.

42. A particle moves on the curve

$$x = a \cos \omega t, \qquad y = b \sin \omega t,$$

where a, b, and ω are constants. Show that the acceleration components are

$$a_x = -\omega^2 x \quad \text{and} \quad a_y = -\omega^2 y.$$

2–11

CONTINUITY

Before we take up further applications of differentiation in Chapter 3, it is desirable to discuss the *continuity* of a function. We shall see that continuity is even more basic than differentiability.

Definition.   *A function f which is defined in some neighborhood of c is said to be continuous at c provided*

a) *the function has a definite finite value $f(c)$ at c, and*
b) *as x approaches c, $f(x)$ approaches $f(c)$ as limit:*

$$\lim_{x \to c} f(x) = f(c).$$

If a function is continuous at all points of an interval $a \le x \le b$ (or $a < x < b$, etc.), then it is said to be continuous on, or in, that interval.

EXAMPLE 1.   As an example of a continuous function, let us investigate

$$f(x) = x^2$$

at some fixed value $x = c$. Certainly

$$f(c) = c^2$$

at $x = c$. Furthermore, the difference

$$f(x) - f(c) = x^2 - c^2 = (x - c)(x + c)$$

approaches zero as a limit when $x - c$ approaches zero, since as $x \to c$ we have

$$\lim \left[f(x) - f(c) \right] = \lim (x - c) \lim (x + c)$$

$$= 0 \cdot 2c = 0.$$

Thus, both requirements of the definition are satisfied. Therefore, $f(x) = x^2$ is continuous at *any* $x = c$; that is, it is continuous for all x, $-\infty < x < +\infty$.

The graph of a function that is continuous on an interval $a \le x \le b$ is an unbroken curve over that interval. This fact is of practical importance in using curves to represent functions. It makes it possible to sketch a curve by constructing a table of values (x, y), plotting relatively few points from this table, and then sketching a continuous (i.e., unbroken) curve through these points. For example, to graph $y = x^2$, we first make a short table of values:

x	0	± 0.5	± 1	± 2
y	0	0.25	1	4

then plot these points and draw a continuous curve through them, as shown in Fig. 2–25. Then we might go one step further and use the curve itself to find the value of x^2 corresponding to an x different from those used in making the table of values. For example, in Fig. 2–25, $x = 1.6$ is indicated on the x-scale and the corresponding reading on the y-scale gives $x^2 \approx 2.6$. Of

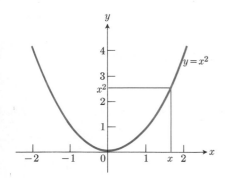

2–25   The graph of $y = x^2$ is a continuous curve. It can be used to read $x^2 = 2.6$ when $x = 1.6$.

course, the graph probably won't give *exact* values except at those points that have been plotted exactly. But it will give values that are *near* the exact values, if the calculated points aren't spread too far apart.

A function that is not continuous at a point $x = c$ is said to be *discontinuous* or to have a *discontinuity* at $x = c$.

EXAMPLE 2. The function $F(t) = 1/t$ is discontinuous at $t = 0$ because it violates both requirements (a) and (b) (see Fig. 2–26). This function has an infinite discontinuity at $t = 0$.

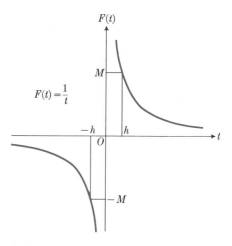

2–26 The function $F(t) = 1/t$ is not continuous at $t = 0$, but is continuous elsewhere.

Removable Discontinuity

A function may have a discontinuity at a point c because the function is not defined at c, or because the limit of $f(x)$ as x approaches c differs from $f(c)$, or because the limit may not exist. One simple type, called a *removable discontinuity*, is illustrated in the next example: The function has a limit as x approaches $c = 0$, but the formula defining the function has no meaning at 0. We remove the discontinuity by defining the function by its original formula for $x \neq 0$ and by the actual limit as its value at $x = 0$.

EXAMPLE 3. The function f defined by

$$f(x) = \frac{\sin x}{x} \qquad \text{for} \quad x \neq 0$$

has a removable discontinuity at $x = 0$. The formula is not valid when $x = 0$, but

$$\lim_{x \to 0} \frac{\sin x}{x} = 1.$$

We therefore extend the domain of f to include the origin by defining its value there to be $f(0) = 1$ (Fig. 2–27). Strictly speaking, when we change the domain we should change the name of the function. But mathematicians often don't make that distinction in a situation of this type, and use the same letter to name the function, saying, let

$$f(x) = \begin{cases} \dfrac{\sin x}{x} & \text{when } x \neq 0, \\[2mm] 1 & \text{when } x = 0. \end{cases}$$

By so defining the value of f at 0, we have made f continuous there, since we now have $f(0) = \lim f(x)$ as x approaches zero.

2–27 The graph of $f(x) = (\sin x)/x$ for $-\pi/2 \leq x \leq \pi/2$, $x \neq 0$, does not include the point $(0, 1)$ because the formula $(\sin x)/x$ is not valid for $x = 0$. But we have removed the discontinuity from the graph by defining $f(0) = 1$. When we have filled in the missing point in this way we get a continuous curve.

Nonremovable Discontinuity

The discontinuity at $x = 0$ in the foregoing example could be removed because f had a limit, namely 1, as x approached zero. On the other hand, if

$$g(x) = \frac{|x|}{x} \qquad \text{for} \quad x \neq 0,$$

then there is a discontinuity of g at 0 that cannot be removed. When x is

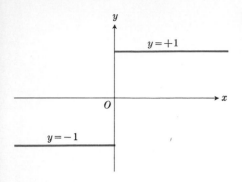

2–28 The graph of $g(x) = |x|/x$ for $x \neq 0$ cannot be made continuous because the righthand limit and the lefthand limit of $g(x)$ as x approaches zero are not equal.

negative, $g(x) = -1$, and when x is positive, $g(x) = +1$ (Fig. 2–28). Therefore, $g(x)$ does not approach a limit as x approaches zero: Its limit as x approaches zero from the left is -1 and its limit as x approaches zero from the right is $+1$. If we assign the value 0 to $g(0)$, the resulting function is the *signum function* (or *sign function*) of x:

$$\operatorname{sgn} x = \begin{cases} +1 & \text{if } x \text{ is positive,} \\ 0 & \text{if } x = 0, \\ -1 & \text{if } x \text{ is negative.} \end{cases}$$

The signum function is defined for all x, but it is not continuous at $x = 0$. It is continuous for $x \neq 0$.

With these examples before us, the question arises as to how, in practice, we can tell whether or not a given function is continuous. When we sketch its graph, should we be sure to sketch a connected, unbroken curve, as for the graph of $y = x^2$, or must we be careful *not* to connect all of the points as, for example, in the case $y = 1/x$, where points in the third quadrant must not be connected with points in the first quadrant?

Since we have studied differentiation, the following theorem, which says that every function that has a derivative at a point is also continuous at that point, enables us to conclude that:

a) Every polynomial

$$f(x) = ax^n + bx^{n-1} + \cdots + px + q$$

is continuous for all x, $-\infty < x < +\infty$, and

b) Every rational function

$$f(x) = \frac{F(x)}{G(x)},$$

$F(x)$ and $G(x)$ being polynomials, is continuous for all x where the denominator $G(x)$ is not zero.

c) The functions $\sin u$ and $\cos u$ are differentiable, and therefore are continuous, wherever $u = f(x)$ is a differentiable function of x.

Thus, for example, the graphs of

$$y = x^3, \qquad y = 2x^2 - x + 3, \qquad y = \frac{x^2 - 1}{x^2 + 1}, \qquad y = \sin 2x$$

are continuous, connected curves over the domain $-\infty < x < +\infty$.

On the other hand, the graph of

$$y = \frac{x^2 + 1}{x^3 - 4x} \tag{1}$$

goes shooting off toward $\pm\infty$ as x approaches one of the three values

$$x = -2, \qquad x = 0, \qquad x = +2,$$

where the denominator vanishes. But, over the intervals $-\infty < x < -2$, $-2 < x < 0$, $0 < x < 2$, and $2 < x < +\infty$, the graph consists of separate continuous curves, since the denominator does not vanish in any of these intervals. (See Fig. 2–29.)

Let us now state and prove the theorem we mentioned above.

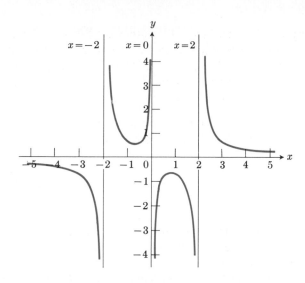

2–29 The function $f(x) = (x^2 + 1)/(x^3 - 4x)$ has infinite discontinuities where $x^3 - 4x = 0$. Elsewhere the function is continuous. The graph is symmetric with respect to the origin.

Theorem 1. *If the function f has a finite derivative*

$$f'(c) = \lim_{\Delta x \to 0} \frac{f(c + \Delta x) - f(c)}{\Delta x} \qquad (2)$$

at $x = c$, then f is continuous at $x = c$.

Proof. For the limit in (2) to exist, it is necessary that $f(c)$ and $f(c + \Delta x)$ both exist, at least for all Δx near zero. We change the notation slightly by writing x in place of $c + \Delta x$. Then

$$x = c + \Delta x$$

is near c when

$$\Delta x = x - c$$

is near zero. Equation (2) now may be written in the form

$$f'(c) = \lim_{x \to c} \frac{f(x) - f(c)}{x - c}.$$

Suppose then that $f'(c)$ exists and is finite. We want to prove that $f(x) - f(c)$ tends to zero as $x \to c$. This follows at once from

$$\lim_{x \to c} [f(x) - f(c)] = \lim_{x \to c} \left[(x - c) \frac{f(x) - f(c)}{x - c} \right],$$

$$= \lim_{x \to c} (x - c) \cdot \lim_{x \to c} \frac{f(x) - f(c)}{x - c}$$

$$= 0 \cdot f'(c) = 0. \qquad \text{Q.E.D.}$$

We have just shown that differentiability implies continuity. The converse, however, is not true.

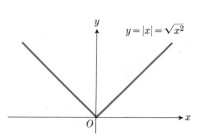

EXAMPLE 4. The function $f(x) = |x|$ is continuous at $x = 0$, but does not have a derivative there. (See Fig. 2–30; also, Example 3, Article 1–8.)

2–30 The absolute value function is continuous everywhere but has no derivative at zero.

Until the middle of the nineteenth century it was generally believed that a continuous function would have a derivative at most places, even though there might be isolated points where the derivative did not exist, as at $x = 0$ in our example. However, the German mathematicians Riemann (1826–1866) and Weierstrass (1815–1897) gave examples of functions that are continuous but that fail to have derivatives anywhere. (For a readable account of this, see *World of Mathematics*, Vol. 3, p. 1963.)

We conclude this chapter with some theorems which we shall state without proofs. Some of these theorems follow rather simply from the corresponding theorems on limits. Others require, for rigorous proofs, a deeper study of the properties of the real number system than we are able to make at this time.

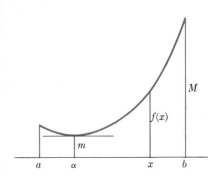

Minimum m at inner point α of interval; maximum M at endpoint b.

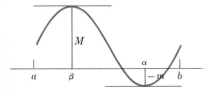

Minimum and maximum at inner points.

Maximum and minimum at endpoints of $[a,b]$.

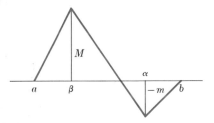

Minimum and maximum at interior points α and β where the slope is not zero. This function is continuous on $[a,b]$ but is not differentiable at α and β.

2–31   A continuous function over the domain $a \le x \le b$ has a minimum and a maximum (low point and high point).

Theorem 2.   *Suppose f and g are two functions that are continuous at $x = c$. Then the functions F_1, F_2, F_3 defined by*

$$F_1(x) = f(x) + g(x),$$
$$F_2(x) = kf(x), \qquad k \text{ any number,}$$
$$F_3(x) = f(x) \cdot g(x)$$

are also continuous at $x = c$. Furthermore, if $g(c)$ is not zero, then

$$F_4(x) = \frac{f(x)}{g(x)}$$

is also continuous at $x = c$.

Theorem 2 says that the sum, product, and quotient of two continuous functions are continuous except where the denominator in a quotient would be zero. The product $kf(x)$ for $k =$ a constant is really a special case, because the function $g(x) = k$ is continuous everywhere.

The next three theorems describe properties of any function f that is continuous on a bounded closed interval $a \le x \le b$. Theorems 3 and 4 together guarantee that the image of such an interval under a continuous mapping f either is a single point (if f is constant) or is a closed bounded interval $m \le f(x) \le M$, where m and M are the least and greatest values of $f(x)$ for x in the interval. We shall have more appreciation for these results as we see how they are used.

Theorem 3 (Existence of maximum and minimum values).   *Suppose that $f(x)$ is continuous for all x in the closed interval $[a, b]$. Then f has a minimum value m and a maximum value M on $[a, b]$. That is, there are numbers α and β in $[a, b]$ such that $f(\alpha) = m, f(\beta) = M$, and*

$$m \le f(x) \le M \qquad \text{for all } x \text{ in } [a, b].$$

Figure 2–31 illustrates that (α, m) is the lowest point, and (β, M) is the highest point of the graph of the function f over the interval $a \le x \le b$.

Theorem 4 (The Intermediate Value Theorem).   *If $f(x)$ is continuous on the closed interval $[a, b]$ and N is any number between $f(a)$ and $f(b)$, then there is at least one number c between a and b such that $f(c) = N$.*

The theorem gets its name, the Intermediate Value Theorem, from the fact that the continuous function $f(x)$ takes on all values between $f(a)$ and $f(b)$ as x varies from a to b. In particular, if f is negative at $x = a$ and positive at $x = b$, then f takes on the value $N = 0$ at some point c between a and b. Thus, the theorem guarantees that there is a solution of the equation $f(x) = 0$ somewhere in the interval (a, b); or, in geometric terms, that the graph of f crosses the x-axis somewhere between a and b. This guarantee is the basis of the approximation technique illustrated in the next example.

EXAMPLE 5. Find a real number x that is one less than its cube.

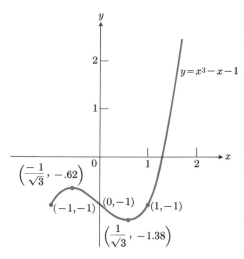

Solution. We want $x = x^3 - 1$, or $x^3 - x - 1 = 0$. Let $f(x) = x^3 - x - 1$. A part of the graph of $y = f(x)$ is shown in Fig. 2–32. We have plotted enough points to find that $f(1.3) = -0.10$ and $f(1.4) = +0.34$ so the curve must cross the x-axis between $x = 1.3$ and $x = 1.4$. With a calculator it is easy to compute values of $f(x)$ for $x = 1.31, 1.32, 1.33$, and so on, until we locate an interval of length 0.01 in which a zero of $f(x)$ lies. In fact, one gets $f(1.32) \approx -0.02$ and $f(1.33) \approx +0.02$, so a solution of $f(x) = 0$ lies between 1.32 and 1.33. The process can be continued, using 1.321, 1.322, 1.323, and so on. Or we can use linear interpolation, or Newton's method. The latter is very good in this example and gives, as the solution of $f(x) = 0$, the answer 1.324717957 (see Example in Article 2–7).

2–32 The graph of $f(x) = x^3 - x - 1$ crosses the x-axis between $x = 1.3$ and $x = 1.4$. (The slope is zero at $x = \pm 1/\sqrt{3}$.)

Epsilons and Deltas and Uniform Continuity

We know that the function $f(x) = x^2$ is everywhere differentiable, so we also know that it is continuous at every $x = c$. Thus the limit of x^2 as x approaches c is c^2, and we can make the difference between $f(x) = x^2$ and $f(c) = c^2$ as small as we please by keeping x sufficiently close to c. The precise way to say that is:

For every real number c and every positive number ϵ there exists a positive number δ such that

$$|f(x) - f(c)| < \epsilon \qquad \text{whenever} \qquad |x - c| < \delta.$$

Figure 2–33 illustrates these ideas for two possible values of c, namely $c = \sqrt{0.5} = 0.707$ and $c = 2.5$, and with $\epsilon = 0.25$. These numbers were chosen solely for the purpose of showing exactly how one might find deltas for given c's and a given positive epsilon. Focus your attention for a moment on one of the two values of c, say $c = \sqrt{0.5}$. Look at c^2 on the y-axis, and go up a distance ϵ and down the same distance. Now look at that part of the graph that is between the lines $y = c^2 + \epsilon$ and $y = c^2 - \epsilon$. It runs from $x = c - \delta_1 = \sqrt{c^2 - \epsilon}$ to $x = c + \delta_2 = \sqrt{c^2 + \epsilon}$.

In this example, $c^2 = 0.5$ and $\epsilon = 0.25$, so $c^2 - \epsilon = 0.25$ and $c^2 + \epsilon = 0.75$. Therefore, to four decimal places, we have

$$c = \sqrt{0.5} = 0.7071, \qquad c - \delta_1 = \sqrt{0.25} = 0.5000,$$

$$c + \delta_2 = \sqrt{0.75} = 0.8660, \qquad \delta_1 = 0.2071, \qquad \delta_2 = 0.1589.$$

We don't have to produce the "best" value of δ but we can see that our curve will stay between $y = c^2 - \epsilon$ and $y = c^2 + \epsilon$ in the neighborhood

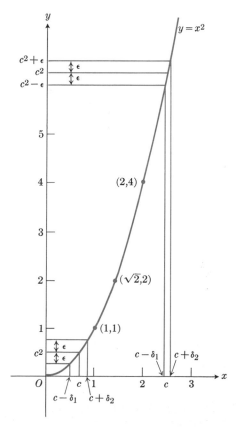

2–33 Graph of $y = x^2$.

$(c - \delta, c + \delta)$ if δ is any number that is positive and less than or equal to the minimum of δ_1 and δ_2. Thus, we can take $\delta = 0.1588$, or 0.15, or 0.01, or 0.0001. Each of these is a positive number that is small enough to guarantee that $f(x)$ stays within the interval $(c^2 - \epsilon, c^2 + \epsilon)$ when x stays in the interval $(c - \delta, c + \delta)$, for $c = \sqrt{0.5}$ and $\epsilon = 0.25$. A different value of c with the same value of epsilon would probably call for a different delta. Also, a different value of epsilon for the same c, or a different c, would probably call for a different delta. For $c = 2.5$ and $\epsilon = 0.25$, one must choose δ less than or equal to the minimum of $\delta_1 = 0.0505$ and $\delta_2 = 0.0495$. The curve is much steeper in the neighborhood of $c = 2.5$ than it is near $c = \sqrt{0.5}$, and this means that we must keep x much closer to $c = 2.5$ if we want $f(x)$ to stay close to $f(c)$.

Continuing to study the function $f(x) = x^2$, observe that we can factor $f(x) - f(c)$ as follows:

$$f(x) - f(c) = x^2 - c^2 = (x - c)(x + c).$$

By keeping x close to c, we make the first factor, $x - c$, as small as we please, and the second factor gets close to $2c$. If we restrict the domain of f to the closed interval $[-3, +5]$, say, then we can be sure that the factor $(x + c)$ will be no greater than $5 + 5 = 10$:

If x and c are in $[-3, +5]$, then

$$|x + c| \le 10 \quad \text{and} \quad |f(x) - f(c)| \le 10|x - c|,$$

and we can guarantee

$$|f(x) - f(c)| < \epsilon \quad \text{when} \quad |x - c| < \delta,$$

provided that δ is any positive number not greater than $\epsilon/10$.

If ϵ is any positive number, then

$$10|x - c| < \epsilon \quad \text{if} \quad |x - c| < \frac{\epsilon}{10}.$$

Therefore, $\delta = \epsilon/10$ will be small enough to work for every value of c in the domain $[-3, +5]$. When a function has the property that, for each positive ϵ, there exists a positive δ such that

$$|f(x) - f(c)| < \epsilon \quad \text{when } x \text{ and } c \text{ are in } D \text{ and } |x - c| < \delta,$$

we say that $f(x)$ is *uniformly continuous on D*.

EXAMPLE 6. Functions that are uniformly continuous on their domains:

1. $f(x) = k$, where k is any real number, and D is the set of all real numbers. For any positive number ϵ we can take $\delta = 1$, because

$$|f(x) - f(c)| = |k - k| = 0 \quad \text{for all } x \text{ and } c \text{ in } D.$$

2. $f(x) = 5x + 3$ and D is the set of all real numbers. For any positive number ϵ we can take $\delta = \epsilon/5$ and have

$$|f(x) - f(c)| = |5(x - c)| < \epsilon \quad \text{when } |x - c| < \frac{\epsilon}{5}.$$

3. $f(x) = \sin x$ and D is the set of all real numbers. For any positive number ϵ we can take $\delta = \epsilon$ because

$$\left| \sin x - \sin c \right| = \left| 2 \sin \left(\frac{x - c}{2} \right) \cos \left(\frac{x + c}{2} \right) \right|$$

$$\leq \left| 2 \left(\frac{x - c}{2} \right) \cdot 1 \right|$$

$$= |x - c| < \epsilon \qquad \text{if} \quad |x - c| < \delta = \epsilon.$$

If the trigonometry here is not familiar, you can see intuitively why the result is true by thinking of the slope of the chord from the point $(c, \sin c)$ to the point $(x, \sin x)$. That slope is not greater than the slope of the sine curve at its steepest, which is -1 or $+1$. Therefore,

$$\left| \frac{(\sin x - \sin c)}{(x - c)} \right| \leq 1, \qquad \text{so} \quad \left| \sin x - \sin c \right| \leq |x - c|.$$

EXAMPLE 7. Functions that are continuous but not uniformly continuous on their domains:

1. $f(x) = 1/x$ and the domain D is the set of all real numbers $x \neq 0$. If c is very small, and x is near c, then

$$|f(x) - f(c)| = \left| \frac{1}{x} - \frac{1}{c} \right| = \left| \frac{x - c}{xc} \right| \approx \frac{1}{c^2} |x - c|.$$

To make this less than a preassigned positive ϵ when $|x - c| < \delta$, we would need to take $\delta \approx c^2 \epsilon$. The smaller the value of c, the smaller must be our δ. No δ that depends upon ϵ alone will work for all c's $\neq 0$.

2. $f(x) = \sin(1/x)$ for $x \neq 0$. This curve gets very steep near $x = 0$ and, although we could find a δ for given ϵ and c, we have to take δ smaller and smaller if c is near zero. That is, δ depends upon c as well as ϵ, and therefore the function is not uniformly continuous on the domain given. On the other hand, if we were to change the domain to the set of all x greater than 0.001, say, then, for a given positive number ϵ, we could in fact find a δ that works for the "steepest" part of the graph over this domain, and that same value of δ would work for the entire domain.

The following theorem tells us that every function that is continuous at each point of a closed bounded interval $[a, b]$ is uniformly continuous on the interval. We do not prove the theorem in this book,* but we use it later.

Theorem 5. *A function f that is continuous for all x in the closed bounded interval $a \leq x \leq b$ is uniformly continuous there. That is, for each positive number ϵ, there is a positive number δ such that*

$$|f(x) - f(x')| < \epsilon \qquad \text{when} \quad a \leq x, \ x' \leq b, \ \text{and} \ |x - x'| < \delta.$$

---

*   For a proof see, for example, *Elementary Calculus from an Advanced Viewpoint* by Moulton, Thomas, and Zelinka, Addison-Wesley Publishing Co., 1967, or *Continuity*, by G. B. Thomas, Jr., Addison-Wesley Publishing Co., 1965 (pp. 35–36).

The following physical interpretation of continuity may help you to understand the difference between the notion of "continuous at every point of an interval" on the one hand and "uniformly continuous in an interval" on the other. We recall that a function is continuous at $x = c$ if $f(c)$ exists and $f(x) \to f(c)$ as $x \to c$. This means that if we are challenged with a positive "tolerance limit" ϵ and required to make

$$|f(x) - f(c)| < \epsilon \tag{3}$$

for *all* x sufficiently close to c, we can produce a positive number δ such that condition (3) is met whenever

$$|x - c| < \delta. \tag{4}$$

Let us translate this into physical terms.

Suppose that we have a pair of dividers (Fig. 2–34) with a meter that reads $|f(x) - f(c)|$ when the points touch x and c. Suppose now we hold one prong of the dividers at c and move the other prong around near c, either to the left of c or to its right. Suppose that to *each* positive number ϵ we are able to assign a band of width 2δ around c,

$$c - \delta < x < c + \delta,$$

such that whenever the second prong is inside this band the meter reading is less than ϵ. Then the function is, by our definition, continuous at c.

Now the "bandwidth" 2δ will in general depend upon ϵ. That is, the smaller the tolerance limit ϵ that is required, the more narrowly must we restrict the range of x around c. Furthermore, the "bandwidth" 2δ will also, in general, depend upon c. That is, for a given function $f(x)$,

$$\delta = \delta(c, \epsilon).$$

But it may happen that there is a positive number $k = k(\epsilon)$ that depends upon ϵ alone such that if x and x' are any two points in the domain of f and

$$|x - x'| < k(\epsilon),$$

then

$$|f(x) - f(x')| < \epsilon.$$

In other words, if the two prongs of the dividers are spread apart any distance less than $k(\epsilon)$ and the dividers are placed so that they touch any two points x and x' in the domain of f, the meter reads less than ϵ. This exemplifies uniform continuity. Theorem 5 says that, when the domain of f is a closed bounded interval, the continuity of f at each point of the domain guarantees uniform continuity.

To summarize these remarks we may say that:

a) *ordinary continuity* at a point c means that the bandwidth depends not only upon the tolerance ϵ but also upon c, whereas

b) *uniform continuity* means that with any positive ϵ we may associate *one* bandwidth that works for *all* points in the domain.

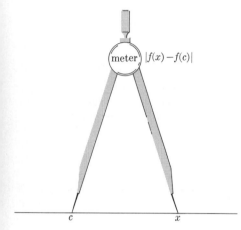

Figure 2–34

PROBLEMS

1. (a) Prove that the function $f(x) = x^3$ is continuous at $x = c$ for any real c. (b) If $c = 5$, and ϵ is a preassigned positive number, find δ such that

$$|x^3 - 5^3| < \epsilon \quad \text{when} \quad |x - 5| < \delta.$$

2. For what values of x is each of the following functions discontinuous?

a) $f(x) = \dfrac{x}{x+1}$ **b)** $f(x) = \dfrac{x+1}{x^2 - 4x + 3}$.

3. Is the function f defined by the rule

$$f(x) = \begin{cases} \dfrac{x^2 - 1}{x - 1}, & \text{when} \quad x \neq 1, \\ 2, & \text{when} \quad x = 1, \end{cases}$$

continuous or discontinuous at $x = 1$? Prove your result.

4. The function $f(x) = |x|$ is continuous at $x = 0$. Given a positive number ϵ, how large may δ be in order that $|f(x) - 0| < \epsilon$ when $|x - 0| < \delta$?

5. What is the maximum of $f(x) = |x|$ for $-1 \leq x \leq 1$? What is the minimum? Sketch.

6. Does the function $f(x) = x^2$ have a maximum for $0 < x < 1$? Does it have a minimum? Give reasons for your answers.

7. A continuous function $y = f(x)$ is known to be negative at $x = 0$ and positive at $x = 1$. Why is it true that the equation $f(x) = 0$ has at least one root between $x = 0$ and $x = 1$? Illustrate with a sketch.

8. Is the function $f(x) = \sqrt[3]{x}$ continuous at $x = 0$? Is it differentiable there? Give reasons for your answers.

9. *Prove the following theorem.* Let f be continuous and positive at $x = c$. Prove that there is some interval around $x = c$, say $c - \delta < x < c + \delta$, throughout which $f(x)$ remains positive. [*Hint.* In the definition of continuity, Eqs. (3) and (4), take $\epsilon = \frac{1}{2}f(c)$.] Illustrate with a sketch.

10. For $x \neq 2$, the function $f(x)$ is equal to $(x^2 + 3x - 10)/(x - 2)$. What value should be assigned to $f(2)$ to make $f(x)$ continuous at $x = 2$?

We have used both y' and dy/dx to denote the derivative of y with respect to x. Can some useful meaning be given to the symbols dy, called the *differential* of y, and dx separately? The answer is *yes*, and we do so as follows.

Definitions. *If x is the independent variable and $y = F(x)$ has a derivative at x_0, we define dx to be an independent variable with domain $(-\infty, +\infty)$ and define dy to be*

$$dy = F'(x_0)\, dx. \tag{1}$$

If $F(x)$ has a derivative at each point x in some domain D, then dy is a function of two independent variables x and dx: $dy = F'(x)\, dx$. Geometrically, we often think of dx as a certain number of units of change in the x-direction, and dy then is the corresponding number of units of change in the y-direction along the tangent to the graph of the function (Fig. 2–35).

If $dx = 0$ in Eq. (1), then $dy = 0$. If $dx \neq 0$, then we can divide both sides of Eq. (1) by dx and have

$$F'(x_0) = \frac{\text{The differential of } y}{\text{The differential of } x}. \tag{2}$$

There is nothing profound about Eq. (2); it just means that our notations $F'(x)$ and dy/dx are compatible.

If $x = f(t)$ and $y = g(t)$ are functions of t that are differentiable at t_0, the differential of t is a new independent variable, dt. The differentials of x and y

2-12

DIFFERENTIALS

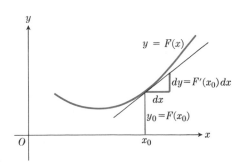

2–35 Geometric interpretations of the differentials dx and dy for a function $y = F(x)$.

are, by definition,

$$dx = f'(t_0)\, dt \qquad \text{and} \qquad dy = g'(t_0)\, dt. \tag{3}$$

Once again, if $dt \neq 0$ and $f'(t_0) \neq 0$, we can divide and write

$$\frac{dy}{dx} = \frac{\text{Differential of } y}{\text{Differential of } x} = \frac{g'(t_0)\, dt}{f'(t_0)\, dt} = \frac{g'(t_0)}{f'(t_0)}$$

$$= \frac{\text{Derivative of } y \text{ with respect to } t}{\text{Derivative of } x \text{ with respect to } t}. \tag{4}$$

Equation (4) is the same as the chain rule. It says that the derivative of y with respect to x is the quotient of the differentials dy and dx when both dy and dx are functions of t and dt, as well as when y is a function of x.

EXAMPLE 1. Use differentials to find approximately how much the function $y = x^{2/3}$ changes when x decreases from $x_0 = 8$ to 7.8.

Solution. Take $x = x_0 = 8$, $dx = -0.2$, and

$$dy = \frac{2}{3} x^{-1/3}\, dx = \frac{2}{3}\left(\frac{1}{2}\right)(-0.2) = \frac{-0.2}{3} \approx -0.0667.$$

This is the tangent-line approximation to the actual change $7.8^{2/3} - 8^{2/3} \approx -0.0669$.

EXAMPLE 2. If $x = \cos t$, $y = \sin t$, and $0 < t < \pi$, find: (a) dx and dy, and (b) dy/dx. Compare your answer in (b) to the derivative of $y = (1 - x^2)^{1/2}$.

Solution

a) $dx = -\sin t\, dt, \quad dy = \cos t\, dt.$

b) $\dfrac{dy}{dx} = \dfrac{\cos t\, dt}{-\sin t\, dt} = \dfrac{x}{-y} = -x/(1 - x^2)^{1/2}.$

From $y = f(x) = (1 - x^2)^{1/2}$ we calculate directly,

$$f'(x) = \tfrac{1}{2}(1 - x^2)^{-1/2}(-2x) = -x/(1 - x^2)^{1/2},$$

which agrees with the result in (b) above.

We often use letters a, b, c and others at the start of the alphabet to denote constants, and x, y, z and other letters at the end of the alphabet for variables. But that is not a hard-and-fast rule. The next example illustrates a situation where a and b are used as variables.

EXAMPLE 3. The dimensions of a rectangle are a cm and b cm. How do small changes in a and b affect the area $A = ab$?

Solution. We can use differentials to estimate small changes. (See Fig.

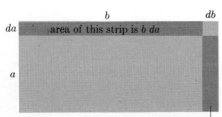

2–36 If b is greater than a and $da = db$, then $b\, da$ is greater than $a\, db$: The product ab is more sensitive to small changes in the smaller factor.

2–36.) The rule for the differential of a product gives

$$dA = a\, db + b\, da.$$

If b is the length of the longer side of the rectangle, and if da and db are assumed to be equal, then the term $b\, da$ is greater than $a\, db$: A change da in the shorter side makes more of a contribution to dA than does an equal change in the longer side.

Second Derivative

The second derivative of y with respect to x is the result obtained from y by doing twice in succession the operation "differentiate with respect to x"; that is,

$$\frac{d^2y}{dx^2} = \frac{d}{dx}\left[\frac{d}{dx}(y)\right].$$

It is also possible to define a second differential, d^2y, in such a way that the second derivative of y with respect to x is equal to d^2y divided by $(dx)^2$. However, things get rather complicated in the case of parametric equations

$$x = f(t), \qquad y = F(x) = F[f(t)] = g(t).$$

In such cases, it is simplest to calculate second and higher order derivatives by using such rules as

$$\frac{dy}{dx} = y' = \frac{dy/dt}{dx/dt},$$

$$\frac{d^2y}{dx^2} = y'' = \frac{dy'}{dx} = \frac{dy'/dt}{dx/dt}.$$

The second of these equations says that, to find the second derivative of y with respect to x, we

1. Express $y' = dy/dx$ in terms of t.
2. Differentiate y' with respect to t.
3. Divide the result by dx/dt.

EXAMPLE 4.   Find d^2y/dx^2 if $x = t - t^2$ and $y = t - t^3$.

Solution

$$y' = \frac{dy}{dx} = \frac{dy/dt}{dx/dt} = \frac{1 - 3t^2}{1 - 2t},$$

$$\frac{d^2y}{dx^2} = \frac{dy'/dt}{dx/dt} = \frac{\dfrac{d}{dt}\left[\dfrac{1 - 3t^2}{1 - 2t}\right]}{(1 - 2t)}$$

$$= \frac{(1 - 2t)\cdot(-6t) - (1 - 3t^2)\cdot(-2)}{(1 - 2t)^3}$$

$$= \frac{2 - 6t + 6t^2}{(1 - 2t)^3}.$$

2-13

FORMULAS FOR DIFFERENTIATION REPEATED IN THE NOTATION OF DIFFERENTIALS

Earlier in this chapter we derived formulas for the derivatives listed below on the left. By multiplying each one by dx we now obtain the corresponding formulas for differentials.

Derivatives	Differentials
I. $\dfrac{dc}{dx} = 0$	I'. $dc = 0$
II. $\dfrac{d(cu)}{dx} = c\dfrac{du}{dx}$	II'. $d(cu) = c\,du$
III. $\dfrac{d(u+v)}{dx} = \dfrac{du}{dx} + \dfrac{dv}{dx}$	III'. $d(u+v) = du + dv$
IV. $\dfrac{d(uv)}{dx} = u\dfrac{dv}{dx} + v\dfrac{du}{dx}$	IV'. $d(uv) = u\,dv + v\,du$
V. $\dfrac{d\left(\dfrac{u}{v}\right)}{dx} = \dfrac{v\dfrac{du}{dx} - u\dfrac{dv}{dx}}{v^2}$	V'. $d\left(\dfrac{u}{v}\right) = \dfrac{v\,du - u\,dv}{v^2}$
VI. $\dfrac{du^n}{dx} = nu^{n-1}\dfrac{du}{dx}$	VI'. $d(u^n) = nu^{n-1}\,du$
VIa. $\dfrac{dcx^n}{dx} = cnx^{n-1}$	VI'a. $d(cx^n) = cnx^{n-1}\,dx$
VII. $\dfrac{d\sin u}{dx} = \cos u\dfrac{du}{dx}$	VII'. $d(\sin u) = \cos u\,du$
VIII. $\dfrac{d\cos u}{dx} = -\sin u\dfrac{du}{dx}$	VIII'. $d(\cos u) = -\sin u\,du$

We collect these formulas primarily for future reference. Any problem involving differentials, say that of finding dy when y is a given function of x, may be handled either

a) by finding the derivative dy/dx and then multiplying by dx, or
b) by direct use of formulas I'–VIII'.

EXAMPLE. Find the differentials of:

a) $\sin(2x)$ b) $\cos^2(3x)$ c) $\dfrac{x}{x^2+1}$

Solutions

a) $d\sin(2x) = \cos(2x)\,d(2x) = 2\cos(2x)\,dx$.

b) $d \cos^2 (3x) = 2 \cos (3x) \, d \cos (3x)$

$$= 2 \cos (3x) \cdot (-\sin 3x) \, d(3x)$$

$$= -6 \sin 3x \cos 3x \, dx$$

$$= -3 \sin (6x) \, dx.$$

c) $d \dfrac{x}{x^2 + 1} = \dfrac{(x^2 + 1) \, dx - x \, d(x^2 + 1)}{(x^2 + 1)^2}$

$$= \frac{(x^2 + 1) \, dx - x(2x \, dx)}{(x^2 + 1)^2}$$

$$= \frac{(1 - x^2) \, dx}{(x^2 + 1)^2}.$$

It should be noted that a *differential* on the left side of an equation, say dy, also calls for a *differential*, usually dx, on the right side of the equation. Thus we never have $dy = 3x^2$, but instead $dy = 3x^2 \, dx$.

The term "differentiate" means either to find the derivative or to find the differential, and either operation is referred to as "differentiation."

PROBLEMS

In each of the following problems (1 through 8), find dy.

1. $y = x^3 - 3x^2 + 5x - 7$ **2.** $y^2 = (3x^2 + 1)^{3/2}$

3. $xy^2 + x^2y = 4$ **4.** $y = \dfrac{2x}{1 + x^2}$

5. $y = x\sqrt{1 - x^2}$ **6.** $y = \dfrac{x + 1}{x^2 - 2x + 4}$

7. $y = \dfrac{(1 - x)^3}{2 - 3x}$ **8.** $y = \dfrac{1 + x - x^2}{1 - x}$

Use differentials to obtain reasonable approximations to the following:

9. $\sqrt{145}$ **10.** $(2.1)^3$

11. $\sqrt[4]{17}$ **12.** $\sqrt[3]{0.126}$

13. $(8.01)^{4/3} + (8.01)^2 - \dfrac{1}{\sqrt[3]{8.01}}$

Given the following functions $x = f(t), \, y = g(t)$.

a) Express dx and dy in terms of t and dt.

b) Use the results of **(a)** to find, at the point for which $t = 2$, the slope of the curve traced by the point (x, y).

c) Use the results of **(b)** to find an equation of the line tangent to the curve at the point for which $t = 2$.

14. $x = t + \dfrac{1}{t}, \quad y = t - \dfrac{1}{t}$

15. $x = \sqrt{2t^2 + 1}, \quad y = (2t + 1)^2$

16. $x = t\sqrt{2t + 5}, \quad y = (4t)^{1/3}$

17. $x = \dfrac{t - 1}{t + 1}, \quad y = \dfrac{t + 1}{t - 1}$ **18.** $x = \dfrac{1}{t^2}, \quad y = \sqrt{t^2 + 12}$

19. Find d^2y/dx^2 from the parametric equations in Problem 14.

20. Find d^2y/dx^2 from the parametric equations in Problem 17.

21. Given the parametric equations $x = f(t), \, y = g(t)$. Show that

$$\frac{d^2y}{dx^2} = \frac{\dfrac{dx}{dt}\dfrac{d^2y}{dt^2} - \dfrac{d^2x}{dt^2}\dfrac{dy}{dt}}{(dx/dt)^3}.$$

22. If $A = ab$ and da and db are small changes in a and b, show that

$$\frac{dA}{A} = \frac{da}{a} + \frac{db}{b}.$$

Interpret the result in terms of percentage changes: If a changes by m percent and b changes by n percent, by what percent (approximately) does ab change? (Assume that m and n are small.)

REVIEW QUESTIONS AND EXERCISES

1. Using the definition of the derivative, deduce the formula for the derivative of a product uv of two differentiable functions.

2. In the formula for the derivative of uv, let $v = u$, and thereby deduce a formula for the derivative of u^2. Repeat the process, with $v = u^2$, and get a formula for the derivative of u^3. Extend the result, by the method of mathematical induction, to deduce the formula for the derivative of u^n for every positive integer n.

3. Explain how the three formulas

a) $\dfrac{d(x^n)}{dx} = nx^{n-1}$,

b) $\dfrac{d(cu)}{dx} = c\dfrac{du}{dx}$,

c) $\dfrac{d(u + v)}{dx} = \dfrac{du}{dx} + \dfrac{dv}{dx}$

are sufficient to differentiate any polynomial.

4. What formula do we need, in addition to the three listed in Problem 3 above, in order to differentiate rational functions?

5. Does the derivative of a polynomial function exist at every point of its domain? What is the largest domain the function can have? Does the derivative of a rational function exist at every point in its domain? What real numbers, if any, must be excluded from the domain of a rational function?

6. *Definition of algebraic function.* Let $y = f(x)$ define a function of x such that every pair of numbers (x, y) belonging to f satisfy an irreducible equation of the form

$$P_0(x)y^n + P_1(x)y^{n-1} + \cdots + P_{n-1}(x)y + P_n(x) = 0 \quad (\alpha)$$

for some positive integer n, with coefficients $P_0(x), \ldots, P_n(x)$ polynomials in x, and $P_0(x)$ not identically zero. Then f is said to be an *algebraic function.* What technique of this chapter can be used to find the derivative of an algebraic function if the polynomial coefficients $P_0(x), \ldots, P_n(x)$ in its defining equation (α) are given?

7. Show that the function f defined by $f(x) = x^{2/3}$ is an algebraic function by finding an appropriate equation of the type (α) in the definition in Problem 6 above. On what domain of values of x is this function defined? Where is it continuous? Where is it differentiable?

8. Show that every rational function is algebraic. Do you think the converse is also true? Explain.

9. It can be shown (though not very easily) that sums, quotients, products, powers, and roots of algebraic functions are algebraic functions. Thus

$$f(x) = x\sqrt{3x^2 + 1} + \frac{5x^{4/3}}{3x + 2}, \qquad x \neq -\frac{2}{3},$$

defines an algebraic function. Find its derivative. What formulas of this chapter are used in finding derivatives of functions like this one?

10. Show that $y = |x|$ satisfies the equation $y^2 - x^2 = 0$. Is the absolute value function algebraic? What is its derivative? Where does the derivative exist? Where is the absolute value function continuous?

11. Develop the formula for $\cos(A - B)$ from the law of cosines.

12. Write expressions for $\sin(A + B)$ and $\sin(A - B)$. Set $\alpha = A + B$, $\beta = A - B$, and develop a formula for $\sin \alpha - \sin \beta$.

13. Under what assumptions is it true that

$$\lim((\sin \theta)/\theta) = 1?$$

Prove the result.

14. Write expressions for $\cos(A + B)$ and $\cos(A - B)$. Set $\alpha = A + B$, $\beta = A - B$, and develop a formula for $\cos \alpha - \cos \beta$. Use the result to develop a formula for the derivative of $\cos x$, from the definition

$$\frac{d(\cos x)}{dx} = \lim_{\Delta x \to 0} \frac{\cos(x + \Delta x) - \cos x}{\Delta x}.$$

15. Let A_n be the area bounded by a regular n-sided polygon inscribed in a circle of radius r. Show that $A_n = (n/2)r^2 \sin(2\pi/n)$. Find $\lim A_n$ as $n \to \infty$. Does the result agree with what you know about the area of a circle?

16. Define differentials. If $y = f(x)$ defines a differentiable function, how are dy and dx related? Give geometrical interpretations of dx and dy.

17. State the chain rule for derivatives. Prove it, with the book closed.

18. Show how the chain rule is used to prove that the derivative of y with respect to x is the ratio of dy to dx when x and y are both differentiable functions of t, and $dx \neq 0$.

19. Give an example of a function that is defined and bounded on $0 \leq t \leq 1$, continuous in the open interval $0 < t < 1$, and discontinuous at $t = 0$.

20. State and prove a theorem about the relationship between continuity and differentiability of a function, at a point in its domain.

21. Read the article "The Lever of Mahomet," by R. Courant and H. Robbins, and the accompanying "Commentary on Continuity," by J. R. Newman, in *World of Mathematics*, Vol. 4, pp. 2410–2413.

MISCELLANEOUS PROBLEMS

Find dy/dx in each of the following problems (1 through 33).

1. $y = \dfrac{x}{\sqrt{x^2 - 4}}$

2. $x^2 + xy + y^2 - 5x = 2$

3. $xy + y^2 = 1$

4. $x^3 + 4xy - 3y^3 = 2$

5. $x^2 y + xy^2 = 6$

6. $y = (x + 1)^2 (x^2 + 2x)^{-2}$

7. $y = \cos(1 - 2x)$

8. $y = \dfrac{\cos x}{\sin x}$

9. $y = \dfrac{x}{x + 1}$

10. $y = \sqrt{2x + 1}$

11. $y = x^2 \sqrt{x^2 - a^2}$

12. $y = \dfrac{2x + 1}{2x - 1}$

13. $y = \dfrac{x^2}{1 - x^2}$

14. $y = (x^2 + x + 1)^3$

15. $y = \sec^2(5x)$

16. $y^3 = \sin^3 x + \cos^3 x$

17. $y = \dfrac{(2x^2 + 5x)^{3/2}}{3}$

18. $y = \dfrac{3}{(2x^2 + 5x)^{3/2}}$

19. $xy^2 + \sqrt{xy} = 2$

20. $x^2 - y^2 = xy$

21. $x^{2/3} + y^{2/3} = a^{2/3}$

22. $x^{1/2} + y^{1/2} = a^{1/2}$

23. $xy = 1$

24. $\sqrt{xy} = 1$

25. $(x + 2y)^2 + 2xy^2 = 6$

26. $y = \sqrt{\dfrac{1 - x}{1 + x^2}}$

27. $y^2 = \dfrac{x}{x + 1}$

28. $x^2 y + xy^2 = 6(x^2 + y^2)$

29. $xy + 2x + 3y = 1$

30. $y = u^2 - 1, \quad x = u^2 + 1$

31. $y = \sqrt{2t + t^2}, \quad t = 2x + 3$

32. $x = \dfrac{t}{1 + t^2}, \quad y = 1 + t^2$

33. $t = \dfrac{x}{1 + x^2}, \quad y = x^2 + t^2$

34. Find the slope of $y = x/(x^2 + 1)$ at the origin. Write the equation of the tangent line at the origin.

35. Write the equation of the tangent at (2, 2) to the curve

$$x^2 - 2xy + y^2 + 2x + y - 6 = 0.$$

36. Determine the constant c such that the straight line joining the points (0, 3) and (5, −2) is tangent to the curve $y = c/(x + 1)$.

37. What is the slope of the curve $y = 2x^2 - 6x + 3$ at the point on the curve where $x = 2$? What is the equation of the tangent line to the curve at this point?

38. Find the points on the curve $y = 2x^3 - 3x^2 - 12x + 20$ where the tangent is parallel to the x-axis.

39. Find the derivatives of the following functions:

a) $y = (x^2 + 2x)^5$;

b) $f(t) = \sqrt{3t^2 - 2t}$;

c) $f(r) = \sqrt{r^2 + 5} + \sqrt{r^2 - 5}$;

d) $f(x) = \dfrac{x^2 - 1}{x^2 + 1}$.

40. Find the equation of the tangent to the curve $y = 2/\sqrt{x - 1}$ at the point on the curve where $x = 10$.

41. Write the equation of the straight line passing through the point (2, 1) and normal to the curve $x^2 = 4y$.

42. Use the definition of the derivative to find dy/dx for $y = \sqrt{2x + 3}$ and then check the result by finding the same derivative by the power formula.

43. Find the value of

$$\lim_{\Delta x \to 0} \frac{[2 - 3(x + \Delta x)]^2 - [2 - 3x]^2}{\Delta x}$$

and specify the function $f(x)$ of which this is the derivative.

44. Find the slope of the curve $x^2 y + xy^2 = 6$ at the point (1, 2).

45. A cylindrical can of height 6 (in.) and radius r (in.) has volume $V = 6\pi r^2$ (in.³). What is the difference between ΔV and its principal part as r varies? What is the geometric significance of the principal part?

46. If a hemispherical bowl of radius 10 in. is filled with water to a depth of x in., the volume of water is given by $v = \pi[10 - (x/3)]x^2$. Find the rate of increase of the volume per inch increase of the depth.

47. A bus will hold 60 people. If the number x of persons per trip who use the bus is related to the fare charged (p nickels), by the law $p = [3 - (x/40)]^2$, write the function expressing the total revenue per trip received by the bus company. What is the number x_1 of people per trip that will make the marginal revenue equal to zero? What is the corresponding fare?

48. Prove Eq. (2), Article 2–3, by mathematical induction.

49. Given $y = x - x^2$, find the rate of change of y^2 with respect to x^2 (expressed in terms of x).

50. If $x = 3t + 1$ and $y = t^2 + t$, find dy/dt, dx/dt, and dy/dx. Eliminate t to obtain y as a function of x, and then determine dy/dx directly. Do the results check?

51. A particle projected vertically upward with a speed of a ft/sec reaches an elevation $s = at - 16t^2$ ft at the end of t sec. What must the initial velocity be in order for the particle to travel 49 ft upward before it starts coming back down?

52. Find the rate of change of $\sqrt{x^2 + 16}$ with respect to $x/(x - 1)$ at $x = 3$.

53. The circle $(x - h)^2 + (y - k)^2 = r^2$, center at (h, k), radius $= r$ (see Article 8–4), is tangent to the curve $y = x^2 + 1$ at the point $(1, 2)$. (a) Find the locus of the point (h, k). (b) If, also, the circle and the curve have the same second derivative at $(1, 2)$, find h, k, and r. Sketch the curve and the circle.

54. If $y = x^2 + 1$ and $u = \sqrt{x^2 + 1}$, find dy/du.

55. If $x = y^2 + y$ and $u = (x^2 + x)^{3/2}$, find dy/du.

56. If $f'(x) = \sqrt{3x^2 - 1}$ and $y = f(x^2)$, find dy/dx.

57. If $f'(x) = \sin(x^2)$ and $y = f((2x - 1)/(x + 1))$, find dy/dx.

58. Given $y = 3 \sin 2x$ and $x = u^2 + \pi$, find the value of dy/du when $u = 0$.

59. If $0 < x < \pi/2$, prove that $x > \sin x > 2x/\pi$.

60. If $y = x\sqrt{2x - 3}$, find d^2y/dx^2.

61. Find the value of d^2y/dx^2 in the equation $y^3 + y = x$ at the point $(2, 1)$.

62. If $x = t - t^2$, $y = t - t^3$, find the values of dy/dx and d^2y/dx^2 at $t = 1$.

63. Prove Leibniz's rule:

a) $\dfrac{d^2(uv)}{dx^2} = \dfrac{d^2u}{dx^2} \cdot v + 2\dfrac{du}{dx}\dfrac{dv}{dx} + u\dfrac{d^2v}{dx^2}$,

b) $\dfrac{d^3(uv)}{dx^3} = \dfrac{d^3u}{dx^3} \cdot v + 3\dfrac{d^2u}{dx^2}\dfrac{dv}{dx} + 3\dfrac{du}{dx}\dfrac{d^2v}{dx^2} + u\dfrac{d^3v}{dx^3}$,

c) $\dfrac{d^n(uv)}{dx^n} =$

$\dfrac{d^nu}{dx^n} \cdot v + n\dfrac{d^{n-1}u}{dx^{n-1}}\dfrac{dv}{dx} + \cdots$

$+ \dfrac{n(n-1)\cdots(n-k+1)}{k!}\dfrac{d^{n-k}u}{dx^{n-k}}\dfrac{d^kv}{dx^k} + \cdots + u\dfrac{d^nv}{dx^n}$.

The terms on the right side of this equation may be obtained from the terms in the binomial expansion $(a + b)^n$ by replacing $a^{n-k}b^k$ by $(d^{n-k}u/dx^{n-k}) \cdot (d^kv/dx^k)$ for $k = 0, 1, 2, \ldots, n$, and interpreting d^0u/dx^0 as being u itself.

64. Find d^3y/dx^3 in each of the following cases:

a) $y = \sqrt{2x - 1}$

b) $y = \dfrac{1}{3x + 2}$

c) $y = ax^3 + bx^2 + cx + d$.

65. If $f(x) = (x - a)^n g(x)$, where $g(x)$ is a polynomial and $g(a) \neq 0$, show that $f(a) = 0 = f'(a) = \cdots = f^{(n-1)}(a)$; but $f^{(n)}(a) = n! \, g(a) \neq 0$.

66. If $y = 2x^2 - 3x + 5$, find Δy for $x = 3$ and $\Delta x = 0.1$. Approximate Δy by finding its principal part.

67. (a) Show that the perimeter P_n of an n-sided regular polygon inscribed in a circle of radius r is $P_n = 2nr \sin(\pi/n)$. (b) Find the limit of P_n as $n \to \infty$. Is the answer consistent with what you know about the circumference of a circle?

68. Find dy/dx and d^2y/dx^2 if $x = \cos 3t$ and $y = \sin^2 3t$.

69. To compute the height h of a lamppost, the length a of the shadow of a six-foot pole is measured. The pole is 20 ft from the lamppost. If $a = 15$ ft, with a possible error of less than one inch, find the height of the lamppost and estimate the possible error in height.

70. Find the differential dy in each of the following cases:

a) $y = x^2/(1 + x)$ **b)** $x^2 - y^2 = 1$ **c)** $xy + y^2 = 1$.

71. Suppose a function f satisfies the following two conditions for all x and y:

a) $f(x + y) = f(x) \cdot f(y)$;

b) $f(x) = 1 + xg(x)$, where $\lim\limits_{x \to 0} g(x) = 1$.

Prove that (a) the derivative $f'(x)$ exists, (b) $f'(x) = f(x)$.

72. Let $f(x) = x^2 + 1$. Given $\epsilon > 0$, find $\delta > 0$ such that $|f(x_1) - f(x_2)| < \epsilon$ whenever $|x_1 - x_2| < \delta$ and x_1, x_2 both lie in the closed interval $-2 \leq x \leq 2$. State precisely what this means concerning the continuity of this function.

73. Given a function $f(x)$, defined for all real x, and a positive constant c such that $|f(x + h) - f(x)| \leq ch^2$ for all real h. Prove that (a) $f(x)$ is uniformly continuous, (b) $f'(x) = 0$ for all x.

74. A function $f(x)$ is said to satisfy a Lipschitz condition of order m on the closed interval $a \leq x \leq b$ if there is a constant C such that

$$|f(x_2) - f(x_1)| \leq C|x_2 - x_1|^m$$

for all values of x_1, x_2 on $[a, b]$. Prove that a function which satisfies a Lipschitz condition of order $m > 0$ on $[a, b]$ is uniformly continuous there.

75. Suppose $[a, b]$ is the interval $[-1, 1]$ and $f(x) = \sqrt{1 - x^2}$. Find appropriate values of C and of m to satisfy the conditions in Problem 74. [*Hint.* Show that if $y_2 > y_1 > 0$ and $y_2 - y_1 = h$, then $|\sqrt{y_2} - \sqrt{y_1}| \leq \sqrt{h}$.]

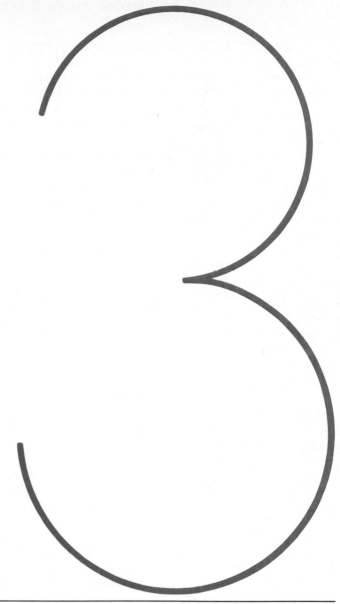

APPLICATIONS

3–1

SIGN OF THE FIRST DERIVATIVE. APPLICATION TO CURVE SKETCHING

We have previously illustrated the use of the slope of a curve to gain information beyond that given by the table of (x, y) values. We wish now to consider just how the sign of the derivative at a point gives information about the curve. Figure 3–1 shows a curve $y = f(x)$ on which we have indicated certain points $A, B, C, D,$ and E. At A we say that y is an increasing function of x, by which we mean that the function values increase as x increases. At such a point the slope of the tangent to the curve, dy/dx, is positive. The same applies at E. At C we say the function f is a decreasing function of x and this will be indicated by a negative value of dy/dx at C. At B and D the slope is zero.

EXAMPLE 1. We apply these ideas to the problem of sketching the curve

$$y = \tfrac{1}{3}x^3 - 2x^2 + 3x + 2.$$

The slope at (x, y) is

$$\frac{dy}{dx} = x^2 - 4x + 3 = (x - 1)(x - 3).$$

To determine where dy/dx is positive and where it is negative, we first determine where it is zero:

$$\frac{dy}{dx} = 0 \qquad \text{when} \quad x = 1 \quad \text{or} \quad x = 3,$$

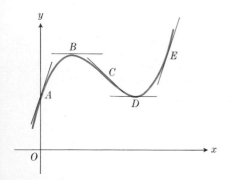

3–1 Tangents to a curve $y = f(x)$. The derivative dy/dx is positive at A and E, negative at C, and zero at B and D.

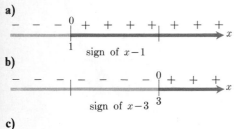

a)

sign of $x-1$

b)

sign of $x-3$

c)

sign of $(x-1)(x-3)$

3–2 The sign pattern of the product $(x - 1)(x - 3)$.

since these points will mark the transition from positive to negative or from negative to positive slopes. The sign of dy/dx depends upon the signs of the two factors $(x - 1)$ and $(x - 3)$. Since the sign of $(x - 1)$ is negative when x is to the left of 1 and positive to the right, we have the pattern of signs indicated in Fig. 3–2(a). Similarly, the sign of $(x - 3)$ is shown in Fig. 3–2(b), and the sign of the product $dy/dx = (x - 1)(x - 3)$ is shown in Fig. 3–2(c). We can get a rough idea of the shape of the curve just from this pattern of signs of its slope, if we sketch a curve which is rising, falling, and rising again for $x < 1$, $1 < x < 3$, and $x > 3$, respectively (Fig. 3–3).

To get a more accurate curve, we would construct a table for some range of values extending, say, from $x = 0$ to $x = 4$, which includes the transition points between rising and falling portions of the curve (Fig. 3–4).

The terms "rising" and "falling," or "increasing" and "decreasing," are always taken to apply to the behavior of the curve as the point that is tracing

3–3 A function whose derivative has the sign pattern shown in Fig. 3–2(c) must have a graph something like this.

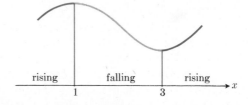

rising   falling   rising

it moves from left to right or, in other words, relative to its behavior as x increases. The same concepts apply to functions that vary with time.

EXAMPLE 2. Figure 3–5 shows a rope running through a pulley at P, bearing a weight W at one end. The other end is held in a worker's hand M at a distance of 5 feet above the ground as the worker walks straight away from the pulley at the rate of 6 ft/sec. If x represents the distance in feet of the worker's hand away from the vertical line PW, and t represents time, then x is an increasing function of t. We are given the rate at which x changes with t, namely, 6 ft/sec. This would be stated in mathematical terms by saying $dx/dt = +6$ ft/sec. On the other hand, if the worker were to walk *toward* the line PW at the rate of 6 ft/sec, we would have $dx/dt = -6$ ft/sec, because x would then be a decreasing function of t.

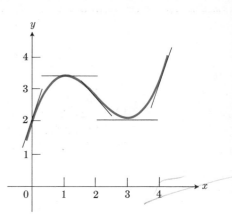

3–4 This graph of $y = \frac{1}{3}x^3 - 2x^2 + 3x + 2$ combines the general information about shape from Fig. 3–3 with a selection of plotted points and slopes.

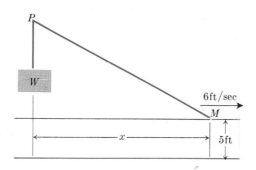

3–5 If the worker at M moves to the right at the speed shown, then $dx/dt = 6$ ft/sec.

PROBLEMS

In each of the following exercises, determine dy/dx and find the sets of values of x where the graph of y versus x is rising (as x moves to the right) and where it is falling. Sketch each curve, showing in particular the points of transition between falling and rising portions of the curve.

1. $y = x^2 - x + 1$

2. $y = \dfrac{x^3}{3} - \dfrac{x^2}{2} - 2x + \dfrac{1}{3}$

3. $y = 2x^3 - 3x^2 + 3$

4. $y = x^3 - 27x + 36$

5. $y = x^4 - 8x^2 + 16$

6. $y = \dfrac{1}{x}$

7. $y = \sin x$

8. $y = \tan x$

9. $y = x|x|$

In this article we look at problems that ask for the rate at which some quantity changes. In each case this rate is a derivative that has to be computed from the rate at which some other quantity is known to change. To find it, we write an equation that relates the first quantity to the second. We then differentiate both sides of the equation to express the derivative we seek in terms of the derivative we know.

3–2
RELATED RATES

a)

b)

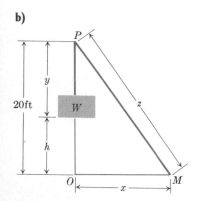

3–6 A typical sketch for a related rate problem shows the situation for any time t, not just for the time in question. The reason for this is that certain distances in the figure vary (here, x, y, z, and h) and it is important to treat them as variables and not as constants.

EXAMPLE 1.   Suppose that the pulley in Example 2 at the end of Article 3–1 is 25 ft above the ground, the rope is 45 ft long, and the worker is walking away from the pulley at the rate of 6 ft/sec. How fast is the weight being raised at the instant when the distance x is 15 ft?

Solution.   To help visualize the problem, we draw and label a preliminary sketch, Fig. 3–6(a). In the figure, M represents the worker's hand, P the pulley, and OM the horizontal line from the worker's hand to a point directly beneath the pulley. The angle at O is a right angle.

The quantities that are changing in the figure are the distance from M to O, the height of the weight above O, the distance from the weight to P, and the length of rope from P to M. The quantities that remain constant are the height of P above O (20 ft, because O is 5 ft above the ground), the total length of the rope (45 ft), and the rate at which the worker walks (6 ft/sec).

The quantity we are asked to find is a rate. If we let h be the height of the weight W above O, and denote time by t, then we can write this rate as dh/dt. We have been asked to find the value of dh/dt when $x = 15$ ft.

We label the other changing dimensions in the sketch (Fig. 3–6(b)), and write down any numerical information we have about them. We choose y, say, for the distance from P to the bottom of the weight, and z for the length of the rope from P to M. These variables, as well as h and x, are to be considered to be functions of t. We have been told that $dx/dt = 6$ ft/sec.

We now write equations to express the relationships that are to hold between the variables at all values of t under consideration:

$$y + z = 45 \text{ (The total length of the rope is 45 ft)}$$

$$h + y = 20 \text{ (P is 20 ft above O)} \tag{1}$$

$$20^2 + x^2 = z^2 \text{ (The angle at O is a right angle).}$$

If these equations are differentiated with respect to t, the new equations so obtained will tell how the derivatives of the variables are related to each other. From this information we can express dh/dt in terms of x and dx/dt.

Actually, it will save time and effort if we first obtain a single equation relating the variable x (whose rate is given) and the variable h (whose rate is wanted) before we take derivatives. Using the equations in (1), we find successively:

$$z = 45 - y, \qquad y = 20 - h,$$

$$z = 45 - (20 - h) = (25 + h), \qquad 20^2 + x^2 = z^2 = (25 + h)^2,$$

that is,

$$20^2 + x^2 = (25 + h)^2.$$

This last equation relates the variables x and h for all values of t under consideration. Both sides of this equation are functions of t, and the equality says they represent the same function of t. Thus when we differentiate both sides of the equation with respect to t, we will have another equation:

$$\frac{d}{dt}(20^2 + x^2) = \frac{d}{dt}(25 + h)^2, \qquad 0 + 2x\frac{dx}{dt} = 2(25 + h)\frac{dh}{dt}.$$

This may be solved for the rate we want, namely,

$$\frac{dh}{dt} = \frac{x}{25 + h} \frac{dx}{dt}. \tag{2}$$

Now at the given instant, we have

$$x = 15, \qquad \frac{dx}{dt} = 6,$$

and we find h at this instant from the equation

$$20^2 + 15^2 = (25 + h)^2: \qquad 25 + h = 25, \qquad h = 0.$$

When we substitute these values in Eq. (2), we obtain

$$\frac{dh}{dt} = \frac{15}{25 + 0} \cdot 6 = \frac{18}{5} = 3\tfrac{3}{5} \text{ ft/sec}$$

as the rate at which the weight is being raised at the instant in question.

The problem in Example 1 is called a problem in related rates. It is typical of such problems that:

a) certain variables are related in a definite way for all values of t under consideration;

b) the values of some or all of these variables and the rates of change of some of them are given at some particular instant; and

c) it is required to find the rate of change of one or more of them at this instant.

The variables may then all be considered to be functions of time, and if the equations that relate them for all values of t are differentiated with respect to t, the new equations so obtained will tell how their rates of change are related. From this information it should be possible to answer the question posed by the problem.

A strategy for solving such problems is this:*

1. *Visualize the problem.* Make a sketch. Note which quantities change, and which stay the same.

2. *Write down what you are asked to find* (in Example 1, a rate). Express it in terms of a variable (dh/dt). Show the variable in the sketch (the h in Fig. 3–6(b)).

3. *Identify the other variables in the problem.* Write down any numerical information that is given about them. Show them in the sketch.

4. *Write equations that relate the variables.*

5. *Use substitution and differentiation* to get a single equation that expresses the desired quantity in terms of the quantities whose values are known.

We carried out these steps in Example 1, and we do so again in Example 2.

---

* See *The Solving of Word Problems in Beginning Calculus, A Strategic Approach*, by Peter Ross, Group in Science and Mathematics Education (SESAME), University of California, Berkeley, May, 1977.

3–7 x increases and y decreases when the foot of the ladder slides away from the wall.

EXAMPLE 2. A ladder 26 ft long leans against a vertical wall. The foot of the ladder is being drawn away from the wall at the rate of 4 ft/sec. How fast is the top of the ladder sliding down the wall at the instant when the foot of the ladder is 10 ft from the wall?

Solution. Figure 3–7 shows the ladder against the wall. The quantities that change are the height of the top of the ladder above the ground and the distance of the base of the ladder from the wall. The quantities that remain constant are the length of the ladder and the rate at which the base moves away from the wall.

We are asked to find a rate. If y denotes the height of the top of the ladder above the ground in feet and t denotes time measured in seconds, then the rate we seek is dy/dt. What is the value of dy/dt when the base of the ladder is 10 ft from the wall?

Denote the distance of the base of the ladder from the wall by x. Then $dx/dt = 4$ ft/sec.

The variables x and y are related by the equation $x^2 + y^2 = 26^2$. To express dy/dt in terms of dx/dt, we differentiate both sides of the equation with respect to t, and get

$$2x\frac{dx}{dt} + 2y\frac{dy}{dt} = 0.$$

Hence

$$\frac{dy}{dt} = \frac{-x}{y}\frac{dx}{dt}.$$

When $x = 10$, $y = 24$, $dx/dt = 4$, this leads to $dy/dt = -\frac{5}{3}$. That is, y is *decreasing* (the top of the ladder is moving *down*) at the rate of $\frac{5}{3}$ ft/sec.

In the next example we combine Steps 1 and 3 of the strategy.

EXAMPLE 3. Water runs into the conical tank shown in Fig. 3–8 at the constant rate of 2 ft³ per minute. How fast is the water level rising when the water is 6 ft deep?

Solution. The quantities that are changing in the problem are:

$v =$ the volume (ft³) of water in the tank at time t (min),

$x =$ the radius (ft) of the surface of the water at time t,

$y =$ the depth (ft) of water in the tank at time t.

The quantities that remain the same are the dimensions of the tank and the rate

$$\frac{dv}{dt} = 2 \text{ ft}^3/\text{min}$$

at which the tank fills.

We are asked to find the rate dy/dt at the instant when $y = 6$.

3–8 To show that the water level is changing in this conical tank, the depth of the water is denoted by a variable, y. The rate at which the level changes is then dy/dt.

The relationship between the volume of water v and depth y is expressed by the equation

$$v = \tfrac{1}{3}\pi x^2 y.$$

But this involves the additional variable x as well as v and y. However, we may eliminate x since, by similar triangles, we have

$$\frac{x}{y} = \frac{5}{10} \qquad \text{or} \qquad x = \tfrac{1}{2}y.$$

Therefore

$$v = \tfrac{1}{12}\pi y^3,$$

and when we differentiate this with respect to t, we have

$$\frac{dv}{dt} = \frac{1}{4}\pi y^2 \frac{dy}{dt}.$$

Hence

$$\frac{dy}{dt} = \frac{4}{\pi y^2}\frac{dv}{dt},$$

and when

$$\frac{dv}{dt} = 2 \qquad \text{and} \qquad y = 6,$$

this gives

$$\frac{dy}{dt} = \frac{4 \cdot 2}{\pi \cdot 36} = \frac{2}{9\pi} \approx 0.071 \text{ ft/min.}$$

PROBLEMS

1. Let A be the area of a circle of radius r. How is dA/dt related to dr/dt?

2. Let V be the volume of a sphere of radius r. How is dV/dt related to dr/dt?

3. Sand falls onto a conical pile at the rate of 10 ft³/min. The radius of the base of the pile is always equal to one-half of its altitude. How fast is the altitude of the pile increasing when it is 5 ft deep?

4. Suppose that a raindrop is a perfect sphere. Assume that, through condensation, the raindrop accumulates moisture at a rate proportional to its surface area. Show that the radius increases at a constant rate.

5. Point A moves along the x-axis at the constant rate of a ft/sec while point B moves along the y-axis at the constant rate of b ft/sec. Find how fast the distance between them is changing when A is at the point $(x, 0)$ and B is at the point $(0, y)$.

6. A spherical balloon is inflated with gas at the rate of 100 ft³/min. Assuming that the gas pressure remains constant, how fast is the radius of the balloon increasing at the instant when the radius is 3 ft?

7. A boat is pulled in to a dock by means of a rope with one end attached to the bow of the boat, the other end passing through a ring attached to the dock at a point 4 ft higher than the bow of the boat. If the rope is pulled in at the rate of 2 ft/sec, how fast is the boat approaching the dock when 10 ft of rope are out?

8. A balloon is 200 ft off the ground and rising vertically at the constant rate of 15 ft/sec. An automobile passes beneath it traveling along a straight road at the constant rate of 45 mi/hr = 66 ft/sec. How fast is the distance between them changing one second later?

9. Water is withdrawn from a conical reservoir 8 ft in diameter and 10 ft deep (vertex down) at the constant rate of 5 ft³/min. How fast is the water level falling when the depth of water in the reservoir is 6 ft?

10. A particle moves around the circle $x^2 + y^2 = 1$ with an x-velocity component $dx/dt = y$. Find dy/dt. Does the particle travel in the clockwise or counterclockwise direction around the circle?

11. A man 6 ft tall walks at the rate of 5 ft/sec toward a street light that is 16 ft above the ground. At what rate is the tip of his shadow moving? At what rate is the length of his shadow changing when he is 10 ft from the base of the light?

12. When air changes volume adiabatically (without any heat being added to it), the pressure p and the volume v satisfy the relationship $pv^{1.4} = $ constant. At a certain instant the pressure is 50 lb/in^2 and the volume is 32 in^3 and is decreasing at the rate of 4 in^3/sec. How rapidly is the pressure changing at this instant?

13. A light is at the top of a pole 50 ft high. A ball is dropped from the same height from a point 30 ft away from the light. How fast is the shadow of the ball moving along

the ground $\frac{1}{2}$ sec later? (Assume the ball falls a distance $s = 16t^2$ ft in t seconds.)

14. A girl flies a kite at a height of 300 ft, the wind carrying the kite horizontally away from her at a rate of 25 ft/sec. How fast must she pay out the string when the kite is 500 ft away from her?

15. A spherical iron ball 8 in. in diameter is coated with a layer of ice of uniform thickness. If the ice melts at the rate of 10 in^3 per minute, how fast is the thickness of the ice decreasing when it is 2 in. thick? How fast is the outer surface area of ice decreasing?

16. Two ships A and B are sailing away from the point O along routes such that the angle $AOB = 120°$. How fast is the distance between them changing if, at a certain instant, $OA = 8$ mi, $OB = 6$ mi, ship A is sailing at the rate of 20 mi/hr, and ship B at the rate of 30 mi/hr? [*Hint.* Use the law of cosines.]

3–3

SIGNIFICANCE OF THE SIGN OF THE SECOND DERIVATIVE

We have already seen how we may use the information given by dy/dx about the slope of the tangent to a curve to help in sketching it. We recall that in an interval where dy/dx is positive, the curve is rising to the right, while if dy/dx is negative the curve is falling to the right. Also it is evident that the regions of rise and fall are usually separated by high or low points where dy/dx is zero and the tangent is horizontal. However, it is possible for dy/dx to be zero at points that are neither high nor low points of the curve.

EXAMPLE 1. If

$$y = (x - 2)^3 + 1,$$

then

$$\frac{dy}{dx} = 3(x - 2)^2,$$

and although

$$\frac{dy}{dx} = 0 \qquad \text{at} \quad x = 2,$$

for all values of x other than 2, the slope is positive and y is an increasing function of x (Fig. 3–9).

The regions of rise and fall may also be separated by points where the derivative fails to exist.

3–9 The point (2, 1) where $dy/dx = 0$ is neither a high point nor a low point of the curve.

EXAMPLE 2. If $y = x^{2/3}$, then

$$\frac{dy}{dx} = \frac{2}{3} x^{-1/3} = \frac{2}{3\sqrt[3]{x}}$$

is positive when x is positive, and negative when x is negative. At the transition point $x = 0$, dy/dx does not exist, but $dx/dy = \frac{3}{2}x^{1/3}$ is zero, which means that the tangent to the curve at $(0, 0)$ is vertical instead of horizontal (Fig. 3–10).

3–10 Here the regions of rise and fall are separated by a point where the derivative does not exist.

Next we shall see that when the second derivative is not zero its sign tells whether the graph of $y = f(x)$ is concave upward (y'' positive) or downward (y'' negative).

Consider, for example, the curve in Fig. 3–11(a). The first and second derivatives are represented by the curves in Fig. 3–11(b) and (c). The arc ABC of the y-curve is concave upward; CDE is concave downward; EF is again concave upward. To focus attention, let us consider a section near A on arc ABC. Here y' is negative and the y-curve slopes downward to the right. But as we travel through A, moving from left to right, we find the slope becomes less negative. That is, y' is an *increasing* function of x. Therefore the y'-curve slopes upward at A'. Hence its own slope, which is y'', is positive there. The same kind of argument applies at all points along the arc ABC; namely, y' is an increasing function of x, so its derivative (that is, y'') is positive. This is indicated by drawing the arc $A''B''C''$ of the y''-curve above the x-axis.

Similarly, where the y-curve is concave downward (along CDE), the y'-curve is falling, so its slope y'' is negative.

The direction of concavity is, therefore,

a)

b)

c)

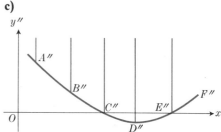

3–11 Compare the graph of the function in (a) with the graphs of its first and second derivatives in (b) and (c).

upward   if the second derivative is *positive*,

downward   if the second derivative is *negative*.

In the first case we could also say the curve is cupped so as to "hold water"; in the second case it would "spill water." Another way to think of concave upward is that locally the curve lies *above* its tangents. Near the points of a region where a curve is concave downward, the curve lies *below* its tangents.

Points of inflection. A point where the curve changes its concavity from downward to upward or vice versa is called a *point of inflection*. Inflection points occur at C and E in Fig. 3–11(a), and are characterized by a change in the sign of d^2y/dx^2. Such a change of sign may occur where

a) $d^2y/dx^2 = 0$,   or

b) d^2y/dx^2 fails to exist (for example, it may become infinite at such a point).

EXAMPLE 3. Figure 3–11 shows case (a). Case (b) is shown in Fig. 3–12, where the curve is

$$y = x^{1/3},$$

from which we find

$$y' = \tfrac{1}{3}x^{-(2/3)},$$

$$y'' = -\tfrac{2}{9}x^{-(5/3)},$$

a)

b)

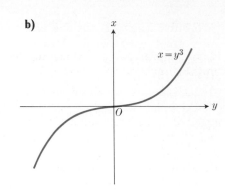

3–12 (a) The graph of $y = x^{1/3}$ shows that a point where y'' fails to exist can be a point of inflection. (b) The same function graphed with the y-axis horizontal and the x-axis vertical.

so that both y' and y'' become infinite when x approaches zero. On the other hand,

$$y' = \frac{1}{3x^{2/3}} = \frac{1}{3y^2}$$

is always positive for both positive and negative values of x, so the curve is always rising and has a vertical tangent at $(0, 0)$. Also,

$$y'' = -\frac{2}{9}\left(\frac{1}{\sqrt[3]{x}}\right)^5 = \frac{-2}{9y^5}$$

is positive (the curve "holds water") when x is negative, and is negative (the curve "spills water") when x is positive, so that $(0, 0)$ is a point of inflection.

REMARK. Another way to discuss Example 3 is to write the equation $y = x^{1/3}$ in the form $x = y^3$, and then

$$\frac{dx}{dy} = 3y^2, \qquad \frac{d^2x}{dy^2} = 6y,$$

so that we have

$$\frac{dx}{dy} = 0 \qquad \text{and} \qquad \frac{d^2x}{dy^2} = 0$$

at $(0, 0)$. It is clear that dx/dy is positive for all y different from zero and d^2x/dy^2 has the same sign as y and therefore changes its sign at $y = 0$. If we interchange the x- and y-axes so as to take the x-axis to be vertical and the y-axis to be horizontal, the curve will be as shown in Fig. 3–12(b).

3–13 The graph of $y = x^4$ has no inflection point at the origin even though $y''(0) = 0$.

WARNING. The condition $y'' = 0$ by itself is not enough to guarantee a point of inflection. The graph of $y = x^4$ (Fig. 3–13) is concave upward at $x = 0$ even though the value of $y'' = 12x^2$ is 0 when $x = 0$.

Here is a procedure for sketching the graph of an equation $y = f(x)$, based on the discussion in Article 3–3.

A. Calculate dy/dx and d^2y/dx^2.

B. Find the values of x for which dy/dx is positive and for which it is negative. Calculate y and d^2y/dx^2 at the points of transition between positive and negative values of dy/dx. These may give maximum or minimum points on the curve. (See Figs. 3–4, 3–10, and 3–11a.)

C. Find the values of x for which d^2y/dx^2 is positive and for which it is negative. Calculate y and dy/dx at the points of transition between positive and negative values of d^2y/dx^2. These may give points of inflection of the curve. (See Figs. 3–11 and 3–12.)

D. Plot a few additional points. In particular, points which lie between the transition points already determined or points which lie to the left or to the right of all of them will ordinarily be useful. The nature of the curve for large values of $|x|$ should also be indicated.

E. Sketch a smooth curve through the points found above, unless there are discontinuities in the curve or its slope. Have the curve pass through its points rising or falling as indicated by the sign of dy/dx, and concave upward or downward as indicated by the sign of d^2y/dx^2.

We shall now apply this procedure to a few examples.

3–4
CURVE PLOTTING

EXAMPLE 1. (See Fig. 3–14b.) Graph the function

$$y = \tfrac{1}{6}(x^3 - 6x^2 + 9x + 6).$$

Solution. We take the five steps listed above.

A.
$$\frac{dy}{dx} = \frac{1}{6}(3x^2 - 12x + 9) = \frac{1}{2}(x^2 - 4x + 3),$$

$$\frac{d^2y}{dx^2} = \frac{1}{2}(2x - 4) = x - 2.$$

a)

b)

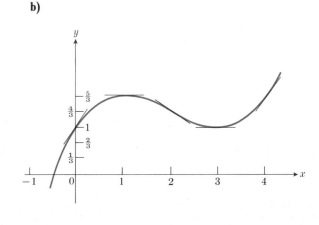

3–14　A graph of $y = \tfrac{1}{6}(x^3 - 6x^2 + 9x + 6)$ drawn after studying the values of y' and y''.

B. When factored,

$$\frac{dy}{dx} = \frac{1}{2}(x - 1)(x - 3),$$

and the two factors change their signs at $x = 1$ and $x = 3$. (See Fig. 3–14a.) When $x = 1$, $d^2y/dx^2 = -1$ and when $x = 3$, $d^2y/dx^2 = 1$. We enter the information in Table 3–1.

C. It is readily seen that $d^2y/dx^2 = x - 2$ is negative to the left of $x = 2$ and is positive to the right of $x = 2$, so that an inflection point occurs at $x = 2$.

D. We calculate y, y', and y'' at a few additional points to get general information about the curve.

E. A fairly good sketch of the curve can now be made (Fig. 3–14(b)) by using the information in the table.

Table 3–1

x	y	y'	y''	**Conclusions**
-1	$-\frac{5}{3}$	$+$	$-$	Rising; concave down
0	1	$+\frac{3}{2}$	$-$	Rising; concave down
1	$\frac{5}{3}$	0	$-$	"Spills water"; max.
2	$\frac{4}{3}$	$-\frac{1}{2}$	0	Falling; point of inflection
3	1	0	$+$	"Holds water"; min.
4	$\frac{5}{3}$	$+\frac{3}{2}$	$+$	Rising; concave up

EXAMPLE 2. (See Fig. 3–15b.)

$$y = x + \frac{1}{x} = x + x^{-1}.$$

Solution

$$\frac{dy}{dx} = 1 - x^{-2} = 1 - \frac{1}{x^2} = \frac{x^2 - 1}{x^2},$$

$$\frac{d^2y}{dx^2} = 2x^{-3} = \frac{2}{x^3}.$$

The sign of dy/dx will be the same as the sign of $x^2 - 1 = (x - 1)(x + 1)$. (See Fig. 3–15a.) But when x is near zero, $|y|$ will be large and y, dy/dx, d^2y/dx^2 all become infinite as x approaches zero. This curve is discontinuous at $x = 0$. Also, for large values of x, the $1/x$ term becomes small and $y \approx x$. In fact,

when $|x|$ is small, $y \approx \frac{1}{x}$,

when $|x|$ is large, $y \approx x$,

so that it is helpful to sketch (as can quickly be done) the curves

$$y_1 = \frac{1}{x}, \qquad y_2 = x,$$

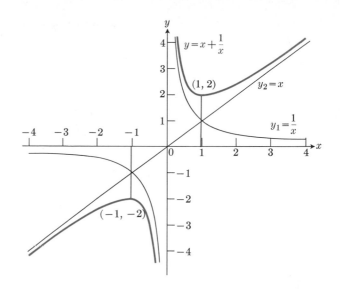

3-15 The graph of $y = x + (1/x)$, from the data in Example 2. The ordinate of each point on the graph is the sum of the ordinates x and $1/x$.

as well as

$$y = x + \frac{1}{x} = y_1 + y_2.$$

Actually, replacing x by $-x$ merely changes the sign of y, so that it would suffice to sketch the portion of the curve in the first quadrant and then reflect the result with respect to the origin to get the portion in the third quadrant (Fig. 3-15b). (See Table 3-2.)

Table 3-2. Data for Fig. 3-15(b).

x	y_1	y_2	y	y'	y''	Conclusions
-4	$-\frac{1}{4}$	-4	$-\frac{17}{4}$	$+$	$-$	Rising; concave down
-2	$-\frac{1}{2}$	-2	$-\frac{5}{2}$	$+$	$-$	Rising; concave down
-1	-1	-1	-2	0	-2	"Spills water"; max.
$-\frac{1}{2}$	-2	$-\frac{1}{2}$	$-\frac{5}{2}$	$-$	$-$	Falling; concave down
$-\frac{1}{4}$	-4	$-\frac{1}{4}$	$-\frac{17}{4}$	$-$	$-$	Falling; concave down
$+\frac{1}{4}$	4	$\frac{1}{4}$	$\frac{17}{4}$	$-$	$+$	Falling; concave up
$\frac{1}{2}$	2	$\frac{1}{2}$	$\frac{5}{2}$	$-$	$+$	Falling; concave up
1	1	1	2	0	$+2$	"Holds water"; min.
2	$\frac{1}{2}$	2	$\frac{5}{2}$	$+$	$+$	Rising; concave up
4	$\frac{1}{4}$	4	$\frac{17}{4}$	$+$	$+$	Rising; concave up

PROBLEMS

In each of the following problems (1 through 6), find intervals of values of x for which the curve is (a) rising, (b) falling, (c) concave upward, (d) concave downward. Sketch the curves, showing the high turning points M, low turning points m, and points of inflection I.

1. $y = x^2 - 4x + 3$

2. $y = \dfrac{x}{x+1}$

3. $y = 4 + 3x - x^3$

4. $y = \dfrac{x^3}{3} - \dfrac{x^2}{2} - 6x$

5. $y = x + \dfrac{4}{x}$

6. $y = \cos x$

7. Sketch a smooth curve $y = f(x)$ illustrating

$$f(1) = 0,$$

$$f'(x) < 0 \quad \text{for} \quad x < 1,$$

$$f'(x) > 0 \quad \text{for} \quad x > 1.$$

8. Sketch a smooth curve $y = f(x)$ illustrating

$$f(1) = 0,$$

$$f''(x) < 0 \quad \text{for} \quad x < 1,$$

$$f''(x) > 0 \quad \text{for} \quad x > 1.$$

Sketch each of the following curves (9 through 14), indicating high and low turning points and points of inflection.

9. $y = 6 - 2x - x^2$ **10.** $y = 2x^2 - 4x + 3$

11. $y = 12 - 12x + x^3$ **12.** $y = x^3 - 3x^2 + 2$

13. $y = -x^4$ **14.** $y = x^4 - 32x + 48$

For the following curves (15 through 18), find vertical tangents and sketch the curves.

15. $x = y^3 + 3y^2 + 3y + 2$ **16.** $x = y^3 + 3y^2 - 9y - 11$

17. $x = y^4 - 2y^2 + 2$ **18.** $x = y^2 + \dfrac{2}{y}$

19. Sketch a continuous curve $y = f(x)$ having the following characteristics:

$$f(-2) = 8, \qquad\qquad f'(2) = f'(-2) = 0,$$

$$f(0) = 4, \qquad\qquad f'(x) < 0 \quad \text{for} \quad |x| < 2,$$

$$f(2) = 0, \qquad\qquad f''(x) < 0 \quad \text{for} \quad x < 0,$$

$$f'(x) > 0 \quad \text{for} \quad |x| > 2, \qquad f''(x) > 0 \quad \text{for} \quad x > 0.$$

20. Sketch a continuous curve $y = f(x)$ having

$$f'(x) > 0 \quad \text{for} \quad x < 2, \qquad f'(x) < 0 \quad \text{for} \quad x > 2,$$

a) if $f'(x)$ is continuous at $x = 2$,
b) if $f'(x) \to 1$ as $x \to 2-$ and $f'(x) \to -1$ as $x \to 2+$,
c) if $f'(x) = 1$ for all $x < 2$ and $f'(x) = -1$ for all $x > 2$.

21. Sketch a continuous curve $y = f(x)$ for $x > 0$ if

$$f(1) = 0 \qquad \text{and} \qquad f'(x) = 1/x \quad \text{for all} \quad x > 0.$$

Is such a curve necessarily concave upward or concave downward?

22. Show that the sum of any positive real number and its reciprocal is at least 2.

23. Sketch the curve

$$y = 2x^3 + 2x^2 - 2x - 1$$

after locating its maximum, minimum, and inflection points. Then answer the following questions from your graph:

a) How many times and approximately where does the curve cross the x-axis?
b) How many times and approximately where would the curve cross the x-axis if $+3$ were added to all the y-values?
c) How many times and approximately where would the curve cross the x-axis if -3 were added to all the y-values?

24. Show that the curve

$$y = x + \sin x$$

has no maximum or minimum points even though it does have points where dy/dx is zero. Sketch the curve.

3-5

**MAXIMA AND MINIMA.
THEORY**

A function f is said to have a relative, or local, *maximum* at $x = a$ if

$$f(a) \geq f(a + h)$$

for all positive and negative values of h sufficiently near zero. For a local *minimum* at $x = b$,

$$f(b) \leq f(b + h)$$

for values of h close to zero. The word *relative* or *local* is used to distinguish such a point from an *absolute* maximum or minimum that would occur if we could say, for example,

$$f(a) \geq f(x)$$

for all x and not just for all x close to a. The function

$$f(x) = x + \frac{1}{x}$$

(Fig. 3–15(b)) has a *relative* minimum at $x = 1$, because

$$x + \frac{1}{x} \geq 2$$

for all values of x close to 1. But certainly when x is negative, the inequality is no longer satisfied. Indeed, the function has a relative maximum at $x = -1$. It has no absolute maximum or absolute minimum.

Figure 3–16 shows the graph of a function $y = f(x)$ defined only for the domain $0 \leq x \leq L$. This function has a relative minimum at $x = c$ which is also an absolute minimum. It also has relative maxima at $x = 0$ and $x = L$, and an absolute maximum at $x = L$.

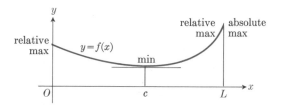

3–16 A relative maximum occurs at each endpoint. The one at $x = L$ is also the absolute maximum.

We have encountered relative maxima and minima in sketching curves and have observed that they occur at transition points between rising and falling portions of a curve. At such transition points we have also observed that dy/dx is usually zero, but may in exceptional cases become infinite (Fig. 3–10). We shall now prove the following theorem.

Theorem. *Let the function f be defined for $a \leq x \leq b$. Suppose that f has a relative maximum or minimum at an interior point $x = c$ of the interval (i.e., $a < c < b$). If the derivative $f'(x)$ exists as a finite number at $x = c$, then*

$$f'(c) = 0.$$

Proof. We shall give the proof for the case of a relative minimum at $x = c$; namely,

$$f(c) \leq f(c + h)$$

for all h close to zero (that is, when $c + h$ is close to c). By hypothesis,

$$f'(c) = \lim_{h \to 0} \frac{f(c + h) - f(c)}{h}$$

exists as a definite number which we want to prove is zero. In the ratio whose limit is $f'(c)$, when h is small, we have

$$\frac{f(c + h) - f(c)}{h} \geq 0 \qquad \text{if} \quad h > 0$$

and

$$\frac{f(c + h) - f(c)}{h} \leq 0 \qquad \text{if} \quad h < 0,$$

because in both cases the numerator either is positive or is zero. Hence if we let $h \to 0$ through positive values, we have

$$f'(c) \geq 0$$

from the first case; but if we let $h \to 0$ through negative values, we also have

$$f'(c) \leq 0$$

from the second case. Since the derivative is assumed to exist, we must have the same limit in both cases, so

$$0 \leq f'(c) \leq 0,$$

and the only way this can happen is to have

$$f'(c) = 0. \qquad\qquad\qquad \text{Q.E.D.}$$

The proof in case of a relative maximum at $x = c$ is similar.

CAUTION.   Be careful not to read into the theorem more than it says. It says that $f' = 0$ at every interior point where f has a relative maximum or minimum and f' exists. It does not say what happens if a maximum or minimum occurs

a) at a point c where the derivative fails to exist, or
b) at an endpoint of the interval of definition of the function.

Neither does it say that the function necessarily does have a maximum or minimum at every place where the derivative is zero.

In Fig. 3–17, the graph represents the continuous function defined by

$$y = f(x) = \begin{cases} 3 - x & \text{for} \quad x \leq 2, \\ \tfrac{1}{2}x^2 - 1 & \text{for} \quad x > 2. \end{cases}$$

The slope is

$$\frac{dy}{dx} = \frac{d(3 - x)}{dx} = -1 \quad \text{for} \quad x < 2,$$

$$\frac{dy}{dx} = \frac{d(\tfrac{1}{2}x^2 - 1)}{dx} = x \quad \text{for} \quad x > 2.$$

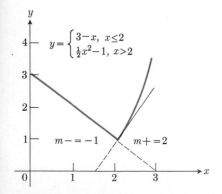

$$y = \begin{cases} 3 - x, & x \leq 2 \\ \tfrac{1}{2}x^2 - 1, & x > 2 \end{cases}$$

$m- = -1 \qquad m+ = 2$

3–17 A function can have a minimum value at a point where its derivative does not exist. One way this can happen is shown in Fig. 3–10, where the tangent to the curve is vertical at $x = 0$. Another way is shown here, where the right and left tangents are different.

At the point $x = 2$, the lefthand tangent has slope $m- = -1$ and the right-hand tangent has slope $m+ = 2$. Clearly, the curve is falling before $x = 2$ and rising after $x = 2$, and has a minimum at $x = 2$, $y = 1$. The derivative at $x = 2$ does not exist because $m+ \neq m-$. This shows that a minimum may occur where the derivative is not zero: where it doesn't even exist.

It is also easy to see from the proof of the theorem that when a maximum or minimum occurs at the *end* of a curve which exists only over a limited interval, the derivative need not vanish at such a point. For example, if the point $x = c$ is at the left end of such a curve, then in the limit in Eq. (2) it is not possible to take h to be negative, because $f(c + h)$ with h negative does not exist in this case. Strictly speaking, $f'(c)$ does not exist in these circumstances, although there may be a righthand tangent at one end of the curve and a lefthand tangent at the other end (Fig. 3–16).

The point $(0, 0)$ on the curve $y = x^3$ is an example of a point where a curve has zero slope without having either a maximum or a minimum there.

It is customary to refer to a point on a curve $y = f(x)$ at which $f'(x) = 0$ as a *stationary point* on the curve. Values of x that satisfy the equation $f'(x) = 0$ are also called *critical values*. In other words, a critical value of x is a value at which the curve $y = f(x)$ has a stationary point.

Conclusion. If f is continuous on the closed interval $a \leq x \leq b$, then Theorem 3 of Article 2–11 tells us that f has both a maximum and a minimum value somewhere on the interval. The theorem of this article now tells us where to look for them. Every point where f has a maximum or a minimum must be one of the following:

1. an endpoint of the interval, or
2. a point where f' does not exist, or
3. an interior point where $f' = 0$.

We need to investigate only these three classes of points to find the extreme values of f. The next article shows how we do this.

The differential calculus is a powerful tool for solving problems that call for minimizing or maximizing a function. We shall illustrate how this is done in several instances, and then summarize the technique in a list of specific rules.

3–6

MAXIMA AND MINIMA. PROBLEMS

EXAMPLE 1. Find two positive numbers whose sum is 20 and whose product is as large as possible.

Solution. If one of the numbers is x, then the other is $(20 - x)$, and their product is

$$y = x(20 - x) = 20x - x^2.$$

Therefore,

$$\frac{dy}{dx} = 20 - 2x = 2(10 - x),$$

which is

positive   when $x < 10$,

negative   when $x > 10$,

zero   when $x = 10$.

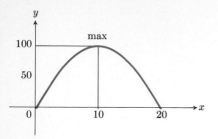

3–18(a) The product $y = x(20 - x)$ reaches a maximum value of 100 when $x = 10$.

Furthermore,

$$\frac{d^2y}{dx^2} = -2$$

is always negative. Thus the graph of y is concave downward at every point. Therefore, y has an absolute maximum at $x = 10$. The two numbers are $x = 10$ and $20 - x = 10$. (See Fig. 3–18a.)

With the same mathematical analysis that we used in Example 1, we can study the rate of the chemical reaction in the next example.

EXAMPLE 2. *Autocatalytic reactions.* A catalyst for a chemical reaction is a substance that controls the rate of the reaction without undergoing any permanent change in itself. An autocatalytic reaction is one whose product is a catalyst for its own formation. Such a reaction may proceed slowly at first if the amount of catalyst present is small, and slowly again at the end when most of the original substance is used up. But in between, when both the substance and its product are abundant, the reaction may proceed at a faster rate.

In some cases it is reasonable to assume that the rate v of the reaction is proportional both to the amount of the original substance present and to the amount of product. That is,

$$v = kx(a - x) = kax - kx^2, \tag{1}$$

where

$x = $ the amount of product,

$a = $ the amount of substance at the beginning,

$k = $ a positive constant.

At what value of x does the rate v have a maximum? What is the maximum value of v?

Solution. From Eq. (1) we find that

$$\frac{dv}{dx} = ka - 2kx = k(a - 2x),$$

which is

$$\text{positive} \quad \text{when } x < \frac{a}{2},$$

$$\text{negative} \quad \text{when } x > \frac{a}{2},$$

$$\text{zero} \quad \text{when } x = \frac{a}{2}.$$

Furthermore,

$$\frac{d^2v}{dx^2} = -2k$$

is always negative, because k is positive. Thus the graph of v is concave downward at every point. Therefore, v has a maximum value at $x = a/2$, that is, when the original substance is half used up. When $x = a/2$,

$$v = k\frac{a}{2}\left(\frac{a}{2}\right) = \frac{ka^2}{4}.$$

Note that the value $x = a/2$ does not depend on the rate constant k. (A graph of v appears in Fig. 3–18b.)

3–18(b) The chemical reaction modeled in Example 2 runs at its fastest ($v = ka^2/4$) when half of the product is formed ($x = a/2$).

EXAMPLE 3. A square sheet of tin a inches on a side is to be used to make an open-top box by cutting a small square of tin from each corner and bending up the sides. How large a square should be cut from each corner in order that the box shall have as large a volume as possible?

Solution. We first draw a figure to illustrate the problem (Fig. 3–19). In the figure, the side of the square cut from each corner is taken to be x inches and the volume of the box in cubic inches is then given by

$$y = x(a - 2x)^2, \qquad 0 \le x \le a/2. \tag{2}$$

The restrictions placed on x in (2) are clearly those imposed by the fact that one can neither cut a negative amount of material from a corner, nor can one cut away an amount which is more than the total amount present. It is also evident that $y = 0$ when $x = 0$ or when $x = a/2$, so that the maximum volume y must occur at some value of x between 0 and $a/2$. The function in (2) possesses a derivative at every such point, and hence

when y is a maximum, dy/dx must be zero.

From (2), we find

$$y = a^2x - 4ax^2 + 4x^3,$$

$$\frac{dy}{dx} = a^2 - 8ax + 12x^2$$

$$= (a - 2x)(a - 6x),$$

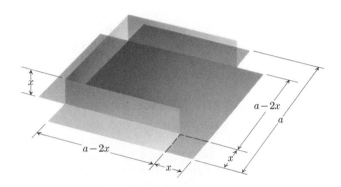

3–19 To make an open box, squares are cut from the corners of a square sheet of tin and the sides are bent up. What value of x gives the largest volume?

so that

$$\frac{dy}{dx} = 0 \quad \text{when} \quad x = \frac{a}{2} \text{ or } \frac{a}{6}.$$

We gain additional information about the shape of the curve representing (2) from

$$\frac{d^2y}{dx^2} = 24x - 8a = 24\left(x - \frac{a}{3}\right),$$

which shows that the curve is

concave downward   for $x < \dfrac{a}{3}$,

concave upward   for $x > \dfrac{a}{3}$.

In particular,

$$\text{at} \quad x = \frac{a}{6}: \quad \frac{dy}{dx} = 0, \quad \frac{d^2y}{dx^2} = -4a,$$

$$\text{at} \quad x = \frac{a}{2}: \quad \frac{dy}{dx} = 0, \quad \frac{d^2y}{dx^2} = +4a. \tag{3}$$

From (3) we see that if we were to draw the graph of the curve (2) it would "spill water" at $x = (a/6)$ and this is the only point between $x = 0$ and $x = (a/2)$ where a relative maximum of the volume y may occur (Fig. 3–20). Each corner square should thus have dimensions $a/6$ by $a/6$ to produce a box of maximum volume.

EXAMPLE 4. An oil can is to be made in the form of a right circular cylinder to contain one quart of oil. What dimensions of the can will require the least amount of material?

Solution. Again we start with a figure (Fig. 3–21). Clearly, the requirement that the can hold a quart of oil is the same as

$$V = \pi r^2 h = a^3, \tag{4a}$$

if the radius r and altitude h are in inches and a^3 is the number of cubic inches in a quart ($a^3 = 57.75$). How shall we interpret the phrase "least material"? A reasonable interpretation arises from neglecting the thickness of the material and the waste due to the manufacturing process. Then we ask for dimensions r and h that make the total surface area

$$A = 2\pi r^2 + 2\pi rh \tag{4b}$$

as small as possible while still satisfying (4a).

We are not quite ready to apply the methods used in Examples 1 and 2, because Eq. (4b) expresses A as a function of *two* variables, r and h, and our methods call for A to be expressed as a function of just *one* variable. However, Eq. (4a) may be used to express one of the variables r or h in terms

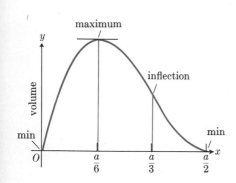

3–20 The volume of the box in Fig. 3–19 graphed as a function of x.

3–21 This one-quart can can be made from the least material when $h = 2r$.

of the other; in fact, we find

$$h = \frac{a^3}{\pi r^2} \qquad \textbf{(4c)}$$

or

$$r = \sqrt{\frac{a^3}{\pi h}}. \qquad \textbf{(4d)}$$

The division in (4c) and (4d) is legitimate because neither r nor h can be zero, and only the positive square root is used in (4d) because the radius r can never be negative. If we substitute from (4c) into (4b), we have

$$A = 2\pi r^2 + \frac{2a^3}{r}, \qquad 0 < r < \infty, \qquad \textbf{(4e)}$$

and now we may apply our previous methods. A minimum of A can occur only at a point where

$$\frac{dA}{dr} = 4\pi r - 2a^3 r^{-2} \qquad \textbf{(4f)}$$

is zero, that is, where

$$4\pi r = \frac{2a^3}{r^2}, \qquad r = \frac{a}{\sqrt[3]{2\pi}}. \qquad \textbf{(4g)}$$

At such a value of r, we shall have

$$\frac{d^2A}{dr^2} = 4\pi + 4a^3 r^{-3} = 12\pi > 0,$$

so the curve representing A as a function of r has $dA/dr = 0$ and d^2A/dr^2 positive ("holds water") at $r = a/\sqrt[3]{2\pi}$, which must therefore produce a relative minimum. Since the second derivative is *always positive* for $0 < r < \infty$, the curve is concave upward everywhere, and there can be no other relative minimum, so we have also found the absolute minimum. From (4g) and (4c), we find

$$r = \frac{a}{\sqrt[3]{2\pi}} = \sqrt[3]{\frac{V}{2\pi}}, \qquad h = \frac{2a}{\sqrt[3]{2\pi}} = 2\sqrt[3]{\frac{V}{2\pi}}$$

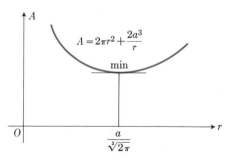

3–22 A graph of $A = 2\pi r^2 + (2a^3/r)$.

as the dimensions of the can of volume V having minimum surface area. Note that the height of the can is equal to its diameter. Figure 3–22 shows a curve representing A as a function of r as given by (4e).

Some problems about maxima and minima have no solution. The next example discusses one such problem.

EXAMPLE 5. A wire of length L is to be cut into two pieces, one of which is bent to form a circle and the other to form a square. How should the wire be cut if the sum of the areas enclosed by the two pieces is to be a maximum?

Solution. In the notation of Fig. 3–23, the sum of the areas is

$$A = \pi r^2 + x^2, \qquad \textbf{(5a)}$$

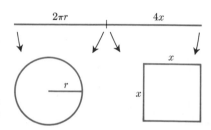

3–23 A circle and a square made from a wire $2\pi r + 4x$ units long. How large an area can they enclose together?

where r and x must satisfy the equation

$$L = 2\pi r + 4x. \tag{5b}$$

We could solve (5b) for x in terms of r, but instead we shall differentiate both (5a) and (5b), treating A and x as functions of r for $0 \le 2\pi r \le L$. Then

$$\frac{dA}{dr} = 2\pi r + 2x \frac{dx}{dr}, \tag{5c}$$

and

$$\frac{dL}{dr} = 2\pi + 4\frac{dx}{dr} = 0, \qquad \frac{dx}{dr} = -\frac{\pi}{2}, \tag{5d}$$

where dL/dr is zero because L is a constant. If we substitute dx/dr from (5d) into (5c), we get

$$\frac{dA}{dr} = \pi(2r - x) \tag{5e}$$

and, for future reference, we note that

$$\frac{d^2A}{dr^2} = \pi\left(2 - \frac{dx}{dr}\right) = \pi\left(2 + \frac{\pi}{2}\right) \tag{5f}$$

is a positive constant, so that the curve which represents A as a function of r is always concave upward (Fig. 3–24).

Now

$$\frac{dA}{dr} = 0 \qquad \text{when} \quad x = 2r,$$

and when we substitute $x = 2r$ into (5b),

$$L = 2\pi r + 4(2r) = (2\pi + 8)r,$$

we have

$$\frac{dA}{dr} = 0 \qquad \text{when} \quad r = \frac{L}{2\pi + 8}, \qquad x = \frac{L}{\pi + 4}.$$

But the fact that the second derivative is positive means that this value of r gives a *minimum* for A. The problem asks for the *maximum* of A.

Since r is limited to

$$0 \le r \le \frac{L}{2\pi},$$

we examine the values of A at the ends of this interval. When

$$r = 0: \qquad x = \frac{L}{4}, \quad A = \tfrac{1}{16}L^2,$$

and when

$$r = \frac{L}{2\pi}: \qquad x = 0, \quad A = \frac{1}{4\pi}L^2.$$

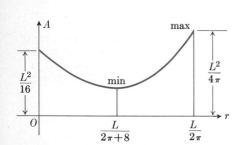

3–24 The sum of the areas in Fig. 3–23 graphed as a function of r.

At the minimum,

$$r = \frac{1}{2}\frac{L}{\pi + 4}, \qquad x = \frac{L}{\pi + 4}, \qquad A = \frac{1}{4\pi + 16}L^2.$$

Using these values to make a rough sketch of A as a function of r (Fig. 3–24), we can readily see that the maximum value of A occurs when $r = L/2\pi$, which means that the wire should not be cut at all, but all of it should be bent into the circle for maximum total area. Or, if we adopt the point of view that the wire *must* be cut, then there is no answer to the problem. For no matter how little of it is used for the square, we could always get a larger total area by using still less of it for the square.

EXAMPLE 6. *Snell's law.* Fermat's principle in optics states that light travels from a point A to a point B along that path for which the time of travel is a minimum. Let us find the path that a ray of light will follow in going from a point A in a medium where the velocity of light is c_1 to a point B in a second medium where the velocity of light is c_2, when both points lie in the xy-plane and the x-axis separates the two media, as shown in Fig. 3–25.

Solution. In either medium, where the velocity of light remains constant, the light ray will follow a straight path, since then "shortest time" and "shortest distance" amount to the same thing. Hence the path will consist of a straight line segment from A to P in the first medium and another line segment PB in the second medium. The time required for the light to travel from A to P is

$$t_1 = \frac{\sqrt{a^2 + x^2}}{c_1},$$

and from P to B the time required is

$$t_2 = \frac{\sqrt{b^2 + (d - x)^2}}{c_2}.$$

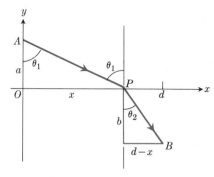

3–25 A light ray is refracted (deflected from its path) when it passes from one medium to another. θ_1 is the angle of incidence. θ_2 is the angle of refraction.

We therefore seek to minimize

$$t = t_1 + t_2 = \frac{\sqrt{a^2 + x^2}}{c_1} + \frac{\sqrt{b^2 + (d - x)^2}}{c_2}. \tag{6a}$$

We find

$$\frac{dt}{dx} = \frac{x}{c_1\sqrt{a^2 + x^2}} - \frac{(d - x)}{c_2\sqrt{b^2 + (d - x)^2}} \tag{6b}$$

or

$$\frac{dt}{dx} = \frac{\sin\theta_1}{c_1} - \frac{\sin\theta_2}{c_2}, \tag{6c}$$

if we make use of the angles θ_1 and θ_2 in the figure.

If we restrict x to the interval $0 \le x \le d$, then t has a negative derivative at $x = 0$ and a positive derivative at $x = d$, while at the value of x, say x_c, for which

$$\frac{\sin\theta_1}{c_1} = \frac{\sin\theta_2}{c_2}, \tag{6d}$$

3–26 These tangents to the graph of Eq. (6a) suggest that t has a minimum at $x = x_c$.

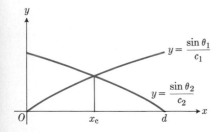

3–27 At $x = x_c$, $(\sin \theta_1)/c_1 = (\sin \theta_2)/c_2$.

dt/dx is zero. Figure 3–26 indicates the directions of the tangents to the curve giving t as a function of x, at these three points, and suggests that t will indeed be a minimum at $x = x_c$. If we want further information on this point, by referring to Fig. 3–25 we see that a decrease in x will cause P to move to the left, making θ_1 smaller, and hence also $\sin \theta_1$ smaller, but will have the opposite effect on θ_2 and $\sin \theta_2$. Figure 3–27 shows that since $(\sin \theta_1)/c_1$ is an increasing function of x which is zero at $x = 0$, while $(\sin \theta_2)/c_2$ is a decreasing function of x which is zero at $x = d$, the two curves can cross at only one point, $x = x_c$, between 0 and d. To the right of x_c, the curve for $(\sin \theta_1)/c_1$ is above the curve for $(\sin \theta_2)/c_2$, but these roles are reversed to the left of x_c, so that

$$\frac{dt}{dx} = \frac{\sin \theta_1}{c_1} - \frac{\sin \theta_2}{c_2} \begin{cases} \text{is negative for } x < x_c, \\ \text{is zero for } x = x_c, \\ \text{is positive for } x > x_c, \end{cases}$$

and the minimum of t does indeed occur at $x = x_c$.

Instead of determining this value of x explicitly, it is customary to characterize the path followed by the ray of light by leaving the equation for $dt/dx = 0$ in the form (6d), which is known as the *law of refraction* or Snell's law. [See Sears, Zemansky, Young, *University Physics*, Fifth edition (1976), Chap. 38.]

REMARK. The following argument can be applied to many problems in which we are trying to find an extreme value, say a maximum, of a function. Suppose that we know that:

1. We can restrict our search to a closed interval I;

2. The function is continuous and differentiable everywhere (we might know this from a formula for the function, or from physical considerations); and

3. The function does not attain a maximum at either endpoint of I.

Then we know that the function has at least one maximum at an interior point of I, at which the derivative must be zero. Therefore, if we find that the derivative of the function is zero at only one interior point of I, then this point is where the function takes on its maximum. A similar argument applies to a search for a minimum value.

EXAMPLE 7. A manufacturing company can sell x items per week at a price $P = 200 - 0.01x$ cents, and it costs $y = 50x + 20,000$ cents to make x items. What is the most profitable number to make?

Solution. The total weekly revenue from x items is

$$xP = 200x - 0.01x^2.$$

The profit T is revenue minus cost:

$$T = xP - y = (200x - 0.01x^2) - (50x + 20,000)$$
$$= 150x - 0.01x^2 - 20,000.$$

For very large values of x, say beyond a million, T is negative. Therefore, T takes on its maximum value somewhere in the interval $0 \le x \le 10^6$. The

STRATEGY FOR FINDING MAXIMA AND MINIMA

First.   When possible, draw a figure to illustrate the problem and label those parts that are important in the problem. Constants and variables should be clearly distinguished.

Second.   Write an equation for the quantity that is to be a maximum or a minimum. If this quantity is denoted by y, it is desirable to express it in terms of a single independent variable x. This may require some algebraic manipulation to make use of auxiliary conditions of the problem.

Third.   If $y = f(x)$ is the quantity to be a maximum or a minimum, find those values of x for which

$$\frac{dy}{dx} = f'(x) = 0.$$

Fourth.   Test each value of x for which $f'(x) = 0$ to determine whether it provides a maximum or minimum or neither. The usual tests are:

a) If $\dfrac{d^2y}{dx^2}$ is positive when $\dfrac{dy}{dx} = 0$, y is a minimum.

   If $\dfrac{d^2y}{dx^2}$ is negative when $\dfrac{dy}{dx} = 0$, y is a maximum.

   If $\dfrac{d^2y}{dx^2} = 0$ when $\dfrac{dy}{dx} = 0$,   the test fails.

b) If

$$\frac{dy}{dx} \text{ is } \begin{cases} \text{positive for } x < x_c, \\ \text{zero for } x = x_c, \\ \text{negative for } x > x_c, \end{cases}$$

then a maximum occurs at x_c. But if dy/dx changes from negative to zero to positive as x advances through x_c, there is a minimum. If dy/dx does not change its sign, neither a maximum nor a minimum need occur.

Fifth.   If the derivative fails to exist at some point, examine this point as possible maximum or minimum. (See Fig. 3–17.)

Sixth.   If the function $y = f(x)$ is defined for only a limited range of values $a \le x \le b$, examine $x = a$ and $x = b$ for possible extreme values of y. (See Fig. 3–24.)

formula for T shows that T is differentiable at every x, and obviously T does not take on its maximum at either endpoint, 0 or 10^6. The derivative

$$\frac{dT}{dx} = 150 - 0.02x$$

is zero only when

$$x = 7500.$$

Therefore, $x = 7500$ is the production level for maximum profit.

___

To solve the problem in Example 7 it would have been as effective to calculate the second derivative $d^2T/dx^2 = -0.02$ and conclude that T has a relative maximum at $x = 7500$. A quick look at the domain of x or the graph of T is all that would then be needed to show that the maximum was absolute. The virtue of the argument that we gave instead is that it can apply to a function whose second derivative is nonexistent or difficult to compute.

As a last example, we derive the order-quantity formula of Example 24 in Article 1–6.

EXAMPLE 8. *Economic Order Quantity* (continued from Article 1–6). As described in Article 1–6, the most economical quantity of merchandise for a retailer to order when supplies run low is

$$Q = \sqrt{\frac{2KM}{h}},$$

where K is the setup cost (fixed cost of placing an order), M is the number of items sold each week (assumed to be a constant), and h is the weekly holding cost for each item. This quantity, it was said, strikes an economical balance between the costs of ordering and holding inventory. To see why this is so, we first derive a formula for the average cost per week of ordering, paying for, and holding merchandise. We then find a value of Q that minimizes this average cost.

We assume that we reorder the same number Q of items each time, and that the supply arrives just when the inventory level at the store falls to zero. Thus, a newly arrived quantity Q takes Q/M weeks to deplete, and the graph of the number of items on hand looks like Fig. 3–28. The average cost per week of carrying the merchandise in question is the sum of three quantities:

1. $K(M/Q)$, the average setup cost per week (the setup cost K divided by the number of weeks Q/M);

2. cM, the average purchase cost per week (c is the purchase cost of one item);

3. $h(Q/2)$, the average holding cost per week ($Q/2$ is the average level of inventory, as you can see from Fig. 3–28).

Thus the average cost per week is given by the formula

$$A(Q) = \frac{KM}{Q} + cM + \frac{hQ}{2}.$$

What values of Q, if any, minimize $A(Q)$?

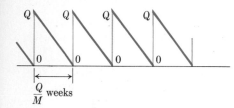

3–28 Graph of a store's inventory level. M is the weekly demand. Q is the quantity reordered.

We find that

$$\frac{dA}{dQ} = -\frac{KM}{Q^2} + \frac{h}{2},$$

which equals zero when

$$Q = \sqrt{\frac{2KM}{h}}.$$

(The negative square root is not a possible value for Q.) The second derivative,

$$\frac{d^2A}{dQ^2} = \frac{2KM}{Q^3},$$

is positive, so that A has a relative minimum at $Q = \sqrt{2KM/h}$. There are no endpoints to worry about because A is defined for all $Q > 0$, and A is differentiable for all $Q > 0$. Hence the minimum is absolute. Incidentally, the graph of A is like the right branch of the graph of $y = x + (1/x)$ in Fig. 3–15.

PROBLEMS

1. Show that the rectangle that has maximum area for a given perimeter is a square.

2. Find the dimensions of the rectangle of greatest area that can be inscribed in a semicircle of radius r.

3. Find the area of the largest rectangle with lower base on the x-axis and upper vertices on the curve $y = 12 - x^2$.

4. An open rectangular box is to be made from a piece of cardboard 8 in. wide and 15 in. long by cutting a square from each corner and bending up the sides. Find the dimensions of the box of largest volume.

5. One side of an open field is bounded by a straight river. How would you put a fence around the other three sides of a rectangular plot in order to enclose as great an area as possible with a given length of fence?

6. An open storage bin with square base and vertical sides is to be constructed from a given amount of material. Determine its dimensions if its volume is a maximum. Neglect the thickness of the material and waste in construction.

7. A box with square base and open top is to hold 32 in³. Find the dimensions that require the least amount of material. Neglect the thickness of the material and waste in construction.

8. A variable line through the point $(1, 2)$ intersects the x-axis at $A(a, 0)$ and the y-axis at $B(0, b)$. Find the area of the triangle AOB of least area if both a and b are positive.

9. A poster is to contain 50 in² of printed matter with margins of 4 in. each at top and bottom and 2 in. at each side. Find the overall dimensions if the total area of the poster is a minimum.

10. A right triangle of given hypotenuse is rotated about one of its legs to generate a right circular cone. Find the cone of greatest volume.

11. It costs a manufacturer c dollars each to manufacture and distribute a certain item. If the items sell at x dollars each, the number sold is given by $n = a/(x - c) + b(100 - x)$, where a and b are certain positive constants. What selling price will bring a maximum profit?

12. A cantilever beam of length L has one end built into a wall, while the other end is simply supported. If the beam weighs w lb per unit length, its deflection y at distance x from the built-in end satisfies the equation

$$48EIy = w(2x^4 - 5Lx^3 + 3L^2x^2),$$

where E and I are constants depending upon the material of the beam and the shape of its cross section. How far from the built-in end does the maximum deflection occur?

13. Determine the constant a in order that the function

$$f(x) = x^2 + \frac{a}{x}$$

may have (a) a relative minimum at $x = 2$, (b) a relative minimum at $x = -3$, (c) a point of inflection at $x = 1$. (d) Show that the function cannot have a relative maximum for any value of a.

14. Determine the constants a and b in order that the function

$$f(x) = x^3 + ax^2 + bx + c$$

may have (a) a relative maximum at $x = -1$ and a relative minimum at $x = 3$, (b) a relative minimum at $x = 4$ and a point of inflection at $x = 1$.

15. A wire of length L is cut into two pieces, one being bent to form a square and the other to form an equilateral triangle. How should the wire be cut (a) if the sum of the two areas is a minimum, (b) if the sum of the areas is a maximum?

16. Find the points on the curve $5x^2 - 6xy + 5y^2 = 4$ that are nearest the origin.

17. Find the point on the curve $y = \sqrt{x}$ nearest the point $(c, 0)$, (a) if $c \geq \frac{1}{2}$, (b) if $c < \frac{1}{2}$.

18. Find the volume of the largest right circular cone that can be inscribed in a sphere of radius r.

19. Find the volume of the largest right circular cylinder that can be inscribed in a sphere of radius r.

20. Show that the volume of the largest right circular cylinder that can be inscribed in a given right circular cone is $\frac{4}{9}$ the volume of the cone.

21. The strength of a rectangular beam is proportional to the product of its width and the square of its depth. Find the dimensions of the strongest beam that can be cut from a circular cylindrical log of radius r.

22. The stiffness of a rectangular beam is proportional to the product of its breadth and the cube of its depth. Find the stiffest beam that can be cut from a log of given diameter.

23. The intensity of illumination at any point is proportional to the product of the strength of the light source and the inverse of the square of the distance from the source. If two sources of relative strengths a and b are a distance c apart, at what point on the line joining them will the intensity be a minimum? Assume the intensity at any point is the sum of intensities from the two sources.

24. A window is in the form of a rectangle surmounted by a semicircle. If the rectangle is of clear glass while the semicircle is of colored glass which transmits only half as much light per square foot as clear glass does, and the total perimeter is fixed, find the proportions of the window that will admit the most light.

25. Right circular cylindrical tin cans are to be manufactured to contain a given volume. There is no waste involved in cutting the tin that goes into the vertical sides of the can, but each end piece is to be cut from a square and the corners of the square wasted. Find the ratio of height to diameter for the most economical cans.

26. A silo is to be made in the form of a cylinder surmounted by a hemisphere. The cost of construction per square foot of surface area is twice as great for the hemisphere as for the cylinder. Determine the dimensions to be used if the volume is fixed and the cost of construction is to be a minimum. Neglect the thickness of the silo and waste in construction.

27. If the sum of the areas of a cube and a sphere is constant, what is the ratio of an edge of the cube to the diameter of the sphere when (a) the sum of their volumes is a minimum, (b) the sum of their volumes is a maximum?

* 28. Two towns, located on the same side of a straight river, agree to construct a pumping station and filtering plant at the river's edge, to be used jointly to supply the towns with water. If the distances of the two towns from the river are a and b and the distance between them is c, show that the sum of the lengths of the pipe lines joining them to the pumping station is at least as great as $\sqrt{c^2 + 4ab}$.

* 29. Light from a source A is reflected to a point B by a plane mirror. If the time required for the light to travel from A to the mirror and then to B is a minimum, show that the angle of incidence is equal to the angle of reflection.

30. Show that a manufacturer's profit is maximized (or minimized) at a level of production where the marginal revenue equals the marginal cost.

31. Suppose the government imposes a tax of ten cents, for each item sold, on the product of Example 7, but other features are unchanged. To maximize the company's profits, how much of the tax should the company absorb and how much should be passed on to the customer? Why? Compare the profits before and after the tax.

32. Shipping costs are likely to depend on order size, and it might be more realistic in modeling the inventory problem of Example 8 to assume that the setup cost is not a constant. Suppose instead that the setup cost is $K + pQ$, the sum of a constant and a multiple of Q. What is the most economical quantity to order now?

33. The reaction of the body to a drug is sometimes represented by the function

$$R(D) = D^2 \left(\frac{C}{2} - \frac{D}{3} \right),$$

where $C =$ the maximum amount of the drug that could be given, $D =$ the amount given $(0 \leq D \leq C)$, and $R =$ a measure of the strength of the reaction (e.g., blood pressure measured in millimeters of mercury). The derivative $R'(D)$ is used as a measure of the sensitivity of the body to the drug. At the point where $R'(D)$ has a maximum, there is the greatest change in R for a small change in D. Show that this point is $D = C/2$, and that

$$R(C) = 2R \left(\frac{C}{2} \right).$$

[From *Some Mathematical Models in Biology*, p. 221.]

---

*   You may prefer to do these problems without calculus.

34. When we cough, the trachea (windpipe) can be observed to contract in a way that increases the velocity of the air going out. This naturally raises the questions of how much it should contract to maximize the velocity, and whether it really contracts that much. Under reasonable assumptions about the elasticity of the tracheal wall, and about how the air flow is slowed near the wall by friction, the overall flow velocity v can be modeled by the equation

$$v = c(r - r_0)r^2 \quad \frac{cm}{sec}, \qquad \frac{r_0}{2} \le r \le r_0,$$

where r_0 is the rest radius of the trachea in centimeters, and $c < 0$ is a constant that depends on the length of the trachea.

Show that v has a maximum when $r = \frac{2}{3}r_0$, that is, when the trachea is about 33 percent contracted. The remarkable fact is that x-ray photographs confirm that the trachea contracts just about this much during a cough. (For more information, see *The Human Cough*, Philip Tuchinsky, UMAP Project, Education Development Center, Newton, MA, 1978.)

35. Find all maxima and minima of $y = \sin x + \cos x$. Sketch.

There is strong geometrical evidence to support the belief that between two points where a smooth curve $y = f(x)$ crosses the x-axis there must be at least one point where it has a horizontal tangent (Fig. 3–29a). But such is not the case if the curve has a corner, as in Fig. 3–29(b), where the derivative fails to exist. More precisely, we have the following theorem.

3–7
ROLLE'S THEOREM

Rolle's Theorem.* Let the function f be defined and continuous on the closed interval $a \le x \le b$ and differentiable in the open interval $a < x < b$. Furthermore, let*

$$f(a) = f(b) = 0.$$

Then there is at least one number c between a and b where $f'(x)$ is zero; i.e.,

$$f'(c) = 0 \quad for\ some\ c, \quad a < c < b.$$

Proof. Either $f(x)$ is identically equal to zero for all x, $a \le x \le b$, or else $f(x)$ is different from zero for some values of x in this interval. In the former case, $f'(x)$ is also identically zero and the theorem is true for this case.

But if $f(x)$ is not zero everywhere between a and b, then either it is positive some place, or negative some place, or both. In any case, the function will then have a maximum positive value or a minimum negative value, or both. That is, it has an extreme value at a point c where $f(c)$ is negative (in the case of a minimum) or $f(c)$ is positive (in the case of a maximum). In either case, c is neither a nor b, since

$$f(a) = f(b) = 0, \quad f(c) \ne 0.$$

Therefore c is between a and b and the theorem of Article 3–5 applies, showing that the derivative must be zero at $x = c$:

$$f'(c) = 0 \quad for\ some\ c, \quad a < c < b. \qquad \text{Q.E.D.}$$

There may be more than one place between a and b where the derivative is zero. In Fig. 3–29(a), for example, dy/dx is zero at c_1 and at c_2 and they both lie between $a = -2$ and $b = +2$.

a)

b)

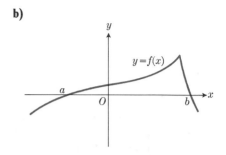

3–29 The functions graphed in (a) and (b) are both continuous. Graph (b), however, has no horizontal tangent between the two points where it crosses the x-axis. This could not have happened if $y = f(x)$ had been differentiable at every point between $x = a$ and $x = b$. The proof of Rolle's theorem explains why.

---

* Published in 1691 in *Méthode pour Résoudre les Egalités* by the French mathematician Michel Rolle. See *Source Book in Mathematics* by D. E. Smith, p. 253.

EXAMPLE 1. The polynomial

$$y = x^3 - 4x = f(x)$$

is continuous and differentiable for all x, $-\infty < x < +\infty$. If we take

$$a = -2, \qquad b = +2,$$

the hypotheses of Rolle's Theorem are satisfied, since

$$f(-2) = f(+2) = 0.$$

Thus

$$f'(x) = 3x^2 - 4$$

must be zero at least once between -2 and $+2$. In fact, we find

$$3x^2 - 4 = 0$$

at

$$x = c_1 = -\frac{2\sqrt{3}}{3} \qquad \text{and} \qquad x = c_2 = +\frac{2\sqrt{3}}{3}.$$

Rolle's Theorem may be combined with the Intermediate Value Theorem of Article 2–11 to obtain a criterion for isolating the real solutions of an equation $f(x) = 0$. Suppose that a and b are two real numbers such that

a) $f(x)$ and its first derivative $f'(x)$ are continuous for $a \le x \le b$,

b) $f(a)$ and $f(b)$ have opposite signs,

c) $f'(x)$ is different from zero for all values of x between a and b.

Then there is one and only one solution of the equation $f(x) = 0$ between a and b. This solution is called a *zero* of the function f. It is also called a *root* of the equation $f(x) = 0$.

EXAMPLE 2. Show that the equation

$$x^3 + 3x + 1 = 0$$

has exactly one real root.

Solution. Let

$$f(x) = x^3 + 3x + 1.$$

Then the derivative

$$f'(x) = 3x^2 + 3$$

is never zero (because it is always positive). Now, if there were even two points $x = a$ and $x = b$ where $f(x)$ was zero, Rolle's Theorem would guarantee the existence of a point $x = c$ where f' was zero. Therefore, f has no more than one zero. It does in fact have one zero, because the Intermediate Value Theorem tells us that the graph of $y = f(x)$ crosses the x-axis somewhere between $x = -1$ (where $y = -3$) and $x = 0$ (where $y = 1$). (See Fig. 3–30.)

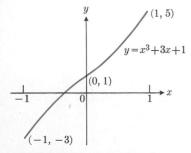

3–30 The only real root of the polynomial $y = x^3 + 3x + 1$ is the one shown here between -1 and 0.

PROBLEMS

Without trying to solve the equations exactly, show that the equation $f(x) = 0$ has one and only one real root between the given pair of numbers for each of the following functions $f(x)$.

1. $x^4 + 3x + 1$, $\quad\quad a = -2$, $\quad b = -1$
2. $x^4 + 2x^3 - 2$, $\quad\quad a = 0$, $\quad b = 1$
3. $2x^3 - 3x^2 - 12x - 6$, $\quad a = -1$, $\quad b = 0$

4. Let $f(x)$, together with its first two derivatives $f'(x)$ and $f''(x)$, be continuous for $a \le x \le b$. Suppose the curve $y = f(x)$ intersects the x-axis in at least three different places between a and b inclusive. Use Rolle's Theorem to show that the equation $f''(x) = 0$ has at least one real root between a and b. Generalize this result.

5. Use Rolle's Theorem to prove that between every two zeros of the polynomial $x^n + a_{n-1}x^{n-1} + \cdots + a_1 x + a_0$ there lies a zero of the polynomial

$$nx^{n-1} + (n-1)a_{n-1}x^{n-2} + \cdots + a_1.$$

6. The function

$$y = f(x) = \begin{cases} x & \text{if } 0 \le x < 1, \\ 0 & \text{if } x = 1, \end{cases}$$

is zero at $x = 0$ and at $x = 1$. Its derivative, $y' = 1$, is different from zero at every point between 0 and 1. Why doesn't that contradict Rolle's Theorem?

In this article we shall prove the Mean Value Theorem, which is a generalization of Rolle's Theorem. Again we shall be concerned with a function $y = f(x)$ that is continuous for $a \le x \le b$ and has a nonvertical tangent at each point between $A[a, f(a)]$ and $B[b, f(b)]$. (See Fig. 3–31.) The tangent may be vertical at one or both of the endpoints A and B. For example, the function might be

$$f(x) = \sqrt{a^2 - x^2}, \quad\quad -a \le x \le a,$$

which represents a semicircle that fulfills the requirements above.

3–8
THE MEAN VALUE THEOREM

DISCUSSION. Geometrically, the Mean Value Theorem states that if the function $y = f(x)$ is continuous for $a \le x \le b$ and has a derivative at each value of x for $a < x < b$, then there is at least one point c between a and b where the tangent to the curve will be parallel to the chord through the two points $A[a, f(a)]$ and $B[b, f(b)]$. This is intuitively plausible, for if we consider displacing the chord AB in Fig. 3–31 upward, keeping it parallel to AB, there will be a transition between positions where it cuts the curve in two nearby points and where it will fail to touch the curve, and the transition will take place at a point C where the line will be tangent to this curve. This transition will occur where the vertical distance between the chord AB and the curve is a maximum. The analytic proof of the Mean Value Theorem has its key idea in this last statement.

The Mean Value Theorem. Let $y = f(x)$ be continuous for $a \le x \le b$, and possess a derivative at each x for $a < x < b$. Then there is at least one number c between a and b such that

$$f(b) - f(a) = f'(c)(b - a).$$

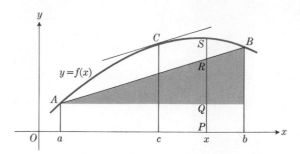

3–31 If $y = f(x)$ is differentiable on (a, b) and continuous on $[a, b]$, then the length RS is a function of x that is differentiable on (a, b) and continuous on $[a, b]$. In fact, RS satisfies all the requirements of Rolle's Theorem because it is zero at $x = a$ and $x = b$. Therefore, its derivative is zero at some value c of x between a and b. When we translate this observation into a statement about the function f, we obtain one of the most useful theorems of calculus.

Proof of the Mean Value Theorem. The vertical distance between the chord and the curve is measured by RS in Fig. 3–31 and

$$RS = PS - PR.$$

Now PS is simply the ordinate y on the curve $y = f(x)$, so that

$$PS = f(x).$$

On the other hand, PR is the ordinate on the chord AB and may be found by using the equation

$$y - f(a) = m(x - a),$$

which is the equation of the straight line AB through the point $A[a, f(a)]$ with slope

$$m = \frac{f(b) - f(a)}{b - a}.$$

That is, the ordinate y of the point R on the line AB is

$$y = PR = f(a) + \frac{f(b) - f(a)}{b - a}(x - a).$$

Hence

$$RS = f(x) - f(a) - \frac{f(b) - f(a)}{b - a}(x - a) \tag{1}$$

measures the vertical displacement from the chord AB to the curve $y = f(x)$ for any x between a and b.

It will simplify the discussion somewhat to change the notation on the left side of Eq. (1) and replace RS by $F(x)$.

That is,

$$F(x) = f(x) - f(a) - \frac{f(b) - f(a)}{b - a}(x - a). \qquad (2)$$

Then

$$F(a) = f(a) - f(a) - \frac{f(b) - f(a)}{b - a}(a - a) = 0$$

and

$$F(b) = f(b) - f(a) - \frac{f(b) - f(a)}{b - a}(b - a) = 0,$$

so that this function $F(x)$ is zero at both $x = a$ and $x = b$. But since $f(x)$ and $x - a$ in Eq. (2) are continuous for $a \leq x \leq b$ and differentiable for $a < x < b$, and the other expressions on the right side of the equation are constants, the function $F(x)$ satisfies all the hypotheses of Rolle's Theorem. Therefore its derivative must be zero at some place between a and b; that is,

$$F'(c) = 0 \qquad \text{for some } c, \qquad a < c < b. \qquad (3a)$$

If we take the derivative of both sides of (2), we get

$$F'(x) = f'(x) - \frac{f(b) - f(a)}{b - a} \cdot \frac{d(x - a)}{dx}$$

and the result (3a) is equivalent to stating

$$f'(c) = \frac{f(b) - f(a)}{b - a} \qquad (3b)$$

or

$$f(b) - f(a) = f'(c)(b - a) \qquad \text{for some } c, \qquad a < c < b, \qquad (4)$$

which is what we wished to prove.

We note that (3b) states that the slope $f'(c)$ of the curve at $C[c, f(c)]$ is the same as the slope $[f(b) - f(a)]/(b - a)$ of the chord joining the point $A[a, f(a)]$ and $B[b, f(b)]$; this is a form that is easily recalled.

When we are presented with a specific function f and specific values of a and b, we find the value or values of c that are guaranteed by the Mean Value Theorem by solving Eq. (4).

EXAMPLE 1.   (See Fig. 3–32.) Let $f(x) = x^3$, $a = -2$, and $b = +2$. Then

$$f'(x) = 3x^2, \qquad f'(c) = 3c^2,$$

$$f(b) = 2^3 = 8, \qquad f(a) = (-2)^3 = -8,$$

$$\frac{f(b) - f(a)}{b - a} = \frac{8 - (-8)}{2 - (-2)} = \frac{16}{4} = 4,$$

so that

$$f'(c) = \frac{f(b) - f(a)}{b - a}$$

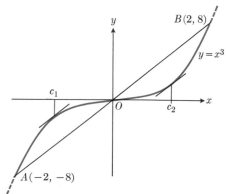

3–32 At $c = \pm\frac{2}{3}\sqrt{3}$, the tangents to the curve are parallel to the chord AB.

becomes

$$3c^2 = 4, \qquad c = \pm\tfrac{2}{3}\sqrt{3}.$$

There are thus two values of c, namely,

$$c_1 = -\tfrac{2}{3}\sqrt{3}, \qquad c_2 = +\tfrac{2}{3}\sqrt{3},$$

between $a = -2$ and $b = +2$, where the tangent to the curve $y = x^3$ is parallel to the chord through the points $(-2, -8)$ and $(+2, +8)$.

EXAMPLE 2.   (See Fig. 3–33.) Let $f(x) = x^{2/3}$, $a = -8$, $b = +8$. Then

$$f'(x) = \frac{2}{3}x^{-1/3} = \frac{2}{3\sqrt[3]{x}}$$

exists everywhere between a and b *except* at $x = 0$. We find that

$$\frac{f(b) - f(a)}{b - a} = \frac{(8)^{2/3} - (-8)^{2/3}}{8 - (-8)} = \frac{4 - 4}{16} = 0,$$

and

$$f'(c) = \frac{2}{3\sqrt[3]{c}}$$

is not zero for any finite value of c. The result (3b) need not hold, and does not hold, in this case due to the failure of the derivative to exist at a point, namely $x = 0$, between $a = -8$ and $b = +8$. Note, however, that the curve $y = x^{2/3}$ does have a tangent at $x = 0$ (it is vertical) and therefore has a tangent everywhere between a and b.

3–33   Having a tangent everywhere does not mean having a derivative everywhere.

REMARK.   The Mean Value Theorem has the following interesting interpretation when applied to an equation of motion $s = f(t)$. Let $\Delta s = f(b) - f(a)$ be the change in s corresponding to $\Delta t = b - a$; then the right side of Eq. (3b) is

$$\frac{\Delta s}{\Delta t} = \frac{f(b) - f(a)}{b - a} = \text{Average velocity from } t = a \text{ to } t = b. \qquad \textbf{(5)}$$

The equation then tells us that there is an instant $t = c$ between a and b at which the instantaneous velocity $f'(c)$ is equal to the average velocity. The theorem may therefore be paraphrased as follows: If a motorist makes a trip in which the *average* velocity is 30 mi/hr, then at least once during the trip the speedometer must also have registered precisely 30 mi/hr.

Corollary 1. *If a function F has a derivative that is equal to zero for all values of x in an interval $a < x < b$,*

$$F'(x) \equiv 0, \qquad a < x < b, \tag{6a}$$

then the function is constant throughout the interval:

$$F(x) \equiv \text{constant}, \qquad a < x < b. \tag{6b}$$

Proof. Suppose (6a) is satisfied. Let x_1 and x_2 be any two points in the interval with $a < x_1 < x_2 < b$. Then, since the function is differentiable for $x_1 \leq x \leq x_2$, it is also continuous in the same closed interval. Hence the Mean Value Theorem applies. That is, there is at least one number c, $x_1 < c < x_2$, such that

$$F(x_1) - F(x_2) = F'(c)(x_1 - x_2).$$

But $F'(c)$ is zero by hypothesis. Therefore

$$F(x_1) = F(x_2).$$

That is, the value of the function at any point x_1 is the same as its value at any other point x_2, for all x_1, x_2 in the interval (a, b). This is what is meant by Eq. (6b).   Q.E.D.

Corollary 2. *If F_1 and F_2 are two functions each of which has its derivative equal to $f(x)$ for $a < x < b$, that is,*

$$\frac{dF_1(x)}{dx} = \frac{dF_2(x)}{dx} = f(x), \qquad a < x < b,$$

then

$$F_1(x) - F_2(x) \equiv \text{constant}, \qquad a < x < b.$$

Proof. Apply Corollary 1, above, to the function $F(x) = F_1(x) - F_2(x)$.

PROBLEMS

In each of the following problems (1 through 5), a, b, and c refer to the equation $f(b) - f(a) = (b - a)f'(c)$, which expresses the Mean Value Theorem. Given $f(x)$, a, and b, find c.

1. $f(x) = x^2 + 2x - 1$; $a = 0$, $b = 1$.
2. $f(x) = x^3$; $a = 0$, $b = 3$.
3. $f(x) = x^{2/3}$; $a = 0$, $b = 1$.
4. $f(x) = x + \dfrac{1}{x}$; $a = \frac{1}{2}$, $b = 2$.
5. $f(x) = \sqrt{x - 1}$; $a = 1$, $b = 3$.

6. Suppose you know that $f(x)$ is differentiable and that $f'(x)$ always has a value between -1 and $+1$. Show that

$$|f(x) - f(a)| \leq |x - a|.$$

7. The Mean Value Theorem gives the equation

$$f(b) = f(a) + (b - a)f'(c),$$

c between a and b. When all terms on the right side of this equation are known, the equation determines $f(b)$ for us. Usually, however, $f'(c)$ is not known unless $f(b)$ is known. But when b is near a, then c will also be near a, and the

approximation

$$f'(c) \approx f'(a)$$

leads to the approximation

$$f(b) \approx f(a) + (b - a)f'(a).$$

Using this approximation, calculate

a) $\sqrt{10}$ by taking $f(x) = \sqrt{x}$, $a = 9$, $b = 10$;
b) $(2.003)^2$ by taking $f(x) = x^2$, $a = 2$, $b = 2.003$;
c) $1/99$ by taking $f(x) = 1/x$, $a = 100$, $b = 99$.

8. Let $P_1(x_1, y_1)$ and $P_2(x_2, y_2)$ be any two points on the parabola

$$y = ax^2 + bx + c,$$

and let $P_3(x_3, y_3)$ be the point on the arc $P_1 P_2$ where the tangent is parallel to the chord $P_1 P_2$. Show that $x_3 = (x_1 + x_2)/2$.

9. Use the Mean Value Theorem to prove that $|\sin b - \sin a| \le |b - a|$.

INDETERMINATE FORMS AND L'HÔPITAL'S RULE

As an application of the Mean Value Theorem, we develop a rule that will significantly extend our ability to calculate limits. The rule is named after Guillaume François Antoine de l'Hôpital (1661–1704), Marquis de St. Mesme, a French nobleman who wrote the first calculus text.

1. The Indeterminate Form 0/0

We sometimes wish to know the value of

$$\lim_{x \to a} \frac{f(x)}{g(x)} \tag{1}$$

at a point a where the functions $f(x)$ and $g(x)$ both vanish. However, if we substitute $x = a$ in the numerator and denominator of the fraction, we are led to the meaningless expression 0/0.

EXAMPLE 1. Both x and $\sin x$ are zero at $x = 0$, so we cannot just put $x = 0$ in the numerator and denominator if we want to find the limit

$$\lim_{x \to 0} \frac{\sin x}{x},$$

which we know (from earlier investigations) is one. This is also the derivative of $\sin x$ at $x = 0$. Indeed, the derivative

$$f'(a) = \lim_{x \to a} \frac{f(x) - f(a)}{x - a}$$

was our first example of the indeterminate form 0/0, since both the numerator and the denominator of the fraction $(f(x) - f(a))/(x - a)$ approach zero when x approaches a.

The key to a rule that will let us deal with indeterminate forms in many cases is a mean value theorem of Augustin L. Cauchy (1789–1857). It involves two functions instead of one.

Theorem 1. Cauchy's Mean Value Theorem.   *Suppose that the functions $f(x)$ and $g(x)$ are continuous for $a \le x \le b$ and differentiable for $a < x < b$, and* *that $g'(x) \neq 0$ for $a < x < b$. Then there exists a number c between a and b such that*

$$\frac{f'(c)}{g'(c)} = \frac{f(b) - f(a)}{g(b) - g(a)}. \qquad (2)$$

Proof. We apply the Mean Value Theorem of Article 3-8 twice. First we use it to show that $g(b) \neq g(a)$. For if $g(b)$ did equal $g(a)$, then the Mean-Value Theorem would apply to g, to give

$$g'(c) = \frac{g(b) - g(a)}{b - a} = 0$$

for some c between a and b. But this cannot happen because $g'(x) \neq 0$ for $a < x < b$.

We next apply the Mean Value Theorem to the function

$$F(x) = f(x) - f(a) - \frac{f(b) - f(a)}{g(b) - g(a)}[g(x) - g(a)]. \qquad (3)$$

This function is continuous and differentiable where f and g are, and $F(b) = F(a) = 0$. Therefore there is a number c between a and b for which $F'(c) = 0$. In terms of f and g this says

$$F'(c) = f'(c) - \frac{f(b) - f(a)}{g(b) - g(a)}[g'(c)] = 0, \qquad (4)$$

or

$$\frac{f'(c)}{g'(c)} = \frac{f(b) - f(a)}{g(b) - g(a)},$$

which is what we wished to prove.

REMARK. The auxiliary function in Eq. (3) has a geometric interpretation similar to the interpretation of the auxiliary function F that appears in the proof of the Mean Value Theorem in Article 3-8. We rewrite Eq. (3) in terms of a parameter t, so that

$$F(t) = f(t) - f(a) - \frac{f(b) - f(a)}{g(b) - g(a)}[g(t) - g(a)]. \qquad (3')$$

Then $F(t)$ is the vertical difference RS between the ordinate $y = f(t)$ on the graph of the parametric equations $x = g(t)$, $y = f(t)$ at S, and the chord through the points A (where $t = a$) and B (where $t = b$). (See Fig. 3-34.) For

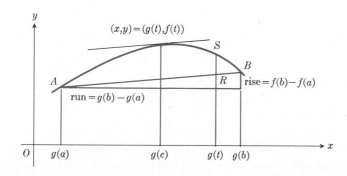

3-34 At $t = c$, the slope of the tangent to the parametric curve is the slope of chord AB.

some value $t = c$ between a and b, the tangent to the curve is parallel to the chord. Using the parametric equations, this says that

$$\frac{dy}{dx}\Big|_{t=c} = \frac{f'(t)}{g'(t)}\Big|_{t=c} = \frac{f'(c)}{g'(c)} = \frac{f(b) - f(a)}{g(b) - g(a)}.$$

We can now prove l'Hôpital's rule.

Theorem 2. l'Hôpital's Rule. *Suppose that the functions $f(x)$ and $g(x)$ are both zero at some point x_0, that is, $f(x_0) = g(x_0) = 0$, and that f and g are both differentiable at every point of an open interval $a < x < b$ that contains x_0. Suppose also that $g'(x) \neq 0$ for every $x \neq x_0$ in (a, b). Then*

$$\lim_{x \to x_0} \frac{f(x)}{g(x)} = \lim_{x \to x_0} \frac{f'(x)}{g'(x)}, \tag{5}$$

provided $f'(x)/g'(x)$ has a limit as x approaches x_0.

Proof.   We first establish Eq. (5) for the case $x \to x_{0+}$. The method needs almost no change to apply to $x \to x_{0-}$, and the combination of these two cases establishes the result.

Suppose that x lies to the right of x_0. Then $g'(x) \neq 0$ and we can apply Cauchy's Mean Value Theorem to the closed interval from x_0 to x. This produces a number c between x_0 and x such that

$$\frac{f'(c)}{g'(c)} = \frac{f(x) - f(x_0)}{g(x) - g(x_0)}. \tag{6}$$

But $f(x_0) = g(x_0) = 0$, so that

$$\frac{f'(c)}{g'(c)} = \frac{f(x)}{g(x)}. \tag{7}$$

As x approaches x_0, c approaches x_0, because it lies between x and x_0. Therefore,

$$\lim_{x \to x_0^+} \frac{f(x)}{g(x)} = \lim_{c \to x_0^+} \frac{f'(c)}{g'(c)} = \lim_{x \to x_0^+} \frac{f'(x)}{g'(x)}.$$

This establishes l'Hôpital's rule for the case where x approaches x_0 from above. The case where x approaches x_0 from below is proved by applying Cauchy's Mean Value Theorem to the closed interval $[x, x_0]$, $x < x_0$.

We apply l'Hôpital's rule first to compute a limit we already know.

EXAMPLE 2

$$\lim_{x \to 0} \frac{\sin x}{x} \qquad\qquad \left[\frac{0}{0}\right]$$

$$= \lim_{x \to 0} \frac{\cos x}{1} = 1.$$

Notice that $f'(x)/g'(x)$ in l'Hôpital's rule is the derivative of f divided by the derivative of g. It is *not* the derivative of the fraction $f(x)/g(x)$.

It may happen that, in applying l'Hôpital's rule, we find that $f'(x_0) = g'(x_0) = 0$. When this happens, we may apply l'Hôpital's rule again, provided $f'(x)$ and $g'(x)$ are differentiable for $a < x < b$, and $g''(x) \neq 0$ near x_0.

EXAMPLE 3

$$\lim_{x \to 0} \frac{\sqrt{1 + x} - 1 - (x/2)}{x^2} \qquad \left[\frac{0}{0}\right]$$

$$= \lim_{x \to 0} \frac{\frac{1}{2}(1 + x)^{-1/2} - \frac{1}{2}}{2x} \qquad \left[\text{still } \frac{0}{0}\right]$$

$$= \lim_{x \to 0} \frac{-\frac{1}{4}(1 + x)^{-3/2}}{2} = -\frac{1}{8}.$$

In practice, the functions we deal with in this book satisfy the hypotheses of l'Hôpital's rule. We apply the method by proceeding to differentiate the numerator and denominator separately so long as we still get the form $0/0$ at $x = x_0$. As soon as one or the other of these derivatives is different from zero at $x = x_0$, we stop differentiating; *l'Hôpital's rule does not apply when either the numerator or the denominator has a finite nonzero limit.*

EXAMPLE 4

$$\lim_{x \to 0} \frac{1 - \cos x}{x + x^2} \qquad \left[\frac{0}{0}\right]$$

$$= \lim_{x \to 0} \frac{\sin x}{1 + 2x} = 0.$$

If we continue to differentiate in an attempt to apply l'Hôpital's rule once more, we get

$$\lim_{x \to 0} \frac{1 - \cos x}{x + x^2} = \lim_{x \to 0} \frac{\sin x}{1 + 2x} = \lim_{x \to 0} \frac{\cos x}{2} = \frac{1}{2},$$

which is wrong.

It may happen that one of the derivatives is zero at $x = x_0$ and the other is not. Then the limit of the fraction is either zero, as in Example 4, or infinity, as in the next example.

EXAMPLE 5

$$\lim_{x \to 0} \frac{\sin x}{x^2} \qquad \left[\frac{0}{0}\right]$$

$$= \lim_{x \to 0} \frac{\cos x}{2x} = \infty.$$

2. The Indeterminate Forms ∞/∞ and $\infty \cdot 0$

In more advanced textbooks it is proved that if $f(t) \to \infty$ and $g(t) \to \infty$ as $t \to a$, then

$$\lim_{t \to a} \frac{f(t)}{g(t)} = \lim_{t \to a} \frac{f'(t)}{g'(t)},$$

provided the limit on the right exists.* This simply says that l'Hôpital's rule applies to the indeterminate form ∞/∞ as well as to the form $0/0$. The form $\infty \cdot 0$ must be reduced to one or the other of these two. In the notation $t \to a$, a may either be finite or infinite.

EXAMPLE 6. Find the limit

$$\lim_{t \to \infty} \frac{t^2 + t}{2t^2 + 1}.$$

Solution. This assumes the form ∞/∞ as $t \to \infty$.

a) We apply l'Hôpital's rule and have

$$\lim_{t \to \infty} \frac{t^2 + t}{2t^2 + 1} = \lim_{t \to \infty} \frac{2t + 1}{4t} \left[\text{still} = \frac{\infty}{\infty} \right] = \lim_{t \to \infty} \frac{2}{4} = \frac{1}{2}.$$

b) Note that this could also have been evaluated by writing $t = 1/h$ and letting $h \to 0$:

$$\lim_{t \to \infty} \frac{t^2 + t}{2t^2 + 1} = \lim_{h \to 0} \frac{\dfrac{1}{h^2} + \dfrac{1}{h}}{\dfrac{2}{h^2} + 1} = \lim_{h \to 0} \frac{1 + h}{2 + h^2} = \frac{1}{2}.$$

c) Another way is to divide both the numerator and denominator by t^2 (the highest power of t that occurs in either numerator or denominator) and observe that $1/t$ and $1/t^2$ approach zero as t increases without bound:

$$\lim_{t \to \infty} \frac{t^2 + t}{2t^2 + 1} = \lim_{t \to \infty} \frac{1 + \dfrac{1}{t}}{2 + \dfrac{1}{t^2}} = \frac{1 + 0}{2 + 0} = \frac{1}{2}.$$

This is actually the same as the method given above in (b).

3. The Indeterminate Form $\infty - \infty$

The differences $n - n = 0$, $n - n^2 = n(1 - n)$, and $n^2 - n = n(n - 1)$ behave entirely differently as $n \to \infty$. They all become formally $\infty - \infty$ and illustrate why such an expression is called an indeterminate form.

It may be possible, by preliminary algebraic manipulations, to reduce an expression $F(x) - G(x)$ that becomes $\infty - \infty$ as x approaches x_0 to a form

---

*   There is also a proof of l'Hôpital's rule for both forms $0/0$ and ∞/∞ in the article "L'Hôpital's Rule," by A. E. Taylor, *American Mathematical Monthly*, 59, 20–24 (1952).

$f(x)/g(x)$ that becomes $0/0$ or ∞/∞. While l'Hôpital's rule does not apply directly to the original expression $F(x) - G(x)$, it does apply to the algebraically equivalent form $f(x)/g(x)$.

EXAMPLE 7. Find

$$\lim_{x \to 0} \left(\frac{1}{\sin x} - \frac{1}{x} \right).$$

Solution. If $x \to 0^+$, then $\sin x \to 0^+$ and $1/\sin x \to +\infty$, while $1/x \to +\infty$. The expression $(1/\sin x) - (1/x)$ formally becomes $+\infty - (+\infty)$, which is indeterminate. On the other hand, if $x \to 0^-$, then $1/\sin x \to -\infty$ and $1/x \to -\infty$, so that $(1/\sin x) - (1/x)$ becomes $-\infty + \infty$, which is also indeterminate. But we may also write

$$\frac{1}{\sin x} - \frac{1}{x} = \frac{x - \sin x}{x \sin x}$$

and apply l'Hôpital's rule to the expression on the right. Thus,

$$\lim_{x \to 0} \left(\frac{1}{\sin x} - \frac{1}{x} \right) = \lim_{x \to 0} \frac{x - \sin x}{x \sin x} \qquad \left[\frac{0}{0} \right]$$

$$= \lim_{x \to 0} \frac{1 - \cos x}{\sin x + x \cos x} \qquad \left[\text{still } \frac{0}{0} \right]$$

$$= \lim_{x \to 0} \frac{\sin x}{2 \cos x - x \sin x} = 0.$$

PROBLEMS

Find the limits in Problems 1 through 18.

1. $\lim\limits_{x \to 2} \dfrac{x - 2}{x^2 - 4}$

2. $\lim\limits_{t \to \infty} \dfrac{6t + 5}{3t - 8}$

3. $\lim\limits_{x \to \infty} \dfrac{5x^2 - 3x}{7x^2 + 1}$

4. $\lim\limits_{x \to 1} \dfrac{x^3 - 1}{4x^3 - x - 3}$

5. $\lim\limits_{t \to 0} \dfrac{\sin t^2}{t}$

6. $\lim\limits_{x \to \pi/2} \dfrac{2x - \pi}{\cos x}$

7. $\lim\limits_{x \to 0} \dfrac{\sin 5x}{x}$

8. $\lim\limits_{t \to 0} \dfrac{\cos t - 1}{t^2}$

9. $\lim\limits_{\theta \to \pi} \dfrac{\sin \theta}{\pi - \theta}$

10. $\lim\limits_{x \to \pi/2} \dfrac{1 - \sin x}{1 + \cos 2x}$

11. $\lim\limits_{x \to 2} \dfrac{\sqrt{x^2 + 5} - 3}{x^2 - 4}$

12. $\lim\limits_{x \to 0} \dfrac{\sqrt{a(a + x)} - a}{x}, \quad a > 0$

13. $\lim\limits_{t \to 0} \dfrac{10 \sin t - t}{t^3}$

14. $\lim\limits_{x \to 0} \dfrac{x(\cos x - 1)}{\sin x - x}$

15. $\lim\limits_{h \to 0} \dfrac{\sin (a + h) - \sin a}{h}$.

16. $\lim\limits_{r \to 1} \dfrac{a(r^n - 1)}{r - 1}, \quad n$ a positive integer

17. $\lim\limits_{x \to 0+} \left(\dfrac{1}{x} - \dfrac{1}{\sqrt{x}} \right)$

18. $\lim\limits_{x \to \infty} \left(x - \sqrt{x^2 + x} \right)$

19. Which is correct, (a) or (b)? Explain.

a) $\lim\limits_{x \to 3} \dfrac{x - 3}{x^2 - 3} = \lim\limits_{x \to 3} \dfrac{1}{2x} = \dfrac{1}{6}$.

b) $\lim\limits_{x \to 3} \dfrac{x - 3}{x^2 - 3} = \dfrac{0}{6} = 0$.

In Problems 20–22, find all values of c that satisfy Eq. (2), the conclusion of Cauchy's Mean Value Theorem, for the given functions and interval.

20. $f(x) = x, \quad g(x) = x^2, \quad (a, b) = (-2, 0)$

21. $f(x) = x, \quad g(x) = x^2, \quad (a, b)$ arbitrary

22. $f(x) = x^3/3 - 4x, \quad g(x) = x^2, \quad (a, b) = (0, 3)$

3–10

**EXTENSION OF THE
MEAN VALUE THEOREM**

In Article 3–8 we established the existence of a number c, between a and b, such that

$$f(b) - f(a) = f'(c)(b - a), \tag{1}$$

under suitable hypotheses on the function f. If the number c is replaced by a on the right side of Eq. (1), the equality must be changed to an approximation, which turns out to be the approximation we obtain by using the line tangent to the curve at $(a, f(a))$ to approximate the curve $y = f(x)$ at $x = b$. When b is close to a, we expect the approximation to be quite good. The following theorem tells us that if the function has a second derivative, as well as a first, then the difference between the tangent approximation and the function itself is proportional to $(b - a)^2$.

Extended Mean Value Theorem (Special case).   *Let $f(x)$ and its first derivative $f'(x)$ be continuous on the closed interval $a \leq x \leq b$, and suppose its second derivative $f''(x)$ exists in the open interval $a < x < b$. Then there is a number c_2 between a and b such that*

$$f(b) = f(a) + f'(a)(b - a) + \tfrac{1}{2}f''(c_2)(b - a)^2. \tag{2}$$

Proof.   Let K be the number defined by the equation

$$f(b) = f(a) + f'(a)(b - a) + K(b - a)^2. \tag{3}$$

Consider the function $F(x)$ that we get by replacing b by x in Eq. (3) and subtracting the right side from the left:

$$F(x) = f(x) - f(a) - f'(a)(x - a) - K(x - a)^2. \tag{4}$$

Then, by substitution in (4), we find

$$F(a) = 0.$$

Also, from (3), we have

$$F(b) = 0.$$

Moreover, F and its first derivative are continuous on $a \leq x \leq b$, and

$$F'(x) = f'(x) - f'(a) - 2K(x - a). \tag{5}$$

Therefore, F satisfies the hypotheses of Rolle's Theorem, so there is a number c_1 between a and b such that

$$F'(c_1) = 0,$$

and, by substitution in (5), we also have

$$F'(a) = 0.$$

The derived function F' satisfies Rolle's Theorem on the interval $a \leq x \leq c_1$. Hence there is a number c_2 between a and c_1 such that

$$F''(c_2) = 0.$$

We differentiate (5) and get

$$F''(x) = f''(x) - 2K. \qquad (6)$$

If we put $x = c_2$ in (6), set the result equal to zero, and solve for K, we have

$$K = \tfrac{1}{2}f''(c_2).$$

When this is substituted into Eq. (3), we have Eq. (2).   Q.E.D.

By a similar method, it is easy to prove the more general Extended Mean Value Theorem.

Extended Mean Value Theorem (General case).   *Let $f(x)$ and its first $n - 1$ derivatives $f'(x)$, $f''(x)$, ..., $f^{(n-1)}(x)$ be continuous on the closed interval $a \leq x \leq b$, and suppose the nth derivative $f^{(n)}(x)$ exists at least in the open interval $a < x < b$. Then there is a number c_n between a and b such that*

$$f(b) = f(a) + f'(a)(b - a) + \tfrac{1}{2}f''(a)(b - a)^2$$
$$+ \tfrac{1}{6}f'''(a)(b - a)^3 + \cdots$$
$$+ \frac{1}{(n-1)!}f^{(n-1)}(a)(b - a)^{n-1} \qquad (7)$$
$$+ \frac{1}{n!}f^{(n)}(c_n)(b - a)^n.$$

REMARK.   The law of formation of the terms on the right side of Eq. (7) may be discovered by continuing a term at a time from $n = 1$ to $n = 2$ (as we have done), then to $n = 3$, and so on. Equation (7) is the basis of a powerful general method for evaluating a large class of functions that have derivatives of all orders. The proof of the general case of the Mean Value Theorem is left as an exercise. (See Problem 74 at the end of this chapter.)

PROBLEMS

1. Prove the special case $n = 3$ of the Extended Mean Value Theorem, Eq. (7).

2. Prove the case $n = 4$ of the Extended Mean Value Theorem, Eq. (7).

3. Verify the validity of the Extended Mean Value Theorem for each of the following polynomials, for the given values of a and n:

a) $f(x) = 3x^2 + 2x + 4$; $a = 1$, $n = 2$.
b) $f(x) = x^3 + 5x - 7$; $a = 1$, $n = 3$.

4. Using the Extended Mean Value Theorem, prove that a polynomial $f(x)$ of degree n may be written, precisely, in the form:

$$f(x) = f(a) + f'(a)(x - a) + \frac{f''(a)}{2}(x - a)^2 + \cdots$$
$$+ \frac{f^{(n)}(a)}{n!}(x - a)^n.$$

5. Use the Extended Mean Value Theorem for $n = 2$, Eq. (2), to prove the following: Let $f(x)$ be continuous and have continuous first and second derivatives. Suppose that $f'(a) = 0$. Then $f(x)$ has:

a) a relative maximum at a if its second derivative is less than or equal to zero throughout some neighborhood of a,

b) a relative minimum at a if its second derivative is greater than or equal to zero throughout some neighborhood of a.

(A "neighborhood" of a is an open interval centered at a, that is, an interval of the form $a - h < x < a + h$ for some positive h.)

*3–11

**APPLICATIONS OF THE
MEAN VALUE THEOREM
TO CURVE TRACING**

The discussion of the signs of dy/dx and d^2y/dx^2 in Articles 3–1 and 3–3 can be made more rigorous by applying the Mean Value Theorems to prove the following results.

Theorem 1. First derivative test for rise and fall.   *Let $y = f(x)$ be continuous in the closed interval $a \leq x \leq b$ and differentiable in the open interval $a < x < b$. Then,*

if dy/dx is positive for $a < x < b$,   the curve $y = f(x)$ steadily rises,

if dy/dx is negative for $a < x < b$,   the curve $y = f(x)$ steadily falls

as x increases from a to b.

Proof.   (We urge you to make your own sketch to illustrate the following statements.) Let x_1 and x_2 be any two points in the closed interval (a, b) with x_1 to the left of x_2; that is,

$$a \leq x_1 < x_2 \leq b.$$

Then by the Mean Value Theorem, there is a number c between x_1 and x_2 such that

$$f(x_2) - f(x_1) = f'(c) \cdot (x_2 - x_1).$$

Since $x_2 - x_1$ is positive, the sign of the right side of this equation is the same as the sign of the derivative $f'(c)$. Therefore

$$y_2 = f(x_2) \quad \text{is greater than } y_1 = f(x_1) \quad \text{if } f'(c) \text{ is positive,}$$

and

$$y_2 = f(x_2) \quad \text{is less than } y_1 = f(x_1) \quad \text{if } f'(c) \text{ is negative.}$$

In other words, when dy/dx is positive, the point $P_2(x_2, y_2)$ is to the right of and above the point $P_1(x_1, y_1)$ and when dy/dx is negative, the point $P_2(x_2, y_2)$ is to the right of and below the point $P_1(x_1, y_1)$, as the theorem asserts.   Q.E.D.

Second Derivative Test for Maxima and Minima

In Article 3–6 we found that we can sometimes tell a relative maximum from a minimum of a function by the sign of the second derivative at a point where the first derivative is zero. When the second derivative is also zero at the same point, the test fails. But we may use the second derivative, even when it is zero at the point a where $f'(a) = 0$, provided there is some *interval* $a - h < x < a + h$, containing a, where the second derivative does not change its sign. Theorem 2 explains this procedure.

Theorem 2. Second derivative test for maxima and minima.   *Let f be continuous and twice differentiable in some open interval containing a, and suppose*

---

*   This section may be omitted without loss of continuity. The results are not used in later chapters.

that the first derivative is zero at a:

$$f'(a) = 0. \tag{1}$$

Then $f(x)$ has a relative maximum at $x = a$ if its second derivative $f''(x)$ is negative or zero for all x in some interval $a - h < x < a + h$, and has a relative minimum if $f''(x)$ is positive or zero there.

Proof. Let h be a number such that $f''(x)$ exists for $a - h < x < a + h$. Let b be any number between $a - h$ and $a + h$. By the Extended Mean Value Theorem for $n = 2$, we know that there is a number c between a and b such that

$$f(b) - f(a) = f'(a)(b - a) + \tfrac{1}{2}f''(c)(b - a)^2.$$

This reduces to

$$f(b) - f(a) = \tfrac{1}{2}f''(c)(b - a)^2, \tag{2}$$

in view of the hypothesis (1). The right side of Eq. (2) has the same sign as $f''(c)$. If the second derivative is negative or zero throughout $a - h < x < a + h$, then $f(b) - f(a) \leq 0$ and $f(b) \leq f(a)$; hence f has a relative maximum at a. If the second derivative is positive or zero throughout $a - h < x < a + h$, then $f(b) \geq f(a)$ and f has a relative minimum at a.   Q.E.D.

EXAMPLE 1. The function

$$f(x) = x^4 - 4x^3 + 6x^2 - 4x + 4$$

is differentiable any number of times for all values of x. Its first two derivatives are

$$f'(x) = 4x^3 - 12x^2 + 12x - 4 = 4(x - 1)^3,$$

$$f''(x) = 12x^2 - 24x + 12 = 12(x - 1)^2.$$

The first derivative is zero at $x = 1$. So is the second derivative. But the second derivative is positive everywhere else, so the function has a minimum at $x = 1$.

Curves Concave Upward or Downward

By using the Extended Mean Value Theorem for $n = 2$, we can now give an analytic proof of the results in Article 3-3 on the direction of concavity of a curve.

Theorem 3. Second derivative test for concavity.   *Let $y = f(x)$ be continuous together with its first derivative $y' = f'(x)$ in the closed interval $a \leq x \leq b$. Let the second derivative $y'' = f''(x)$ exist at least over the open interval $a < x < b$. Then the curve $y = f(x)$ is*

concave upward if $f''(x)$ is positive,

and

concave downward if $f''(x)$ is negative,

for $a < x < b$.

REMARK.   To prove Theorem 3 we need a more precise formulation of what the phrases "concave upward" and "concave downward" mean. A portion of

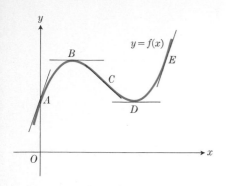

3–35 The second derivative $f''(x)$ is negative between A and C, zero at C, and positive between C and E.

a)

b)

3–36 The portion of the curve $y = f(x)$ shown here is concave upward. Each chord lies above its arc.

a curve is *concave upward* if the chord PQ lies above the arc PQ for all pairs of points P and Q on it, as it would in the region CDE in Fig. 3–35. Similarly, it is *concave downward* when each chord lies below its arc, as it would in the region ABC in the figure.

Proof of Theorem 3. In Fig. 3–36(a), $P_1(x_1, y_1)$ and $P_2(x_2, y_2)$ represent two points on the curve $y = f(x)$ with $a \le x_1 < x_2 \le b$. The point P_L is on the chord $P_1 P_2$. Its abscissa x lies between x_1 and x_2. By similar triangles, we have

$$\frac{y_L - y_1}{h_1} = \frac{y_2 - y_L}{h_2} \quad \text{or} \quad y_L = \frac{h_1 y_2 + h_2 y_1}{h_1 + h_2}.$$

Suppose now that $P(x, y)$ is the point of abscissa x on the curve $y = f(x)$. Then we know that:

$$P \text{ lies above the chord} \quad \text{if } y > y_L,$$
$$P \text{ lies on the chord} \quad \text{if } y = y_L,$$
$$P \text{ lies below the chord} \quad \text{if } y < y_L.$$

To be specific, let us consider the case where the second derivative $f''(x)$ is positive for $a < x < b$. By the Extended Mean Value Theorem with $n = 2$, we have:

$$f(x_1) - f(x) = f'(x)(x_1 - x) + \tfrac{1}{2}f''(c)(x_1 - x)^2, \tag{3a}$$
$$f(x_2) - f(x) = f'(x)(x_2 - x) + \tfrac{1}{2}f''(e)(x_2 - x)^2 \tag{3b}$$

for some numbers c, between x_1 and x, and e, between x and x_2 (Fig. 3–36b). We multiply (3a) by $x_2 - x = h_2$ and (3b) by $x - x_1 = h_1$ and add, thereby eliminating the terms in $f'(x)$. We obtain

$$h_2[f(x_1) - f(x)] + h_1[f(x_2) - f(x)] = \tfrac{1}{2}[h_2\, f''(c)h_1^2 + h_1\, f''(e)h_2^2]. \tag{4}$$

If f'' is positive throughout the interval (a, b), all terms on the right side of (4) are positive and we have

$$h_2\, f(x_1) + h_1\, f(x_2) - (h_1 + h_2)f(x) > 0$$

or

$$\frac{h_2\, f(x_1) + h_1\, f(x_2)}{h_1 + h_2} > f(x) \tag{5}$$

or

$$\frac{h_1 y_2 + h_2 y_1}{h_1 + h_2} > y.$$

The expression on the left side of this inequality is the ordinate y_L of the point P_L on the chord $P_1 P_2$. Since y is less than y_L, the point $P(x, y)$ is below the chord. Since this is true for any position of the points P_1 and P_2, provided only that $a \le x_1 < x_2 \le b$, and for any intermediate point P of abscissa x between x_1 and x_2, it follows that the curve is concave upward in this case, that is, when the second derivative is positive for $a < x < b$.

In case the second derivative is negative over $a < x < b$, the inequalities above are reversed, and we find that

$$y_L < y \qquad \text{when} \quad f''(x) \text{ is negative.}$$

That is, the curve-point $P(x, y)$ is above the chord-point $P_L(x, y_L)$. This means that the curve is concave downward when the second derivative is negative.   Q.E.D.

REVIEW QUESTIONS AND EXERCISES

1. Discuss the significance of the signs of the first and second derivatives. Sketch a small portion of a curve, illustrating how it looks near a point where:

a) both y' and y'' are positive;

b) $y' > 0$, $y'' < 0$;   **c)** $y' < 0$, $y'' > 0$;

d) $y' < 0$, $y'' < 0$.

2. Define *point of inflection*. How do you find points of inflection from an equation of a curve?

3. How do you locate local maximum and minimum points of a curve? Discuss exceptional points, such as endpoints and points where the derivative fails to exist, in addition to the nonexceptional type. Illustrate with graphs.

4. Let n be a positive integer. For which values of n does the curve $y = x^n$ have (a) a local minimum at the origin, (b) a point of inflection at the origin?

5. Outline a general method for solving "related rates" problems.

6. Outline a general method for solving "max-min" problems.

7. What are the hypotheses of Rolle's theorem? What is the conclusion?

8. Is the converse of Rolle's theorem true?

9. With the book closed, state and prove the Mean Value Theorem. What is its geometrical interpretation?

10. We know that if $F(x) = x^2$, then $F'(x) = 2x$. If someone knows a function G such that $G'(x) = 2x$ but $G(x) \neq x^2$, what can be said about the difference $G(2) - G(1)$? Explain.

11. Describe a method of finding

$$\lim_{x \to a} f(x)/g(x) \text{ if } f(a) = g(a) = 0.$$

Illustrate with an example.

12. Read the article "Mathematics in warfare" by F. W. Lanchester, *World of Mathematics*, **4**, pp. 2138–2157, as a discussion of a practical problem in "related rates."

MISCELLANEOUS PROBLEMS

In each of the following problems (1 through 14) find y' and y''. Determine in each case the sets of values of x for which:

a) y is increasing (as x increases),

b) y is decreasing (as x increases),

c) the graph is concave upward,

d) the graph is concave downward.

Also sketch the graph in each case, indicating *high* and *low* turning points and points of inflection.

1. $y = 9x - x^2$

2. $y = x^3 - 5x^2 + 3x$

3. $y = 4x^3 - x^4$

4. $y = 4x + x^{-1}$

5. $y = x^2 + 4x^{-1}$

6. $y = x + 4x^{-2}$

7. $y = 5 - x^{2/3}$

8. $y = \dfrac{x - 1}{x + 1}$

9. $y = x - \dfrac{4}{x}$

10. $y = x^4 - 2x^2$

11. $y = \dfrac{x^2}{ax + b}$; $a > 0$, $b > 0$

12. $y = 2x^3 - 9x^2 + 12x$

13. $y = (x - 1)(x + 1)^2$

14. $y = x^2 - \frac{1}{6}x^3$

15. The slope of a curve at any point (x, y) is given by the equation

$$\frac{dy}{dx} = 6(x - 1)(x - 2)^2(x - 3)^3(x - 4)^4.$$

a) For what value (or values) of x is y a maximum? Why?

b) For what value (or values) of x is y a minimum? Why?

16. A particle moves along the x-axis with velocity $v = dx/dt = f(x)$. Show that its acceleration is $f(x)f'(x)$.

17. A meteorite entering the earth's atmosphere has velocity inversely proportional to $\sqrt{s}$ when at distance s from the center of the earth. Show that its acceleration is inversely proportional to s^2.

18. If the velocity of a falling body is $k\sqrt{s}$ at the instant when the body has fallen a distance s, find its acceleration.

19. The volume of a cube is increasing at a rate of 300 in^3/min at the instant when the edge is 20 in. Find the rate at which the edge is changing.

20. Sand falling at the rate of 3 ft^3/min forms a conical pile whose radius always equals twice the height. Find the rate at which the height is changing at the instant when the height is 10 ft.

21. The volume of a sphere is decreasing at the rate of 12π ft^3/min. Find the rates at which the radius and the surface area are changing at the instant when the radius is 20 ft. Also find approximately how much the radius and surface area may be expected to change in the following 6 sec.

22. At a certain instant airplane A is flying a level course at 500 mi/hr. At the same time, airplane B is straight above airplane A and flying at the rate of 700 mi/hr on a course that intercepts A's course at a point C that is 4 mi from B and 2 mi from A. (a) At the instant in question, how fast is the distance between the airplanes decreasing? (b) What is the minimum distance between the airplanes, if they continue on the present courses at constant speed?

23. A point moves along the curve $y^2 = x^3$ in such a way that its distance from the origin increases at the constant rate of 2 units per second. Find dx/dt at $(2, 2\sqrt{2})$.

24. Refer to the triangle in Fig. 3–7. How fast is its area changing when $x = 17\sqrt{2}$?

25. Suppose the cone in Fig. 3–8 has a small opening at the vertex through which the water escapes at the rate of $0.08\sqrt{y}$ ft^3/min when its depth is y. Water is also running into the cone at a constant rate of c ft^3/min. When the depth is $6\frac{1}{4}$ ft, the depth of the water is observed to be increasing at the rate of 0.02 ft/min. Under these conditions, will the tank fill? Give a reason for your answer.

26. A particle projected vertically upward from the surface of the earth with initial velocity v_0 has velocity $\sqrt{v_0^2 - 2gR[1 - (R/s)]}$ when it reaches a distance $s \geq R$ from the *center* of the earth. Here R is the radius of the earth. Show that the acceleration is inversely proportional to s^2.

27. Given a triangle ABC. Let D and E be points on the sides AB and AC, respectively, such that DE is parallel to BC. Let the distance between BC and DE equal x. Show that the derivative, with respect to x, of the area $BCED$ is equal to the length of DE.

28. Points A and B move along the x- and y-axes, respectively, in such a way that the perpendicular distance r (inches) from the origin to AB remains constant. How fast is OA changing, and is it increasing or decreasing, when $OB = 2r$ and B is moving toward O at the rate of $0.3r$ in/sec?

29. Ships A and B start from O at the same time. Ship A travels due east at a rate of 15 mi/hr. Ship B travels in a straight course making an angle of 60° with the path of ship A at a rate of 20 mi/hr. How fast are they separating at the end of 2 hr?

30. Water is being poured into an inverted conical tank (vertex down) at the rate of 2 ft^3/min. How fast is the water

level rising when the depth of the water is 5 ft? The radius of the base of the cone is 3 ft and the altitude is 10 ft.

31. Divide 20 into two parts (not necessarily integers) such that the product of one part with the square of the other shall be a maximum.

32. Find the largest value of $f(x) = 4x^3 - 8x^2 + 5x$ for $0 \leq x \leq 2$. Give reasons for your answer.

33. Find two *positive* numbers whose sum is 36 and whose product is as large as possible. Can the problem be solved if the product is to be as small as possible?

34. Determine the coefficients a, b, c, d so that the curve whose equation is $y = ax^3 + bx^2 + cx + d$ has a maximum at $(-1, 10)$ and an inflection point at $(1, -6)$.

35. Find that number which most exceeds its square.

36. The perimeter p and area A of a circular sector ("piece of pie") of radius r and arc length s are given by $p = 2r + s$; $A = \frac{1}{2}rs$. If the perimeter is 100 ft, what value of r will produce a maximum area?

37. If a ball is thrown vertically upward with a velocity of 32 ft/sec, its height after t sec is given by the equation $s = 32t - 16t^2$. At what instant will the ball be at its highest point, and how high will it rise?

38. A right circular cone has altitude 12 ft and radius of base 6 ft. A cone is inscribed with its vertex at the center of the base of the given cone and its base parallel to the base of the given cone. Find the dimensions of the cone of maximum volume that can be so inscribed.

39. An oil can is to be made in the form of a right circular cylinder to contain 16π in^3. What dimensions of the can will require the least amount of material?

40. An isosceles triangle is drawn with its vertex at the origin, its base parallel to and above the x-axis and the vertices of its base on the curve $12y = 36 - x^2$. Determine the area of the largest such triangle.

41. A tire manufacturer is able to make x (hundred) grade A tires and y (hundred) grade B tires per day, where $y = (40 - 10x)/(5 - x)$, with $0 \leq x \leq 4$. If the profit on each grade A tire is twice the profit on a grade B tire, what is the most profitable number of grade A tires per day to make?

42. Find the points on the curve $x^2 - y^2 = 1$ that are nearest the point $P(a, 0)$ in case (a) $a = 4$, (b) $a = 2$, (c) $a = \sqrt{2}$.

43. A motorist, stranded in a desert 5 mi from a point A, which is the nearest point on a long straight road, wishes to get to a point B on the road. If the car can travel at 15 mi/hr on the desert and 39 mi/hr on the road, find the point where it must meet the road to get to B in the shortest possible time if (a) B is 5 mi from A, (b) B is 10 mi from A, (c) B is 1 mi from A.

44. Points A and B are ends of a diameter of a circle and C is a point on the circumference. Which of the following statements about triangle ABC is (or are) true?

a) The area is a maximum when the triangle is isosceles.

b) The area is a minimum when the triangle is isosceles.

c) The perimeter is a maximum when the triangle is isosceles.

d) The perimeter is a minimum when the triangle is isosceles.

45. The base and the perimeter of a triangle are fixed. Determine the remaining two sides if the area is to be a maximum.

46. The base b and the area k of a triangle are fixed. Determine the base angles if the angle at the vertex opposite b is to be a maximum.

47. A line is drawn through a fixed point (a, b) to meet the axes Ox, Oy in P and Q. Show that the minimum values of PQ, $OP + OQ$, and $OP \cdot OQ$ are, respectively,

$$(a^{2/3} + b^{2/3})^{3/2}, \qquad (\sqrt{a} + \sqrt{b})^2, \qquad \text{and} \qquad 4ab.$$

48. Find the smallest value of the constant m if $mx - 1 + (1/x)$ is to be greater than or equal to zero for all positive values of x.

49. Let s be the distance between the fixed point $P_1(x_1, y_1)$ and a point $P(x, y)$ on the line

$$L: \quad ax + by + c = 0.$$

Using calculus methods, (a) show that s^2 is a minimum when $P_1 P$ is perpendicular to L, and (b) show that the minimum distance is

$$|ax_1 + by_1 + c|/\sqrt{a^2 + b^2}.$$

50. A playing field is to be built in the shape of a rectangle plus a semicircular area at each end. A 400-m race track is to form the perimeter of the field. Find the dimensions of the field if the rectangular part is to have as large an area as possible.

51. If $ax + (b/x) \geq c$ for all positive values of x, where a, b, and c are positive constants, show that $ab \geq c^2/4$.

52. Prove that if $ax^2 + (b/x) \geq c$ for all positive values of x, where a, b, and c are positive constants, then $27ab^2 \geq 4c^3$.

53. Given $f(x) = ax^2 + 2bx + c$ with $a > 0$. By considering the minimum, prove that $f(x) \geq 0$ for all real x if, and only if, $b^2 - ac \leq 0$.

54. In Problem 53, take

$$f(x) = (a_1 x + b_1)^2 + (a_2 x + b_2)^2 + \cdots + (a_n x + b_n)^2,$$

and deduce Schwarz's inequality:

$$(a_1 b_1 + a_2 b_2 + \cdots + a_n b_n)^2$$
$$\leq (a_1^2 + a_2^2 + \cdots + a_n^2)(b_1^2 + b_2^2 + \cdots + b_n^2).$$

55. In Problem 54, prove that equality can hold only in case there is a real number x such that $b_i = -a_i x$ for every $i = 1, 2, \ldots, n$.

56. If x is positive and m is greater than one, prove that $x^m - 1 - m(x - 1)$ is not negative.

57. What are the dimensions of the rectangular plot of greatest area which can be laid out within a triangle of base 36 ft and altitude 12 ft? Assume that one side of the rectangle lies on the base of the triangle.

58. Find the width across the top of an isosceles trapezoid of base 12 in. and slant sides 6 in. if its area is a maximum.

59. A fence h m high runs parallel to and w m from a vertical wall. Find the length of the shortest ladder that will reach from the ground across the top of the fence to the wall.

60. Assuming that the cost per hour of running the *Queen Elizabeth II* is $a + bv^n$, where a, b, and n are positive constants, $n > 1$, and v is the velocity through the water, find the speed for making the run from Liverpool to New York at minimum cost.

61. A flower bed is to be in the shape of a circular sector of radius r and central angle θ (i.e., like a piece of pie). Find r and θ if the area is fixed and the perimeter is a minimum.

62. A reservoir is to be built in the form of a right circular cone and the lateral area waterproofed. If the capacity of the reservoir is to be 72π ft^3 and one gallon of waterproofing material will cover 80 ft^2, how many gallons are required?

63. Given two concentric circles, C_1 of radius r_1 and C_2 of radius r_2, $r_2 > r_1 > 0$. Let A be the area between them.

a) How fast is A increasing (or decreasing) when $r_1 = 4$ cm and is increasing at the rate of 0.02 cm/sec while $r_2 = 6$ cm and is increasing at the rate of 0.01 cm/sec?

b) Suppose that at time $t = 0$, r_1 is 3 cm and r_2 is 5 cm, and that for $t > 0$, r_1 increases at the constant rate of a cm/sec and r_2 increases at the constant rate of b cm/sec. If $(\frac{3}{5})a < b < a$, find when the area A will be a maximum.

64. Given two concentric spheres, S_1 of radius r_1 and S_2 of radius r_2, $r_2 > r_1 > 0$. Let V be the volume between them. Suppose that at time $t = 0$, $r_1 = r$ in. and $r_2 = R$ in., and that for $t > 0$, r_1 increases at the constant rate of a in/sec and r_2 increases at the constant rate of b in/sec. If $a > b > ar^2/R^2$, find when V will be a maximum.

65. The motion of a particle in a straight line is given by $s = \lambda t - (1 + \lambda^4)t^2$. Show that the particle moves forward initially when λ is positive but ultimately retreats. Show also that for different values of λ the maximum possible distance that the particle can move forward is $\frac{1}{8}$.

66. Let $h(x) = f(x)g(x)$ be the product of two functions that have first and second derivatives and are positive; that is, $f(x) > 0$, $g(x) > 0$.

a) Is it true, if f and g both have a relative maximum at $x = a$, that h has a relative maximum at $x = a$?

b) Is it true, if f and g both have a point of inflection at $x = a$, that h has a point of inflection at $x = a$?

For both (a) and (b) either give a proof or construct a numerical example showing that the statement is false.

67. The numbers $c_1, c_2, \ldots, c_n$ are recorded in an experiment. It is desired to determine a number x with the property that

$$(c_1 - x)^2 + (c_2 - x)^2 + (c_3 - x)^2 + \cdots + (c_n - x)^2$$

shall be a minimum. Find x.

68. The four points

$$(-2, -\tfrac{1}{2}), \quad (0, 1), \quad (1, 2), \quad \text{and} \quad (3, 3)$$

are observed to lie more or less close to a straight line of equation $y = mx + 1$. Find m if the sum

$$(y_1 - mx_1 - 1)^2 + (y_2 - mx_2 - 1)^2$$
$$+ (y_3 - mx_3 - 1)^2 + (y_4 - mx_4 - 1)^2$$

is to be a minimum, where $(x_1, y_1), \ldots, (x_4, y_4)$ are the coordinates of the given points.

69. The *geometric mean* of the n positive numbers $a_1, a_2, \ldots, a_n$ is the nth root of $a_1 a_2 \cdots a_n$ and the arithmetic mean is $(a_1 + a_2 + \cdots + a_n)/n$. Show that if $a_1, a_2, \ldots, a_{n-1}$ are fixed and $a_n = x$ is permitted to vary over the set of positive real numbers, the ratio of the arithmetic mean to the geometric mean is a minimum when x is the arithmetic mean of $a_1, a_2, \ldots, a_{n-1}$.

70. The curve $(y + 1)^3 = x^2$ passes through the points $(1, 0)$ and $(-1, 0)$. Does Rolle's Theorem justify the conclusion that dy/dx vanishes for some value of x in the interval $-1 \le x \le 1$? Give reasons for your answer.

71. If $a < 0 < b$ and $f(x) = x^{-1/3}$, show that there is no c that satisfies Eq. (4), Article 3–8. Illustrate with a sketch of the graph.

72. If $a < 0 < b$ and $f(x) = x^{1/3}$, show that there is a value of c that satisfies Eq. (4), Article 3–8, even though the function fails to have a derivative at $x = 0$. Illustrate with a sketch of the graph.

73. Show that the equation $f(x) = 2x^3 - 3x^2 + 6x + 6 = 0$ has exactly one real root and find its value accurate to two significant figures. [*Hint.* $f(-1) = -5$, $f(0) = +6$, and $f'(x) > 0$ for all real x.]

74. *Extended Mean Value Theorem.* Suppose $f(x)$ and its derivatives $f'(x), f''(x), \ldots, f^{(n-1)}(x)$ of order one through $(n - 1)$ are continuous on $a \le x \le b$, and $f^{(n)}(x)$ exists for $a < x < b$. If

$$F(x) = f(x) - f(a) - (x - a)f'(a) - (x - a)^2 f''(a)/2! - \cdots$$
$$- \frac{(x - a)^{n-1} f^{(n-1)}(a)}{(n - 1)!} - K(x - a)^n,$$

where K is chosen so that $F(b) = 0$, show that:

a) $F(a) = F(b) = 0$,
b) $F'(a) = F''(a) = \cdots = F^{(n-1)}(a) = 0$,
c) there exist numbers $c_1, c_2, c_3, \ldots, c_n$ such that

$$a < c_n < c_{n-1} < \cdots < c_2 < c_1 < b$$

and such that

$$F'(c_1) = 0 = F''(c_2) = F'''(c_3) = \cdots$$
$$= F^{(n-1)}(c_{n-1}) = F^{(n)}(c_n).$$

d) Hence, deduce that $K = [f^{(n)}(c_n)]/n!$ for c_n as above in (c); or, in other words, since $F(b) = 0$,

$$f(b) = f(a) + f'(a)(b - a) + \frac{f''(a)}{2!}(b - a)^2 + \cdots$$
$$+ \frac{f^{(n-1)}(a)}{(n - 1)!}(b - a)^{n-1} + \frac{f^{(n)}(c_n)}{n!}(b - a)^n$$

for some c_n, $a < c_n < b$. [*Amer. Math. Monthly,* **60** (1953), p. 415, James Wolfe.]

75. Suppose that it costs a company $y = a + bx$ dollars to produce x units per week. It can sell x units per week at a price of $P = c - ex$ dollars per unit. (a) What production level maximizes the profit? (b) What is the corresponding price? (c) What is the weekly profit at this level of production? (d) At what price should each item be sold to maximize profits if the government imposes a tax of t dollars per item sold? Comment on the difference between this price and the price before tax.

76. Evaluate the following limits.

a) $\displaystyle\lim_{x \to 0} \frac{2 \sin 5x}{3x}$

b) $\displaystyle\lim_{x \to 0} \sin 5x \cot 3x$

c) $\displaystyle\lim_{x \to 0} x \csc^2 \sqrt{2x}$

d) $\displaystyle\lim_{x \to \pi/2} (\sec x - \tan x)$

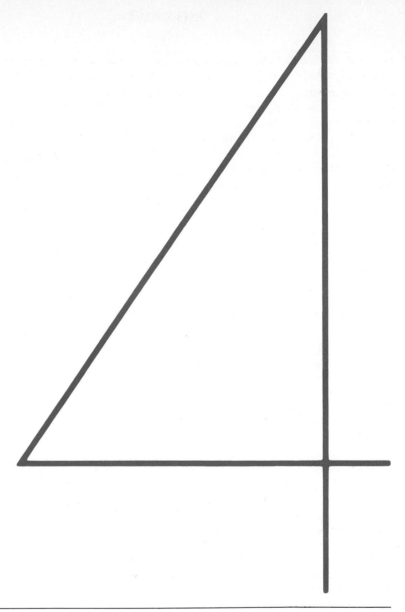

4

INTEGRATION

4-1
INTRODUCTION

In the preceding chapters we have pursued one of the two main branches of the calculus, namely, *differential calculus*. We shall now turn our attention to the other main branch of the subject, *integral calculus*. Today, "to integrate" has two meanings in calculus. The deeper and more fundamental meaning is nearly the same as the nontechnical definition: "to indicate the whole of; to give the sum or total of" (Webster). The mathematical meaning of the word in this sense will be amply illustrated in finding areas bounded by curves, volumes of various solids, lengths of curves, centers of gravity, and other applications.

The second mathematical meaning of the verb "to integrate" is "to find a function whose derivative is given." This is the aspect of integration that we shall discuss in the next two articles.

The two kinds of integration are called respectively *definite* and *indefinite*, and the connection between the two is given by a theorem called the *fundamental theorem* of integral calculus.

4-2
THE INDEFINITE INTEGRAL

Suppose that we are given a derivative dy/dx as a function

$$\frac{dy}{dx} = f(x), \qquad a < x < b, \tag{1}$$

and are asked to find $y = F(x)$.

For example, we might be asked to find y as a function of x if

$$\frac{dy}{dx} = 2x.$$

From our experience with derivatives, we can find one answer, namely,

$$y = x^2.$$

On the other hand, we realize that this is not the only answer, since

$$y = x^2 + 1, \qquad y = x^2 - \sqrt{2}, \qquad y = x^2 + 5\pi$$

are also valid answers. Indeed,

$$y = x^2 + C$$

is an answer if C is any constant.

Definition 1. *An equation such as* (1), *which specifies the derivative as a function of x (or as a function of x and y), is called a **differential equation.***

For example,

$$\frac{dy}{dx} = 2xy^2$$

is a differential equation. Second, third, and higher order derivatives may also occur in differential equations, such as

$$\frac{d^2y}{dx^2} + 6xy\frac{dy}{dx} + 3x^2y^3 = 0,$$

and so on. For the time being we shall restrict attention to the special type of differential equation considered in Eq. (1). Differential equations of more general types will be considered in Chapter 18.

Definition 2. *A function* $y = F(x)$ *is called a* **solution** *of the differential equation* (1) *if, over the domain* $a < x < b$, $F(x)$ *is differentiable and*

$$\frac{dF(x)}{dx} = f(x). \tag{2}$$

We also say, in these circumstances, that $F(x)$ *is* **an integral** *of* $f(x)$ *with respect to* x.

It is clear from this definition that if $F(x)$ is an integral of $f(x)$ with respect to x, then $F(x) + C$ is also such an integral when C is any constant whatever. For if $F(x)$ satisfies Eq. (2), then

$$\frac{d}{dx}[F(x) + C] = \frac{dF(x)}{dx} + \frac{dC}{dx}$$

$$= f(x) + 0 = f(x).$$

What is not clear, however, is whether there are other integrals of $f(x)$ besides those given by the formula $F(x) + C$.

We know that $y = x^2 + C$ is a solution of the differential equation $dy/dx = 2x$ for any constant C. But are there any other solutions? This question is answered by the second corollary of the Mean Value Theorem, Article 3–8. For if both $F_1(x)$ and $F_2(x)$ are integrals of $f(x)$, then

$$\frac{dF_1(x)}{dx} = \frac{dF_2(x)}{dx} = f(x),$$

so that

$$\frac{d[F_1(x) - F_2(x)]}{dx} = 0,$$

and hence

$$F_1(x) - F_2(x) = C,$$

where C is a constant. Hence, if we take $F_2(x) = F(x)$, we have $F_1(x) = F(x) + C$.

Therefore, if

$$y = F(x)$$

is any solution whatever of Eq. (1), then *all* solutions are contained in the formula

$$y = F(x) + C,$$

where C is an arbitrary constant. This is indicated by writing

$$\int f(x)\, dx = F(x) + C, \tag{3}$$

where the symbol $\int$ is called an "integral sign" and Eq. (3) is read "The integral of $f(x)\, dx$ is $F(x)$ plus C." This is a standard notation. We may interpret it in either of two ways:

1. We may think of the symbol

$$\int \ldots dx \tag{4}$$

as meaning "integral, with respect to x, of ...." The symbol (4) is then interpreted as the inverse of the symbol

$$\frac{d}{dx}\ldots,$$

which means "derivative, with respect to x, of ...." In this interpretation the integral sign and the dx go together; the integral sign specifies the operation of integration, and the dx tells us that the *variable of integration* is x.

2. Or we may think of Eq. (2) as written in *differential* form:

$$dF(x) = f(x)\, dx, \tag{5}$$

before the operation indicated by the integral sign is performed. Then, when we introduce the integral sign in Eq. (5) (that is, when we "integrate" both sides of the equation), we get

$$\int dF(x) = \int f(x)\, dx.$$

If we compare this with Eq. (3), we have

$$\int dF(x) = F(x) + C. \tag{6}$$

In other words, when we integrate the *differential* of a function we get that function plus an arbitrary constant. In this interpretation, the symbol $\int$ for integration without the dx stands for the operation that is the inverse of the operation denoted by the symbol d for differentiation. This is the interpretation which we shall adopt in this book. We will refer to the differential $f(x)\, dx$ in Eq. (3) as the *integrand* of the integral.

EXAMPLE 1. Solve the differential equation

$$\frac{dy}{dx} = 3x^2.$$

Solution. We write the given equation in the differential form

$$dy = 3x^2\, dx.$$

Now we know, from past experience, that

$$d(x^3) = 3x^2\, dx.$$

Hence we have

$$y = \int 3x^2 \, dx = \int d(x^3) = x^3 + C.$$

If both x and y occur in the differential equation, but in such a way that we can separate the variables to combine all y terms with dy and all x terms with dx, we then integrate as in the following example.

EXAMPLE 2. Solve the differential equation

$$\frac{dy}{dx} = x^2 \sqrt{y}, \qquad y > 0. \tag{7}$$

Solution. We change to differentials:

$$dy = x^2 \sqrt{y} \, dx.$$

We divide both sides of the equation by $\sqrt{y}$ to separate the variables and obtain

$$y^{-(1/2)} \, dy = x^2 \, dx.$$

The left side of this equation is

$$d(2y^{1/2}) = y^{-(1/2)} \, dy,$$

while the right side is

$$d\left(\frac{x^3}{3}\right) = x^2 \, dx.$$

Therefore

$$d(2y^{1/2}) = d\left(\frac{x^3}{3}\right).$$

When we integrate this equation, we may write

$$2y^{1/2} + C_1 = \frac{x^3}{3} + C_2$$

or

$$2y^{1/2} = \frac{x^3}{3} + C,$$

where we have combined the two constants C_1 and C_2 into a single constant

$$C = C_2 - C_1.$$

Arbitrary Constants

The equation

$$2y^{1/2} + C_1 = \frac{x^3}{3} + C_2$$

or

$$2y^{1/2} = \frac{x^3}{3} + (C_2 - C_1)$$

in Example 2 describes the family of solutions of Eq. (7). There is one solution for each value of $(C_2 - C_1)$. The equation

$$2y^{1/2} = \frac{x^3}{3} + C$$

describes the very same family of functions, one for each value of C. Clearly there is no need to describe the family with two constants when one will do, nor is any greater generality achieved by doing so.

When we integrate the two sides of a differential equation, it always suffices to add the arbitrary constant C to just one side of the equation since, in any case, if we add constants to both sides of the equation they may always be combined into a single constant.

Integration, as described above, requires the ability to guess the answer. But the following formulas help to reduce the amount of guesswork in many cases. In these formulas, u and v denote differentiable functions of some independent variable (say of x), and a, n, and C are constants.

a) $$\int du = u + C,$$

b) $$\int a \, du = a \int du,$$

c) $$\int (du + dv) = \int du + \int dv,$$

d) $$\int u^n \, du = \frac{u^{n+1}}{n+1} + C, \quad (n \neq -1).$$

In words, these formulas say that:

a) The integral of the differential of a function u is u plus an arbitrary constant C.

b) A constant may be moved across the integral sign. [*Caution.* Variables must *not* be moved across the integral sign.]

c) The integral of the sum of two differentials is the sum of their integrals. This may be extended to the sum of any *finite* number of differentials:

$$\int (du_1 + du_2 + \cdots + du_n) = \int du_1 + \int du_2 + \cdots + \int du_n.$$

d) If n is not minus one, the integral of $u^n \, du$ is obtained by adding one to the exponent, dividing by the new exponent, and adding an arbitrary constant.

EXAMPLE 3

$$\int (5x - x^2 + 2) \, dx = \frac{5}{2} x^2 - \frac{x^3}{3} + 2x + C.$$

$$\int x^{1/2} \, dx = \frac{x^{3/2}}{3/2} + C = \frac{2}{3} x^{3/2} + C.$$

CAUTION.   One *must* have precisely du and u^n in order to apply formula (d).

EXAMPLE 4

$$\int \sqrt{2x + 1} \, dx$$

The integral does not fit the formula

$$\int u^n \, du$$

with

$$u = 2x + 1, \qquad n = \tfrac{1}{2},$$

because then

$$du = \frac{du}{dx} \cdot dx = 2 \, dx$$

is *not* precisely dx. The constant factor 2 is missing from the integral. However, this factor can be introduced after the integral sign provided we compensate for it by a factor of $\frac{1}{2}$ in front of the integral sign, by (b). Thus we write

$$\int \sqrt{2x + 1} \, dx = \tfrac{1}{2} \int \sqrt{2x + 1} \cdot 2 \, dx$$

$$= \tfrac{1}{2} \int u^{1/2} \, du \qquad [u = 2x + 1, \quad du = 2 \, dx]$$

$$= \frac{1}{2} \frac{u^{3/2}}{3/2} + C$$

$$= \tfrac{1}{3}(2x + 1)^{3/2} + C.$$

PROBLEMS

Solve the following differential equations. Remember to separate the variables when necessary.

1. $\dfrac{dy}{dx} = x^2 + 1$

2. $\dfrac{dy}{dx} = \dfrac{1}{x^2} + x, \quad x > 0$

3. $\dfrac{dy}{dx} = \dfrac{x}{y}, \quad y > 0$

4. $\dfrac{dy}{dx} = \sqrt{xy}, \quad x > 0, \quad y > 0$

5. $\dfrac{dy}{dx} = \sqrt[3]{y/x}, \quad x > 0, \quad y > 0$

6. $\dfrac{dy}{dx} = 2xy^2, \quad y > 0$

7. $\dfrac{dy}{dx} = 3x^2 - 2x + 5$

8. $\dfrac{ds}{dt} = 3t^2 + 4t - 6$

9. $\dfrac{dr}{dz} = (2z + 1)^3$

10. $\dfrac{du}{dv} = 2u^2(4v^3 + 4v^{-3}), \quad v > 0, \quad u > 0$

11. $\dfrac{dx}{dt} = 8\sqrt{x}, \quad x > 0$

12. $\dfrac{dy}{dt} = (2t + t^{-1})^2, \quad t > 0$

13. $\dfrac{dy}{dz} = \sqrt{(z^2 - z^{-2})^2 + 4}, \quad z > 0$

Evaluate the following integrals:

14. $\displaystyle\int (2x + 3) \, dx$

15. $\displaystyle\int (x^2 - \sqrt{x}) \, dx$

16. $\displaystyle\int (3x - 1)^{234} \, dx$

17. $\displaystyle\int (2 - 7t)^{2/3} \, dt$

18. $\displaystyle\int \sqrt{2 + 5y} \, dy$

19. $\displaystyle\int \dfrac{dx}{(3x + 2)^2}$

20. $\displaystyle\int \dfrac{3r \, dr}{\sqrt{1 - r^2}}$

21. $\displaystyle\int \sqrt{2x^2 + 1} \, x \, dx$

22. $\displaystyle\int t^2(1 + 2t^3)^{-(2/3)} \, dt$

23. $\displaystyle\int \dfrac{y \, dy}{\sqrt{2y^2 + 1}}$

24. $\displaystyle\int \left(\sqrt{x} + \dfrac{1}{\sqrt{x}}\right) dx$

25. $\displaystyle\int \dfrac{(z + 1) \, dz}{\sqrt[3]{z^2 + 2z + 2}}$

4-3

APPLICATIONS OF INDEFINITE INTEGRATION

Differential equations, such as Eq. (1) or (7) of Article 4–2, arise in chemistry, physics, mathematics, and all branches of engineering. Some of these applications will be illustrated in the examples that follow. Before proceeding with these, however, let us consider the meaning of the arbitrary constant C, which always enters when we integrate a differential equation. If we draw the integral curve $y = F(x)$ (corresponding to taking $C = 0$), then any other integral curve $y = F(x) + C$ is obtained by shifting this curve through a vertical displacement C. Thus we obtain, as in Fig. 4–1, a family of "parallel" curves. They are parallel in the sense that the slope of the tangent to any one of them, at the point of abscissa x, is $f(x)$, the same for all curves $y = F(x) + C$. Now clearly this family of parallel curves has the property that, given any point (x_0, y_0) with x_0 in the allowed domain of the independent variable x, there is one and only one curve of the family that passes through this particular point. For in order that the curve shall pass through the point, the equation must be satisfied by these particular coordinates. This uniquely specifies the value of C to be

$$C = y_0 - F(x_0).$$

With C thus determined, we get a definite function expressing y in terms of x.

The condition imposed that $y = y_0$ when $x = x_0$ is often referred to as an *initial condition*. This is particularly appropriate in problems where time is the independent variable and initial velocities or initial positions of moving bodies are specified.

EXAMPLE 1. The velocity, at time t, of a moving body is given by

$$v = at,$$

where a is a constant. If the body's coordinate is s_0 at time $t = 0$, find the distance s as a function of t.

Solution. The velocity v is the same as the derivative ds/dt. Hence we want to solve the problem that consists of

$$\text{The differential equation:} \quad \frac{ds}{dt} = at \tag{1}$$

and

$$\text{The initial condition:} \quad s = s_0 \quad \text{when} \quad t = 0. \tag{2}$$

We write Eq. (1) in differential form,

$$ds = at\, dt,$$

and integrate:

$$s = \int at\, dt = a\frac{t^2}{2} + C.$$

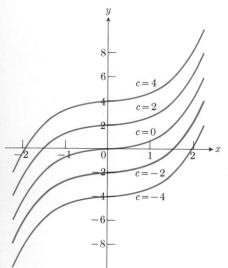

4–1 Selected curves of the family $y = x^3 + C$.

The constant of integration may now be determined from the initial condition, which requires that

$$s_0 = C.$$

Hence, the solution of the problem is

$$s = a\frac{t^2}{2} + s_0.$$

EXAMPLE 2. (See Fig. 4–1.) Find the curve whose slope at the point (x, y) is $3x^2$ if the curve is also required to pass through the point $(1, -1)$.

Solution. In mathematical language, we have the following problem:

Differential equation: $\dfrac{dy}{dx} = 3x^2$;

Initial condition: $y = -1$ when $x = 1$.

First, we integrate the differential equation:

$$dy = 3x^2 \, dx,$$

$$y = \int 3x^2 \, dx = x^3 + C.$$

Then we impose the initial condition to evaluate the constant C:

$$-1 = 1^3 + C; \qquad C = -2.$$

We substitute the value of C into the solution of the differential equation, and obtain the particular integral curve that passes through the given point, namely,

$$y = x^3 - 2.$$

The total revenue $R(x)$ from selling x units of a product can be determined by integrating the marginal revenue dR/dx and using an initial condition to evaluate the constant of integration.

EXAMPLE 3. For quantities x up to a certain production level $x = L$, a company found that its marginal revenue was

$$\frac{dR}{dx} = 5 + \frac{4}{(2x + 1)^2}.$$

Find $R(x)$ for $0 \le x \le L$, if $R(0) = 0$.

Solution

$$\int dR = \int \left[5 + \frac{4}{(2x + 1)^2} \right] dx,$$

$$R(x) = 5x - \frac{2}{2x + 1} + C.$$

Since $R(0) = 0$,

$$0 = 0 - 2 + C, \quad C = 2.$$

The revenue function for $0 \le x \le L$ is

$$R(x) = 5x - \frac{2}{2x + 1} + 2.$$

PROBLEMS

In each of the following problems (1 through 6), find the position s as a function of t from the given velocity $v = ds/dt$. Evaluate the constant of integration so as to have $s = s_0$ when $t = 0$.

1. $v = 3t^2$ **2.** $v = 2t + 1$

3. $v = (t + 1)^2$ **4.** $v = (t^2 + 1)^2$

5. $v = (t + 1)^{-2}$ **6.** $v = \sqrt{2gs}$ (g = constant)

In each of the following problems (7 through 11), find the velocity v and position s as functions of t from the given acceleration $a = dv/dt$. Evaluate the constants of integration so as to have $v = v_0$ and $s = s_0$ when $t = 0$.

7. $a = g$ (constant)   **8.** $a = t$

9. $a = \sqrt[3]{2t + 1}$ **10.** $a = (2t + 1)^{-3}$

11. $a = (t^2 + 1)^2$

12. The gravitational attraction exerted by the earth on a particle of mass m at distance s from the center is given by $F = -mgR^2 s^{-2}$, where R is the radius of the earth and F is negative because the force acts in opposition to increasing s (Fig. 4–2). If a particle is projected vertically upward from the surface of the earth with initial velocity $v_0 = \sqrt{2gR}$, apply Newton's second law $F = ma$ with $a = v(dv/ds)$ to show that $v = v_0\sqrt{R/s}$ and that $s^{3/2} = R^{3/2}[1 + (3v_0 t/2R)]$.

REMARK. The initial velocity $v_0 = \sqrt{2gR}$ (approximately 11.2 kilometers per second) is known as the "velocity of escape," since the displacement s tends to infinity with increasing t provided the initial velocity is this large. Actually, a somewhat larger initial velocity is required for escape from the earth's gravitational attraction, due to the retardation effect of air resistance, which we have neglected here for the sake of simplicity.

Solve the following differential equations subject to the prescribed initial conditions.

13. $\dfrac{dy}{dx} = 9x^2 - 4x + 5,$ $x = -1, \quad y = 0$

14. $\dfrac{dy}{dx} = 4(x - 7)^3,$ $x = 8, \quad y = 10$

15. $\dfrac{dy}{dx} = x^{1/2} + x^{1/4},$ $x = 0, \quad y = -2$

16. $\dfrac{dy}{dx} = \dfrac{x^2 + 1}{x^2},$ $x = 1, \quad y = 1$

17. $\dfrac{dy}{dx} = x\sqrt{y},$ $x = 0, \quad y = 1$

18. $\dfrac{dy}{dx} = 2xy^2,$ $x = 1, \quad y = 1$

19. $\dfrac{dy}{dx} = x\sqrt{1 + x^2},$ $x = 0, \quad y = -3$

20. $\dfrac{dy}{dx} = \dfrac{4\sqrt{(1 + y^2)^3}}{y},$ $x = 0, \quad y = 1$

21. (a) Find the total revenue $R(x)$ from selling x units if the marginal revenue in dollars per unit for $0 < x \le 400$ is

$$\frac{dR}{dx} = \frac{125}{\sqrt{x}} - \frac{100}{x^2}$$

and the revenue from selling the first 100 units is $2400. (b) What additional income comes from selling the next 100 units?

mass m

$F = -\dfrac{mgR^2}{s^2}$

s

R

center of the earth

4–2 A mass m that is s km from the earth's center.

Corresponding to the derivative formulas VII and VIII (see Article 2–13), we also have the differential formulas

$$d(\sin u) = \cos u \, du, \qquad \text{VII}'$$

$$d(\cos u) = -\sin u \, du, \qquad \text{VIII}'$$

4–4

INTEGRATION OF SINES AND COSINES

and the integration formulas

$$\int \cos u \, du = \sin u + C,$$

$$\int \sin u \, du = -\cos u + C. \qquad \textbf{(1)}$$

EXAMPLE 1

$$\int \cos 2t \, dt = \tfrac{1}{2} \int \cos 2t \cdot 2 \, dt$$

$$= \tfrac{1}{2} \int \cos u \, du \qquad (u = 2t)$$

$$= \tfrac{1}{2} \sin u + C$$

$$= \tfrac{1}{2} \sin 2t + C.$$

EXAMPLE 2. Evaluate the integral

$$\int \frac{\cos 2x}{\sin^3 2x} \, dx.$$

Solution. Since

$$d(\sin 2x) = 2 \cos 2x \, dx,$$

we recognize the numerator as being

$$\tfrac{1}{2} d(\sin 2x).$$

Hence we have

$$\int \frac{\cos 2x \, dx}{\sin^3 2x} = \int (\sin 2x)^{-3} \cdot \tfrac{1}{2} d(\sin 2x)$$

$$= \tfrac{1}{2} \int u^{-3} \, du \qquad (u = \sin 2x)$$

$$= \frac{1}{2} \frac{u^{-2}}{-2} + C$$

$$= \frac{-1}{4 \sin^2 2x} + C.$$

In Examples 1 and 2 we used a combination of substitution and algebraic manipulation to reduce the integrands to standard forms that we knew how to integrate. The standard forms available to us at the moment are

$$\int du = u + C \qquad\qquad \int u^n \, du = \frac{u^{n+1}}{n+1} + C, \quad n \neq -1 \qquad (2)$$

$$\int \sin u \, du = -\cos u + C \qquad \int \cos u \, du = \sin u + C,$$

and the rules we can use for algebraic manipulation of integrals are

$$\int a \, du = a \int du, \qquad \int du + dv = \int du + \int dv. \qquad (3)$$

However, it may not always be clear, when you first see an integral, how to find a combination of substitutions and manipulations that will reduce it to one of the standard forms. (Occasionally no such combination exists, but that will not be an issue here.)

There is a procedure you can try if you don't see how to integrate a given function right away. The procedure assumes that you have enough experience to make a reasonable guess at the answer, but it does not require you to guess absolutely right the first time. The steps are: (1) write down your guess; (2) compare its differential with the one in the integral; (3) modify your guess accordingly; and (4) check the result and make any further improvements necessary. Make sure to add a C.

We use this procedure in the next example.

EXAMPLE 3. Evaluate the integral

$$\int \sin (7x + 5) \, dx.$$

Solution. We try

$$\cos (7x + 5) + C.$$

Its differential is

$$-\sin (7x + 5) \cdot 7 \, dx.$$

This differs from the original differential $\sin (7x + 5) \, dx$ by a factor of -7. We divide the trial function by -7, obtaining

$$-\frac{1}{7} \cos (7x + 5) + C.$$

The differential of this new function is

$$-\frac{1}{7} \cdot -\sin (7x + 5) \cdot 7 \, dx = \sin (7x + 5) \, dx,$$

which is what we want. We conclude that

$$\int \sin (7x + 5) \, dx = -\frac{1}{7} \cos (7x + 5) + C.$$

EXAMPLE 4. Find

$$\int x \sin x \, dx.$$

Solution. We try

$$x \cos x + C.$$

Its differential is

$$\cos x \, dx - x \sin x \, dx.$$

There are two things wrong here. First, we have $-x \sin x \, dx$ when we want $+x \sin x \, dx$, and second, we have $\cos x \, dx$ which we do not want at all. Correcting the sign is easy: we just take

$$-x \cos x + C$$

as our new trial function. Now the differential is

$$-\cos x \, dx + x \sin x \, dx,$$

which is partly what we want but still has a term, $-\cos x \, dx$, that we don't want. To eliminate it we add to the trial function a term whose differential is $+\cos x \, dx$, namely, $\sin x$. This changes the trial function to

$$\sin x - x \cos x + C,$$

whose differential is

$$\cos x \, dx - \cos x \, dx + x \sin x \, dx = x \sin x \, dx.$$

This is just what we want:

$$\int x \sin x \, dx = \sin x - x \cos x + C.$$

PROBLEMS

Evaluate the following integrals.

1. $\int \sin 3x \, dx$

2. $\int \cos (2x + 4) \, dx$

3. $\int x \sin (2x^2) \, dx$

4. $\int (\cos \sqrt{x}) \dfrac{dx}{\sqrt{x}}$

5. $\int \sin 2t \, dt$

6. $\int \cos (3\theta - 1) \, d\theta$

7. $\int 4 \cos 3y \, dy$

8. $\int 2 \sin z \cos z \, dz$

9. $\int \sin^2 x \cos x \, dx$

10. $\int \cos^2 2y \sin 2y \, dy$

11. $\int (1 - \sin^2 3t) \cos 3t \, dt$

12. $\int \dfrac{\sin x \, dx}{\cos^2 x}$

13. $\int \dfrac{\cos x \, dx}{\sin^2 x}$

14. $\int \sqrt{2 + \sin 3t} \cos 3t \, dt$

15. $\int \dfrac{\sin 2t \, dt}{\sqrt{2 - \cos 2t}}$

16. $\int \sin^3 \dfrac{y}{2} \cos \dfrac{y}{2} \, dy$

17. $\int \dfrac{\sin [(z - 1)/3] \, dz}{\cos^2 [(z - 1)/3]}$

18. $\int \cos^2 \dfrac{2x}{3} \sin \dfrac{2x}{3} \, dx$

19. $\int (1 + \sin 2t)^{3/2} \cos 2t \, dt$

20. $\int (3 \sin 2x + 4 \cos 3x) \, dx$

21. $\int \sin t \cos t (\sin t + \cos t) \, dt$

22. $\int (\sin x + x \cos x) \, dx$

Solve the following differential equations subject to the given initial conditions.

23. $2y \dfrac{dy}{dx} = 5x - 3 \sin x, \qquad x = 0, \quad y = 0$

24. $\dfrac{dy}{dx} = \dfrac{\pi \cos \pi x}{\sqrt{y}}, \qquad\qquad x = \tfrac{1}{2}, \quad y = 1$

25. We can treat the integral of $2 \sin x \cos x \, dx$ in three different ways:

i) $\int 2 \sin x \cos x \, dx = \int 2 \sin x \, d(\sin x)$

$$= \sin^2 x + C_1$$

ii) $\int 2 \sin x \cos x \, dx = \int -2 \cos x \, d(\cos x)$

$$= -\cos^2 x + C_2$$

iii) $\int 2 \sin x \cos x \, dx = \int \sin 2x \, dx$

$$= -\tfrac{1}{2} \cos 2x + C_3.$$

Can all three integrations be correct? Explain.

4–5

AREA UNDER A CURVE

In geometry we learned how to find areas of certain polygons: rectangles, triangles, parallelograms, trapezoids. Indeed, the area of any polygon can be found by cutting it into triangles.

The area of a circle is easily computed from the familiar formula $A = \pi r^2$. But the idea behind this simple formula isn't so simple. In fact, it is the subtle concept of a *limit*, the area of the circle being *defined* as the limit of areas of inscribed (or circumscribed) regular polygons as the number of sides *increases without bound*. A similar idea is involved in the definition we now introduce for other plane areas.

Let $y = f(x)$ define a continuous function of x on the closed interval $a \leq x \leq b$. For simplicity, we shall also suppose that $f(x)$ is positive for $a \leq x \leq b$. We consider the problem of calculating the area bounded above by the graph of the function, on the sides by vertical lines through $x = a$ and $x = b$, and below by the x-axis (Fig. 4–3).

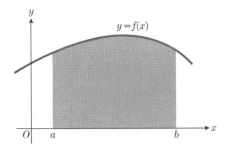

4–3 Area under a curve.

We divide the area into n thin strips of uniform width $\Delta x = (b - a)/n$ by lines perpendicular to the x-axis through the endpoints $x = a$ and $x = b$ and many intermediate points, which we number as $x_1, x_2, \ldots, x_{n-1}$ (Fig. 4–4). We use an inscribed rectangle to approximate the area in each strip. For instance, in the figure, we approximate the area of the strip $aP_0 P_1 x_1$ by the shaded rectangle of altitude aP_0 and base $a \cdots x_1$. The area of this rectangle is

$$f(a) \cdot (x_1 - a) = f(a) \cdot \Delta x,$$

since the length of the altitude aP_0 is the value of f at $x = a$, and the length of the base is $x_1 - a = \Delta x$. Similarly, the inscribed rectangle in the second strip has area

$$f(x_1) \cdot \Delta x.$$

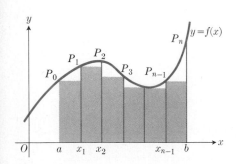

4–4 Area under a curve $y = f(x)$ divided into strips. Each strip is approximated by a rectangle.

Continuing in this fashion, we inscribe a rectangle in each strip.

If the function increases with x as in Fig. 4–5, then the altitude of each rectangle is the length of its left edge, and we have

$$\text{Area of first rectangle} = f(a) \cdot \Delta x,$$
$$\text{Area of second rectangle} = f(x_1) \cdot \Delta x,$$
$$\text{Area of third rectangle} = f(x_2) \cdot \Delta x,$$
$$\vdots$$
$$\text{Area of } n\text{th and last rectangle} = f(x_{n-1}) \cdot \Delta x.$$

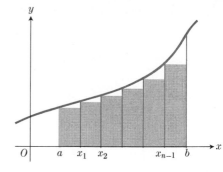

4–5 Rectangles under the graph of an increasing function.

EXAMPLE 1. Suppose $f(x) = 1 + x^2$; $a = 0$, $b = 1$, and $n = 4$. There are $n - 1 = 3$ intermediate points $x_1 = \frac{1}{4}$, $x_2 = \frac{1}{2}$, and $x_3 = \frac{3}{4}$, which divide the interval $0 \le x \le 1$ into $n = 4$ subintervals, each of length $\Delta x = \frac{1}{4}$. The inscribed rectangles (Fig. 4–6) have areas

$$f(0) \cdot \Delta x = 1 \cdot \tfrac{1}{4} = \tfrac{16}{64}$$
$$f(\tfrac{1}{4}) \cdot \Delta x = \tfrac{17}{16} \cdot \tfrac{1}{4} = \tfrac{17}{64}$$
$$f(\tfrac{1}{2}) \cdot \Delta x = \tfrac{5}{4} \cdot \tfrac{1}{4} = \tfrac{20}{64}$$
$$f(\tfrac{3}{4}) \cdot \Delta x = \tfrac{25}{16} \cdot \tfrac{1}{4} = \tfrac{25}{64}$$
$$\overline{\text{Sum} = \tfrac{78}{64} = 1.21875.}$$

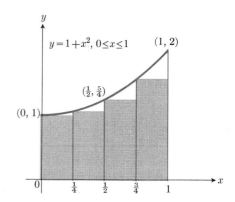

4–6 Rectangles under the graph of $y = 1 + x^2$, $0 \le x \le 1$.

Since the area under the curve is larger than the sum of the areas of these inscribed rectangles, we may expect it to be somewhat larger than 1.22. In fact, by using methods we shall soon develop, we shall find that the area is exactly $\frac{4}{3}$. Thus our estimate of 1.22 is about 8 percent too small. There are easy ways of improving the accuracy, for example by using trapezoids in place of rectangles to approximate each strip, but we defer that to a later time.

If the curve slopes downward as in Fig. 4–7, then the altitude of each inscribed rectangle is the length of its right edge, and we have areas as follows:

$$\text{First rectangle} \quad f(x_1) \cdot \Delta x,$$
$$\text{Second rectangle} \quad f(x_2) \cdot \Delta x,$$
$$\text{Third rectangle} \quad f(x_3) \cdot \Delta x,$$
$$\vdots$$
$$n\text{th and last} \quad f(b) \cdot \Delta x.$$

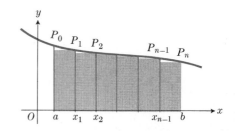

4–7 Rectangles under the graph of a decreasing function.

More generally, the curve may rise and fall between $x = a$ and $x = b$, as in Fig. 4–8. But there is a number c_1, between a and x_1 inclusive, such that the first inscribed rectangle has area $f(c_1) \cdot \Delta x$; and a number c_2 in the second closed subinterval such that the area of the second inscribed rec-

4–8 Rectangles under a curve which rises and falls between a and b.

tangle is $f(c_2) \cdot \Delta x$; and so on. The number c_1 is the place between a and x_1, inclusive, where f is minimized for the first subinterval. Similarly, the minimum value of f for x in the second subinterval is attained at c_2, and so on.

The sum of the areas of these inscribed rectangles is

$$S_n = f(c_1) \cdot \Delta x + f(c_2) \cdot \Delta x + \cdots + f(c_n) \cdot \Delta x. \qquad (1)$$

We may also write this in more abbreviated form by using the sigma notation,

$$S_n = \sum_{k=1}^{n} f(c_k) \cdot \Delta x. \qquad (2)$$

The Greek letter $\sum$ (capital sigma) is used this way in mathematics to denote a sum. Note that each term of the sum in (1) is of the form $f(c_k) \cdot \Delta x$, with only the subscript on c changing from one term to another. We have indicated the subscript by k, but we could equally well have used i or j or any other symbol except a letter that is currently in use for something else. In the first term in the sum on the right side of Eq. (1) the subscript is $k = 1$; in the second, $k = 2$; and so on to the last, or nth, in which $k = n$. We indicate this by writing $k = 1$ below the $\sum$ in (2), to say that the sum is to *start* with the term we get by replacing k in the expression that follows by 1. The n above the sigma tells us where to *stop*. For instance, if $n = 4$, we have

$$\sum_{k=1}^{4} f(c_k) \cdot \Delta x = f(c_1) \cdot \Delta x + f(c_2) \cdot \Delta x + f(c_3) \cdot \Delta x + f(c_4) \cdot \Delta x.$$

The only thing that changes from one summand to the next is the numeral in the place indicated by k. First we replace k by 1, then by 2, then 3, then 4. Then we add.

Here are a few other examples of $\sum$ notation:

EXAMPLE 2

a) $\displaystyle\sum_{k=1}^{5} k^2 = 1^2 + 2^2 + 3^2 + 4^2 + 5^2,$

b) $\displaystyle\sum_{k=1}^{3} \frac{k}{k+1} = \frac{1}{1+1} + \frac{2}{2+1} + \frac{3}{3+1},$

c) $\displaystyle\sum_{j=0}^{2} \frac{j+1}{j+2} = \frac{0+1}{0+2} + \frac{1+1}{1+2} + \frac{2+1}{2+2},$

d) $\displaystyle\sum_{i=1}^{4} x_i = x_1 + x_2 + x_3 + x_4,$

e) $\displaystyle\sum_{k=1}^{4} x^k = x + x^2 + x^3 + x^4.$

We turn our attention once more to the area under the graph of a positive continuous function $y = f(x)$, $a \leq x \leq b$. We *define* the area to be *the limit of the sums of the areas of inscribed rectangles as their common base length Δx approaches zero and their number increases without bound.*

In symbols,

$$A = \lim_{n\to\infty} [f(c_1)\,\Delta x + f(c_2)\,\Delta x + \cdots + f(c_n)\,\Delta x]$$

$$= \lim_{n\to\infty} \sum_{k=1}^{n} f(c_k)\,\Delta x. \tag{3}$$

REMARK 1.   The existence of the limit in (3) is a consequence of the continuity of f, but proving this fact is beyond the scope of our discussion and will be left to more advanced courses in mathematical analysis. However, it is a fact that, by taking larger and larger values of n and computing the sum of the areas of inscribed rectangles for each n, we get answers that differ from one another (and from what we would intuitively call the area under the curve) by amounts that become arbitrarily small as n increases.

REMARK 2.   We could have used circumscribed instead of inscribed rectangles. We would then replace the c_k in Eq. (3) by other numbers, say e_k. These would be the places in the subintervals where the function takes on its *maximum* instead of minimum values. The corresponding sums would tend to overestimate the exact area, but in the limit we would get the same answer whether we used inscribed or circumscribed rectangles. The fact that the two kinds of sums of areas of rectangles give the same limit is a consequence of the *uniform continuity* of the function f over the domain $a \le x \le b$. Again, this is a theorem which is usually proved in more advanced courses in mathematical analysis. (It is also implied by the inequalities and equations (10) through (14) of Article 4–8.)

REMARK 3.   Just as we use the simple formula $A = \pi r^2$ to find the area of a circle, rather than resorting to a calculation of the limit of areas of inscribed polygons, so with the area under a curve. We shall not compute many areas directly from the definition in Eq. (3). Rather we shall develop from it a method for getting answers very quickly and simply. But we need the definition of area, as given above, as a starting place.

PROBLEMS

In each of the following problems (1 through 5), sketch the graph of the given equation over the interval $a \le x \le b$. Divide the interval into $n = 4$ subintervals each of length $\Delta x = (b - a)/4$. (a) Sketch the inscribed rectangles and compute the sum of their areas. (b) Do the same using the circumscribed, in place of the inscribed rectangle in each subinterval (Fig. 4–9).

1. $y = 2x + 1, \quad a = 0, \quad b = 1.$
2. $y = x^2, \quad a = -1, \quad b = 1.$
3. $y = \sin x, \quad a = 0, \quad b = \pi.$
4. $y = 1/x, \quad a = 1, \quad b = 2.$
5. $y = \sqrt{x}, \quad a = 0, \quad b = 4.$

Write out the following sums, as in Example 2.

6. $\displaystyle\sum_{k=1}^{5} \frac{1}{k}$ 7. $\displaystyle\sum_{i=-1}^{3} 2^i$ 8. $\displaystyle\sum_{n=1}^{4} \cos n\pi x$

Find the value of each sum.

9. $\displaystyle\sum_{n=0}^{4} \frac{n}{4}$ 10. $\displaystyle\sum_{k=1}^{3} \frac{k-1}{k}$ 11. $\displaystyle\sum_{m=0}^{5} \sin \frac{m\pi}{2}$

inscribed rectangles

circumscribed rectangles

Figure 4–9

4-6

**COMPUTATION OF
AREAS AS LIMITS**

In Article 4–5 we defined the area under the graph of $y = f(x)$ over the interval $a \leq x \leq b$ as the *limit* of sums of areas of inscribed rectangles. We computed a few sums, but no limits. To compute the limits we need some algebraic formulas. We now develop these. Then we compute some areas as limits to show how it can be done. In Article 4–7 we show how much easier it is using integral calculus.

We need the following formulas:

$$\sum_{k=1}^{n} k = 1 + 2 + 3 + \cdots + n = \frac{n(n+1)}{2},$$

$$\sum_{k=1}^{n} k^2 = 1^2 + 2^2 + 3^2 + \cdots + n^2 = \frac{n(n+1)(2n+1)}{6},$$

which we shall prove by the method of mathematical induction. This consists of showing that each formula is true when $n = 1$, and that if the formula is true for any integer n, then it is also true for the next integer, $n + 1$. We shall also show how such formulas might be discovered.

First, consider the sum of first powers:

$$F(n) = 1 + 2 + 3 + \cdots + n.$$

Table 4–1 shows briefly how $F(n)$ increases with n. The last column exhibits $F(n)/n$, the ratio of $F(n)$ to n.

Table 4–1

n	$F(n) = 1 + 2 + 3 + \cdots + n$	$F(n)/n$
1	1	$1 = \frac{2}{2}$
2	$1 + 2 = 3$	$\frac{3}{2} = \frac{3}{2}$
3	$1 + 2 + 3 = 6$	$\frac{6}{3} = \frac{4}{2}$
4	$1 + 2 + 3 + 4 = 10$	$\frac{10}{4} = \frac{5}{2}$
5	$1 + 2 + 3 + 4 + 5 = 15$	$\frac{15}{5} = \frac{6}{2}$
6	$1 + 2 + 3 + 4 + 5 + 6 = 21$	$\frac{21}{6} = \frac{7}{2}$

The last column suggests that the ratio $F(n)/n$ is equal to $(n + 1)/2$. At least this is the case for all the entries ˙ the table ($n = 1, 2, 3, 4, 5, 6$). In other words, the formula

$$\frac{F(n)}{n} = \frac{n + 1}{2}$$

or

$$1 + 2 + 3 + \cdots + n = \frac{n(n+1)}{2} \qquad (1)$$

is true for $n = 1, 2, 3, 4, 5, 6$. Suppose now that n is any integer for which (1) is known to be true (at the moment, n could be any integer from 1 through

6). Then if $(n + 1)$ were added to both sides of the equation, the new equation

$$1 + 2 + 3 + \cdots + n + (n + 1) = \frac{n(n + 1)}{2} + (n + 1) \qquad (2)$$

would also be true for that same n. But the right side of (2) is

$$\frac{n(n + 1)}{2} + (n + 1) = \frac{(n + 1)}{2}(n + 2) = \frac{(n + 1)(n + 2)}{2},$$

so that (2) becomes

$$1 + 2 + 3 + \cdots + n + (n + 1) = \frac{(n + 1)((n + 1) + 1)}{2},$$

which is just like Eq. (1) except that n is replaced by $n + 1$. Thus if Eq. (1) is true for an integer n, it is also true for the next integer $n + 1$. Hence we now know that it is true for $n + 1 = 7$, since it was true for $n = 6$. Then we can say it is true for $n + 1 = 8$, since it is true for $n = 7$. By the principle of mathematical induction, then, it is true for every positive integer n.

Now let's consider the squares. Let

$$Q(n) = 1^2 + 2^2 + 3^2 + \cdots + n^2$$

be the sum of the squares of the first n positive integers. Obviously this grows faster than $F(n)$, the sum of first powers, but let us look at the ratio of $Q(n)$ to $F(n)$ to compare them. (See Table 4–2.)

Table 4–2

n	$F(n)$	$Q(n) = 1^2 + 2^2 + 3^2 + \cdots + n^2$	$Q(n)/F(n)$
1	1	$1^2 = 1$	$\frac{1}{1} = \frac{3}{3}$
2	3	$1^2 + 2^2 = 5$	$\frac{5}{3} = \frac{5}{3}$
3	6	$1^2 + 2^2 + 3^2 = 14$	$\frac{14}{6} = \frac{7}{3}$
4	10	$1^2 + 2^2 + 3^2 + 4^2 = 30$	$\frac{30}{10} = \frac{9}{3}$
5	15	$1^2 + 2^2 + 3^2 + 4^2 + 5^2 = 55$	$\frac{55}{15} = \frac{11}{3}$
6	21	$1^2 + 2^2 + 3^2 + 4^2 + 5^2 + 6^2 = 91$	$\frac{91}{21} = \frac{13}{3}$

We note how regular the last column is: $\frac{3}{3}, \frac{5}{3}, \frac{7}{3}$, and so on. In fact it is just $(2n + 1)/3$ for $n = 1, 2, 3, 4, 5, 6$; that is,

$$Q(n) = F(n) \cdot \frac{2n + 1}{3}.$$

But from Eq. (1), $F(n) = n(n + 1)/2$, and hence

$$Q(n) = 1^2 + 2^2 + 3^2 + \cdots + n^2 = \frac{n(n + 1)(2n + 1)}{6} \qquad (3)$$

is true for the integers n from 1 through 6. To establish it for all other positive integers, we proceed as before. Start with any n for which (3) is true

and add $(n + 1)^2$. Then

$$1^2 + 2^2 + 3^2 + \cdots + n^2 + (n + 1)^2 = \frac{n(n + 1)(2n + 1)}{6} + (n + 1)^2$$

$$= \frac{(n + 1)}{6}[n(2n + 1) + 6(n + 1)]$$

$$= \frac{(n + 1)}{6}(2n^2 + 7n + 6) = \frac{(n + 1)(n + 2)(2n + 3)}{6}. \qquad \textbf{(4)}$$

We note that the last expression in (4) is the same as the last expression in (3) with n replaced by $n + 1$. In other words, if the formula in (3) is true for any integer n, we have just shown that it is true for $n + 1$. Since we know it is true for $n = 6$, it is also true for $n + 1 = 7$. And now that we know it is true for $n = 7$, it follows that it is true for $n + 1 = 8$, and so on. It is true for every positive integer n by the principle of mathematical induction.

We now apply these formulas to find areas under two graphs.

EXAMPLE 1.   Let a and b be positive numbers, with $a < b$. Find the area under the graph $y = mx$, $a \leq x \leq b$ (Fig. 4–10).

Solution.   Let n be a positive integer and divide the interval (a, b) into n subintervals each of length $\Delta x = (b - a)/n$, by inserting the points

$$x_1 = a + \Delta x,$$
$$x_2 = a + 2\,\Delta x,$$
$$x_3 = a + 3\,\Delta x,$$
$$\vdots \qquad \vdots$$
$$x_{n-1} = a + (n - 1)\,\Delta x.$$

$y = mx$, $a \leq x \leq b$

4–10   The area under $y = mx$, $a \leq x \leq b$.

The inscribed rectangles have areas

$$f(a)\,\Delta x = ma \cdot \Delta x,$$
$$f(x_1)\,\Delta x = m(a + \Delta x) \cdot \Delta x,$$
$$f(x_2)\,\Delta x = m(a + 2\,\Delta x) \cdot \Delta x,$$
$$\vdots \qquad \vdots$$
$$f(x_{n-1})\,\Delta x = m[a + (n - 1)\,\Delta x] \cdot \Delta x,$$

whose sum is

$$S_n = m[a + (a + \Delta x) + (a + 2\,\Delta x) + \cdots + (a + (n - 1)\,\Delta x)] \cdot \Delta x$$

$$= m[na + (1 + 2 + \cdots + (n - 1))\,\Delta x]\,\Delta x = m\left[na + \frac{(n - 1)n}{2}\,\Delta x\right]\Delta x$$

$$= m\left[a + \frac{n - 1}{2}\,\Delta x\right]n\,\Delta x \qquad \left(\Delta x = \frac{b - a}{n}\right)$$

$$= m\left[a + \frac{b - a}{2} \cdot \frac{n - 1}{n}\right] \cdot (b - a).$$

The area under the graph is defined to be the limit of S_n as $n \to \infty$. In the final form, the only place n appears is in the fraction

$$\frac{n-1}{n} = 1 - \frac{1}{n},$$

and $1/n \to 0$ as $n \to \infty$, so

$$\lim \frac{n-1}{n} = 1 - 0 = 1.$$

Therefore,

$$\lim S_n = m\left(a + \frac{b-a}{2}\right) \cdot (b-a)$$

$$= \frac{ma + mb}{2} \cdot (b-a).$$

This is easily interpreted as the area of a trapezoid, with "bases" (in this case vertical) ma and mb and with altitude $(b-a)$.

EXAMPLE 2.   Find the area under the graph of $y = x^2$, $0 \le x \le b$ (Fig. 4–11).

Solution.   Divide the interval $0 \le x \le b$ into n (> 0) subintervals each of length $\Delta x = b/n$, by inserting the points

$$x_1 = \Delta x, \quad x_2 = 2\,\Delta x, \quad x_3 = 3\,\Delta x, \quad \ldots, \quad x_{n-1} = (n-1)\,\Delta x.$$

The inscribed rectangles have areas

$$f(0)\,\Delta x = 0,$$
$$f(x_1)\,\Delta x = (\Delta x)^2\,\Delta x,$$
$$f(x_2)\,\Delta x = (2\,\Delta x)^2\,\Delta x,$$
$$f(x_3)\,\Delta x = (3\,\Delta x)^2\,\Delta x,$$
$$\vdots \qquad\qquad \vdots$$
$$f(x_{n-1})\,\Delta x = ((n-1)\,\Delta x)^2\,\Delta x.$$

The sum of these areas is

$$S_n = (1^2 + 2^2 + 3^2 + \cdots + (n-1)^2)(\Delta x)^3$$

$$= \frac{(n-1)n(2n-1)}{6} \cdot \left(\frac{b}{n}\right)^3$$

$$= \frac{b^3}{6} \cdot \frac{n-1}{n} \cdot \frac{n}{n} \cdot \frac{2n-1}{n}$$

$$= \frac{b^3}{6} \cdot \left(1 - \frac{1}{n}\right) \cdot \left(2 - \frac{1}{n}\right).$$

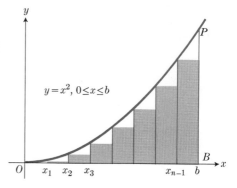

4–11   The area under $y = x^2$, $0 \le x \le b$.

To find the area under the graph, we let n increase without bound and get

$$A = \lim S_n = \frac{b^3}{6} \cdot 1 \cdot 2 = \frac{b^3}{3}.$$

Therefore the area under the curve is $\frac{1}{3}$ the base b times the "altitude" b^2. The triangle OBP in Fig. 4–11 has area $\frac{1}{2}b \cdot b^2 = b^3/2$, and the area under the curve turns out to be somewhat smaller, as we should expect.

PROBLEMS

1. Verify the formula

$$\sum_{k=1}^{n} k^3 = 1^3 + 2^3 + \cdots + n^3 = \left(\frac{n(n+1)}{2}\right)^2$$

for $n = 1, 2, 3$. Then add $(n + 1)^3$ and thereby prove by mathematical induction (as in the text) that the formula is true for all positive integers n.

2. Using the result of Problem 1 and the method of Example 2 in the text, show that the area under the graph of $y = x^3$ over the interval $0 \le x \le b$ is $b^4/4$.

3. Find the area under the graph of $y = mx$ over the interval $a \le x \le b$ by using *circumscribed* rectangles in place of the inscribed rectangles of Example 1 in the text.

4. Find the area under the curve $y = x^2$ over the interval $0 \le x \le b$ by using circumscribed rectangles in place of the inscribed rectangles of Example 2 in the text.

5. Do Problem 2 above by using circumscribed rectangles instead of inscribed rectangles.

6. Establish the formulas given below, for every positive integer n, by showing (a) that the formula is correct for $n = 1$, and (b) if true for n, the formula is also true for $n + 1$.

$$\sum_{k=1}^{n} (2k - 1) = 1 + 3 + 5 + \cdots + (2n - 1) = n^2,$$

$$\sum_{k=1}^{n} \frac{1}{k(k + 1)} = \frac{1}{1 \cdot 2} + \frac{1}{2 \cdot 3} + \cdots + \frac{1}{n \cdot (n + 1)} = \frac{n}{n + 1}.$$

4–7

AREAS BY CALCULUS

In Article 4–5 we defined the area under a curve and showed how we could estimate it by computing sums of areas of rectangles. Nothing more than arithmetic is involved in these calculations, but we pay the price of getting only an estimate of the true area. On the other hand, in Article 4–6 we used algebraic techniques and actually computed *limits*, thus getting exact areas at the cost of fairly extensive algebraic preliminaries. In this article we shall follow the path blazed by Leibniz and Newton to show how exact areas can be computed easily by using integral calculus.

To begin we need some preliminary results. We consider a function f which is positive-valued and continuous over the domain $a \le x \le b$. Let A_a^c, A_c^b, A_a^b denote the areas under the graph and above the x-axis from a to c, from c to b, and from a to b, respectively (Fig. 4–12). If c is between a and b, we have

$$A_a^c + A_c^b = A_a^b. \tag{1}$$

And this is also true when $c = a$ if we define the area from a to a to be zero,

$$A_a^a = 0. \tag{2}$$

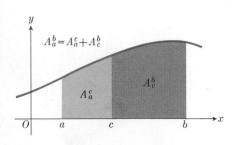

4–12 $A_a^c + A_c^b = A_a^b.$

Equation (1) is also true if c is beyond b, provided we adopt some conventions about signed areas. Let us say that area above the x-axis is positive if we go from left to right, and negative if we go from right to left. Thus, in Fig.

4–12, A_a^c, A_c^b, and A_a^b are all positive, while

$$A_c^a = -A_a^c, \qquad A_b^c = -A_c^b, \qquad A_b^a = -A_a^b \qquad \text{(3)}$$

are negative. So formula (1) is also true in the form

$$A_a^b + A_b^c = A_a^c, \qquad \text{(4)}$$

because adding A_b^c to A_a^b just subtracts A_c^b from the latter, leaving A_a^c.

The following theorem will also be used.

The Intermediate Value Theorem.   *Let f be a positive-valued continuous function over the domain $a \le x \le b$. Let A_a^b denote the area under the graph of f over the domain. Then there is at least one number c between a and b such that*

$$A_a^b = f(c) \cdot (b - a). \qquad \text{(5)}$$

Proof. Suppose m and M are respectively the minimum and maximum values of f over the domain $a \le x \le b$. Then

$$m(b - a) \le A_a^b \le M(b - a),$$

and therefore

$$m \le \frac{A_a^b}{b - a} \le M.$$

Since $A_a^b/(b - a)$ lies between the minimum and maximum values of $f(x)$ for $a \le x \le b$, there is at least one place c between a and b where

$$f(c) = \frac{A_a^b}{b - a}$$

(Article 2–11, Theorem 4). Equation (5) follows.

REMARK.   The geometric interpretation of the Intermediate Value Theorem is this. A line drawn parallel to the x-axis at the right place between m and M units above the x-axis will serve as upper boundary of a rectangle having the same area as that under the curve, and it will surely cut the curve at least once between $x = a$ and $x = b$. The abscissa of that cut is a suitable value of c in Eq. (5) (See Fig. 4–13).

To compute the area A_a^b, we now consider any abscissa x between a and b, the area A_a^x, and the area $A_a^{x + \Delta x}$, where $\Delta x \ne 0$ (Fig. 4–14). We shall derive a differential equation for the area function A_a^x. The solution of this differential equation, with the initial condition

$$A_a^a = 0,$$

will enable us to compute the area from a to any x and, in particular, from a to b.

From Eq. (1) we have

$$A_a^x + A_x^{x + \Delta x} = A_a^{x + \Delta x},$$

so that

$$\Delta(A_a^x) = A_a^{x + \Delta x} - A_a^x = A_x^{x + \Delta x}. \qquad \text{(6a)}$$

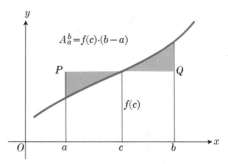

4–13   The area under the curve is equal to the area of the rectangle $aPQb$: The shaded regions above and below the curve have equal areas.

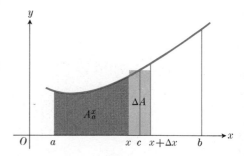

4–14   An increment of the area function.

Then, by Eq. (5),

$$A_x^{x+\Delta x} = f(c) \cdot \Delta x, \tag{6b}$$

where c is a number between x and $x + \Delta x$, which must therefore approach x as Δx approaches zero. Combining (6a) and (6b) and dividing by Δx, we get

$$\frac{\Delta A_a^x}{\Delta x} = f(c), \tag{7}$$

and therefore

$$\frac{dA_a^x}{dx} = \lim_{\Delta x \to 0} \frac{\Delta A_a^x}{\Delta x}$$

$$= \lim_{c \to x} f(c)$$

$$= f(x),$$

where the last line follows from the fact that f is continuous.

Therefore the area function A_a^x satisfies the differential equation

$$\frac{dA_a^x}{dx} = f(x) \tag{8a}$$

and the initial condition

$$A_a^a = 0. \tag{8b}$$

Thus if $F(x)$ is any integral of $f(x)\,dx$, we have

$$A_a^x = \int f(x)\,dx = F(x) + C. \tag{9a}$$

We also have

$$A_a^a = 0 = F(a) + C.$$

Hence

$$C = -F(a)$$

and

$$A_a^x = F(x) - F(a).$$

Finally, by taking $x = b$ we get

$$A_a^b = F(b) - F(a). \tag{9b}$$

Equations (9a) and (9b) summarize the method for finding the area under the graph of a positive-valued continuous function by integration. If the equation of the curve is $y = f(x)$, we integrate f to find

$$F(x) + C = \int f(x)\,dx. \tag{10a}$$

If the interval is $a \leq x \leq b$, we then compute

$$A_a^b = F(x)]_a^b = F(b) - F(a). \tag{10b}$$

The notation $F(x)]_a^b$ in Eq. (10b) simply means: first replace x by the upper value b to calculate $F(b)$, then subtract the value $F(a)$ obtained by setting $x = a$. For example,

$$2x + 3]_1^5 = 13 - 5 = 8.$$

The constant of integration may be omitted in evaluating Eq. (10b). For if we use $F(x) + C$ in place of $F(x)$ in (10b), we find

$$F(x) + C]_a^b = [F(b) + C] - [F(a) + C]$$
$$= F(b) - F(a)$$
$$= F(x)]_a^b.$$

EXAMPLE 1. The area under the graph of $y = mx$, $a \leq x \leq b$ (Fig. 4–10) is

$$\int mx \, dx \Big]_a^b = \frac{mx^2}{2} \Big]_a^b = \frac{mb^2}{2} - \frac{ma^2}{2}$$
$$= \frac{mb + ma}{2} \cdot (b - a).$$

Compare the result and the method with Example 1 of Article 4–6.

EXAMPLE 2. The area under the graph of $y = x^2$, $0 \leq x \leq b$ (Fig. 4–11) is

$$\int x^2 \, dx \Big]_0^b = \frac{x^3}{3} \Big]_0^b = \frac{b^3}{3}.$$

Compare the result and the method with Example 2 of Article 4–6.

EXAMPLE 3. Calculate the area bounded by the parabola $y = 6 - x - x^2$ and the x-axis.

Solution. We find where the curve crosses the x-axis by setting

$$y = 0 = 6 - x - x^2 = (3 + x)(2 - x),$$

which gives

$$x = -3 \qquad \text{or} \qquad x = 2.$$

The curve is sketched in Fig. 4–15.
According to Eqs. (10a, b), the area is

$$A_{-3}^2 = \int (6 - x - x^2) \, dx \Big]_{-3}^2 = 6x - \frac{x^2}{2} - \frac{x^3}{3} \Big]_{-3}^2$$
$$= (12 - 2 - \tfrac{8}{3}) - (-18 - \tfrac{9}{2} + \tfrac{27}{3}) = 20\tfrac{5}{6}.$$

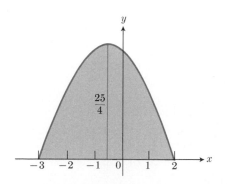

4–15 The parabolic arch
$y = 6 - x - x^2$, $-3 \leq x \leq 2$.

The curve in Fig. 4–15 is an arch of a parabola, and it is interesting to note that the area is exactly equal to two-thirds the base times the altitude:

$$\tfrac{2}{3}(5)(\tfrac{25}{4}) = \tfrac{125}{6} = 20\tfrac{5}{6}.$$

EXAMPLE 4. Show that the area under one arch of the curve $y = \sin x$ is 2.

Solution. One arch of the sine curve extends from $x = 0$ to $x = \pi$ (Fig. 4–16). Therefore the area is

$$A_0^\pi = \int \sin x \, dx \Big]_0^\pi = -\cos x \Big]_0^\pi$$

$$= -\cos \pi - (-\cos 0) = -(-1) + 1 = 2.$$

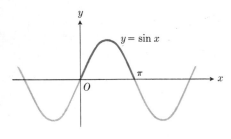

4–16 One arch of the curve $y = \sin x$.

PROBLEMS

In Problems 1 through 10, find the area bounded by the x-axis, the given curve $y = f(x)$, and the given vertical lines:

1. $y = x^2 + 1$; $x = 0$, $x = 3$.

2. $y = 2x + 3$; $x = 0$, $x = 1$.

3. $y = \sqrt{2x + 1}$; $x = 0$, $x = 4$.

4. $y = \dfrac{1}{\sqrt{2x + 1}}$; $x = 0$, $x = 4$.

5. $y = \dfrac{1}{(2x + 1)^2}$; $x = 1$, $x = 2$.

6. $y = (2x + 1)^2$; $x = -1$, $x = 3$.

7. $y = x^3 + 2x + 1$; $x = 0$, $x = 2$.

8. $y = x\sqrt{2x^2 + 1}$; $x = 0$, $x = 2$.

9. $y = \dfrac{x}{\sqrt{2x^2 + 1}}$; $x = 0$, $x = 2$.

10. $y = \dfrac{x}{(2x^2 + 1)^2}$; $x = 0$, $x = 2$.

11. Find the area bounded by the coordinate axes and the line $x + y = 1$.

12. Find the area between the curve $y = 4 - x^2$ and the x-axis.

13. Find the area between the curve $y = 1/\sqrt{x}$, the x-axis, and the lines $x = 1$, $x = 4$.

14. Find the area between the curve $y = \sqrt{1 - x}$ and the coordinate axes.

15. Find the area between the curve $x = 1 - y^2$ and the y-axis.

16. Find the area contained between the x-axis and one arch of the curve $y = \cos 3x$.

*17. Take $B = A$ in Eq. (11a), Article 2–9, and show that

$$\cos 2A = \cos^2 A - \sin^2 A.$$

Combine this with the identity

$$1 = \cos^2 A + \sin^2 A$$

to show that

$$\cos^2 A = \tfrac{1}{2}(1 + \cos 2A), \qquad \sin^2 A = \tfrac{1}{2}(1 - \cos 2A).$$

Use the last of these identities to find the area contained between the x-axis and one arch of the curve $y = \sin^2 3x$.

18. The graph of $y = \sqrt{a^2 - x^2}$ over $-a \le x \le a$ is a semicircle of radius a.

a) Using this fact, explain why it is true that

$$\int \sqrt{a^2 - x^2} \, dx \Big]_{-a}^{a} = \tfrac{1}{2}\pi a^2.$$

b) Evaluate

$$\int \sqrt{a^2 - x^2} \, dx \Big]_0^a.$$

19. The integral in Problem 18 above can be evaluated by using the substitution

$$x = a \cos \theta, \qquad \pi \ge \theta \ge 0$$

to replace $\sqrt{a^2 - x^2} \, dx$ by $-a^2 \sin^2 \theta \, d\theta$. Combine this with Problem 17 above to show that

$$\int \sqrt{a^2 - x^2} \, dx \Big]_{-a}^{a} = \int -a^2 \sin^2 \theta \, d\theta \Big]_\pi^0$$

$$= -\frac{a^2}{2} \int (1 - \cos 2\theta) \, d\theta \Big]_\pi^0,$$

and thus verify the result given in Problem 18(a), by evaluating this final integral.

---

*   The method used in this problem should be used in several later problems involving integration of squares of sines and cosines.

In Articles 4–5, 4–6, and 4–7, we made a systematic study of the area prob-lem. We have arrived at the following result.

If the function f is positive and continuous over the domain $a \le x \le b$, then the area under its graph is

$$A_a^b = \lim \sum f(c_k)\, \Delta x = \int_a^b f(x)\, dx \bigg]_a^b = F(x) \bigg]_a^b = F(b) - F(a). \quad (1)$$

The first part of this equation is just the definition of the area as the limit of the sum of areas of inscribed rectangles. The last part of the equation gives a short way to evaluate this limit by calculus. Therein lies one of the most powerful ideas of post-Renaissance mathematics, for the key idea is this: The limit can be evaluated by integration. This, essentially, is what is known as the *Fundamental Theorem* of integral calculus. It ties together the summation process (which Archimedes used over two thousand years ago for finding areas, volumes, and centers of gravity) and the differentiation process, from which one may find the tangent to a curve. It is a remarkable fact that the inverse of the "tangent problem" (that is, the inverse of differentiation) pro-vides a ready tool for solving the summation problem. And its applications, as we shall see, extend far beyond the finding of areas; e.g., finding volumes of solids, lengths of curves, areas of surfaces of revolution, centers of gravity, work done by a variable force, gravitational and electrical potential, popula-tion growth, and cardiac output, to mention only a few.

While Eq. (1) above is expressed in terms of area, and up until now has been restricted to positive-valued functions, the Fundamental Theorem is less restrictive.

Fundamental Theorem of Integral Calculus.   *Let f be a function that is contin-uous over the domain $a \le x \le b$. Let*

$$a, \quad x_1, \quad x_2, \quad \dots, \quad x_{n-1}, \quad b \qquad (2)$$

be a set of numbers $a < x_1 < x_2 < \cdots < x_{n-1} < b$, which partition the interval (a, b) into n equal subintervals each of length

$$\Delta x = \frac{(b-a)}{n}. \qquad (3)$$

Let $c_1, c_2, \dots, c_n$ be a set of n numbers, one in each subinterval,

$$a \le c_1 \le x_1, \qquad x_1 \le c_2 \le x_2, \qquad \dots, \qquad x_{n-1} \le c_n \le b. \qquad (4)$$

Let

$$S_n = f(c_1)\, \Delta x + f(c_2)\, \Delta x + \cdots + f(c_n)\, \Delta x$$

$$= \sum_{k=1}^{n} f(c_k)\, \Delta x. \qquad (5)$$

Finally, let $F(x)$ be any integral of $f(x)\, dx$,

$$F(x) = \int f(x)\, dx. \qquad (6)$$

4–8

THE DEFINITE INTEGRAL AND THE FUNDAMENTAL THEOREM OF INTEGRAL CALCULUS

Then, as $n \to \infty$,

$$\lim S_n = \lim \sum f(c_k) \, \Delta x = F(b) - F(a). \tag{7}$$

Proof. We shall first prove (7) for the special set of numbers $c_1, c_2, \ldots, c_n$ that we get by applying the Mean Value Theorem of Article 3–8 to the function F in each subinterval. We can do this because F is differentiable and continuous. Thus, remembering that $F'(x) = f(x)$, we have

$$F(x_1) - F(a) = F'(c_1) \cdot (x_1 - a) = f(c_1) \, \Delta x,$$

$$F(x_2) - F(x_1) = F'(c_2) \cdot (x_2 - x_1) = f(c_2) \, \Delta x,$$

$$F(x_3) - F(x_2) = F'(c_3) \cdot (x_3 - x_2) = f(c_3) \, \Delta x, \tag{8}$$

$$\vdots \qquad\qquad \vdots \qquad\qquad \vdots$$

$$F(x_{n-1}) - F(x_{n-2}) = F'(c_{n-1}) \cdot (x_{n-1} - x_{n-2}) = f(c_{n-1}) \, \Delta x,$$

$$F(b) - F(x_{n-1}) = F'(c_n) \cdot (b - x_{n-1}) = f(c_n) \, \Delta x.$$

We add Eqs. (8), and note that $F(x_1), F(x_2), \ldots, F(x_{n-1})$ all appear twice on the left side, once positive and once negative. Hence these terms cancel out, leaving only $F(b) - F(a)$ in the sum. Thus we get

$$F(b) - F(a) = f(c_1) \, \Delta x + f(c_2) \, \Delta x + \cdots + f(c_n) \, \Delta x. \tag{9}$$

Since the left side of this equation does not in any way involve n, it remains fixed as we let $n \to \infty$, thus establishing Eq. (7), for this particular way of choosing the numbers $c_1, c_2, \ldots, c_n$.

But the theorem states that the same answer is obtained no matter how the c's are chosen in the subintervals, so long as there is one c in each subinterval. To establish this final result, we recall that the function f is continuous on the closed interval $a \le x \le b$, and therefore is *uniformly* continuous there [Article 2–11, Theorem 5]. Hence, if ϵ is any positive number, there exists a positive number δ, depending only upon ϵ, such that

$$|f(c_k) - f(c_k')| < \epsilon \tag{10}$$

whenever

$$|c_k - c_k'| < \delta. \tag{11}$$

And we can make $\Delta x = (b - a)/n < \delta$ by making

$$n > \frac{(b - a)}{\delta}. \tag{12}$$

For all sufficiently large n, (12) is satisfied. Now let c_1, c_1' be two numbers in the first subinterval, c_2, c_2' in the second, and so on. Form the sums

$$S_n = \sum_{k=1}^{n} f(c_k) \, \Delta x,$$

$$S_n' = \sum_{k=1}^{n} f(c_k') \, \Delta x.$$

Their difference is less than or equal to

$$|f(c_1) - f(c_1')| \, \Delta x + |f(c_2) - f(c_2')| \, \Delta x + \cdots + |f(c_n) - f(c_n')| \, \Delta x.$$

$$(13)$$

Every term in (13) is less than $\epsilon \cdot \Delta x$, by (10), and there are n terms. Therefore

$$|S_n - S_n'| < n \cdot (\epsilon \cdot \Delta x) = \epsilon \cdot (n \, \Delta x) = \epsilon \cdot (b - a), \qquad (14)$$

provided condition (12) is satisfied. This inequality, (14), says that the sums S_n and S_n' that we get from two different choices of the c's in the subintervals can be made to differ by as little as we please [no more than $\epsilon \cdot (b - a)$] by making n sufficiently large. But for the particular choice of the c's in Eqs. (8), we have

$$S_n = F(b) - F(a).$$

Therefore S_n' differs arbitrarily little from $F(b) - F(a)$ when n is sufficiently large. This means that

$$\lim S_n' = F(b) - F(a). \qquad (15)$$

Equation (15) completes the proof.

REMARK.   The integral sign, $\int$, is a modified capital S (for sum), intended to remind us of the close connection between integration and summation.

The limit

$$\lim \sum f(c_k) \, \Delta x$$

in Eq. (7) is called the *definite integral* of f *from* a *to* b. It is denoted by the symbol

$$\int_a^b f(x) \, dx.$$

The numbers a and b are called the *limits of integration* of the integral, a being the *lower limit* and b the *upper limit*.

The Fundamental Theorem tells us that we can evaluate a definite integral if we know any indefinite integral $F(x)$ of the integrand $f(x) \, dx$. We just subtract $F(a)$ from $F(b)$.

EXAMPLE 1

$$\int_0^{\pi/2} \cos x \, dx = \sin x \Big]_0^{\pi/2}$$

$$= \sin \frac{\pi}{2} - \sin 0$$

$$= 1.$$

Three Properties of Definite Integrals

Definite integrals of continuous functions have simple algebraic properties that are often used in computations.

First, the integral of a constant multiple of a function is that same constant times the integral of the function:

(A) $$\int_a^b kf(x)\,dx = k \int_a^b f(x)\,dx, \quad k \text{ any constant.}$$

EXAMPLE 2

$$\int_0^\pi 5 \sin x\,dx = 5 \int_0^\pi \sin x\,dx$$

$$= 5 \left[-\cos x \right]_0^\pi$$

$$= 5[-\cos \pi + \cos 0] = 10.$$

EXAMPLE 3

$$\int_0^4 -x^2\,dx = -\int_0^4 x^2\,dx = -\left[\frac{x^3}{3} \right]_0^4 = -\frac{64}{3}.$$

Second, the integral of the sum of two functions is the sum of their integrals:

(B) $$\int_a^b [f(x) + g(x)]\,dx = \int_a^b f(x)\,dx + \int_a^b g(x)\,dx.$$

A similar rule holds for the difference of two functions.

EXAMPLE 4

$$\int_1^2 \left[3 - \frac{6}{x^2} \right]\,dx = \int_1^2 3\,dx - \int_1^2 \frac{6}{x^2}\,dx$$

$$= \left[3x \right]_1^2 - \left[-\frac{6}{x} \right]_1^2$$

$$= 6 - 3 + 3 - 6 = 0.$$

Third, the sign of an integral changes when its limits of integration are interchanged.

(C) $$\int_b^a f(x)\,dx = -\int_a^b f(x)\,dx.$$

EXAMPLE 5

$$\int_1^0 [4 - 5x^2]\,dx = \int_0^1 [5x^2 - 4]\,dx$$

$$= \left[5\left(\frac{x^3}{3} \right) - 4x \right]_0^1 = -\frac{7}{3}.$$

As you might suspect, the first two of the three properties of definite integrals, Properties (A) and (B), are related to the analogous properties of indefinite integrals. We will make the relationship explicit when we return to the three properties later in this article. For the moment, however, we will turn our attention to the relation between definite integrals and area.

If a continuous function $f(x)$ has no negative values over $a \le x \le b$, then the definite integral

$$\int_a^b f(x)\,dx = F(x)\Big]_a^b = F(b) - F(a) \tag{16}$$

represents the area under its graph, above the x-axis, between the ordinates at $x = a$ and $x = b$. If, on the other hand, the function f were everywhere negative between a and b, the summands $f(c_k)\,\Delta x$ would all be negative (assuming $b > a$ and $\Delta x = (b - a)/n$ is positive) and the integral, (16), would be negative.

EXAMPLE 6. For $|x| < 2$, $f(x) = x^2 - 4$ is negative (Fig. 4–17(a)).

$$\int_{-2}^2 f(x)\,dx = \frac{x^3}{3} - 4x\Big]_{-2}^2 = (\tfrac{8}{3} - 8) - (-\tfrac{8}{3} + 8) = -\tfrac{32}{3}.$$

The area between the curve and the x-axis, from $x = -2$ to $x = +2$, contains $\tfrac{32}{3}$ units of area. The sign is negative because the curve lies below the x-axis. Clearly, the graph (Fig. 4–17(b)) of

$$y - g(x) - -f(x) = 4 - x^2, \qquad -2 \le x \le 2$$

is just the mirror image, with respect to the x-axis as mirror, of the curve in Fig. 4–17(a). The area between the graph of $y = g(x)$ and the x-axis is

$$\int_{-2}^2 g(x)\,dx = 4x - \frac{x^3}{3}\Big]_{-2}^2 = \tfrac{32}{3}.$$

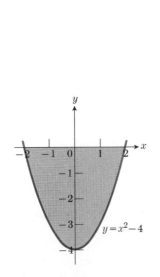

4–17 These graphs enclose the same amount of area with the x-axis, but the definite integrals of the two functions from -2 to 2 differ in sign.

The absolute value is the same as for the integral of $f(x)\,dx$ between the same limits. For $g(x)\,dx$ the sign is positive, since the area between the g-curve and the x-axis is above the axis.

If the graph of $y = f(x)$, $a \le x \le b$, is partly below and partly above the x-axis, as in Fig. 4–18, then

$$\lim \sum f(c_k)\,\Delta x = \int_a^b f(x)\,dx = F(x)\Big]_a^b = F(b) - F(a)$$

is the algebraic sum of *signed* areas, positive areas above the x-axis, negative areas below. For example, if the absolute values of the areas between the curve and the x-axis in Fig. 4–18 are A_1, A_2, A_3, A_4, then the definite integral of f from a to b is equal to

$$\int_a^b f(x)\,dx = -A_1 + A_2 - A_3 + A_4.$$

4–18 The integral $\int_a^b f(x)\,dx$ is the algebraic sum of signed areas.

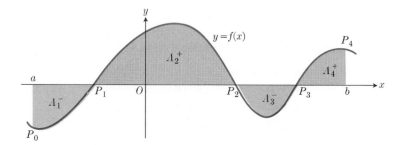

Thus if we wanted the sum of the absolute values of these signed areas, that is,

$$A = |-A_1| + A_2 + |-A_3| + A_4,$$

we should need to find the abscissas s_1, s_2, s_3 of the points P_1, P_2, P_3 where the curve crosses the x-axis. We would then compute, separately,

$$-A_1 = \int_a^{s_1} f(x)\,dx, \qquad A_2 = \int_{s_1}^{s_2} f(x)\,dx,$$

$$-A_3 = \int_{s_2}^{s_3} f(x)\,dx, \qquad A_4 = \int_{s_3}^b f(x)\,dx,$$

and add their absolute values.

EXAMPLE 7. Find the total area bounded by the curve $y = x^3 - 4x$ and the x-axis.

Solution. The graph in Fig. 4–19 lies above the x-axis from -2 to 0, below from 0 to $+2$. (The polynomial $x^3 - 4x$ factors as

$$x^3 - 4x = x(x-2)(x+2),$$

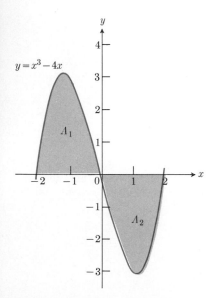

4–19 Graph of $y = x^3 - 4x$, $-2 \le x \le 2$.

and we determine the sign of the product from the signs of the three factors.)

$$A_1 = \int_{-2}^{0} (x^3 - 4x)\, dx = \frac{x^4}{4} - 2x^2 \bigg]_{-2}^{0} = 0 - (4 - 8) = +4,$$

$$-A_2 = \int_{0}^{2} (x^3 - 4x)\, dx = \frac{x^4}{4} - 2x^2 \bigg]_{0}^{2} = (4 - 8) - 0 = -4,$$

$$A_1 + |-A_2| = 4 + |-4| = 8.$$

The definite integral, as a limit of sums, provides a new way of defining functions. The integral of any continuous function $f(t)$ from $t = a$ to $t = x$ defines a number

$$F(x) = \int_{a}^{x} f(t)\, dt, \tag{17a}$$

which can be computed as a limit (at least in theory). The function F defined by this formula has the property that its derivative at any x is the value of the integrand f at x:

$$F'(x) = f(x). \tag{17b}$$

To show this, we use the definition of the derivative

$$F'(x) = \lim_{\Delta x \to 0} \frac{F(x + \Delta x) - F(x)}{\Delta x}$$

$$= \lim_{\Delta x \to 0} \frac{1}{\Delta x} \int_{x}^{x + \Delta x} f(t)\, dt.$$

By the Intermediate Value Theorem, Article 4–7, Eq. (5), we have

$$\int_{x}^{x + \Delta x} f(t)\, dt = f(c)\, \Delta x$$

for some c between x and $x + \Delta x$. When we divide both sides of this equation by Δx, and then let Δx approach zero, c approaches x and $f(c)$ approaches $f(x)$. (Why?) Hence

$$F'(x) = \lim_{\Delta x \to 0} \left[\frac{1}{\Delta x} f(c) \cdot \Delta x \right] = \lim_{c \to x} f(c) = f(x).$$

In other words,

$$\frac{d}{dx} \left(\int_{a}^{x} f(t)\, dt \right) = f(x). \tag{18}$$

EXAMPLE 8. Suppose

$$F(x) = \int_{0}^{x} \sqrt{1 - t^2}\, dt, \qquad 0 < x < 1.$$

Then

$$F'(x) = \sqrt{1 - x^2}.$$

Equation (18) tells us that, if f is a continuous function, then there is a function of which it is the derivative. That is, *every continuous function has an indefinite integral.* We can use this fact to establish Properties (A), (B), and (C) for definite integrals of continuous functions.

Verification of Properties (A), (B), and (C)

Let $f(x)$ and $g(x)$ be continuous for $a \le x \le b$, and let

$$F(x) = \int f(x)\, dx, \qquad G(x) = \int g(x)\, dx.$$

These indefinite integrals have the properties that

$$\int kf(x)\, dx = kF(x) \tag{19}$$

and

$$\int [f(x) + g(x)]\, dx = F(x) + G(x). \tag{20}$$

Equations (19) and (20) lead immediately to properties (A) and (B) for definite integrals, as follows:

$$\text{(A)} \qquad \int_a^b kf(x)\, dx = kF(x)\Big]_a^b = kF(b) - kF(a)$$
$$= k[F(b) - F(a)]$$
$$= k \int_a^b f(x)\, dx.$$

$$\text{(B)} \qquad \int_a^b [f(x) + g(x)]\, dx = \Big[F(x) + G(x)\Big]_a^b$$
$$= [F(b) + G(b)] - [F(a) + G(a)]$$
$$= [F(b) - F(a)] + [G(b) - G(a)]$$
$$= \int_a^b f(x)\, dx + \int_a^b g(x)\, dx.$$

As for Property (C), we have

$$\text{(C)} \qquad \int_b^a f(x)\, dx = F(a) - F(b)$$
$$= -[F(b) - F(a)]$$
$$= -\int_a^b f(x)\, dx.$$

Two Further Properties of Definite Integrals

There are two other properties of definite integrals of continuous functions that are worth mentioning now for later use.

The first is that the integral of a nonnegative function is never negative:

(D) If $f(x) \geq 0$ for $a \leq x \leq b$, then $\displaystyle\int_a^b f(x)\, dx \geq 0$.

The reason is that none of the approximating sums $\sum f(c_k)$ is ever negative, so the smallest limiting value they could possibly have is zero.

The second is that integrals preserve order:

(E) If $f(x) \leq g(x)$ for $a \leq x \leq b$, then $\displaystyle\int_a^b f(x)\, dx \leq \int_a^b g(x)\, dx$.

The reason for (E) is that $[g(x) - f(x)] \geq 0$ for $a \leq x \leq b$, so that, by Properties (B) and (D),

$$\int_a^b g(x)\, dx - \int_a^b f(x)\, dx = \int_a^b [g(x) - f(x)]\, dx \geq 0.$$

The Fundamental Theorem is sometimes used as a tool for approximating sums. This is the reverse of what we did in Article 4–6. There we found formulas for sums of first powers, and of squares, of the positive integers 1 through n. Then we used these formulas to compute limits of sums of areas of inscribed rectangles for the graphs of $y = mx$, $a \leq x \leq b$, and of $y = x^2$, $0 \leq x \leq b$. In the following example, we work back from the definite integral (or, what amounts to the same thing, the area under the graph) to an approximation for the sum of the square roots of the integers 1 through n. The process is not completely reversible. We can go from exact formulas for sums to definite integrals by way of limits, but we cannot go back from the definite integral to an exact formula for the sum, because we don't know which terms went to zero in the limit process, and hence we cannot recover them.

EXAMPLE 9. Consider the function defined by $f(x) = \sqrt{x}$, $0 \leq x \leq 1$. Let n be a positive integer, and $\Delta x = 1/n$. In Eq. (5) take $c_1 = x_1 = \Delta x$, $c_2 = x_2 = 2\,\Delta x, \ldots, c_n = b = 1 = n\,\Delta x$. Then

$$S_n = \sqrt{c_1}\,\Delta x + \sqrt{c_2}\,\Delta x + \cdots + \sqrt{c_n}\,\Delta x$$

$$= \frac{\sqrt{1} + \sqrt{2} + \cdots + \sqrt{n}}{n^{3/2}}$$

$$\to \int \sqrt{x}\, dx \Big]_0^1 = \frac{x^{3/2}}{3/2}\Big]_0^1 = \frac{2}{3}, \quad \text{as } n \to \infty.$$

When n is large, S_n will be close to its limit $\frac{2}{3}$. This means that the numerator

$$\sqrt{1} + \sqrt{2} + \cdots + \sqrt{n} \text{ is approximately equal to } \tfrac{2}{3}n^{3/2}.$$

For $n = 10$, the sum of the square roots is 22.5^-, while $\frac{2}{3}n^{3/2}$ is 21.1^-, so that the approximation is in error by about 6 percent.

PROBLEMS

1. For each of the following cases, integrate the given function f to find a new function F, defined by $F(x) = \int f(x)\, dx$. Apply the Mean Value Theorem to this new function F to find an expression for c_k in terms of x_k and x_{k-1}

such that

$$F(x_k) - F(x_{k-1}) = F'(c_k)(x_k - x_{k-1}).$$

a) $f(x) = x$ **b)** $f(x) = x^2$

c) $f(x) = x^3$ **d)** $f(x) = 1/\sqrt{x}$.

2. Consider the function defined by $f(x) = x$ and take $a = 0$, $b > 0$. Show that by taking

$$c_k = \tfrac{1}{2}(x_k + x_{k-1})$$

in Eq. (5), the resulting sum has the constant value

$$S_n = \tfrac{1}{2}b^2,$$

independent of the value of n. (Let $a = x_0$ and $b = x_n$.)

3. Take $f(x) = x^2$, $a = 0$, $b > 0$, and form S_n (Eq. (5)), using

$$c_k = \sqrt{\frac{x_k^2 + x_k x_{k-1} + x_{k-1}^2}{3}}.$$

Show that no matter what value n has, the resulting sum S_n has the constant value

$$S_n = \tfrac{1}{3}b^3.$$

(Let $a = x_0$ and $b = x_n$.) What is the limit of S_n as $n \to \infty$? Note that one should substitute $x_k - x_{k-1}$ for Δx and recognize that

$$\left(\frac{x_k^2 + x_k x_{k-1} + x_{k-1}^2}{3}\right)\Delta x = \frac{x_k^3 - x_{k-1}^3}{3}.$$

4. Take $f(x) = x^3$, $a = 0$, $b > 0$, and calculate S_n (Eq. (5)), taking

$$c_k = \sqrt[3]{\frac{x_k^3 + x_k^2 x_{k-1} + x_k x_{k-1}^2 + x_{k-1}^3}{4}}.$$

Express the result in a form that is independent of the number of subdivisions n. (Let $a = x_0$ and $b = x_n$.)

5. Take $f(x) = 1/\sqrt{x}$, $a = 1$, $b > 1$. Use the intermediate values

$$c_k = \left(\frac{\sqrt{x_{k-1}} + \sqrt{x_k}}{2}\right)^2$$

and calculate S_n (Eq. (5)). Express the result in a form that is

independent of the number of subdivisions. (Let $a = x_0$, and $b = x_n$.)

Evaluate each of the following definite integrals (6 through 16).

6. $\displaystyle\int_1^2 (2x + 5)\, dx$ **7.** $\displaystyle\int_0^1 (x^2 - 2x + 3)\, dx$

8. $\displaystyle\int_{-1}^1 (x + 1)^2\, dx$ **9.** $\displaystyle\int_0^2 \sqrt{4x + 1}\, dx$

10. $\displaystyle\int_0^\pi \sin x\, dx$ **11.** $\displaystyle\int_0^\pi \cos x\, dx$

12. $\displaystyle\int_{\pi/4}^{\pi/2} \frac{\cos x\, dx}{\sin^2 x}$ (Let $u = \sin x$.)

13. $\displaystyle\int_0^{\pi/6} \frac{\sin 2x}{\cos^2 2x}\, dx$ ***14.** $\displaystyle\int_0^\pi \sin^2 x\, dx$

***15.** $\displaystyle\int_0^{2\pi/\omega} \cos^2 (\omega t)\, dt$ (ω constant)

16. $\displaystyle\int_0^1 \frac{dx}{(2x + 1)^3}$

17. (a) Express the area between the curves $y = x^2$, $y = 18 - x^2$ as a *limit of a sum* of areas of rectangles. (b) Evaluate the area of part (a) by Eq. (7).

In each of the following problems (18 through 21), use Eq. (18) to find $F'(x)$ for the given functions F:

18. $\displaystyle F(x) = \int_0^x \sqrt{1 + t^2}\, dt$ **19.** $\displaystyle F(x) = \int_1^x \frac{dt}{t}$

20. $\displaystyle F(x) = \int_x^1 \sqrt{1 - t^2}\, dt$ **21.** $\displaystyle F(x) = \int_0^x \frac{dt}{1 + t^2}$

22. $\displaystyle F(x) = \int_1^{2x} \cos (t^2)\, dt$

[*Hint.* Use the chain rule with $u = 2x$.]

23. $\displaystyle F(x) = \int_1^{x^2} \frac{dt}{1 + \sqrt{1 - t}}$ **24.** $\displaystyle F(x) = \int_{\sin x}^0 \frac{dt}{2 + t}$

---

* See Problem 17, Article 4–7.

4–9

RULES FOR APPROXIMATING INTEGRALS

Any definite integral may be thought of as an area, or an algebraic sum of signed areas, as discussed in Article 4–8. We know how to evaluate a definite integral when an indefinite integral of the integrand is known. But there are simple functions, for example $(\sin x)/x$, for which no simple indefinite integral is known. In such instances, as long as the integrand is continuous, the definite integral still exists and we may wish to evaluate it numerically. We can often obtain good accuracy by using numerical methods for approximating a definite integral. These methods are also important for computations done by machines. One of the simplest of these numerical methods is the *trapezoidal rule*, which we shall now derive. (See Fig. 4-20.)

Suppose that the definite integral $\int_a^b f(x)\,dx$ is to be evaluated. We divide the interval $a \le x \le b$ into n subintervals, each of length $h = (b - a)/n$, in the usual way by inserting the points

$$x_1 = a + h, \quad x_2 = a + 2h, \quad \ldots, \quad x_{n-1} = a + (n-1)h$$

between

$$x_0 = a \quad \text{and} \quad x_n = b.$$

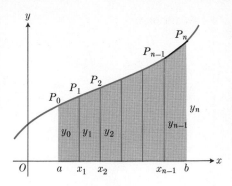

4-20 The sum of areas of trapezoids can give a good approximation of area under a curve.

The integral from a to b is just the sum of the integrals from a to x_1, from x_1 to x_2, etc.:

$$\int_a^b f(x)\,dx = \int_a^{x_1} f(x)\,dx + \int_{x_1}^{x_2} f(x)\,dx + \cdots + \int_{x_{n-1}}^b f(x)\,dx$$

$$= \sum_{k=1}^n \int_{x_{k-1}}^{x_k} f(x)\,dx.$$

The integral over the first subinterval is now *approximated* by the area of the trapezoid $aP_0P_1x_1$, which equals $\frac{1}{2}(y_0 + y_1)h$; over the second subinterval by the area of the trapezoid $x_1P_1P_2x_2$, which is $\frac{1}{2}(y_1 + y_2)h$; and so on. The *trapezoidal rule* is: To estimate the definite integral $\int_a^b f(x)\,dx$, use the *trapezoidal approximation* T given by

$$T = \tfrac{1}{2}(y_0 + y_1)h + \tfrac{1}{2}(y_1 + y_2)h + \cdots$$
$$\quad + \tfrac{1}{2}(y_{n-2} + y_{n-1})h + \tfrac{1}{2}(y_{n-1} + y_n)h$$
$$= \frac{h}{2}(y_0 + 2y_1 + 2y_2 + \cdots + 2y_{n-1} + y_n), \tag{1a}$$

where

$$y_0 = f(x_0), \quad y_1 = f(x_1), \quad \ldots, \quad y_{n-1} = f(x_{n-1}), \quad y_n = f(x_n).$$

Since $h = (b - a)/n$, we may write the approximation in the following alternative form.

TRAPEZOIDAL RULE

$$\int_a^b f(x)\,dx \approx T = \frac{b-a}{2n}(y_0 + 2y_1 + 2y_2 + \cdots + 2y_{n-1} + y_n) \tag{1b}$$

EXAMPLE 1.   Use the trapezoidal rule with $n = 4$ to estimate $\int_1^2 x^2\,dx$ and compare this approximation with the exact value of the integral.

Solution.   The exact value of this integral is

$$\int_1^2 x^2\,dx = \frac{x^3}{3}\bigg]_1^2 = \frac{7}{3} \approx 2.33333.$$

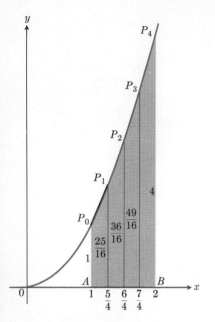

4–21 The trapezoidal approximation to the area under the graph of $y = x^2$, $1 \le x \le 2$, is a slight overestimate.

For the trapezoidal approximation we have

$$a = 1, \qquad b = 2, \qquad n = 4, \qquad h = \tfrac{1}{4},$$

so that

$$x_0 = a \qquad\quad = 1, \qquad y_0 = f(x_0) = \;\; 1^2 = \tfrac{16}{16}$$

$$x_1 = a + \;\; h = \tfrac{5}{4}, \qquad y_1 = f(x_1) = (\tfrac{5}{4})^2 = \tfrac{25}{16}$$

$$x_2 = a + 2h = \tfrac{6}{4}, \qquad y_2 = f(x_2) = (\tfrac{6}{4})^2 = \tfrac{36}{16}$$

$$x_3 = a + 3h = \tfrac{7}{4}, \qquad y_3 = f(x_3) = (\tfrac{7}{4})^2 = \tfrac{49}{16}$$

$$x_4 = b \qquad\quad = 2, \qquad y_4 = f(x_4) = (\tfrac{8}{4})^2 = \tfrac{64}{16}$$

and

$$T = \frac{b-a}{2n}\,(y_0 + 2y_1 + 2y_2 + 2y_3 + y_4)$$

$$= \tfrac{1}{8}(\tfrac{75}{4}) = \tfrac{75}{32} = 2.34375.$$

Thus the approximation is too large by about half a percent. As the graph in Fig. 4–21 shows, each approximating trapezoid contains slightly more area than the corresponding strip of area under the curve.

Accuracy of the Trapezoidal Approximation

As n increases and $h = \Delta x$ approaches zero, the trapezoidal approximation approaches the exact value of the definite integral as limit. For we have

$$T = (y_1 + y_2 + \cdots + y_n)\,\Delta x + \tfrac{1}{2}(y_0 - y_n)\,\Delta x$$

$$= \sum_{k=1}^{n} f(x_k)\,\Delta x + \tfrac{1}{2}[f(a) - f(b)]\,\Delta x. \qquad (2)$$

When n increases without bound and Δx approaches zero, the sum indicated by the sigma approaches $\int_a^b f(x)\,dx$ as limit, and the last term in (2) approaches zero. Therefore,

$$\lim T = \int_a^b f(x)\,dx.$$

This means, of course, that by taking n sufficiently large, we can make the difference between T and the integral as small as desired.

By methods studied in more advanced calculus (an extension of the Mean Value Theorem), it is possible to prove* that, if f is continuous on $a \le x \le b$, and twice differentiable on $a < x < b$, then there is a number c between a and b such that

$$\int_a^b f(x)\,dx = T - \frac{b-a}{12}\,f''(c)\cdot h^2. \qquad (3)$$

---

* See, for example, J. M. H. Olmsted, *Intermediate Analysis* (Appleton-Century-Crofts, 1956), p. 145.

Thus as h approaches zero, the "error," that is, the difference between the integral and the trapezoidal approximation, approaches zero as the *square* of h. By estimating the size of the second derivative of f between a and b, we can get a good estimate of how accurately T approximates the integral.

EXAMPLE 2. In Example 1, $f(x) = x^2, f''(x) = 2$, and the error predicted by (3) is

$$-\frac{b-a}{12} f''(c) \cdot h^2 = -\frac{2-1}{12} \cdot 2 \cdot \frac{1}{16} = -\frac{1}{96}.$$

This is precisely what we find when we subtract $T = \frac{75}{32}$ from $\int_1^2 x^2 \, dx = \frac{7}{3}$, since $\frac{7}{3} - \frac{75}{32} = -\frac{1}{96}$. Here we are able to give the error *exactly*, since the second derivative of $f(x) = x^2$ is a constant and we have no uncertainty caused by not knowing c in the term $f''(c)$. Of course we are not always this lucky, and in most cases the best we can do is to *estimate* the difference between the integral and T.

EXAMPLE 3. Find how many subdivisions are required to approximate

$$\int_1^2 \frac{1}{x} \, dx$$

with the trapezoidal rule with an error of less than 10^{-4}.

Solution. The question is how small an h we need to make

$$E = \left| \frac{b-a}{12} f''(c) \cdot h^2 \right| < 10^{-4}.$$

Once we know this, we can decide how many subdivisions to make (the value of n). Since

$$f''(x) = 2x^{-3} = \frac{2}{x^3},$$

$f''(x)$ decreases steadily from

$$f''(1) = 2 \qquad \text{to} \qquad f''(2) = \tfrac{1}{4}.$$

Therefore, $|f''(c)| \le 2$, and

$$E = \left| \frac{2-1}{12} f''(c) \cdot h^2 \right| \le \frac{1}{12} \cdot 2 \cdot h^2 = \frac{h^2}{6}.$$

If we make $h^2/6 < 10^{-4}$, then E will be less than 10^{-4}. This can be achieved by taking

$$h^2 < 6 \times 10^{-4},$$

which will hold if

$$0 < h < 2.44 \times 10^{-2}.$$

Since $h = (b-a)/n = 1/n$, we can rewrite the inequality above in terms of n

and conclude that

$$n = \frac{1}{h} > 40.98.$$

The first integer beyond 40.98 is $n = 41$. With $n = 41$ subdivisions, we can guarantee $E < 10^{-4}$. Of course, any larger n will work, too.

Simpson's Rule

Another method for approximating integrals, called *Simpson's method*, is based on the formula

$$A_p = \frac{h}{3}[y_0 + 4y_1 + y_2]$$

for the area under the arc of the parabola

$$y = Ax^2 + Bx + C$$

between $x = -h$ and $x = +h$, as in Fig. 4–22.*

This result is readily established as follows: In the first place,

$$A_p = \int_{-h}^{h} (Ax^2 + Bx + C)\, dx$$

$$= \frac{2Ah^3}{3} + 2Ch.$$

Since the curve passes through the three points $(-h, y_0)$, $(0, y_1)$, and (h, y_2), we also have

$$y_0 = Ah^2 - Bh + C, \qquad y_1 = C, \qquad y_2 = Ah^2 + Bh + C,$$

from which there follows

$$C = y_1,$$
$$Ah^2 - Bh = y_0 - y_1,$$
$$Ah^2 + Bh = y_2 - y_1,$$
$$2Ah^2 = y_0 + y_2 - 2y_1.$$

Hence, expressing the area A_p in terms of the ordinates y_0, y_1, and y_2, we have

$$A_p = \frac{h}{3}[2Ah^2 + 6C] = \frac{h}{3}[(y_0 + y_2 - 2y_1) + 6y_1]$$

or

$$A_p = \frac{h}{3}[y_0 + 4y_1 + y_2]. \tag{4}$$

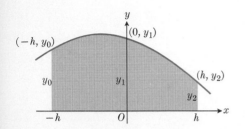

4–22 The shaded area under the parabola is $(h/3)(y_0 + 4y_1 + y_2)$.

---

*   We choose the interval $-h \le x \le h$ to simplify the algebra. There is no loss in generality in so doing, because the area does not depend on the location of the y-axis.

Simpson's rule follows from applying the formula for A_p to successive pieces of the curve $y = f(x)$ between $x = a$ and $x = b$. Each separate piece of the curve, covering an x-subinterval of width $2h$, is approximated by an arc of a parabola through its ends and its midpoint. The areas under the parabolic arcs are then added to give Simpson's rule.

SIMPSON'S RULE

$$\int_a^b f(x)\, dx \simeq S$$

$$= \frac{h}{3}[y_0 + 4y_1 + 2y_2 + 4y_3 + 2y_4 + \cdots + 2y_{n-2} + 4y_{n-1} + y_n] \quad \textbf{(5)}$$

The y's in Eq. (5) are the values of $y = f(x)$ at the points

$$x_0 = a, \quad x_1 = a + h, \quad x_2 = a + 2h, \quad \ldots, \quad x_n = a + nh = b,$$

corresponding to a subdivision of the interval $a \le x \le b$ into n equal subintervals of width $h = (b - a)/n$. (See Fig. 4–23.) The number n must be even in order to apply the method.

To estimate the error in the Simpson approximation, we have the formula*

$$\int_a^b f(x)\, dx = S - \frac{b - a}{180} f^{(4)}(c) \cdot h^4, \quad \textbf{(6)}$$

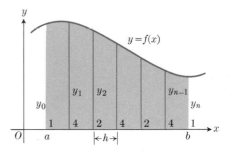

4–23 The number of subdivisions must be even if Simpson's rule is to work.

which applies when f is continuous on $a \le x \le b$ and four times differentiable on $a < x < b$. The fact that Eq. (6) has an $h^4/180$ while the estimate for the trapezoidal rule in Eq. (3) has an $h^2/12$ suggests that Simpson's rule will generally give more accurate results than the trapezoidal rule for a given h when h is small.

If $f(x)$ is a polynomial of degree less than four, then $f^{(4)}(c) = 0$ in Eq. (6) and the approximation S gives the exact value of the integral. We illustrate this in the next example, in which, for comparison, we approximate the value of an integral whose value we already know.

EXAMPLE 4. Approximate $\int_0^1 4x^3\, dx$ by the trapezoidal rule and by Simpson's rule with $n = 2$.

Solution. The exact value of the integral is

$$\int_0^1 4x^3\, dx = x^4 \Big|_0^1 = 1.$$

The trapezoidal rule gives

$$T = \frac{1}{2 \cdot 2}[0 + 2 \cdot 4(\tfrac{1}{2})^3 + 4(1)^3] = \tfrac{1}{4}[1 + 4] = \tfrac{5}{4}.$$

---

* See, for example, J. M. H. Olmsted, *Intermediate Analysis* (Appleton-Century-Crofts), p. 146.

Simpson's rule gives

$$S = \frac{1}{2 \cdot 3}[0 + 4 \cdot 4(\tfrac{1}{2})^3 + 4(1)^3] = \tfrac{1}{6}[6] = 1.$$

Simpson's rule gives the exact value in this case because $f(x) = 4x^3$ is a polynomial of degree less than four. The fourth derivative of f is zero, and the error term in Eq. (6) vanishes.

Both of the approximation rules of this article can give good estimates of the integral of a continuous function from a table of values of the function when the increment h is small enough. Thus we can sometimes expect to obtain useful estimates of the integral of a function even when we do not know a formula for the function. This is the case in many practical applications in which the source of our information about a function is a set of specific values of the function measured in the laboratory or in the field.

EXAMPLE 5 *Measuring cardiac output.** The rate R at which a person's heart pumps blood is usually measured in liters per minute and is called the person's *cardiac output*. For a person at rest, this rate is usually about 5 liters per minute. But during strenuous exercise it can rise to more than 30 liters per minute. It can also change significantly as a result of disease.

One way to measure cardiac output is to inject a known amount D of dye into a main vein near the heart. The dyed blood circulates through the right side of the heart, the lungs, and the left side of the heart, and begins to enter the arteries. The concentration of the dye can be monitored in the aorta, say, where the first of the dye can be expected to appear a few seconds after injection. After entering the aorta, the dyed blood takes about 20 seconds to complete its trip through the body, heart, lungs and heart again, and to start past the monitoring point once more. A typical set of dye concentration readings resulting from an injection of $D = 5.0$ milligrams of dye are shown in Table 4–3 and plotted in Fig. 4–24.

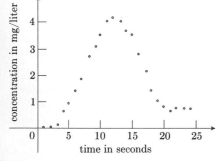

4–24 Dye concentrations measured in the aorta near the heart at one-second intervals.

Table 4–3. Data (in mg/l) for the dye-dilution method of measuring cardiac output

Seconds after injection	Concentration	Seconds after injection	Concentration	Seconds after injection	Concentration
0	0	9	3.0	18	1.5
1	0	10	3.7	19	1.1
2	0	11	4.0	20	0.9
3	0.1	12	4.1	21	0.8
4	0.6	13	4.0	22	0.9
5	0.9	14	3.8	23	0.9
6	1.4	15	3.7	24	0.9
7	1.9	16	2.9		
8	2.7	17	2.2		

* From *Measuring Cardiac Output*, by B. Horelick and S. Koont, Project UMAP, Education Development Center, Inc., 1978.

Table 4–3 shows measurements taken at the aorta every second for 24 seconds. The concentrations are recorded in milligrams of dye per liter of blood. The data show that most of the dye passed through the aorta in the first 15 or 20 seconds, but that the concentration did not taper to zero during the last three seconds. In fact, after $t = 21$ seconds, the dye concentration rose slightly. The dye that had been pumped through during the first seconds had circulated through the body and was beginning to reappear.

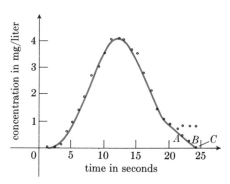

4-25 Dye concentration $C(t)$ pictured with a smooth curve that fits the real and adjusted data points.

To measure the cardiac output, therefore, we *assume* that the concentration of first-time-through dye did taper off even though the concentration readings did not. The concentration seemed to be falling steadily just before $t = 21$, and we simply continue the trend by replacing the last three data points in the table with the three fictitious data points $A(22, 0.5)$, $B(23, 0.3)$, and $C(24, 0)$, as shown in Fig. 4–25. In Fig. 4–25 we have fitted a smooth curve to the data points to represent the dye concentration $C(t)$ as a continuous function of time. This is a reasonable thing to do because there is no reason for the dye concentration to change abruptly.

The amount of blood that flows past the monitoring point in the aorta in a time interval Δt is $R \, \Delta t$ (rate times time). The amount of *dye* that flows past in Δt seconds is approximately $C(t_i)R \, \Delta t$, where $C(t_i)$ is the concentration observed at the beginning of the time interval. The total amount D of dye flowing by in the interval $0 \leq t \leq 24$ is approximately

$$D = \sum C(t_i)R \, \Delta t = R \sum C(t_i) \, \Delta t. \tag{7}$$

The sum on the right of Eq. (7) is an approximating sum for the definite integral

$$\int_0^{24} C(t) \, dt.$$

If we knew $C(t)$ as a continuous function of t, we could then write

$$D = R \int_0^{24} C(t) \, dt, \tag{8}$$

and compute the cardiac output R from the equation

$$R = \frac{D}{\int_0^{24} C(t) \, dt}. \tag{9}$$

However, we know $C(t)$ only at a set of isolated values of t. Fortunately, these values permit us to approximate the integral. The trapezoidal rule gives

$$\int_0^{24} C(t) \, dt \approx \frac{24 - 0}{2(24)}(0 + 0 + 0 + 0.2 + 1.2 + \cdots + 1.6 + 1.0 + 0.6 + 0)$$

$$= \tfrac{1}{2}(88.2) = 44.1. \tag{10}$$

We conclude that

$$R \approx \frac{D}{44.1} = \frac{5.0}{44.1} \approx 0.113 \text{ liters/second}$$

$$\approx 6.8 \text{ liters/minute.}$$

Simpson's rule gives

$$\int_0^{24} C(t)\, dt \approx \frac{24 - 0}{3(24)}\,[0 + 4(0) + 2(0) + 4(0.1)$$
$$+\, 2(0.6) + 4(0.9) + \cdots + 2(0.9) + 4(0.8)$$
$$+\, 2(0.5) + 4(0.3) + 0]$$
$$=\tfrac{1}{3}(132.2) \approx 44.1 \text{ (to the nearest tenth).} \qquad \textbf{(11)}$$

Again, $R \approx 6.8$ liters/minute.

The fact that there is no significant difference in the results of the two rules in this case can be traced to two factors. First, the increment $h = 1$ is fairly large. The h^4 in the Simpson error formula is no smaller than the h^2 in the trapezoidal error formula. Second, the data given are nearest-tenth estimates, and are not accurate enough to justify rounding the $\tfrac{1}{3}(132.2)$ in the Simpson calculation to anything more refined than 44.1.

PROBLEMS

1. Interpret the meaning of the sign of the error term in Eq. (3) in case the graph of $y = f(x)$ is: (a) concave upward over $a < x < b$; (b) concave downward. Illustrate both cases with sketches.

Approximate each of the following integrals (2–7) with $n = 4$ by (a) the trapezoidal rule and (b) Simpson's rule. Compare your answers with (c) the exact value in each case. Use the error terms in (d) Eq. (3) and (e) Eq. (6) to estimate the minimum number of subdivisions needed to approximate the integral with an error of less than 10^{-5} by each of the two rules.

2. $\displaystyle\int_0^2 x\, dx$ **3.** $\displaystyle\int_0^2 x^2\, dx$ **4.** $\displaystyle\int_0^2 x^3\, dx$

5. $\displaystyle\int_1^2 \frac{1}{x^2}\, dx$ **6.** $\displaystyle\int_1^4 \sqrt{x}\, dx$ **7.** $\displaystyle\int_0^\pi \sin x\, dx$

8. Estimate the error in using (a) the trapezoidal rule and (b) Simpson's rule to approximate $\int_1^2 (1/x)\, dx$ with $n = 10$.

9. Repeat Example 3 with Simpson's rule in place of the trapezoidal rule.

10. In what units should one express the integral

$$\int_0^{24} C(t)\, dt$$

in Example 5?

11. (*Calculator*) Carry out the calculation in Eq. (10).

12. (*Calculator*) The rate at which flashbulbs give off light varies during the flash. For some bulbs, the light, measured in *lumens*, reaches a peak and fades quickly, as shown in Fig. 4–26(a). For other bulbs, the light, instead of reaching a

a)

b)

4–26 Flashbulb output data from Tables 4–4 and 4–5 plotted and connected by smooth curves.

peak, stays at a moderate level for a relatively longer period of time, as shown in Fig. 4–26(b). To calculate how much light reaches the film in a camera, we must know when the shutter opens and closes. A typical focal-plane shutter opens 20 milliseconds and closes 70 milliseconds after the button is pressed. The amount A of light emitted by the flashbulb in this interval is

$$A = \int_{20}^{70} L(t)\, dt \quad \text{lumen-milliseconds,}$$

where $L(t)$ is the lumen output of the bulb as a function of time. Use the trapezoidal rule and the numerical data from Tables 4–4 and 4–5 to estimate A for each of the given bulbs, and find out which bulb gets more light to the film.*

Table 4–4.† Light output (in millions of lumens) vs. time (in milliseconds) for No. 22 flashbulb

Time after ignition	Light output	Time after ignition	Light output
0	0	30	1.7
5	0.2	35	0.7
10	0.5	40	0.35
15	2.6	45	0.2
20	4.2	50	0
25	3.0		

---

* From *Integration*, by W. U. Walton, *et al.*, Project CALC, Education Development Center, Inc., Newton, MA (1975), p. 83.

† Data from *Photographic Lamp and Equipment Guide*, P4–15P, Gen. Elec. Company, Cleveland, Ohio.

Table 4–5.‡ Light output (in millions of lumens) vs. time (in milliseconds) for No. 31 flashbulb

Time after ignition	Light output	Time after ignition	Light output	Time after ignition	Light output
0	0	35	0.9	65	1.0
5	0.1	40	1.0	70	0.8
10	0.3	45	1.1	75	0.6
15	0.7	50	1.3	80	0.3
20	1.0	55	1.4	85	0.2
25	1.2	60	1.3	90	0
30	1.0				

‡ Data from *Photographic Lamp and Equipment Guide*, P4–15P, Gen. Electric Company, Cleveland, Ohio.

4–10
SOME COMMENTS ON NOTATION

In each application of the definite integral it is reasonably easy to set up sums that approximate the answer to some physical problem. In general, it will even be possible (though not necessary) to find *particular* choices of the points c_k such that the *particular* sums

$$S_n = \sum_{k=1}^{n} f(c_k)\, \Delta x$$

give the *exact* value. Then

$$\lim_{n \to \infty} S_n = \int_a^b f(x)\, dx = F(x) \Big]_a^b = F(b) - F(a)$$

also gives the *exact* value. But since all sums S_n give the *same* answer in the limit (provided the function $f(x)$ is continuous for $a \le x \le b$, and this condition will usually be satisfied by the functions we shall encounter), we could get the same limit from

$$S_n = \sum_{k=1}^{n} f(x_k)\,\Delta x. \tag{1a}$$

Finally, we modify this notation slightly by dropping the subscript k entirely and writing simply

$$S_a^b = \sum_a^b f(x)\,\Delta x, \tag{1b}$$

where we write a and b to indicate that we have a sum of expressions, each of the form $f(x)\,\Delta x$, extending over a set of subintervals from $x = a$ to $x = b$. Of course it is not the *sum* (1b) that we are interested in, but rather the *limit* of the sum as given by the definite integral, and the notation (1b) is most suggestive of the final form, namely,

$$\lim_{\Delta x \to 0} S_a^b = \lim_{\Delta x \to 0} \sum_a^b f(x)\,\Delta x = \int_a^b f(x)\,dx = F(x)\Big]_a^b. \tag{2}$$

As remarked in Article 4–8, it was the close relationship between sums and integrals that led to the adoption of the symbol $\int$ (a modified S) to denote integration.

It should also be noted that *since it is the integral* that gives the *exact* answer in (2), and since the expression $f(x)\,dx$ after the integral sign is the same as the differential of $F(x)$,

$$\frac{dF(x)}{dx} = f(x), \tag{3a}$$

$$dF(x) = f(x)\,dx, \tag{3b}$$

we would arrive at the *correct final result* for the area under the curve $y = f(x) \geq 0$ between $x = a$ and $x = b$, say, if we were to write

$$dA = f(x)\,dx, \qquad A = \int_a^b f(x)\,dx. \tag{4}$$

It is easy to attach a geometric interpretation to (4), but it is also easy to be misled by this interpretation into feeling that the integral in (4) gives only an approximation to the area, rather than giving its exact value. Enough has already been said on this latter point, however, so that the careful reader need not be a victim of this delusion. If we accept the interpretation simply as a shortcut for setting up the *integral whose value gives the exact result*, we may thereby gain from its simplicity. Namely, if we again think of the area from the left boundary a to a right boundary x, this area is a function of x, with derivative $dA/dx = y = f(x)$, as we found in Article 4–7. When we multiply both sides of this equation by dx, we get the result $dA = f(x)\,dx$, as in (4). But if we think of dx as a small increment in x, we may also interpret dA as the area of a small rectangle with base extending along the x-axis from x to $x + dx$, and with altitude $f(x) = y$ equal to the ordinate of the curve (see Fig. 4–27. Then this rectangle gives an *approximation* to that portion of the

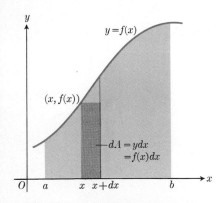

4–27 If dx is a small increment in x, then the area of the shaded rectangle is $f(x)\,dx$.

area under the curve lying between x and $x + dx$, and we think of the integral

$$A = \int_a^b f(x)\, dx$$

as adding together all of these small rectangles from $x = a$ to $x = b$ and then taking the *limit* of the sum so as to give the *exact value*.

It should be borne in mind that what has just been discussed should in no way obscure the fact that a *precise* formulation of the problem would involve a process of

a) subdividing the interval $a \leq x \leq b$,

b) forming a sum $\sum_a^b f(x)\, \Delta x$,

c) taking the limit, $\displaystyle\lim_{\Delta x \to 0} \sum_a^b f(x)\, \Delta x$, and

d) applying the fundamental theorem to evaluate this limit,

$$\lim_{\Delta x \to 0} \sum_a^b f(x)\, \Delta x = \int_a^b f(x)\, dx = F(x)\Big|_a^b.$$

Insofar as the shortcut described above leads to the same final answer, without leading to confusion or feelings of misgiving, it may be helpful and time-saving. But whenever we suspect that the final answer may be only an approximation instead of a mathematically exact answer, a reconsideration, along the lines that led up to the fundamental theorem, should be made. It is probably desirable, at least in the beginning, to go through the precise formulation first, and then it is but a matter of seconds to repeat the setup of the problem by the shortcut method.

SUMMARY

Much that we have done in this chapter is related to area. This is useful and gives us a way of interpreting sums like those in Eq. (5), Article 4–8, and Eq. (1a) in Article 4–10. But it is also good to express the main results in ways that don't depend upon area. In this article we shall summarize six results of major importance. Although we have appealed to the notion of area in presenting them in earlier sections, they can all be proved by purely analytical methods, with no reference to area. (See, for example, Apostol, *Modern Mathematical Analysis*, or Buck, *Advanced Calculus*, or Rudin, *Principles of Analysis*.)

Once again we start with a function f defined on an interval $a \leq x \leq b$. We partition the interval into n subintervals by inserting points $x_1, x_2, \ldots, x_{n-1}$ between $a = x_0$ and $b = x_n$. We do not require that the points be uniformly spaced. The kth subinterval has length $\Delta x_k = x_k - x_{k-1}$, which may vary with k. In the kth subinterval a number c_k is chosen arbitrarily, for each k from 1 through n. Then we form the sum

$$\sum_{k=1}^{n} f(c_k) \cdot (x_k - x_{k-1}). \tag{1}$$

This sum depends upon the function f, the points $x_0, x_1, x_2, \ldots, x_n$ and upon the c's. However, for a given function f and interval $[a, b]$ it may happen that all sums like (1) are nearly equal to some constant, provided the subintervals are all sufficiently short. If this is true, then that constant is called the *Riemann integral* of f from a to b, and is variously denoted by

$$R_a^b(f), \quad \text{or} \int_a^b f, \quad \text{or} \int_a^b f(x)\,dx, \quad \text{or} \int_a^b f(t)\,dt, \quad \text{or} \int_a^b f(u)\,du, \quad \text{and so on.}$$

Definition of Riemann Integral. *Let f be a function whose domain includes the interval $[a, b]$, $a < b$. Let f have the property that there exists a number $R_a^b(f)$ so related to f that to each positive number ϵ there corresponds a positive number δ such that every sum (1) differs from $R_a^b(f)$ by less than ϵ whenever all subintervals have lengths Δx_k less than δ. Then:*

a) *f is said to be **Riemann integrable** (or, more briefly, integrable) over $[a, b]$, and*

b) *$R_a^b(f)$ is called the **Riemann integral** (or, more briefly, the integral) of f from a to b.*

Theorem 1. *If f is Riemann integrable over an interval $[a, b]$, then it is also integrable over any subinterval contained in $[a, b]$.*

Theorem 2. *Every function that is continuous on a closed bounded interval $[a, b]$ is Riemann integrable there.*

REMARK. Although we are mainly interested in continuous functions, they are not the only ones that are integrable. All bounded functions that are *piecewise* continuous are also integrable. "Piecewise continuous" means that the interval can be divided into a finite number of nonoverlapping open subintervals over each of which the function is continuous. "Bounded" means that, for some finite constant M, $|f(x)| \leq M$ for all values of x in the interval. Figure 4–28 shows the graph of a bounded piecewise-continuous function over $[a, b]$. For this example, the integral $R_a^b(f)$ would be computed

4–28 The graph of a bounded piecewise continuous function.

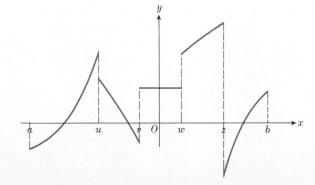

as the sum

$$R_a^b(f) = R_a^u(f) + R_u^v(f) + R_v^w(f) + R_w^z(f) + R_z^b(f).$$

If $b < a$ and $R_b^a(f)$ exists, then we define $R_a^b(f)$ to be its negative:

$$R_a^b(f) = -R_b^a(f). \tag{2}$$

If $a = b$, we define $R_a^a(f)$ to be zero.

Theorem 3.   *Let a, b, c be three numbers belonging to an interval over which the Riemann integral of f exists. Then*

$$R_a^c(f) = R_a^b(f) + R_b^c(f). \tag{3}$$

Theorem 4.   *Let f be Riemann integrable over [a, b]. Let x be any number between a and b at which f is continuous. Then $R_a^x(f)$ is differentiable at x and its derivative there is $f(x)$:*

$$\frac{d}{dx} R_a^x(f) = f(x). \tag{4}$$

Theorem 5. The Mean Value Theorem for Integrals.   *Let f be continuous on [a, b]. Then there exists at least one number c between a and b such that*

$$R_a^b(f) = f(c) \cdot (b - a). \tag{5}$$

Theorem 6. Fundamental Theorem of Integral Calculus.   *Let f be Riemann integrable over [a, b]. Let F be any continuous indefinite integral of f, that is,*

$$F'(x) = f(x) \quad \text{for} \quad a < x < b.$$

Then

$$R_a^b(f) = F(b) - F(a). \tag{6}$$

PROBLEMS

1. Rewrite Eqs. (2) through (6), Article 4–11, using the notation $\int_a^b f(t)\, dt$ in place of $R_a^b(f)$ for the Riemann integral of f from a to b.

2. Sketch graphs of each of the following piecewise-continuous functions on $(0, 2)$ and compute $\int_0^2 f(x)\, dx$:

a) $f(x) = \begin{cases} x, & \text{for } 0 \le x < 1, \\ \sin(\pi x), & \text{for } 1 \le x \le 2. \end{cases}$

b) $f(x) = \begin{cases} \sqrt{1 - x}, & \text{for } 0 \le x \le 1, \\ (7x - 6)^{-1/3}, & \text{for } 1 < x \le 2. \end{cases}$

3. Find $F'(x)$ for $x = \frac{1}{2}$ and for $x = \frac{3}{2}$ if $F(x) = \int_0^x f(t)\, dt$ and (a) f is defined as in Problem 2(a) above; (b) f is defined as in Problem 2(b) above; (c) $f(t) = (\sin(\pi t))/(1 + t)$.

REVIEW QUESTIONS AND EXERCISES

1. The process of "indefinite integration" is sometimes called "antidifferentiation." Explain why the two terms should be synonymous.

2. Can there be more than one indefinite integral of a given function? If more than one exist, how are they related? What theorem of Chapter 3 is the key to this relationship?

3. If the acceleration of a moving body is given as a function of time (t), what further information do you need in order to find the law of motion, $s = f(t)$? How is s found?

4. Write a formula for the area bounded above by the semicircle

$$y = \sqrt{r^2 - t^2},$$

below by the t-axis, on the left by the y-axis, and on the right by the line $t = x$. Without making any calculations, what do you know must be the derivative, with respect to x, of this expression? Explain.

5. What numerical methods do you know for approximating a definite integral? How can an approximation usually be improved upon to give greater accuracy?

6. What property of continuous functions is used in the proof of the Intermediate Value Theorem?

7. Is every Riemann-integrable function also differentiable? Give a reason for your answer.

8. Is the function f defined on the domain $0 \le x \le 1$ by

$$f(x) = \begin{cases} 0 & \text{when } x \text{ is rational,} \\ 1 & \text{when } x \text{ is irrational,} \end{cases}$$

Riemann-integrable over $(0, 1)$? Give a reason for your answer.

MISCELLANEOUS PROBLEMS

Solve the differential equations in Problems 1–5.

1. $\dfrac{dy}{dx} = xy^2$

2. $\dfrac{dy}{dx} = \sqrt{1 + x + y + xy}$

3. $\dfrac{dy}{dx} = \dfrac{x^2 - 1}{y^2 + 1}$

4. $\dfrac{dx}{dy} = \dfrac{y - \sqrt{y}}{x + \sqrt{x}}$

5. $\dfrac{dx}{dy} = \left(\dfrac{2 + x}{3 - y}\right)^2$

6. Solve each of the following differential equations subject to the prescribed initial conditions:

a) $\dfrac{dy}{dx} = x\sqrt{x^2 - 4}; \quad x = 2, \quad y = 3.$

b) $\dfrac{dy}{dx} = xy^3; \quad x = 0, \quad y = 1.$

7. Can there be a curve satisfying the following conditions? d^2y/dx^2 is everywhere equal to zero and, when $x = 0$, $y = 0$ and $dy/dx = 1$. Give a reason for your answer.

8. Find an equation of the curve whose slope at the point (x, y) is $3x^2 + 2$, if the curve is required to pass through the point $(1, -1)$.

9. A particle moves along the x-axis. Its acceleration is $a = -t^2$. At $t = 0$, the particle is at the origin. In the course of its motion, it reaches the point $x = b$, where $b > 0$, but no point beyond b. Determine its velocity at $t = 0$.

10. A particle moves with acceleration $a = \sqrt{t} - (1/\sqrt{t})$. Assuming that the velocity $v = 4/3$ and the distance $s = -4/15$ when $t = 0$, find (a) the velocity v in terms of t, (b) the distance s in terms of t.

11. A particle is accelerated with acceleration $3 + 2t$, where t is the time. At $t = 0$, the velocity is 4. Find the velocity as a function of time and the distance between the position of the particle at time zero and at time 4.

12. The acceleration of a particle moving along the x-axis is given by $d^2x/dt^2 = -4x$. If the particle starts from rest at $x = 5$, find the velocity when it first reaches $x = 3$.

13. Let $f(x)$, $g(x)$ be two continuously differentiable functions satisfying the relationships $f'(x) = g(x)$ and $f''(x) = -f(x)$. Let $h(x) = f^2(x) + g^2(x)$. If $h(0) = 5$, find $h(10)$.

14. The family of straight lines $y = ax + b$ (a, b arbitrary constants) can be characterized by the relation $y'' = 0$. Find a similar relation satisfied by the family of all circles

$$(x - h)^2 + (y - h)^2 = r^2,$$

where h and r are arbitrary constants. [*Hint.* Eliminate h and r from the set of three equations including the given one and two obtained by successive differentiation.]

15. Assume that the brakes of an automobile produce a constant deceleration of k ft/sec². (a) Determine what k must be to bring an automobile traveling 60 mi/hr (88 ft/sec) to rest in a distance of 100 ft from the point where the brakes are applied. (b) With the same k, how far would a car traveling 30 mi/hr travel before being brought to a stop?

16. Solve the differential equation $dy/dx = x\sqrt{1 + x^2}$ subject to the condition that $y = -2$ when $x = 0$.

17. The acceleration due to gravity is -32 ft/sec². A stone is thrown upward from the ground with a speed of 96 ft/sec. Find the height to which the stone rises in t sec. What is the maximum height reached by the stone?

18. (*Amer. Math. Monthly* (1955), M. S. Klamkin.) Show that the following procedure will produce a continuous polygonal "curve" whose slope at the point (x_k, y_k) will be $f(x_k)$. First, sketch the auxiliary curve $C: y = xf(x)$. Then through the point $P_0(x_0, y_0)$, construct the line $x = x_0$ intersecting C in $Q_0(x_0, x_0 f(x_0))$. Through P_0 draw a line segment $P_0 P_1$ parallel to OQ_0. Then the slope of $P_0 P_1$ is $f(x_0)$. Now take $P_1(x_1, y_1)$ on this segment to lie close to P_0. For example, take $x_1 = x_0 + h$, where h is small. Then find $Q_1(x_1, x_1 f(x_1))$ on C and through P_1 draw a line segment $P_1 P_2$ parallel to OQ_1. Continue the process by taking $P_2(x_2, y_2)$ close to P_1, with $x_2 = x_1 + h$; then find $Q_2(x_2, x_2 f(x_2))$ on C and through P_2 draw a line segment $P_2 P_3$ parallel to OQ_2; and so on.

19. (a) Apply the procedure of Problem 18 to the case $f(x) = 1/x$ with $x_0 = 1$, $y_0 = 1$, and $h = \frac{1}{4}$. Continue the process until you reach the point $P_4(x_4, y_4)$. What is your value of y_4? **(b)** Repeat the construction of part (a), but with $h = \frac{1}{8}$, and continue until you reach $x_8 = 2$. What is your value of y_8?

20. A body is moving with velocity 16 ft/sec when it is suddenly subjected to a deceleration. If the deceleration is proportional to the square root of the velocity, and the body comes to rest in 4 sec, **(a)** how fast is the body moving 2 sec after it begins decelerating, and **(b)** how far does the body travel before coming to rest?

Evaluate the integrals in Problems 21 through 33:

21. $\int \dfrac{x^3 + 1}{x^2}\, dx$

22. $\int y\sqrt{1 + y^2}\, dy$

23. $\int t^{1/3}(1 + t^{4/3})^{-7}\, dt$

24. $\int \dfrac{(1 + \sqrt{u})^{1/2}\, du}{\sqrt{u}}$

25. $\int \dfrac{dr}{\sqrt[3]{(7 - 5r)^2}}$

26. $\int \cos 4x\, dx$

27. $\int \sin^2 3x \cos 3x\, dx$

28. $\int \dfrac{\cos x\, dx}{\sqrt{\sin x}}$

29. $\int \cos (2x - 1)\, dx$

30. $\int \dfrac{y\, dy}{\sqrt{25 - 4y^2}}$

31. $\int \dfrac{dt}{t\sqrt{2t}}$

32. $\int (x^2 - \sqrt{x})\, dx$

33. $\int \dfrac{dx}{(2 - 3x)^2}$

34. If one side and the opposite angle of a triangle are fixed, prove that the area is a maximum when the triangle is isosceles.

35. A light hangs above the center of a table of radius r ft. The illumination at any point on the table is directly proportional to the cosine of the angle of incidence (i.e., the angle a ray of light makes with the normal) and is inversely proportional to the square of the distance from the light. How far should the light be above the table in order to give the strongest illumination at the edge of the table?

36. If A, B, C are constants, $AB \neq 0$, prove that the graph of the curve $y = A \sin (Bx + C)$ is always concave toward the x-axis except at its points of inflection, which are its points of intersection with the x-axis.

37. Two particles move on the same straight line so that their distances from a fixed point O, at any time t, are

$$x_1 = a \sin bt \quad \text{and} \quad x_2 = a \sin [bt + (\pi/3)],$$

where a and b are constants, $ab \neq 0$. Find the greatest distance between them.

38. If the identity $\sin (x + a) = \sin x \cos a + \cos x \sin a$ is differentiated with respect to x, is the resulting equation also an identity? Does this principle apply to the equation $x^2 - 2x - 8 = 0$? Explain.

39. A revolving beacon light in a lighthouse $\frac{1}{2}$ mile offshore makes two revolutions per minute. If the shoreline is a straight line, how fast is the ray of light moving along the shore when it passes a point one mile from the lighthouse?

40. The coordinates of a moving particle are $x = a \cos^3 \theta$ and $y = a \sin^3 \theta$. If a is a positive constant and θ increases at the constant rate of ω rad/sec, find the magnitude of the velocity vector.

41. The area bounded by the x-axis, the curve $y = f(x)$, and the lines $x = 1$, $x = b$, is equal to $\sqrt{b^2 + 1} - \sqrt{2}$ for all $b > 1$. Find $f(x)$.

42. Let $f(x)$ be a continuous function. Express

$$\lim_{n \to \infty} \frac{1}{n}\left[f\left(\frac{1}{n}\right) + f\left(\frac{2}{n}\right) + \cdots + f\left(\frac{n}{n}\right) \right]$$

as a definite integral.

43. Use the result of Problem 42 to evaluate:

a) $\displaystyle\lim_{n \to \infty} \frac{1}{n^{16}}[1^{15} + 2^{15} + 3^{15} + \cdots + n^{15}]$,

b) $\displaystyle\lim_{n \to \infty} \frac{\sqrt{1} + \sqrt{2} + \sqrt{3} + \cdots + \sqrt{n}}{n^{3/2}}$,

c) $\displaystyle\lim_{n \to \infty} \frac{1}{n}\left[\sin \frac{\pi}{n} + \sin \frac{2\pi}{n} + \sin \frac{3\pi}{n} + \cdots + \sin \frac{n\pi}{n} \right]$

Find:

d) $\displaystyle\lim_{h \to 0} \frac{1}{h} \int_x^{x+h} \frac{du}{u + \sqrt{u^2 + 1}}$,

e) $\displaystyle\lim_{x \to x_1} \left[\frac{x}{x - x_1} \int_{x_1}^x f(t)\, dt \right]$.

44. Variables x and y are related by the equation

$$x = \int_0^y \frac{1}{\sqrt{1 + 4t^2}}\, dt.$$

Show that d^2y/dx^2 is proportional to y and find the constant of proportionality.

APPLICATIONS OF THE DEFINITE INTEGRAL

5–1

INTRODUCTION

In Chapter 4 we discovered a close connection between sums of the form

$$S_a^b = \sum_a^b f(x)\, \Delta x \tag{1}$$

and integration, the inverse of differentiation. When f is continuous on $a \le x \le b$, we found that the *limit* of S_a^b as Δx approaches zero is just $F(b) - F(a)$, where F is any integral of f:

$$F(x) = \int f(x)\, dx. \tag{2}$$

We applied this to the problem of computing the area between the x-axis and the graph of $y = f(x)$, $a \le x \le b$. In this chapter we shall extend the applications to the following topics: area between two curves, distance, volumes, lengths of curves, areas of surfaces of revolution, average value of a function, center of mass, centroid, work, and hydrostatic force.

5–2

AREA BETWEEN TWO CURVES

Suppose that

$$y_1 = f_1(x) \qquad \text{and} \qquad y_2 = f_2(x)$$

define two functions of x that are continuous for $a \le x \le b$, and furthermore, suppose that

$$f_1(x) \ge f_2(x) \qquad \text{for} \quad a \le x \le b.$$

Then the y_1 curve is above the y_2 curve from a to b (Fig. 5–1) and we consider the problem of finding the area bounded above by the y_1 curve, below by the y_2 curve, and on the sides by the vertical lines $x = a$, $x = b$.

If the x-interval from a to b is divided into n equal subintervals, each of width $\Delta x = (b - a)/n$, and a rectangle of width Δx and altitude extending from the y_2 curve to the y_1 curve is used to approximate that portion of the

5–1 The area between two curves can be approximated by adding the areas of rectangular strips that reach from one curve to the other.

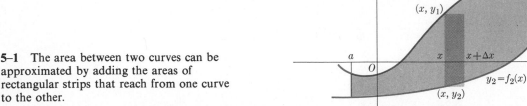

area between the curves that lies between x and $x + \Delta x$, then the area of the rectangle is

$$(y_1 - y_2) \, \Delta x = [f_1(x) - f_2(x)] \, \Delta x.$$

The total area in question is *approximated* by adding together the areas of all such rectangles

$$A \approx \sum_a^b [f_1(x) - f_2(x)] \, \Delta x.$$

Finally, if we let $\Delta x \to 0$, we obtain a number we call the exact area:

$$A = \lim_{\Delta x \to 0} \sum_a^b [f_1(x) - f_2(x)] \, \Delta x = \int_a^b [f_1(x) - f_2(x)] \, dx. \qquad \textbf{(1)}$$

by definition of a definite integral

EXAMPLE. Find the area (Fig. 5–2) bounded by the parabola

$$y = 2 - x^2$$

and the straight line

$$y = -x.$$

Solution. We first find where the curves intersect by finding points that satisfy both equations simultaneously. That is, we solve

$$2 - x^2 = -x$$

or

$$x^2 - x - 2 = 0, \qquad (x - 2)(x + 1) = 0, \qquad x = -1, 2.$$

The points of intersection are thus $A(-1, 1)$ and $B(2, -2)$. For all values of x between -1 and $+2$, the curve

$$y_1 = 2 - x^2$$

is above the line

$$y_2 = -x$$

by an amount

$$y_1 - y_2 = (2 - x^2) - (-x) = 2 - x^2 + x.$$

This is the altitude of a typical rectangle used to approximate that portion of the area lying between x and $x + \Delta x$. The total area is approximated by

$$A_{-1}^2 \approx \sum_{-1}^2 (y_1 - y_2) \, \Delta x = \sum_{-1}^2 (2 - x^2 + x) \, \Delta x$$

and is given exactly by

$$A_{-1}^2 = \lim_{\Delta x \to 0} \sum_{-1}^2 (2 - x^2 + x) \, \Delta x = \int_{-1}^2 (2 - x^2 + x) \, dx = 4\tfrac{1}{2}.$$

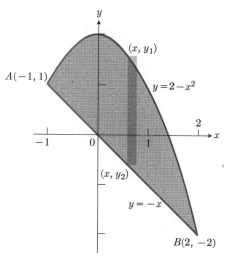

5–2 Calculating the area between $y = 2 - x^2$ and $y = -x$.

PROBLEMS

1. Make a sketch to represent a region that is bounded on the right by a continuous curve $x = f(y)$, on the left by a continuous curve $x = g(y)$, below by the line $y = a$, and above by the line $y = b$. Divide the region into n horizontal strips each of altitude $\Delta y = (b - a)/n$ and express the area of the region (a) as a limit of a sum of areas of rectangles, and (b) as an appropriate definite integral.

2. Find the area bounded by the x-axis and the curve $y = 2x - x^2$.

3. Find the area bounded by the y-axis and the curve $x = y^2 - y^3$.

4. Find the area bounded by the curve $y^2 = x$ and the line $x = 4$.

5. Find the area bounded by the curve $y = 2x - x^2$ and the line $y = -3$.

6. Find the area bounded by the curve $y = x^2$ and the line $y = x$.

7. Find the area bounded by the curve $x = 3y - y^2$ and the line $x + y = 3$.

8. Find the area bounded by the curves $y = x^4 - 2x^2$ and $y = 2x^2$.

9. Find the area of the "triangular" region in the first quadrant bounded by the y-axis and the curves $y = \sin x$, $y = \cos x$.

10. The area bounded by the curve $y = x^2$ and the line $y = 4$ is divided into two equal portions by the line $y = c$. Find c.

11. Find the area bounded by the curve $\sqrt{x} + \sqrt{y} = 1$ and the coordinate axes.

12. Use Simpson's rule with $n = 10$ to approximate the area between the curves $y = 1/(1 + x^2)$ and $y = -1/(1 + x^2)$, $-1 \le x \le 1$.

 DISTANCE

As a second application of the basic principles involved in the use of the Fundamental Theorem of the calculus, we shall calculate the distance traveled by a body moving with velocity

$$v = f(t). \tag{1}$$

To simplify the discussion we shall assume that $f(t)$ is nonnegative, as well as continuous, for $a \le t \le b$. This means that the body moves in only one direction and does not back up.

Now there are two ways in which we can calculate the distance traveled by the body between $t = a$ and $t = b$.

FIRST METHOD. If we can integrate the differential equation

$$ds = f(t)\, dt, \tag{2}$$

which we get by substituting ds/dt for v in Eq. (1), then we can determine the position s of the body as a function of t, say

$$s = F(t) + C. \tag{3}$$

The distance traveled by the body between $t = a$ and $t = b$ is then given by

$$s\Big|_{t=a}^{t=b} = F(t) + C\Big|_{a}^{b} = F(b) - F(a).$$

We recognize this, of course, as saying that the distance is given by the definite integral

$$s\Big|_{t=a}^{t=b} = \int_{a}^{b} f(t)\, dt = F(t)\Big|_{a}^{b} = F(b) - F(a). \tag{4}$$

SECOND METHOD. In this method, we imagine the total time interval $a \le t \le b$ as divided into n subintervals, each of duration $\Delta t = (b - a)/n$.

The velocity at the beginning of the first subinterval is

$$v_1 = f(t_1) = f(a).$$

If Δt is small, the velocity remains nearly constant throughout the time from a to $a + \Delta t$. Hence during the first subinterval of time, the body travels a distance Δs_1 which is approximately equal to $v_1 \Delta t$:

$$\Delta s_1 \approx v_1 \Delta t = f(t_1) \Delta t. \tag{5}$$

If, instead of using the velocity v_1 at time t_1, we were to use the *average velocity*

$$\bar{v}_1 = \frac{\Delta s_1}{\Delta t}, \tag{6a}$$

we could write

$$\Delta s_1 = \bar{v}_1 \Delta t \tag{6b}$$

exactly. Now by the Mean Value Theorem, we know that there is some instant, say T_1, between t_1 and $t_1 + \Delta t$, where the instantaneous velocity is equal to the average velocity $\bar{v}_1$. In other words,

$$f(T_1) = \bar{v}_1 \quad \text{for some } T_1, \qquad t_1 < T_1 < t_1 + \Delta t, \tag{6c}$$

and therefore

$$\Delta s_1 = f(T_1) \Delta t$$

exactly. By reasoning in the same manner for the second, third, ..., nth subintervals, we conclude that there are instants of time $T_2, T_3, \ldots, T_n$ in these intervals for which

$$\Delta s_2 = f(T_2) \Delta t,$$
$$\Delta s_3 = f(T_3) \Delta t,$$
$$\vdots$$
$$\Delta s_n = f(T_n) \Delta t,$$

where $\Delta s_2, \Delta s_3, \ldots, \Delta s_n$ represent the distances traveled during these respective time subintervals. Therefore the total distance traveled between $t = a$ and $t = b$ is

$$\begin{aligned} s]_{t=a}^{t=b} &= \Delta s_1 + \Delta s_2 + \Delta s_3 + \cdots + \Delta s_n \\ &= f(T_1) \Delta t + f(T_2) \Delta t + \cdots + f(T_n) \Delta t \\ &= \sum_{k=1}^{n} f(T_k) \Delta t. \end{aligned} \tag{7}$$

Let us now take finer and finer subdivisions Δt and let n increase without limit. For each n we select the appropriate instants of time $T_1, T_2, \ldots, T_n$ according to the method described above. Then the particular sums used in Eq. (7) tend to the definite integral

$$\lim_{n \to \infty} \sum_{k=1}^{n} f(T_k) \Delta t = \int_a^b f(t) \, dt \tag{8}$$

as limit, by virtue of the Fundamental Theorem. On the other hand, these sums all give the distance traveled by the body. Therefore the distance traveled is equal to the integral in Eq. (8) [or Eq. (4)].

REMARK 1. If, instead of using the velocities at the instants of time T_1, $T_2, \ldots, T_n$ described above, we had used the velocities

$$v_1 = f(t_1), \qquad v_2 = f(t_2), \qquad \ldots, \qquad v_n = f(t_n)$$

at the beginnings of the various subintervals, then we would have had n *approximations* like (5) with subscripts $1, 2, \ldots, n$. Then we would have obtained an *approximation*

$$\Delta s_1 + \Delta s_2 + \cdots + \Delta s_n \approx f(t_1)\, \Delta t + f(t_2)\, \Delta t + \cdots + f(t_n)\, \Delta t,$$

or

$$s \Big]_{t=a}^{t=b} \approx \sum_{k=1}^{n} f(t_k)\, \Delta t. \tag{9}$$

Now since $f(t)$ is continuous, the sums (7) and (9) have the same *limit* as $n \to \infty$. In other words, the approximation (9) gets better as n increases, and the *limit* again gives the exact value, namely, the integral in Eq. (8).

REMARK 2. Of course, the two methods give the same result, Eqs. (4) and (8). The second method is useful primarily (a) because it shows how the simple formula

Distance = Velocity × Time,

which applies only to the case of *constant* velocity, can be extended to the case of variable velocity, provided we apply it to short subintervals Δt; and (b) because it can be used [in the form of the approximation (9)] to estimate the distance in cases where the velocity is given empirically by a table of values or a graph instead of by a formula $f(t)$ with known indefinite integral $F(t)$. (See Problem 15.)

REMARK 3. If the velocity changes sign during the interval (a, b), then the integral in Eq. (4) gives only the *net* change in s. This permits cancellation of distances traveled forward and backward. For example, it would give an answer of 2 miles if the body traveled forward 7 miles and backed up 5 miles. If we want to determine the total distance traveled, we calculate the integral of the *absolute value* of the velocity,

$$\int_a^b |f(t)|\, dt. \tag{10}$$

This can be done in practice by integrating separately over the intervals where v is positive and where v is negative and adding the absolute values of the results.

REMARK 4. The preceding discussion shows that the distance traveled is given by precisely the same expression as that for the area bounded by the curve

$$v = f(t)$$

and the t-axis from a to b. All of the discussion above can be interpreted geometrically. For example, T is chosen between t and $t + \Delta t$ in such a way that the area of the rectangle of base Δt and altitude $f(T)$ (Fig. 5–3(a)) is precisely equal to the area under the velocity curve between t and $t + \Delta t$. This is also the place where the slope of the curve $s = F(t)$ (Fig. 5–3(b)) is equal to the slope of the chord.

a)

b)

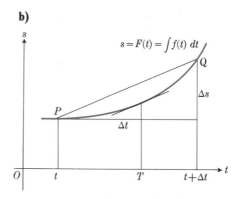

5–3 Two geometric interpretations of the equation

$$f(T)\,\Delta t = \int_{t}^{t+\Delta t} f(t)\,dt = F(t + \Delta t) - F(t):$$

(a) The area of the shaded rectangle equals the area under the curve between t and $(t + \Delta t)$; (b) At $t = T$ the slope $f(T)$ of the curve $s = F(t)$ equals the slope $[F(t + \Delta t) - F(t)]/\Delta t$ of the chord PQ.

PROBLEMS

In each of the following problems (1 through 8), the function $v = f(t)$ represents the velocity v (ft/sec) of a moving body as a function of the time t (sec). Sketch the graph of v versus t and find that portion of the given time interval $a \le t \le b$ in which the velocity is (a) positive, and (b) negative. Then find the total distance traveled by the body between $t = a$ and $t = b$.

1. $v = 2t + 1; \quad 0 \le t \le 2$

2. $v = t^2 - t - 2; \quad 0 \le t \le 3$

3. $v = t - \dfrac{8}{t^2}; \quad 1 \le t \le 3$

4. $v = |t - 1|; \quad 0 \le t \le 2$

5. $v = 6 \sin 3t; \quad 0 \le t \le \dfrac{\pi}{2}$

6. $v = 4 \cos 2t; \quad 0 \le t \le \pi$

7. $v = \sin t + \cos t; \quad 0 \le t \le \pi$

8. $v = \sin t \sqrt{2 + 2 \cos t}; \quad 0 \le t \le \pi$

In each of the following problems (9 through 13), the function $a = f(t)$ represents the acceleration (ft/sec^2) of a

moving body and v_0 is its velocity at time $t = 0$. Find the *distance* traveled by the body between time $t = 0$ and $t = 2$.

9. $a = \sin t; \quad v_0 = 2$

10. $a = 1 - \cos t; \quad v_0 = 0$

11. $a = g$ (const.); $\quad v_0 = 0$

12. $a = \sqrt{4t + 1}; \quad v_0 = -4\frac{1}{3}$

13. $a = \dfrac{1}{\sqrt{4t + 1}}; \quad v_0 = 1$

14. Suppose water flows into a tank at the rate of $f(t)$ gal/min, where f is a given, positive, continuous function of t. Let the amount of water in the tank at time $t = 0$ be Q_0 gal. Apply the Fundamental Theorem to show that the amount of water in the tank at any later time $t = b$ is

$$Q = Q_0 + \int_{0}^{b} f(t)\,dt.$$

15. (*Calculator*) Table 5–1 shows the speed of an automobile every 10 seconds from start to stop on a two-minute trip. Use Simpson's rule to estimate how far the car went.

Table 5–1.   Selected speeds of a car on a two-minute trip

Time (sec)	Velocity (mph)	Time (sec)	Velocity (mph)
0	0	70	66
10	32	80	66
20	51	90	58
30	57	100	40
40	54	110	6
50	64	120	0
60	66		

5–4

VOLUMES (SLICES)

The volumes of many solids can be found by the "method of slicing." Suppose, for example, that the solid is bounded by two parallel planes perpendicular to the x-axis at $x = a$ and $x = b$. Imagine the solid cut into thin slices of thickness Δx by planes perpendicular to the x-axis. Then the total volume V of the solid is the sum of the volumes of these slices (see Fig. 5–4).

Let ΔV be the volume of a representative slice between x and $x + \Delta x$. Then if A' and A'' are, respectively, the smallest and largest cross-sectional areas of the solid between x and $x + \Delta x$, it will be seen at once that

$$A' \, \Delta x \leq \Delta V \leq A'' \, \Delta x$$

or

$$\Delta V = A(\bar{x}) \, \Delta x,$$

where $A(\bar{x})$ denotes an appropriate intermediate cross-sectional area of the solid at some $\bar{x}$ between x and $x + \Delta x$. Then

$$V = \sum_a^b A(\bar{x}) \, \Delta x$$

will give the total volume of the solid exactly. If, instead of choosing the exactly appropriate intermediate point $\bar{x}$ in the typical subinterval, we use the area $A(x)$ of the cross section at x, we have only an approximation,

$$V \approx \sum_a^b A(x) \, \Delta x.$$

But now let $\Delta x \to 0$. Then, if the cross-sectional area is a continuous function of x, all these sums will approach the same limit. Since one sequence of sums always gives the value V, it will have this value as its limit. Hence the other sums will also give the value V in the limit, that is,

$$V = \lim_{\Delta x \to 0} \sum_a^b A(x) \, \Delta x = \int_a^b A(x) \, dx. \tag{1}$$

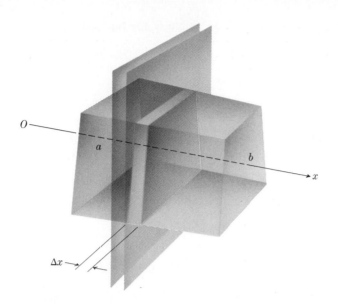

5–4 The volume of the solid is the sum of the volumes of slices of thickness Δx.

Volume of a Solid of Revolution

The solid generated by rotating a plane area about an axis in its plane is called a solid of revolution. To find the volume of a solid like the one in Fig. 5–5, we need only observe that the cross-sectional area $A(x)$ in Eq. (1) is the area of a circle of radius $r = y = f(x)$, so that

$$A(x) = \pi r^2 = \pi [f(x)]^2. \qquad (2)$$

EXAMPLE 1. Suppose the curve in Fig. 5–5 represents the graph of

$$y = \sqrt{x}$$

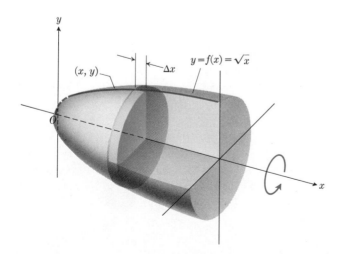

5–5 A slice perpendicular to the axis of a solid of revolution.

from (0, 0) to (4, 2). Then the volume of the representative slice is

$$\Delta V \approx \pi y^2 \, \Delta x = \pi(\sqrt{x})^2 \, \Delta x,$$

and the total volume is approximately

$$V \approx \sum_0^4 \pi x \, \Delta x.$$

Exactly, we have

$$V = \lim_{\Delta x \to 0} \sum_0^4 \pi x \, \Delta x = \int_0^4 \pi x \, dx = \pi \frac{x^2}{2} \bigg]_0^4 = 8\pi.$$

EXAMPLE 2.   The circle

$$x^2 + y^2 = a^2$$

is rotated about the x-axis to generate a sphere. Find its volume.

Solution.   We imagine the sphere cut into thin slices by planes perpendicular to the x-axis (Fig. 5–6). The volume of a typical slice between two planes at x and $x + \Delta x$ is approximately

$$\pi y^2 \, \Delta x = \pi(a^2 - x^2) \, \Delta x,$$

and the sum of all slices is approximately

$$V^a_{-a} \approx \sum_{-a}^a \pi(a^2 - x^2) \, \Delta x.$$

The exact volume is given by

$$V^a_{-a} = \lim_{\Delta x \to 0} \sum_{-a}^a \pi(a^2 - x^2) \, \Delta x = \int_{-a}^a \pi(a^2 - x^2) \, dx$$

$$= \pi \left[a^2 x - \frac{x^3}{3} \right]_{-a}^a = \frac{4}{3}\pi a^3.$$

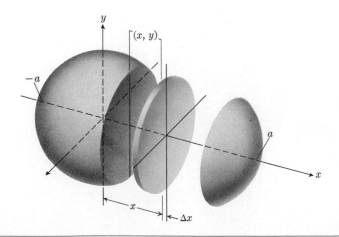

5–6 The sphere generated by rotating the circle $x^2 + y^2 = a^2$ about the x-axis.

Various methods for finding volumes are illustrated in the following examples.

EXAMPLE 3. A wedge is cut from a right circular cylinder of radius r by two planes, one perpendicular to the axis of the cylinder while the second makes an angle α with the first and intersects it at the center of the cylinder. Find the volume of the wedge.

Solution. The volume ΔV of the slice between y and $y + \Delta y$ in Fig. 5–7 is approximately

$$\Delta V \approx A(y)\,\Delta y,$$

where

$$A(y) = \tfrac{1}{2}xh$$

is the area of the triangle that forms one face of the slice and is to be expressed as a function of y. By trigonometry,

$$h = x \tan \alpha,$$

and by the theorem of Pythagoras,

$$x^2 + y^2 = r^2$$

or

$$x^2 = r^2 - y^2.$$

Hence

$$A(y) = \tfrac{1}{2}x^2 \tan \alpha = \tfrac{1}{2} \tan \alpha (r^2 - y^2).$$

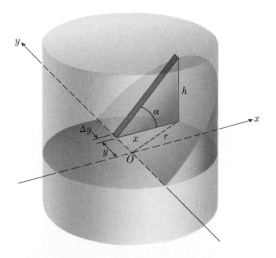

5–7 The curved wedge can be cut into triangular slices.

The total volume is given by

$$V = \lim_{\Delta y \to 0} \sum_{-r}^{r} A(y)\, \Delta y$$

$$= \int_{-r}^{r} \tfrac{1}{2} \tan \alpha (r^2 - y^2)\, dy.$$

Remembering that the factor $\frac{1}{2} \tan \alpha$ is a constant, we find

$$V = \tfrac{2}{3} r^3 \tan \alpha.$$

a)

b)

5–8 A solid with a triangular base (a), and square sections (b).

EXAMPLE 4. The base of the solid in Fig. 5–8 is an equilateral triangle of side s, with one vertex at the origin; one altitude of the triangle lies along the x-axis. Each plane section perpendicular to the x-axis is a square, one side of which lies in the base of the solid. Find the volume of the solid.

Solution. Figure 5–8(a) shows the base of the solid with a strip of width Δx, which corresponds to a slice of the solid of volume

$$\Delta V \approx A(x)\, \Delta x,$$

where

$$A(x) = (2y)^2 = 4y^2$$

is the area of a face of the slice. The slice extends upward from the xy-plane of Fig. 5–8(a). It is possible to find the required volume from the statement of the problem by reference to this figure and without visualizing the actual solid. A perspective view of the solid is, however, given in Fig. 5–8(b). It is required to find y in terms of x so that the area $A(x)$ will be given as a function of x. Since the base triangle is equilateral, its altitude h is given by

$$h^2 = s^2 - (s/2)^2 = \tfrac{3}{4}s^2$$

or

$$h = \frac{s}{2}\sqrt{3}.$$

Then, by similar triangles, we find

$$\frac{2y}{x} = \frac{s}{h} = \frac{2}{\sqrt{3}}$$

or

$$y = \frac{x}{\sqrt{3}}.$$

$$\therefore A(x) = \frac{4x^2}{3}$$

Then

$$V = \int_0^h A(x)\, dx$$

$$= \int_0^{s\sqrt{3}/2} \frac{4}{3} x^2\, dx = \frac{s^3}{2\sqrt{3}} = \frac{1}{3} hs^2.$$

PROBLEMS

In Problems 1 through 8, find the volumes generated when the areas bounded by the given curves and lines are rotated about the x-axis. [*Note.* $x = 0$ is the y-axis and $y = 0$ is the x-axis.]

~~boundaries~~

1. $x + y = 2$; $x = 0$, $y = 0$

2. $y = \sin x$, $y = 0$ $(0 \le x \le \pi)$
[See Problem 17, Article 4–7.]

3. $y = x - x^2$; $y = 0$ 4. $y = -3x - x^2$; $y = 0$

5. $y = x^2 - 2x$; $y = 0$ 6. $y = x^3$; $x = 2$, $y = 0$

7. $y = x^4$; $x = 1$, $y = 0$ 8. $y = \sqrt{\cos x}$, $0 \le x \le \pi/2$;
$x = 0$; $y = 0$

9. Find the volume generated when the area bounded by $y = \sqrt{x}$, $y = 2$, and $x = 0$ is rotated (a) about the y-axis, (b) about the line $y = 2$.

10. By integration find the volume generated by rotating the triangle with vertices at $(0, 0)$, $(h, 0)$, (h, r),

a) about the x-axis,   b) about the y-axis.

11. (a) A hemispherical bowl of radius a contains water to a depth h. Find the volume of water in the bowl. (b) (Review problem on related rates.) Water runs into a hemispherical bowl of radius 5 ft at the rate of 0.2 ft³/sec. How fast is the water level in the bowl rising when the water is 4 ft deep?

12. A football has a volume that is approximately the same as the volume generated by rotating the area inside the ellipse $b^2x^2 + a^2y^2 = a^2b^2$ (where a and b are constants) about the x-axis. Find the volume so generated.

13. The cross sections of a certain solid by planes perpendicular to the x-axis are circles with diameters extending from the curve $y = x^2$ to the curve $y = 8 - x^2$. The solid lies between the points of intersection of these two curves. Find its volume.

14. The base of a certain solid is the circle $x^2 + y^2 = a^2$. Each plane section of the solid cut out by a plane perpendicular to the x-axis is a square with one edge of the square in the base of the solid. Find the volume of the solid.

15. Two great circles, lying in planes that are perpendicular to each other, are marked on a sphere of radius a. A portion of the sphere is then shaved off in such a manner that any plane section of the remaining solid, perpendicular to the common diameter of the two great circles, is a square with vertices on these circles. Find the volume of the solid that remains.

16. The base of a certain solid is the circle $x^2 + y^2 = a^2$. Each plane section of the solid cut out by a plane perpendicular to the y-axis is an isosceles right triangle with one leg in the base of the solid. Find the volume.

17. The base of a certain solid is the region between the x-axis and the curve $y = \sin x$ between $x = 0$ and $x = \pi/2$. Each plane section of the solid perpendicular to the x-axis is an equilateral triangle with one side in the base of the solid. Find the volume.

18. A rectangular swimming pool is 30 ft wide and 50 ft long. The depth of water h ft at distance x ft from one end of the pool is measured at 5-ft intervals and found to be as follows:

x (ft)	0	5	10	15	20	25
h (ft)	6.0	8.2	9.1	9.9	10.5	11.0
x (ft)	30	35	40	45	50	
h (ft)	11.5	11.9	12.3	12.7	13.0	

Use the trapezoidal rule to estimate the volume of water in the pool.

Sometimes when we rotate an area about a line in the plane of the area, the volume swept out by a rectangular strip in the area is a washer or a cylinder instead of a disk. The calculation of the volume in these cases is straightforward, but involves modeling that differs enough from the examples of Article 5–4 to warrant separate attention.

5–5

VOLUMES (SHELLS AND WASHERS)

Suppose the area $PQRS$ in Fig. 5–9 is revolved around the y-axis. We can compute the volume generated in the following way. Consider a strip of area between the ordinate at x and the ordinate at $x + \Delta x$. When this strip is revolved around the y-axis, it generates a hollow, thin-walled shell of inner radius x, outer radius $x + \Delta x$, and volume ΔV. The base of this shell is a ring bounded by two concentric circles. The inner radius is

$$r_1 = x$$

and the outer radius is

$$r_2 = x + \Delta x.$$

The area of the ring is

$$\Delta A = \pi(r_2^2 - r_1^2) = 2\pi \left(\frac{r_2 + r_1}{2}\right)(r_2 - r_1) = 2\pi r \, \Delta x.$$

Here

$$r = \frac{r_2 + r_1}{2} = x + \frac{\Delta x}{2}$$

is the radius of the circle midway between the inner and outer boundaries of the ring, and $2\pi r$ is its circumference.

Now if we had a cylindrical shell of constant altitude y standing on this base, its volume would be

$$\text{Altitude} \times \text{base} = y \, \Delta A.$$

In the present case, the altitude of the shell varies between y and $y + \Delta y$. Its

5–9 The volume swept out when $PQRS$ is revolved about the y-axis is a union of cylindrical shells like the one shown here.

volume therefore lies between $y \, \Delta A$ and $(y + \Delta y) \, \Delta A$. That is,

$$y \, \Delta A \le \Delta V \le (y + \Delta y) \, \Delta A$$

or

$$y \cdot 2\pi r \, \Delta x \le \Delta V \le (y + \Delta y) \cdot 2\pi r \, \Delta x.$$

The total volume V is contained between the "lower" sum

$$s = \sum_a^b y \cdot 2\pi \left(x + \frac{\Delta x}{2}\right) \Delta x$$

and the "upper" sum

$$S = \sum_a^b (y + \Delta y) \cdot 2\pi \left(x + \frac{\Delta x}{2}\right) \Delta x.$$

As Δx approaches zero, both of these sums approach the integral

$$\int_a^b y \cdot 2\pi x \, dx$$

as limit (see Article 5–6). Hence this limit must also be equal to the volume V, namely,

$$V = \lim_{\Delta x \to 0} s = \lim_{\Delta x \to 0} S = \int_a^b y \cdot 2\pi x \, dx = \int_a^b 2\pi x f(x) \, dx.$$

REMARK.   An easy way to visualize this result is to imagine that the volume element ΔV has been cut along a generator of the cylinder and that the shell has been rolled out flat like a thin sheet of tin. The sheet then has dimensions very nearly equal to $2\pi x$ by $y = f(x)$ by Δx. Hence

$$\Delta V \approx 2\pi x \cdot f(x) \cdot \Delta x,$$

and the total volume is given approximately by

$$V \approx \sum_a^b 2\pi x \cdot f(x) \cdot \Delta x.$$

As Δx approaches zero, we obtain a limit that is equal to the exact volume:

$$V = \lim_{\Delta x \to 0} \sum_a^b 2\pi x \cdot f(x) \cdot \Delta x = \int_a^b 2\pi x f(x) \, dx.$$

EXAMPLE 1.   The area bounded by $y = \sqrt{x}$, $y = 0$, and $x = 4$ is revolved about the x-axis. Find the volume swept out.

Solution. Instead of beginning with a vertical strip to generate a disk, as in Example 1 of Article 5–4, we begin with a horizontal strip of area between the lines at distances y and $y + \Delta y$ above the x-axis. (See Fig. 5–10.) The volume generated by revolving this strip around the x-axis is a hollow cylindrical shell of inner circumference $2\pi y$, inner length $4 - x$, and wall

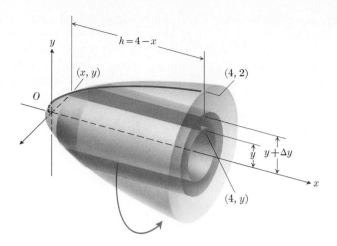

5–10 The volume of the cylindrical shell generated by the horizontal strip is about

Circumference · Length · Thickness

$$\approx 2\pi y \cdot (4 - x) \cdot \Delta y$$

thickness Δy. Hence, the total volume V is approximately

$$V \approx \sum_{y=0}^{2} 2\pi y(4 - x)\,\Delta y$$

and is exactly equal to the limit of this sum as Δy approaches zero:

$$V = \lim_{\Delta y \to 0} \sum_{y=0}^{2} 2\pi y(4 - x)\,\Delta y = \int_{0}^{2} 2\pi y(4 - y^2)\,dy$$

$$= 2\pi \left[2y^2 - \frac{y^4}{4}\right]_{0}^{2} = 8\pi.$$

EXAMPLE 2. A hole of diameter a is bored through the center of the sphere in Example 2 of Article 5–4. Find the remaining volume.

Solution. The volume could be generated by rotating about the y-axis the area inside the circle $x^2 + y^2 = a^2$ lying to the right of the line $x = a/2$ (Fig. 5–11(a)). The line and the circle intersect at the points $(a/2, \pm a\sqrt{3}/2)$. There are at least three methods for finding the required volume.

METHOD 1. Figure 5–11(b) shows an exploded view of the solid sphere with the core pulled out. Note that the core is a cylinder with a spherical cap at each end. Essentially, what we shall do is subtract the volume of this core from the volume of the sphere, but we shall simplify matters slightly by imagining that the two caps have been sliced off first, by planes perpendicular to the y-axis at $y = \pm a\sqrt{3}/2$. When these two caps have been removed, the truncated sphere has a volume V_1. From this truncated sphere we remove a right circular cylinder of radius $a/2$ and altitude $2(a\sqrt{3}/2) = a\sqrt{3}$. Then the volume of this flat-ended cylinder is

$$V_2 = \pi \left(\frac{a}{2}\right)^2 (a\sqrt{3}) = \frac{\sqrt{3}}{4}\pi a^3.$$

The desired volume is $V = V_1 - V_2$. We find V_1 by the same method we used for the spherical ball in Example 2 of Article 5–4, but we keep in mind that the two caps have been removed at top and bottom. Imagine the solid as cut into slices by planes perpendicular to the y-axis. The slice between y and $y + \Delta y$ is approximated by a cylinder of altitude Δy and cross-sectional area

$$\pi x^2 = \pi(a^2 - y^2),$$

so that we have the approximation

$$V_1 \approx \sum_{-a\sqrt{3}/2}^{a\sqrt{3}/2} \pi(a^2 - y^2)\,\Delta y$$

and the exact value

$$V_1 = \int_{-a\sqrt{3}/2}^{a\sqrt{3}/2} \pi(a^2 - y^2)\,dy = \frac{3\sqrt{3}}{4}\pi a^3.$$

Thus

$$V = V_1 - V_2 = \frac{3\sqrt{3}}{4}\pi a^3 - \frac{\sqrt{3}}{4}\pi a^3 = \frac{\sqrt{3}}{2}\pi a^3.$$

METHOD 2. Instead of subtracting volumes, we may work directly with the volume required. Again we imagine the solid to be cut into thin slices by planes perpendicular to the y-axis. Each slice (Fig. 5–11(c)) is now like a washer of thickness Δy, inner radius

$$r_1 = \frac{a}{2},$$

and outer radius

$$r_2 = x = \sqrt{a^2 - y^2}.$$

The area of a face of such a washer is

$$\pi r_2^2 - \pi r_1^2 = \pi(\tfrac{3}{4}a^2 - y^2),$$

and the volume of the solid is approximately

$$V \approx \sum_{-a\sqrt{3}/2}^{a\sqrt{3}/2} \pi(\tfrac{3}{4}a^2 - y^2)\,\Delta y,$$

while its exact value is

$$V = \lim_{\Delta y \to 0} \sum_{-a\sqrt{3}/2}^{a\sqrt{3}/2} \pi(\tfrac{3}{4}a^2 - y^2)\,\Delta y$$

$$= \int_{-a\sqrt{3}/2}^{a\sqrt{3}/2} \pi(\tfrac{3}{4}a^2 - y^2)\,dy$$

$$= \frac{\sqrt{3}}{2}\pi a^3.$$

METHOD 3. This time we shall use the cylindrical-shell approach (see Fig. 5–11(a)). We imagine the solid to be cut into a number of hollow cylindrical

a)

c)

b)

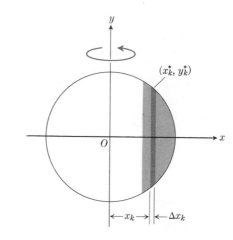

d)

5–11 (a) The tinted region generates the volume of revolution. (b) An exploded view showing the sphere with the core removed. (c) A phantom view showing a cross-sectional slice of the sphere with core removed. (d) The strip of area indicated by darker tint generates a cylindrical shell.

shells by cylinders having the y-axis as their common axis and having radii

$$x_1 = \frac{a}{2}, \quad x_2, \quad x_3, \quad \ldots, \quad x_n, \quad x_{n+1} = a.$$

The first shell has inner radius x_1 and outer radius x_2, the second shell has inner radius x_2 and outer radius x_3, and so on, the kth shell having inner radius x_k and outer radius x_{k+1}. This kth shell fills the region swept out when the dark strip in Fig. 5–11(d) is revolved about the y-axis. If we imagine this region to have been cut along a line parallel to the y-axis and flattened out, we see that the volume V_k of the kth cylindrical shell is approximately

$$2\pi x_k^* \cdot 2y_k^* \cdot \Delta x_k = 4\pi x_k^* \sqrt{a^2 - (x_k^*)^2} \, \Delta x_k,$$

where (x_k^*, y_k^*) (Fig. 5–11(d)) is the point of abscissa

$$x_k^* = \tfrac{1}{2}(x_k - x_{k+1})$$

on the circle in the first quadrant. Then the entire volume will be approximated by

$$V \approx \sum_{k=1}^{n} 4\pi x_k^* \sqrt{a^2 - (x_k^*)^2} \, \Delta x_k$$

$$\approx \sum_{a/2}^{a} 4\pi x \sqrt{a^2 - x^2} \, \Delta x.$$

The exact value will be the *limit* of this sum, namely,

$$V = \lim_{x \to 0} \sum_{a/2}^{a} 4\pi x \sqrt{a^2 - x^2} \, \Delta x$$

$$= \int_{a/2}^{a} 4\pi x \sqrt{a^2 - x^2} \, dx.$$

To evaluate this integral, we let

$$u = a^2 - x^2;$$

then

$$V = 4\pi \int_{a/2}^{a} \sqrt{a^2 - x^2} \, (x \, dx)$$

$$= 4\pi \int u^{1/2}(-\tfrac{1}{2} \, du) = -\frac{4\pi}{3} \left[(a^2 - x^2)^{3/2} \right]_{a/2}^{a}$$

$$= \frac{\sqrt{3}}{2} \pi a^3.$$

PROBLEMS

In Problems 1–8 find the volume generated when the area bounded by the given curves and lines is rotated about the x-axis. [*Note.* $x = 0$ is the y-axis and $y = 0$ is the x-axis.]

1. $x + y = 2$; $x = 0$, $y = 0$ **2.** $x = 2y - y^2$; $x = 0$
3. $y = 3x - x^2$; $y = x$ **4.** $y = x$; $y = 1$, $x = 0$
5. $y = x^2$; $y = 4$ **6.** $y = 3 + x^2$; $y = 4$
7. $y = x^2 + 1$; $y = x + 3$ **8.** $y = 4 - x^2$; $y = 2 - x$

In Problems 9–16, find the volume generated by revolving the given area about the given axis.

9. The area bounded by $y = x^4$, $x = 1$, and $y = 0$ about the y-axis.

10. The area bounded by $y = x^3$, $x = 2$, and $y = 0$, about the y-axis.

11. The triangle with vertices $(1, 1)$, $(1, 2)$, $(2, 2)$, (a) about the x-axis; (b) about the y-axis.

12. The area bounded by the curve $x = y - y^3$ and the lines $x = 0$, $y = 0$, $y = 1$, about the x-axis.

13. The area bounded by $y = \sqrt{x}$, $y = 2$, $x = 0$, (a) about the x-axis; (b) about the line $x = 4$.

14. The area bounded by the y-axis, and by the curves $y = \cos x$ and $y = \sin x$ for $0 \leq x \leq \pi/4$, about the x-axis.

15. The area bounded by $y = 0$ and the curve $y = 8x^2 - 8x^3$, $0 \leq x \leq 1$, about the y-axis.

16. The area between the curves $y = 2x^2$ and $y = x^4 - 2x^2$ about the y-axis.

17. Use cylindrical shells and the result of Example 4, Article 4–4, to find the volume generated by revolving about the y-axis the area bounded by $y = 0$ and the curve $y = \sin x$, $0 \leq x \leq \pi$.

18. The area bounded by the curve $y = x^2$ and the line $y = 4$ generates various solids of revolution when rotated as follows:

a) about the y-axis,   **b)** about the line $y = 4$,

c) about the x-axis,   **d)** about the line $y = -1$,

e) about the line $x = 2$.

Find the volume generated in each case.

19. The circle $x^2 + y^2 = a^2$ is rotated about the line $x = b$ $(b > a)$ to generate a torus. Find the volume generated. [*Hint.* $\int_{-a}^{a} \sqrt{a^2 - x^2}\, dx = \pi a^2/2$, since it is the area of a semicircle of radius a.]

APPROXIMATIONS

By now it is apparent that each application of the Fundamental Theorem that we have made so far has involved the following steps:

1. Select an independent variable, say x, such that the quantity U to be computed can be represented as a sum of pieces ΔU, where ΔU is that part of U that is associated with the subinterval $(x,\ x + \Delta x)$ of the domain $a \leq x \leq b$ of the variable x.

2. Subdivide the domain (a, b) into n subintervals. For simplicity we usually take the lengths all to be the same, namely, equal to $\Delta x = (b - a)/n$.

3. Approximate that portion ΔU of U that is associated with the subinterval $(x, x + \Delta x)$ by an expression of the form

$$\Delta U \approx f(X)\, \Delta x. \tag{1}$$

In this expression, X is to be some point in the subinterval $(x,\ x + \Delta x)$ and the function f is to be continuous over the entire domain $a \leq x \leq b$.

4. Then the total quantity U is *approximately*

$$U \approx \sum_{a}^{b} f(X)\, \Delta x. \tag{2}$$

5. Take the limit, as Δx approaches zero, of the sum in Eq. (2). This limit is the definite integral

$$\lim_{\Delta x \to 0} \sum_{a}^{b} f(X)\, \Delta x = \int_{a}^{b} f(x)\, dx. \tag{3}$$

Is this limit also an approximation to U or does it give U exactly?

In the case of area, distance, and volume we have seen that the *limit* in (3) does give U exactly. To be able to apply these methods to new situations as they arise, we need an answer to the following question.

QUESTION. How accurate must the approximations in (1) and (2) be to say that all of the error is squeezed out in going to the limit, (3), with the result that the exact value of U is given by the limit

$$U = \lim_{\Delta x \to 0} \sum_{a}^{b} f(X)\, \Delta x = \int_{a}^{b} f(x)\, dx? \tag{4}$$

ANSWER.   Denote by $\alpha\,\Delta x$ the correction that must be added to the right side of Eq. (1) to give ΔU exactly. That is, suppose that

$$\Delta U = f(X)\,\Delta x + \alpha\,\Delta x, \tag{5}$$

exactly.

FIRST CASE.   Suppose these correction terms are no larger than a constant K times $(\Delta x)^2$,

$$|\alpha\,\Delta x| \le K(\Delta x)^2,$$

where K is a constant the same for all subintervals and all methods of subdivision. Then we have

$$\Delta U = f(X)\,\Delta x + \alpha\,\Delta x,$$

$$U = \sum_a^b f(X)\,\Delta x + \sum_a^b \alpha\,\Delta x$$

and

$$\left| U - \sum_a^b f(X)\,\Delta x \right| = \left| \sum_a^b \alpha\,\Delta x \right| \le \sum_a^b K(\Delta x)^2. \tag{6}$$

This last sum consists of n terms each of which is equal to $K(\Delta x)^2$, where $\Delta x = (b - a)/n$. Therefore

$$\sum_a^b K(\Delta x)^2 = nK(b - a)^2/n^2 = K(b - a)^2/n = K(b - a)\,\Delta x,$$

and (6) becomes

$$\left| U - \sum_a^b f(X)\,\Delta x \right| \le K(b - a)\,\Delta x. \tag{7}$$

In other words, if the error in the approximation (1) to each individual ΔU is no more than a constant times the *square* of Δx, then the error in the approximation (2) to the *total U* is no more than a constant times the *first power* of Δx. Now let Δx approach zero in (7). The sum on the left becomes the definite integral (3), and the term on the right becomes zero. In other words, U is exactly equal to the definite integral in this case.

SECOND CASE.   Suppose the correction terms are numerically no larger than a constant K' times Δx times δy:

$$|\alpha\,\Delta x| \le K'\,\Delta x\,\delta y,$$

where K' is the same for all subintervals and all methods of subdivision, and where δy is the oscillation in the interval $(x, x + \Delta x)$ of a function $y = \phi(x)$ that is continuous over the closed interval (a, b). Then one finds in this case that the total error in the approximation (2) is no larger than

$$K'(b - a) \text{ times } (\max \delta y).$$

But the maximum δy also approaches zero when Δx does, so again we find that U is given exactly by the definite integral.

We have given criteria such as

$$|\alpha \, \Delta x| \leq K(\Delta x)^2 \qquad \text{or} \qquad |\alpha \, \Delta x| \leq K' \, \Delta x \, \delta y,$$

where K and K' are constants. Usually, in an application, we have a function of x in place of K or K' in these inequalities. But a function of x that is continuous over the closed interval $a \leq x \leq b$ has a maximum absolute value M on that interval, and we could take K (or K') equal to M in such a case. Also, the correction terms $\alpha \, \Delta x$ could involve finite combinations of the two cases discussed above, provided the inequality

$$|\alpha \, \Delta x| \leq K(\Delta x)^2 + K' \, \Delta x \, \delta y$$

is satisfied for some choice of the constants K and K'.

Roughly speaking, we may say that in the approximation

$$\Delta U \approx f(X) \, \Delta x$$

we must include all first power Δx terms but we may omit higher-power terms like $(\Delta x)^2$, $(\Delta x)^3$, and so on, or we may omit such mixed terms as

$$(\Delta x)(\Delta y), \qquad (\Delta x)^2(\Delta y), \qquad (\Delta x)(\Delta y)^2,$$

and so on. If each separate piece ΔU is estimated to this degree of accuracy, then the total quantity U which is given approximately by the sum (2) will be given exactly by the limit of the sum, namely, by the integral (4).

In discussing the cylindrical shell method of finding a volume of revolution, Article 5–5, we found that we could estimate the volume ΔV in a hollow shell as follows:

$$2\pi \left(x + \frac{\Delta x}{2} \right) \cdot y \cdot \Delta x \leq \Delta V \leq 2\pi \left(x + \frac{\Delta x}{2} \right)(y + \Delta y) \, \Delta x. \tag{8}$$

Multiplied out, this becomes

$$2\pi xy \, \Delta x + \pi y (\Delta x)^2 \leq \Delta V$$

$$\leq 2\pi xy \, \Delta x + \pi y (\Delta x)^2 + 2\pi x \, \Delta x \, \Delta y + \pi \, \Delta y (\Delta x)^2.$$

If we ignore all except the first power terms in Δx, we have the approximation

$$\Delta V \approx 2\pi xy \, \Delta x,$$

with an error that involves combinations like

$$\pi y (\Delta x)^2, \qquad 2\pi x \, \Delta y \, \Delta x, \qquad \pi \, \Delta y (\Delta x)^2.$$

All such terms may be safely ignored when we go to the *limit* of the sum:

$$V = \lim_{\Delta x \to 0} \sum_a^b 2\pi xy \, \Delta x = \int_a^b 2\pi xy \, dx = \int_a^b 2\pi x f(x) \, dx.$$

Infinitesimals.   A variable, such as Δx above, that approaches zero as a limit is called an infinitesimal. Terms that approach zero as the first power of Δx are said to be of the *same order* as Δx, but terms which approach zero as $(\Delta x)^2$ or as $\Delta y \, \Delta x$ are called infinitesimals of *higher order* than Δx. In setting up a definite integral, we must retain those infinitesimals that are of the same order as Δx, but we may omit those infinitesimals that are of higher order than Δx. Thus we may omit the term $\alpha \, \Delta x$, Eq. (5), if α is an infinitesimal of the same order as Δx (or higher order) or of the same order as δy (or higher order), and the *limit* in (4) will give the exact value of U.

PROBLEMS

1. In Fig. 5–9, Article 5–5, let V_a^x denote the volume generated by rotating about the y-axis the area under the curve $y = f(x)$ between the ordinate at a and the ordinate at x, $(x > a)$. Use inequality (8) to show that

$$\frac{dV_a^x}{dx} = \lim_{\Delta x \to 0} \frac{\Delta V_a^x}{\Delta x} = 2\pi x f(x).$$

From this, deduce that

$$V_a^b = \int_a^b 2\pi x f(x) \, dx.$$

2. Let U_a^x denote the amount of the quantity U associated with the interval (a, x), and let ΔU in Eq. (5) represent $U_a^{x+\Delta x} - U_a^x = U_x^{x+\Delta x}$. If the function $f(x)$ in Eq. (5) is continuous over the closed interval $a \le x \le b$ and $|\alpha \, \Delta x| \le K(\Delta x)^2$, where K is a constant, show that

$$\frac{dU_a^x}{dx} = \lim_{\Delta x \to 0} \frac{\Delta U}{\Delta x} = f(x).$$

From this, deduce that $U_a^b = \int_a^b f(x) \, dx.$

3. In Problem 2, replace the condition $|\alpha \, \Delta x| < K(\Delta x)^2$ by the condition

$$|\alpha \, \Delta x| \le |K' \, \Delta x \, \delta y|,$$

where K' is a constant and δy is the oscillation over the interval $(x, x + \Delta x)$ of a function $y = g(x)$ that is continuous over the closed interval $a \le x \le b$. Then derive the same conclusion as in Problem 2.

5–7

LENGTH OF A PLANE CURVE

Divide the arc AB (Fig. 5–12) into n pieces and join the successive points of division by straight lines. A representative line, such as PQ, will have length

$$PQ = \sqrt{(\Delta x_k)^2 + (\Delta y_k)^2}.$$

The length of the curve AB is approximately

$$L_A^B \approx \sum_{k=1}^{n} \sqrt{(\Delta x_k)^2 + (\Delta y_k)^2}.$$

When the number of division points is increased indefinitely while the lengths of the individual segments tend to zero, we obtain

$$L_A^B = \lim_{n \to \infty} \sum_{k=1}^{n} \sqrt{(\Delta x_k)^2 + (\Delta y_k)^2}, \tag{1}$$

provided the limit exists.* The sum on the right side of (1) is not in the standard form to which we can apply the Fundamental Theorem of the integral calculus, but it can be put into such a form, as follows:

Suppose that the function $y = f(x)$ is continuous and possesses a continuous derivative at each point of the curve from $A[a, f(a)]$ to $B[b, f(b)]$. Then, by the Mean Value Theorem, there is some point $P^*(x_k^*, y_k^*)$ between P and

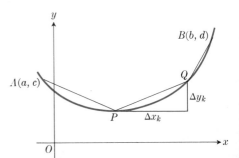

5–12 The arc AB is approximated by the polygonal path $APQB$. The length of the arc is defined to be the limit (when it exists) of the lengths of successively finer polygonal approximations.

---

* For most smooth curves encountered in practice, the limit does exist. Such curves are called *rectifiable*. An example of a continuous curve that is not rectifiable is given by the curve

$$y = \begin{cases} x \sin 1/x & \text{when} \quad x \ne 0, \\ 0 & \text{when} \quad x = 0, \end{cases} \quad \frac{-\pi}{2} \le x \le \frac{\pi}{2}.$$

Q on the curve where the tangent to the curve is parallel to the chord PQ. That is,

$$f'(x_k^*) = \frac{\Delta y_k}{\Delta x_k}$$

or

$$\Delta y_k = f'(x_k^*)\, \Delta x_k.$$

Hence (1) may also be written in the form

$$L_A^B = \lim_{n \to \infty} \sum_{k=1}^{n} \sqrt{(\Delta x_k)^2 + (f'(x_k^*)\, \Delta x_k)^2}$$

$$= \lim_{\Delta x \to 0} \left(\sum_{a}^{b} \sqrt{1 + (f'(x^*))^2}\, \Delta x \right)$$

or

$$L_A^B = \int_a^b \sqrt{1 + \left(\frac{dy}{dx}\right)^2}\, dx, \qquad (2a)$$

where we have written dy/dx for $f'(x)$.

It is sometimes convenient, if x can be expressed as a function of y, to interchange the roles of x and y. The analogue of Eq. (2a) in this case is

$$L_A^B = \int_c^d \sqrt{1 + \left(\frac{dx}{dy}\right)^2}\, dy. \qquad (2b)$$

There is a particularly useful formula for calculating the length of a curve that is given parametrically. Let the equations of motion be

$$x = g(t), \qquad y = h(t), \qquad (3)$$

and let t_k, t_{k+1} be the values of t at P and Q respectively. Suppose the arc AB is described just once by $P(x, y)$ as t goes from t_a at A to t_b at B. If the functions $g(t)$ and $h(t)$ are continuously differentiable for t between t_a and t_b inclusive, the Mean Value Theorem may be applied to Eq. (3) to give

$$\Delta x_k = x_{k+1} - x_k = g(t_{k+1}) - g(t_k) = g'(t_k')\, \Delta t_k,$$

$$\Delta y_k = y_{k+1} - y_k = h(t_{k+1}) - h(t_k) = h'(t_k'')\, \Delta t_k,$$

where t_k' and t_k'' are two suitably chosen values of t between t_k and t_{k+1}. Then (1) becomes

$$L_A^B = \lim_{n \to \infty} \sum_{k=1}^{n} \sqrt{(g'(t_k'))^2 + (h'(t_k''))^2}\, \Delta t_k$$

$$= \int_{t_a}^{t_b} \sqrt{\left(\frac{dx}{dt}\right)^2 + \left(\frac{dy}{dt}\right)^2}\, dt. \qquad (4)$$

Clearly, there is nothing inherently dependent upon the fact that t stands for time in Eqs. (3) and (4). Any other variable could serve as well, and if θ is used instead of t in (3) in representing the curve, then we need only replace t by θ in (4) as well.

EXAMPLE 1. The coordinates (x, y) of a point on a circle of radius r can be expressed in terms of the central angle θ (Fig. 5–13) as

$$x = r \cos \theta, \qquad y = r \sin \theta.$$

The point $P(x, y)$ moves once around the circle as θ varies from 0 to 2π, so that the circumference of the circle is given by

$$C = \int_0^{2\pi} \sqrt{\left(\frac{dx}{d\theta}\right)^2 + \left(\frac{dy}{d\theta}\right)^2} \, d\theta.$$

We find

$$\frac{dx}{d\theta} = -r \sin \theta, \qquad \frac{dy}{d\theta} = r \cos \theta,$$

so that

$$\left(\frac{dx}{d\theta}\right)^2 + \left(\frac{dy}{d\theta}\right)^2 = r^2(\sin^2 \theta + \cos^2 \theta) = r^2,$$

and hence

$$C = \int_0^{2\pi} r \, d\theta = r[\theta]_0^{2\pi} = 2\pi r.$$

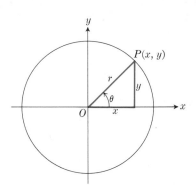

5–13 As θ grows from $\theta = 0$ to $\theta = 2\pi$, the point $P(x, y)$ travels around the circle exactly once.

Equation (4) is frequently written in terms of differentials in place of derivatives. This is done formally by writing $(dt)^2$ under the radical in place of the dt outside the radical, and then writing

$$\left(\frac{dx}{dt}\right)^2 (dt)^2 = \left(\frac{dx}{dt} \, dt\right)^2 = (dx)^2$$

and

$$\left(\frac{dy}{dt}\right)^2 (dt)^2 = \left(\frac{dy}{dt} \, dt\right)^2 = (dy)^2.$$

It is also customary to eliminate the parentheses in $(dx)^2$ and write dx^2 instead, so that Eq. (4) is written

$$L = \int \sqrt{dx^2 + dy^2}. \qquad (5)$$

Of course, dx and dy must both be expressed in terms of one and the same variable, and appropriate limits must be supplied in (5) before the integration can be performed.

A useful mnemonic device for Eq. (5) is to write

$$ds = \sqrt{dx^2 + dy^2} \qquad (6)$$

and treat ds as the differential of arc length, which can be integrated (between appropriate limits) to give the total length of a curve. Figure 5–14(a) gives the exact interpretation of ds corresponding to Eq. (6). Figure 5–14(b) is not strictly accurate, but is to be thought of as a simplified version of Fig.

a)

b)

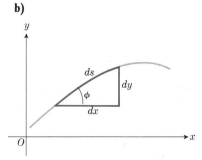

5–14 Diagrams for the equation $ds = \sqrt{dx^2 + dy^2}$.

5–14(a). The inaccuracies in this simplified version will be compensated for if the arc of the curve is treated as the hypotenuse ds of a right triangle of sides dx and dy.

EXAMPLE 2. Find the length of the curve $y = x^{2/3}$ between $x = -1$ and $x = 8$.

Solution. From the equation of the curve, we find

$$\frac{dy}{dx} = \frac{2}{3} x^{-1/3}.$$

Since this becomes infinite at the origin (see Fig. 5–15), we use Eq. (2b) instead of (2a) to find the length of the curve. Then we need to find dx/dy. Since the equation of the curve,

$$y = x^{2/3},$$

can also be written as

$$x = \pm y^{3/2},$$

we find

$$\frac{dx}{dy} = \pm \frac{3}{2} y^{1/2},$$

or

$$dx = \pm \tfrac{3}{2} y^{1/2}\, dy.$$

Then

$$= \tfrac{9}{4} y\, dy^2 + dy^2$$

$$ds^2 = dx^2 + dy^2 = \left(\tfrac{9}{4} y + 1 \right) dy^2,$$

so that

$$ds = \sqrt{\tfrac{9}{4} y + 1}\; dy.$$

The portion of the curve between $A(-1, 1)$ and the origin has length

$$L_1 = \int_0^1 \sqrt{\tfrac{9}{4} y + 1}\; dy,$$

while the rest of the curve from the origin to $B(8, 4)$ has length

$$L_2 = \int_0^4 \sqrt{\tfrac{9}{4} y + 1}\; dy,$$

and the total length is

$$L = L_1 + L_2.$$

It is necessary to calculate the length of the curve with two separate integrals since $x = \pm y^{3/2}$ needs to be separated into two distinct functions of y. For the portion AO of the curve, we have $x = -y^{3/2}$, $0 \le y \le 1$; while on the arc OB, we have $x = +y^{3/2}$, $0 \le y \le 4$.

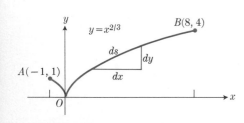

5–15 To compute the length of $y = x^{2/3}$ between A and B one writes $x = -y^{3/2}$ for the part from A to O, and $x = y^{3/2}$ for the part from O to B, and uses Eq. (2b) twice. The discussion at the end of Example 2 explains why.

To evaluate the given integrals, we let

$$u = \tfrac{9}{4}y + 1,$$

then

$$du = \tfrac{9}{4}\, dy, \qquad dy = \tfrac{4}{9}\, du,$$

and

$$\int (\tfrac{9}{4}y + 1)^{1/2}\, dy = \tfrac{4}{9} \int u^{1/2}\, du = \tfrac{8}{27}u^{3/2}.$$

Therefore,

$$L = \frac{8}{27} \left\{ \left(\frac{9}{4}y + 1\right)^{3/2} \Big]_0^1 + \left(\frac{9}{4}y + 1\right)^{3/2} \Big]_0^4 \right\}$$

$$= \tfrac{1}{27}(13\sqrt{13} + 80\sqrt{10} - 16) = 10.5.$$

To check against gross errors, we calculate the sum of the lengths of the two inscribed chords:

$$AO + OB = \sqrt{2} + \sqrt{80} = 10.4,$$

which appears to be satisfactory.

The curve in Fig. 5–15 has a cusp at $(0, 0)$ where the slope becomes infinite. If we were to reconstruct the derivation of Eq. (2) for this particular curve, we would see that the crucial step that required an application of the Mean Value Theorem could not have been taken for the case of a chord PQ from a point P to the left of the cusp to a point Q to its right. For this reason, if for no other, when one or more cusps occur between the ends of a portion of a curve whose length is to be calculated, it is best to calculate the lengths of portions of the curve between cusps and add the results. We recall that the Mean Value Theorem is still valid even when the derivative becomes infinite at an extremity of the interval where it is to be applied, so that the derivation of Eq. (2) would be valid for the separate portions of a curve lying *between* cusps (or other discontinuities of dy/dx, such as occur at corners). Thus in the example just worked, we find the lengths L_1 from $A(-1, 1)$ to O (up to the cusp) and L_2 from O to $B(8, 4)$, then add the results to obtain $L = L_1 + L_2$. This was done by the sum of the two integrals. Had there been no point of discontinuity of dy/dx, it would not have been necessary to take two separate integrals, and Eq. (2a) could have been used.

EXAMPLE 3.　The coordinates of the point $P(x, y)$ on the four-cusped hypocycloid are given by

$$x = a \cos^3 \theta, \qquad y = a \sin^3 \theta.$$

Find the total length of the curve (Fig. 5–16).

Solution.　When θ varies from 0 to $\pi/2$, P traces out the portion of the curve in the first quadrant. Also, from the fact that

$$x^{2/3} + y^{2/3} = a^{2/3}(\cos^2 \theta + \sin^2 \theta) = a^{2/3},$$

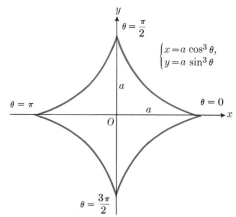

5–16　The hypocycloid $x = a \cos^3 \theta$, $y = a \sin^3 \theta$, $0 \le \theta \le 2\pi$

it will be seen that, for every point (x, y) on the curve in the first quadrant, the corresponding points

$$(-x, y), \qquad (-x, -y), \qquad \text{and} \qquad (x, -y)$$

in the other three quadrants are also on the curve, which is therefore symmetrical about both axes. The portion of the curve in the first quadrant lies *between* two cusps and is one-quarter of the total length of the curve. Therefore

$$L = 4 \int_{\theta=0}^{\theta=\pi/2} \sqrt{dx^2 + dy^2}.$$

From the equation of the curve, we find

$$\frac{dx}{d\theta} = -3a \cos^2 \theta \sin \theta, \qquad dx = 3a \cos \theta \sin \theta (-\cos \theta) \, d\theta,$$

$$\frac{dy}{d\theta} = 3a \sin^2 \theta \cos \theta, \qquad dy = 3a \cos \theta \sin \theta (\sin \theta) \, d\theta,$$

and hence

$$ds^2 = dx^2 + dy^2 = (3a \cos \theta \sin \theta)^2 (\cos^2 \theta + \sin^2 \theta)(d\theta)^2$$

or

$$ds^2 = (3a \cos \theta \sin \theta \, d\theta)^2.$$

Hence, for θ between 0 and $\pi/2$,

$$ds = 3a \cos \theta \sin \theta \, d\theta$$

and

$$L = 4 \int_0^{\pi/2} 3a \cos \theta \sin \theta \, d\theta.$$

To evaluate this integral, we let

$$u = \sin \theta, \qquad du = \cos \theta \, d\theta,$$

and

$$\int \cos \theta \sin \theta \, d\theta = \int u \, du = \tfrac{1}{2}u^2 = \tfrac{1}{2} \sin^2 \theta,$$

so that

$$L = (12a)(\tfrac{1}{2} \sin^2 \theta)\Big]_0^{\pi/2} = 6a.$$

PROBLEMS

Find the lengths of the curves in Problems 1 through 6.

1. $y = \tfrac{1}{3}(x^2 + 2)^{3/2}$ from $x = 0$ to $x = 3$.
2. $y = x^{3/2}$ from $(0, 0)$ to $(4, 8)$.
3. $9x^2 = 4y^3$ from $(0, 0)$ to $(2\sqrt{3}, 3)$.
4. $y = (x^3/3) + (1/4x)$ from $x = 1$ to $x = 3$.

5. $x = (y^4/4) + 1/(8y^2)$ from $y = 1$ to $y = 2$.
6. $(y + 1)^2 = 4x^3$ from $x = 0$ to $x = 1$.
7. Find the distance traveled between $t = 0$ and $t = \pi/2$ by a particle $P(x, y)$ whose position at time t is given by

$$x = a \cos t + at \sin t, \qquad y = a \sin t - at \cos t,$$

where a is a positive constant.

8. Find the length of the curve

$$x = t - \sin t, \qquad y = 1 - \cos t, \qquad 0 \le t \le 2\pi.$$

[*Hint.* $\sqrt{2 - 2\cos t} = 2\sqrt{(1 - \cos t)/2}.$]

9. Find the distance traveled by the particle $P(x, y)$ between $t = 0$ and $t = 4$ if the position at time t is given by

$$x = \frac{t^2}{2}, \qquad y = \frac{1}{3}(2t + 1)^{3/2}.$$

10. The position of a particle $P(x, y)$ at time t is given by

$$x = \frac{1}{3}(2t + 3)^{3/2}, \qquad y = \frac{t^2}{2} + t.$$

Find the distance it travels between $t = 0$ and $t = 3$.

11. (*Calculator*) The length of one arch of the curve $y = \sin x$ is given by

$$L = \int_0^\pi \sqrt{1 + \cos^2 x}\, dx.$$

Estimate L by Simpson's rule with $n = 8$.

Suppose that the curve in Fig. 5–17 is rotated about the x-axis. It will generate a surface in space. The inscribed polygonal line segments will generate inscribed frustums of cones. The sum of the lateral areas of these frustums will be an approximation to the area of the surface. To obtain an analytic expression for this approximation, we require the formula

5–8

AREA OF A SURFACE OF REVOLUTION

$$A = \pi(r_1 + r_2)l \tag{1}$$

for the lateral area A of a frustum of slant height l, where r_1 and r_2 are the radii of its bases.

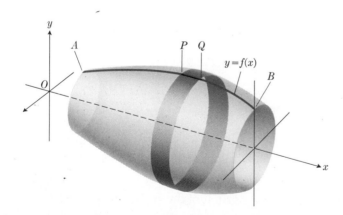

5–17 The surface swept out by a plane curve rotated about an axis in the plane of this curve is a union of bands.

To establish Eq. (1), imagine the frustum of a cone to be the limit of inscribed frustums of pyramids (see Fig. 5–18). If each base of an inscribed frustum of a pyramid is a regular polygon of n sides, and b_1 is the length of one side in the upper face, while b_2 is the length of a side in the lower face, then the lateral area will consist of n trapezoids each having an area

$$\tfrac{1}{2}(b_1 + b_2)h.$$

5–18 The frustum of a cone approximated by the frustum of a pyramid.

The n trapezoids have area

$$\tfrac{1}{2}(nb_1 + nb_2)h.$$

As n increases indefinitely, we have

$$\lim_{n \to \infty} nb_1 = 2\pi r_1, \qquad \lim_{n \to \infty} nb_2 = 2\pi r_2,$$

and

$$\lim_{n \to \infty} h = l,$$

so that

$$A = \lim_{n \to \infty} \tfrac{1}{2}(nb_1 + nb_2)h = \tfrac{1}{2}(2\pi r_1 + 2\pi r_2)l = \pi(r_1 + r_2)l,$$

which establishes Eq. (1). Note that if $r_1 = r_2$, Eq. (1) reduces to the correct formula for the lateral area of a cylinder, and if $r_1 = 0$, it gives the correct result for the lateral area of a cone. It can also be put into the form

$$A = 2\pi r l$$

where

$$r = \tfrac{1}{2}(r_1 + r_2)$$

is the radius of the mid-section of the frustum. In this form, (1) says that the lateral area of a frustum of a cone = (circumference of mid-section) × (slant height).

We now consider the portion of the surface ΔS generated by the arc PQ, and its inscribed frustum of a cone generated by the chord PQ. Let's call (x, y) the coordinates of P, and $(x + \Delta x, y + \Delta y)$ the coordinates of Q, and then take

$$r_1 = y, \qquad r_2 = y + \Delta y, \qquad l = \sqrt{(\Delta x)^2 + (\Delta y)^2}$$

in Eq. (1). Then we have the approximation

$$S \approx \sum_{x=a}^{b} \pi(2y + \Delta y)\sqrt{(\Delta x)^2 + (\Delta y)^2}$$

or

$$S \approx \sum_a^b 2\pi \left(y + \frac{1}{2} \Delta y \right) \sqrt{1 + \left(\frac{\Delta y}{\Delta x} \right)^2} \, \Delta x.$$

If y and dy/dx are continuous functions of x and we omit products like $(\Delta y)(\Delta x)$ and higher powers of Δx in this approximation, we have

$$S \approx \sum_a^b 2\pi y \sqrt{1 + \left(\frac{dy}{dx} \right)^2} \, \Delta x.$$

Then taking the limit as Δx tends to zero, we get

$$S = \lim_{\Delta x \to 0} \sum_a^b 2\pi y \sqrt{1 + \left(\frac{dy}{dx} \right)^2} \, \Delta x$$

or

$$S = \int_a^b 2\pi y \sqrt{1 + \left(\frac{dy}{dx} \right)^2} \, dx. \qquad (2)$$

Our end result, Eq. (2), is easily remembered if we write

$$\sqrt{1 + \left(\frac{dy}{dx} \right)^2} \, dx = ds$$

and take

$$S = \int 2\pi y \, ds. \qquad (3)$$

If we let

$$dS = 2\pi y \, ds,$$

so that

$$S = \int dS,$$

we may interpret dS as the product of a

$$\text{Circumference} = 2\pi y$$

and a

$$\text{Slant height} = ds.$$

Thus dS gives the lateral area of a frustum of a cone of slant height ds if the point (x, y) is the midpoint of the element of arc length ds (Fig. 5–19).

 Why not approximate the surface area S by inscribed *cylinders* and arrive at a result

$$S = \int 2\pi y \, dx,$$

having dx instead of ds, to replace Eq. (3)? Since we know from our discussion on volume that inscribed cylinders work perfectly well for *volumes* of revolution, why not use them for *surfaces* of revolution also? The answer

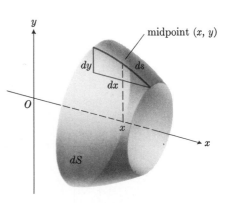

5–19 $dS = 2\pi y \, ds.$

hinges on the fact that the approximation

$$\Delta V \approx \pi y^2 \, \Delta x$$

for the volume of a slice involves, at worst, terms that are products like $(\Delta x)(\Delta y)$ and higher powers of Δx and these contribute zero to the *limit* of the sum of volumes of the inscribed cylinders. (See Article 5–6.) But the approximations

(a) $\qquad \Delta S \approx 2\pi y \, \Delta x \quad$ (Inscribed cylinder)

and

(b) $\qquad \Delta S \approx 2\pi y \sqrt{(\Delta x)^2 + (\Delta y)^2} \quad$ (Inscribed conical band)

for the surface area of a slice cannot *both* be this accurate. For their ratio is

$$\frac{2\pi y \sqrt{(\Delta x)^2 + (\Delta y)^2}}{2\pi y \, \Delta x} = \sqrt{1 + \left(\frac{\Delta y}{\Delta x}\right)^2},$$

which has the limiting value

$$\lim_{\Delta x \to 0} \sqrt{1 + \left(\frac{\Delta y}{\Delta x}\right)^2} = \sqrt{1 + \left(\frac{dy}{dx}\right)^2},$$

and this will be different from one (unless $dy/dx = 0$, which would not be generally true), whereas two approximations that differ only by terms involving products like $(\Delta y)(\Delta x)$ and higher powers of Δx have a ratio whose limiting value is unity. Since the approximations (a) and (b) above will usually lead to different answers when we pass to the corresponding definite integrals, they cannot both be correct, and we must abandon one or both of them. But the approximation (b) is clearly the one that corresponds to a natural way of defining the surface area of a surface of revolution and it leads to (3).

If the axis of revolution is the y-axis, the corresponding formula that replaces (3) is

$$S = \int_c^d 2\pi x \sqrt{1 + \left(\frac{dx}{dy}\right)^2} \, dy. \tag{4}$$

If the curve that sweeps out the surface is given in parametric form with x and y as functions of a third variable t that varies from t_a to t_b, then we may compute S from the formula

$$S = \int_{t_a}^{t_b} 2\pi \rho \sqrt{\left(\frac{dx}{dt}\right)^2 + \left(\frac{dy}{dt}\right)^2} \, dt, \tag{5}$$

where ρ is the distance from the axis of revolution to the element of arc length, and is expressed as a function of t.

More generally we may write

$$S = \int 2\pi \rho \, ds, \tag{6}$$

where, again, ρ is the distance from the axis of revolution to the element of arc length ds. Both ρ and ds need to be expressed in terms of some one variable and proper limits must be supplied to (6) in any particular problem.

EXAMPLE 1.   The circle

$$x^2 + y^2 = r^2$$

is revolved about the x-axis (Fig. 5–20). Find the area of the sphere generated.

Solution.   We write

$$dS = 2\pi y \, ds,$$
$$ds = \sqrt{dx^2 + dy^2},$$

and use

$$x = r \cos \theta, \qquad y = r \sin \theta$$

to represent the circle. Then

$$dx = -r \sin \theta \, d\theta, \qquad dy = r \cos \theta \, d\theta,$$

so that

$$ds = r \, d\theta$$

and

$$dS = 2\pi y \, ds = 2\pi (r \sin \theta) r \, d\theta$$
$$= 2\pi r^2 \sin \theta \, d\theta.$$

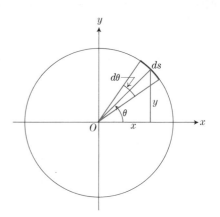

5–20   To compute the surface area of the sphere obtained by revolving the circle $x^2 + y^2 = r^2$ about the x-axis, let θ vary from $\theta = 0$ to $\theta = \pi$. The top half of the circle generates the entire sphere.

The top half of the circle generates the entire sphere, and the representative point (x, y) traces out this upper semicircle as θ varies from 0 to π. Hence

$$S = \int_0^\pi 2\pi r^2 \sin \theta \, d\theta$$
$$= 2\pi r^2 [-\cos \theta]_0^\pi = 4\pi r^2.$$

EXAMPLE 2.   The circle in Example 1 is revolved about the line $y = -r$, which is tangent to the circle at the point $(0, -r)$ (Fig. 5–21). Find the area of the surface generated.

Solution.   Here it takes the whole circle to generate the surface, and in terms of the previous example, this means that we must let θ vary from 0 to 2π. The radius of rotation now becomes

$$\rho = y + r,$$

and we have

$$dS = 2\pi \rho \, ds = 2\pi (y + r) r \, d\theta = 2\pi (r \sin \theta + r) r \, d\theta.$$

Hence

$$S = \int_0^{2\pi} 2\pi (\sin \theta + 1) r^2 \, d\theta = 2\pi r^2 [-\cos \theta + \theta]_0^{2\pi} = 4\pi^2 r^2.$$

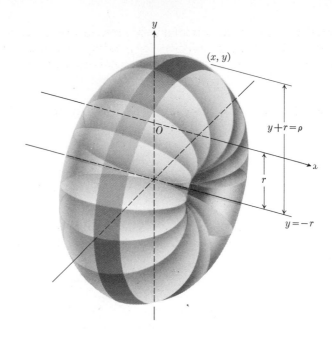

5–21 The circle of Fig. 5–20 revolved about the line $y = -r$.

PROBLEMS

1. Find the area of the surface generated by rotating the portion of the curve $y = \frac{1}{3}(x^2 + 2)^{3/2}$ between $x = 0$ and $x = 3$ about the y-axis.

2. Find the area of the surface generated by rotating about the x-axis the arc of the curve $y = x^3$ between $x = 0$ and $x = 1$.

3. Find the area of the surface generated by rotating about the y-axis the arc of the curve $y = x^2$ between $(0, 0)$ and $(2, 4)$.

4. The arc of the curve $y = (x^3/3) + (1/4x)$ from $x = 1$ to $x = 3$ is rotated about the line $y = -1$. Find the surface area generated.

5. The arc of the curve $x = (y^4/4) + (1/8y^2)$ from $y = 1$ to $y = 2$ is rotated about the x-axis. Find the surface area generated.

6. Find the area of the surface generated by rotating about the y-axis the curve $y = (x^2/2) + \frac{1}{2}$, $0 \le x \le 1$.

7. Find the area of the surface generated by rotating the curve $x = t^2$, $y = t$, $0 \le t \le 1$, about the x-axis.

8. Find the area of the surface generated by rotating the hypocycloid $x = a \cos^3 \theta$, $y = a \sin^3 \theta$, about the x-axis.

9. The curve described by the particle $P(x, y)$,

$$x = t + 1, \qquad y = \frac{t^2}{2} + t,$$

from $t = 0$ to $t = 4$, is rotated about the y-axis. Find the surface area that is generated.

10. The loop of the curve $9x^2 = y(3 - y)^2$ is rotated about the x-axis. Find the surface area generated.

5–9

AVERAGE VALUE OF A FUNCTION

The process of finding the average value of a finite number of data is familiar to all students. For example, if $y_1, y_2, \ldots, y_n$ are the grades of a class of n students on a certain calculus quiz, then the class average on that quiz is

$$y_{\text{av}} = \frac{y_1 + y_2 + \cdots + y_n}{n}. \tag{1}$$

When the number of data is infinite, it is not feasible to use Eq. (1) (since it is likely to take on the meaningless form ∞/∞). This situation arises, in particular, when the data y are given by a continuous function

$$y = f(x), \qquad a \leq x \leq b.$$

In this case, the average value of y, with respect to x, is defined to be

$$(y_{av})_x = \frac{1}{b-a} \int_a^b f(x)\, dx. \tag{2}$$

The curve in Fig. 5–22, for example, might represent temperature as a function of time over a twenty-four hour period. Equation (2) would then give the "average temperature" for the day.

REMARK 1.   It may be possible to express y as a function of x, or, alternatively, as a function of u. Then $(y_{av})_x$ and $(y_{av})_u$ need not be equal. For example, for a freely falling body starting from rest,

$$s = \tfrac{1}{2}gt^2, \qquad v = gt, \qquad v = \sqrt{2gs}.$$

Suppose we calculate the average velocity, first with respect to t and second with respect to s, from $t_1 = 0$, $s_1 = 0$, to $t_2 > 0$, $s_2 = \tfrac{1}{2}g(t_2)^2$. Then, by definition,

$$(v_{av})_t = \frac{1}{t_2 - 0} \int_0^{t_2} gt\, dt = \frac{1}{2}\, gt_2 = \frac{1}{2}\, v_2,$$

$$(v_{av})_s = \frac{1}{s_2 - 0} \int_0^{s_2} \sqrt{2gs}\, ds = \frac{2}{3}\sqrt{2gs_2} = \frac{2}{3}\, v_2.$$

REMARK 2.   If both sides of Eq. (2) are multiplied by $b - a$, we have

$$(y_{av})_x \cdot (b-a) = \int_a^b f(x)\, dx. \tag{3}$$

The right side of Eq. (3) represents the area bounded above by the curve $y = f(x)$, below by the x-axis, and on the sides by the ordinates $x = a, x = b$. The left side of the equation can be interpreted as the area of a rectangle of altitude $(y_{av})_x$ and of base $b - a$. Hence, Eq. (3) provides a geometric interpretation of $(y_{av})_x$ as that ordinate of the curve $y = f(x)$ that should be used as altitude if one wishes to construct a rectangle whose base is the interval $a \leq x \leq b$ and whose area is equal to the area under the curve (Fig. 5–22). In the narrower sense of area, this statement is valid only when the curve lies above the x-axis. If the curve lies partly or entirely below the x-axis, we would count areas below the x-axis as negative. In such a case there might well be a certain amount of canceling of positive and negative areas.

REMARK 3.   Equation (2) is a *definition*, and hence is not subject to proof. Nevertheless, some discussion may help to explain why this particular formula is used to define the average. One might arrive at it as follows. From the total "population" of x-values, $a \leq x \leq b$, we select a representative "sample," $x_1, x_2, \ldots, x_n$, uniformly distributed between a and b. Then, using Eq. (1), we calculate the average of the functional values

$$y_1 = f(x_1), \qquad y_2 = f(x_2), \qquad \ldots, \qquad y_n = f(x_n)$$

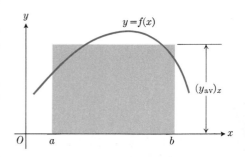

5-22 One interpretation of $(y_{av})_x = [1/(b-a)] \int_a^b f(x)\, dx$ comes from interpreting the integral as an area.

associated with these representative x's. This gives us

$$\frac{y_1 + y_2 + \cdots + y_n}{n} = \frac{f(x_1) + f(x_2) + \cdots + f(x_n)}{n}. \tag{4}$$

Since we require that the x's be uniformly distributed between a and b, let us take the spacing to be Δx, with

$$x_2 - x_1 = x_3 - x_2 = \cdots = x_n - x_{n-1} = \Delta x$$

and

$$\Delta x = \frac{b - a}{n}.$$

Then, in (4), let us replace the n in the denominator by $(b - a)/\Delta x$, thus obtaining

$$\frac{f(x_1) + f(x_2) + \cdots + f(x_n)}{(b - a)/\Delta x} = \frac{f(x_1)\,\Delta x + f(x_2)\,\Delta x + \cdots + f(x_n)\,\Delta x}{b - a}$$

If, now, n is very large and Δx small, the expression

$$f(x_1)\,\Delta x + f(x_2)\,\Delta x + \cdots + f(x_n)\,\Delta x = \sum_{k=1}^{n} f(x_k)\,\Delta x$$

is very nearly equal to $\int_a^b f(x)\,dx$. In fact, if we take limits, letting $n \to \infty$, we obtain precisely

$$\lim_{n \to \infty} \frac{f(x_1)\,\Delta x + f(x_2)\,\Delta x + \cdots + f(x_n)\,\Delta x}{b - a} = \frac{1}{b - a} \int_a^b f(x)\,dx.$$

This is the expression that defines the average value of y in Eq. (2).

EXAMPLE 1. The costs of warehouse space, utilities, insurance, and security can be a large part of the cost of doing business, and a firm's average daily inventory can play a significant role in determining these costs.

For example, suppose that a wholesale grocer receives a shipment of 1200 cases of chocolate bars every 30 days. The chocolate is sold to retailers at a steady rate; and x days after the shipment arrives, the inventory $I(x)$ of cases still on hand is

$$I(x) = 1200 - 40x.$$

From Eq. (2) we compute the average daily inventory to be

$$I_{av} = \tfrac{1}{30} \int_0^{30} (1200 - 40x)\,dx = \tfrac{1}{30}[1200x - 20x^2]_0^{30} = 600.$$

From I_{av} we can compute the firm's daily holding cost for the chocolate bars. If the cost of holding one case is 3¢ per day, then the total daily holding cost for the chocolate is

$$(600)(0.03) = \$18 \text{ per day.}$$

EXAMPLE 2 *Delesse's rule.** To find out what proportion of a tissue is composed of particles of a certain kind, life scientists sometimes study thin slices of the tissue a few thousandths of a millimeter thick. Under reasonable circumstances, for example, if the particles do not cluster and are fairly evenly distributed throughout the tissue, the proportion of the slice occupied by the traces of the particles will be the same as the proportion of the tissue occupied by the uncut particles. The equality of these proportions was discovered by a French geologist, Achille Ernest Delesse, in the 1840's. The mathematical justification for it lies in the notion of average value.

Suppose that the tissue under investigation is a cube whose sides have length L, as shown in Fig. 5–23. The particles make up a volume u less than L^3, say

$$u = kL^3, \qquad 0 < k < 1. \tag{5}$$

We wish to estimate the proportionality constant k by examining a slice of the cube of width dx perpendicular to the x-axis. The volume of the slice is

$$dV = L^2 \, dx.$$

The space occupied by the traces of the particles in the slice can be written as

$$du = r(x) \, dV = r(x)L^2 \, dx, \tag{6}$$

where the proportionality factor $r(x)$ depends on the location x where the slice is cut. From Eq. (2), the average value of r is

$$\bar{r} = \frac{1}{L} \int_0^L r(x) \, dx. \tag{7}$$

From Eq. (6) we have

$$u = \int_0^L r(x)L^2 \, dx = L^2 \int_0^L r(x) \, dx, \tag{8}$$

or, using Eq. (7),

$$u = \bar{r}L^3. \tag{9}$$

A comparison of this equation with Eq. (5) shows that

$$k = \bar{r}.$$

This is Delesse's rule.

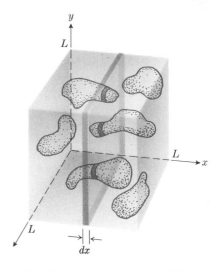

5–23 Particles in a sample of tissue. (Adapted from E. R. Weibel, *Morphometry of the Human Lung.* New York: Academic Press, 1963, p. 13.)

---

*   A. E. Delesse, "A mechanical procedure for determining the composition of rocks," *Annales des Mines,* **13,** 1848, pp. 379–388.

PROBLEMS

In each of the following problems (1 through 5), find the average value with respect to x, over the given domain, of the given function $f(x)$. In each case, draw a graph of the curve $y = f(x)$, and sketch a rectangle whose altitude is the average ordinate.

1. a) $\sin x, \quad 0 \le x \le \pi/2$ **b)** $\sin x, \quad 0 \le x \le 2\pi$

2. a) $\sin^2 x, \quad 0 \le x \le \pi/2$ **b)** $\sin^2 x, \quad \pi \le x \le 2\pi$

3. $\sqrt{2x + 1}, \quad 4 \le x \le 12$

4. $\frac{1}{2} + \frac{1}{2} \cos 2x, \quad 0 \le x \le \pi$

5. $\alpha x + \beta; \quad a \le x \le b \quad [\alpha, \beta, a, b, \text{constants}]$

6. Solon Container receives 450 drums of plastic pellets every 30 days. The inventory function (drums on hand as a function of days) is $I(x) = 450 - x^2/2$. Find the average daily inventory. If the holding cost for one drum is 2¢ per day, find the total daily holding cost.

7. Mitchell Mailorder receives a shipment of 600 cases of athletic socks every 60 days. The number of cases on hand t days after the shipment arrives is $I(t) = 600 - 20\sqrt{15t}$. Find the average daily inventory. If the holding cost for one case is $\frac{1}{2}$¢ per day, find the total daily holding cost.

8. (*Calculator*) Compute the average value of the temperature function

$$f(x) = 37 \sin\left[\frac{2\pi}{365}(x - 101)\right] + 25$$

for a 365-day year (see the Example in Article 2-9). This is one way to estimate the annual mean air temperature in Fairbanks, Alaska. The National Weather Service's official figure, a numerical average of the daily normal mean air temperatures for the year, is 25.7°F, which is slightly higher than the average value of $f(x)$. Figure 2-19 shows why.

9. (*Calculator*) (a) Use the trapezoidal rule to estimate the average lumen output of the No. 22 flashbulb of Problem 12, Article 4-9, for the time interval from $t = 0$ to $t = 60$ milliseconds. Take the data from Table 4-4. (b) How long would a 60-watt incandescent light bulb rated at 765 lumens have to burn to put out as much light as the No. 22 flashbulb did in (a)?

10. Given a circle C of radius a, and a diameter AB of C. Chords are drawn perpendicular to AB, intercepting equal segments along AB. Find the limit of the average of the lengths of these chords, as the number of chords tends to infinity. [*Hint.* $\int_{-a}^{a} \sqrt{a^2 - x^2}\, dx$ is $\frac{1}{2}\pi a^2$, since it is the area of a semicircle of radius a.]

11. Solve Problem 10 under the modified assumption that the chords intercept equal arcs along the circumference of C.

12. Solve Problem 10 using the *squares* of the lengths, in place of the lengths of the chords.

13. Solve Problem 11 using the *squares* of the lengths, in place of the lengths of the chords.

5–10

MOMENTS AND CENTER OF MASS

If masses $m_1, m_2, \ldots, m_n$ are placed along the x-axis at distances $x_1, x_2, \ldots, x_n$ from the origin (Fig. 5–24), then their moment about the origin is defined to be

$$x_1 m_1 + x_2 m_2 + \cdots + x_n m_n = \sum_{k=1}^{n} x_k m_k. \tag{1}$$

If all the mass

$$m_1 + m_2 + \cdots + m_n = \sum_{k=1}^{n} m_k \tag{2}$$

is concentrated at one point of abscissa x, the total moment is

$$x\left(\sum_{k=1}^{n} m_k\right).$$

5–24 Masses on the x-axis.

The position of $\bar{x}$ for which this is the same as the total moment in (1) is called the *center of mass*. The condition

$$\bar{x} \sum_{k=1}^{n} m_k = \sum_{k=1}^{n} x_k m_k$$

thus determines

$$\bar{x} = \frac{\sum_{k=1}^{n} x_k m_k}{\sum_{k=1}^{n} m_k}. \tag{3}$$

EXAMPLE 1.   The principle of a moment underlies the simple seesaw. For instance (Fig. 5–25), suppose one child weighs 80 lb and sits 5 ft from the point O, while the other child weighs 100 lb and is 4 ft from O. Then the child at the left end of the seesaw produces a moment of $5 \times 80 = 400$ ft-lb, which tends to rotate the plank counterclockwise about O. The child at the right end of the plank produces a moment of $4 \times 100 = 400$ ft-lb, which tends to rotate the plank clockwise around O. If we introduce coordinates $x_1 = -5$ and $x_2 = +4$, we find

$$x_1 m_1 + x_2 m_2 = (-5)(80) + (4)(100)$$
$$= -400 + 400 = 0$$

as the resultant moment about O. The same moment, zero, would be obtained if both children were at O, which is the center of their mass.

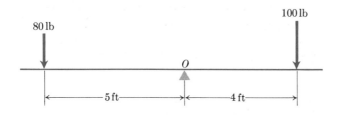

5–25 A 100-lb weight four feet to the right of O balances an 80-lb weight five feet to the left of O.

If, instead of being placed on the x-axis, the masses are located in the xy-plane at points

$$(x_1, y_1),\quad (x_2, y_2),\quad \ldots,\quad (x_n, y_n),$$

in that order, then we define their moments with respect to the y-axis and with respect to the x-axis as

$$M_y = x_1 m_1 + x_2 m_2 + \cdots + x_n m_n = \sum_{k=1}^{n} x_k m_k,$$

$$M_x = y_1 m_1 + y_2 m_2 + \cdots + y_n m_n = \sum_{k=1}^{n} y_k m_k.$$

The center of mass is the point $(\bar{x}, \bar{y})$,

$$\bar{x} = \frac{\sum x_k m_k}{\sum m_k}, \qquad \bar{y} = \frac{\sum y_k m_k}{\sum m_k}, \tag{4}$$

where the total mass could be concentrated and still give the same total moments M_y and M_x.

In space, three coordinates are needed to specify the position of a point. If the masses are located at the points

$$(x_1, y_1, z_1),\quad (x_2, y_2, z_2),\quad \ldots,\quad (x_n, y_n, z_n),$$

we define their moments with respect to the various coordinate planes as

$$M_{yz} = x_1 m_1 + x_2 m_2 + \cdots + x_n m_n = \sum_{k=1}^{n} x_k m_k,$$

$$M_{zx} = y_1 m_1 + y_2 m_2 + \cdots + y_n m_n = \sum_{k=1}^{n} y_k m_k,$$

$$M_{xy} = z_1 m_1 + z_2 m_2 + \cdots + z_n m_n = \sum_{k=1}^{n} z_k m_k.$$

(M_{yz} = Moment with respect to the yz-plane, etc.)

The center of mass $(\bar{x}, \bar{y}, \bar{z})$ is the point where the total mass could be concentrated without altering these moments. Its coordinates therefore are given by

$$\bar{x} = \frac{\sum x_k m_k}{\sum m_k}, \qquad \bar{y} = \frac{\sum y_k m_k}{\sum m_k}, \qquad \bar{z} = \frac{\sum z_k m_k}{\sum m_k}. \tag{5}$$

Now most physical objects with which we deal are composed of enormously large numbers of molecules. It would be extremely difficult, and in most cases unnecessary, for us to concern ourselves with the molecular structure of a physical object, such as a pendulum, whose motion as a whole is to be studied. Instead, we make certain simplifying assumptions which we recognize as being only approximately correct. One such assumption is that the matter in a given solid is continuously distributed throughout the solid. Furthermore, if P is a point in the solid and ΔV is an element of volume that contains P, and if Δm is the mass of ΔV, then we assume that the ratio $\Delta m / \Delta V$ tends to a definite limit

$$\delta = \lim_{\Delta V \to 0} \frac{\Delta m}{\Delta V}, \tag{6}$$

as the largest dimension of ΔV approaches zero. The limit δ is called the *density* of the solid at the point P. It is customary to write Eq. (6) in the alternative forms

$$\delta = dm/dV, \qquad dm = \delta \, dV. \tag{7}$$

If now a solid is divided into small pieces ΔV of mass Δm and if $P(\tilde{x}, \tilde{y}, \tilde{z})$ is a point in ΔV and δ is the density at P, then

$$\Delta m \approx \delta \, \Delta V.$$

The moments of Δm with respect to the coordinate planes are not defined by what we have done thus far. But now we may think of replacing the Δm that fills the volume ΔV by an equal mass all concentrated at the point P. The moments of this concentrated mass with respect to the coordinate planes are

$$\tilde{x} \, \Delta m, \qquad \tilde{y} \, \Delta m, \qquad \tilde{z} \, \Delta m.$$

Now we add the moments of all the concentrated masses in all the volume elements ΔV and take the limit as the ΔV's approach zero. This leads us to the following *definitions* of the moments M_{yz}, etc., for the mass as a whole:

$$M_{yz} = \lim_{\Delta m \to 0} \sum \tilde{x}\, \Delta m = \int \tilde{x}\, dm,$$

$$M_{zx} = \lim_{\Delta m \to 0} \sum \tilde{y}\, \Delta m = \int \tilde{y}\, dm,$$

$$M_{xy} = \lim_{\Delta m \to 0} \sum \tilde{z}\, \Delta m = \int \tilde{z}\, dm.$$

From these, we then deduce the equations

$$\bar{x} = \frac{\int \tilde{x}\, dm}{\int dm}, \qquad \bar{y} = \frac{\int \tilde{y}\, dm}{\int dm}, \qquad \bar{z} = \frac{\int \tilde{z}\, dm}{\int dm} \tag{8}$$

for the center of mass of the solid as a whole.

In theory, the element dm is approximately the mass in a volume element dV which has three small dimensions as in Fig. 5–26. In a later chapter we shall see how to evaluate the integrals (8) which arise when this is done. In practice, however, we can usually take

$$dm = \delta\, dV$$

with a volume element dV which has only one small dimension. Then we must interpret $\tilde{x}, \tilde{y}, \tilde{z}$ in the integrands in (8) as the coordinates of the *center of mass* of the *element dm*.

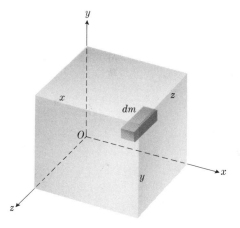

5–26 Mass dm = density $\times$ dV.

In many problems of practical importance the density δ is constant and the solid possesses a plane of symmetry. Then it is easy to see that the center of mass lies in this plane of symmetry. For we may, with no loss of generality, choose our coordinate reference frame in such a way that the yz-plane is the plane of symmetry. Then for every element of mass Δm with a positive $\tilde{x}$ there is a symmetrically located element of mass with a corresponding negative $\tilde{x}$. These two elements have moments that are equal in magnitude and of opposite signs. The whole mass is made up of such symmetric pairs of elements and the sum of their moments about the yz-plane is zero. Therefore $\bar{x} = 0$; that is, the center of mass lies in the plane of symmetry. If there are two planes of symmetry, their intersection is an axis of symmetry and the center of mass must lie on this axis, since it lies in both planes of symmetry.

The most frequently encountered distributions of mass are

a) along a thin wire or filament: $dm = \delta_1\, ds$,
b) in a thin plate or shell: $dm = \delta_2\, dA$ or $\delta_2\, dS$,
c) in a solid: $dm = \delta_3\, dV$,

where

$$ds = \text{element of arc length,}$$

$$\delta_1 = \text{mass per unit length of the wire,}$$

$$dA \quad \text{or} \quad dS = \text{element of area,}$$

$$\delta_2 = \text{mass per unit area of the plate or shell,}$$

$$dV = \text{element of volume,}$$

$$\delta_3 = \text{mass per unit volume of the solid.}$$

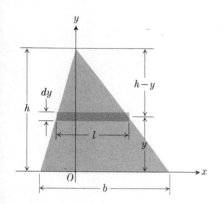

5–27 Calculating the mass of a thin triangular plate.

EXAMPLE 1. Find the center of mass of a thin homogeneous triangular plate of base b and altitude h.

Solution. Divide the triangle into strips of width dy parallel to the x-axis. A representative strip is shown in Fig. 5–27. The mass of the strip is approximately

$$dm = \delta_2 \, dA,$$

where

$$dA = l \, dy$$

and l is the width of the triangle at distance y above its base. By similar triangles,

$$\frac{l}{b} = \frac{h-y}{h}$$

or

$$l = \frac{b}{h}(h-y),$$

so that

$$dm = \delta_2 \frac{b}{h}(h-y) \, dy.$$

For the y-coordinate of the center of mass of the element dm, we have $\tilde{y} = y$. For the entire plate,

$$\bar{y} = \frac{\int y \, dm}{\int dm} = \frac{\int_0^h \delta_2 \frac{b}{h} y(h-y) \, dy}{\int_0^h \delta_2 \frac{b}{h}(h-y) \, dy} = \frac{1}{3}h.$$

Thus the center of mass lies above the base of the triangle at a distance one-third of the way toward the opposite vertex. By considering each side in turn as being a base of the triangle, this result shows that the center of gravity lies at the intersection of the medians.

EXAMPLE 2. A thin homogeneous wire is bent to form a semicircle of radius r (Fig. 5–28). Find its center of mass.

Solution. Here we take

$$dm = \delta_1 \, ds,$$

where ds is an element of arc length of the wire and

$$\delta_1 = \frac{M}{L} = \frac{M}{\pi r}$$

5–28 Calculating the mass of a semicircular wire.

is the mass per unit length of the wire. In terms of the central angle θ

measured in radians (as usual), we have

$$ds = r \, d\theta$$

and

$$\tilde{x} = r \cos \theta, \qquad \tilde{y} = r \sin \theta.$$

Hence

$$\bar{x} = \frac{\int_0^\pi r \cos \theta \, \delta_1 r \, d\theta}{\int_0^\pi \delta_1 r \, d\theta} = \frac{\delta_1 r^2 [\sin \theta]_0^\pi}{\delta_1 r [\theta]_0^\pi} = 0,$$

$$\bar{y} = \frac{\int_0^\pi r \sin \theta \, \delta_1 r \, d\theta}{\int_0^\pi \delta_1 r \, d\theta} = \frac{\delta_1 r^2 [-\cos \theta]_0^\pi}{\delta_1 r [\theta]_0^\pi} = \frac{2}{\pi} r.$$

The center of mass is therefore on the y-axis at a distance $2/\pi$ (roughly $\frac{2}{3}$) of the way up from the origin toward the intercept $(0, r)$.

EXAMPLE 3.   Find the center of mass of a solid hemisphere of radius r if its density at any point P is proportional to the distance between P and the base of the hemisphere.

Solution.   Imagine the solid cut into slices of thickness dy by planes perpendicular to the y-axis (Fig. 5–29), and take

$$dm = \delta_3 \, dV,$$

where

$$dV = A(y) \, dy$$

is the volume of the representative slice at distance y above the base of the hemisphere, which is in the xz-plane, and where

$$\delta_3 = ky \qquad (k = \text{constant})$$

is the density of the solid in this slice. The area of a face of the slice dV is

$$A(y) = \pi x^2,$$

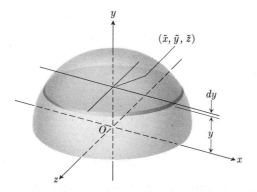

5–29 Finding the mass of a hemispherical solid by slicing parallel to its base.

where $x^2 + y^2 = r^2$; that is,

$$dV = A(y)\, dy = \pi(r^2 - y^2)\, dy;$$

so that

$$dm = k\pi(r^2 - y^2)y\, dy.$$

The center of mass of the slice may be taken at its geometric center,

$$(\tilde{x}, \tilde{y}, \tilde{z}) = (0, y, 0),$$

so that

$$\bar{x} = \bar{z} = 0$$

and

$$\bar{y} = \frac{\int y\, dm}{\int dm}$$

$$= \frac{\displaystyle\int_0^r k\pi(r^2 - y^2)y^2\, dy}{\displaystyle\int_0^r k\pi(r^2 - y^2)y\, dy} = \frac{k\pi\left[\dfrac{r^2 y^3}{3} - \dfrac{y^5}{5}\right]_0^r}{k\pi\left[\dfrac{r^2 y^2}{2} - \dfrac{y^4}{4}\right]_0^r}$$

$$= \frac{8}{15}r.$$

PROBLEMS

In each of the following problems (1 through 5), find the center of mass of a thin homogeneous plate covering the given portion of the xy-plane.

1. The first quadrant of the circle $x^2 + y^2 = a^2$.

2. The area bounded by the parabola $y = h^2 - x^2$ and the x-axis.

3. The "triangular" area in the first quadrant between the circle $x^2 + y^2 = a^2$ and the lines $x = a$, $y = a$.

4. The area between the x-axis and the curve $y = \sin x$ between $x = 0$ and $x = \pi$. [*Hint.* Take $dA = y\, dx$ and $\tilde{y} = \frac{1}{2}y$.]

5. The area between the y-axis and the curve $x = 2y - y^2$.

6. Find the distance, from the base, of the center of mass of a thin triangular plate of base b and altitude h if its density varies as the square root of the distance from the base.

7. In Problem 6, suppose that the density varies as the square of the distance.

8. Find the center of mass of a homogeneous solid right circular cone.

9. Find the center of mass of a solid right circular cone if the density varies as the distance from the base.

10. In Problem 9 suppose that the density varies as the square of the distance.

11. In Example 2 (see Fig. 5–28) suppose that the density is $\delta_1 = k \sin \theta$, k being constant. Find the center of mass.

5–11

CENTROID AND CENTER OF GRAVITY

For a mass of uniform density, Eqs. (8), Article 5–10, reduce to

$$\bar{x} = \frac{\int \tilde{x}\, \delta_3\, dV}{\int \delta_3\, dV} = \frac{\delta_3 \int \tilde{x}\, dV}{\delta_3 \int dV} = \frac{\int \tilde{x}\, dV}{\int dV},$$

$$\bar{y} = \frac{\int \tilde{y}\, dV}{\int dV}, \qquad \bar{z} = \frac{\int \tilde{z}\, dV}{\int dV} \tag{1}$$

for a solid, with similar equations having dA or ds in place of dV in the case of a plate or a wire. Since these expressions involve only the geometric objects, namely, volumes, areas, and curves, we speak of the point $(\bar{x}, \bar{y}, \bar{z})$ in such cases as the *centroid* of the object. The term *center of gravity* is also used, since the line of action of the forces due to gravity acting on the elements of the object passes through this point. (See Sears, Zemansky, Young, *University Physics*, Fifth edition (1976), Chapters 2 and 3, for a discussion of physical concepts involved.)

EXAMPLE 1. Find the center of gravity of a solid hemisphere of radius r.

Solution. As in Example 3, Article 5–10, imagine the solid (Fig. 5–29) cut into slices of thickness dy by planes perpendicular to the y-axis. The centroid of a slice is its geometric center, on the y-axis, at $(0, y, 0)$. Its moment with respect to the xz-plane is

$$dM_{xz} = y \, dV$$
$$= y\pi(r^2 - y^2) \, dy.$$

Hence

$$M_{xz} = \pi \int_0^r (r^2 y - y^3) \, dy = \frac{\pi r^4}{4}.$$

Since the volume of the hemisphere is

$$V = \tfrac{2}{3}\pi r^3,$$

we have

$$\bar{y} = \frac{M_{xz}}{V} = \frac{3}{8} r.$$

EXAMPLE 2. Find the center of gravity of a thin hemispherical shell of inner radius r and thickness t.

Solution. We shall solve this problem, (a) exactly, by using the results of the preceding example; then (b) we shall see how the position of the center of gravity changes as we hold r fixed and let $t \to 0$. Finally, (c) we shall solve the problem approximately without using the results of Example 1, by considering the center of mass of an imaginary distribution of mass over the surface of the hemisphere of radius r, assuming that the thickness t is negligible in comparison with r (as, for example, the gold leaf covering the dome of the State House in Boston).

a) Let M_1, M_2, and M; V_1, V_2, and V denote, respectively, the moments with respect to the xz-plane and the volumes of the solid hemisphere of radius r, the solid hemisphere of radius $(r + t)$, and the hemispherical shell of thickness t and inner radius r. Since the moment of the sum of two masses is the sum of their moments and

$$V_1 + V = V_2,$$

we also have

$$M_1 + M = M_2;$$

that is

$$M = M_2 - M_1.$$

But, by Example 1,

$$M_2 = \frac{\pi}{4}(r + t)^4, \qquad M_1 = \frac{\pi}{4}r^4,$$

so that

$$M = \frac{\pi}{4}[(r + t)^4 - r^4]$$

$$= \frac{\pi}{4}[4r^3t + 6r^2t^2 + 4rt^3 + t^4],$$

while

$$V = V_2 - V_1 = \tfrac{2}{3}\pi[(r + t)^3 - r^3]$$
$$= \tfrac{2}{3}\pi(3r^2t + 3rt^2 + t^3);$$

hence

$$\bar{y} = \frac{M}{V} = \frac{1}{2}\frac{[r^3 + \frac{3}{2}r^2t + rt^2 + \frac{1}{4}t^3]}{[r^2 + rt + \frac{1}{3}t^2]}.$$

b) In the case of a shell where the thickness t is negligible in comparison with r, this reduces to $\bar{y} = \frac{1}{2}r$, by writing

$$\bar{y} = \frac{1}{2}\frac{r^3\left[1 + \dfrac{3}{2}\left(\dfrac{t}{r}\right) + \left(\dfrac{t}{r}\right)^2 + \dfrac{1}{4}\left(\dfrac{t}{r}\right)^3\right]}{r^2\left[1 + \left(\dfrac{t}{r}\right) + \dfrac{1}{3}\left(\dfrac{t}{r}\right)^2\right]},$$

and then letting $(t/r) \to 0$.

c) To solve the problem directly, without reference to Example 1, consider the mass of the shell to be uniformly distributed over its surface so that the mass of any portion cut from the shell will be proportional to its (inner) surface area. The proportionality factor,

$$\sigma = \delta t,$$

where δ is the volume density and t the thickness of the shell, is frequently referred to as a surface density factor. (Thus in working with sheet metal stock, say, aluminum of uniform thickness and density, we might speak of it as weighing so many pounds *per square foot*. This would be our σ, and A square feet of this particular stock would weigh σA pounds.) Then the slice of shell between planes perpendicular to the y-axis at distances y and $y + \Delta y$, respectively, above the xz-plane has mass

$$\Delta m = \sigma \, \Delta S,$$

where ΔS is the surface area of the slice (see Fig. 5–30). The moment of this slice with respect to the xz-plane then lies between

$$y \, \Delta m \qquad \text{and} \qquad (y + \Delta y) \, \Delta m,$$

and hence differs from $y \, \Delta m$ by at most $\Delta y \, \Delta m$. The sum of the moments of the slices has a limit, as Δy approaches zero, equal to $\int y \, dm$. We are thus led to

$$\bar{y} = \frac{\int y \, dm}{\int dm} = \frac{\int \sigma y \, dS}{\int \sigma \, dS} = \frac{\sigma \int y \, dS}{\sigma \int dS},$$

since σ is constant by our hypothesis. Here

$$dS = 2\pi x \, ds = 2\pi (r \cos \theta) r \, d\theta$$

if we use

$$x = r \cos \theta, \qquad y = r \sin \theta$$

to represent the circle $x^2 + y^2 = r^2$. Hence

$$\bar{y} = \frac{\int_0^{\pi/2} r \sin \theta \cdot 2\pi (r \cos \theta) \cdot r \, d\theta}{\int_0^{\pi/2} 2\pi (r \cos \theta) r \, d\theta}$$

$$= \frac{2\pi r^3 \int_0^{\pi/2} \sin \theta \cos \theta \, d\theta}{2\pi r^2 \int_0^{\pi/2} \cos \theta \, d\theta} = r \frac{[\frac{1}{2} \sin^2 \theta]_0^{\pi/2}}{[\sin \theta]_0^{\pi/2}} = \frac{1}{2} r.$$

Observe that the element of arc ds which, when rotated about the y-axis, generates dS, need only move along the arc of the circle in the first quadrant, namely, $0 \le \theta \le \pi/2$, in order to give us the entire hemisphere.

By the symmetry of the shell, the center of gravity lies on the y-axis, that is,

$$(\bar{x}, \bar{y}, \bar{z}) = (0, \tfrac{1}{2} r, 0).$$

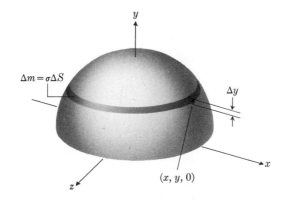

5–30 $\Delta m = \sigma \, \Delta S$, where σ is a density factor measured in mass per unit area.

PROBLEMS

In Problems 1 through 5, find the center of gravity of the areas bounded by the given curves and lines.

1. The x-axis and the curve $y = c^2 - x^2$.

2. The y-axis and the curve $x = y - y^3$, $0 \le y \le 1$.

3. The curve $y = x^2$ and the line $y = 4$.

4. The curve $y = x - x^2$ and the line $x + y = 0$.

5. The curve $x = y^2 - y$ and the line $y = x$.

6. Find the center of gravity of a solid right circular cone of altitude h and base-radius r.

7. Find the center of gravity of the solid generated by rotating, about the y-axis, the area bounded by the curve $y = x^2$ and the line $y = 4$.

8. The area bounded by the curve $x = y^2 - y$ and the line $y = x$ is rotated about the x-axis. Find the center of gravity of the solid thus generated.

9. Find the center of gravity of a very thin right circular conical shell of base-radius r and altitude h.

10. Find the center of gravity of the surface area generated by rotating about the line $x = -r$, the arc of the circle $x^2 + y^2 = r^2$ that lies in the first quadrant. (Use $x = r \cos \theta$, $y = r \sin \theta$, to represent the circle.)

11. Find the moment, about the x-axis, of the arc of the parabola $y = \sqrt{x}$ lying between $(0, 0)$ and $(4, 2)$.

12. Find the center of gravity of the arc length of one quadrant of a circle.

5–12

THE THEOREMS OF PAPPUS

When a plane area, such as A in Fig. 5–31, is rotated about an axis in its plane that does not intersect the area, there is a useful formula that relates the volume swept out by the area to the path described by its centroid.

Theorem 1. *If a plane area is revolved about a line that lies in its plane but does not intersect the area, then the volume generated is equal to the product of the area and the distance traveled by its center of gravity.*

To prove this result, which is one of the Theorems of Pappus, let the x-axis coincide with the axis of revolution and divide the area into strips of width Δy by lines parallel to the x-axis. The entire volume is the sum of the volumes generated by these strips of area. Let $l = f(y)$ be the width of the area at distance y above the x-axis, $c \leq y \leq d$. By the same argument we used in Article 5–5 to justify the cylindrical shell method of computing volumes, we have

$$V = \lim_{\Delta y \to 0} \sum 2\pi y l \, \Delta y$$

$$= \int_c^d 2\pi y l \, dy. \tag{1}$$

But the ordinate $\bar{y}_A$ of the center of gravity of the area A is given by

$$\bar{y}_A = \frac{\int y \, dA}{\int dA} = \frac{\int_c^d y l \, dy}{A},$$

so that

$$\int_c^d y l \, dy = A \bar{y}_A,$$

and hence Eq. (1) becomes

$$V = 2\pi \bar{y}_A A. \tag{2}$$

Since $2\pi \bar{y}_A$ is the distance traveled by the center of gravity of the area, the theorem is established.

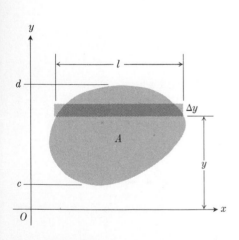

5–31 The shape above is to be revolved about the x-axis to generate a volume. A 1700-year-old theorem says that the volume can be calculated by multiplying the shape's area by the distance traveled by the shape's center of gravity.

EXAMPLE 1. (See Fig. 5–32.) Find the volume of the torus (doughnut) generated by rotating a circle of radius r about an axis in its plane at a distance b from its center, $b > r$.

Solution. The center of the circle is its center of gravity, and this travels a distance $2\pi b$. The area of the circle is πr^2, so by Eq. (2) the volume of the torus is

$$V = (2\pi b)(\pi r^2) = 2\pi^2 b r^2.$$

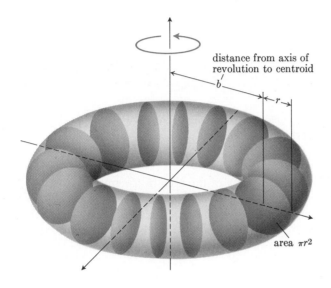

distance from axis of revolution to centroid

b

r

area πr^2

5–32 The volume swept out by the revolving disk is $(2\pi b)(\pi r^2)$.

Theorem 2. *If an arc of a plane curve is revolved about a line that lies in its plane but does not intersect the arc, then the surface area generated by the arc is equal to the product of the length of the arc and the distance traveled by its center of gravity.*

In this, another Theorem of Pappus, the center of gravity is that of the curve (or of a fine homogeneous wire whose centerline coincides with the curve), and is generally different from the center of gravity of the enclosed plane area (if the curve is a closed curve). To prove the theorem, refer the curve to x- and y-axes in its plane and let the x-axis coincide with the axis of revolution (see Fig. 5–33). Then the surface area generated is

$$S = \int_{x=a}^{x=b} 2\pi y \, ds, \qquad (3)$$

as we found in Article 5–8. But the center of gravity of the curve has ordinate

$$\bar{y}_c = \frac{\int y \, ds}{\int ds} = \frac{\int y \, ds}{L},$$

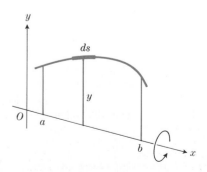

5–33 Arc of a plane curve.

where

$$L = \int ds$$

is the length of the arc. Hence

$$S = 2\pi \int_{x=a}^{x=b} y \, ds = 2\pi \bar{y}_c L \tag{4}$$

Q.E.D.

EXAMPLE 2.   The surface area of the torus in the previous example is given by

$$S = (2\pi b)(2\pi r) = 4\pi^2 b r.$$

The two Theorems of Pappus can be used to determine the center of gravity of a known volume or surface.

EXAMPLE 3.   Use the first Theorem of Pappus and the fact that the volume of a sphere of radius r is

$$V = \tfrac{4}{3}\pi r^3$$

to find the center of gravity of the area of a semicircle.

Solution.   Note that we generate a sphere by rotating a semicircle about its diameter (Fig. 5–34). Then the axis of revolution does not intersect the area, and since

$$A = \tfrac{1}{2}\pi r^2,$$

while

$$V = 2\pi \bar{y} A,$$

we find

$$\bar{y} = \frac{V}{2\pi A} = \frac{\tfrac{4}{3}\pi r^3}{2\pi \cdot \tfrac{1}{2}\pi r^2} = \frac{4}{3\pi} r.$$

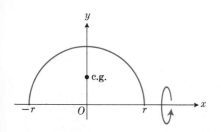

5–34   The y-coordinate of the center of gravity of a semicircular area can be calculated from Pappus' theorem without integration.

PROBLEMS

1. Use the Theorems of Pappus to find the lateral surface area and the volume of a right circular cone.

2. Use the second Theorem of Pappus and the fact that the surface area of a sphere of radius r is $4\pi r^2$ to find the center of gravity of the semicircular arc

$$y = \sqrt{r^2 - x^2}, \qquad -r \le x \le r.$$

3. The semicircular arc $y = \sqrt{r^2 - x^2}$, $-r \le x \le r$, is rotated about the line $y = r$. Use the second Theorem of

Pappus together with the answer to the preceding problem to find the surface area generated.

4. The center of gravity of the area bounded by the x-axis and the semicircle $y = \sqrt{r^2 - x^2}$ is at $[0, (4/3\pi)r]$ (see Example 3, above). Find the volume generated when this area is rotated about the line $y = -r$.

5. The area in the preceding example is rotated about the line $y = x - r$. Find the volume generated.

6. Use the answer to Problem 2 above to find the surface area generated by rotating the semicircular arc $y = \sqrt{r^2 - x^2}$, $-r \le x \le r$, about the line $y = x - r$.

7. Find the moment about the x-axis of the area in the semicircle of Fig. 5–34, Example 3, above. (If you use

results already known, you won't need to integrate.)

8. Find the moment about the line $y = -r$ of the area in the semicircle of Fig. 5–34.

9. Find the moment about the line $y = x - r$ of the area in the semicircle of Fig. 5–34.

If a flat-bottomed container is filled with water to a depth h, the force against the bottom of the container due to the pressure of the liquid is

$$F = whA, \tag{1}$$

5-13

HYDROSTATIC PRESSURE

where w is the weight-density, which is nearly 62.5 lb/ft^3, and A is the area of the bottom of the container. Obviously, the units in Eq. (1) must be compatible, say h in feet, A in square feet, w in pounds per cubic foot, giving F in pounds. It is a remarkable fact that this force does not depend upon the shape of the sides of the vessel, the force on the bottom being the same in both (a) and (b) in Fig. 5–35, for example, if both containers have the same area at their bases and both have the same "head" h. (See Sears, Zemansky, Young, *University Physics*, Fifth edition (1976), Chapter 12.) The *pressure*, or *force per unit area*, at the bottom of the container is therefore

$$p = wh. \tag{2}$$

Next, consider any body of water, such as the water in a reservoir or behind a dam. According to Pascal's principle, the pressure $p = wh$ at depth h in such a body of water is the same *in all directions*. For a flat plate submerged *horizontally*, the downward *force* acting on its upper face due to this liquid pressure is the same as that given by Eq. (1). If the plate is submerged *vertically*, however, then the pressure against it will be different at different depths and Eq. (1) no longer is usable in that form because we would have different h factors for points at different depths. We circumvent this difficulty in a manner that should by now be fairly familiar, namely, by dividing the plate into many narrow strips, the representative strip having its upper edge at depth h and its lower edge at depth $h + \Delta h$ below the surface of the water. If the area of this strip is called ΔA, and the force on one side of it ΔF, then Eq. (1) suggests that

$$wh\,\Delta A \le \Delta F \le w(h + \Delta h)\,\Delta A,$$

since the pressure will vary from wh to $w(h + \Delta h)$ in this strip. When we add the forces for all strips, then take the limit of such sums as $\Delta h \to 0$, we may disregard the infinitesimals of higher order, such as $\Delta h\,\Delta A$, and we are led to

$$F = \lim_{\Delta h \to 0} \sum_a^b wh\,\Delta A$$

5-35 The hydrostatic pressure on the bottoms of these containers is the same.

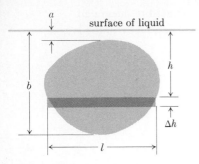

5–36 A plate submerged vertically beneath the surface of a liquid. The force exerted by the liquid on one side of the rectangular strip is approximately $whl \, \Delta h$, where w is the weight-density of the liquid.

or

$$F = \int_{h=a}^{h=b} wh \, dA = \int_{a}^{b} whl \, dh, \qquad (3)$$

where $dA = l \, dh$ (see Fig. 5–36).

As a corollary of Eq. (3), if we denote the depth of the center of gravity of the area A by $\bar{h}$, then

$$\bar{h} = \frac{\int h \, dA}{\int dA} \qquad \text{or} \qquad \int h \, dA = \bar{h}A.$$

Since w is a constant that may be moved across the integral sign in (3), we have

$$F = w\bar{h}A. \qquad (4)$$

This states that the total force of the liquid pressing against one face of the plate (an equal and opposite force presses against the other face unless the plate forms part of a wall of the container) is the same as it would be according to (1) if all of the area A were at the depth $\bar{h}$ below the surface.

Equation (4) is the working tool used most frequently by engineers in finding such hydrostatic forces as we have discussed. They can refer to a handbook to obtain the center of gravity of simple plane areas, and from this they quickly find $\bar{h}$. Of course, the location of the center of gravity given in the handbook was calculated by someone who performed an integration equivalent to evaluating the integral in Eq. (3). We recommend that, for now, you solve problems of this type by thinking through the steps which lead up to Eq. (3) by integration, and then checking your results, when you can conveniently do so, by Eq. (4).

EXAMPLE 1. A trapezoid is submerged vertically in water with its upper edge 4 ft below the surface and its lower edge 10 ft below the surface. If the upper and lower edges are respectively 6 ft and 8 ft long, find the total force on one face of the trapezoid.

Solution. In Fig. 5–37(a) we have, by similar triangles,

$$\frac{l - 6}{2} = \frac{h - 4}{6},$$

so that

$$l = \frac{h + 14}{3}.$$

Then the force is

$$F = \int_{4}^{10} wh \left(\frac{h + 14}{3} \right) dh = 300w.$$

Since

$$w = 62.5 \text{ lb/ft}^3 = \tfrac{1}{32} \text{ ton/ft}^3,$$

we have

$$F = 9\tfrac{3}{8} \text{ tons.}$$

Now we check by using Eq. (4). The trapezoid can be resolved into a parallelogram plus a triangle (Fig. 5–37(b)). For the parallelogram,

$$\bar{h}_1 = 7, \qquad A_1 = 36; \qquad F_1 = 252w.$$

For the triangle,

$$\bar{h}_2 = 8, \qquad A_2 = 6; \qquad F_2 = 48w.$$

For the trapezoid,

$$F = F_1 + F_2 = 300w.$$

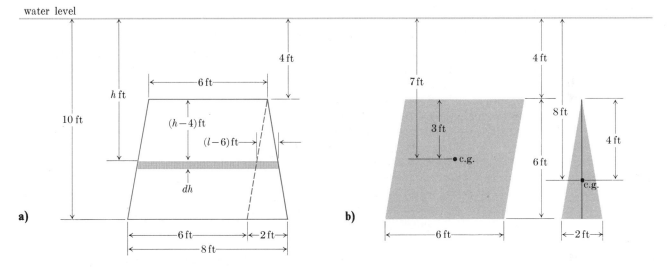

water level

a)

b)

5–37 (a) The trapezoid of Example 1 submerged vertically beneath the surface of the water. (b) To calculate the force on one side, the trapezoid is divided into a parallelogram and an isosceles triangle. The resulting centroids are marked "c.g." (center of gravity).

EXAMPLE 2. Find the moment produced about the lower edge of the trapezoid by the forces in the preceding example.

Solution. The force on the representative strip may be denoted by

$$dF = wh\, dA = wh\left(\frac{h+14}{3}\right)dh.$$

For the moment of this force about the lower edge of the trapezoid, we must multiply this force by the moment arm,

$$r = 10 - h,$$

to give the moment

$$dM = r\, dF = wh(10 - h)\frac{h+14}{3}\, dh.$$

The total moment due to forces on all the strips is

$$M = \frac{w}{3} \int_4^{10} (140h - 4h^2 - h^3) \, dh = 732w$$

or

$$M = 22\tfrac{7}{8} \text{ foot-tons.}$$

PROBLEMS

1. The vertical ends of a water trough are isosceles triangles of base 4 ft and altitude 3 ft. Find the force on one end if the trough is full of water weighing 62.5 lb/ft^3.

2. Find the force in the previous problem if the water level in the trough is lowered one foot.

3. A triangular plate ABC is submerged in water with its plane vertical. The side AB, 4 ft long, is 1 ft below the surface, while C is 5 ft below AB. Find the total force on one face of the plate.

4. Find the force on one face of the triangle ABC of Problem 3 if AB is one foot below the surface as before, but the triangle is rotated 180° about AB so as to bring the vertex C 4 ft *above* the surface.

5. A semicircular plate is submerged in water with its plane vertical and its diameter in the surface. Find the force on one face of the plate if its diameter is 2 ft.

6. The face of a dam is a rectangle, $ABCD$, of dimensions $AB = CD = 100$ ft, $AD = BC = 26$ ft. Instead of being vertical, the plane $ABCD$ is inclined as indicated in Fig. 5–38, so that the top of the dam is 24 ft higher than the

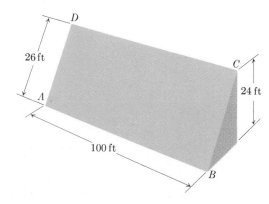

5–38   The dam of Problem 6.

bottom. Find the force due to water pressure on the dam when the surface of the water is level with the top of the dam.

7. Find the moment, about AB, of the force in Problem 6.

5–14

WORK

When a constant force F (pounds) acts throughout a distance s (feet), the *work* done (in foot-pounds) is the product of force and distance,

$$W = Fs. \tag{1}$$

When the force is not constant, as for instance in stretching or compressing a spring, then Eq. (1) cannot be used directly to give the work done. The law in (1) can be used, however, to estimate the work done over a *short* interval Δs if the force is a continuous function of s. The integral process then enables us to extend the law in (1) to find the total work done.

For most springs there is a range over which the amount of force F required to stretch or compress the spring from its natural length can be approximated by the equation

$$F = cx, \tag{2}$$

where x is the amount the spring has been displaced from its natural or unstressed length, and c is a constant characteristic of the spring, called the *spring constant* (Fig. 5–39(a)). Beyond this range, the metal of the spring becomes distorted and Eq. (2) is no longer a reliable description. We assume that the springs in this article are never stretched or compressed to such an extent. Equation (2) is known as *Hooke's law*.

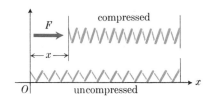

(a)

(b)

EXAMPLE 1. Find the work done in compressing a spring from its natural length L to a length of $\frac{3}{4}L$.

Solution. To compress the spring by an amount $L/4$, the force must be increased from

$$F_0 = c \times 0 = 0$$

to

$$F_1 = c\left(\frac{L}{4}\right).$$

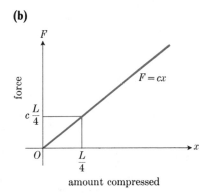

The point of application of the force will move from $x = 0$ to $x = L/4$ as the force increases (Fig. 5–39(b)). To find the work done during the process, we imagine the x-interval from 0 to $L/4$ to be divided into a large number of subintervals, each of length Δx. As the spring is compressed from x to $x + \Delta x$, the *force* varies from cx to $c(x + \Delta x)$. Since the force acts through a *distance* Δx, the work done to achieve this small compression will lie between

$$cx \, \Delta x \qquad \text{and} \qquad c(x + \Delta x) \, \Delta x.$$

5-39 The force F required to hold a spring under compression increases linearly as the spring is compressed.

Therefore, the total work of compression is approximately

$$W \approx \sum_{x=0}^{L/4} cx \, \Delta x,$$

or

$$W = \sum_{x=0}^{L/4} c\tilde{x} \, \Delta x$$

for appropriate choices of the $\tilde{x}$ between x and $x + \Delta x$. In the limit as Δx tends to zero, we have

$$W = \lim_{\Delta x \to 0} \sum_{x=0}^{L/4} cx \, \Delta x = \int_0^{L/4} cx \, dx = \frac{cL^2}{32}$$

or

$$W = \frac{1}{2}\left(\frac{cL}{4}\right)\left(\frac{L}{4}\right).$$

In this last form, the factor $\frac{1}{2}c(L/4)$ is one-half the final value reached by F when the spring has been compressed to $\frac{3}{4}$ of its original length, and the factor $L/4$ is the total distance through which the variable force has acted. This suggests

$$W = \bar{F}s \qquad\qquad\qquad (3)$$

as a suitable modification of Eq. (1) when the force is variable, where $\bar{F}$ represents the *average* value of the variable force throughout the total displacement. However, the determination of $\bar{F}$ itself involves an integration in the general case, so that it is usually as easy to apply the principles illustrated in the example just considered as it is to apply Eq. (3). In fact, Eq. (3) may be interpreted as *defining* $\bar{F}$.

In a manner entirely analogous to that in the example above, it is easily seen that

$$W = \int_a^b F \, ds \qquad \textbf{(4)}$$

gives the work done by a variable force (which, however, always acts along a given direction) as the point of application undergoes a displacement from $s = a$ to $s = b$.

EXAMPLE 2.   A spring has a natural length of $L = 3$ ft. A force of 10 lbs stretches the spring to a length of 3.5 ft. Find the spring constant. Then calculate the amount of work done in stretching the spring from its natural length to a length of 5 ft. How much work is done in stretching the spring from 4 ft to 5 ft? How far beyond its natural length will a 15-lb force stretch the spring?

Solution.   We find the spring constant from Eq. (2). A force of 10 lbs stretches the spring 0.5 ft, so that

$$10 = c(0.5), \qquad c = 20 \text{ lb/ft}.$$

To calculate the work done in stretching the spring 2 ft beyond its natural length, imagine the spring hanging parallel to the x-axis, as shown in Fig. 5–40. Then, by Eq. (4),

$$W = \int_0^2 20x \, dx = 10x^2 \Big]_0^2 = 40 \text{ foot-pounds}.$$

To find the work done in stretching the spring from a length of 4 ft to a length of 5 ft, we calculate

$$W = \int_1^2 20x \, dx = 10x^2 \Big]_1^2 = 30 \text{ foot-pounds}.$$

To learn how far a 15 lb force will stretch the spring, we solve Eq. (1) with $F = 15$ and $c = 20$:

$$15 = 20x, \qquad x = \tfrac{15}{20} \text{ ft} = 9 \text{ in}.$$

No calculus is involved in this last computation.

$x = 0$

$\frac{1}{2}$

10 lbs

1

ft

5–40 A 10-lb weight stretches the spring half a foot beyond its unstressed length.

Equation (4) leads to an interesting theorem of mechanics.

Theorem.   *Let F denote the resultant of all forces acting on a particle of mass m. Let the direction of F remain constant. Then, whether the magnitude of F is* *constant or variable, the work done on the particle by the force F is equal to the change in the kinetic energy of the particle.*

The ingredients required for a proof of this theorem are:

a) Eq. (4), which gives the work,
b) the definition of kinetic energy, K.E. $= \frac{1}{2}mv^2$, and
c) Newton's second law: $F = m(dv/dt)$.

The fact that

$$v = \frac{ds}{dt}$$

and

$$\frac{dv}{dt} = \frac{dv}{ds}\frac{ds}{dt} = \frac{dv}{ds}v$$

and Newton's second law enable us to write Eq. (4) in the form

$$W = \int_{s=a}^{s=b} mv\frac{dv}{ds}ds = \int_{v=v_a}^{v=v_b} mv\,dv,$$

which leads to

$$W = \frac{1}{2}mv^2\Big]_{v_a}^{v_b} = \frac{1}{2}mv_b^2 - \frac{1}{2}mv_a^2.$$

That is, the work done by the force F is the kinetic energy at b minus the kinetic energy at a or, more simply, the change in kinetic energy:

$$W = \Delta(\text{K.E.}).$$

We now consider another situation where the simple Eq. (1) cannot be applied to the *total* but can be applied to a *small piece.*

EXAMPLE 3.   Calculate the amount of work required to pump all the water from a full hemispherical bowl of radius r ft to a distance h ft above the top of the bowl (Fig. 5–41).

Solution.   We introduce coordinate axes as shown in Fig. 5–41 and imagine the bowl to be divided into thin slices by planes perpendicular to the x-axis between $x = 0$ and $x = r$. The representative slice between the planes at x and $x + \Delta x$ has volume ΔV which, if we neglect only infinitesimals of higher order than Δx, is given approximately by

$$\Delta V \approx \pi y^2\,\Delta x = \pi(r^2 - x^2)\,\Delta x.$$

To the same order of approximation, the force F required to lift *this slice* is equal to its weight:

$$w\,\Delta V \approx \pi w(r^2 - x^2)\,\Delta x,$$

where w is the weight of a cubic foot of water. Finally, the *distance* through which this force must act lies between

$$h + x \qquad \text{and} \qquad h + x + \Delta x,$$

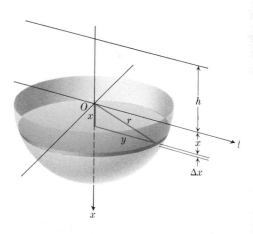

5–41 To calculate the work required to pump the water from a bowl, think of lifting the water out one slab at a time.

so that the work ΔW done in *lifting this one slice* is approximately

$$\Delta W \approx \pi w(r^2 - x^2)(h + x)\,\Delta x,$$

where we again have suppressed all higher powers of Δx. This is justified in the *limit* of the sum, and the total work is

$$W = \lim_{\Delta x \to 0} \sum_0^r \pi w(r^2 - x^2)(h + x)\,\Delta x$$

$$= \int_0^r \pi w(h + x)(r^2 - x^2)\,dx$$

$$= hw \int_0^r \pi(r^2 - x^2)\,dx + w \int_0^r \pi x(r^2 - x^2)\,dx$$

$$= hwV + \bar{x}wV.$$

Here wV is the weight of the whole bowlful of water of volume V, and the second integral may be interpreted physically as giving the work required in pumping *all* the water from the depth of the center of gravity of the bowl to the level $x = 0$, while the first integral gives the work done in pumping the whole bowlful of water from the level $x = 0$ up a distance of h feet. The actual evaluation of the integrals leads to

$$W = \tfrac{2}{3}\pi r^3 w(h + \tfrac{3}{8}r).$$

Can you prove for yourself that, no matter what the shape of the container in Fig. 5–41, the total work is the sum of two terms, one of which is

$$W_1 = hw \int dV$$

and represents the total work done in lifting a bowlful of water a distance h, while the other is

$$W_2 = w \int x\,dV$$

and represents the work done in lifting a bowlful of water a distance equal to the depth of the center of gravity of the bowl?

PROBLEMS

1. If the spring in Fig. 5–39 has natural length $L = 18$ in., and a force of 10 lb is sufficient to compress it to a length of 16 in., what is the value of the "spring constant" c for the particular spring in question? How much work is done in compressing it from a length of 16 in. to a length of 12 in.?

2. A spring has a natural length of 10 in. An 800 lb force stretches the spring to 14 in. (a) Find the spring constant. (b) How much work is done in stretching the spring from 10 in. to 12 in.? (c) How far beyond its natural length will a 1600 lb force stretch the spring?

3. A 10,000 lb force compresses a spring from its natural length of 12 in. to a length of 11 in. How much work is done in compressing the spring (a) from 12 to 11.5 in.? (b) from 11.5 in. to 11 in.?

4. A spring has a natural length of 2 ft. A 1 lb force stretched the spring 5 ft (from 2 ft to 7 ft). How much work did the 1 lb force do? If the spring is stretched by a 2 lb force, what will its total length be?

5. A bathroom scale is depressed $\tfrac{1}{16}$ in. when a 150 lb person stands on it. Assuming that the scale behaves like a spring, find how much work is required to depress the scale $\frac{1}{8}$ in. from its natural height. How much weight is required to compress the scale this much?

6. Answer the questions of Problem 1 if the law of force is $F = c \sin(\pi x/2L)$ in place of Eq. (2).

7. Two electrons repel each other with a force inversely proportional to the square of the distance between them. Suppose one electron is held fixed at the point $(1, 0)$ on the x-axis. Find the work required to move a second electron along the x-axis from the point $(-1, 0)$ to the origin.

8. If two electrons are held stationary at the points $(-1, 0)$ and $(1, 0)$ on the x-axis, find the work done in moving a third electron from $(5, 0)$ to $(3, 0)$ along the x-axis.

9. If a straight hole could be bored through the center of the earth, a particle of mass m falling in this hole would be attracted toward the center of the earth with a force $mg(r/R)$ when it is at distance r from the center. (R is the radius of earth; g is the acceleration due to gravity at the surface of the earth.) How much work is done on the particle as it falls from the surface to the center of the earth?

10. A bag of sand originally weighing 144 lb is lifted at a constant rate of 3 ft/min. The sand leaks out uniformly at such a rate that half of the sand is lost when the bag has

been lifted 18 ft. Find the work done in lifting the bag this distance.

11. Gas in a cylinder of constant cross-sectional area A expands or is compressed by the motion of a piston. If p is the pressure of the gas in pounds per square inch and v is its volume in cubic inches, show that the work done by the gas as it goes from an initial state (p_1, v_1) to a second state (p_2, v_2) is

$$W = \int_{(p_1, v_1)}^{(p_2, v_2)} p \, dv \quad \text{inch-pounds.}$$

[*Hint.* Take the x-axis perpendicular to the face of the piston. Then $dv = A \, dx$ and $F = pA$.]

12. Use the result of Problem 11 to find the work done on the gas in compressing it from $v_1 = 243$ in^3 to $v_2 = 32$ in^3 if the initial pressure $p_1 = 50$ lb/in^2 and the pressure and volume satisfy the law for adiabatic change of state, $pv^{1.4} = $ constant.

13. Find the work done in pumping all the water out of a conical reservoir of radius 10 ft at the top, altitude 8 ft, to a height of 6 ft above the top of the reservoir.

14. Find the work done in Problem 13 if, at the beginning, the reservoir is filled to a depth of 5 ft and the water is pumped just to the top of the reservoir.

REVIEW QUESTIONS AND EXERCISES

1. List nine applications of the definite integral presented in this chapter.

2. How do you define the area bounded above by a curve $y = f_1(x)$, below by a curve $y = f_2(x)$, and on the sides by $x = a$ and $x = b$, $a < b$?

3. How do you define the volume generated by rotating a plane area about an axis in its plane and not intersecting the area?

4. How do you define the length of a plane curve? Can

you extend this to a curve in three-dimensional space?

5. How do you define the surface area of a sphere? Of other surfaces of revolution?

6. How do you define the average value of a function over an interval?

7. How do you define center of mass?

8. How do you define work done by a variable force?

9. How do you define the hydrostatic force on the face of a dam?

MISCELLANEOUS PROBLEMS

1. Sketch the graphs of the equations $y = 2 - x^2$ and $x + y = 0$ in one diagram, and find the area bounded by them.

2. Find the maximum and minimum points of the curve $y = x^3 - 3x^2$ and find the total area bounded by this curve and the x-axis. Sketch.

In the following problems (3–15), find the area bounded by the given curves and lines. A sketch is usually helpful.

3. $y = x, \quad y = \dfrac{1}{x^2}, \quad x = 2$

4. $y = x, \quad y = \dfrac{1}{\sqrt{x}}, \quad x = 2$

5. $y = x + 1, \quad y = 3 - x^2$

6. $y = 2x^2, \quad y = x^2 + 2x + 3$

7. $x = 2y^2, \quad x = 0, \quad y = 3$

8. $4x = y^2 - 4, \quad 4x = y + 16$

9. $x^{1/2} + y^{1/2} = a^{1/2}, \quad x = 0, \quad y = 0$

10. $y = \sin x, \quad y = \sqrt{2}x/2$

11. $y^2 = 9x, \quad y = \dfrac{3x^2}{8}$

12. $y = \sin x$, $y = x$, $0 \le x \le \dfrac{\pi}{4}$

13. $y = x\sqrt{2x^2 + 1}$, $x = 0$, $x = 2$

14. $y^2 = 4x$ and $y = 4x - 2$

15. $y = 2 - x^2$ and $y = x^2 - 6$

16. The function $v = 3t^2 - 15t + 18$ represents the velocity v (ft/sec) of a moving body as a function of the time t (sec). (a) Find that portion of the time interval $0 \le t \le 3$ in which the velocity is positive. (b) Find that portion where v is negative. (c) Find the total distance traveled by the body from $t = 0$ to $t = 3$.

17. The area from 0 to x under a certain graph is given to be

$$A = (1 + 3x)^{1/2} - 1, \quad x \ge 0.$$

a) Find the *average* rate of change of A with respect to x as x increases from 1 to 8.

b) Find the *instantaneous* rate of change of A with respect to x at $x = 5$.

c) Find the ordinate (height) y of the graph as a function of x.

d) Find the average value of the ordinate (height) y, with respect to x, as x increases from 1 to 8.

18. A solid is generated by rotating, about the x-axis, the area bounded by the curve $y = f(x)$, the x-axis, and the lines $x = a$, $x = b$. Its volume, for all $b > a$, is $b^2 - ab$. Find $f(x)$.

19. Find the volume generated by rotating the area bounded by the given curves and lines about the line indicated:

a) $y = x^2$, $y = 0$, $x = 3$; about the x-axis.

b) $y = x^2$, $y = 0$, $x = 3$; about the line $x = -3$.

c) $y = x^2$, $y = 0$, $x = 3$; about the y-axis, first integrating with respect to x and then integrating with respect to y.

d) $x = 4y - y^2$, $x = 0$; about the y-axis.

e) $x = 4y - y^2$, $x = 0$; about the x-axis.

20. A solid is generated by rotating the curve $y = f(x)$, $0 \le x \le a$, about the x-axis. Its volume for all a is $a^2 + a$; find $f(x)$.

21. The area bounded by the curve $y^2 = 4x$ and the straight line $y = x$ is rotated about the x-axis. Find the volume generated.

22. Sketch the area bounded by the curve $y^2 = 4ax$, the line $x = a$, and the x-axis. Find the respective volumes generated by rotating this area in the following ways: (a) about the x-axis, (b) about the line $x = a$, (c) about the y-axis.

23. The area bounded by the curve $y = x/\sqrt{x^3 + 8}$, the x-axis, and the line $x = 2$ is rotated about the y-axis, generating a certain volume. Set up the integral that should be used to evaluate the volume and then evaluate the integral.

24. Find the volume of the solid generated by rotating the larger area bounded by $y^2 = x - 1$, $x = 3$, and $y = 1$ about the y-axis.

25. The area bounded by the curve $y^2 = 4ax$ and the line $x = a$ is rotated about the line $x = 2a$. Find the volume generated.

26. A twisted solid is generated as follows: We are given a fixed line L in space, and a square of side s in a plane perpendicular to L. One vertex of the square is on L. As this vertex moves a distance h along L, the square turns through a full revolution, with L as the axis. Find the volume generated by this motion. What would the volume be if the square had turned through two full revolutions in moving the same distance along L?

27. Two circles have a common diameter and lie in perpendicular planes. A square moves in such a way that its plane is perpendicular to this diameter and its diagonals are chords of the circles. Find the volume generated.

28. Find the volume generated by rotating about the x-axis the area bounded by the x-axis and one arch of the curve $y = \sin 2x$.

29. A round hole of radius $\sqrt{3}$ ft is bored through the center of a solid sphere of radius 2 ft. Find the volume cut out.

30. The cross section of a certain solid in any plane perpendicular to the x-axis is a circle having diameter AB with A on the curve $y^2 = 4x$ and B on the curve $x^2 = 4y$. Find the volume of the solid lying between the points of intersection of the curves.

31. The base of a solid is the area bounded by $y^2 = 4ax$ and $x = a$. Each cross section perpendicular to the x-axis is an equilateral triangle. Find the volume of the solid.

32. Find the length of the curve $y = (\tfrac{2}{3})x^{3/2} - (\tfrac{1}{2})x^{1/2}$ from $x = 0$ to $x = 4$.

33. Find the surface area generated when the curve of Problem 32 is rotated about the y-axis.

34. Find the length of the curve $x = (\tfrac{3}{5})y^{5/3} - (\tfrac{3}{4})y^{1/3}$ from $y = 0$ to $y = 1$.

35. Find the surface area generated when the curve of Problem 34 is rotated about the line $y = -1$.

36. Find the average value of y with respect to x for that part of the curve $y = \sqrt{ax}$ between $x = a$ and $x = 3a$.

37. Find the average value of y^2 with respect to x for the curve $ay = b\sqrt{a^2 - x^2}$ between $x = 0$ and $x = a$. Also find the average value of y with respect to x^2 for $0 \le x \le a$.

38. Consider the curve $y = f(x)$, $x \ge 0$ such that $f(0) = a$. Let $s(x)$ denote the arc length along the curve from $(0, a)$ to $(x, f(x))$. Find $f(x)$ if (a) $s(x) = Ax$. (What are the permissible values of A?) (b) Is it possible for $s(x)$ to equal x^n, $n > 1$? Give a reason for your answer.

39. A point moves in a straight line during the time from $t = 0$ to $t = 3$ according to the law $s = 120t - 16t^2$. (a) Find the average value of the velocity, with respect to time, for these three seconds. [Compare with the "average velocity," Article 1–9, Eq. (6).] (b) Find the average value of the velocity with respect to the distance s during the three seconds.

40. Sketch a smooth curve through the points

$$A(1, 3), \quad B(3, 5), \quad C(5, 6), \quad D(7, 6), \quad E(9, 7), \quad F(11, 10).$$

The area bounded by this curve, the x-axis, and the lines $x = 1$, $x = 11$, is rotated about the x-axis to generate a solid. Use the trapezoidal rule to approximate the volume generated. Also determine approximately the average value of the circular cross-sectional area (with respect to x.)

41. Determine the center of mass of a thin homogeneous plate covering the area enclosed by the curves $y^2 = 8x$ and $y = x^2$.

42. Find the center of mass of a homogeneous plate covering the area in the first quadrant bounded by the curve $4y = x^2$, the y-axis, and the line $y = 4$.

43. Find the center of gravity of the area bounded by the curve $y = 4x - x^2$ and the line $2x - y = 0$.

44. Find the center of mass of a thin homogeneous plate covering the portion of the xy-plane, in the first quadrant, bounded by the curve $y = x^2$, the x-axis, and the line $x = 1$.

45. Consider a thin metal plate of area A and constant density and thickness. Show that, if its first moment about the y-axis is M, its moment about the line $x = b$ is $M - bA$. Indicate why this result actually shows that the center of gravity is a physical property of the body, independent of the coordinate system used for finding its location.

46. Find the center of mass of a thin plate covering the region bounded by the curve $y^2 = 4ax$ and the line $x = a$, $a = $ positive constant, if the density at (x, y) is directly proportional to (a) x, (b) $|y|$.

47. Find the centroid of the area, in the first quadrant, bounded by two concentric circles and the coordinate axes, if the circles have radii a and b, $b > a > 0$, and their centers are at the origin. Also find the limits of the coordinates of the centroid as a approaches b, and discuss the meaning of the result.

48. (a) Find the centroid of the arc of the curve $x = a \cos^3 \phi$, $y = a \sin^3 \phi$ that is in the first quadrant. (b) Find the centroid of the surface generated by rotating the arc of part (a) about the y-axis.

49. A triangular corner is cut from a square 1 ft on a side.

The area of the cutoff triangle is 36 in². If the centroid of the remaining area is 7 in. from one side of the original square, how far is it from the remaining sides?

50. A triangular plate ABC is submerged in water with its plane vertical. The side AB, 4 ft long, is 6 ft below the surface of the water, while the vertex C is 2 ft below the surface. Find the force of liquid pressure on one face of the plate.

51. A dam is in the form of a trapezoid, with its two horizontal sides 200 and 100 ft, respectively, the longer side being at the top; the height is 20 ft. What is the force of pressure on the dam when the water is level with the top of the dam?

52. The center of pressure on a submerged plane area is defined to be the point at which the total force could be applied without changing its total moment about any axis in the plane. Find the depth to the center of pressure (a) on a vertical rectangle of height h and width b if its upper edge is in the surface of the water, (b) on a vertical triangle of height h and base b if the vertex opposite b is a ft, and the base b is $(a + h)$ ft below the surface of the water.

53. A container is filled with two nonmixing liquids with respective densities d_1 and d_2, $d_1 < d_2$. Find the force on one face of a square $ABCD$, $6\sqrt{2}$ feet on a side, immersed in the liquids with the diagonal AC normal to the free surface, if the highest point A of the square is 2 ft below the free surface and BD lies on the surface separating the two liquids.

54. A particle of mass M starts from rest at time $t = 0$ and is moved with constant acceleration a from $x = 0$ to $x = h$ against a variable force $F(t) = t^2$. Find the work done.

55. When a particle of mass M is at $(x, 0)$, it is attracted toward the origin with a force whose magnitude is k/x^2. If the particle starts from rest at $x = b$ and is acted upon by no other forces, find the work done on it by the time it reaches $x = a$, $0 < a < b$.

56. Below the surface of the earth the force of its gravitational attraction is directly proportional to the distance from its center. Find the work done in lifting an object, whose weight at the surface is w lb, from a distance r ft below the earth's surface to the surface.

57. A storage tank is a right circular cylinder 20 ft long and 8 ft in diameter with its axis horizontal. If the tank is half full of oil weighing w lb/ft³, find the work done in emptying it through a pipe that runs from the bottom of the tank to an outlet that is 6 ft above the top of the tank.

TRANSCENDENTAL FUNCTIONS

THE TRIGONOMETRIC FUNCTIONS

We have learned how to differentiate and integrate polynomials and certain other algebraic functions including some rational functions and fractional powers. By definition, y is an *algebraic* function of x if it is a function that satisfies an irreducible algebraic equation of the form

$$P_0(x)y^n + P_1(x)y^{n-1} + \cdots + P_{n-1}(x)y + P_n(x) = 0,$$

with n a positive integer and with coefficients $P_0(x)$, $P_1(x)$, ... that are polynomials in x. For instance, $y = \sqrt{x}$, $x > 0$, defines an algebraic function whose elements (x, y) satisfy the irreducible equation

$$y^2 - x = 0.$$

Sums, products, quotients, powers, and roots of algebraic functions are in turn algebraic functions.

A function that is not algebraic is called *transcendental*. The class of transcendental functions includes the trigonometric, logarithmic, exponential, and inverse trigonometric functions, and many more that are less familiar.

We have learned how to differentiate and integrate two transcendental functions—the sine and cosine. In this chapter we shall add to this list the derivatives of the remaining trigonometric functions, their inverse functions, and the logarithmic and exponential functions.

At this stage it is well to recall the following formulas for derivatives and differentials:

	Derivatives		**Differentials**
I.	$\dfrac{dc}{dx} = 0.$	I'.	$dc = 0.$
II.	$\dfrac{d(cu)}{dx} = c\dfrac{du}{dx}.$	II'.	$d(cu) = c\,du.$
III.	$\dfrac{d(u+v)}{dx} = \dfrac{du}{dx} + \dfrac{dv}{dx}.$	III'.	$d(u+v) = du + dv.$
IV.	$\dfrac{d(uv)}{dx} = u\dfrac{dv}{dx} + v\dfrac{du}{dx}.$	IV'.	$d(uv) = u\,dv + v\,du.$
V.	$\dfrac{d\left(\dfrac{u}{v}\right)}{dx} = \dfrac{v\dfrac{du}{dx} - u\dfrac{dv}{dx}}{v^2}.$	V'.	$d\left(\dfrac{u}{v}\right) = \dfrac{v\,du - u\,dv}{v^2}.$
VI.	$\dfrac{d(u^n)}{dx} = nu^{n-1}\dfrac{du}{dx}.$	VI'.	$d(u^n) = nu^{n-1}\,du.$
VII.	$\dfrac{d(\sin u)}{dx} = \cos u\dfrac{du}{dx}.$	VII'.	$d(\sin u) = \cos u\,du.$
VIII.	$\dfrac{d(\cos u)}{dx} = -\sin u\dfrac{du}{dx}.$	VIII'.	$d(\cos u) = -\sin u\,du.$

The first six of these formulas by themselves enable us to differentiate the *algebraic* functions, which include polynomials, ratios of polynomials, and roots or powers of either of these types. VII, VII′, VIII, and VIII′ are discussed in Article 2–10.

When we combine formulas V, VII, and VIII and apply them to the trigonometric identities

$$\tan u = \frac{\sin u}{\cos u}, \qquad \cot u = \frac{\cos u}{\sin u},$$

$$\sec u = \frac{1}{\cos u}, \qquad \csc u = \frac{1}{\sin u}, \tag{1}$$

it is a simple matter to complete the list of formulas for differentiating the trigonometric functions and, doing so, we obtain:

IX. $\dfrac{d(\tan u)}{dx} = \sec^2 u \dfrac{du}{dx}.$ IX′. $d(\tan u) = \sec^2 u\, du.$

X. $\dfrac{d(\cot u)}{dx} = -\csc^2 u \dfrac{du}{dx}.$ X′. $d(\cot u) = -\csc^2 u\, du.$

XI. $\dfrac{d(\sec u)}{dx} = \sec u \tan u \dfrac{du}{dx}.$ XI′. $d(\sec u) = \sec u \tan u\, du.$

XII. $\dfrac{d(\csc u)}{dx} = -\csc u \cot u \dfrac{du}{dx}.$ XII′. $d(\csc u) = -\csc u \cot u\, du.$

The proofs of these formulas should be carried through by the reader.

These are the forms that are customarily used, though there are alternative forms such as

$$\frac{d(\sec u)}{dx} = \frac{\sin u}{\cos^2 u} \frac{du}{dx},$$

which are obtained from the expressions given by using some trigonometric identities. One reason for preferring the numbered forms above is that they are quite easy to remember if we note that *the derivative of every cofunction* (i.e., cos, cot, csc) *can be obtained from the derivative of the corresponding function* (i.e., sin, tan, sec) by

a) *introducing a minus sign*, and

b) *replacing each function by its cofunction.*

Apply this, for example, to the formula

$$\frac{d(\sec u)}{dx} = \sec u \tan u \frac{du}{dx}.$$

Replace sec u and tan u by their *cofunctions* on *both sides* of the equation and put in a *minus* sign; the result is

$$\frac{d(\csc u)}{dx} = -\csc u \cot u \frac{du}{dx}.$$

Thus it is really only necessary to "memorize" the two new formulas

$$\frac{d(\tan u)}{dx} = \sec^2 u \frac{du}{dx},$$

$$\frac{d(\sec u)}{dx} = \sec u \tan u \frac{du}{dx},$$

and the rule above produces the other two.

The formulas IX′–XII′ for differentials immediately produce the four new integration formulas:

$$\int \sec^2 u \, du = \tan u + C, \qquad \int \sec u \tan u \, du = \sec u + C,$$

$$\int \csc^2 u \, du = -\cot u + C, \qquad \int \csc u \cot u \, du = -\csc u + C. \tag{2}$$

EXAMPLE 1. Find dy/dx if $y = \tan^2 3x$.

Solution. First we apply the power formula VI,

$$\frac{dy}{dx} = 2 \tan 3x \frac{d(\tan 3x)}{dx}$$

and then IX,

$$\frac{d(\tan 3x)}{dx} = \sec^2 3x \frac{d(3x)}{dx},$$

and then II,

$$\frac{d(3x)}{dx} = 3 \frac{dx}{dx} = 3.$$

When these are combined, we get

$$\frac{dy}{dx} = 6 \tan 3x \sec^2 3x.$$

EXAMPLE 2. Integrate $\int \tan^2 3x \, dx$.

Solution. At first sight, this seems to be impossible with the formulas we have for integration. But the trigonometric identity

$$\sin^2 3x + \cos^2 3x = 1$$

becomes

$$\tan^2 3x + 1 = \sec^2 3x$$

when we divide both sides by $\cos^2 3x$. Hence,

$$\tan^2 3x = \sec^2 3x - 1$$

and

$$\int \tan^2 3x \, dx = \int (\sec^2 3x - 1) \, dx = \int \sec^2 3x \, dx - \int 1 \, dx$$

$$= \tfrac{1}{3} \int \sec^2 3x \, d(3x) - \int 1 \, dx = \tfrac{1}{3} \tan 3x - x + C.$$

EXAMPLE 3 (*Optimal branching angle for blood vessels*). When a smaller artery branches off from a larger one, it is reasonable to suppose that the angle formed by the central axes of the arteries is such as to be "best" from some energy-conserving viewpoint. We assume, for instance, that energy loss due to friction is minimized along the section AOB shown in Fig. 6–1. In this diagram, B is a given point to be reached by the smaller artery, A is a point in the larger artery upstream from B, and O is the point where branching occurs. A law due to Poiseuille states that the loss of energy due to friction in nonturbulent flow is proportional to the length of the path and inversely proportional to the fourth power of the radius. Thus, the loss along AO is $(kd_1)/R^4$ and along OB is $(kd_2)/r^4$, where k is a constant, d_1 is the length of AO, d_2 is the length of OB, R is the radius of the larger artery, and r is the radius of the smaller branch. The angle θ is to be such as to minimize the sum of these two losses:

$$L = k\frac{d_1}{R^4} + k\frac{d_2}{r^4}.$$

In our model, we assume that $AC = a$ and $BC = b$ are fixed. Thus we have the relations

$$d_1 + d_2 \cos \theta = a, \qquad d_2 \sin \theta = b,$$

so that

$$d_2 = b \csc \theta \qquad \text{and} \qquad d_1 = a - d_2 \cos \theta = a - b \cot \theta.$$

We can express the total loss L as a function of θ:

$$L = k\left(\frac{a - b \cot \theta}{R^4} + \frac{b \csc \theta}{r^4}\right). \tag{3}$$

When we differentiate Eq. (3) with respect to θ we get

$$\frac{dL}{d\theta} = k\left(\frac{b \csc^2 \theta}{R^4} - \frac{b \csc \theta \cot \theta}{r^4}\right) = \frac{kb \csc^2 \theta}{r^4}\left(\frac{r^4}{R^4} - \cos \theta\right).$$

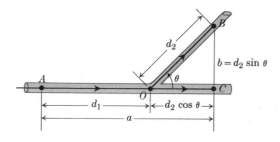

6–1 The smaller artery OB branches away from the larger artery AOC at an angle θ that minimizes the friction loss along AO and OB. The optimum angle is found to be $\theta_c = \cos^{-1}(r^4/R^4)$, where r is the radius of the smaller artery and R is the radius of the larger.

The critical value of θ, for which $dL/d\theta$ is zero, is

$$\theta_c = \cos^{-1}\left(\frac{r^4}{R^4}\right). \tag{4}$$

A slightly smaller value of θ makes $\cos\theta$ larger and $dL/d\theta$ negative, while a slightly larger θ makes $\cos\theta$ smaller and $dL/d\theta$ positive. Therefore, L has a minimum value at $\theta = \theta_c$.

PROBLEMS

Sketch the graphs of the equations in Problems 1–10.

1. $y = \sin x$ **2.** $y = \cos x$

3. $y = \tan x$ **4.** $y = \cot x$

5. $y = \sec x$ **6.** $y = \csc x$

7. $y = 3 \sin 2x$ **8.** $y = 4 \cos (x/3)$

9. $y = \sin^2 x$ **10.** $y = \frac{1}{2} + \frac{1}{2} \cos 2x$

11. a) Derive formula IX. **b)** Derive formula XI.

12. a) Derive formula X. **b)** Derive formula XII.

Find dy/dx in each of the following problems (13 through 33):

13. $y = \tan (3x^2)$ **14.** $y = \tan^2 (\cos x)$

15. $y = \cot (3x + 5)$ **16.** $y = \sqrt{\cot x}$

17. $y = \sec^2 x - \tan^2 x$ **18.** $y = \frac{1}{3} \sec^3 x$

19. $y = 3x + \tan 3x$ **20.** $y = 3 \tan 2x$

21. $y = x - \tan x$ **22.** $y = \sec^4 x - \tan^4 x$

23. $y = (\csc x + \cot x)^2$ **24.** $y = 2 \sin^2 3x$

25. $y = \frac{1}{2}x - \frac{1}{4} \sin 2x$ **26.** $y = \frac{1}{2}x + \frac{1}{4} \sin 2x$

27. $y = \sin^3 \frac{x}{3} - 3 \sin \frac{x}{3}$ **28.** $y = 3 \cos^2 \frac{x}{2}$

29. $y = 2 \sin \frac{1}{2}x - x \cos \frac{1}{2}x$ **30.** $x^2 = \sin y + \sin 2y$

31. $y = \sin^3 x - \sin 3x$ **32.** $y = \frac{1}{3} \sin^3 5x - \sin 5x$

33. $x + \tan (xy) = 0$

34. Find the maximum height of the curve $y = 6 \cos x - 8 \sin x$ above the x-axis.

35. Find the maximum and minimum values of the function $y = 2 \sin x + \cos 2x$ for $0 \le x \le \pi/2$.

36. (*Calculator or tables*) If the ratio of the radii of the arteries in Example 3 is $r/R = 5/6$, estimate to the nearest degree the optimal branching angle given by Eq. (4).

37. Show that the curve $y = x \sin x$ is tangent to the line $y = x$ whenever $\sin x = 1$, and is tangent to the line $y = -x$ whenever $\sin x = -1$.

38. A revolving light 3 miles from a straight shoreline makes 8 revolutions per minute. Find the velocity of the beam of light along the shore at the instant when it makes an angle of 45° with the shoreline.

39. A rope with a ring in one end is looped over two pegs in a horizontal line. The free end, after being passed through the ring, has a weight suspended from it, so that the rope hangs taut. If the rope slips freely over the pegs and through the ring, the weight will descend as far as possible. Assume that the length of the rope is at least four times as great as the distance between the pegs, and that the configuration of the rope is symmetric with respect to the line of the vertical part of the rope. (The symmetry assumption can be justified on the grounds that the rope and weight will take a rest position that minimizes the potential energy of the system. See Problem 25, Article 8–6.) Find the angle formed at the bottom of the loop.

Evaluate the following integrals:

40. $\displaystyle\int \sin 3t \, dt$ **41.** $\displaystyle\int \sec^2 2\theta \, d\theta$

42. $\displaystyle\int \tan^3 x \sec^2 x \, dx$ **43.** $\displaystyle\int \sec^3 x \tan x \, dx$

44. $\displaystyle\int \sec \frac{x}{2} \tan \frac{x}{2} \, dx$ **45.** $\displaystyle\int \cos^2 y \, dy$

46. $\displaystyle\int \frac{d\theta}{\cos^2 \theta}$ **47.** $\displaystyle\int \frac{d\theta}{\sin^2 (\theta/3)}$

48. Find the area bounded by the curve $y = \tan x \sec^2 x$, the x-axis, and the line $x = \pi/3$.

49. The area bounded above by the curve $y = \tan x$, below by the x-axis, and on the right by the line $x = \pi/4$ is revolved about the x-axis. Find the volume generated.

Evaluate the following limits, by showing that l'Hôpital's rule may be applied, and then applying it:

50. $\displaystyle\lim_{h \to 0} \frac{\tan h}{3h}$ **51.** $\displaystyle\lim_{x \to 0} \frac{\sec x - 1}{x^2}$

52. $\displaystyle\lim_{y \to 0} 2y \cot y$ **53.** $\displaystyle\lim_{t \to \pi} \frac{t - \pi}{2 \tan 3t}$

54. Let $f(x) = (\tan x)/x$ for $0 < |x| < \pi/2$. Show that:

a) $\lim_{x \to 0} f(x) = 1$

b) $f(-x) = f(x)$

c) $f'(x) = [(\sec^2 x)/x][1 - (\sin 2x)/2x]$ and therefore $f'(x)$ is positive for $0 < x < \pi/2$.

d) $f(x)$ increases without bound as $x \to \pi/2^-$.

Use the information above to sketch the graph of $y = f(x)$.

THE INVERSE TRIGONOMETRIC FUNCTIONS

There are two reasons for studying the inverses of the trigonometric functions: first, because the inverse of any function is worth some study in its own right, and second, because the derivatives of the inverse trigonometric functions lead to useful integration formulas. We recall that the inverse of the function $y = f(x)$ comes from the equation $x = f(y)$ that we get by interchanging the letters x and y in the original function. So we begin our study of the inverse of the sine function by investigating the equation

$$x = \sin y. \tag{1}$$

In this equation, infinitely many values of y correspond to each x in the range $-1 \leq x \leq 1$.

For example, if $x = \frac{1}{2}$ then we ask for all angles y such that $\sin y = \frac{1}{2}$. The two angles 30° and 150° in the first and second quadrants occur to us immediately. But any whole multiple of 360° may be either added to or subtracted from these and the sine of the resulting angle will still be $\frac{1}{2}$. Expressing these facts in mathematical language and using radian measure for the angles, we have $\sin y = \frac{1}{2}$ if

$$y = \begin{cases} \dfrac{\pi}{6} + 2n\pi \\[2ex] \dfrac{5\pi}{6} + 2n\pi \end{cases} \qquad n = 0, \pm 1, \pm 2, \ldots$$

Similarly, we find that $\sin y = -\frac{1}{2}$ if

$$y = \begin{cases} -\dfrac{\pi}{6} + 2n\pi \\[2ex] -\dfrac{5\pi}{6} + 2n\pi \end{cases} \qquad n = 0, \pm 1, \pm 2, \ldots$$

Now it is desirable, for some of our later applications, to adopt a rule for picking a *principal value* of y. We shall require that the rule (a) produce one and only one value of y for each x, $-1 \leq x \leq 1$, such that $\sin y = x$; and (b) give two "nearly equal" values of y for two "nearly equal" values of x.

To state requirement (b) more specifically, we require that if x_1 and x_2 are two values of x both between -1 and $+1$, and y_1 and y_2 are the corresponding values of y such that $\sin y = x$, then $y_2 - y_1$ should tend to zero if $x_2 - x_1$ does. The portion of the curve AOB shown heavily marked in Fig. 6–2 fulfills these requirements. For any x between -1 and $+1$ there is one and only one corresponding point (x, y) on this portion of the curve, and the y-value satisfies $\sin y = x$. Furthermore, this is a continuous curve, so that if (x_1, y_1) and (x_2, y_2) are two points on it and $(x_2 - x_1) \to 0$, then also $(y_2 - y_1) \to 0$.

To be sure that the point (x, y) stays on the portion AOB of Fig. 6–2, we need only restrict y:

$$\sin y = x, \qquad -\frac{\pi}{2} \leq y \leq \frac{\pi}{2}. \tag{2}$$

6–2 $y = \sin^{-1} x.$

The restrictions placed on y give a continuous function

$$y = \sin^{-1} x, \qquad -\frac{\pi}{2} \le y \le \frac{\pi}{2}, \tag{3}$$

called the "inverse sine of x," which is defined on the domain $-1 \le x \le 1$ and has values on the range $-\pi/2 \le y \le +\pi/2$. Note that the minus one in Eq. (3), although written as an exponent, does *not* mean

$$(\sin x)^{-1} = \frac{1}{\sin x} = \csc x.$$

Actually, Eq. (3) merely gives a name to the new function that is defined implicitly by Eq. (2). The symbol $f^{-1}(x)$ is often used to denote the function y defined implicitly by $f(y) = x$, that is,

$$y = f^{-1}(x).$$

The notation arcsin x is also used to represent the function that we have denoted by $\sin^{-1} x$, but the latter notation is now more commonly used. Thus,

$$\sin^{-1}\left(\frac{1}{2}\right) = \frac{\pi}{6}, \qquad \sin^{-1}\left(-\frac{1}{2}\right) = -\frac{\pi}{6}.$$

In terms of angles referred to standard position in the various quadrants, Eq. (2) and the restriction $-\pi/2 \le y \le \pi/2$ mean that the answer to the question: "What is the angle y whose sine is x?" is always an angle in the *first* or *fourth* quadrant, but if it is in the *fourth* quadrant, it is to be expressed as the *negative* of an angle between 0 and $\pi/2$ and not as a positive angle $\ge 3\pi/2$, since the latter would violate the restriction in (2).

At the risk of appearing to labor a point which is already clear, we also note that the inverse sine is an *odd* function of x. This means that

$$\sin^{-1}(-x) = -\sin^{-1}(x). \tag{4}$$

Keeping this fact firmly in mind will prevent us from using values of y corresponding to points on the discontinuous curve composed of the portions OB and CD on the curve in Fig. 6–3. The objection to using these is that for a small positive value of x, say $x_1 = +0.01$, the point is near O and $y_1 \approx 0.01$; while for a small negative value of x, say $x_2 = -0.01$, the point is near D and $y_2 \approx 2\pi - 0.01$. The difference $y_2 - y_1$ is nearly $2\pi = 6.28+$, whereas the difference $x_1 - x_2$ is, in this case, only 0.02. This difficulty is not encountered if we restrict the value of y as in (3), which confines us to the *continuous* curve AOB of Fig. 6–2.

To each of the other trigonometric functions there also corresponds an *inverse* trigonometric function. In each case, we restrict the angle in such a way that the function is *single-valued*.

The reasoning that led us to adopt the particular range

$$-\frac{\pi}{2} \le y \le \frac{\pi}{2}$$

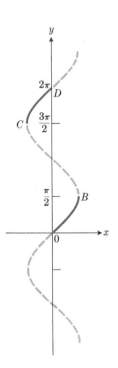

6–3 If $y = \sin^{-1} x$ were the function graphed here, it would not be continuous at $x = 0$.

for the principal value of $y = \sin^{-1} x$ prompts us to adopt a similar range for the principal value of y satisfying the equation $x = \tan y$ (see Fig. 6–4). Thus we write

$$y = \tan^{-1} x, \qquad -\frac{\pi}{2} < y < \frac{\pi}{2} \qquad \text{(5a)}$$

to mean the same as

$$\tan y = x, \qquad -\frac{\pi}{2} < y < \frac{\pi}{2}. \qquad \text{(5b)}$$

The inverse tangent function, (5a), is defined on the *domain* $-\infty < x < +\infty$, that is, for all real x. Its *range* is $-\pi/2 < y < +\pi/2$. The values $y = \pm\pi/2$ are to be excluded, since the tangent becomes infinite as the angle approaches $\pm\pi/2$.

When we come to the inverse cosine function, we simply *define* it by the equation

$$\cos^{-1} x = \frac{\pi}{2} - \sin^{-1} x. \qquad \text{(6)}$$

Since

$$-\frac{\pi}{2} \leq \sin^{-1} x \leq \frac{\pi}{2},$$

the range of principal values for (6) is

$$0 \leq \cos^{-1} x \leq \pi. \qquad \text{(7)}$$

The *domain* of the inverse cosine function is $-1 \leq x \leq 1$. Its *range* is $0 \leq y \leq \pi$. The principal value is thus represented by the heavily marked portion of the curve

$$x = \cos y$$

shown in Fig. 6–5.

The reason for defining $\cos^{-1} x$ by Eq. (6) is as follows. In the right triangle in Fig. 6–6, the acute angles α and β are complementary, that is

$$\alpha + \beta = \frac{\pi}{2}.$$

But we also have

$$\sin \alpha = x = \cos \beta,$$

so that

$$\alpha = \sin^{-1} x, \qquad \beta = \cos^{-1} x,$$

and the relation $\alpha + \beta = \pi/2$ is the same as $\beta = \pi/2 - \alpha$; that is,

$$\cos^{-1} x = \frac{\pi}{2} - \sin^{-1} x.$$

Thus Eq. (6) expresses the fact that the angle whose cosine is x is the complement of the angle whose sine is x.

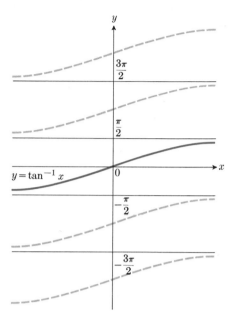

6–4 The branch chosen for $y = \tan^{-1} x$ is the one through the origin.

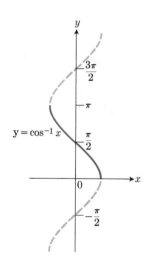

6–5 $y = \cos^{-1} x$.

6–6 $\alpha + \beta = \pi/2$.

For exactly analogous reasons, we also define the inverse cotangent to be

$$\cot^{-1} x = \frac{\pi}{2} - \tan^{-1} x, \tag{8}$$

and we thus restrict the principal value to

$$0 < \cot^{-1} x < \pi. \tag{9}$$

The inverse secant and inverse cosecant functions will be single-valued functions of x on the domain $|x| \geq 1$ if we adopt the definitions

$$\sec^{-1} x = \cos^{-1}\left(\frac{1}{x}\right), \tag{10a}$$

$$\csc^{-1} x = \sin^{-1}\left(\frac{1}{x}\right), \tag{10b}$$

with their principal values confined to the ranges

$$0 \leq \sec^{-1} x \leq \pi, \tag{11a}$$

$$-\frac{\pi}{2} \leq \csc^{-1} x \leq \frac{\pi}{2}. \tag{11b}$$

The reason for adopting the definitions above is the following. If $\sec y = x$, then $\cos y = 1/x$, and we simply ask that the principal values of y be the same in these two cases, that is

$$y = \sec^{-1} x = \cos^{-1}\left(\frac{1}{x}\right).$$

It should be noted, however, that some writers choose the principal value of the inverse secant of x to lie between 0 and $\pi/2$ when x is positive, and between $-\pi$ and $-\pi/2$ (hence, as a negative angle in the third quadrant) when x is negative. This latter method has the advantage of simplifying the formula for the derivative of $\sec^{-1} x$, but has the disadvantage of failing to satisfy the relationship expressed in Eq. (10a) when x is negative. Either method leads to a function that is discontinuous, as is inherent in the nature of the secant function itself, since to pass from a point where the secant is negative to a point where the secant is positive requires crossing one of the discontinuities of the curve (Fig. 6–7).

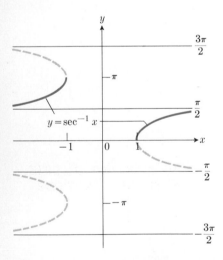

6–7 $y = \sec^{-1} x$ is defined for $|x| \geq 1$.

In Problem 7, you are asked to establish the following identities:

$$\tan^{-1}(-x) = -\tan^{-1} x, \tag{12a}$$

$$\cos^{-1}(-x) = \pi - \cos^{-1} x, \tag{12b}$$

$$\sec^{-1}(-x) = \pi - \sec^{-1} x. \tag{12c}$$

These are easy to interpret graphically. We list them here for future reference.

PROBLEMS

1. Given that $\alpha = \sin^{-1} \frac{1}{2}$, find $\cos \alpha$, $\tan \alpha$, $\sec \alpha$, $\csc \alpha$.

2. Given that $\alpha = \cos^{-1}\left(-\frac{1}{2}\right)$, find $\sin \alpha$, $\tan \alpha$, $\sec \alpha$, $\csc \alpha$.

3. Evaluate $\sin^{-1}(1) - \sin^{-1}(-1)$.

4. Evaluate $\tan^{-1}(1) - \tan^{-1}(-1)$.

5. Evaluate $\sec^{-1}(2) - \sec^{-1}(-2)$.

6. A picture a feet high is placed on a wall with its base b feet above the level of an observer's eye. If the observer stands x feet from the wall, show that the angle of vision α subtended by the picture is given by

$$\alpha = \cot^{-1} \frac{x}{a+b} - \cot^{-1} \frac{x}{b}.$$

7. Prove:

a) $\tan^{-1}(-x) = -\tan^{-1}x$

b) $\cos^{-1}(-x) = \pi - \cos^{-1}x$

c) $\sec^{-1}(-x) = \pi - \sec^{-1}x$

8. Simplify each of the following expressions:

a) $\sin(\sin^{-1} 0.735)$ **b)** $\cos(\sin^{-1} 0.8)$

c) $\sin(2\sin^{-1} 0.8)$ **d)** $\tan^{-1}(\tan \pi/3)$

e) $\cos^{-1}(-\sin \pi/6)$ **f)** $\sec^{-1}(\sec(-30°))$

9. When a ray of light passes from one medium (say air) where it travels with a velocity c_1, into a second medium (for example, water) where it travels with velocity c_2, the angle of incidence θ_1 and angle of refraction θ_2 are related by Snell's law:

$$\frac{\sin \theta_1}{c_1} = \frac{\sin \theta_2}{c_2}$$

(Fig. 6–8). The quotient $c_1/c_2 = n_{12}$ is called the index of refraction of medium 2 with respect to medium 1. (a) Express θ_2 as a function of θ_1. (b) Find the largest value of θ_1 for which the expression for θ_2 in part (a) is defined. (For values of θ_1 larger than this, the incoming light will be reflected.) [*Remark.* Snell's law also applies in acoustics. See, for example, R. G. Lindsay and K. D. Kryter, "Acoustics," *American Institute of Physics Handbook*, 3rd Edition, 1972.]

10. Find all values of c that satisfy the conclusion of Cauchy's Mean Value Theorem for $f(x) = \sin x$, $g(x) = \cos x$, on the interval $0 \le x \le \pi/2$.

angle of incidence

angle of refraction

6–8 A ray refracted as it passes from one medium to another.

The following formulas may now be derived.

6–3

DERIVATIVES OF THE INVERSE TRIGONOMETRIC FUNCTIONS

XIII. $\dfrac{d(\sin^{-1} u)}{dx} = \dfrac{du/dx}{\sqrt{1 - u^2}}$.

XIII′. $d(\sin^{-1} u) = \dfrac{du}{\sqrt{1 - u^2}}$.

XIV. $\dfrac{d(\cos^{-1} u)}{dx} = -\dfrac{du/dx}{\sqrt{1 - u^2}}$.

XIV′. $d(\cos^{-1} u) = -\dfrac{du}{\sqrt{1 - u^2}}$.

XV. $\dfrac{d(\tan^{-1} u)}{dx} = \dfrac{du/dx}{1 + u^2}$.

XV′. $d(\tan^{-1} u) = \dfrac{du}{1 + u^2}$.

XVI. $\dfrac{d(\cot^{-1} u)}{dx} = -\dfrac{du/dx}{1 + u^2}$.

XVI′. $d(\cot^{-1} u) = -\dfrac{du}{1 + u^2}$.

XVII. $\dfrac{d(\sec^{-1} u)}{dx} = \dfrac{du/dx}{|u|\sqrt{u^2 - 1}}$.

XVII′. $d(\sec^{-1} u) = \dfrac{du}{|u|\sqrt{u^2 - 1}}$.

XVIII. $\dfrac{d(\csc^{-1} u)}{dx} = \dfrac{-du/dx}{|u|\sqrt{u^2 - 1}}$.

XVIII′. $d(\csc^{-1} u) = \dfrac{-du}{|u|\sqrt{u^2 - 1}}$.

To illustrate how these are derived, we shall prove formulas XIII and XVII. Let

$$y = \sin^{-1} u, \qquad -\frac{\pi}{2} \le y \le \frac{\pi}{2}.$$

Then

$$\sin y = u,$$

$$\cos y \frac{dy}{dx} = \frac{du}{dx}, \qquad \frac{dy}{dx} = \frac{1}{\cos y}\frac{du}{dx}.$$

To express the right side in terms of u, we use the fact that

$$\cos y = \pm\sqrt{1 - \sin^2 y} = \pm\sqrt{1 - u^2}.$$

Since $-\pi/2 \le y \le \pi/2$, $\cos y$ is not negative; hence

$$\cos y = +\sqrt{1 - u^2}$$

and

$$\frac{dy}{dx} = \frac{1}{\sqrt{1 - u^2}}\frac{du}{dx},$$

which establishes XIII.

Next, let

$$y = \sec^{-1} u, \qquad 0 \le y \le \pi.$$

Then

$$\sec y = u, \qquad \sec y \tan y \frac{dy}{dx} = \frac{du}{dx},$$

$$\frac{dy}{dx} = \frac{1}{\sec y \tan y}\frac{du}{dx}.$$

Substituting

$$\sec y = u, \qquad \tan y = \pm\sqrt{\sec^2 y - 1} = \pm\sqrt{u^2 - 1},$$

we have

$$\frac{dy}{dx} = \frac{1}{u(\pm\sqrt{u^2 - 1})}\frac{du}{dx}.$$

The ambiguous sign is determined by the sign of $\tan y$, and hence is

$$+ \quad \text{if } 0 < y < \frac{\pi}{2}, \qquad \text{that is, if } u \text{ is } +;$$

$$- \quad \text{if } \frac{\pi}{2} < y < \pi, \qquad \text{that is, if } u \text{ is } -.$$

That is,

$$\frac{dy}{dx} = \begin{cases} \dfrac{1}{u\sqrt{u^2-1}}\dfrac{du}{dx} & \text{if } u > 1, \\[3ex] \dfrac{1}{-u\sqrt{u^2-1}}\dfrac{du}{dx} & \text{if } u < -1, \end{cases}$$

and both of these are summarized in the single formula

$$\frac{dy}{dx} = \frac{1}{|u|\sqrt{u^2-1}}\frac{du}{dx}.$$

The formulas XIII to XVIII are used directly as given, but even more important are the integration formulas obtained immediately from the differential formulas XIII′ to XVIII′, namely,

$$\int \frac{du}{\sqrt{1-u^2}} = \sin^{-1} u + C, \qquad \int \frac{du}{1+u^2} = \tan^{-1} u + C,$$

$$\int \frac{du}{u\sqrt{u^2-1}} = \int \frac{d(-u)}{(-u)\sqrt{u^2-1}} = \sec^{-1} |u| + C. \tag{1}$$

Note that $\sec^{-1} u$ and $\sec^{-1} |u|$ are meaningless unless $|u| \geq 1$ (see Fig. 6–7).

REMARK.   Something more should be said about the last formula in Eqs. (1). In the first place, if we are evaluating a *definite* integral of the form

$$\int_a^b \frac{dx}{x\sqrt{x^2-1}},$$

both a and b should be greater than 1 or both should be less than -1, for otherwise we would be attempting to integrate an expression that becomes infinite, or imaginary, or both, within the interval of integration. (Why?) On the other hand, if we are looking for all curves of the form $y = f(x)$ such that $f'(x) = 1/(x\sqrt{x^2-1})$, then our answer is

$$y = \begin{cases} \sec^{-1} x + C_1 & \text{if } x > 1, \\ \sec^{-1}(-x) + C_2 & \text{if } x < -1; \end{cases}$$

and the two constants C_1 and C_2 need not be the same.

We can also replace $\sec^{-1}(-x)$ by $\pi - \sec^{-1} x$ by Eq. (12c) of Article 6–2 and then let $C_2 + \pi = C'$, and write

$$y = \begin{cases} \sec^{-1} x + C & \text{if } x > 1, \\ -\sec^{-1} x + C' & \text{if } x < -1. \end{cases}$$

EXAMPLE 1.   Evaluate:

a) $\displaystyle\int_0^1 \frac{dx}{1+x^2}$ and   **b)** $\displaystyle\int_{2/\sqrt{3}}^{2/\sqrt{2}} \frac{dx}{x\sqrt{x^2-1}}.$

Solutions

a) $\tan^{-1} x\big]_0^1 = \tan^{-1} 1 - \tan^{-1} 0 = \dfrac{\pi}{4} - 0 = \dfrac{\pi}{4}$.

b) $\sec^{-1} x\big]_{2/\sqrt{3}}^{2/\sqrt{2}} = \cos^{-1}(\sqrt{2}/2) - \cos^{-1}(\sqrt{3}/2) = \dfrac{\pi}{4} - \dfrac{\pi}{6} = \dfrac{\pi}{12}$.

EXAMPLE 2. Find a curve whose slope at the point (x, y) is $1/(x\sqrt{x^2 - 1})$ and that passes through the points $(-2, -2)$ and $(\sqrt{2}, 0)$.

Solution. From the discussion above, we can write

$$y = \begin{cases} \sec^{-1} x + C & \text{if } x > 1, \\ -\sec^{-1} x + C' & \text{if } x < -1. \end{cases} \qquad \begin{matrix} \textbf{(2a)} \\ \textbf{(2b)} \end{matrix}$$

Using Eq. (2a) with $x = \sqrt{2}$ and $y = 0$, we have

$$0 = \sec^{-1}\sqrt{2} + C, \qquad C = -\sec^{-1}\sqrt{2} = -\frac{\pi}{4}.$$

To find the value of C' we use Eq. (2b) and the point $(-2, -2)$ to get

$$-2 = -\sec^{-1}(-2) + C',$$

$$C' = \sec^{-1}(-2) - 2 = \frac{2\pi}{3} - 2.$$

Therefore the curve is described by the equations

$$y = \begin{cases} \sec^{-1} x - \dfrac{\pi}{4} & \text{if } x > 1, \\[2mm] -\sec^{-1} x + \dfrac{2\pi}{3} - 2 & \text{if } x < -1. \end{cases}$$

The graph is shown in Fig. 6-9.

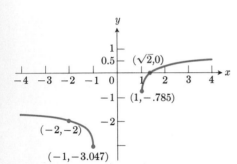

6-9 Graph of curve satisfying $dy/dx = 1/(x\sqrt{x^2 - 1})$ and passing through the points $(-2, -2)$ and $(\sqrt{2}, 0)$. The two branches have the same shape. Either branch can be moved up or down any number of units without changing the slope.

PROBLEMS

1. Derive formula XIV.   **2.** Derive formula XV.

3. Derive formula XVI.   **4.** Derive formula XVIII.

Find dy/dx in each of the following:

5. $y = \sin^{-1} \dfrac{x}{2}$

6. $y = \dfrac{1}{3}\tan^{-1}\dfrac{x}{3}$

7. $y = \sec^{-1} 5x$

8. $y = \cos^{-1} 2x$

9. $y = \cot^{-1}\dfrac{2}{x} + \tan^{-1}\dfrac{x}{2}$

10. $y = \sin^{-1}\dfrac{x-1}{x+1}$

11. $y = \tan^{-1}\dfrac{x-1}{x+1}$

12. $y = x\sin^{-1} x + \sqrt{1 - x^2}$

13. $y = x(\sin^{-1} x)^2 - 2x + 2\sqrt{1-x^2}\,\sin^{-1} x$

14. $y = x\cos^{-1} 2x - \dfrac{1}{2}\sqrt{1 - 4x^2}$

15. How far from the wall should the observer stand in order to maximize the angle of vision α in Problem 6, Article 6-2?

Evaluate the following integrals:

16. $\displaystyle\int_0^{1/2} \dfrac{dx}{\sqrt{1 - x^2}}$

17. $\displaystyle\int_{-1}^{1} \dfrac{dx}{1 + x^2}$

18. $\displaystyle\int_{\sqrt{2}}^{2} \dfrac{dx}{x\sqrt{x^2 - 1}}$

19. $\displaystyle\int_{-2}^{-\sqrt{2}} \dfrac{dx}{x\sqrt{x^2 - 1}}$

20. $\displaystyle\int \frac{dx}{\sqrt{1-4x^2}}$

21. $\displaystyle\int_{1/\sqrt{3}}^{1} \frac{dx}{x\sqrt{4x^2-1}}$

22. Find a curve whose slope at $P(x, y)$ is $1/(x\sqrt{4x^2-1})$ if it contains the points $A(-1, -1)$ and $B(1, 2)$.

23. Evaluate the limits:

a) $\displaystyle\lim_{x\to 0} \frac{\sin^{-1} 2x}{x}$

b) $\displaystyle\lim_{x\to 0} \frac{2\tan^{-1} 3x}{5x}$

c) $\displaystyle\lim_{x\to 0} x^{-3}(\sin^{-1} x - x)$

d) $\displaystyle\lim_{x\to 0} x^{-3}(\tan^{-1} x - x)$

24. Use Simpson's method with $n = 2$ to approximate the area under the curve $y = \sin^{-1} x$ over the interval $[0, 1]$. Compare your answer with the trapezoidal approximation using two trapezoids, those for $0 \le x \le \frac{1}{2}$ and $\frac{1}{2} \le x \le 1$.

25. Verify that the derivative of $f(x) = x\sin^{-1} x + \sqrt{1-x^2}$ is $\sin^{-1} x$. Use this result to find the exact value of $\int_0^1 \sin^{-1} x\, dx$.

THE NATURAL LOGARITHM

We have so far studied functions that are fairly familiar. Polynomials, rational functions, and other algebraic functions result from the familiar operations of arithmetic and algebra. The trigonometric functions can be identified with coordinates of points on a unit circle and with their ratios and reciprocals. The inverse trigonometric functions are probably less familiar, but nevertheless they can be understood without any knowledge of the calculus. But we are now going to study a function, the natural logarithm,* which depends upon the calculus for its very definition.

The natural logarithm of x, which is indicated by the notation $\ln x$, is defined, for positive x, as the integral

$$\ln x = \int_1^x \frac{1}{t}\, dt. \tag{1}$$

For any x greater than 1, this integral represents the area bounded above by the curve $y = 1/t$, below by the t-axis, on the left by the line $t = 1$, and on the right by the line $t = x$. (See Fig. 6–10.)

If $x = 1$, the left and right boundaries of the area are identical and the area is zero,

$$\ln 1 = \int_1^1 \frac{1}{t}\, dt = 0. \tag{2}$$

If x is less than 1, then the left boundary is the line $t = x$ and the right boundary is $t = 1$. In this case,

$$\ln x = \int_1^x \frac{1}{t}\, dt = -\int_x^1 \frac{1}{t}\, dt \tag{3}$$

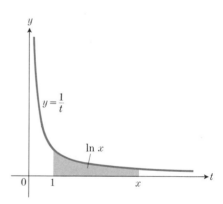

6–10 The shaded area is $\ln x$.

is the negative of the area under the curve between x and 1.

In all cases, if x is any positive number, the value of the definite integral in Eq. (1) can be calculated to as many decimal places as may be desired by using inscribed rectangles, circumscribed rectangles, or trapezoids to approximate the appropriate area. (See Chapter 4. Another method for computing natural logarithms, by means of series, will also be discussed in

---

* The first discovery of logarithms is credited to a Scottish nobleman, John Napier (1550–1617). For a biographical sketch of Napier, see the *World of Mathematics*, Vol. 1, "The Great Mathematicians," by H. W. Turnbull. New York: Simon and Schuster, 1962; pp. 121–125.

Chapter 16. Also see Problem 8 below.) In any event, Eq. (1) defines a computable function of x over the domain $0 < x < +\infty$. We study its range in Article 6–7.

REMARK. No doubt you have learned about logarithms in your earlier studies in mathematics. Common logarithms, or logarithms to the base 10, are related to the natural logarithms by a rule that we shall come to in Article 6–10. Any function $f(x)$ that is defined on the domain of positive numbers x and that satisfies the condition

$$f(ax) = f(a) + f(x)$$

may be called a logarithmic function. The function that we have introduced as $\ln x$ has these properties: that is,

$$\ln x = \int_1^x \frac{1}{t}\, dt$$

is defined for all positive values of x, and, as we shall see in Article 6–6,

$$\ln ax = \ln a + \ln x. \tag{4}$$

(One method of establishing Eq. (4) is outlined in Problem 9. We shall prove it by a different method in Article 6–6.) Fundamentally, it is the property of areas under the curve $y = 1/t$ expressed by Eq. (4) that motivates the definition of $\ln x$ that we have given.

PROBLEMS

Use trapezoids of altitude $\Delta t = 0.1$ to approximate the appropriate areas to obtain approximations to the following natural logarithms, Problems 1–4.

1. $\ln 1.2$ **2.** $\ln 1.4$

3. $\ln 2$ **4.** $\ln 0.5$

5. (a) Suppose h is small and positive. Does the approximation $\ln (1 + h) \approx h$ correspond to using an inscribed rectangle or a circumscribed rectangle to approximate the area from 1 to $1 + h$ under the curve $y = 1/t$? (b) Answer the same question in case h is negative.

6. Approximate $\ln (1 + h)$ by using the line L that is tangent to the curve $y = 1/t$ at $A(1, 1)$, as upper boundary of a trapezoid of altitude $|h|$. Sketch. Show that this leads to the approximation

$$\ln (1 + h) \approx h - \frac{h^2}{2}.$$

Use this result to approximate (a) $\ln 1.04$; (b) $\ln 0.96$.

7. Find the volume generated by rotating about the x-axis the area in the first quadrant bounded by $y = 1/\sqrt{x}$, the x-axis, the line $x = 1$, and the line $x = 2$.

8. a) Show, by long division or otherwise, that

$$\frac{1}{1 + u} = 1 - u + u^2 - \frac{u^3}{1 + u}.$$

(The division could be continued. We stop here only for the sake of illustration.)

b) In Eq. (1), make the substitution

$$t = 1 + u, \qquad dt = du$$

and make the corresponding change in the limits of integration, thus obtaining

$$\ln x = \int_0^{x-1} \frac{du}{1 + u}.$$

c) Combine the results of (a) and (b) to obtain

$$\ln x = \int_0^{x-1} \left(1 - u + u^2 - \frac{u^3}{1 + u} \right) du,$$

or

$$\ln x = (x - 1) - \tfrac{1}{2}(x - 1)^2 + \tfrac{1}{3}(x - 1)^3 - R,$$

where

$$R = \int_0^{x-1} \frac{u^3}{1 + u}\, du.$$

d) Show that, if $x > 1$ and $0 \le u \le x - 1$, then

$$\frac{u^3}{1 + u} \le u^3.$$

Hence, deduce that

$$R \le \int_0^{x-1} u^3 \, du = \frac{(x-1)^4}{4}.$$

e) Combining the results of (c) and (d), show that the approximation

$$\ln x \approx (x-1) - \tfrac{1}{2}(x-1)^2 + \tfrac{1}{3}(x-1)^3$$

tends to overestimate the value of ln x, but with an error not greater than $(x-1)^4/4$.

f) Use the result of (e) to estimate ln 1.2.

9. (*A proof of Eq. (4)*) **a)** Prove that the area under the curve $y = 1/t$ over $[1, x]$ is equal to the area under the same curve over $[a, ax]$ where a is any positive constant. *Suggestion.* Take any partition of $[1, x]$ and multiply each co-ordinate by a to get the corresponding partition of $[a, ax]$. Sketch. If $f(t_i) \Delta t_i$ is the area of a rectangle over one of the subdivisions in $[1, x]$, what is the rectangle whose area is represented by $f(at_i)(a \, \Delta t_i)$? Are these two rectangles equal in area?

b) In part (a) you have shown that the area under the curve $y = 1/t$ over $[a, ax]$ is equal to ln x. By Eq. (1), the area over $[1, a]$ is ln a. Now combine these results to show that ln ax = ln a + ln x. (*Remark.* It is easier to see what goes on if you assume that both a and x are greater than 1 in the foregoing. The language has to be different if either a or x is less than 1, but the final conclusion ln ax = ln a + ln x is still true. Our proof in Article 6–6 is more straightforward and does not require special cases.)

Since the function $F(x) = \ln x$ is defined by the integral

$$F(x) = \int_1^x \frac{1}{t} \, dt \qquad (x > 0) \tag{1}$$

(see Fig. 6–11), it follows at once, from Theorem 4 of Article 4–10, that

$$F'(x) = \frac{1}{x}.$$

That is,

$$\frac{d(\ln x)}{dx} = \frac{1}{x}. \tag{2}$$

We obtain a more general formula by considering ln u, where u is a positive, differentiable function of x. By the chain rule for derivatives,

$$\frac{d \ln u}{dx} = \frac{d \ln u}{du} \frac{du}{dx} = \frac{1}{u} \frac{du}{dx}, \qquad \textbf{XIX}$$

or, in terms of differentials,

$$d \ln u = \frac{du}{u}. \qquad \textbf{XIX}'$$

6–5

THE DERIVATIVE OF ln x

6–11 $\ln x = \int_1^x \frac{1}{t} \, dt, \quad \frac{d(\ln x)}{dx} = \frac{1}{x}.$

EXAMPLE 1. Find dy/dx if $y = \ln (3x^2 + 4)$.

Solution

$$\frac{dy}{dx} = \frac{1}{3x^2 + 4} \frac{d(3x^2 + 4)}{dx} = \frac{6x}{3x^2 + 4}.$$

Equation (XIX′) leads at once to the integration formula

$$\int \frac{du}{u} = \ln u + C, \tag{3a}$$

provided u is positive. On the other hand, if u is negative then $-u$ is positive and

$$\int \frac{du}{u} = \int \frac{d(-u)}{-u} = \ln (-u) + C'. \tag{3b}$$

The two results (3a, b) can be combined into a single result, namely,

$$\int \frac{du}{u} = \begin{cases} \ln u + C & \text{if } u > 0, \\ \ln (-u) + C' & \text{if } u < 0, \end{cases} \tag{4a}$$

or, if u does not change sign on the given domain,

$$\int \frac{du}{u} = \ln |u| + C. \tag{4b}$$

EXAMPLE 2. Find a function $y = f(x)$ such that $dy/dx = 1/x$, and $f(1) = 1$ and $f(-1) = 2$. Sketch the solution.

Solution. There are constants C and C' such that

$$y = \begin{cases} \ln x + C & \text{if } x \text{ is positive,} \\ \ln (-x) + C' & \text{if } x \text{ is negative.} \end{cases}$$

Substituting $y = 1$ when $x = 1$, we get

$$1 = \ln 1 + C = 0 + C, \quad \text{so} \quad C = 1.$$

Likewise, putting $y = 2$ when $x = -1$, we get

$$2 = \ln (-(-1)) + C' = \ln 1 + C' = 0 + C', \quad \text{so} \quad C' = 2.$$

The complete solution is, therefore,

$$y = f(x) = \begin{cases} \ln x + 1 & \text{if } x \text{ is positive,} \\ \ln (-x) + 2 & \text{if } x \text{ is negative.} \end{cases}$$

A graph of the solution is shown in Fig. 6–12. (For a general analysis of the graph of $y = \ln x$, see Article 6–7.)

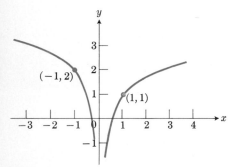

6–12 Graph of function $f(x)$ whose derivative is $1/x$ with $f(-1) = 2$ and $f(1) = 1$:

$$f(x) = \begin{cases} 2 + \ln(-x) & \text{when } x \text{ is negative,} \\ 1 + \ln x & \text{when } x \text{ is positive,} \end{cases}$$

The two constants of integration C and C' are not equal.

We recall that the formula

$$\int u^n \, du = \frac{u^{n+1}}{n+1} + C', \quad n \neq -1$$

failed to cover one case, namely, $n = -1$. Equation (4b) now covers this for us, since it tells us that

$$\int u^{-1} \, du = \int \frac{du}{u} = \ln |u| + C.$$

It is important, of course, to remember that

$$\int \frac{dx}{x^2} = \int x^{-2}\,dx = \frac{x^{-1}}{-1} + C$$

is *not* a logarithm.

EXAMPLE 2. Integrate

$$\int \frac{\cos\theta\,d\theta}{1 + \sin\theta}.$$

Solution. In Eq. (4b), let

$$u = 1 + \sin\theta.$$

Then

$$du = \frac{du}{d\theta}\,d\theta = \cos\theta\,d\theta$$

so that

$$\int \frac{\cos\theta\,d\theta}{1 + \sin\theta} = \int \frac{du}{u} = \ln|u| + C$$

$$= \ln|1 + \sin\theta| + C.$$

PROBLEMS

Find dy/dx in each of the following problems (1 through 18).

1. $y = \ln(x^2 + 2x)$

2. $y = (\ln x)^3$

3. $y = \ln(\cos x)$

4. $y = \ln(\tan x + \sec x)$

5. $y = \ln(x\sqrt{x^2 + 1})$

6. $y = \ln(3x\sqrt{x + 2})$

7. $y = x\ln x - x$

8. $y = x^3\ln(2x)$

9. $y = \frac{1}{2}\ln\frac{1 + x}{1 - x}$

10. $y = \frac{1}{3}\ln\frac{x^3}{1 + x^3}$

11. $y = \ln\frac{x}{2 + 3x}$

12. $y = \ln(x^2 + 4) - x\tan^{-1}\frac{x}{2}$

13. $y = \ln x - \frac{1}{2}\ln(1 + x^2) - \frac{\tan^{-1}x}{x}$

14. $y = x(\ln x)^3$

15. $y = x[\sin(\ln x) + \cos(\ln x)]$

16. $y = x\sec^{-1}x - \ln(x + \sqrt{x^2 - 1}), \quad (x > 1)$

17. $y = x\ln(a^2 + x^2) - 2x + 2a\tan^{-1}\frac{x}{a}$

18. $y = \ln(\ln x)$

Evaluate the following integrals:

19. $\displaystyle\int \frac{dx}{2x + 3}$

20. $\displaystyle\int \frac{dx}{2 - 3x}$

21. $\displaystyle\int \frac{x\,dx}{4x^2 + 1}$

22. $\displaystyle\int \frac{\sin x\,dx}{2 - \cos x}$

23. $\displaystyle\int \frac{\cos x\,dx}{\sin x}$

24. $\displaystyle\int \frac{2x - 5}{x}\,dx$

25. $\displaystyle\int \frac{x\,dx}{x + 1}$

26. $\displaystyle\int \frac{x^2\,dx}{4 - x^3}$

27. $\displaystyle\int \frac{x\,dx}{1 - x^2}$

28. $\displaystyle\int \frac{dx}{\sqrt{x}(1 + \sqrt{x})}$

29. $\displaystyle\int (\ln x)^2\frac{dx}{x}$

30. $\displaystyle\int \frac{dx}{(2x + 3)^2}$

31. $\displaystyle\int \tan x\,dx$

32. $\displaystyle\int \frac{dx}{x\ln x}$

33. $\displaystyle\int \frac{\ln x}{x}\,dx$

34. Evaluate the following limits (using l'Hôpital's rule):

   a) $\displaystyle\lim_{t\to 0} \frac{\ln(1 + 2t) - 2t}{t^2}$

   b) $\displaystyle\lim_{x\to\infty} \frac{\ln x}{x}$

   c) $\displaystyle\lim_{h\to 0^+} h\ln h$

   d) $\displaystyle\lim_{\theta\to 0^+} \frac{\ln(\sin\theta)}{\cot\theta}$

35. Find the length of the curve $y = \ln\sec x$ from $x = 0$ to $x = \pi/4$, using at some stage the result of Problem 4.

PROPERTIES OF NATURAL LOGARITHMS

In this article we shall establish the following properties of the natural logarithm:

$$\ln ax = \ln a + \ln x, \tag{1}$$

$$\ln \frac{x}{a} = \ln x - \ln a, \tag{2}$$

$$\ln x^n = n \ln x, \tag{3}$$

provided x and a are positive and n is a rational number.

The proofs of these results are all based on the fact that

$$y = \ln x$$

satisfies the differential equation

$$\frac{dy}{dx} = \frac{1}{x} \qquad \text{for all} \quad x > 0,$$

plus the fact that if two functions have the same derivative for all $x > 0$, then the two functions can differ only by a constant. That is, if

$$\frac{dy_1}{dx} = \frac{dy_2}{dx} \qquad \text{for all} \quad x > 0,$$

then

$$y_1 = y_2 + \text{constant} \qquad \text{for all} \quad x > 0.$$

Now, to prove Eq. (1), let

$$y_1 = \ln ax, \qquad y_2 = \ln x.$$

Then

$$\frac{dy_1}{dx} = \frac{1}{ax}\frac{d(ax)}{dx} = \frac{a}{ax} = \frac{1}{x} = \frac{dy_2}{dx}. \tag{4}$$

Therefore we have

$$\ln ax = \ln x + C. \tag{5}$$

To evaluate C it suffices to substitute $x = 1$:

$$\ln a = \ln 1 + C = 0 + C,$$

which gives

$$C = \ln a.$$

Hence, by (5),

$$\ln ax = \ln x + \ln a. \qquad \text{Q.E.D.}$$

To prove Eq. (2), we first put $x = 1/a$ in Eq. (1) and recall that $\ln 1 = 0$:

$$0 = \ln 1 = \ln a + \ln \left(\frac{1}{a}\right)$$

so that

$$\ln \frac{1}{a} = -\ln a. \tag{6}$$

Now apply Eq. (1) with a replaced by $1/a$ and $\ln a$ replaced by $\ln (1/a) = -\ln a$. The result is Eq. (2).

To prove Eq. (3), let

$$y_1 = \ln x^n.$$

Then

$$\frac{dy_1}{dx} = \frac{1}{x^n} \cdot nx^{n-1} = \frac{n}{x} = \frac{d}{dx}(n \ln x).$$

Hence $y_1 = \ln x^n$ and $y_2 = n \ln x$ have equal derivatives, so they differ at most by a constant:

$$\ln x^n = n \ln x + C. \tag{7}$$

But by taking $x = 1$, and remembering that $\ln 1 = 0$, we find $C = 0$, which gives Eq. (3). In particular, if $n = 1/m$, where m is a positive integer, we have

$$\ln \sqrt[m]{x} = \ln x^{1/m} = \frac{1}{m} \ln x. \tag{8}$$

PROBLEMS

Express the following logarithms in terms of the two given logarithms $a = \ln 2$, $b = \ln 3$. [For example: $\ln 1.5 = \ln \frac{3}{2} = \ln 3 - \ln 2 = b - a$.]

4. $\ln 0.25$ **5.** $\ln \frac{4}{9}$ **6.** $\ln 12$

7. $\ln \frac{9}{8}$ **8.** $\ln 36$ **9.** $\ln 4.5$

1. $\ln 16$ **2.** $\ln \sqrt[3]{9}$ **3.** $\ln 2\sqrt{2}$ **10.** $\ln \sqrt{13.5}$

The slope of the curve

$$y = \ln x \tag{1}$$

is given by

$$\frac{dy}{dx} = \frac{1}{x}, \tag{2}$$

6–7

GRAPH OF $y = \ln x$

which is positive for all $x > 0$. Hence the graph of $y = \ln x$ steadily rises from left to right. Since the derivative is continuous, the function $\ln x$ is itself continuous, and the curve has a continuously turning tangent.

The second derivative,

$$\frac{d^2 y}{dx^2} = -\frac{1}{x^2}, \tag{3}$$

is always negative, so the curve (1) is everywhere concave downward.

The curve passes through the point $(1, 0)$, since $\ln 1 = 0$. At this point its slope is $+1$, so the tangent line at this point makes an angle of $45°$ with the x-axis (if we use equal units on the x- and y-axes).

If we refer to the definition of $\ln 2$ as an integral,

$$\ln 2 = \int_1^2 \frac{1}{t}\, dt,$$

we see that it may be interpreted as the area in Fig. 6–11 with $x = 2$. By considering the areas of rectangles of base 1 and altitudes 1 or $\frac{1}{2}$, respectively circumscribed over and inscribed under the given area, we see that

$$0.5 < \ln 2 < 1.0.$$

In fact, by more extensive calculations, the value of $\ln 2$ to 5 decimal places can be found to be

$$\ln 2 \approx 0.69315.$$

By Eq. (3) of Article 6–6 we have

$$\ln 4 = \ln 2^2 = 2 \ln 2 \approx 1.38630,$$

$$\ln 8 = \ln 2^3 = 3 \ln 2 \approx 2.07944,$$

$$\ln \tfrac{1}{2} = \ln 2^{-1} = -\ln 2 \approx -0.69315,$$

$$\ln \tfrac{1}{4} = \ln 2^{-2} = -2 \ln 2 \approx -1.38630,$$

and so on.

We now plot the points that correspond to $x = \frac{1}{4}, \frac{1}{2}, 1, 2, 4, 8$ on the curve $y = \ln x$ and connect them with a smooth curve. The curve we draw should have slope $1/x$ at the point of abscissa x and should everywhere be concave downward. The curve is shown in Fig. 6–13.

Since $\ln 2$ is greater than 0.5 and $\ln 2^n = n \ln 2$, it is clear that

$$\ln 2^n > 0.5n,$$

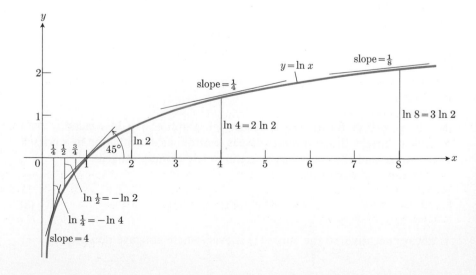

6–13　Graph of $y = \ln x$.

and hence $\ln x$ increases without limit as x does. That is,

$$\ln x \to +\infty \qquad \text{as} \quad x \to +\infty. \tag{4}$$

On the other hand, as x approaches zero through positive values, $1/x$ tends to plus infinity. Hence, taking Eq. (6) of Article 6–6 into account, we have

$$\ln x = -\ln \frac{1}{x} \to -\infty \qquad \text{as} \quad x \to 0^+. \tag{5}$$

Summary

The natural logarithm, $y = \ln x$, is a function with the following properties:

1. Its *domain* is the set of positive real numbers, $x > 0$.

2. Its *range* is the set of all real numbers, $-\infty < y < +\infty$.

3. It is a *continuous*, *increasing* function of x everywhere on its domain. If $x_1 > x_2 > 0$, then $\ln x_1 > \ln x_2$. It provides a one-to-one mapping from its domain to its range.

4. *Multiplication* of numbers in the domain corresponds to *addition* of numbers in the range. That is, if

$$x_1 > 0, \qquad y_1 = \ln x_1,$$
$$x_2 > 0, \qquad y_2 = \ln x_2,$$

then

$$x_1 x_2 > 0 \qquad \text{and} \qquad y_1 + y_2 = \ln (x_1 x_2).$$

5. The *derivative* of $y = \ln x$ is $dy/dx = 1/x$.

PROBLEMS

1. Take $\ln 3 = 1.09861$ as known. Plot the points corresponding to $x = \frac{1}{9}, \frac{1}{3}, 1, 3,$ and 9 on the curve $y = \ln x$. Also construct, through each of these points, a line segment tangent to the curve. Then sketch the curve itself. From the curve, read off $\ln 2$.

2. Let x_0 be the abscissa of the point $(x_0, 1)$ in which the line $y = 1$ intersects the curve $y = \ln x$. Show that the curve $y = x \ln x$ has a minimum at $[1/x_0, -(1/x_0)]$ and sketch the curve for $x > 0$. Does this curve possess a point of inflection? If so, find it (or them), and if not, state why not. (See Problem 5.)

3. Sketch the curve $x = \ln y$ for $y > 0$. What is its slope at the point (x, y)? Is it always concave upward, or downward, or does it have inflection points? Give reasons for your answers.

4. The curve $y = \ln x$ in Fig. 6–13 has the property that y becomes infinite when x does. But the ratio $(\ln x)/x$ approaches zero as x becomes infinite. Prove this latter statement by showing, first, that for $x > 1$

$$\ln x = \int_1^x \frac{1}{t}\, dt \leq \int_1^x \frac{1}{\sqrt{t}}\, dt = 2(\sqrt{x} - 1).$$

[*Hint.* Compare the areas under the curves $y_1 = 1/t$ and $y_2 = 1/\sqrt{t}$ for $1 \leq t \leq x$.]

5. From the result of Problem 4 that

$$\lim_{x \to +\infty} \frac{\ln x}{x} = 0,$$

deduce that $\lim_{x \to 0^+} x \ln x = 0$. [*Hint.* Let $x = 1/u$, $u \to +\infty$.]

6. Show that the curve

$$y = \ln x - (x - 1) + \tfrac{1}{2}(x - 1)^2$$

has a point of inflection and a horizontal tangent at $(1, 0)$. Sketch the curve for $0 < x < 2$. (Compare Problem 8, Article 6–4.)

7. Suppose you had a table of natural logarithms giving $\ln x$ for each $x > 0$. How could you use this to find $\log_{10} N$, where

$$\log_{10} N = b \quad \text{means} \quad N = 10^b?$$

In particular, find $\log_{10} 2$, given $\ln 2 = 0.69315$, $\ln 10 = 2.30259$.

6–8

THE EXPONENTIAL FUNCTION

In Article 6–7 we discussed and sketched the graph of the curve $y = \ln x$ (Fig. 6–13). We now make the observation that the curve $y = \ln x$ must cross the horizontal line $y = 1$ for some value of x between 2 and 4, since $\ln x$ is continuous and $\ln 2$ is less than 1 while $\ln 4$ is greater than 1. The value of x for which $\ln x = 1$ is denoted by the letter e. It is one of the most important numbers in mathematics. It satisfies the basic equation

$$\ln e = 1. \tag{1}$$

From our discussion above, it follows that e lies between 2 and 4. (In Chapter 16 we shall see how its value may be computed to any desired number of decimal places by using series.) Its value to 15 decimal places is

$$e = 2.7 \ 1828 \ 1828 \ 45 \ 90 \ 45 \ldots \tag{2}$$

By Eq. (3), Article 6–6, and Eq. (1) above, we have

$$\ln e^n = n \ln e = n \tag{3}$$

for any rational number n. Thus, for example, we have

$$\ln e^2 = 2, \qquad \ln e^3 = 3, \qquad \ln e^{-1} = -1, \qquad \ln \sqrt{e} = \tfrac{1}{2},$$

and so on. Since only one number can have its natural logarithm equal to n, for any given n, we may restate Eq. (3) by saying that the number whose natural logarithm is n is e^n; that is, the anti-natural-logarithm of n is e^n.

We now propose to study the antilogarithm, i.e., the *inverse of the logarithm*, as a function. To obtain this inverse function, we let

$$y = \text{Inverse natural logarithm of } x$$

or

$$x = \ln y. \tag{4}$$

The equation $x = \ln y$ defines a unique x for each positive real number y. Values of y greater than 1 correspond to x greater than zero; $y = 1$ to $x = 0$; $y < 1$ to $x < 0$. To each positive real number y there corresponds just one real number x such that $x = \ln y$. And conversely, to each real number x there corresponds just one positive real number y such that $x = \ln y$. The correspondence is one-to-one between the sets $y > 0$ and $-\infty < x < +\infty$, and hence it may be used to *define y as a function of x*, on the domain of all real numbers $-\infty < x < +\infty$. The *range* of this function is the set of all positive real numbers $y > 0$.

We have just seen (Eq. (3)) that $x = \ln y = n$ if and only if $y = e^n$, provided n is a rational number. That is, Eq. (4) is equivalent to the equation

$$y = e^x \tag{5}$$

for all rational values of x. We are therefore led to define e^x for all real values of x, irrational as well as rational, to be that number y whose natural logarithm is x:

$$y = e^x \qquad \text{if and only if} \qquad x = \ln y. \tag{6}$$

The resulting function is a continuous, single-valued function of x, defined for all real x, $-\infty < x < +\infty$. It is called the *exponential function*, with e as base and exponent x. *The exponential function is the inverse of the natural logarithm.* Its graph, Fig. 6–14 may be obtained by reflecting the curve in Fig. 6–13 across the 45° line $y = x$. Note, in particular, that $e^0 = 1$ since $\ln 1 = 0$.

To find the derivative of

$$y = e^x, \qquad (7)$$

we differentiate both sides of the equivalent equation

$$x = \ln y$$

implicitly with respect to x. Then

$$1 = \frac{1}{y}\frac{dy}{dx} \qquad \text{or} \qquad \frac{dy}{dx} = y. \qquad (8)$$

Taking account of Eq. (7), we therefore have

$$\frac{de^x}{dx} = e^x.$$

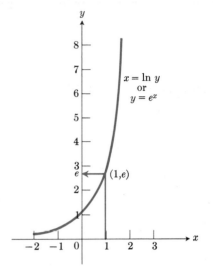

6–14　$y = e^x$ or $x = \ln y$.

Here is a function that is not changed by differentiation! It is indestructible. It can be differentiated again and again without changing. In this, the exponential function is like the story of a student who asked a guru what was holding up the earth. The answer was that the earth was upheld by an elephant, and the student naturally wanted to know what held up that elephant. The guru paused a moment, then replied "It's elephants all the way down."

In Fig. 6–15, the line QP through the points $Q(x - 1, 0)$ and $P(x, e^x)$ is tangent to the curve $y = e^x$ at P, for the slope of QP is $y/1$ and the slope of the curve, at P, is also equal to y, by Eq. (8).

We obtain a slightly more general formula for the derivative of e^u, where u is a differentiable function of x, by applying the chain rule

$$\frac{de^u}{dx} = \frac{de^u}{du}\frac{du}{dx} = e^u\frac{du}{dx}. \qquad \text{XX}$$

In terms of differentials, we have, from XX,

$$de^u = e^u\,du. \qquad \text{XX}'$$

This in turn leads to the integration formula

$$\int e^u\,du = e^u + C. \qquad (9)$$

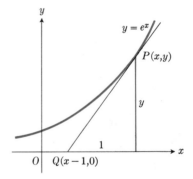

6–15　Line QP is tangent to the curve at P.

EXAMPLE 1.　Find dy/dx if $y = e^{\tan^{-1} x}$.

Solution

$$\frac{dy}{dx} = e^{\tan^{-1} x}\frac{d\,\tan^{-1} x}{dx}$$

$$= e^{\tan^{-1} x} \cdot \frac{1}{1 + x^2} \cdot \frac{dx}{dx}$$

$$= \frac{e^{\tan^{-1} x}}{1 + x^2}.$$

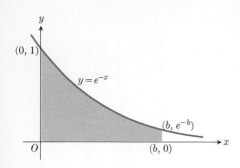

6-16   The shaded area is $1 - e^{-b}$.

EXAMPLE 2. Find the area under the curve $y = e^{-x}$ from $x = 0$ to $x = b(> 0)$ and show that this area *remains finite* as $b \to +\infty$. (See Fig. 6-16.)

Solution. The area from $x = 0$ to $x = b$ is given by

$$A_0^b = \int_0^b y \, dx = \int_0^b e^{-x} \, dx.$$

To evaluate this integral, we compare it with our standard forms and see that it is almost, but not exactly, like

$$\int e^u \, du = e^u + C.$$

To bring it into precisely this form, we let

$$u = -x, \qquad du = -dx,$$

or

$$dx = -du,$$

so that

$$\int e^{-x} \, dx = \int e^u(-du) = -\int e^u \, du = -e^u + C = -e^{-x} + C.$$

Therefore

$$A_0^b = -e^{-x}]_0^b = -e^{-b} + e^0 = 1 - e^{-b}.$$

From this we see that the number of square units of area in the shaded region of Fig. 6-16 is somewhat less than unity, for b large and positive, and moreover

$$\lim_{b \to +\infty} A_0^b = \lim_{b \to +\infty} (1 - e^{-b}) = 1,$$

since [see Eq. (11) below]

$$\lim_{b \to +\infty} e^{-b} = \lim_{b \to +\infty} \frac{1}{e^b} = 0.$$

Some properties of the function

$$y = e^x$$

are worthy of additional comment.

In the first place, the exponential function satisfies the law

$$e^{x_1} \cdot e^{x_2} = e^{x_1 + x_2}. \tag{10}$$

For, if

$$y_1 = e^{x_1} \qquad \text{and} \qquad y_2 = e^{x_2},$$

then, by definition,

$$x_1 = \ln y_1 \qquad \text{and} \qquad x_2 = \ln y_2,$$

so that

$$x_1 + x_2 = \ln y_1 + \ln y_2 = \ln y_1 y_2$$

by Eq. (1), Article 6–6. Therefore, by definition,

$$y_1 y_2 = e^{x_1 + x_2},$$

which establishes Eq. (10).

Again, we have

$$e^{-x} = \frac{1}{e^x} \qquad (11)$$

for any real number x. For, if

$$y = e^{-x}$$

then, by definition,

$$-x = \ln y$$

or, from Eq. (6), Article 6–6,

$$x = -\ln y = \ln \left(\frac{1}{y}\right).$$

Therefore

$$\frac{1}{y} = e^x \qquad \text{or} \qquad y = \frac{1}{e^x},$$

which establishes Eq. (11).

A table of e^x and e^{-x} is included at the end of the book for convenience and to give an appreciation of the rapid rate of increase of the exponential function for positive values of x. Many small calculators give $\ln x$ and e^x, as well as other elementary functions.

PROBLEMS

1. Simplify each of the following expressions:

a) $e^{\ln x}$ **b)** $\ln (e^x)$ **c)** $e^{-\ln (x^2)}$

d) $\ln (e^{-x^2})$ **e)** $\ln (e^{1/x})$ **f)** $\ln (1/e^x)$

g) $e^{\ln (1/x)}$ **h)** $e^{-\ln (1/x)}$ **i)** $e^{\ln 2 + \ln x}$

j) $e^{2 \ln x}$ **k)** $\ln (e^{x - x^2})$ **l)** $\ln (x^2 e^{-2x})$

m) $e^{x + \ln x}$ **n)** $e^{\ln x - 2 \ln y}$

Find dy/dx in each of the following problems (2 through 19).

2. $y = x^2 e^x$

3. $y = e^{2x}(2 \cos 3x + 3 \sin 3x)$

4. $y = \ln \dfrac{e^x}{1 + e^x}$ **5.** $y = \frac{1}{2}(e^x - e^{-x})$

6. $y = \frac{1}{2}(e^x + e^{-x})$ **7.** $y = \dfrac{e^x - e^{-x}}{e^x + e^{-x}}$

8. $y = e^{\sin^{-1} x}$ **9.** $y = (1 + 2x)e^{-2x}$

10. $y = (9x^2 - 6x + 2)e^{3x}$ **11.** $y = \dfrac{ax - 1}{a^2} e^{ax}$

12. $y = e^{-x^2}$ **13.** $y = x^2 e^{-x^2}$

14. $y = e^x \ln x$ **15.** $y = \tan^{-1} (e^x)$

16. $y = \sec^{-1} (e^{2x})$ **17.** $e^{2x} = \sin (x + 3y)$

18. $y = e^{1/x}$ **19.** $\tan y = e^x + \ln x$

20. (a) Show that $y = Ce^{ax}$ is a solution of the differential equation $dy/dx = ay$ for any choice of the constant C. (b) Using the result of (a), find a solution of the differential equation $dy/dt = -2y$ satisfying the initial condition $y = 3$ when $t = 0$.

21. Use l'Hôpital's rule to evaluate the following limits:

a) $\displaystyle\lim_{h \to 0} \dfrac{e^h - (1 + h)}{h^2}$ **b)** $\displaystyle\lim_{x \to \infty} \dfrac{e^x}{x^5}$

Evaluate the following integrals:

22. $\displaystyle\int e^{2x} \, dx$ **23.** $\displaystyle\int xe^{x^2} \, dx$ **24.** $\displaystyle\int e^{\sin x} \cos x \, dx$

25. $\displaystyle\int e^{x/3} \, dx$ **26.** $\displaystyle\int \dfrac{4 \, dx}{e^{3x}}$ **27.** $\displaystyle\int \dfrac{e^x \, dx}{1 + 2e^x}$

28. $\displaystyle\int_{e}^{e^2} \frac{dx}{x \ln x}$ **29.** $\displaystyle\int \frac{(e^x - e^{-x})\, dx}{(e^x + e^{-x})}$

30. $\displaystyle\int xe^x\, dx$ (See Example 4, Article 4–4.)

Sketch the graphs of the functions in Problems 31 through 34, taking extreme values and inflection points into account.

31. $y = x,\ y = e^x,$ and $y = \ln x$ (in a common graph)

32. $y = (\ln x)/x,\quad x > 0$ **33.** $y = (1 + t)e^{-t}$

34. $y = e^{-t} \cos t,\quad 0 \le t \le 2\pi$

35. The area between the curve $y = e^{-x}$ and the x-axis from $x = 1$ to $x = \ln 10$ is revolved about the x-axis. Find the volume thus swept out.

36. Find the length of the curve $x = e^t \sin t,\ y = e^t \cos t,$ $0 \le t \le \pi$.

37. If a particle moves along the x-axis so that its position at time t is given by $x = ae^{\omega t} + be^{-\omega t}$, where a, b, ω, are constants, show that it is repelled from the origin with a force proportional to the displacement. [Assume that force = mass × acceleration.]

Problems 38–41 deal with hyperbolic functions. These are treated in greater detail in Chapter 9.

Certain combinations of e^x and e^{-x} behave in some respects like the trigonometric functions (and quite unlike the trigonometric functions in other ways). The hyperbolic cosine of x, written $\cosh x$, and hyperbolic sine of x, written $\sinh x$, are defined by the relations:

$$\cosh x = \tfrac{1}{2}(e^x + e^{-x}), \qquad \sinh x = \tfrac{1}{2}(e^x - e^{-x}).$$

Using these definitions, prove the following:

38. $\displaystyle\frac{d}{dx}(\cosh x) = \sinh x, \qquad \frac{d}{dx}(\sinh x) = \cosh x$

39. $\cosh^2 x - \sinh^2 x = 1,\quad \cosh^2 x + \sinh^2 x = \cosh(2x)$

40. $\cosh(-x) = \cosh x,\quad \sinh(-x) = -\sinh x$

41. Using the tables of e^x and e^{-x} in the back of the book, sketch graphs of $y = \cosh x$ and $y = \sinh x$.

6–9

THE FUNCTION a^u

If a is any positive real number and

$$b = \ln a, \tag{1a}$$

then

$$a = e^b. \tag{1b}$$

The two equations (1a, b) may be combined to give the result

$$a = e^{\ln a}. \tag{2}$$

In words, ln a *is the power to which the base e may be raised to give a.*

Suppose we now raise both sides of Eq. (2) to the power u, where u is any real number. We would like to have the law of exponents

$$(e^{\ln a})^u = e^{u \ln a}$$

be true. Hence we now make the following *definition*:

$$a^u = e^{u \ln a}. \tag{3}$$

This definition is equivalent to saying that

$$\ln a^u = u \ln a, \tag{3'}$$

since both Eqs. (3) and (3′) say that $u \ln a$ is the power to which e may be raised to produce a^u. But (3′) is the same as Eq. (3), Article 6–6, in case $u = n$ is a rational number. What we are now considering is the case where u may be any real number, rational or irrational, $-\infty < u < +\infty$. Our new definition of a^u includes the old case but goes beyond and extends it.

Equation (3) is the basis for the algorithm used by some small calculators to compute y^x. Humans have no trouble computing $(-2)^3$, because we know that it is just $-(2^3)$, or -8. But suppose that we thought we should calculate the result using Eq. (3):

$$(-2)^3 = e^{3 \ln(-2)},$$

and we have learned that -2 is not in the domain of the function $\ln x$. We would do something similar to what the calculator does: flash a signal that signifies "error." The number a in Eq. (3) should be positive.

Derivative of a^u

We are ready to calculate the derivative of $y = a^u$ in case u is a differentiable function of x. We apply formula XX, Article 6–8, and, remembering that $\ln a$ is constant when a is, we obtain

$$\frac{da^u}{dx} = \frac{de^{u \ln a}}{dx}$$

$$= e^{u \ln a} \cdot \frac{du}{dx} \cdot \ln a,$$

$$\frac{da^u}{dx} = a^u \cdot \frac{du}{dx} \cdot \ln a. \tag{4}$$

This gives us a formula for the derivative of any positive constant a raised to a variable power. There is very little reason to memorize the result, since it may always be derived very quickly by the method of logarithmic differentiation, which will presently be discussed. It illustrates the fact that the base e is the most desirable one to encounter, since $\ln e = 1$ and Eq. (4) is the same as formula XX in case $a = e$. It also enables us to write down a formula for the integral of $a^u \, du$. For, if we multiply both sides of Eq. (4) by dx to change it to differential form,

$$da^u = \ln a \cdot a^u \, du,$$

and then divide by $\ln a$, provided $a \neq 1$, we see that

$$\int a^u \, du = \int \frac{1}{\ln a} da^u = \frac{a^u}{\ln a} + C, \qquad a > 0, \quad a \neq 1. \tag{5}$$

Logarithmic differentiation

The properties

a) $\ln uv = \ln u + \ln v$

b) $\ln \dfrac{u}{v} = \ln u - \ln v$

c) $\ln u^n = n \ln u$ $\tag{6}$

d) $\ln a^u = u \ln a$

can be used to advantage in calculating derivatives of products, quotients, roots, and powers, as illustrated in the examples that follow. The method, known as logarithmic differentiation, is to take the natural logarithm of both sides of an equation

$$y = f(x),$$

$$\ln y = \ln f(x),$$

simplify $\ln f(x)$ as much as possible by making use of the properties in Eq. (6), and then differentiate implicitly with respect to x:

$$\frac{d}{dx} \ln y = \frac{1}{y} \frac{dy}{dx}.$$

EXAMPLE 1. Find where the curves $y = x^2$ and $y = 2^x$ intersect.

Solution. (See Fig. 6–17.) It is easy to plot points on the two curves for

$$x = -3, \quad -2, \quad -1, \quad 0, \quad 1, \quad 2, \quad 3, \quad 4, \quad 5,$$

and then sketch a smooth curve for each of the two equations. The curves obviously intersect at $x = 2$ and 4. There is a third intersection between -1 and 0. To find it, we put $f(x) = 2^x - x^2$ and use Newton's method to locate a root of $f(x) = 0$. Recall that the general procedure is to make an initial guess (we shall put $x_1 = -1$), and then use the formula

$$x_{n+1} = x_n - \frac{f(x_n)}{f'(x_n)}$$

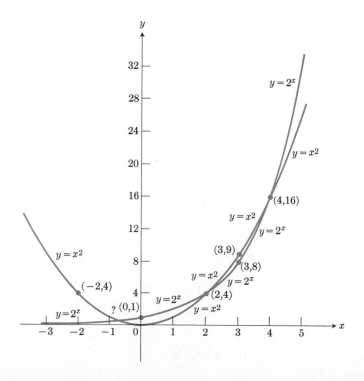

6–17   Where do the curves $y = x^2$ and $y = 2^x$ intersect? (At $x = 2$, $x = 4$, and $x = ?$.)

to get other approximations. For $f(x) = 2^x - x^2$ we get

$$x' = x - \frac{2^x - x^2}{2^x \ln 2 - 2x}$$

where, for simplicity of notation, we have written x' in place of x_{n+1} on the left and x in place of x_n on the right. The successive approximations are:

$x_1 = -1$

$x_2 = -0.7869$

$x_3 = -0.7668$

$x_4 = -0.7667$

$x_5 = -0.766665$

$x_6 = -0.76666470$

$x_7 = -0.766664696$ $x_7 = x_8$ $(x_7)^2 = 0.587774756$

$x_8 = -0.766664696$ $2^{x_7} = 0.587774756$

We continued the iterations until we got nine-decimal agreement. For accuracy to three decimals, $x = -0.767$, and we have the answer in three iterations.

EXAMPLE 2. If n is a real constant and u is a positive differentiable function of x, show that

$$\frac{du^n}{dx} = nu^{n-1}\frac{du}{dx}.$$

Solution. Let $y = u^n$. Then

$$\ln y = \ln u^n = n \ln u,$$

$$\frac{1}{y}\frac{dy}{dx} = n\frac{1}{u}\frac{du}{dx},$$

$$\frac{dy}{dx} = n\frac{y}{u}\frac{du}{dx} = n\frac{u^n}{u}\frac{du}{dx}$$

$$= nu^{n-1}\frac{du}{dx}. \qquad\qquad \text{Q.E.D.}$$

EXAMPLE 3. Find dy/dx if $y = x^x$, $x > 0$.

Solution. $\ln y = \ln x^x = x \ln x,$

$$\frac{1}{y}\frac{dy}{dx} = x \cdot \frac{1}{x} + \ln x = 1 + \ln x,$$

$$\frac{dy}{dx} = y(1 + \ln x) = x^x(1 + \ln x).$$

EXAMPLE 4. Find dy/dx if

$$y^{2/3} = \frac{(x^2 + 1)(3x + 4)^{1/2}}{\sqrt[5]{(2x - 3)(x^2 - 4)}}, \qquad (x > 2).$$

Solution

$$\ln y^{2/3} = \tfrac{2}{3} \ln y$$

$$= \ln (x^2 + 1) + \tfrac{1}{2} \ln (3x + 4) - \tfrac{1}{5} \ln (2x - 3) - \tfrac{1}{5} \ln (x^2 - 4) \quad \textbf{(a)}$$

and

$$\frac{2}{3} \cdot \frac{1}{y} \frac{dy}{dx} = \frac{2x}{x^2 + 1} + \frac{1}{2} \cdot \frac{3}{3x + 4} - \frac{1}{5} \cdot \frac{2}{2x - 3} - \frac{1}{5} \cdot \frac{2x}{x^2 - 4},$$

so that

$$\frac{dy}{dx} = \frac{3y}{2} \left[\frac{2x}{x^2 + 1} + \frac{\frac{3}{2}}{3x + 4} - \frac{\frac{2}{5}}{2x - 3} - \frac{2x/5}{x^2 - 4} \right].$$

REMARK. The restriction $x > 2$ ensures that all the quantities whose logarithms are indicated in (a) above are positive. If we want dy/dx at a point where y is negative, we may multiply our equation by -1 before taking logarithms; for if y is negative, then $-y$ is positive and $\ln (-y)$ is defined.

EXAMPLE 5 *Point elasticity of total cost.* Economists define the ratio of marginal cost to average cost as the point elasticity of total cost. That is, if the total cost of producing x units of a given product is $y = f(x)$ dollars, then the "average cost" is y/x dollars per unit. The "marginal cost," which is, roughly speaking, the additional cost of producing one more unit, is dy/dx. Then, by definition,

$$\text{Point elasticity of total cost} = \frac{dy/dx}{y/x} = \frac{dy/y}{dx/x} = \frac{d(\ln y)}{d(\ln x)}.$$

When the point elasticity of total cost equals one, then marginal cost equals average cost (that is, $dy/dx = y/x$) and average cost has a stationary value (that is, $d(y/x)/dx = 0$). [For further discussion, see Alpha C. Chiang, *Fundamental Methods of Mathematical Economics*, Second edition, McGraw-Hill Book Company, 1974, pp. 202ff.]

PROBLEMS

Use the method of logarithmic differentiation to find dy/dx in each of the following problems (1 through 8).

1. $y^2 = x(x + 1) \quad (x > 0)$ **2.** $y = \sqrt[3]{\dfrac{x + 1}{x - 1}} \quad (x > 1)$

3. $y = \dfrac{x\sqrt{x^2 + 1}}{(x + 1)^{2/3}} \quad (x > 0)$

4. $y = \sqrt[3]{\dfrac{x(x + 1)(x - 2)}{(x^2 + 1)(2x + 3)}} \quad (x > 2)$

5. $y = x^{\sin x} \quad (x > 0)$ **6.** $y = (\sin x)^{\tan x} \quad (\sin x > 0)$

7. $y = 2^{\sec x}$ **8.** $y = x^{\ln x} \quad (x > 0)$

9. Show that $(ab)^u = a^u b^u$ if a and b are any positive numbers and u is any real number.

10. Show that the derivative of average cost is zero when marginal cost and average cost are equal.

Evaluate the following integrals (11–15):

11. $\displaystyle\int_0^{\ln 2} e^{-2x} \, dx$ **12.** $\displaystyle\int_0^{1.2} 3^x \, dx$

13. $\displaystyle\int_1^{\sqrt{2}} x2^{-x^2}\,dx$ **14.** $\displaystyle\int_0^1 5^{2t-2}\,dt$

15. $\displaystyle\int_0^{\pi/6} (\cos\theta)4^{-\sin\theta}\,d\theta$

16. Let a be a number greater than one. Prove that the graph of $y = a^x$ has the following characteristics:

a) If $x_1 > x_2$, then $a^{x_1} > a^{x_2}$.

b) The graph is everywhere concave upward.

c) The graph lies entirely above the x-axis.

d) The slope at any point is proportional to the ordinate there, and the proportionality factor is the slope at the y-intercept of the graph.

e) The curve approaches the negative x-axis as $x \to -\infty$.

17. Suppose that a and b are positive numbers such that $a^b = b^a$. (For example, $2^4 = 4^2$.)

a) Show that $(\ln a)/a = (\ln b)/b$.

b) Show that the graph of the function $f(x) = (\ln x)/x$ has a maximum at $x = e$, a point of inflection at $x = e^{3/2}$, approaches minus infinity as x approaches zero through positive values, and approaches zero as x approaches plus infinity. Sketch its graph.

c) Use the results of parts (a) and (b) to show that:

  i) If $0 < a \le 1$ and $a^b = b^a$ then $b = a$, and

  ii) If $1 < a < e$, or if $a > e$, then there is exactly one number $b \ne a$ such that $a^b = b^a$.

18. In Example 1, we found three zeros for the function $f(x) = 2^x - x^2$. Might there be others? One way to find out is to study the derived function $f'(x)$ to see how many zeros it has.

a) Show that each zero of $f'(x)$ corresponds to an intersection of the graphs of $y = 2^x \ln 2$ and $y = 2x$. Further, show that the first of these is everywhere concave upward while the second is a straight line. Sketch their graphs.

b) From the analysis of part (a), what can you conclude about the number of zeros of $f'(x)$? Of $f(x)$?

c) (*Calculator*) If you have a calculator that can easily evaluate $2^x \ln 2$ and $2^x(\ln 2)^2$, find the zeros of $f'(x)$ to three-decimal accuracy. Compare your answers with what you might expect from Fig. 6–17.

19. For what positive values of x does $x^{(x^x)} = (x^x)^x$?

We know that $\ln u$ is the power to which e may be raised to give u. For that reason, we say that e is the base of the system of natural logarithms in keeping with the following definition.

THE FUNCTION $\log_a u$

Definition.   *If u is positive and a is a positive number different from 1, we say that y is the logarithm of u to the base a, and write*

$$y = \log_a u, \tag{1a}$$

provided y is the power to which a may be raised to give u:

$$a^y = u. \tag{1b}$$

For example,

$$\log_5 25 = 2 \qquad \text{since} \qquad 5^2 = 25,$$

$$\log_2 \tfrac{1}{4} = -2 \qquad \text{since} \qquad 2^{-2} = \tfrac{1}{4}.$$

To find $x = \log_4 8$, we rewrite the equation as

$$4^x = 2^{2x} = 8 = 2^3,$$

from which we read $2x = 3$, $x = \tfrac{3}{2}$. In other words,

$$\log_4 8 = \tfrac{3}{2} \qquad \text{since} \qquad 4^{3/2} = (\sqrt{4})^3 = 8.$$

We may solve Eq. (1b) for y, and thereby obtain an expression for $\log_a u$, by taking natural logarithms and applying Eq. (3′) of Article 6–9:

$$\ln u = \ln a^y = y \ln a.$$

If $\ln a \ne 0$ (which is the case when a is different from 1), we may solve for y.

The result is that

$$y = \frac{\ln u}{\ln a}$$

is the power to which a may be raised to produce u. In other words,

$$\log_a u = \frac{\ln u}{\ln a}. \tag{2}$$

Properties of $\log_a u$

The following properties follow readily from Eq. (2) above and the analogous properties of $\ln u$.

$$\textbf{a)} \ \log_a uv = \log_a u + \log_a v$$

$$\textbf{b)} \ \log_a \frac{u}{v} = \log_a u - \log_a v \tag{3}$$

$$\textbf{c)} \ \log_a u^v = v \log_a u$$

Equation (3c), for example, is derived as follows:

$$\log_a u^v = \frac{\ln u^v}{\ln a} = \frac{v \ln u}{\ln a} = v \log_a u,$$

where we make use of Eq. (2), then Eq. (3′) of Article 6–9, and then Eq. (2) again.

If u is a differentiable positive function of x, we may differentiate both sides of Eq. (2) and thus obtain

$$\frac{d \log_a u}{dx} = \frac{1}{u \ln a} \frac{du}{dx}. \tag{4}$$

It is clear that this formula is simpler for logarithms to the base e than for any other base. The only bases of practical importance are $a = e$ (natural logarithms) and $a = 10$ (common logarithms). Since $\ln 10 = 2.30259 \ldots$, Eq. (4) is certainly less attractive for the case $a = 10$ than it is for the case $a = e$. This is the primary reason why natural logarithms are to be preferred over common logarithms in applications of the calculus.

Common logarithms are often used in scientific formulas. For example, earthquake intensity is reported on the Richter scale. Here the formula is

$$m = \log\left(\frac{a}{T}\right) + B, \tag{5}$$

where a is the amplitude of the ground motion in microns at the receiving station, T is the period of the seismic wave in seconds, and B is an empirical factor that allows for weakening of the seismic wave with increasing distance from the epicenter of the earthquake. Other familiar examples include the measurement of noise in decibels and acidity in pH values.

If y is any function of x of the general form

$$y = A \cdot C^x, \tag{6}$$

the range of values of y may be very large, especially if C is large compared to one. To compensate for such a large spread of the values of y, we can take logarithms to any base. If the base is 10, we get

$$\log y = \log A + x \log C, \qquad (7)$$

so that the graph of $\log y$ as a function of x is a straight line with slope $\log C$ and with intercept $(0, \log A)$. A change of one unit in $\log y$ corresponds to multiplying or dividing y by a factor of 10.

PROBLEMS

Determine the following logarithms:

1. a) $\log_4 16$ **b)** $\log_8 32$
   c) $\log_5 0.04$ **d)** $\log_{0.5} 4$

2. a) $\log_2 4$ **b)** $\log_4 2$
   c) $\log_8 16$ **d)** $\log_{32} 4$

3. Find x if $3^x = 2^{x+1}$.

4. Find x if $3^{\log_3 7} + 2^{\log_2 5} = 5^{\log_5 x}$.

5. Show that $\log_b u = \log_a u \cdot \log_b a$ if $a, b,$ and u are positive numbers, $a \neq 1, b \neq 1$.

6. Given $\ln 2 = 0.69315$, $\ln 10 = 2.30259$, and $\log_{10} 2 = 0.30103$. Find:

a) $\log_{10} 20$, $\log_{10} 200$, $\log_{10} 0.2$, $\log_{10} 0.02$;
b) $\ln 20$, $\ln 200$, $\ln 0.2$, $\ln 0.02$.

7. Which function is changing faster at $x = 10$,

$$f_1(x) = \ln x \qquad \text{or} \qquad f_2(x) = \log_2 x?$$

8. Stirling's formula says that, if n is large, then

$$n! \sim \sqrt{2\pi}\, n^{n+(1/2)} e^{-n}.$$

For what value of the constant m can we replace e^{-n} by 10^{-mn} in the formula?

9. Find the derivatives of the following:

a) $y = 3^{\tan x}$ **b)** $y = (x^2 + 1)^{\ln x}$
c) $s = 2^{-t^2}$ **d)** $r = \theta e^{-2\theta}$

We are all familiar with arithmetic progressions and geometric progressions. In an arithmetic progression

$$a, \quad a + b, \quad a + 2b, \quad a + 3b, \quad \ldots$$

each term is a fixed amount more (or less) than the term before it. In a geometric progression

$$a, \quad ar, \quad ar^2, \quad ar^3, \quad \ldots$$

each term is a fixed *multiple* of the term before it. The way money on deposit in a savings account grows is like a geometric progression. For example, if a bank pays 6 percent annual interest and compounds interest quarterly, an amount A at the start of an interest period receives an additional

$$\frac{0.06}{4} A = \frac{r}{4} A \qquad (r = 0.06)$$

at the end of the interest period. Because the interest is added to the original amount A, the amount at the end of the period is

$$A + \frac{r}{4} A = \left(1 + \frac{r}{4}\right) A,$$

6–11

COMPOUND INTEREST AND EXPONENTIAL GROWTH

and the amounts at the ends of successive interest periods form a geometric progression

$$A, \quad \left(1 + \frac{r}{4}\right)A, \quad \left(1 + \frac{r}{4}\right)^2 A, \quad \ldots, \quad \left(1 + \frac{r}{4}\right)^n A.$$

In particular, at the end of t years the number of interest periods is $n = 4t$ and the amount is

$$A_t = \left(1 + \frac{r}{4}\right)^{4t} A_0 \qquad (t = \text{an integer}), \qquad (1)$$

where A_0 is the original amount.

EXAMPLE 1. A bank agrees to pay 6 percent interest compounded quarterly for the next eight years. How much should you deposit now in order to have \$1000 in the account eight years from now?

Solution. We put $A_8 = 1000$ in Eq. (1), with $r = 0.06$ and $t = 8$:

$$1000 = A_0(1.015)^{32}$$

and solve for A_0:

$$A_0 = 1000(1.015)^{-32} = 620.9929 \quad \text{(to four decimals)}.$$

Thus a deposit of \$621 would yield \$1000 in eight years if the interest is 6 percent compounded quarterly.

More generally, suppose the rate r per year is fixed, but the number of compounding periods per year is k. Then Eq. (1) becomes

$$A_t = A_0 \left(1 + \frac{r}{k}\right)^{kt} = A_0 \left[\left(1 + \frac{r}{k}\right)^k\right]^t. \qquad (2)$$

The expression

$$f(k) = \left(1 + \frac{r}{k}\right)^k \qquad (3)$$

has a limit as k increases without bound. To find what that limit is, we take the natural logarithm

$$\ln f(k) = k \ln \left(1 + \frac{r}{k}\right) \qquad (4)$$

and then put

$$\frac{r}{k} = h, \quad \text{so} \quad k = \frac{r}{h}$$

and

$$\ln f(k) = \frac{r}{h} \ln (1 + h) = r \frac{\ln (1 + h)}{h}. \qquad (4')$$

As k increases without bound, h approaches zero through positive values and, by l'Hôpital's rule,

$$\lim_{h \to 0+} \frac{\ln (1 + h)}{h} = \lim_{h \to 0+} \frac{1}{1 + h} = 1.$$

Hence, $\ln f(k)$ in Eq. (4') has the limit r as k approaches infinity and $f(k)$ has the limit e^r. Thus, from Eq. (2), as k increases without bound, we get

$$\lim A_t = A_0 e^{rt}. \tag{5}$$

REMARK 1.   When we took the limit as k increases without bound in Eq. (2) above, we went to the extreme of compounding the interest continuously. The result is the function

$$A(t) = A_0 e^{rt}. \tag{6}$$

In this relation, we need not restrict t to be an integer—it can be any real number greater than or equal to zero. The derivative of this function is

$$\frac{dA}{dt} = rA_0 e^{rt} = rA. \tag{7}$$

If we rewrite Eq. (7) in differential form, we get

$$dA = rA \, dt = A(r \, dt). \tag{7'}$$

This equation can be interpreted as the increase that would be added to A during a very short interval of time from t to $t + dt$. The increase is jointly proportional to the amount A at time t and to the annual interest rate r multiplied by dt, which we can interpret as a very small fraction of a year.

REMARK 2.   There are many physical, biological, ecological, and economic phenomena in which some quantity x grows, or declines, at a rate that is proportional to the amount that is present at time t. This is expressed by the differential equation

$$\frac{dx}{dt} = kx. \tag{8}$$

If we know the value of x at some instant of time, we take that as $t = 0$ and use the initial condition

$$x = x_0 \qquad \text{when} \quad t = 0 \tag{9}$$

to determine x as a function of t.

The general solution of the differential equation

$$\frac{dx}{dt} = kx \qquad \text{with } x = x_0 \text{ when } t = 0$$

is

$$x = x_0 e^{kt}. \tag{10}$$

Positive values of k correspond to exponential growth; negative values correspond to decrease. For example, if a body of water has become polluted with some substance but the polluting source has been stopped and fresh water is being continuously introduced with thorough mixing, then we can expect the rate of decrease of the amount of the pollutant in the water to be proportional to the amount still remaining. Equation (10), with an appropriate negative value of k, would then describe the amount of pollutant at time t after the cleanup had begun.

EXAMPLE 2. Suppose \$621 is deposited in an account with interest at the rate of 6 percent and the interest is compounded continuously for eight years. Find the amount at the time $t = 8$.

Solution. The phrase "compounded continuously" corresponds mathematically to the limit we got in Eq. (5) as $k \to \infty$. Thus, we put $r = 0.06$, $t = 8$, and $A_0 = 621$, to obtain the answer

$$A_8 = 621e^{0.48} = 1003.5822 \quad \text{(to four decimals)}.$$

The effect of continuous compounding, as compared with quarterly, has been an addition of \$3.58. A bank might decide it would be worth this additional amount to be able to advertise "we compound your money every second, night and day—better than that, we compound the interest continuously."

EXAMPLE 3. Suppose that the amount of substance x follows the exponential law of Eq. (10). If x decreases by 10 percent in 18 months, how long will it be until x is less than $0.005x_0$?

Solution. Let t be measured in months and put $x = 0.9x_0$ and $t = 18$ in Eq. (10). Thus,

$$0.9x_0 = x_0 e^{18k}, \qquad 18k = \ln 0.9 = -0.1054, \qquad k = -0.0059.$$

With k known, we now substitute $x = 0.005x_0$ and solve for t:

$$0.005x_0 = x_0 e^{kt}, \qquad kt = \ln 0.005, \qquad t = \frac{\ln 0.005}{k} = \frac{-5.2983}{-0.0059},$$

or $t = 906$ months, or about 75.5 years. The 75 years is 50 times 18 months: Each 18 months corresponds to multiplying by 0.90, and $(0.90)^{50}$ is approximately 0.005.

Benjamin Franklin's Will. The Franklin Technical Institute of Boston owes its existence to a codicil to the will of Benjamin Franklin. In part, that codicil reads:

> I was born in Boston, New England and owe my first instruction in Literature to the free Grammar Schools established there: I have therefore already considered those schools in my Will.... I have considered that among Artisans good Apprentices are most likely to make good citizens ... I wish to be useful even after my Death, if possible, in forming and advancing other young men that may be serviceable to their Country in both Boston and Philadelphia. To this end I devote Two

thousand Pounds Sterling, which I give, one thousand thereof to the Inhabitants of the Town of Boston in Massachusetts, and the other thousand to the inhabitants of the City of Philadelphia, in Trust and for the Uses, Interests and Purposes hereinafter mentioned and declared.

Franklin's plan was to lend money to young apprentices at 5 percent interest with the provision that each borrower should pay each year "with the yearly Interest, one tenth part of the Principal, which sums of Principal and Interest shall be again let to fresh Borrowers.

"If this plan is executed and succeeds as projected without interruption for one hundred Years, the Sum will then be one hundred and thirty-one thousand Pounds of which I would have the Managers of the Donation to the Inhabitants of the Town of Boston, then lay out at their discretion one hundred thousand Pounds in Public Works.... The remaining thirty-one thousand Pounds, I would have continued to be let out on Interest in the manner above directed for another hundred Years.... At the end of this second term if no unfortunate accident has prevented the operation the sum will be Four Millions and Sixty-one Thousand Pounds."

It was not always possible to find as many borrowers as Franklin had planned, but the managers of the trust did the best they could; they lent money to medical students as well as others. At the end of one hundred years from the reception of the Franklin gift, January, 1894, the fund had grown from one thousand pounds to almost exactly ninety thousand pounds. In one hundred years the original capital had multiplied about ninety times instead of the one hundred and thirty-one times Franklin had anticipated.

QUESTION. What rate of interest, compounded continuously for one hundred years, would multiply the original capital by 90?

The mathematical model we assume is that which is expressed by the equation

$$A = A_0 e^{rt},$$

where A_0 is the original capital, r is the interest rate per year (but compounded continuously), and t is the time in years. If we put $t = 100$ and $A = 90A_0$, we get

$$90A_0 = A_0 e^{100r},$$

which leads to

$$100r = \ln 90 = 4.50$$

or

$$r = 0.045 \quad \text{or} \quad 4.5 \text{ percent.}$$

PROBLEMS

1. Suppose that the GNP in a country is increasing at an annual rate of 4 percent. How many years, at that rate of growth, are required in order to double the present GNP?

2. In Benjamin Franklin's estimate that the original one thousand pounds would grow to 131 thousand in 100 years,

he was using an annual rate of 5 percent and compounding once each year. What rate of interest per year when compounded continuously for 100 years would produce such a result as to multiply the original amount by 131?

3. If you use the approximation $\ln 2 \approx 0.70$ (in place of

0.69315...), you can derive a rule of thumb that says "If a quantity grows at the rate of 5 percent per year compounded continuously over the next 70 years, then it will double in about $\frac{70}{5} = 14$ years, so it will be multiplied by $2^5 = 32$ during the 70-year span. If the annual rate is r percent, it will be multiplied by about 2^r during a life span of 70 years." Show how this is derived.

4. Suppose a body of mass m moving in a straight line with velocity v encounters a resistance proportional to the velocity and this is the only force acting on the body. If the body starts with velocity v_0, how far does it travel in time t? Assume $F = d(mv)/dt$.

5. A radioactive substance disintegrates at a rate propor-

tional to the amount present. How much of the substance remains at time t if the initial amount is Q_0?

6. If the bacteria in a culture increase continuously at a rate proportional to the number present, and the initial number is N_0, find the number at time t.

In Problems 7–10, substitute $y = e^{rx}$ and find values of the constant r for which $y = e^{rx}$ is a solution of the given differential equation.

7. $\dfrac{d^2y}{dx^2} - 4\dfrac{dy}{dx} + 3y = 0$ **8.** $\dfrac{d^2y}{dx^2} - \dfrac{dy}{dx} - 2y = 0$

9. $\dfrac{d^3y}{dx^3} + 6\dfrac{d^2y}{dx^2} + 5\dfrac{dy}{dx} = 0$ **10.** $\dfrac{d^4y}{dx^4} - 13\dfrac{d^2y}{dx^2} + 36y = 0$

REVIEW QUESTIONS AND EXERCISES

1. Review the formulas for derivatives of sums, products, quotients, powers, sines, and cosines. Using these, develop formulas for derivatives of the other trigonometric functions.

2. Define the inverse sine, inverse cosine, inverse tangent, and inverse secant functions. What is the *domain* of each? What is its *range*? What is the derivative of each? Sketch the graph of each.

3. Define the natural logarithm function. What is its domain? What is its range? What is its derivative? Sketch its graph.

4. What is the inverse function of the natural logarithm called? What is the domain of this function? What is its range? What is its derivative? Sketch its graph.

5. Define the term "algebraic function." Define "transcendental function." To which class (algebraic or transcendental) do you think the greatest integer function (Fig. 1–45) belongs?

[It is often difficult to prove that a particular function belongs to one class or the other. Numbers are also classified as algebraic and transcendental. *References:* (1) W. J. Le Veque, *Topics in Number Theory*, Addison-Wesley, Vol. II, Chap. 5, pp. 161–200; (2) I. M. Niven, *Irrational Numbers*, Carus monograph number 11 of the Mathematical Association of America, (1956). Both π and e are transcendental numbers, and proofs may be found in the references cited.

That π is transcendental was first proved by Ferdinand Lindemann in 1882. One result that follows from the transcendence of π is that it is impossible to construct, with unmarked straightedge and compass alone, a square whose area is equal to the area of a given circle. The first proof that e is transcendental was published by Charles Hermite in 1873. You may also enjoy reading about an interesting related feature of the graph of $y = \ln x$ in the article on logarithms on p. 301 of Vol. 14 of the *Encyclopedia Britannica* (1956 edition).]

6. Let n be an integer greater than 1. Divide the interval $1 \le x \le n$ into n equal subintervals and write an expression for the trapezoidal approximation to the area under the graph of $y = 1/x$, $1 \le x \le n$, based on this subdivision. Is this approximation less than, equal to, or greater than $\ln n$? Give a reason for your answer.

7. Prove that $\lim_{x \to \infty} (\ln x)/x = 0$, starting with the definition of $\ln x$ as an integral.

8. The *Encyclopedia Britannica* article on logarithms begins with the statement: "By shortening processes of computation, logarithms have doubled the working speed of astronomers and engineers." What property or properties of logarithms do you think the author of the article had in mind when he made that statement?

9. What is the meaning of the differential equation $dy/dt = ky$? What is the solution of this equation that satisfies the initial condition $y = y_0$ when $t = 0$?

MISCELLANEOUS PROBLEMS

In each of the following problems (1 through 25), (a) find dy/dx, and (b) sketch the curve.

1. $y = \sin 2x$

2. $y = 4 \cos (2x + \pi/4)$

3. $y = 2 \sin x + \sin 2x$

4. $y = \dfrac{\sin x}{1 + \cos x}$

5. $x = \cos y$

6. $x = \tan y$

7. $y = 4 \sin \left(\dfrac{x}{2} + \pi\right)$

8. $y = 1 - \sin x$

9. $y = x - \sin x$

10. $y = \dfrac{\sin x}{x}$ (What happens as $x \to 0$? As $x \to \infty$?)

11. $y = \dfrac{\sin x}{x^2}$ (What happens as $x \to 0$? As $x \to \infty$?)

12. $y = x \sin \dfrac{1}{x}$ (What happens as $x \to \infty$? As $x \to 0$?)

13. $y = x^2 \sin \dfrac{1}{x}$ (What happens as $x \to \infty$? As $x \to 0$?)

14. $x = \tan \dfrac{\pi y}{2}$ **15.** $y = \dfrac{e^x - e^{-x}}{e^x + e^{-x}}$

16. $y = xe^{-x}$

17. a) $y = x \ln x$,   **b)** $y = \sqrt{x} \ln x$

18. a) $y = \dfrac{\ln x}{x}$,   **b)** $y = \dfrac{\ln x}{\sqrt{x}}$,   **c)** $y = \dfrac{\ln x}{x^2}$

19. $y = e^{-x} \sin 2x$

20. a) $y = 2x - \frac{1}{2}e^{2x}$,   **b)** $y = e^{[2x - (1/2)e^{2x}]}$

21. a) $y = x - e^x$,   **b)** $y = e^{(x - e^x)}$

22. $y = \ln (x + \sqrt{x^2 + 1})$ **23.** $y = \frac{1}{2} \ln \dfrac{1 + x}{1 - x}$

24. $y = \ln (x^2 + 4)$ **25.** $y = x \tan^{-1} \dfrac{x}{2}$

Find dy/dx in Problems 26–42.

26. $y = \dfrac{e^{2x} - e^{-2x}}{e^{2x} + e^{-2x}}$ **27.** $y = \ln \dfrac{\sec x + \tan x}{\sec x - \tan x}$

28. $y = x^2 e^{2x} \sin 3x$ **29.** $y = \sin^{-1}(x^2) - xe^{x^2}$

30. $y = \ln \left(\dfrac{x^4}{1 + x^3} \right) + 7^{x^{2/3}}$ **31.** $y = (x^2 + 2)^{2 - x}$

32. $y = \dfrac{\ln x}{e^x}$ **33.** $y = \ln \dfrac{x}{\sqrt{x^2 + 1}}$

34. $y = \ln (4 - 3x)$ **35.** $y = \ln (3x^2 + 4x)$

36. $y = x(\ln x)^3$ **37.** $y = x \ln (x^3)$

38. $y = x^3 \ln x$ **39.** $y = \ln e^x$

40. $y = x^2 e^x$ **41.** $x = \ln y$

42. $y = \ln (\ln x)$

43. Find dy/dx by logarithmic differentiation for

a) $y = \dfrac{x}{x^2 + 1}$, $x > 0$;   **b)** $y = \sqrt[3]{\dfrac{x(x - 2)}{x^2 + 1}}$, $x > 2$.

44. If $f(x) = x + e^{4x}$, find $f(0)$ and $f'(0)$, and find an approximation for $f(0.01)$.

45. Find dy/dx for each of the following:

a) $y = a^{x^2 - x}$,   **b)** $y = \ln \dfrac{e^x}{1 + e^x}$,

c) $y = x \ln x - x$ **d)** $y = x^{1/x}$.

46. Sketch the graphs of $y = \ln (1 - x)$ and $y = \ln (1/x)$.

47. Sketch (in a common figure) the graphs of $y = e^{-x}$ and $y = -e^{-x}$.

48. Solve for x: $\tan^{-1} x - \cot^{-1} x = \pi/4$.

49. If $\dfrac{dy}{dx} = \dfrac{e^x - e^{-x}}{e^x + e^{-x}}$,   find $\dfrac{d^2y}{dx^2}$ and y.

50. If $dy/dx = 2/e^y$ and $y = 0$ when $x = 5$, find y as a function of x.

51. $P(x_1, y_1)$ and $Q(x_2, y_2)$ are any two points (in the first quadrant) lying on the hyperbola $xy = R$ (R positive). Show that the area bounded by the arc PQ, the lines $x = x_1$, $x = x_2$, and the x-axis is equal to the area bounded by the arc PQ, the lines $y = y_1$, $y = y_2$, and the y-axis.

52. By the trapezoidal rule, find $\int_0^2 e^{-x^2}\, dx$, using $n = 4$.

53. In a capacitor discharging electricity, the rate of change of the voltage in volts per second is proportional to the voltage, being numerically equal to minus one-fortieth of the voltage. Express the voltage as a function of the time. In how many seconds will the voltage decrease to 10 percent of its original value?

54. A curve $y = f(x)$ goes through the points $(0, 0)$ and (x_1, y_1). It divides the rectangle $0 \le x \le x_1, 0 \le y \le y_1$ into two regions: A above the curve and B below. Find the curve if the area of A is twice the area of B for all choices of $x_1 > 0$ and $y_1 > 0$.

55. Find a curve passing through the origin and such that the length s of the curve between the origin and any point (x, y) of the curve is given by

$$s = e^x + y - 1.$$

56. A particle starts at the origin and moves along the x-axis in such a way that its velocity at the point $(x, 0)$ is given by the formula $dx/dt = \cos^2 \pi x$. How long will it take to cover the distance from the origin to the point $x = \frac{1}{4}$? Will it ever reach the point $x = \frac{1}{2}$? Why?

57. A particle moves in a straight line with acceleration $a = 4/(4 - t)^2$. If when $t = 0$ the velocity is equal to 2, find how far the particle moves between $t = 1$ and $t = 2$.

58. The velocity of a certain particle moving along the x-axis is proportional to x. At time $t = 0$ the particle is located at $x = 2$ and at time $t = 10$ it is at $x = 4$. Find its position at $t = 5$.

59. Solve the differential equation $dy/dx = y^2 e^{-x}$ if $y = 2$ when $x = 0$.

60. It is estimated that the population of a certain country is now increasing at a rate of 2 percent per year. Assuming that this (instantaneous) rate will continue indefinitely, estimate what the population N will be t years from now, if the population now is N_0. How many years will it take for the population to double?

61. If $y = (e^{2x} - 1)/(e^{2x} + 1)$, show that $dy/dx = 1 - y^2$.

62. Determine the inflection points of the curve $y = e^{-(x/a)^2}$, where a is a positive constant. Sketch the curve. (This is closely related to the normal curve used in statistics.)

63. Find the volume generated when the area bounded by $x = \sec y$, $x = 0$, $y = 0$, $y = \pi/3$, is rotated about the y-axis.

64. Find the length of the curve

$$\frac{x}{a} = \left(\frac{y}{b}\right)^2 - \frac{1}{8}\left(\frac{b^2}{a^2}\right)\ln\left(\frac{y}{b}\right)$$

from $y = b$ to $y = 3b$, assuming a and b to be positive constants.

65. Find the volume generated by rotating about the x-axis the area bounded by $y = e^x$, $y = 0$, $x = 0$, $x = 2$.

66. Find the area bounded by the curve

$$y = \left(\frac{a}{2}\right)(e^{x/a} + e^{-x/a}),$$

the x-axis, and the lines $x = -a$ and $x = +a$.

67. The portion of a tangent to a curve included between the x-axis and the point of tangency is bisected by the y-axis. If the curve passes through $(1, 2)$, find its equation.

Evaluate the integrals in Problems 68–78.

68. $\displaystyle\int \frac{dx}{4 - 3x}$

69. $\displaystyle\int \frac{5\,dx}{x - 3}$

70. $\displaystyle\int_0^2 \frac{x\,dx}{x^2 + 2}$

71. $\displaystyle\int_0^2 \frac{x\,dx}{(x^2 + 2)^2}$

72. $\displaystyle\int \frac{x + 1}{x}\,dx$

73. $\displaystyle\int \frac{x}{2x + 1}\,dx$

74. $\displaystyle\int_0^1 \frac{x^2\,dx}{2 - x^3}$

75. $\displaystyle\int_0^3 x(e^{x^2 - 1})\,dx$

76. $\displaystyle\int_1^3 \frac{dx}{x}$

77. $\displaystyle\int_0^5 \frac{x\,dx}{x^2 + 1}$

78. $\displaystyle\int_0^1 (e^x + 1)\,dx$

79. In the inversion of raw sugar, the time rate of change of the amount of raw sugar present varies as the amount of raw sugar remaining. If 1000 lb of raw sugar has been reduced to 800 lb after 10 hr, how much raw sugar will remain after 24 hr?

80. A cylindrical tank of radius 10 ft and height 20 ft, with its axis vertical, is full of water but has a leak at the bottom. Assuming that water escapes at a rate proportional to the depth of water in the tank and that 10 percent escapes during the first hour, find a formula for the volume of water left in the tank after t hr.

81. Let p be a positive integer ≥ 2. Show that

$$\lim_{n \to \infty}\left(\frac{1}{n + 1} + \frac{1}{n + 2} + \cdots + \frac{1}{p \cdot n}\right) = \ln p.$$

82. (a) If $(\ln x)/x = (\ln 2)/2$, does it necessarily follow that $x = 2$? (b) If $(\ln x)/x = -2\ln 2$, does it necessarily follow that $x = \frac{1}{2}$? Give reasons for your answers.

83. Given that $\lim_{x \to \infty} (\ln x)/x = 0$ (see Article 6–7, Problem 4). Prove that (a) $\lim_{x \to \infty} (\ln x)/x^h = 0$ if h is any positive constant, (b) $\lim_{x \to +\infty} x^n/e^x = 0$ if n is any constant.

84. Show that $\lim_{h \to 0} (e^h - 1)/h = 1$, by considering the definition of the derivative of e^x at $x = 0$.

85. Prove that if x is any positive number, $\lim_{n \to \infty} n(\sqrt[n]{x} - 1) = \ln x$. [*Hint.* Take $x = e^{nh}$ and apply Problem 84.] *Remark.* This result provides a method for finding $\ln x$ (to any desired finite number of decimal places) using nothing fancier than repeated use of the operation of extracting square roots. For we may take $n = 2^k$, and then $\sqrt[n]{x}$ is obtained from x by taking k successive square roots.

86. Show that $(x^2/4) < x - \ln(1 + x) < (x^2/2)$ if

$$0 < x < 1.$$

[*Hint.* Let $f(x) = x - \ln(1 + x)$ and show that $(x/2) < f'(x) < x$.]

87. Prove that the area under the graph of $y = 1/x$ over the interval $a \leq x \leq b$ $(a > 0)$ is the same as the area over the interval $ka \leq x \leq kb$, for any $k > 0$.

88. Find the limit, as $n \to \infty$, of

$$\frac{e^{1/n} + e^{2/n} + \cdots + e^{(n - 1)/n} + e^{n/n}}{n}.$$

METHODS OF INTEGRATION

7–1

BASIC FORMULAS

Since indefinite integration is defined as the inverse of differentiation, evaluating an integral

$$\int f(x)\, dx \tag{1}$$

is equivalent to finding a function F such that

$$dF(x) = f(x)\, dx. \tag{2}$$

At first sight, this may seem like a hopeless task when we think of adopting a "trial-and-error" approach, and realize that it is simply impossible to try *all functions* as F in Eq. (2) hoping to find one that does the job.* In fact, it is even possible to write down fairly simple integrals, such as

$$\int \sin x^2\, dx, \qquad \int e^{-x^2}\, dx, \qquad \int \sqrt{1 + x^4}\, dx, \tag{3}$$

which cannot be expressed in terms of finite combinations of the so-called "elementary functions" that we have studied thus far. We shall leave a discussion of such integrals as (3) to Chapter 16, and say simply that the words "finite combinations" must give way and an integral like (3) may then be expressed in terms of an infinite series.

In order to reduce the amount of trial and error involved in integration, it is useful to build up a table of standard types of integral formulas by inverting formulas for differentials, as we have done in the previous chapters. Then we try to match any integral that confronts us against one of the standard types. This usually involves a certain amount of algebraic manipulation.

A table of integrals, more extensive than the list of basic formulas given here, may be found inside the covers of this book. To use such a table intelligently, it is necessary to become familiar with certain basic techniques that one can apply to reduce a given integral to a form that matches an entry in the table. The examples and problems in this book should serve to develop skill with these techniques. To concentrate on the techniques without becoming entangled in a mass of algebra, these problems and examples have been kept fairly simple. In fact, *these particular problems* can frequently be solved immediately by consulting an integral table. But solving them this way right now would defeat the purpose of developing the skill likely to be needed for later work. And it is this skill that is important, rather than the specific answer to any given problem.

Perhaps a good way to develop the skill we are aiming for is to build your own table of integrals. You may, for example, make a notebook in which the various sections are headed by standard forms like

$$\int u^n\, du, \qquad \int \frac{du}{u}, \qquad \int e^u\, du, \qquad \text{etc.,}$$

---

* If f is continuous, then an integral function F satisfying Eq. (2) always exists. For example, for $F(x)$ we could take the area A_a^x discussed in Article 4–7. Theoretically, this, together with the fact that such an area can be calculated as a limit of sums of areas of rectangles, gives us a rule for computing $F(x)$. However, we are interested in avoiding these arithmetical calculations, if possible. Hence we prefer to find simple closed-form expressions for the integral whenever possible.

and then under each heading include several examples to illustrate the range of application of the particular formula.

Making such a notebook probably has educational value. But once it is made, it should rarely be necessary to refer to it!

Success in integration hinges on the ability to spot what part of the integrand should be called u in order that one will also have du, so that a known formula can be applied. This means that the *first requirement* for skill in integration is a thorough mastery of the formulas for differentiation. We therefore list certain formulas for differentials that have been derived in previous chapters, together with their integral counterparts. (See page 334.)

At present, let us just consider this list a handy reference and *not* a challenge to our memories! A bit of examination will probably convince us that we are already rather familiar with the first twelve formulas for *differentials* and, so far as *integration* is concerned, our training in technique will show us how to get the *integrals* in the last six cases without memorizing the formulas for the differentials of the inverse trigonometric functions.

Just what types of functions can we integrate directly with this short table of integrals?

Powers

$$\int u^n \, du, \qquad \int \frac{du}{u}.$$

Exponentials

$$\int e^u \, du, \qquad \int a^u \, du.$$

Trigonometric functions

$$\int \sin u \, du, \qquad \int \cos u \, du.$$

Algebraic functions

$$\int \frac{du}{\sqrt{1 - u^2}}, \qquad \int \frac{du}{1 + u^2}, \qquad \int \frac{du}{u\sqrt{u^2 - 1}}.$$

Of course, there are additional combinations of trigonometric functions such as $\int \sec^2 u \, du$, etc., which are integrable accidentally, so to speak.

What common types of functions are *not* included in the table?

Logarithms

$$\int \ln u \, du, \qquad \int \log_a u \, du.$$

Trigonometric functions

$$\int \tan u \, du, \qquad \int \cot u \, du, \qquad \int \sec u \, du, \qquad \int \csc u \, du.$$

Algebraic functions

$$\int \frac{du}{a^2 + u^2}, \qquad \text{etc.,} \quad \text{with } a^2 \neq 1.$$

$$\int \sqrt{a^2 \pm u^2} \, du, \qquad \int \sqrt{u^2 - a^2} \, du, \qquad \text{etc.}$$

Summary of Differential Formulas and Corresponding Integrals

1. $du = \dfrac{du}{dx}\,dx$

1. $\displaystyle\int du = u + C$

2. $d(au) = a\,du$

2. $\displaystyle\int a\,du = a\int du$

3. $d(u + v) = du + dv$

3. $\displaystyle\int (du + dv) = \int du + \int dv$

4. $d(u^n) = nu^{n-1}\,du$

4. $\displaystyle\int u^n\,du = \dfrac{u^{n+1}}{n+1} + C, \quad n \neq -1$

5. $d(\ln u) = \dfrac{du}{u}$

5. $\displaystyle\int \dfrac{du}{u} = \ln\,|u| + C$

6. a) $d(e^u) = e^u\,du$

6. a) $\displaystyle\int e^u\,du = e^u + C$

b) $d(a^u) = a^u \ln a\,du$

b) $\displaystyle\int a^u\,du = \dfrac{a^u}{\ln a} + C$

7. $d(\sin u) = \cos u\,du$

7. $\displaystyle\int \cos u\,du = \sin u + C$

8. $d(\cos u) = -\sin u\,du$

8. $\displaystyle\int \sin u\,du = -\cos u + C$

9. $d(\tan u) = \sec^2 u\,du$

9. $\displaystyle\int \sec^2 u\,du = \tan u + C$

10. $d(\cot u) = -\csc^2 u\,du$

10. $\displaystyle\int \csc^2 u\,du = -\cot u + C$

11. $d(\sec u) = \sec u \tan u\,du$

11. $\displaystyle\int \sec u \tan u\,du = \sec u + C$

12. $d(\csc u) = -\csc u \cot u\,du$

12. $\displaystyle\int \csc u \cot u\,du = -\csc u + C$

13. $d(\sin^{-1} u) = \dfrac{du}{\sqrt{1 - u^2}}$

14. $d(\cos^{-1} u) = \dfrac{-du}{\sqrt{1 - u^2}}$

13. and **14.** $\displaystyle\int \dfrac{du}{\sqrt{1 - u^2}} = \begin{cases} \sin^{-1} u + C \\ -\cos^{-1} u + C' \end{cases}$

15. $d(\tan^{-1} u) = \dfrac{du}{1 + u^2}$

16. $d(\cot^{-1} u) = \dfrac{-du}{1 + u^2}$

15. and **16.** $\displaystyle\int \dfrac{du}{1 + u^2} = \begin{cases} \tan^{-1} u + C \\ -\cot^{-1} u + C' \end{cases}$

17. $d(\sec^{-1} u) = \dfrac{du}{|u|\sqrt{u^2 - 1}}$

18. $d(\csc^{-1} u) = \dfrac{-du}{|u|\sqrt{u^2 - 1}}$

17. and **18.** $\displaystyle\int \dfrac{du}{u\sqrt{u^2 - 1}} = \begin{cases} \sec^{-1}|u| + C \\ -\csc^{-1}|u| + C' \end{cases}$

Inverse functions

$$\int \sin^{-1} u \, du, \qquad \int \tan^{-1} u \, du, \qquad \text{etc.}$$

We shall eventually see how to evaluate all of these and some others, but there are no methods that will solve *all* integration problems in terms of elementary functions.

PROBLEMS

Evaluate each of the integrals 1 through 44 by reducing the integrand to one of the standard forms. In each case, indicate what you have called u and refer by number to the standard formula used.

1. $\displaystyle\int \sqrt{2x+3} \, dx$

2. $\displaystyle\int \frac{dx}{3x+5}$

3. $\displaystyle\int \frac{dx}{(2x-7)^2}$

4. $\displaystyle\int \frac{(x+1)\,dx}{x^2+2x+3}$

5. $\displaystyle\int \frac{\sin x \, dx}{2+\cos x}$

6. $\displaystyle\int \tan^3 2x \sec^2 2x \, dx$

7. $\displaystyle\int \frac{x \, dx}{\sqrt{1-4x^2}}$

8. $\displaystyle\int x^{1/3}\sqrt{x^{4/3}-1} \, dx$

9. $\displaystyle\int \frac{2 \, dx}{\sqrt{1-4x^2}}$

10. $\displaystyle\int \frac{2v \, dv}{\sqrt{1-v^4}}$

11. $\displaystyle\int \frac{x \, dx}{(3x^2+4)^3}$

12. $\displaystyle\int x^2\sqrt{x^3+5} \, dx$

13. $\displaystyle\int \frac{x^2 \, dx}{\sqrt{x^3+5}}$

14. $\displaystyle\int \frac{x \, dx}{4x^2+1}$

15. $\displaystyle\int e^{2x} \, dx$

16. $\displaystyle\int e^{\cos x}\sin x \, dx$

17. $\displaystyle\int \frac{dx}{e^{3x}}$

18. $\displaystyle\int \frac{e^{\sqrt{x+1}}}{\sqrt{x+1}} \, dx$

19. $\displaystyle\int \frac{e^x \, dx}{1+e^{2x}}$

20. $\displaystyle\int \frac{dt}{1+9t^2}$

21. $\displaystyle\int \cos^2 x \sin x \, dx$

22. $\displaystyle\int \frac{\cos x \, dx}{\sin^3 x}$

23. $\displaystyle\int \cot^3 x \csc^2 x \, dx$

24. $\displaystyle\int \tan 3x \sec^2 3x \, dx$

25. $\displaystyle\int \frac{e^{2x}+e^{-2x}}{e^{2x}-e^{-2x}} \, dx$

26. $\displaystyle\int \sin 2x \cos^2 2x \, dx$

27. $\displaystyle\int (1+\cos\theta)^3 \sin\theta \, d\theta$

28. $\displaystyle\int te^{-t^2} \, dt$

29. $\displaystyle\int \frac{dt}{t\sqrt{4t^2-1}}$

30. $\displaystyle\int \frac{dx}{\sqrt{e^{2x}-1}}$ [*Hint.* Multiply numerator and denominator by e^x.]

31. $\displaystyle\int \frac{\cos x \, dx}{\sin x}$

32. $\displaystyle\int \frac{\cos x \, dx}{1+\sin x}$

33. $\displaystyle\int \sec^3 x \tan x \, dx$

34. $\displaystyle\int \frac{\sin\theta \, d\theta}{\sqrt{1+\cos\theta}}$

35. $\displaystyle\int e^{\tan 3x}\sec^2 3x \, dx$

36. $\displaystyle\int \cos 2t\sqrt{4-\sin 2t} \, dt$

37. $\displaystyle\int \frac{1+\cos 2x}{\sin^2 2x} \, dx$

38. $\displaystyle\int \frac{\sin^2 2x}{1+\cos 2x} \, dx$

39. $\displaystyle\int \frac{\csc^2 2t}{\sqrt{1+\cot 2t}} \, dt$

40. $\displaystyle\int e^{3x} \, dx$

41. $\displaystyle\int \frac{e^{\tan^{-1} 2t}}{1+4t^2} \, dt$

42. $\displaystyle\int xe^{-x^2} \, dx$

43. $\displaystyle\int 3^x \, dx$

44. $\displaystyle\int 10^{2x} \, dx$

45. Can both of the following integrations be correct? Explain.

a) $\displaystyle\int \frac{dx}{\sqrt{1-x^2}} = \sin^{-1} x + C$

b) $\displaystyle\int \frac{dx}{\sqrt{1-x^2}} = -\int \frac{-dx}{\sqrt{1-x^2}} = \cos^{-1}(-x) + C$

46. Solve for C in each of the following equations.
a) $\tan^{-1} u + \cot^{-1} u = C$
b) $\sec^{-1}|u| + \csc^{-1}|u| = C$

47. Each of the integrals in (a) through (c) may be evaluated easily for a particular numerical value of n. Choose this value and integrate. For example,

$$\int x^n \cos(x^2) \, dx$$

is evaluated easily for $n = 1$:

$$\int x \cos(x^2) \, dx = \tfrac{1}{2} \sin(x^2) + C.$$

a) $\displaystyle\int x^n \ln x \, dx$,   **b)** $\displaystyle\int x^n e^{x^3} \, dx$,   **c)** $\displaystyle\int x^n \sin\sqrt{x} \, dx$.

48. The integral $\int_a^\infty e^{-x^2}\,dx$ arises in statistics and elsewhere. It is defined to mean the same thing as

$$\lim_{b\to+\infty}\int_a^b e^{-x^2}\,dx.$$

Show that if $x > a \geq 1$, then $e^{-x^2} < e^{-ax}$. Hence, by comparing the integral from a to ∞ of e^{-x^2} with the integral of e^{-ax} and evaluating the latter integral, show that

$$\int_a^\infty e^{-x^2}\,dx < \frac{1}{a}e^{-a^2}, \qquad \text{if} \quad a \geq 1.$$

7–2

POWERS OF TRIGONOMETRIC FUNCTIONS

The formula

$$\int u^n\,du = \begin{cases} \dfrac{u^{n+1}}{n+1} + C, & n \neq -1, \\[2mm] \ln|u| + C, & n = -1, \end{cases}$$

may be used to evaluate certain integrals involving powers of the trigonometric functions, as illustrated by the examples that follow. The same methods work for powers of other functions. Pay attention to the *methods* rather than trying to remember specific results.

EXAMPLE 1

$$\int \sin^n ax \cos ax\,dx.$$

Solution. If we let $u = \sin ax$, then

$$du = \cos ax\,d(ax) = a\cos ax\,dx,$$

so that we need only multiply the integral by unity in the form of a times $1/a$. Since a and $1/a$ are constants, we may write a inside the integral sign and $1/a$ in front of the integral sign to have

$$\int \sin^n ax \cos ax\,dx = \frac{1}{a}\int (\sin ax)^n(a\cos ax\,dx)$$

$$= \frac{1}{a}\int u^n\,du$$

$$= \begin{cases} \dfrac{1}{a}\dfrac{u^{n+1}}{n+1} + C, & n \neq -1, \\[2mm] \dfrac{1}{a}\ln|u| + C, & n = -1; \end{cases}$$

that is,

$$\int \sin^n ax \cos ax\,dx = \frac{\sin^{n+1}ax}{(n+1)a} + C, \qquad n \neq -1, \tag{1a}$$

and if $n = -1$, we get

$$\int \cot ax\,dx = \int \frac{\cos ax\,dx}{\sin ax} = \frac{1}{a}\ln|\sin ax| + C. \tag{1b}$$

Note that the success of the method depended upon having cos ax to go with the dx as part of du.

By a similar method we can obtain

$$\int \cos^n ax \, \sin ax \, dx = \frac{-\cos^{n+1} ax}{(n+1)a} + C, \qquad n \neq -1, \qquad \textbf{(2a)}$$

and, when $n = -1$,

$$\int \tan ax \, dx = \int \frac{\sin ax}{\cos ax} dx = -\frac{1}{a} \ln \, |\cos ax| + C. \qquad \textbf{(2b)}$$

EXAMPLE 2

$$\int \sin^3 x \, dx.$$

Solution. The method of the previous example does not work because there is no cos x to go with dx to give du if we try letting $u = \sin x$. But if we write

$$\sin^3 x = \sin^2 x \cdot \sin x = (1 - \cos^2 x) \cdot \sin x$$

and let

$$u = \cos x, \qquad du = -\sin x \, dx,$$

we have

$$\int \sin^3 x \, dx = \int (1 - \cos^2 x) \cdot \sin x \, dx = \int (1 - u^2) \cdot (-du)$$

$$= \int (u^2 - 1) \, du = \tfrac{1}{3}u^3 - u + C = \tfrac{1}{3} \cos^3 x - \cos x + C.$$

This method may be applied whenever an *odd* power of sin x or cos x is to be integrated. For example, any positive odd power of cos x has the form

$$\cos^{2n+1} x = \cos^{2n} x \cdot \cos x = (\cos^2 x)^n \cdot \cos x = (1 - \sin^2 x)^n \cdot \cos x,$$

with n an integer ≥ 0. Then if we let $u = \sin x$, $du = \cos x \, dx$, we have

$$\int \cos^{2n+1} x \, dx = \int (1 - \sin^2 x)^n \cdot \cos x \, dx = \int (1 - u^2)^n \cdot du.$$

The expression $(1 - u^2)^n$ may now be expanded by the binomial theorem and the result evaluated as a sum of individual integrals of the type $\int u^m \, du$.

EXAMPLE 3

$$\int \sec x \, \tan x \, dx.$$

Solution. Of course this is a standard form already, so there is no real problem in finding an answer. But in trigonometry we often express all trigonometric functions in terms of sines and cosines, and we now investigate what this does to the integral in question:

$$\int \sec x \tan x \, dx = \int \frac{1}{\cos x} \frac{\sin x}{\cos x} dx = \int \frac{\sin x \, dx}{\cos^2 x}.$$

Taking a cue from the previous examples (keeping in mind du as well as u), we let

$$u = \cos x, \qquad du = -\sin x \, dx,$$

and then

$$\int \frac{\sin x \, dx}{\cos^2 x} = \int \frac{-du}{u^2} = -\int u^{-2} \, du = \frac{-u^{-1}}{-1} + C = \frac{1}{u} + C$$

$$= \frac{1}{\cos x} + C = \sec x + C.$$

EXAMPLE 4

$$\int \tan^4 x \, dx.$$

Solution. This does not lend itself readily to the use of sines and cosines, since both of them occur to even powers. We say: $u = \tan x$ would require $du = \sec^2 x \, dx$. Is there some way to include $\sec^2 x$? Yes; there is an identity involving tangents and secants. How does it go? Since

$$\sin^2 x + \cos^2 x = 1,$$

if we divide through by $\cos^2 x$ we get

$$\tan^2 x + 1 = \sec^2 x \qquad \text{or} \qquad \tan^2 x = \sec^2 x - 1.$$

Then

$$\int \tan^4 x \, dx = \int \tan^2 x \cdot \tan^2 x \, dx = \int \tan^2 x \cdot (\sec^2 x - 1) \, dx$$

$$= \int \tan^2 x \sec^2 x \, dx - \int \tan^2 x \, dx.$$

The first of these is all set. But how about the $\tan^2 x$? Oh, yes,

$$\tan^2 x = \sec^2 x - 1,$$

so

$$\int \tan^4 x \, dx = \int \tan^2 x \sec^2 x \, dx - \int \tan^2 x \, dx$$

$$= \int \tan^2 x \sec^2 x \, dx - \int (\sec^2 x - 1) \, dx$$

$$= \int \tan^2 x \sec^2 x \, dx - \int \sec^2 x \, dx + \int dx.$$

In the first two of these, let

$$u = \tan x, \qquad du = \sec^2 x \, dx$$

and have

$$\int u^2 \, du - \int du = \tfrac{1}{3}u^3 - u + C'.$$

The other is a standard form, so

$$\int \tan^4 x \, dx = \tfrac{1}{3} \tan^3 x - \tan x + x + C.$$

This method works for any *even* power of tan x, but what is still better is a *reduction formula* derived as follows:

$$\int \tan^n x \, dx = \int \tan^{n-2} x (\sec^2 x - 1) \, dx$$

$$= \int \tan^{n-2} x \sec^2 x \, dx - \int \tan^{n-2} x \, dx$$

$$= \frac{\tan^{n-1} x}{n-1} - \int \tan^{n-2} x \, dx.$$

This reduces the problem of integrating $\tan^n x \, dx$ to the problem of integrating $\tan^{n-2} x \, dx$. Since this decreases the exponent on tan x by 2, a repetition with the same formula will reduce the exponent by 2 again, and so on. Applying this to the problem above, we have

$$n = 4: \qquad \int \tan^4 x \, dx = \frac{\tan^3 x}{3} - \int \tan^2 x \, dx,$$

$$n = 2: \qquad \int \tan^2 x \, dx = \frac{\tan x}{1} - \int \tan^0 x \, dx,$$

$$\int \tan^0 x \, dx = \int 1 \, dx = x + C.$$

Therefore,

$$\int \tan^4 x \, dx = \tfrac{1}{3} \tan^3 x - [\tan x - x + C]$$

$$= \tfrac{1}{3} \tan^3 x - \tan x + x + C'.$$

This reduction formula works whether the original exponent n is even or odd, but if the exponent is odd, say $2m + 1$, then after m steps it will be reduced by $2m$, leaving

$$\int \tan x = -\ln |\cos x| + C$$

as the final integral to be evaluated.

These examples illustrate how it is possible to use the trigonometric identities

$$\sin^2 x + \cos^2 x = 1, \qquad \tan^2 x + 1 = \sec^2 x,$$

and others readily derived from these, to evaluate the integrals of

a) *odd* powers of sin x or cos x,

b) *any* integral powers of tan x (or cot x), and

c) *even* powers of sec x (or csc x).

The even powers of sec x, say $\sec^{2n} x$, can all be reduced to powers of tan x by employing the substitution $\sec^2 x = 1 + \tan^2 x$, and then using the reduction formula for integrating powers of tan x after expanding $\sec^{2n} x = (1 + \tan^2 x)^n$ by the binomial theorem. But it is even simpler to use the method below:

$$\int \sec^{2n} x \, dx = \int \sec^{2n-2} x \sec^2 x \, dx = \int (\sec^2 x)^{n-1} \sec^2 x \, dx$$

$$= \int (1 + \tan^2 x)^{n-1} \sec^2 x \, dx$$

$$= \int (1 + u^2)^{n-1} \, du \qquad (u = \tan x).$$

When $(1 + u^2)^{n-1}$ is expanded by the binomial theorem, the resulting polynomial in u may be integrated term by term.

For example,

$$\int \sec^6 x \, dx = \int \sec^4 x \cdot \sec^2 x \, dx = \int (1 + \tan^2 x)^2 \cdot \sec^2 x \, dx$$

$$= \int (1 + 2u^2 + u^4) \, du \qquad (u = \tan x)$$

$$= u + \frac{2u^3}{3} + \frac{u^5}{5} + C$$

$$= \tan x + 2\frac{\tan^3 x}{3} + \frac{\tan^5 x}{5} + C.$$

EXAMPLE 5

$$\int \sec x \, dx.$$

Solution. This is hard to evaluate unless one has seen the following trick!

$$\sec x = \frac{\sec x(\tan x + \sec x)}{\sec x + \tan x} = \frac{\sec x \tan x + \sec^2 x}{\sec x + \tan x}.$$

In this form the numerator is the derivative of the denominator. Therefore

$$\int \sec x \, dx = \int \frac{\sec x \tan x + \sec^2 x}{\sec x + \tan x} \, dx$$

$$= \int \frac{du}{u} \qquad (u = \sec x + \tan x)$$

$$= \ln |u| + C.$$

That is,

$$\int \sec x \, dx = \ln |\sec x + \tan x| + C. \qquad (3)$$

EXAMPLE 6 *Mercator's world map.*　The integral of the secant plays an important role in making maps for compass navigation. The easiest course for a sailor to steer is a course whose compass heading is constant. This might be a course of 45° (northeast), for example, or a course of 225° (southwest), or whatever. Such a course will lie along a spiral that winds around the globe toward one of the poles (Fig. 7–1), unless the course runs due north or south, or lies parallel to the equator.

In 1569, Gerhard Krämer, a Flemish surveyor and geographer known to us by his Latinized last name, Mercator, made a world map on which all spirals of constant compass heading appeared as straight lines (Fig. 7–2).

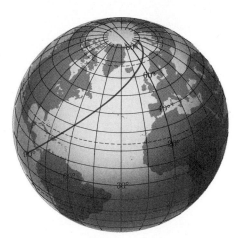

7–1　A flight with a constant bearing of 45° E of N from the Galapagos Islands in the Pacific to Franz Josef Land in the Arctic Ocean.

7–2　Sketch of Mercator's map of 1569.

This fantastic achievement met what must have been one of the most pressing navigational needs of all time. For a sailor could then read the compass heading for a voyage between any two points from the direction of a straight line connecting them on Mercator's map (Fig. 7–3).

If you look closely at Fig. 7–3, you will see that the vertical lines of longitude that meet at the poles on a globe have been spread apart to lie parallel on the map. The horizontal lines of latitude that are shown every 10° are parallel also, as they are on the globe, but they are not evenly spaced. The spacing between them increases toward the poles.

The secant function plays a role in determining the correct spacing of all these lines. The scaling factor by which horizontal distances are increased at a fixed latitude θ° to spread the lines of longitude apart is precisely sec θ. There is no spread at the equator, where sec 0° = 1. At latitude 30° north or south, the spreading is accomplished by multiplying all horizontal distances by the factor sec 30° = $2/\sqrt{3} \approx 1.15$. At 60°, the factor is sec 60° = 2. The closer you move toward the poles, the more the longitudes have to be spread to be parallel. The lines of latitude are spread apart toward the poles to match the spreading of the longitudes, but the formula for the spreading is complicated by the fact that the scaling factor sec θ increases with the latitude θ. Thus, the factor to be used for stretching an interval of latitude is not a constant on the interval. This difficulty is overcome by integration. If R is the radius of the globe being modeled (Fig. 7–4), then the distance D between

7–3　The flight of Fig. 1 traced on a Mercator map.

the lines that are drawn on the map to show the equator and the latitude $\alpha°$ is R times the integral of the secant from zero to α:

$$D = R \int_0^\alpha \sec x \, dx. \tag{4}$$

Therefore, the map distance between two lines of north latitude, say, at $\alpha°$ and $\beta°$ $(\alpha < \beta)$ is

$$R \int_0^\beta \sec x \, dx - R \int_0^\alpha \sec x \, dx = R \int_\alpha^\beta \sec x \, dx$$

$$= R \ln \left| \sec x + \tan x \right| \Big]_\alpha^\beta. \tag{5}$$

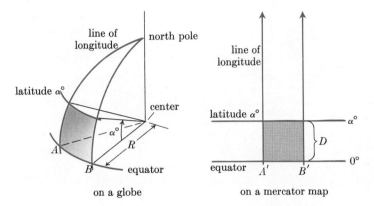

7–4   Lines of latitude and longitude.

on a globe   on a mercator map

EXAMPLE 7.   Suppose that the equatorial length of a Mercator map just matches the equator of a globe of radius 25 cm. Then Eq. (4) gives the spacing on the map between the equator and the latitude 20° north as

$$25 \int_0^{20°} \sec x \, dx = 25 \ln \left| \sec x + \tan x \right| \Big]_0^{20°} \approx 9 \text{ cm.}$$

The spacing between 60° and 80° north is given by Eq. (5) as

$$25 \int_{60°}^{80°} \sec x \, dx = 25 \ln \left| \sec x + \tan x \right| \Big]_{60°}^{80°} \approx 28 \text{ cm.}$$

The navigational properties of a Mercator map are achieved at the expense of a considerable distortion of distance. (For a very readable derivation and discussion of the formula in Eq. (4), see Philip Tuchinsky's *Mercator's World Map and the Calculus*, Project UMAP, Education Development Center, Newton, MA, 1978.)

PROBLEMS

Evaluate the integrals 1 through 33.

1. $\displaystyle\int \sin^{3/2} x \cos x \, dx$

2. $\displaystyle\int \sqrt{\cos x} \sin x \, dx$

3. $\displaystyle\int \sin t \sqrt{1 + \cos t} \, dt$

4. $\displaystyle\int \frac{\sin \theta \, d\theta}{2 - \cos \theta}$

5. $\displaystyle\int \frac{\sec^2 2x \, dx}{1 + \tan 2x}$

6. $\displaystyle\int \tan 3x \, dx$

7. $\int \cos^3 x \, dx$

8. $\int \tan^2 4\theta \, d\theta$

9. a) $\int \sin^3 x \cos^2 x \, dx$

10. $\int \sec^n x \tan x \, dx$

b) $\int \dfrac{\sin^3 x \, dx}{\cos^2 x}$

11. $\int \tan^n x \sec^2 x \, dx$

12. $\int \sin^n x \cos x \, dx$

13. $\int \cos^n x \sin x \, dx$

14. $\int \sin^2 3x \cos 3x \, dx$

15. $\int \cos^3 2x \sin 2x \, dx$

16. $\int \sec^4 3x \tan 3x \, dx$

17. $\int \sec^4 3x \, dx$

18. $\int \cos^3 2x \, dx$

19. $\int \tan^3 2x \, dx$

20. $\int \tan^3 x \sec x \, dx$

21. $\int \sin^3 x \, dx$

22. $\int \dfrac{\cos x \, dx}{(1 + \sin x)^2}$

23. $\int \dfrac{\sec^2 x \, dx}{2 + \tan x}$

24. $\int \dfrac{\cos^3 t \, dt}{\sin^2 t}$

25. $\int \dfrac{e^x \, dx}{1 + e^x}$

26. $\int (\ln ax)^n \dfrac{dx}{x}$

27. $\int \dfrac{dx}{x \ln 3x}$

28. $\int \cot^3 x \, dx$

29. $\int \csc^3 2t \cot 2t \, dt$

30. $\int \csc^4 x \, dx$

31. $\int \dfrac{dx}{\cos x}$

32. $\int_0^{\pi/4} \dfrac{dx}{\sqrt{1 - \sin^2 x}}$

33. $\int \csc \theta \, d\theta$ [*Hint.* Repeat Example 5 with cofunctions.]

34. (*Calculator, or tables*) How far apart should the following lines of latitude be on the Mercator map of Example 7?

  a) 30° and 45° north (about the latitudes of New Orleans, La., and Minneapolis, Minn.);

  b) 45° and 60° north (about the latitudes of Salem, Ore., and Seward, Al.).

35. Find the area of the surface generated by revolving the arc

$$x = t^{2/3}, \quad y = t^2/2, \quad 0 \le t \le 2,$$

about the x-axis.

36. Derive a reduction formula for $\int \cot^n ax \, dx$ and use the result to evaluate $\int \cot^4 3x \, dx$.

37. Find the length of the curve

$$y = \ln (\cos x), \quad 0 \le x \le \pi/3.$$

In Article 7–2 we saw how to evaluate integrals of odd powers of sines and cosines. Indeed, any integral of the form

$$\int \sin^m x \cos^n x \, dx, \tag{1}$$

in which at least one of the exponents m and n is a positive odd integer, may be evaluated by these methods.

To set the stage for our discussion of even powers, we begin by looking at the technique we would normally use for odd powers, and then examine what goes wrong when we try to use the same technique for even powers.

7–3
EVEN POWERS OF SINES AND COSINES

EXAMPLE 1

$$\int \cos^{2/3} x \sin^5 x \, dx.$$

Solution. Here we have $\sin x$ to an *odd* power. So we put one factor of $\sin x$ with dx and the remaining sine factors, namely $\sin^4 x$, can be expressed in terms of $\cos x$ without introducing any square roots, as follows:

$$\sin^4 x = (\sin^2 x)^2 = (1 - \cos^2 x)^2.$$

The sin x goes well with dx when we take

$$u = \cos x, \qquad du = -\sin x \, dx$$

and evaluate the integral as follows:

$$\int \cos^{2/3} x \sin^5 x \, dx = \int \cos^{2/3} x (1 - \cos^2 x)^2 \sin x \, dx$$

$$= \int u^{2/3}(1 - u^2)^2(-du)$$

$$= -\int (u^{2/3} - 2u^{8/3} + u^{14/3}) \, du$$

$$= -[\tfrac{3}{5}u^{5/3} - \tfrac{6}{11}u^{11/3} + \tfrac{3}{17}u^{17/3}] + C$$

$$= -\cos^{5/3} x \, [\tfrac{3}{5} - \tfrac{6}{11} \cos^2 x + \tfrac{3}{17} \cos^4 x] + C.$$

DISCUSSION.   If sin x had appeared to an *even* power in the integral, as it does, say, in the integral

$$\int \cos^{2/3} x \sin^4 x \, dx,$$

then the method above would not work. The substitution $\sin^4 x = (1 - \cos^2 x)^2$ would reduce the integral to

$$\int \cos^{2/3} x \sin^4 x \, dx = \int \cos^{2/3} x (1 - \cos^2 x)^2 \, dx,$$

and there would be no $-\sin x \, dx = du$ to go with the cos $x = u$.

When both the exponents m and n in the integral (1) are even integers, we turn to one or both of the following trigonometric identities:

$$\sin^2 A = \tfrac{1}{2}(1 - \cos 2A), \tag{2a}$$

$$\cos^2 A = \tfrac{1}{2}(1 + \cos 2A). \tag{2b}$$

These identities may be derived by adding or subtracting the equations

$$\cos^2 A + \sin^2 A = 1, \qquad \cos^2 A - \sin^2 A = \cos 2A,$$

and dividing by two.

EXAMPLE 2

$$\int \cos^4 x \, dx = \int (\cos^2 x)^2 \, dx = \int \tfrac{1}{4}(1 + \cos 2x)^2 \, dx \tag{a}$$

$$= \tfrac{1}{4} \int (1 + 2 \cos 2x + \cos^2 2x) \, dx \tag{b}$$

$$= \tfrac{1}{4} \int [1 + 2 \cos 2x + \tfrac{1}{2}(1 + \cos 4x)] \, dx$$

$$= \tfrac{3}{8}x + \tfrac{1}{4} \sin 2x + \tfrac{1}{32} \sin 4x + C.$$

In (a), we used Eq. (2b) with $A = x$, and in (b), we used Eq. (2b) with $A = 2x$. The final integrations involve

$$\int \cos ax \, dx = \frac{1}{a} \int \cos ax \, d(ax) = \frac{1}{a} \sin ax + C'.$$

An integral like

$$\int \sin^2 x \cos^4 x \, dx,$$

which involves even powers of both $\sin x$ and $\cos x$, can be changed to a sum of integrals that involve only powers of one of them. Then these may be handled by the method of Example 2.

EXAMPLE 3

$$\int \sin^2 x \cos^4 x \, dx = \int (1 - \cos^2 x) \cos^4 x \, dx = \int \cos^4 x \, dx - \int \cos^6 x \, dx.$$

We evaluated $\int \cos^4 x \, dx$ above, and

$$\int \cos^6 x \, dx = \int (\cos^2 x)^3 \, dx = \tfrac{1}{8} \int (1 + \cos 2x)^3 \, dx$$

$$= \tfrac{1}{8} \int (1 + 3 \cos 2x + 3 \cos^2 2x + \cos^3 2x) \, dx.$$

We now know how to handle each term of the integrand. The result is

$$\int \cos^6 x \, dx = \tfrac{5}{16}x + \tfrac{1}{4} \sin 2x + \tfrac{3}{64} \sin 4x - \tfrac{1}{48} \sin^3 2x + C.$$

Combining this with the result of Example 2 gives:

$$\int \sin^2 x \cos^4 x \, dx = \int \cos^4 x \, dx - \int \cos^6 x \, dx$$

$$= \tfrac{1}{16}x - \tfrac{1}{64} \sin 4x + \tfrac{1}{48} \sin^3 2x + C.$$

PROBLEMS

Evaluate the following integrals:

1. $\displaystyle\int \sin^2 x \cos^2 x \, dx$

2. $\displaystyle\int \sin^4 y \cos^2 y \, dy$

3. $\displaystyle\int \sin^2 2t \, dt$

4. $\displaystyle\int \cos^2 3\theta \, d\theta$

5. $\displaystyle\int \sin^4 ax \, dx$

6. $\displaystyle\int \frac{\sin^4 x \, dx}{\cos^2 x}$

7. $\displaystyle\int \frac{dx}{\cos^2 x}$

8. $\displaystyle\int \frac{dx}{\sin^4 x}$

9. $\displaystyle\int \frac{\cos 2t \, dt}{\sin^4 2t}$

10. $\displaystyle\int \sin^6 x \, dx$

11. $\displaystyle\int_0^{2\pi} \sqrt{\frac{1 - \cos t}{2}} \, dt$

12. $\displaystyle\int_0^{\pi} \sqrt{1 - \cos 2x} \, dx$

13. $\displaystyle\int_0^{\pi/10} \sqrt{1 + \cos 5\theta} \, d\theta$

14. $\displaystyle\int_0^{2\pi} \sqrt{1 + \cos (y/4)} \, dy$

15. The graph of $x = t - \sin t$, $y = 1 - \cos t$, $0 \le t \le 2\pi$, is an arch standing on the x-axis. Find the surface area generated by rotating the arch about the axis.

16. Find the volume generated by revolving one arch of the curve $y = \sin x$ about the x-axis.

7—4

INTEGRALS INVOLVING
$\sqrt{a^2 - u^2}, \sqrt{a^2 + u^2}, \sqrt{u^2 - a^2},$
$a^2 + u^2,$ **and** $a^2 - u^2$

Some of these follow directly from the integral formulas in Article 7–1. For example, we have

$$\int \frac{du}{1 + u^2} = \tan^{-1} u + C, \tag{1}$$

and, to evaluate

$$\int \frac{du}{a^2 + u^2}, \tag{2}$$

we factor a^2 out of the denominator and proceed as follows:

$$\int \frac{du}{a^2 + u^2} = \int \frac{du}{a^2 \left[1 + \left(\dfrac{u}{a} \right)^2 \right]} = \frac{1}{a^2} \int \frac{a d\left(\dfrac{u}{a} \right)}{1 + \left(\dfrac{u}{a} \right)^2} = \frac{1}{a} \int \frac{dz}{1 + z^2}$$

$$= \frac{1}{a} \tan^{-1} z + C = \frac{1}{a} \tan^{-1} \frac{u}{a} + C \qquad \left[z = \frac{u}{a} \right].$$

That is,

$$\int \frac{du}{a^2 + u^2} = \frac{1}{a} \tan^{-1} \frac{u}{a} + C. \tag{3}$$

The essential feature here was the introduction of a new variable by the substitution

$$z = \frac{u}{a} \qquad \text{or} \qquad u = az.$$

Such a substitution allows the a terms to be brought outside the integral sign, and the resulting integral may then match one of the inverse trigonometric formulas.

An alternative approach will show, however, that one may bypass the job of learning these formulas. In addition, this method, which we shall soon illustrate, permits the evaluation of many additional integrals.

The method uses the following identities.

$$1 - \sin^2 \theta = \cos^2 \theta,$$
$$1 + \tan^2 \theta = \sec^2 \theta, \tag{4}$$
$$\sec^2 \theta - 1 = \tan^2 \theta.$$

These identities may be multiplied by a^2, with the result that the substitutions listed below have the following effects:

a) $u = a \sin \theta$ replaces $a^2 - u^2$ by $a^2 \cos^2 \theta.$

b) $u = a \tan \theta$ replaces $a^2 + u^2$ by $a^2 \sec^2 \theta.$ (5)

c) $u = a \sec \theta$ replaces $u^2 - a^2$ by $a^2 \tan^2 \theta.$

It is thus seen that corresponding to each of the *binomial* expressions

$$a^2 - u^2, \qquad a^2 + u^2, \qquad \text{and} \qquad u^2 - a^2,$$

we have a substitution that replaces the binomial by a single squared term. The particular substitution to use will depend upon the form of the integrand. In the examples that follow, a is a positive constant.

EXAMPLE 1

$$\int \frac{du}{\sqrt{a^2 - u^2}}, \qquad |a| > |u|.$$

Solution.   We try the substitution (5a):

$$u = a \sin \theta, \qquad du = a \cos \theta \; d\theta,$$

$$a^2 - u^2 = a^2(1 - \sin^2 \theta) = a^2 \cos^2 \theta.$$

Then

$$\int \frac{du}{\sqrt{a^2 - u^2}} = \int \frac{a \cos \theta \; d\theta}{\sqrt{a^2 \cos^2 \theta}} = \int \frac{a \cos \theta \; d\theta}{\pm a \cos \theta} \quad (\pm \text{ depends on sign of } \cos \theta)$$

$$= \pm \int d\theta = \pm (\theta + C).$$

Since $\sin \theta = u/a$,

$$\theta = \sin^{-1} \frac{u}{a}$$

and

$$\int \frac{du}{\sqrt{a^2 - u^2}} = \pm \left(\sin^{-1} \frac{u}{a} + C \right).$$

Using only the *principal value* of $\sin^{-1} u/a$ means that θ will lie between $-\pi/2$ and $\pi/2$; hence $\cos \theta \geq 0$ and the ambiguous sign is $+$; that is,

$$\int \frac{du}{\sqrt{a^2 - u^2}} = \sin^{-1} \frac{u}{a} + C. \tag{6}$$

EXAMPLE 2

$$\int \frac{du}{\sqrt{a^2 + u^2}}, \qquad a > 0.$$

Solution.   This time we try

$$u = a \tan \theta,$$

$$du = a \sec^2 \theta \; d\theta,$$

$$a^2 + u^2 = a^2(1 + \tan^2 \theta) = a^2 \sec^2 \theta.$$

Then

$$\int \frac{du}{\sqrt{a^2 + u^2}} = \int \frac{a \sec^2 \theta \; d\theta}{\sqrt{a^2 \sec^2 \theta}}$$

$$= \pm \int \sec \theta \; d\theta \quad (\pm \text{ depends on sign of } \sec \theta).$$

By Eq. (3), Article 7–2, we know that

$$\int \sec \theta \, d\theta = \ln \, |\sec \theta + \tan \theta| + C.$$

If we take

$$\theta = \tan^{-1} \frac{u}{a}, \qquad -\frac{\pi}{2} < \theta < \frac{\pi}{2},$$

then $\sec \theta$ is positive, and

$$\int \frac{du}{\sqrt{a^2 + u^2}} = \int \sec \theta \, d\theta$$

$$= \ln \, |\sec \theta + \tan \theta| + C = \ln \left| \frac{\sqrt{a^2 + u^2}}{a} + \frac{u}{a} \right| + C$$

$$= \ln \, |\sqrt{a^2 + u^2} + u| + C',$$

where

$$C' = C - \ln a.$$

That is,

$$\int \frac{du}{\sqrt{a^2 + u^2}} = \ln \, |\sqrt{a^2 + u^2} + u| + C'. \tag{7}$$

EXAMPLE 3

$$\int \frac{du}{\sqrt{u^2 - a^2}}, \qquad |u| > a > 0.$$

Solution.   We try the substitution

$$u = a \sec \theta,$$

$$du = a \sec \theta \tan \theta \, d\theta,$$

$$u^2 - a^2 = a^2(\sec^2 \theta - 1) = a^2 \tan^2 \theta.$$

Then

$$\int \frac{du}{\sqrt{u^2 - a^2}} = \int \frac{a \sec \theta \tan \theta \, d\theta}{\sqrt{a^2 \tan^2 \theta}}$$

$$= \pm \int \sec \theta \, d\theta \quad (\pm \text{ depends on sign of } \tan \theta).$$

If we take

$$\theta = \sec^{-1} \frac{u}{a}, \qquad 0 \le \theta \le \pi,$$

then

$$\tan \theta \text{ is positive} \quad \text{if } 0 < \theta < \pi/2,$$

$$\tan \theta \text{ is negative} \quad \text{if } \pi/2 < \theta < \pi,$$

and, from Eq. (3) of Article 7–2,

$$\pm \int \sec \theta \, d\theta = \pm \ln \, |\sec \theta + \tan \theta| + C.$$

When $\tan \theta$ is positive, we must use the plus sign; when $\tan \theta$ is negative, the minus sign. Moreover,

$$\sec \theta = \frac{u}{a}, \qquad \tan \theta = \pm \frac{\sqrt{u^2 - a^2}}{a}.$$

So we have

$$\int \frac{du}{\sqrt{u^2 - a^2}} = \pm \ln \left| \frac{u}{a} \pm \frac{\sqrt{u^2 - a^2}}{a} \right| + C$$

$$= \begin{cases} \ln \left| \frac{u}{a} + \frac{\sqrt{u^2 - a^2}}{a} \right| + C \\ \text{or} \\ -\ln \left| \frac{u}{a} - \frac{\sqrt{u^2 - a^2}}{a} \right| + C. \end{cases}$$

But the two forms are actually equal, because

$$-\ln \left| \frac{u}{a} - \frac{\sqrt{u^2 - a^2}}{a} \right| = \ln \left| \frac{a}{u - \sqrt{u^2 - a^2}} \right|$$

$$= \ln \left| \frac{a(u + \sqrt{u^2 - a^2})}{(u - \sqrt{u^2 - a^2})(u + \sqrt{u^2 - a^2})} \right|$$

$$= \ln \left| \frac{a(u + \sqrt{u^2 - a^2})}{a^2} \right|$$

$$= \ln \left| \frac{u + \sqrt{u^2 - a^2}}{a} \right|.$$

Therefore

$$\int \frac{du}{\sqrt{u^2 - a^2}} = \ln \left| u + \sqrt{u^2 - a^2} \right| + C', \qquad \text{(8)}$$

where we have replaced $C - \ln a$ by C'.

EXAMPLE 4

$$\int \frac{du}{a^2 + u^2}, \qquad a > 0.$$

Solution.   We try

$$u = a \tan \theta, \qquad du = a \sec^2 \theta \, d\theta,$$

$$a^2 + u^2 = a^2(1 + \tan^2 \theta) = a^2 \sec^2 \theta.$$

Then

$$\int \frac{du}{a^2 + u^2} = \int \frac{a \sec^2 \theta \, d\theta}{a^2 \sec^2 \theta}$$

$$= \frac{1}{a} \int d\theta = \frac{1}{a} \theta + C.$$

Since $u = a \tan \theta$,

$$\tan \theta = \frac{u}{a}, \qquad \theta = \tan^{-1} \frac{u}{a},$$

and

$$\int \frac{du}{a^2 + u^2} = \frac{1}{a} \tan^{-1} \frac{u}{a} + C. \qquad (9)$$

EXAMPLE 5

$$\int \frac{x^2 \, dx}{\sqrt{9 - x^2}}.$$

Solution.   If we substitute

$$x = 3 \sin \theta, \qquad \frac{-\pi}{2} < \theta < \frac{\pi}{2},$$

$$dx = 3 \cos \theta \, d\theta,$$

$$9 - x^2 = 9(1 - \sin^2 \theta) = 9 \cos^2 \theta,$$

then we find

$$\int \frac{x^2 \, dx}{\sqrt{9 - x^2}} = \int \frac{9 \sin^2 \theta \cdot 3 \cos \theta \, d\theta}{3 \cos \theta} = 9 \int \sin^2 \theta \, d\theta.$$

This is considerably simpler than the integral we started with. To evaluate it, we use the identity

$$\sin^2 \theta = \tfrac{1}{2}(1 - \cos 2\theta).$$

Then

$$\int \sin^2 \theta \, d\theta = \tfrac{1}{2} \int (1 - \cos 2\theta) \, d\theta = \tfrac{1}{2}[\theta - \tfrac{1}{2} \sin 2\theta] + C$$

$$= \tfrac{1}{2}[\theta - \sin \theta \cos \theta] + C.$$

Substituting this above, we get

$$\int \frac{x^2 \, dx}{\sqrt{9 - x^2}} = \frac{9}{2}[\theta - \sin \theta \cos \theta] + C$$

$$= \frac{9}{2}\left[\sin^{-1} \frac{x}{3} - \frac{x\sqrt{9 - x^2}}{9} \right] + C.$$

The trigonometric substitutions (a), (b), and (c) of Eq. (5) can be remembered by thinking of the theorem of Pythagoras and taking a and u as two of the sides and θ as an angle in a right triangle. Thus $\sqrt{a^2 - u^2}$ suggests a as hypotenuse and u as a leg, $\sqrt{a^2 + u^2}$ suggests a and u as the legs, and $\sqrt{u^2 - a^2}$ suggests u as hypotenuse and a as a leg. These situations are shown in Fig. 7–5.

a)

$u = a \sin \theta$

b)

$u = a \tan \theta$

c)

$u = a \sec \theta$

7–5 If $u = a \sin \theta$, then the values of the trigonometric functions of θ can be read from Triangle (a). Triangles (b) and (c) give the values of the trigonometric functions of θ for the substitutions $u = a \tan \theta$ and $u = a \sec \theta$.

The trigonometric identities, Eqs. (4), are simply equivalent expressions of the theorem of Pythagoras applied to the right triangles in Fig. 7–6.

Note that whenever we evaluate an indefinite integral by changing variables, i.e., by substitution, we express the final result in terms of the original variable of integration. When we integrate

$$\int \frac{du}{a^2 + u^2}$$

by substituting $u = a \tan \theta$, we state the final result as

$$\int \frac{du}{a^2 + u^2} = \frac{1}{a} \tan^{-1} \frac{u}{a} + C,$$

and not as

$$\int \frac{du}{a^2 + u^2} = \frac{1}{a} \theta + C.$$

However, when we have a definite integral to evaluate, there is another course of action open to us. We can transform the limits of integration by the same formula we use to change the variable of integration, and then evaluate the transformed integral with the transformed limits. We do this in the next example.

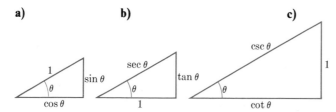

a)

$\cos \theta$

b)

1

c)

$\cot \theta$

7–6 The triangles in (b) and (c) are obtained from the basic triangle in (a) by dividing its sides all by cos θ or sin θ, respectively, to obtain similar triangles.

EXAMPLE 6.   Find the area of the quarter circle bounded by the curve $y = \sqrt{1 - x^2}$ in the first quadrant.

Solution.   The area of the quarter circle is

$$\int_0^1 \sqrt{1 - x^2} \, dx.$$

If we substitute $x = \sin \theta$, $dx = \cos \theta \, d\theta$, then $\theta = 0$ when $x = 0$, and

$\theta = \pi/2$ when $x = 1$. Accordingly,

$$\int_0^1 \sqrt{1 - x^2}\, dx = \int_0^{\pi/2} \sqrt{1 - \sin^2 \theta}\, \cos \theta\, d\theta$$

$$= \int_0^{\pi/2} \cos^2 \theta\, d\theta$$

$$= \int_0^{\pi/2} \frac{1 + \cos 2\theta}{2}\, d\theta = \frac{\theta}{2} + \left. \frac{\sin 2\theta}{4} \right]_0^{\pi/2} = \frac{\pi}{4} + 0 = \frac{\pi}{4}.$$

REMARK. We could have calculated the area of the quarter circle in Example 6 by expressing

$$\frac{\theta}{2} + \frac{\sin 2\theta}{4}$$

in terms of x and evaluating the result in terms of the original limits, but it would have been more work to do so. In some integrations, however, finding the new limits of integration after a change of variable seems to take as much work as changing the result of the integration back into an expression involving the original variable. You will have to use your own judgment about which course to take in any given instance.

PROBLEMS

Evaluate the integrals 1 through 20.

1. $\displaystyle\int_0^{0.6a} \frac{x\, dx}{\sqrt{a^2 - x^2}}$

2. $\displaystyle\int \frac{dx}{\sqrt{1 - 4x^2}}$

3. $\displaystyle\int_0^a \sqrt{a^2 - x^2}\, dx$

4. $\displaystyle\int \frac{dx}{\sqrt{4 - (x - 1)^2}}$

5. $\displaystyle\int \sec 2t\, dt$

6. $\displaystyle\int_0^2 \frac{dx}{\sqrt{4 + x^2}}$

7. $\displaystyle\int_0^1 \frac{dx}{\sqrt{4 - x^2}}$

8. $\displaystyle\int \frac{x\, dx}{\sqrt{4 + x^2}}$

9. $\displaystyle\int_0^2 \frac{x\, dx}{4 + x^2}$

10. $\displaystyle\int_0^2 \frac{dx}{4 + x^2}$

11. $\displaystyle\int_0^1 \frac{dx}{4 - x^2}$

12. $\displaystyle\int_0^1 \frac{x^3\, dx}{\sqrt{x^2 + 1}}$

13. $\displaystyle\int \frac{dx}{x\sqrt{a^2 + x^2}}$

14. $\displaystyle\int \frac{x + 1}{\sqrt{4 - x^2}}\, dx$

15. $\displaystyle\int \frac{dx}{\sqrt{2 - 5x^2}}$

16. $\displaystyle\int \frac{\sin \theta\, d\theta}{\sqrt{2 - \cos^2 \theta}}$

17. $\displaystyle\int \frac{dx}{x\sqrt{x^2 - a^2}}$

18. $\displaystyle\int \frac{dx}{x\sqrt{a^2 - x^2}}$

19. $\displaystyle\int \frac{dx}{(a^2 - x^2)^{3/2}}$

20. $\displaystyle\int \frac{dx}{(a^2 + x^2)^2}$

21. Find the area bounded by the curve $y = \sqrt{1 - (x^2/9)}$ in the first quadrant.

22. Find the area between the x-axis and the curve $y = \sqrt{1 + \cos 4x}$, $0 \le x \le \pi$.

23. Suppose $\theta = \sin^{-1}(u/2)$. Express $\cos \theta$ and $\tan \theta$ in terms of u. (See Fig. 7–5.)

24. Express in terms of u and a:

a) $\sin\left(\tan^{-1} \dfrac{u}{a}\right)$

b) $\cos\left(\sec^{-1} \dfrac{u}{a}\right)$

The general quadratic

$$f(x) = ax^2 + bx + c, \qquad a \neq 0 \tag{1}$$

can be reduced to the form $a(u^2 + B)$ by completing the square, as follows:

$$ax^2 + bx + c = a\left(x^2 + \frac{b}{a}x\right) + c = a\left(x^2 + \frac{b}{a}x + \frac{b^2}{4a^2}\right) + c - \frac{b^2}{4a}$$

$$= a\left(x + \frac{b}{2a}\right)^2 + \frac{4ac - b^2}{4a},$$

and then substituting

$$u = x + \frac{b}{2a}, \qquad B = \frac{4ac - b^2}{4a^2}, \tag{2}$$

which gives us

$$f(x) = ax^2 + bx + c = a(u^2 + B).$$

When the integrand involves the square root of $f(x) = ax^2 + bx + c$, we restrict attention to the case where $f(x)$ is not negative. If a is negative and B is positive, the square root is imaginary. We disregard this case, and consider

$$\sqrt{a(u^2 + B)}$$

1. when a is positive, and
2. when a and B are both negative.

In the first case, the relation

$$\sqrt{a(u^2 + B)} = \sqrt{a}\sqrt{u^2 + B}$$

allows us to reduce the problem to a consideration of $\sqrt{u^2 + B}$, which we handle by the methods of Article 7–4. In the second case, when a and B are both negative, then $-a$ and $-B$ are positive and

$$\sqrt{a(u^2 + B)} = \sqrt{-a(-B - u^2)}$$

$$= \sqrt{-a}\sqrt{-B - u^2} \qquad (-a > 0,\ -B > 0),$$

and, taking $-B = A^2$, say, we consider $\sqrt{A^2 - u^2}$ as in Article 7–4.

When the integrand does not involve an even root of $f(x)$, there need be no restriction on the signs of a and B. In these cases also, we try to use the trigonometric substitutions of the previous section, or to apply the integration formulas derived there.

EXAMPLE 1

$$\int \frac{dx}{\sqrt{2x - x^2}}.$$

Solution. The algebraic transformations proceed as follows:

$$\sqrt{2x - x^2} = \sqrt{-(x^2 - 2x)} = \sqrt{-(x^2 - 2x + 1) + 1}$$

$$= \sqrt{1 - u^2} \qquad (u = x - 1).$$

Then, with $u = x - 1$,

$$du = dx$$

and

$$\int \frac{dx}{\sqrt{2x - x^2}} = \int \frac{du}{\sqrt{1 - u^2}} = \sin^{-1} u + C;$$

that is,

$$\int \frac{dx}{\sqrt{2x - x^2}} = \sin^{-1} (x - 1) + C.$$

EXAMPLE 2

$$\int \frac{dx}{4x^2 + 4x + 2}.$$

Solution.   Again we start with the algebraic transformations:

$$4x^2 + 4x + 2 = 4(x^2 + x) + 2$$
$$= 4(x^2 + x + \tfrac{1}{4}) + (2 - \tfrac{4}{4})$$
$$= 4(x + \tfrac{1}{2})^2 + 1.$$

Then we let

$$u = x + \tfrac{1}{2}, \qquad du = dx,$$

and

$$\int \frac{dx}{4x^2 + 4x + 2} = \int \frac{du}{4u^2 + 1}$$
$$= \frac{1}{4} \int \frac{du}{u^2 + \tfrac{1}{4}}$$
$$= \frac{1}{4} \int \frac{du}{u^2 + a^2} \qquad (a = \tfrac{1}{2})$$
$$= \frac{1}{4} \frac{1}{a} \tan^{-1} \frac{u}{a} + C$$
$$= \frac{1}{2} \tan^{-1} (2x + 1) + C.$$

EXAMPLE 3

$$\int \frac{(x + 1)\, dx}{\sqrt{2x^2 - 6x + 4}}.$$

Solution.   The quadratic part may be reduced as follows:

$$2x^2 - 6x + 4 = 2(x^2 - 3x) + 4$$
$$= 2(x^2 - 3x + \tfrac{9}{4}) + 4 - \tfrac{9}{2} = 2(u^2 - a^2)$$

with

$$u = x - \tfrac{3}{2}, \qquad a = \tfrac{1}{2}.$$

Then

$$x = u + \tfrac{3}{2}, \qquad dx = du, \qquad x + 1 = u + \tfrac{5}{2},$$

and

$$\int \frac{(x + 1)\, dx}{\sqrt{2x^2 - 6x + 4}} = \int \frac{(u + \tfrac{5}{2})\, du}{\sqrt{2(u^2 - a^2)}}$$

$$= \frac{1}{\sqrt{2}} \int \frac{u\, du}{\sqrt{u^2 - a^2}} + \frac{5}{2\sqrt{2}} \int \frac{du}{\sqrt{u^2 - a^2}}.$$

In the former of these, we let

$$z = u^2 - a^2, \qquad dz = 2u\, du, \qquad u\, du = \tfrac{1}{2}\, dz,$$

and to the latter we apply Eq. (8), Article 7-4. That is,

$$\frac{1}{\sqrt{2}} \int \frac{u\, du}{\sqrt{u^2 - a^2}} = \frac{1}{2\sqrt{2}} \int \frac{dz}{\sqrt{z}} = \frac{1}{2\sqrt{2}} \int z^{-(1/2)}\, dz = \frac{1}{2\sqrt{2}} \frac{z^{1/2}}{\tfrac{1}{2}} + C_1$$

$$= \sqrt{\frac{u^2 - a^2}{2}} + C_1$$

and

$$\frac{5}{2\sqrt{2}} \int \frac{du}{\sqrt{u^2 - a^2}} = \frac{5}{2\sqrt{2}} \ln \left| u + \sqrt{u^2 - a^2} \right| + C_2,$$

so that

$$\int \frac{(x + 1)\, dx}{\sqrt{2x^2 - 6x + 4}}$$

$$= \sqrt{\frac{u^2 - a^2}{2}} + \frac{5}{2\sqrt{2}} \ln \left| u + \sqrt{u^2 - a^2} \right| + C$$

$$= \sqrt{\frac{x^2 - 3x + 2}{2}} + \frac{5}{2\sqrt{2}} \ln \left| x - \frac{3}{2} + \sqrt{x^2 - 3x + 2} \right| + C.$$

PROBLEMS

1. $\displaystyle \int_1^3 \frac{dx}{x^2 - 2x + 5}$

2. $\displaystyle \int \frac{x\, dx}{\sqrt{x^2 - 2x + 5}}$

7. $\displaystyle \int \frac{(1 - x)\, dx}{\sqrt{8 + 2x - x^2}}$

8. $\displaystyle \int \frac{x\, dx}{\sqrt{x^2 + 4x + 5}}$

3. $\displaystyle \int \frac{(x + 1)\, dx}{\sqrt{2x - x^2}}$

4. $\displaystyle \int \frac{(x - 1)\, dx}{\sqrt{x^2 - 4x + 3}}$

9. $\displaystyle \int \frac{x\, dx}{x^2 + 4x + 5}$

10. $\displaystyle \int \frac{(2x + 3)\, dx}{4x^2 + 4x + 5}$

5. $\displaystyle \int \frac{x\, dx}{\sqrt{5 + 4x - x^2}}$

6. $\displaystyle \int \frac{dx}{\sqrt{x^2 - 2x - 8}}$

7-6

INTEGRATION BY THE METHOD OF PARTIAL FRACTIONS

In algebra we learned how to combine fractions over a common denominator. In integration, it is desirable to reverse the process and split a fraction into a sum of fractions with simpler denominators. The technique of doing this is called the *method of partial fractions*.

EXAMPLE 1

$$\frac{2}{x+1} + \frac{3}{x-3} = \frac{2(x-3) + 3(x+1)}{(x+1)(x-3)} = \frac{5x-3}{(x+1)(x-3)}.$$

The reverse process consists in finding constants A and B such that

$$\frac{5x-3}{(x+1)(x-3)} = \frac{A}{x+1} + \frac{B}{x-3}.$$

(Pretend, for a moment, that we don't know that $A = 2$, $B = 3$ will work. We call A and B *undetermined coefficients*.) Clearing of fractions, we have

$$5x - 3 = A(x-3) + B(x+1)$$
$$= (A + B)x - 3A + B.$$

This will be an identity in x if and only if coefficients of like powers of x on the two sides of the equation are equal:

$$A + B = 5, \qquad -3A + B = -3.$$

These two equations in two unknowns determine

$$A = 2, \qquad B = 3.$$

More generally, suppose we wish to separate a rational function

$$\frac{f(x)}{g(x)} \tag{1}$$

into a sum of partial fractions. Success in doing so hinges upon two things:

1. *The degree of $f(x)$ should be less than the degree of $g(x)$.* (If this is not the case, we first perform a long division, then work with the remainder term. This remainder can always be put into the required form.)

2. *The factors of $g(x)$ should be known.* (Theoretically, any polynomial $g(x)$ with real coefficients can be expressed as a product of real linear and quadratic factors. In practice, it may be difficult to perform the factorization.)

If these two conditions prevail we can carry out the following steps.

FIRST. Let $x - r$ be a linear factor of $g(x)$. Suppose $(x - r)^m$ is the highest power of $x - r$ that divides $g(x)$. Then assign the sum of m partial fractions to this factor, as follows:

$$\frac{A_1}{x-r} + \frac{A_2}{(x-r)^2} + \cdots + \frac{A_m}{(x-r)^m}.$$

Do this for each distinct linear factor of $g(x)$.

SECOND.   Let $x^2 + px + q$ be a quadratic factor of $g(x)$. Suppose

$$(x^2 + px + q)^n$$

is the highest power of this factor that divides $g(x)$. Then, to this factor, assign the sum of the n partial fractions:

$$\frac{B_1 x + C_1}{x^2 + px + q} + \frac{B_2 x + C_2}{(x^2 + px + q)^2} + \cdots + \frac{B_n x + C_n}{(x^2 + px + q)^n}.$$

Do this for each distinct quadratic factor of $g(x)$.

THIRD.   Set the original fraction $f(x)/g(x)$ equal to the sum of all these partial fractions. Clear the resulting equation of fractions and arrange the terms in decreasing powers of x.

FOURTH.   Equate the coefficients of corresponding powers of x, and solve the resulting equations for the undetermined coefficients.

EXAMPLE 2.   Express

$$\frac{f(x)}{g(x)} = \frac{-2x + 4}{(x^2 + 1)(x - 1)^2}$$

as a sum of partial fractions.

Solution.   The degree of $f(x)$ is less than the degree of $g(x)$, and $g(x)$ is already written as a product of linear and quadratic factors. To carry out the steps listed above, we write

$$\frac{-2x + 4}{(x^2 + 1)(x - 1)^2} = \frac{Ax + B}{x^2 + 1} + \frac{C}{x - 1} + \frac{D}{(x - 1)^2}.$$

Then

$$-2x + 4 = (Ax + B)(x - 1)^2 + C(x - 1)(x^2 + 1) + D(x^2 + 1)$$
$$= (A + C)x^3 + (-2A + B - C + D)x^2$$
$$+ (A - 2B + C)x + (B - C + D).$$

In order for this to be an identity in x, it is both necessary and sufficient that the coefficient of each power of x be the same on the left side of the equation as it is on the right side. Equating these coefficients leads to the following equations:

Coefficient of x^3: $0 = A + C,$

Coefficient of x^2: $0 = -2A + B - C + D$

Coefficient of x^1: $-2 = A - 2B + C,$

Coefficient of x^0: $4 = B - C + D.$

If we subtract the fourth equation from the second, we obtain

$$-4 = -2A, \qquad A = 2.$$

Then from the first equation, we have

$$C = -A = -2.$$

Knowing A and C, we find B from the third equation,

$$B = 1.$$

Finally, from the fourth equation, we have

$$D = 4 - B + C = 1.$$

Hence

$$\frac{-2x + 4}{(x^2 + 1)(x - 1)^2} = \frac{2x + 1}{x^2 + 1} - \frac{2}{x - 1} + \frac{1}{(x - 1)^2}.$$

EXAMPLE 3. Evaluate

$$\int \frac{x^5 - x^4 - 3x + 5}{x^4 - 2x^3 + 2x^2 - 2x + 1} \, dx.$$

Solution. The integrand is a fraction, but not a proper fraction. Hence we divide first, obtaining

$$\frac{x^5 - x^4 - 3x + 5}{x^4 - 2x^3 + 2x^2 - 2x + 1} = x + 1 + \frac{-2x + 4}{x^4 - 2x^3 + 2x^2 - 2x + 1}. \quad (2)$$

The denominator factors as follows:

$$x^4 - 2x^3 + 2x^2 - 2x + 1 = (x^2 + 1)(x - 1)^2.$$

By the result of Example 2, we have, for the remainder term,

$$\frac{-2x + 4}{(x^2 + 1)(x - 1)^2} = \frac{2x + 1}{x^2 + 1} - \frac{2}{x - 1} + \frac{1}{(x - 1)^2}. \quad (3)$$

Hence, substituting from (3) into (2), multiplying by dx, and integrating, we have

$$\int \frac{x^5 - x^4 - 3x + 5}{x^4 - 2x^3 + 2x^2 - 2x + 1} \, dx$$

$$= \int \left[x + 1 + \frac{2x + 1}{x^2 + 1} - \frac{2}{x - 1} + \frac{1}{(x - 1)^2} \right] dx$$

$$= \int \left[x + 1 + \frac{2x}{x^2 + 1} + \frac{1}{x^2 + 1} - \frac{2}{x - 1} + \frac{1}{(x - 1)^2} \right] dx$$

$$= \frac{x^2}{2} + x + \ln (x^2 + 1) + \tan^{-1} x - 2 \ln |x - 1| - \frac{1}{x - 1} + C.$$

In theory, any rational function of x can be integrated by the method of partial fractions. Once the necessary algebra has been done, the problem reduces to that of evaluating integrals of the following two types:

$$\int \frac{dx}{(x-r)^h},$$ (4a)

$$\int \frac{(ax+b)\,dx}{(x^2+px+q)^k}.$$ (4b)

The first of these becomes simply $\int u^{-h}\,du$ when we let $u = x - r$. In the second type it is preferable to complete the square in the denominator:

$$x^2 + px + q = \left(x + \frac{p}{2}\right)^2 + q - \frac{p^2}{4}.$$

The quadratic $x^2 + px + q$ has no real roots. (If it had real roots, it would have been replaced by its linear factors in the original partial-fractions expansion.) Its discriminant, $p^2 - 4q$, is therefore negative. In other words,

$$4q - p^2 > 0, \quad \text{or} \quad q - \frac{p^2}{4} > 0.$$

Let

$$u = x + \frac{p}{2}, \qquad c^2 = q - \frac{p^2}{4}.$$

Then

$$ax + b = a\left(u - \frac{p}{2}\right) + b = au + b', \qquad b' = b - a\frac{p}{2},$$

and we consider

$$\int \frac{au + b'}{(u^2 + c^2)^k}\,du = \frac{a}{2}\int (u^2 + c^2)^{-k}(2u\,du) + b'\int \frac{du}{(u^2 + c^2)^k}.$$ (5)

The first integral on the right in (5) readily yields to the substitution $z = u^2 + c^2$. In the second integral, we let

$$u = c\tan\theta, \qquad du = c\sec^2\theta\,d\theta, \qquad u^2 + c^2 = c^2\sec^2\theta,$$

and obtain

$$\int \frac{du}{(u^2 + c^2)^k} = c^{1-2k}\int \cos^{2k-2}\theta\,d\theta \qquad \left(\theta = \tan^{-1}\frac{u}{c}\right).$$ (6)

In the next article we shall obtain a reduction formula for $\int \cos^n\theta\,d\theta$, which may be used to evaluate the integral in (6). The trigonometric identity

$$\cos^2\theta = \frac{1 + \cos 2\theta}{2}$$ (7)

may also be used to advantage.

The Heaviside Method

When the degree of the polynomial $f(x)$ is less than the degree of $g(x)$, and

$$g(x) = (x - r_1)(x - r_2)\cdots(x - r_n)$$ (8)

is a product of n different linear factors, each to the first power, there is a quick way to expand $f(x)/g(x)$ by partial fractions.

EXAMPLE 4.   Find A, B and C in the partial-fractions expansion

$$\frac{x^2 + 1}{(x - 1)(x - 2)(x - 3)} = \frac{A}{x - 1} + \frac{B}{x - 2} + \frac{C}{x - 3}. \tag{9}$$

Solution.   If we multiply both sides of Eq. (9) by $(x - 1)$ to get

$$\frac{x^2 + 1}{(x - 2)(x - 3)} = A + \frac{B(x - 1)}{x - 2} + \frac{C(x - 1)}{x - 3}, \tag{10}$$

and set $x = 1$, the resulting equation gives the value of A:

$$\frac{(1)^2 + 1}{(1 - 2)(1 - 3)} = A + 0 + 0,$$

$$A = 1.$$

Thus, the value of A is the number we would have obtained if we had covered the factor $x - 1$ in the denominator of the original fraction

$$\frac{x^2 + 1}{(x - 1)(x - 2)(x - 3)} \tag{11}$$

and evaluated what was left at $x = 1$. Similarly, we can find the value of B in Eq. (9) by covering up the factor $x - 2$ in (11) and evaluating the result,

$$\frac{x^2 + 1}{(x - 1)(x - 3)}, \tag{12}$$

at $x = 2$. That is,

$$B = \frac{(2)^2 + 1}{(2 - 1)(2 - 3)} = -5.$$

Finally, the value of C can be found by covering the factor $x - 3$ in (11) to get

$$\frac{x^2 + 1}{(x - 1)(x - 2)}, \tag{13}$$

and evaluating this fraction at $x = 3$:

$$C = \frac{(3)^2 + 1}{(3 - 1)(3 - 2)} = 5.$$

In general, to expand a quotient of polynomials $f(x)/g(x)$ by partial fractions when the degree of $f(x)$ is less than the degree of $g(x)$, and $g(x)$ is the product of n linear factors, each to the first power, one may proceed in the following way. First, write the quotient with $g(x)$ factored:

$$\frac{f(x)}{g(x)} = \frac{f(x)}{(x - r_1)(x - r_2) \cdots (x - r_n)}. \tag{14}$$

Then, cover the factors $(x - r_i)$ of $g(x)$ in (14) one at a time, each time replacing all the uncovered x's by the number r_i. This gives a number A_i for each root r_i:

$$A_1 = \frac{f(r_1)}{(r_1 - r_2) \cdots (r_1 - r_n)},$$

$$A_2 = \frac{f(r_2)}{(r_2 - r_1)(r_2 - r_3) \cdots (r_2 - r_n)}, \qquad \textbf{(15)}$$

$$\vdots$$

$$A_n = \frac{f(r_n)}{(r_n - r_1)(r_n - r_2) \cdots (r_n - r_{n-1})}.$$

The partial-fraction expansion of $f(x)/g(x)$ is then

$$\frac{f(x)}{g(x)} = \frac{A_1}{(x - r_1)} + \frac{A_2}{(x - r_2)} + \cdots + \frac{A_n}{(x - r_n)}. \qquad \textbf{(16)}$$

EXAMPLE 5. Evaluate

$$\int \frac{x + 4}{x^3 + 3x^2 - 10x} \, dx.$$

Solution. The degree of $f(x) = x + 4$ is less than the degree of $g(x) = x^3 + 3x^2 - 10x$, and, with $g(x)$ factored,

$$\frac{x + 4}{x^3 + 3x^2 - 10x} = \frac{x + 4}{x(x - 2)(x + 5)}.$$

The roots of $g(x)$ are $r_1 = 0$, $r_2 = 2$, and $r_3 = -5$. We find

$$A_1 = \frac{0 + 4}{(0 - 2)(0 + 5)} = -\frac{2}{5},$$

$$A_2 = \frac{2 + 4}{2(2 + 5)} = \frac{3}{7},$$

$$A_3 = \frac{-5 + 4}{(-5)(-5 - 2)} = -\frac{1}{35}.$$

Therefore,

$$\frac{x + 4}{x(x - 2)(x + 5)} = -\frac{2}{5x} + \frac{3}{7(x - 2)} - \frac{1}{35(x + 5)},$$

and

$$\int \frac{x + 4}{x(x - 2)(x + 5)} \, dx = -\frac{2}{5} \ln |x| + \frac{3}{7} \ln |x - 2| - \frac{1}{35} \ln |x + 5| + C.$$

EXAMPLE 6. The equation that describes the autocatalytic reaction of Example 2, Article 3–6, can be written as

$$\frac{dx}{dt} = kx(a - x).$$

Find x as a function of t if the initial amount of product is x_0; that is, $x = x_0$ when $t = 0$.

Solution.   We separate variables to obtain

$$\frac{dx}{x(a - x)} = k\,dt, \tag{17}$$

and integrate both sides of the equation:

$$\int \frac{dx}{x(a - x)} = kt + C. \tag{18}$$

Since

$$\frac{1}{x(a - x)} = \frac{1}{ax} + \frac{1}{a(a - x)},$$

the integral on the left of Eq. (18) is

$$\int \frac{dx}{x(a - x)} = \frac{1}{a}\ln x - \frac{1}{a}\ln (a - x) + C = \frac{1}{a}\ln \frac{x}{a - x} + C. \tag{19}$$

We can omit the usual absolute-value signs because neither x nor $a - x$ is negative in the context of this application. Equations (18) and (19) together give

$$\frac{1}{a}\ln \frac{x}{a - x} = kt + C. \tag{20}$$

Substituting $x = x_0$, $t = 0$, in this equation, we find that

$$\frac{1}{a}\ln \frac{x_0}{a - x_0} = C.$$

When we substitute this expression for C in Eq. (20) and simplify the equation, the result is

$$\ln \frac{x(a - x_0)}{x_0(a - x)} = akt. \tag{21}$$

PROBLEMS

Evaluate the integrals 1 through 18.

1. $\displaystyle\int \frac{dx}{1 - x^2}$

2. $\displaystyle\int \frac{d\theta}{\theta^3 + \theta^2 - 2\theta}$

3. $\displaystyle\int \frac{x\,dx}{x^2 + 4x - 5}$

4. $\displaystyle\int \frac{x\,dx}{x^2 - 2x - 3}$

5. $\displaystyle\int \frac{(x + 1)\,dx}{x^2 + 4x - 5}$

6. $\displaystyle\int \frac{x^2\,dx}{x^2 + 2x + 1}$

7. $\displaystyle\int \frac{dx}{x(x + 1)^2}$

8. $\displaystyle\int \frac{dx}{(x + 1)(x^2 + 1)}$

9. $\displaystyle\int \frac{(x + 3)\,dx}{2x^3 - 8x}$

10. $\displaystyle\int \frac{\cos x\,dx}{\sin^2 x + \sin x - 6}$

11. $\displaystyle\int \frac{5x^2\,dx}{x^2 + 1}$

12. $\displaystyle\int \frac{x^3\,dx}{x^2 - 2x + 1}$

13. $\displaystyle\int \frac{dx}{x(x^2 + x + 1)}$

14. $\displaystyle\int \frac{\sin \theta\,d\theta}{\cos^2 \theta + \cos \theta - 2}$

15. $\displaystyle\int \frac{e^t\,dt}{e^{2t} + 3e^t + 2}$

16. $\displaystyle\int \frac{dx}{(x^2 + 1)^2}$

17. $\int \dfrac{x^4 \, dx}{(x^2 + 1)^2}$ **18.** $\int \dfrac{(4x^3 - 20x) \, dx}{x^4 - 10x^2 + 9}$

19. To integrate $\int x^2 \, dx/(x^2 - 1)$ by partial fractions, we would first divide x^2 by $x^2 - 1$ to get

$$\frac{x^2}{x^2 - 1} = 1 + \frac{1}{x^2 - 1}.$$

Suppose that we ignore the fact that x^2 and $x^2 - 1$ have the same degree, and try to write

$$\frac{x^2}{x^2 - 1} = \frac{x^2}{(x - 1)(x + 1)} = \frac{A}{x - 1} + \frac{B}{x + 1}.$$

What goes wrong? Find out by trying to solve for A and B.

20. Many chemical reactions are the result of an interaction of two molecules that undergo a change to produce a new product. The rate of the reaction typically depends on the concentration of the two kinds of molecules. If a is the amount of substance A and b is the amount of substance B at time $t = 0$ and if x is the amount of product at time t, then the rate of formation of x may be given by the differential equation

$$\frac{dx}{dt} = k(a - x)(b - x),$$

where k is a positive constant. Find a relation between x and t, (a) if $a = b$, and (b) if $a \neq b$. [See Example 6.]

There are really just two general methods of integration. One of these is the method of substitution, which we have illustrated in Articles 7–2 through 7–5. The method of partial fractions is really not a method of integration so much as it is a method of algebraic transformation of a rational function into an integrable form. The second general method of integration, called *integration by parts*, depends upon the formula for the differential of a product:

$$d(uv) = u \, dv + v \, du$$

or

$$u \, dv = d(uv) - v \, du.$$

When this is integrated, we have

$$\int u \, dv = uv - \int v \, du + C. \qquad \textbf{(1)}$$

Formula (1) expresses one integral, $\int u \, dv$, in terms of a second integral, $\int v \, du$. If, by proper choice of u and dv, the second integral is simpler than the first, we may be able to evaluate it quite simply and thus arrive at an answer.

REMARK. In a definite integral, appropriate limits must be supplied. We may then interpret the formula for integration by parts,

$$\int_{v_1}^{v_2} u \, dv = (u_2 v_2 - u_1 v_1) - \int_{u_1}^{u_2} v \, du,$$

geometrically in terms of areas (see Fig. 7–7).

EXAMPLE 1

$$\int \ln x \, dx.$$

7–7

INTEGRATION BY PARTS

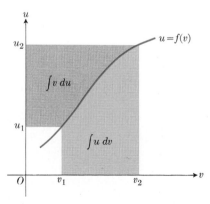

7-7 $\displaystyle \int_{v_1}^{v_2} u \, dv = (u_2 v_2 - u_1 v_1) - \int_{u_1}^{u_2} v \, du.$

Solution.   If we try to match ln $x\,dx$ with $u\,dv$, we may take $u = \ln x$ and $dv = dx$. Then, to use (1), we see that we also require

$$du = d(\ln x) = \frac{dx}{x}$$

and

$$v = \int dv = \int dx = x + C_1,$$

so that

$$\int \ln x\,dx = (\ln x)(x + C_1) - \int (x + C_1)\frac{dx}{x} + C_2$$

$$= x \ln x + C_1 \ln x - \int dx - \int C_1\frac{dx}{x} + C_2$$

$$= x \ln x + C_1 \ln x - x - C_1 \ln x + C_2 = x \ln x - x + C_2.$$

Note that the first constant of integration C_1 does not appear in the final answer. This is generally true, for if we write $v + C_1$ in place of v in the right side of (1), we obtain

$$u(v + C_1) - \int (v + C_1)\,du = uv + C_1 u - \int v\,du - \int C_1\,du = uv - \int v\,du,$$

where it is understood that a constant of integration must still be added in the final result. It is therefore customary to drop the first constant of integration when determining v as $\int dv$.

EXAMPLE 2

$$\int \tan^{-1} x\,dx.$$

Solution.   This is typical of the inverse trigonometric functions. Let

$$u = \tan^{-1} x \qquad \text{and} \qquad dv = dx;$$

then

$$du = \frac{dx}{1 + x^2} \qquad \text{and} \qquad v = x,$$

so that

$$\int \tan^{-1} x\,dx = x \tan^{-1} x - \int \frac{x\,dx}{1 + x^2} = x \tan^{-1} x - \frac{1}{2} \ln (1 + x^2) + C.$$

Sometimes an integration by parts must be repeated to obtain an answer, as in the following example.

EXAMPLE 3

$$\int x^2 e^x\,dx.$$

Solution.   Let

$$u = x^2 \quad \text{and} \quad dv = e^x \, dx.$$

Then

$$du = 2x \, dx \quad \text{and} \quad v = e^x,$$

so that

$$\int x^2 e^x \, dx = x^2 e^x - 2 \int x e^x \, dx.$$

The integral on the right is similar to the original integral, except that we have reduced the power of x from 2 to 1. If we could now reduce it from 1 to 0, we could see success ahead. In $\int x e^x \, dx$, we therefore let

$$U = x \quad \text{and} \quad dV = e^x \, dx,$$

so that

$$dU = dx \quad \text{and} \quad V = e^x.$$

Then

$$\int x e^x \, dx = x e^x - \int e^x \, dx = x e^x - e^x + C,$$

and

$$\int x^2 e^x \, dx = x^2 e^x - 2x e^x + 2 e^x + C.$$

EXAMPLE 4.   Obtain a reduction formula for the integral

$$J_n = \int \cos^n x \, dx.$$

Solution.   We may think of $\cos^n x$ as $\cos^{n-1} x \cdot \cos x$. Then we let

$$u = \cos^{n-1} x \quad \text{and} \quad dv = \cos x \, dx,$$

so that

$$du = (n-1) \cos^{n-2} x (-\sin x \, dx) \quad \text{and} \quad v = \sin x.$$

Hence

$$J_n = \cos^{n-1} x \sin x + (n-1) \int \sin^2 x \cos^{n-2} x \, dx$$

$$= \cos^{n-1} x \sin x + (n-1) \int (1 - \cos^2 x) \cos^{n-2} x \, dx,$$

or

$$\int \cos^n x \, dx$$

$$= \cos^{n-1} x \sin x + (n-1) \int \cos^{n-2} x \, dx - (n-1) \int \cos^n x \, dx.$$

The last integral on the right may now be transposed to the left to give

$$[1 + (n-1)]J_n = nJ_n.$$

We then divide by n, and the final result is

$$\int \cos^n x \, dx = \frac{\cos^{n-1} x \sin x}{n} + \frac{n-1}{n} \int \cos^{n-2} x \, dx. \qquad (2)$$

This allows us to reduce the exponent on $\cos x$ by 2 and is a very useful formula. When n is a positive integer, we may apply the formula repeatedly until the remaining integral is either

$$\int \cos x \, dx = \sin x + C \qquad \text{or} \qquad \int \cos^0 x \, dx = \int dx = x + C.$$

For example, with $n = 4$, we get

$$\int \cos^4 x \, dx = \frac{\cos^3 x \sin x}{4} + \frac{3}{4} \int \cos^2 x \, dx,$$

and with $n = 2$,

$$\int \cos^2 x \, dx = \frac{\cos x \sin x}{2} + \frac{1}{2} \int dx.$$

Therefore,

$$\int \cos^4 x \, dx = \frac{\cos^3 x \sin x}{4} + \frac{3}{4} \left(\frac{\cos x \sin x}{2} + \tfrac{1}{2}x \right) + C.$$

You may find it instructive to derive the companion formula:

$$\int \sin^n x \, dx = -\frac{\sin^{n-1} x \cos x}{n} + \frac{n-1}{n} \int \sin^{n-2} x \, dx. \qquad (3)$$

The integral in the following example occurs in electrical engineering problems. Its evaluation requires two integrations by parts, followed by solving for the unknown integral in a method analogous to that used above in finding reduction formulas.

EXAMPLE 5

$$\int e^{ax} \cos bx \, dx.$$

Solution. Let

$$u = e^{ax} \qquad \text{and} \qquad dv = \cos bx \, dx.$$

Then

$$du = ae^{ax} \, dx \qquad \text{and} \qquad v = \frac{1}{b} \sin bx,$$

so that

$$\int e^{ax} \cos bx \, dx = \frac{e^{ax} \sin bx}{b} - \frac{a}{b} \int e^{ax} \sin bx \, dx.$$

The second integral is like the first except that it has $\sin bx$ in place of $\cos bx$. If we apply integration by parts to it, letting

$$U = e^{ax} \qquad \text{and} \qquad dV = \sin bx \, dx,$$

then

$$dU = ae^{ax} \, dx \qquad \text{and} \qquad V = -\frac{1}{b}\cos bx,$$

so that

$$\int e^{ax} \cos bx \, dx = \frac{e^{ax} \sin bx}{b} - \frac{a}{b}\left[-\frac{e^{ax} \cos bx}{b} + \frac{a}{b}\int e^{ax} \cos bx \, dx \right].$$

Now the unknown integral appears on the left with a coefficient of unity and on the right with a coefficient of $-a^2/b^2$. Transposing this term to the left and dividing by the new coefficient

$$1 + \frac{a^2}{b^2} = \frac{a^2 + b^2}{b^2},$$

we have

$$\int e^{ax} \cos bx \, dx = e^{ax}\left(\frac{b \sin bx + a \cos bx}{a^2 + b^2} \right) + C. \tag{4}$$

PROBLEMS

Evaluate the integrals 1 through 16.

1. $\int x \ln x \, dx$

2. $\int x^n \ln ax \, dx \quad (n \neq -1)$

3. $\int x \tan^{-1} x \, dx$

4. $\int \sin^{-1} ax \, dx$

5. $\int x \sin ax \, dx$

6. $\int x^2 \cos ax \, dx$

7. $\int x \sec^2 ax \, dx$

8. $\int e^{ax} \sin bx \, dx$

9. $\int \sin (\ln x) \, dx$

10. $\int \cos (\ln x) \, dx$

11. $\int \ln (a^2 + x^2) \, dx$

12. $\int x \cos (2x + 1) \, dx$

13. $\int x \sin^{-1} x \, dx$

14. $\int_1^2 x \sec^{-1} x \, dx$

15. $\int_1^4 \sec^{-1} \sqrt{x} \, dx$

16. $\int x^2 \tan^{-1} x \, dx$

Derive the reduction formulas given in part (a) of each of the following problems, and apply each one to the specific problems given there.

17. a) $\int x^m (\ln x)^n \, dx = \frac{x^{m+1}(\ln x)^n}{m + 1}$

$$- \frac{n}{m + 1}\int x^m (\ln x)^{n-1} \, dx$$

b) $\int x^3 (\ln x)^2 \, dx$

18. a) $\int \sin^n x \, dx = -\frac{\sin^{n-1} x \cos x}{n}$

$$+ \frac{n - 1}{n}\int \sin^{n-2} x \, dx$$

b) $\int_0^{\pi/6} \sin^4 3x \, dx$

19. a) $\int x^n e^x \, dx = x^n e^x - n \int x^{n-1} e^x \, dx;$ **b)** $\int x^3 e^x \, dx$

20. a) $\int \sec^n x \, dx = \dfrac{\sec^{n-2} x \tan x}{(n-1)} + \dfrac{n-2}{n-1} \int \sec^{n-2} x \, dx$

b) $\int \sec^3 x \, dx$ [See Eq. (3), Article 7–2.]

c) $\int \sqrt{a^2 + x^2} \, dx$ [*Hint.* Let $x = a \tan \theta$.]

21. Find the second degree polynomial $P(x)$ that has the following properties: (a) $P(0) = 1$, (b) $P'(0) = 0$, and (c) the indefinite integral

$$\int \frac{P(x) \, dx}{x^3(x-1)^2}$$

is a rational function. (That is, no logarithmic terms occur in the answer.)

22. Use cylindrical shells to find the volume of the solid obtained by revolving the area bounded by $x = 0$, $y = 0$, and $y = \cos x$, $0 \le x \le \pi/2$, about the y-axis.

23. Find the centroid of the area bounded by $y = x^2 e^x$, $y = 0$, $x = 1$.

24. Find the centroid of the area bounded by $y = \ln x$, $x = 1$, $y = 1$.

25. Evaluate $\displaystyle\int_0^1 e^{\sqrt{x}} \, dx$.

7–8

INTEGRATION OF RATIONAL FUNCTIONS OF $\sin x$ AND $\cos x$, AND OTHER TRIGONOMETRIC INTEGRALS

It has been discovered that the substitution

$$z = \tan \frac{x}{2} \tag{1}$$

enables us to reduce the problem of integrating any rational function of $\sin x$ and $\cos x$ to a problem involving a rational function of z. This in turn can be integrated by the method of partial fractions discussed in Article 7–6. Thus the substitution (1) is a very powerful tool. This method is cumbersome, however, and is used only when the simpler methods outlined previously have failed.

To see the effect of the substitution, we calculate

$$\cos x = 2 \cos^2 \frac{x}{2} - 1 = \frac{2}{\sec^2 (x/2)} - 1$$

$$= \frac{2}{1 + \tan^2 (x/2)} - 1 = \frac{2}{1 + z^2} - 1$$

or

$$\cos x = \frac{1 - z^2}{1 + z^2}, \tag{2a}$$

and

$$\sin x = 2 \sin \frac{x}{2} \cos \frac{x}{2} = 2 \frac{\sin (x/2)}{\cos (x/2)} \cdot \cos^2 \frac{x}{2}$$

$$= 2 \tan \frac{x}{2} \cdot \frac{1}{\sec^2 (x/2)} = \frac{2 \tan (x/2)}{1 + \tan^2 (x/2)}$$

or

$$\sin x = \frac{2z}{1 + z^2}. \tag{2b}$$

Finally,

$$x = 2 \tan^{-1} z,$$

so that

$$dx = \frac{2\,dz}{1+z^2}.$$ (2c)

EXAMPLE 1

$$\int \sec x\,dx = \int \frac{dx}{\cos x} \quad \text{becomes} \quad \int \frac{2\,dz}{1+z^2} \cdot \frac{1+z^2}{1-z^2} = \int \frac{2\,dz}{1-z^2}.$$

To this we apply the method of partial fractions:

$$\frac{2}{1-z^2} = \frac{A}{1-z} + \frac{B}{1+z},$$

$$2 = A(1+z) + B(1-z)$$

$$= (A+B) + (A-B)z,$$

which requires

$$A+B = 2, \qquad A-B = 0.$$

Hence

$$A = B = 1$$

and

$$\int \frac{2\,dz}{1-z^2} = \int \frac{dz}{1-z} + \int \frac{dz}{1+z} = -\ln|1-z| + \ln|1+z| + C$$

$$= \ln \left| \frac{1+z}{1-z} \right| + C$$

$$= \ln \left| \frac{1+\tan(x/2)}{1-\tan(x/2)} \right| + C$$

$$= \ln \left| \frac{\tan(\pi/4) + \tan(x/2)}{1 - \tan(\pi/4)\tan(x/2)} \right| + C$$

$$= \ln \left| \tan\left(\frac{\pi}{4} + \frac{x}{2}\right) \right| + C.$$

That is,

$$\int \sec x\,dx = \ln \left| \tan\left(\frac{\pi}{4} + \frac{x}{2}\right) \right| + C$$ (3)

is an alternative form, which may be used in place of Eq. (3), Article 7–2.

EXAMPLE 2

$$\int \frac{dx}{1+\cos x} = \int \frac{2\,dz}{1+z^2} \frac{1+z^2}{2} = \int dz = z + C = \tan \frac{x}{2} + C.$$

EXAMPLE 3

$$\int \frac{dx}{2 + \sin x} = \int \frac{2\,dz}{1 + z^2} \left[\frac{1 + z^2}{2 + 2z + 2z^2} \right] = \int \frac{dz}{z^2 + z + 1} = \int \frac{dz}{(z + \frac{1}{2})^2 + \frac{3}{4}}$$

$$= \int \frac{du}{u^2 + a^2} \qquad \left[u = z + \frac{1}{2}, \quad a = \frac{\sqrt{3}}{2} \right]$$

$$= \frac{1}{a} \tan^{-1} \frac{u}{a} + C = \frac{2}{\sqrt{3}} \tan^{-1} \frac{2z + 1}{\sqrt{3}} + C$$

$$= \frac{2}{\sqrt{3}} \tan^{-1} \frac{1 + 2 \tan (x/2)}{\sqrt{3}} + C.$$

We have already made repeated use of trigonometric identities to aid us in evaluating integrals. The following types of integrals:

$$\int \sin mx \sin nx \, dx, \qquad \int \sin mx \cos nx \, dx, \qquad \int \cos mx \cos nx \, dx, \qquad \textbf{(4)}$$

arise in connection with alternating-current theory, heat transfer problems, bending of beams, cable stress analysis in suspension bridges, and many other places where trigonometric series (or Fourier series) are applied to problems in mathematics, science, and engineering. The integrals in (4) can be evaluated by the method of integration by parts, but two such integrations are required in each case. A simpler way to evaluate them is to exploit the trigonometric identities

a) $\quad \sin mx \sin nx = \frac{1}{2}[\cos (m - n)x - \cos (m + n)x],$

b) $\quad \sin mx \cos nx = \frac{1}{2}[\sin (m - n)x + \sin (m + n)x],$ $\qquad$ **(5)**

c) $\quad \cos mx \cos nx = \frac{1}{2}[\cos (m - n)x + \cos (m + n)x].$

These identities follow at once from

$$\cos (A + B) = \cos A \cos B - \sin A \sin B,$$
$$\cos (A - B) = \cos A \cos B + \sin A \sin B, \qquad \textbf{(6a)}$$

and

$$\sin (A + B) = \sin A \cos B + \cos A \sin B,$$
$$\sin (A - B) = \sin A \cos B - \cos A \sin B. \qquad \textbf{(6b)}$$

For example, if we add the two equations in (6a) and then divide by 2, we obtain (5c) by taking $A = mx$ and $B = nx$. The identity in (5a) is obtained in a similar fashion by subtracting the first equation in (6a) from the second equation. Finally, if we add the two equations in (6b) we are led to the identity in (5b).

EXAMPLE 4

$$\int \sin 3x \cos 5x \, dx = \tfrac{1}{2} \int \left[\sin(-2x) + \sin 8x \right] dx$$

$$= \tfrac{1}{2} \int (\sin 8x - \sin 2x) \, dx$$

$$= -\frac{\cos 8x}{16} + \frac{\cos 2x}{4} + C.$$

PROBLEMS

Evaluate integrals 1 through 8.

1. $\displaystyle\int_0^\pi \frac{dx}{1 + \sin x}$

2. $\displaystyle\int_{\pi/2}^\pi \frac{dx}{1 - \cos x}$

3. $\displaystyle\int \frac{dx}{1 - \sin x}$

4. $\displaystyle\int_0^{\pi/2} \frac{dx}{2 + \cos x}$

5. $\displaystyle\int \frac{\cos x \, dx}{2 - \cos x}$

6. $\displaystyle\int_0^{\pi/2} \cos 3x \sin 2x \, dx$

7. $\displaystyle\int_{-\pi}^{\pi} \sin 3x \sin 2x \, dx$ **8.** $\displaystyle\int_{-\pi}^{\pi} \sin^2 3x \, dx$

9. Two functions f and g are said to be *orthogonal* on an interval $a \le x \le b$ if $\int_a^b f(x)g(x) \, dx = 0$. (a) Prove that $\sin mx$ and $\sin nx$ are orthogonal on any interval of length 2π provided m and n are integers such that $m^2 \ne n^2$. (b) Prove the same for $\cos mx$ and $\cos nx$. (c) Prove the same for $\sin mx$ and $\cos nx$ even if $m = n$.

Some integrals involving fractional powers of the variable x may be simplified by substituting $x = z^n$, where n is the least common multiple of the denominators of the exponents.

For example

$$\int \frac{\sqrt{x} \, dx}{1 + \sqrt[4]{x}}$$

7–9

FURTHER SUBSTITUTIONS

may be simplified by taking

$$x = z^4, \qquad dx = 4z^3 \, dz.$$

This leads to

$$\int \frac{\sqrt{x} \, dx}{1 + \sqrt[4]{x}} = \int \frac{z^2 \cdot 4z^3 \, dz}{1 + z}$$

$$= 4 \int \left(z^4 - z^3 + z^2 - z + 1 - \frac{1}{z + 1} \right) dz$$

$$= 4 \left[\frac{z^5}{5} - \frac{z^4}{4} + \frac{z^3}{3} - \frac{z^2}{2} + z - \ln|z + 1| \right] + C$$

$$= \tfrac{4}{5}x^{5/4} - x + \tfrac{4}{3}x^{3/4} - 2x^{1/2} + 4x^{1/4} - 4 \ln|1 + x^{-1/4}| + C.$$

In $\int x^3 \sqrt{x^2 + a^2} \, dx$, on the other hand, the substitution

$$z^2 = x^2 + a^2$$

or

$$x^2 = z^2 - a^2$$

and

$$2x \, dx = 2z \, dz$$

leads to

$$\int x^3 \sqrt{x^2 + a^2} \, dx = \int x^2 \sqrt{x^2 + a^2} \cdot x \, dx = \int (z^2 - a^2) \cdot z^2 \cdot dz$$

$$= \int (z^4 - a^2 z^2) \, dz$$

$$= \tfrac{1}{5}(x^2 + a^2)^{5/2} - \tfrac{1}{3}a^2(x^2 + a^2)^{3/2} + C$$

$$= \frac{3x^2 - 2a^2}{15}(x^2 + a^2)^{3/2} + C.$$

Even when it is not clear at the start that a substitution will work, it is advisable to try one that seems reasonable and pursue it until it either gives results or appears to make matters worse. In the latter case, try something else! Sometimes a chain of substitutions

$$u = f(x), \qquad v = g(u), \qquad z = h(v), \qquad \text{etc.,}$$

will produce results when it is by no means obvious that this will work. The criterion of success is whether the new integrals so obtained appear to be simpler than the original integral. In this regard, it is handy to remember that any rational function of x can be integrated by the method of partial fractions and that any rational function of $\sin x$ and $\cos x$ can be integrated by using the substitution $z = \tan x/2$. If we can reduce a given integral to one of these types, we then know how to finish the job.

Even in these cases, however, it is frequently simpler to use special methods suggested by the particular integrand rather than to use the general methods. For instance, one would hardly let $z = \tan x/2$ in order to evaluate $\int \sin x \, dx = -\cos x + C$. And reference to Eqs. (5) and (6), Article 7–6, and the accompanying discussion shows that a trigonometric substitution is used to evaluate certain of the integrals that arise in the method of partial fractions. It may be more convenient to use the same substitution *before* going through the algebraic reductions instead of *after* doing so.

For example, consider the integral

$$\int_{-1}^{0} \sqrt{\frac{1 + x}{1 - x}} \, dx. \tag{1}$$

If we let

$$\frac{1 + x}{1 - x} = z^2, \tag{2}$$

we shall, of course, get rid of the radical. Whether this is really a good substitution or not depends upon how complicated the expression is for dx

in terms of z and dz. To settle this question, we solve for x as follows:

$$1 + x = z^2 - xz^2,$$

$$x(z^2 + 1) = z^2 - 1,$$

$$x = \frac{z^2 - 1}{z^2 + 1}. \tag{3}$$

Hence

$$dx = \frac{4z\,dz}{(z^2 + 1)^2}$$

and the integral becomes

$$\int \sqrt{\frac{1 + x}{1 - x}}\,dx = \int \frac{4z^2\,dz}{(z^2 + 1)^2}.$$

Now the integrand on the right is a rational function of z and we could proceed by the method of partial fractions. But the $z^2 + 1$ in the denominator also lends itself to the substitution

$$z = \tan\theta. \tag{4}$$

We try this, and have

$$dz = \sec^2\theta\,d\theta, \qquad z^2 + 1 = \tan^2\theta + 1 = \sec^2\theta,$$

so that

$$\int \frac{4z^2\,dz}{(z^2 + 1)^2} = \int \frac{4\tan^2\theta \cdot \sec^2\theta\,d\theta}{\sec^4\theta}$$

$$= 4\int \frac{\sin^2\theta}{\cos^2\theta} \cdot \frac{1}{\sec^2\theta}\,d\theta = 4\int \sin^2\theta\,d\theta,$$

and the last integral can now be evaluated at once to give

$$4\int \sin^2\theta\,d\theta = 2\left[\theta - \frac{\sin 2\theta}{2}\right] + C. \tag{5}$$

We now have two alternative courses of action for evaluating the *definite integral*, (1): namely,

a) we may reverse the substitutions (3) and (4) and replace (5) by its equivalent in terms of x. Then the definite integral (1) could be evaluated by substituting the original limits of integration; or,

b) we may determine new limits of integration corresponding to the new variable of integration.

We illustrate the second line of attack. In the original integral, (1), x varies from -1 to 0. As this happens, the left side of (2) varies from 0 to 1, and since we have tacitly taken

$$z = \sqrt{\frac{1 + x}{1 - x}}$$

as the *positive* square root, we see that then z varies from 0 to 1. Finally, from (4) we have $\theta = \tan^{-1} z$, so that θ varies from 0 to $\pi/4$ as z varies from 0 to 1. Combining these results, we have

$$\int_{-1}^{0} \sqrt{\frac{1+x}{1-x}}\, dx = \int_{0}^{1} \frac{4z^2\, dz}{(z^2+1)^2} \qquad \left[z = \sqrt{\frac{1+x}{1-x}}\right]$$

$$= 4 \int_{0}^{\pi/4} \sin^2 \theta\, d\theta \qquad [\theta = \tan^{-1} z]$$

$$= 2 \left[\theta - \frac{\sin 2\theta}{2}\right]_{0}^{\pi/4} = \frac{\pi}{2}.$$

It is also instructive to evaluate the integral in (1) by making the alternative substitution

$$x = \cos 2t, \qquad dx = -2\sin 2t\, dt = -4\sin t \cos t\, dt,$$

which is particularly well adapted to the integrand in question, since

$$1 + \cos 2t = 2\cos^2 t$$

and

$$1 - \cos 2t = 2\sin^2 t.$$

But the shortest way of all is to notice that for the interval of integration $-1 \le x \le 0$ we have

$$\sqrt{\frac{1+x}{1-x}} = \frac{1+x}{\sqrt{1-x^2}},$$

and hence

$$\int \sqrt{\frac{1+x}{1-x}}\, dx = \int \frac{1+x}{\sqrt{1-x^2}}\, dx$$

$$= \sin^{-1} x - \sqrt{1-x^2} + C. \qquad \textbf{(6)}$$

PROBLEMS

1. $\int \dfrac{1-\sqrt{x}}{1+\sqrt{x}}\, dx$

2. $\int \dfrac{dx}{a + b\sqrt{x}}$ (a and b constants)

3. $\int x^2 \sqrt{x+a}\, dx$

4. $\int \dfrac{\sqrt{x+a}\, dx}{x+b}$ $(b>a)$

5. $\int \sqrt{\dfrac{a+x}{b+x}}\, dx$ $(b \neq a)$

6. $\int \dfrac{dx}{x + \sqrt{x^2+a^2}}$ $(a>0)$

7. $\int_{0}^{1} \dfrac{x^3\, dx}{(x^2+1)^{3/2}}$

8. $\int \dfrac{dx}{x(ax^n + c)}$ $(anc \neq 0)$

9. $\int_{3}^{8} \dfrac{(t+2)\, dt}{t\sqrt{t+1}}$

10. $\int \dfrac{dx}{x - x^{2/3}}$

11. $\int_{0}^{3} \dfrac{\sqrt{x+1}-1}{\sqrt{x+1}+1}\, dx$

12. $\int \dfrac{dx}{x(1 - \sqrt[4]{x})}$

13. $\int \dfrac{y^{2/3}\, dy}{y+1}$

14. $\int \dfrac{z^5\, dz}{\sqrt{1+z^3}}$

15. $\int \dfrac{\sqrt{t^3-1}}{t}\, dt$

16. $\int_{0}^{\ln 2} \dfrac{dw}{(1+e^w)}$

17. $\int_{0}^{\pi/2} \dfrac{\sin 2\theta\, d\theta}{2 + \cos \theta}$

18. $\int \dfrac{\sin x\, dx}{\tan x + \cos x}$

19. $\int \dfrac{dx}{x^3 + 1}$

20. $\int \dfrac{dy}{y^{1/3} - y^{1/2}}$

When the integral discussed in the previous article is changed to

$$\int_{-1}^{+1} \sqrt{\frac{1+x}{1-x}}\, dx,$$

which arises in the so-called "lifting line theory" in aerodynamics, the result is called an *improper* integral because the integrand

$$f(x) = \sqrt{\frac{1+x}{1-x}}$$

becomes infinite at one of the limits of integration, in this case at $x = +1$. More generally, integrals of the following two types are called improper integrals:

a) $\int_a^b f(x)\, dx$,   where $f(x)$ becomes infinite at a value of x between a and b inclusive,

b) $\int_a^\infty f(x)\, dx$ or $\int_{-\infty}^b f(x)\, dx$,   where one or both of the limits of integration are infinite.

EXAMPLE 1

$$\int_{-1}^{1} \sqrt{\frac{1+x}{1-x}}\, dx = \int_0^\infty \frac{4z^2\, dz}{(z^2+1)^2} \qquad \left[z = \sqrt{\frac{1+x}{1-x}} \right],$$

where the integral on the left is an improper integral of the first type and the integral on the right is an improper integral of the second type.

An integral can be improper for more than one reason.

EXAMPLE 2. In

$$\int_0^\infty \frac{1}{x^3}\, dx,$$

the function $1/x^3$ becomes infinite as x approaches 0, and also one of the limits of integration is infinite.

Figure 7–8 illustrates another case where the function becomes infinite at one of the limits of integration. If we interpret the integral in Example 1 in terms of area under the curve $y = f(x)$, say from -1 to $+1$, we see that the curve extends to infinity as x approaches 1 and the area from -1 to $+1$ is not well defined. Nevertheless, we can certainly define the area from $x = -1$ to $x = b$, where b is any positive number *less* than one; for example, we can take $b = 0.999$. This defines a function of b:

$$g(b) = \int_{-1}^b f(x)\, dx.$$

If this function has a finite limit as b approaches $+1$ from the left, we *define*

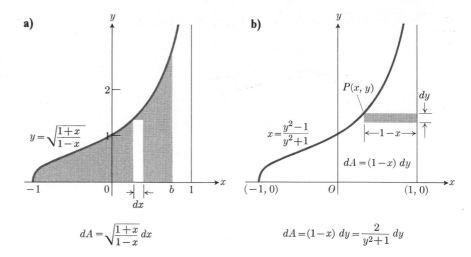

7–8 Two schemes for calculating $\int_{-1}^{1} \sqrt{(1+x)/(1-x)}\,dx$ as an area.

the value of the improper integral to be this limit:

$$\int_{-1}^{+1} f(x)\,dx = \lim_{b \to 1^-} \int_{-1}^{b} f(x)\,dx.$$

In this case we also say that the improper integral *converges*. On the other hand, we say that the integral *diverges* if the function g has no definite finite limit as $b \to 1^-$.

EXAMPLE 3. We find from Eq. (6) of Article 7–9 that

$$\int_{-1}^{b} \sqrt{\frac{1+x}{1-x}}\,dx = \sin^{-1} x - \sqrt{1-x^2}\,\Big]_{-1}^{b}$$

$$= \sin^{-1} b - \sqrt{1-b^2} + \frac{\pi}{2}.$$

This is the number denoted above by $g(b)$. When b is slightly less than $+1$, $\sin^{-1} b$ is slightly less than $\pi/2$ and $\sqrt{1-b^2}$ is nearly zero. Hence,

$$\lim_{b \to 1^-} \int_{-1}^{b} \sqrt{\frac{1+x}{1-x}}\,dx = \lim_{b \to 1^-} \left[\sin^{-1} b - \sqrt{1-b^2} + \frac{\pi}{2}\right]$$

$$= \frac{\pi}{2} - 0 + \frac{\pi}{2} = \pi.$$

The given integral therefore converges and its value is π.

The same result is obtained if, instead of finding the area by summing vertical elements (Fig. 7–8(a)), we sum horizontal elements (Fig. 7–8(b)). Then we find

$$A = \int_{y=0}^{\infty} (1-x)\,dy = \int_{0}^{\infty} \frac{2}{y^2+1}\,dy.$$

This time, the integral to be evaluated is an improper integral of the second type because the range of integration extends to infinity. In this case we investigate the integral from $y = 0$ to $y = c$ for large values of c:

$$\int_0^c \frac{2\, dy}{y^2 + 1} = 2 \tan^{-1} c,$$

and we *define* the integral from 0 to ∞ as the limit of this as $c \to \infty$ (if the limit exists). That is,

$$\int_0^\infty \frac{2\, dy}{y^2 + 1} = \lim_{c \to \infty} \int_0^c \frac{2\, dy}{y^2 + 1} = \lim_{c \to \infty} (2 \tan^{-1} c) = \pi.$$

The limit does exist, since $\tan^{-1} c$ approaches $\pi/2$ as c increases indefinitely.

EXAMPLE 4. In the integral

$$\int_0^1 \frac{dx}{x},$$

the function f is defined by

$$f(x) = \frac{1}{x},$$

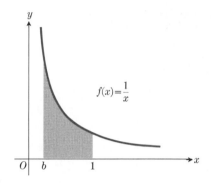

which becomes infinite at $x = 0$. We cut off the point $x = 0$ and start our integration at some positive number $b < 1$. (See Fig. 7–9.) That is, we consider the integral

7–9 $\int_0^1 \frac{dx}{x} = \lim_{b \to 0^+} \int_b^1 \frac{dx}{x}.$

$$\int_b^1 \frac{dx}{x} = \ln x \Big]_b^1 = \ln 1 - \ln b = \ln \frac{1}{b},$$

and investigate its behavior as b approaches zero from the right. Since

$$\lim_{b \to 0^+} \int_b^1 \frac{dx}{x} = \lim_{b \to 0^+} \left(\ln \frac{1}{b} \right) = +\infty,$$

we say that the integral from $x = 0$ to $x = 1$ *diverges*.

The method to be used when the function f becomes infinite at an interior point of the range of integration is illustrated in the following example.

EXAMPLE 5. In the integral

$$\int_0^3 \frac{dx}{(x - 1)^{2/3}},$$

the function

$$f(x) = \frac{1}{(x - 1)^{2/3}}$$

becomes infinite at $x = 1$, which lies between the limits of integration 0 and 3. In such a case, we again cut out the point where $f(x)$ becomes infinite. This time we integrate from 0 to b, where b is slightly less than 1, and start again on the other side of 1 at c and integrate from c to 3 (Fig. 7–10). Then we get the two integrals

$$\int_0^b \frac{dx}{(x-1)^{2/3}} \quad \text{and} \quad \int_c^3 \frac{dx}{(x-1)^{2/3}}$$

to investigate. If the first of these has a definite limit as $b \to 1^-$ and if the second also has a definite limit as $c \to 1^+$, then we say that the improper integral converges and that its value is given by

$$\int_0^3 \frac{dx}{(x-1)^{2/3}} = \lim_{b \to 1^-} \int_0^b \frac{dx}{(x-1)^{2/3}} + \lim_{c \to 1^+} \int_c^3 \frac{dx}{(x-1)^{2/3}}.$$

If either limit fails to exist, we say that the given improper integral *diverges*. For this example,

$$\lim_{b \to 1^-} \int_0^b (x-1)^{-2/3}\, dx = \lim_{b \to 1^-} [3(b-1)^{1/3} - 3(0-1)^{1/3}] = +3$$

and

$$\lim_{c \to 1^+} \int_c^3 (x-1)^{-2/3}\, dx = \lim_{c \to 1^+} [3(3-1)^{1/3} - 3(c-1)^{1/3}] = 3\sqrt[3]{2}.$$

Since both limits exist and are finite, the original integral is said to converge and its value is $3 + 3\sqrt[3]{2}$.

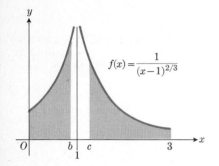

$$f(x) = \frac{1}{(x-1)^{2/3}}$$

7–10 $\displaystyle \int_0^3 f(x)\, dx = \lim_{b \to 1^-} \int_0^b f(x)\, dx$

$\displaystyle \qquad\qquad + \lim_{c \to 1^+} \int_c^3 f(x)\, dx.$

The convergence of the integral

$$\int_1^\infty \frac{dx}{x^p}$$

depends on the size of the exponent p. The next example illustrates this with $p = 1$ and $p = 2$.

EXAMPLE 6. Determine whether the following improper integrals converge or diverge:

$$\int_1^\infty \frac{dx}{x} \quad \text{and} \quad \int_1^\infty \frac{dx}{x^2}.$$

Solution. The two curves

$$y_1 = \frac{1}{x} \quad \text{and} \quad y_2 = \frac{1}{x^2}$$

both approach the x-axis as $x \to \infty$ (Fig. 7–11). In the first case,

$$\int_1^b \frac{dx}{x} = \ln x \Big]_1^b = \ln b.$$

If we now let b take on larger and larger positive values, the logarithm of b increases indefinitely and

$$\lim_{b \to \infty} \int_1^b \frac{dx}{x} = \infty.$$

a)

b)

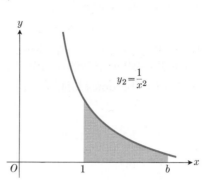

7–11 (a) The shaded area, ln b, does not approach a finite limit as $b \to \infty$. (b) The shaded area, $1 - (1/b)$, approaches 1 as $b \to \infty$.

We therefore say that

$$\int_1^\infty \frac{dx}{x} = \infty$$

and that the integral *diverges*.

In the second case,

$$\int_1^b \frac{dx}{x^2} = -\frac{1}{x}\Big]_1^b = 1 - \frac{1}{b}.$$

This does have a definite limit, namely 1, as b increases indefinitely, and we say that the integral from 1 to ∞ converges and that its value is 1. That is,

$$\int_1^\infty \frac{dx}{x^2} = \lim_{b \to \infty} \int_1^b \frac{dx}{x^2} = \lim_{b \to \infty} \left(1 - \frac{1}{b}\right) = 1.$$

More generally, the integral

$$\int_1^\infty \frac{dx}{x^p}$$

converges when $p > 1$ but diverges when $p \leq 1$ (Problem 22).

Sometimes we can determine whether a given integral converges or diverges by comparing it with a simpler integral. This is the case with the integral in the next example, an integral that is central to the study of continuous probability.

EXAMPLE 7. Determine whether the integral

$$\int_1^\infty e^{-x^2}\, dx$$

converges or diverges.

Solution. Even though we cannot find any simpler expression for

$$I(b) \equiv \int_1^b e^{-x^2}\, dx,$$

we can show that

$$\lim_{b \to \infty} I(b)$$

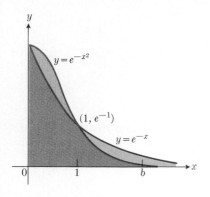

7–12 The graphs of $y = e^{-x^2}$ and $y = e^{-x}$.

exists and is finite, for the function $I(b)$ represents the area between the x-axis and the curve

$$y = e^{-x^2}$$

between $x = 1$ and $x = b$. Clearly, this is an increasing function of b, so that there are two alternatives: either

a) $I(b)$ becomes infinite as $b \to \infty$,

or

b) $I(b)$ has a finite limit as $b \to \infty$.

We show that the first alternative cannot be the true one. We do this by comparing the area under the given curve $y = e^{-x^2}$ with the area under the curve $y = e^{-x}$ (Fig. 7–12). The latter area, from $x = 1$ to $x = b$, is given by the integral

$$\int_1^b e^{-x}\, dx = -e^{-x} \Big]_1^b = e^{-1} - e^{-b},$$

which approaches the finite limit e^{-1} as $b \to \infty$. Since e^{-x^2} is less than e^{-x} for all x greater than one, the area under the given curve is certainly no greater than e^{-1} no matter how large b is.

The discussion above is summarized in the following inequalities:

$$I(b) = \int_1^b e^{-x^2}\, dx \le \int_1^b e^{-x}\, dx = e^{-1} - e^{-b} \le e^{-1};$$

that is,

$$I(b) \le e^{-1} < 0.37.$$

Therefore $I(b)$ does not become infinite as $b \to \infty$, so alternative (a) is ruled out and alternative (b) must hold; that is,

$$\int_1^\infty e^{-x^2}\, dx = \lim_{b \to \infty} \int_1^b e^{-x^2}\, dx$$

converges to a definite finite value. We have not calculated what this limit is, but we know that it exists and is less than 0.37.

An improper integral may diverge without becoming infinite.

EXAMPLE 8. The integral

$$\int_0^b \cos x\, dx = \sin b$$

takes all values between -1 and $+1$ as b varies between $2n\pi - \pi/2$ and $2n\pi + \pi/2$, where n is any integer. Hence,

$$\lim_{b \to \infty} \int_0^b \cos x\, dx$$

does not exist. We might say that this integral "diverges by oscillation."

Improper integrals appear in the study of economics in several ways. We illustrate one of them in the next example.

EXAMPLE 9 (*Discounting and present value*). If P dollars are invested at an interest rate r compounded continuously for t years, then the value of the asset at the end of the compounding process is

$$A = Pe^{rt}. \tag{1}$$

For instance, \$60.65 invested at 5 percent compounded continuously will be worth

$$A = 60.65e^{0.05 \times 10} = 60.65e^{0.5} \approx 100 \text{ dollars}$$

in ten years.

Closely related to compounding interest is the concept of *discounting*. The problem of discounting is that of finding the *present value P* of an amount of money A that will become available in t years. What is a 5 percent savings bond that will pay \$100 ten years from now worth today? It is worth what we would have to bank today at 5 percent to accumulate \$100 in ten years. That is, the bond is worth $P = \$60.65$. More generally, the present value of an investment that will pay A dollars after t years of continuous compounding at rate r is

$$P = Ae^{-rt}, \tag{2}$$

an equation obtained by solving Eq. (1) for P. The amount P is the present value of A *discounted at the rate of r per year*. Thus, $P = \$60.65$ is the present value of $A = \$100$ payable ten years from now discounted at 5 percent per year.

Many investments operate differently from savings accounts. Rather than compounding interest on the investment continuously, they make periodic payments to the investor. How is the present value of all the future revenue from such an investment to be calculated? If the revenue from the investment is given as a function of time $R(t)$, then the amount paid in a future time interval of length Δt will be $R(t) \Delta t$ for some t in that interval. The present value of this part of the total revenue, when discounted at the rate of r per year, is about $R(t)e^{-rt} \Delta t$. The present value of the revenue from the whole investment period is then approximately

$$\sum R(t)e^{-rt} \Delta t. \tag{3}$$

In the limit, we can calculate this value as

$$P(T) = \int_0^T R(t)e^{-rt} \, dt, \tag{4}$$

where T is the duration of the investment. If the investment is a perpetual bond or an indestructible capital asset like land, then the present value of the total revenue from the investment may be taken to be

$$P = \int_0^\infty R(t)e^{-rt} \, dt. \tag{5}$$

For instance, if $R(t)$ is a constant C dollars a year, then

$$P = \int_0^\infty Ce^{-rt}\, dt = \lim_{b \to \infty} -\frac{C}{r} e^{-rt}\Big]_0^b$$

$$= \lim_{b \to \infty} \frac{C}{r}(1 - e^{-rb})$$

$$= \frac{C}{r}.$$

PROBLEMS

Show that the following improper integrals converge and evaluate them.

1. $\int_0^\infty \dfrac{dx}{x^2 + 1}$

2. $\int_0^1 \dfrac{dx}{\sqrt{x}}$

3. $\int_{-1}^1 \dfrac{dx}{x^{2/3}}$

4. $\int_1^\infty \dfrac{dx}{x^{1.001}}$

5. $\int_0^4 \dfrac{dx}{\sqrt{4 - x}}$

6. $\int_0^1 \dfrac{dx}{\sqrt{1 - x^2}}$

7. $\int_0^\infty e^{-x} \cos x \, dx$

8. $\int_0^1 \dfrac{dx}{x^{0.999}}$

Determine whether each of the following improper integrals converges or diverges.

9. $\int_1^\infty \dfrac{dx}{\sqrt{x}}$

10. $\int_1^\infty \dfrac{dx}{x^3}$

11. $\int_1^\infty \dfrac{dx}{x^3 + 1}$

12. $\int_0^\infty \dfrac{dx}{x^3}$

13. $\int_0^\infty \dfrac{dx}{x^3 + 1}$

14. $\int_0^\infty \dfrac{dx}{1 + e^x}$

15. $\int_0^{\pi/2} \tan x \, dx$

16. $\int_{-1}^1 \dfrac{dx}{x^2}$

17. $\int_{-1}^1 \dfrac{dx}{x^{2/5}}$

18. $\int_0^\infty \dfrac{dx}{\sqrt{x}}$

19. $\int_0^\infty \dfrac{dx}{\sqrt{x + x^4}}$

[*Hint.* Compare the integral with $\int dx/\sqrt{x}$ for x near zero and with $\int dx/x^2$ for large x.]

20. Show that

$$\int_3^\infty e^{-3x}\, dx = \tfrac{1}{3}e^{-9} = 0.000041,$$

and hence that $\int_3^\infty e^{-x^2}\, dx < 0.000041$. Therefore, $\int_0^\infty e^{-x^2}\, dx$ can be replaced by $\int_0^3 e^{-x^2}\, dx$ without introducing any errors in the first three decimal places of the answer. Evaluate this last integral by Simpson's rule with $n = 6$.

(This illustrates one method by which a convergent improper integral may be approximated numerically.)

21. As Example 6 shows, the integral $\int_1^\infty (dx/x)$ diverges. This means that the integral

$$\int_1^\infty 2\pi \frac{1}{x}\sqrt{1 + \frac{1}{x^4}}\, dx,$$

which measures the surface area of the solid of revolution traced out by revolving the curve $y = 1/x$, $1 \leq x$, about the x-axis, diverges also. For, by comparing the two integrals, we see that, for every finite value b,

$$\int_1^b 2\pi \frac{1}{x}\sqrt{1 + \frac{1}{x^4}}\, dx > \int_1^b \frac{dx}{x}.$$

However, the integral

$$\int_1^\infty \pi \left(\frac{1}{x}\right)^2 dx$$

for the volume of the solid converges. Calculate it. This solid of revolution is sometimes described as a can that does not hold enough paint to cover its own outside surface.

22. Show that

$$\int_1^\infty \frac{dx}{x^p} = \frac{1}{p - 1} \qquad \text{when } p > 1,$$

but that the integral is infinite when $p < 1$. Example 6 shows what happens when $p = 1$.

23. Find the present value of the revenue from a perpetual bond that pays $300 a year discounted at 6 percent per year.

24. A U.S. savings bond that will yield $25 in 5 years can be purchased for $18.75. Assuming that the interest is compounded continuously, find the rate at which the bond has been discounted.

25. A perpetual investment pays $100 a year, but, to compensate for inflation, the revenue function $R(t)$ of Example 9 is chosen to be $R(t) = 100(0.95)^t$.
a) Estimate the present value of the revenue from this investment discounted at 5 percent a year.
b) What would the present value of the revenue be if there were no inflation?

REVIEW QUESTIONS AND EXERCISES

1. What are some of the general methods presented in this chapter for finding an indefinite integral?

2. What substitution(s) would you consider trying if the integrand contained the following?

a) $\sqrt{x^2 + 9}$
b) $\sqrt{x^2 - 9}$

c) $\sqrt{9 - x^2}$
d) $\sin^3 x \cos^2 x$

e) $\sin^2 x \cos^2 x$
f) $\dfrac{1 + \sin \theta}{2 + \cos \theta}$

3. What method(s) would you try if the integrand contained the following?

a) $\sin^{-1} x$
b) $\ln x$

c) $\sqrt{1 + 2x - x^2}$
d) $x \sin x$

e) $\dfrac{2x + 3}{x^2 - 5x + 6}$
f) $\sin 5x \cos 3x$

g) $\dfrac{1 - \sqrt{x}}{1 + \sqrt[4]{x}}$
h) $x\sqrt{2x + 3}$

4. Discuss two types of improper integral. Define convergence and divergence of each type. Give examples of convergent and divergent integrals of each type.

MISCELLANEOUS PROBLEMS

Evaluate the following integrals:

1. $\displaystyle\int \frac{\cos x \, dx}{\sqrt{1 + \sin x}}$

2. $\displaystyle\int \frac{\sin^{-1} x \, dx}{\sqrt{1 - x^2}}$

3. $\displaystyle\int \frac{\tan x \, dx}{\cos^2 x}$

4. $\displaystyle\int \frac{dx}{1 - \sin x}$

5. $\displaystyle\int e^{\ln \sqrt{x}} \, dx$

6. $\displaystyle\int \frac{\cos \sqrt{x}}{\sqrt{x}} \, dx$

7. $\displaystyle\int \frac{dx}{\sqrt{x^2 + 2x + 2}}$

8. $\displaystyle\int \frac{(3x - 7) \, dx}{(x - 1)(x - 2)(x - 3)}$

9. $\displaystyle\int x^2 e^x \, dx$

10. $\displaystyle\int \sqrt{x^2 + 1} \, dx$

11. $\displaystyle\int \frac{e^t \, dt}{1 + e^{2t}}$

12. $\displaystyle\int \frac{dx}{e^x + e^{-x}}$

13. $\displaystyle\int \frac{dx}{1 + \sqrt{x}}$

14. $\displaystyle\int \frac{dx}{\sqrt{1 + \sqrt{x}}}$

15. $\displaystyle\int t^{2/3}(t^{5/3} + 1)^{2/3} \, dt$

16. $\displaystyle\int \frac{\cot x \, dx}{\ln (\sin x)}$

17. $\displaystyle\int \frac{dt}{\sqrt{e^t + 1}}$

18. $\displaystyle\int \frac{dt}{\sqrt{1 - e^{-t}}}$

19. $\displaystyle\int \frac{\sin x e^{\sec x}}{\cos^2 x} \, dx$

20. $\displaystyle\int \frac{\cos x \, dx}{1 + \sin^2 x}$

21. $\displaystyle\int \frac{dx}{\sqrt{2x - x^2}}$

22. $\displaystyle\int \frac{\sin x \, dx}{1 + \cos^2 x}$

23. $\displaystyle\int \frac{\cos 2t}{1 + \sin 2t} \, dt$

24. $\displaystyle\int \frac{dx}{\sin x \cos x}$

25. $\displaystyle\int \sqrt{1 + \sin x} \, dx$

26. $\displaystyle\int \sqrt{1 - \sin x} \, dx$

27. $\displaystyle\int \frac{dx}{\sqrt{(a^2 - x^2)^3}}$

28. $\displaystyle\int \frac{dx}{\sqrt{(a^2 + x^2)^3}}$

29. $\displaystyle\int \frac{\sin x \, dx}{\cos^2 x - 5 \cos x + 4}$

30. $\displaystyle\int \frac{e^{2x} \, dx}{\sqrt[3]{1 + e^x}}$

31. $\displaystyle\int \frac{dx}{x(x + 1)(x + 2) \cdots (x + m)}$

32. $\displaystyle\int \frac{dx}{x^6 - 1}$

33. $\displaystyle\int \frac{dy}{y(2y^3 + 1)^2}$

34. $\displaystyle\int \frac{x \, dx}{1 + \sqrt{x}}$

35. $\displaystyle\int \frac{dx}{x(x^2 + 1)^2}$

36. $\displaystyle\int \ln \sqrt{x - 1} \, dx$

37. $\displaystyle\int \frac{dx}{e^x - 1}$

38. $\displaystyle\int \frac{d\theta}{1 - \tan^2 \theta}$

39. $\displaystyle\int \frac{(x + 1) \, dx}{x^2(x - 1)}$

40. $\displaystyle\int \frac{x \, dx}{x^2 + 4x + 3}$

41. $\displaystyle\int \frac{du}{(e^u - e^{-u})^2}$

42. $\displaystyle\int \frac{4 \, dx}{x^3 + 4x}$

43. $\displaystyle\int \frac{dx}{5x^2 + 8x + 5}$

44. $\displaystyle\int \frac{\sqrt{x^2 - a^2}}{x} \, dx$

45. $\displaystyle\int e^x \cos 2x \, dx$

46. $\displaystyle\int \frac{dx}{x(3\sqrt{x} + 1)}$

47. $\displaystyle\int \frac{dx}{x(1 + \sqrt[3]{x})}$

48. $\displaystyle\int \frac{\cot \theta \, d\theta}{1 + \sin^2 \theta}$

49. $\displaystyle\int \frac{z^5 \, dz}{\sqrt{1 + z^2}}$

50. $\displaystyle\int \frac{e^{4t} \, dt}{(1 + e^{2t})^{2/3}}$

51. $\int \dfrac{dx}{x^{1/5}\sqrt{1 + x^{4/5}}}$

52. $\int x \sec^2 x \, dx$

93. $\int (\sin^{-1} x)^2 \, dx$

94. $\int x \ln \sqrt[3]{3x + 1} \, dx$

53. $\int x \sin^{-1} x \, dx$

54. $\int \dfrac{(x^3 + x^2) \, dx}{x^2 + x - 2}$

95. $\int \dfrac{x^3 \, dx}{(x^2 + 1)^2}$

96. $\int \dfrac{x \, dx}{\sqrt{1 - x}}$

55. $\int \dfrac{x^3 + 1}{x^3 - x} \, dx$

56. $\int \dfrac{x \, dx}{(x - 1)^2}$

97. $\int x\sqrt{2x + 1} \, dx$

98. $\int \ln (x + \sqrt{x^2 - 1}) \, dx$

57. $\int \dfrac{(2e^{2x} - e^x) \, dx}{\sqrt{3e^{2x} - 6e^x - 1}}$

58. $\int \dfrac{(x + 1) \, dx}{(x^2 + 2x - 3)^{2/3}}$

99. $\int \ln (x - \sqrt{x^2 - 1}) \, dx$

100. $\int \dfrac{dt}{t - \sqrt{1 - t^2}}$

59. $\int \dfrac{dy}{(2y + 1)\sqrt{y^2 + y}}$

60. $\int \dfrac{dx}{x^2\sqrt{a^2 - x^2}}$

101. $\int e^{-x} \tan^{-1} (e^x) \, dx$

102. $\int \sin^{-1} \sqrt{x} \, dx$

61. $\int (1 - x^2)^{3/2} \, dx$

62. $\int \ln (x + \sqrt{1 + x^2}) \, dx$

103. $\int \ln (x + \sqrt{x}) \, dx$

104. $\int \tan^{-1} \sqrt{x} \, dx$

63. $\int x \tan^2 x \, dx$

64. $\int \dfrac{\tan^{-1} x}{x^2} \, dx$

105. $\int \ln (x^2 + x) \, dx$

106. $\int \ln (\sqrt{x} + \sqrt{1 + x}) \, dx$

65. $\int x \cos^2 x \, dx$

66. $\int x^2 \sin x \, dx$

107. $\int \cos \sqrt{x} \, dx$

108. $\int \sin \sqrt{x} \, dx$

67. $\int x \sin^2 x \, dx$

68. $\int \dfrac{dt}{t^4 + 4t^2 + 3}$

109. $\int \tan^{-1} \sqrt{x + 1} \, dx$

110. $\int \sqrt{1 - x^2} \sin^{-1} x \, dx$

69. $\int \dfrac{du}{e^{4u} + 4e^{2u} + 3}$

70. $\int x \ln \sqrt{x + 2} \, dx$

111. $\int x \sin^2 (2x) \, dx$

112. $\int \dfrac{\tan x \, dx}{\tan x + \sec x}$

71. $\int (x + 1)^2 e^x \, dx$

72. $\int \sec^{-1} x \, dx$

113. $\int \dfrac{dt}{\sqrt{e^{2t} + 1}}$

73. $\int \dfrac{8 \, dx}{x^4 + 2x^3}$

74. $\int \dfrac{x \, dx}{x^4 - 16}$

114. $\int \dfrac{dx}{(\cos^2 x + 4 \sin x - 5) \cos x}$

75. $\int_0^{\pi/2} \dfrac{\cos x \, dx}{\sqrt{1 + \cos x}}$

76. $\int \dfrac{\cos x \, dx}{\sin^3 x - \sin x}$

115. $\int \dfrac{dt}{a + be^{ct}}, \qquad a, b, c \neq 0$

77. $\int \dfrac{du}{(e^u + e^{-u})^2}$

78. $\int \dfrac{x \, dx}{1 + \sqrt{x} + x}$

79. $\int \dfrac{\sec^2 t \, dt}{\sec^2 t - 3 \tan t + 1}$

80. $\int \dfrac{dt}{\sec^2 t + \tan^2 t}$

116. $\int \sqrt{\dfrac{1 - \cos x}{\cos \alpha - \cos x}} \, dx, \qquad \alpha \text{ constant,}$

$0 < \alpha < x < \pi$

81. $\int \dfrac{dx}{1 + \cos^2 x}$

82. $\int e^{2t} \cos (e^t) \, dt$

117. $\int \dfrac{dx}{\sin x - \cos x}$

118. $\int \ln \sqrt{1 + x^2} \, dx$

83. $\int \ln \sqrt{x^2 + 1} \, dx$

84. $\int x \ln (x^3 + x) \, dx$

119. $\int \ln (2x^2 + 4) \, dx$

120. $\int \dfrac{x^3}{\sqrt{1 - x^2}} \, dx$

85. $\int x^3 e^{x^2} \, dx$

86. $\int \dfrac{\cos x \, dx}{\sqrt{4 - \cos^2 x}}$

121. $\int \dfrac{dx}{x(2 + \ln x)}$

122. $\int \dfrac{\cos 2x - 1}{\cos 2x + 1} \, dx$

87. $\int \dfrac{\sec^2 x \, dx}{\sqrt{4 - \sec^2 x}}$

88. $\int x^2 \sin (1 - x) \, dx$

123. $\int \dfrac{dx}{x^3 + 1}$

124. $\int \dfrac{e^{2x} \, dx}{\sqrt[4]{e^x + 1}}$

89. $\int \dfrac{dx}{1 + \sin x}$

90. $\int \dfrac{dx}{1 + 2 \sin x}$

125. $\int \dfrac{e^x \, dx}{1 + e^{2x}}$

126. $\int e^{\sqrt{t}} \, dt$

91. $\int \dfrac{dx}{\sin^3 x}$

92. $\int \dfrac{dx}{\cot^3 x}$

127. $\int \sin \sqrt{x + 1} \, dx$

128. $\int \cos \sqrt{1 - x} \, dx$

Evaluate each of the following limits, Problems 129–135, by identifying it with an appropriate definite integral and evaluating the latter.

129. $\lim\limits_{n \to \infty} \left(\dfrac{1}{n+1} + \dfrac{1}{n+2} + \cdots + \dfrac{1}{2n} \right)$

130. $\lim\limits_{n \to \infty} \left(\dfrac{1}{\sqrt{n^2}} + \dfrac{1}{\sqrt{n^2+n}} + \dfrac{1}{\sqrt{n^2+2n}} + \cdots \right.$
$\left. + \dfrac{1}{\sqrt{n^2+(n-1)n}} \right)$

131. $\lim\limits_{n \to \infty} \left(\sin 0 + \sin (\pi/n) + \sin (2\pi/n) + \cdots \right.$
$\left. + \sin [(n-1)\pi/n] \right) / n$

132. $\lim\limits_{n \to \infty} \left(\dfrac{1 + \sqrt[n]{e} + \sqrt[n]{e^2} + \sqrt[n]{e^3} + \cdots + \sqrt[n]{e^{n-1}}}{n} \right)$

133. $\lim\limits_{n \to \infty} \left(\dfrac{n}{n^2+0^2} + \dfrac{n}{n^2+1^2} + \dfrac{n}{n^2+2^2} + \cdots \right.$
$\left. + \dfrac{n}{n^2+(n-1)^2} \right)$

134. $\lim\limits_{n \to \infty} \sum\limits_{k=1}^{n} \ln \sqrt[n]{1 + \dfrac{k}{n}}$

135. $\lim\limits_{n \to \infty} \sum\limits_{k=0}^{n-1} \dfrac{1}{\sqrt{n^2 - k^2}}$

136. Show that $\int_0^\infty x^3 e^{-x^2} \, dx$ is a convergent integral, and evaluate it.

137. Show that $\int_0^1 \ln x \, dx$ is a convergent integral and find its value. Sketch the integrand $y = \ln x$ for $0 < x \le 1$.

138. Assuming that $|\alpha| \ne |\beta|$, prove that

$$\lim\limits_{T \to \infty} \frac{1}{T} \int_0^T \sin \alpha x \sin \beta x \, dx = 0.$$

139. Evaluate

$$\lim\limits_{h \to 0} \frac{1}{h} \int_2^{2+h} e^{-x^2} \, dx.$$

140. At points of the curve $y^2 = 4px$, lines of length $h = y$ are drawn perpendicular to its plane. Find the area of the surface formed by these lines at points of the curve between $(0, 0)$ and $(p, 2p)$.

141. A plane figure is bounded by a 90° arc of a circle of radius r and a straight line. Find its area and its centroid.

142. Find the coordinates of the center of gravity of the area bounded by the curves $y = e^x$, $x = 1$, and $y = 1$.

143. At points on a circle of radius r, perpendiculars to its plane are erected, the perpendicular at each point P being of length ks, where s is the arc of the circle from a fixed point A to P. Find the area of the surface formed by the perpendiculars along the arc beginning at A and extending once around the circle.

144. A plate in the first quadrant, bounded by the curves $y = e^x$, $y = 1$, and $x = 4$, is submerged vertically in water with its upper corner on the surface. The surface of the water is given by the line $y = e^4$. Find the total force on one side of the plate if the weight of water is 62.5 lb/ft^3, and if the units of x and y are also measured in feet.

145. The area under the curve $y = e^{-x}$, for $x \ge 0$, is rotated about the x-axis. If A is the area under the curve, V is the volume generated, and S is the surface area of this volume: (a) is A finite? (b) is V finite? (c) is S finite? Give reasons for your answers.

146. Find the length of arc of $y = \ln x$ from $x = 1$ to $x = e$.

147. The arc of Problem 146 is rotated about the y-axis. Find the surface area generated. Check your answer by comparing it with the area of a frustum of a suitably related cone.

148. Find the length of arc of the curve $y = e^x$ from $x = 0$ to $x = 2$.

149. The arc of Problem 148 is rotated about the x-axis. Find the surface area generated. Compare this area with the area of a suitably related frustum of a cone to check your answer.

150. One arch of the curve $y = \cos x$ is rotated about the x-axis. Find the surface area generated.

151. Use Simpson's rule with $n = 8$ to approximate the length of arc of $y = \cos x$ from $x = 0$ to $x = \pi/2$. Check your answer by consulting a table of elliptic integrals if one is available.

152. A thin wire is bent into the shape of one arch of the curve $y = \cos x$. Find its center of mass (see Problems 150, 151).

153. The area between the graph of $y = \ln (1/x)$, the x-axis, and the y-axis is revolved around the x-axis. Find the volume of the solid it generates.

154. Find the total perimeter of the curve $x^{2/3} + y^{2/3} = a^{2/3}$.

155. Find the area of the surface generated by rotating the curve $x^{2/3} + y^{2/3} = a^{2/3}$ about the x-axis.

156. A thin homogeneous wire is bent into the shape of one arch of the curve $x^{2/3} + y^{2/3} = a^{2/3}$. Find its center of mass (see Problems 154, 155).

157. Determine whether the integral $\int_1^\infty \ln x (dx/x^2)$ converges or diverges.

158. Sketch the curves:

a) $y = x - e^x$; show behavior for large $|x|$;

b) $y = e^{(x - e^x)}$; show behavior for large $|x|$.

Show that the following integrals converge and compute their values:

c) $\int_{-\infty}^{b} e^{(x-e^x)} \, dx$ d) $\int_{-\infty}^{\infty} e^{(x-e^x)} \, dx$

159. The gamma function $\Gamma(x)$ is defined, for $x > 0$, by the definite integral

$$\Gamma(x) = \int_{0}^{\infty} t^{x-1} e^{-t} \, dt.$$

a) Sketch graphs of the integrand $y = t^{x-1} e^{-t}$ vs. t, $t > 0$, for the three typical cases $x = \frac{1}{2}, 1, 3$. Find maxima, minima, and points of inflection (if they exist).

b) Show that the integral converges if $x > 0$.

c) Show that the integral diverges if $x \leq 0$.

d) Using integration by parts, show that $\Gamma(x + 1) = x\Gamma(x)$, for $x > 0$.

e) Using the result of part (d), show that, if n is a positive integer, $\Gamma(n) = (n - 1)!$, where $0! = 1$ (by definition) and if

m is a positive integer, $m!$ is the product of the positive integers from 1 through m inclusive.

f) Discuss how one might compute a table of values of $\Gamma(x)$ for the domain $1 \leq x \leq 2$, say. Consult such a table, if available, and sketch the graph of $y = \Gamma(x)$ for $0 < x \leq 3$.

160. Determine whether the integral $\int_{0}^{\infty} t^{x-1}(\ln t) e^{-t} \, dt$ converges or diverges for fixed $x > 0$. Sketch the integrand $y = t^{x-1} \ln t e^{-t}$ vs. t, $t > 0$, for the two cases $x = \frac{1}{2}$ and $x = 3$.

161. Solve the differential equation $d^2x/dt^2 = -k^2x$, subject to the initial conditions $x = a$, $dx/dt = 0$ when $t = 0$. [*Hint*. Let $dx/dt = v$, $d^2x/dt^2 = dv/dt = v \, dv/dx$.]

162. Find $\lim\limits_{n \to \infty} \int_{0}^{1} \frac{ny^{n-1}}{1 + y} \, dy$.

163. Prove that if n is a positive integer, or zero, then

$$\int_{-1}^{1} (1 - x^2)^n \, dx = \frac{2^{2n+1}(n!)^2}{(2n + 1)!},$$

with $0! = 1$; $n! = 1 \cdot 2 \cdots n$ for $n \geq 1$.

PLANE ANALYTIC GEOMETRY

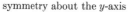

CURVES AND EQUATIONS

Analytic geometry combines algebra and calculus with geometry to study the geometric properties of curves when their equations are given, and to find equations for curves when their geometric properties are known.

An equation

$$F(x, y) = 0 \qquad (1)$$

determines a curve that is the set of all and only those points $P(x, y)$ whose coordinates satisfy the equation. This curve is called the graph of the equation. We have already had some experience in analyzing equations to find turning points and points of inflection. We shall now see how equations may reveal other important characteristics of curves as well.

In this chapter we shall assume that the scales on the x- and y-axes are the same, unless we specifically note otherwise.

Symmetry

Symmetries that are easily detected are:

Symmetry about the y-axis. If the equation of the curve is unaltered when x is replaced by $-x$, that is, if

$$F(x, y) = F(-x, y),$$

then the points (x, y) and $(-x, y)$ both lie on the curve when either one of them does. In particular, an equation that contains only even powers of x represents such a curve (Fig. 8–1(a)).

Symmetry about the x-axis if the equation is unaltered when y is replaced by $-y$; in particular if only even powers of y occur (Fig. 8–1(b)).

Symmetry about the origin if the equation is unaltered when x and y are replaced by $-x$ and $-y$, respectively (Fig. 8–1(c)).

Symmetry about the 45° line $y = x$ if the equation is unaltered when x and y are interchanged (Fig. 8–1(d)).

EXAMPLE 1

$$x^2 + y^2 = 1.$$

Symmetric about both axes, about the origin, and about the line $y = x$.

EXAMPLE 2

$$x^2 - y^2 = 1.$$

Symmetric about both axes and the origin. Not symmetric about the line $y = x$.

EXAMPLE 3

$$xy = 1.$$

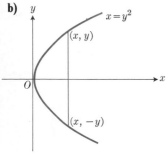

a) symmetry about the y-axis

b) symmetry about the x-axis

c) symmetry about the origin

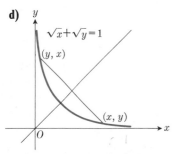

d) symmetry about the line $y = x$

8–1 Coordinate tests for symmetry.

Not symmetric about either axis. Symmetric about the origin and about the line $y = x$.

Extent

Only real values of x and y are considered in determining the points (x, y) whose coordinates satisfy a given equation. When even powers of a variable appear in the equation, the solution for that variable may involve square roots (or other even roots). The *extent* of the curve may then be limited by the condition that negative numbers do not have real square roots.

EXAMPLE 4

$$x^2 + y^2 = 1.$$

When this equation is solved for y, we get

$$y = \pm\sqrt{1 - x^2}.$$

The quantity under the radical is negative if $|x| > 1$. The extent of the curve in the x-direction is therefore limited to the interval $-1 \le x \le 1$. By symmetry about the line $y = x$, the curve is also limited in the y-direction to $-1 \le y \le 1$.

EXAMPLE 5

$$x^2 - y^2 = 1.$$

Solving for y, we get

$$y = \pm\sqrt{x^2 - 1}.$$

In this case, y is imaginary unless $|x| \ge 1$. No portion of the curve lies between the two lines $x = -1$ and $x = +1$. Solving for x, we get

$$x = \pm\sqrt{1 + y^2}.$$

The quantity under the radical is positive (actually it is greater than or equal to one) for all real values of y, $-\infty < y < +\infty$. The extent of this curve is not limited in the y-direction.

Intercepts

The point or points where a given curve crosses the x-axis can be found by setting $y = 0$ in the equation and solving for x. These points are called the *x-intercepts*. The y-intercepts are found in an analogous way by setting $x = 0$. If the labor involved in finding the intercepts is not excessive, they are worth determining to give specific points on the curve.

EXAMPLE 6

$$x^2 + y^2 = 1.$$

Setting $y = 0$, we have $x^2 = 1$. Therefore $(1, 0)$ and $(-1, 0)$ are the x-intercepts. By symmetry, $(0, 1)$ and $(0, -1)$ are the y-intercepts.

EXAMPLE 7

$$x^2 - y^2 = 1.$$

Setting $y = 0$, we find the x-intercepts are $(1, 0)$ and $(-1, 0)$. Setting $x = 0$, we obtain $y^2 = -1$, which has no real solutions. The curve does not have intercepts on the y-axis (see Example 5).

EXAMPLE 8

$$xy = 1.$$

Setting either $x = 0$ or $y = 0$ leads to the equation $0 = 1$, which has no solutions. There are no x- or y-intercepts.

Asymptotes

As the point $P(x, y)$ on a given curve moves farther and farther away from the vicinity of the origin, it may happen that the distance between P and some fixed line tends to zero. In such a case the line is called an *asymptote* of the curve. More generally, if the equation of the curve has the form

$$y = \frac{N(x)}{D(x)}, \tag{2}$$

where $N(x)$ and $D(x)$ are polynomials without any factors in common, and if $x = c$ is a root of the equation

$$D(x) = 0, \tag{3}$$

then as the x-coordinate of the tracing point $P(x, y)$ approaches c, two things will occur:

1. $y \to \infty$; hence the distance $OP \to \infty$; and

2. the horizontal distance $P'P$ between the curve and the vertical line $x = c$ tends to zero (Fig. 8–2).

In other words, *the line $x = c$ is an asymptote of the graph of Eq. (2) if $x = c$ makes the denominator $D(x)$ vanish.* Such asymptotes are found by solving the equation explicitly for y in terms of x. If the result is a fraction, we set the denominator of the fraction equal to zero and solve for the numerical values of x. A similar procedure with the roles of x and y reversed shows that values of y that cause the denominator to vanish in the expression

$$x = \frac{f(y)}{g(y)} \tag{4}$$

may give horizontal asymptotes of the curve. An alternate method for finding such asymptotes is to let $x \to \pm\infty$ in Eq. (2)—provided the extent of the curve does not prohibit this—and find the limiting values of y.

EXAMPLE 9.　(See Fig. 8–3.)

$$y^2(x^2 - x) = x^2 + 1. \tag{5}$$

We solve for y to obtain

$$y = \pm\sqrt{\frac{x^2 + 1}{x(x - 1)}}. \tag{6}$$

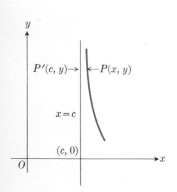

8–2　As $x \to c$, the point $P(x, y)$ rises along the curve toward the line $x = c$.

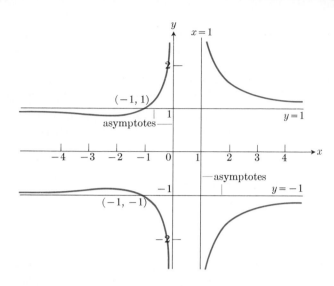

8–3 The graph of $y^2(x^2 - x) = x^2 + 1$ has four asymptotes.

The expression under the radical must not be negative, so no portion of the curve lies between the lines $x = 0$ and $x = 1$. But all values of $x > 1$ and all negative values of x, that is, $x < 0$, are permissible. As x approaches zero *from the left*, $y \to \pm\infty$ and as x approaches one *from the right*, $y \to \pm\infty$. The lines $x = 0$ and $x = 1$ are asymptotes of the curve. Since arbitrarily large values of $|x|$ are permitted, we also investigate the behavior of the curve as $x \to -\infty$ and again as $x \to +\infty$. The expression

$$\frac{\infty^2 + 1}{\infty(\infty - 1)},$$

which appears if we substitute $x = \infty$ directly into (6), is meaningless, but if we write the equation of the curve in the equivalent form

$$y^2 = \frac{x^2 + 1}{x^2 - x} = \frac{1 + (1/x^2)}{1 - (1/x)}, \tag{7}$$

we readily see that $y^2 \to 1$ as $x \to \infty$ or as $x \to -\infty$. Thus the lines $y = 1$ and $y = -1$ are also asymptotes of the curve. We reexamine Eq. (7) to see if y^2 is necessarily always greater than one, or always less than one, or may be equal to one. Certainly when x tends to $+\infty$, the numerator in (7) is greater than one, while the denominator is less than one; hence the fraction is larger than one, that is,

$$y^2 > 1, \qquad y^2 \to 1 \qquad \text{as} \quad x \to +\infty. \tag{8}$$

On the other hand, when x tends to $-\infty$, both $1/x^2$ and $-1/x$ are positive, so that both the numerator and denominator in (7) are greater than one. However, $1/x^2$ will be less than $-1/x$, so that the numerator is less than the denominator; that is,

$$y^2 < 1, \qquad y^2 \to 1 \qquad \text{as} \quad x \to -\infty. \tag{9}$$

To determine whether y^2 may ever equal 1, we try it, say in (5), and find

$$y^2 = 1 \qquad \text{when} \quad x = -1. \tag{10}$$

We now have quite a bit of information about the curve represented by Eq. (5). It is immediately evident that the curve is symmetric about the

x-axis, because y may be replaced by $-y$ without changing the equation. There is no curve between $x = 0$ and $x = 1$. The lines $x = 0$, $x = 1$, $y = 1$, $y = -1$ are asymptotes of the curve. It crosses $y = 1$ and $y = -1$ at $x = -1$. There is no x-intercept, because putting $y = 0$ in Eq. (5) requires $0 = x^2 + 1$, which has only imaginary roots. Using this information, we may sketch the curve with a fair degree of accuracy (see Fig. 8–3). In fact, it becomes apparent that the curve has a minimum somewhat to the left of $x = -1$, and a symmetrically located maximum, and that there is also a point of inflection to the left of this turning point. To find these points accurately requires that we determine dy/dx and d^2y/dx^2. The turning points will be found to occur at $(-1 - \sqrt{2}, \pm\sqrt{2\sqrt{2} - 2})$. The algebra involved in finding the points of inflection is excessive.

Direction at a Point

The three curves

a) $\qquad\qquad y = x, \qquad dy/dx = 1,$

b) $\qquad\qquad y = x^2, \qquad dy/dx = 2x,$

c) $\qquad\qquad y = \sqrt{x}, \qquad dy/dx = 1/(2\sqrt{x})$

all pass through the origin and the point $(1, 1)$. But their behavior for small values of x is radically different. The individual nature of any one of them in the vicinity of $(0, 0)$ is better indicated if the *direction* of the curve at that point is also given. This, of course, means that it is desirable to find the slope of each of them at $(0, 0)$. We find that the inclination angles are respectively $45°$, $0°$, and $90°$ (see Fig. 8–4).

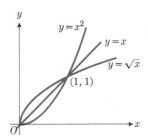

8–4 The curves $y = x$, $y = x^2$, and $y = \sqrt{x}$ have different directions at the origin.

EXAMPLE 10. (See Fig. 8–5.)

$$y^2 = x^2(1 - x^2).$$

This curve has symmetry with respect to both axes and the origin. Its extent in the x-direction is limited to $|x| \le 1$. Differentiating implicitly, we find

$$y' = \frac{x - 2x^3}{y}.$$

At one x-intercept, $(1, 0)$, the slope is infinite. At the origin, which is another intercept, the expression we have for y' becomes 0/0, which is meaningless. However, if we replace y in the denominator by its equivalent expression in terms of x, we obtain

$$y' = \frac{x(1 - 2x^2)}{\pm x\sqrt{1 - x^2}} = \pm\frac{1 - 2x^2}{\sqrt{1 - x^2}}.$$

At $x = 0$, this gives $y' = \pm 1$. The same result can be obtained by considering the limit, as P approaches the origin O, of the slope of the secant line through O and a second point $P(x, y)$ on the curve. Denoting this slope by m_{sec}, we have

$$m_{\text{sec}} = \frac{\text{rise}}{\text{run}} = \frac{y - 0}{x - 0} = \pm\sqrt{1 - x^2}.$$

When $P \to O$, $x \to 0$, and $m_{\text{sec}} \to \pm 1$. The double sign means, of course, that if P approaches O along the branch of the curve given by

$$y = x\sqrt{1 - x^2},$$

the limit of the slope of the secant is $+1$, while the branch given by

$$y = -x\sqrt{1 - x^2}$$

has slope -1 at the origin (Fig. 8–5). We also find turning points at $x = \pm\sqrt{\frac{1}{2}}$, $y = \pm\frac{1}{2}$. We may determine the extent of the curve in the y-direction by comparing the equation of the curve in the form

$$x^4 - x^2 + y^2 = 0$$

with the quadratic equation

$$az^2 + bz + c = 0,$$

whose solutions are

$$z = \frac{-b \pm \sqrt{b^2 - 4ac}}{2a}.$$

Taking $z = x^2$, $a = 1$, $b = -1$, and $c = y^2$, this leads to

$$x^2 = \frac{1 \pm \sqrt{1 - 4y^2}}{2}.$$

This requires $1 - 4y^2 \geq 0$, so there is no portion of the curve above the line $y = \frac{1}{2}$ or below the line $y = -\frac{1}{2}$.

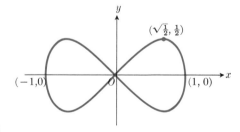

8–5 The graph of $y^2 = x^2(1 - x^2)$.

The equation in Example 10 is of the second degree in y and of the fourth degree in x. A line parallel to the y-axis has the equation $x = $ constant. Solving the equation of the curve and the equation of the line simultaneously will therefore produce at most two values of y; that is, such a line will cut the curve in at most two points. Similarly, because $y^2 = x^2(1 - x^2)$ is of the fourth degree in x, a line parallel to the x-axis will cut the curve in at most four points. The line $y = c$ and the curve will, in fact, have

a) no intersections if $|c| > \frac{1}{2}$,
b) two intersections if $|c| = \frac{1}{2}$,
c) four intersections if $0 < |c| < \frac{1}{2}$,
d) three intersections if $c = 0$.

The results in cases (b) and (d) may be interpreted as limiting cases of (c) with some of the intersections coinciding.

PROBLEMS

Analyze each of the equations below to investigate the following properties of the curve: (a) symmetry, (b) extent, (c) intercepts, (d) asymptotes, (e) slope at the intercepts. Locate a few points, and sketch the curve, taking into account the information discovered above.

1. $y^2 = x(x - 2)$

2. $y^2 = \dfrac{x}{x - 2}$

3. $x^4 + y^4 = 1$

4. $x^2 = \dfrac{1 + y^2}{1 - y^2}$

5. $x^2 = \dfrac{y^2 + 1}{y^2 - 1}$

6. $y = x + \dfrac{1}{x}$

7. $y = x^2 + 1$

8. $y = \dfrac{1}{x^2 + 1}$

9. $y = x^2 - 1$

10. $y = \dfrac{1}{x^2 - 1}$

8–2

TANGENTS AND NORMALS

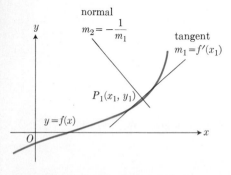

8–6 The normal and tangent to a smooth curve.

In Chapter 1 we learned that

$$y - y_1 = m(x - x_1) \tag{1}$$

is an equation for the line of slope m which passes through the point (x_1, y_1). The equation of a line *tangent* to a given curve $y = f(x)$ at a given point (x_1, y_1) on the curve can be found by taking

$$m = \left(\frac{dy}{dx}\right)_{(x_1, y_1)} = f'(x_1)$$

in Eq. (1). Equation (1) then becomes:

Tangent

$$y - y_1 = f'(x_1)(x - x_1). \tag{2}$$

The numbers x_1, y_1, and $f'(x_1)$ are all *constants* in this equation.

The line through $P_1(x_1, y_1)$ perpendicular to the tangent line is called the *normal* to the curve at P_1 (Fig. 8–6). Its slope m_2 is the negative reciprocal of the slope m_1 of the tangent; that is,

$$m_2 = -\frac{1}{m_1} = \frac{-1}{f'(x_1)}.$$

The point slope equation of the *normal* is therefore:

Normal

$$y - y_1 = \frac{-1}{f'(x_1)}(x - x_1). \tag{3}$$

EXAMPLE 1. Find the lines tangent and normal to the curve

$$y^2 - 6x^2 + 4y + 19 = 0 \qquad (4)$$

at the point $(2, 1)$.

Solution. We differentiate both sides of the equation with respect to x and solve for (dy/dx):

$$2y\frac{dy}{dx} - 12x + 4\frac{dy}{dx} = 0, \qquad (5)$$

$$\frac{dy}{dx}(2y + 4) = 12x,$$

$$\frac{dy}{dx} = \frac{6x}{y + 2}.$$

We then evaluate the derivative at $x = 2$, $y = 1$, to obtain

$$\left.\frac{dy}{dx}\right|_{(2,1)} = \left.\frac{6x}{y + 2}\right|_{(2,1)} = \frac{12}{3} = 4. \qquad (6)$$

Therefore, the tangent to the curve at the point $(2, 1)$ is

$$y - 1 = 4(x - 2),$$

and the normal is

$$y - 1 = -\tfrac{1}{4}(x - 2).$$

EXAMPLE 2. Find the tangents to the curve $y = x^3 - 7x$ that are parallel to the line $y = 5x - 1$.

Solution. The slope of the curve at a point (x, y) on the curve is

$$y' = 3x^2 - 7.$$

The slope of the given line is $m = 5$. We equate the two slopes to get

$$3x^2 - 7 = 5,$$

$$x^2 = \tfrac{12}{3} = 4,$$

$$x = \pm 2.$$

Thus, the tangents to the curve have slope 5 when $x = +2$ and $x = -2$. The y-coordinate of the point on the curve at $x = +2$ is

$$y = (2)^3 - 7(2) = -6.$$

The point–slope equation of the tangent at the point $(2, -6)$ is therefore

$$y + 6 = 5(x - 2).$$

The slope–intercept equation of this line is

$$y = 5x - 16.$$

When $x = -2$ on the curve,

$$y = (-2)^3 - 7(-2) = 6.$$

The tangent to the curve at the point $(-2, 6)$ is

$$y - 6 = 5(x + 2),$$

or

$$y = 5x + 16.$$

EXAMPLE 3. Show that the normal to the curve

$$x^2 + y^2 = a^2 \tag{7}$$

at any point (x_1, y_1) on it passes through the origin.

Solution. Differentiating (7) implicitly and solving for dy/dx, we find

$$\frac{dy}{dx} = -\frac{x}{y}$$

as the slope of the *tangent* at (x, y). The slope of the *normal* at (x_1, y_1) is therefore

$$m = \frac{y_1}{x_1},$$

and the equation of the normal is

$$y - y_1 = \frac{y_1}{x_1}(x - x_1). \tag{8}$$

When we clear of fractions, (8) reduces to

$$x_1 y = y_1 x.$$

Clearly, the origin lies on this line, since the coordinates $x = 0$, $y = 0$ satisfy the equation.

EXAMPLE 4. Show that the number of tangent lines that can be drawn from the point $Q(h, k)$ to the curve

$$y = x^2 \tag{9}$$

is two, one, or zero according as k is less than h^2, equal to h^2, or greater than h^2, respectively.

Solution. Figure 8–7 represents the curve and the three cases $k < h^2$, $k = h^2$, $k > h^2$. From the fact that $d^2y/dx^2 = 2$ is always positive, so that the curve is concave upward, we see that the results stated are equivalent to saying that two tangents can be drawn from a point on the convex side of the curve, no tangents from a point on the concave side of the curve, and only one tangent from a point on the curve. This is geometrically evident, but we shall adopt an analytical approach as follows.

Suppose that a tangent *can* be drawn to the curve from Q, touching the curve at some point $P_1(x_1, y_1)$ which is at present not known. Then, using Eq. (2), we find the equation of this tangent line to be

$$y - y_1 = 2x_1(x - x_1).$$

a)

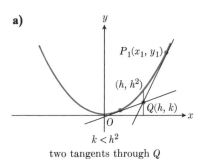

$k < h^2$

two tangents through Q

b)

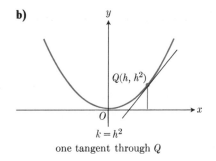

$k = h^2$

one tangent through Q

c)

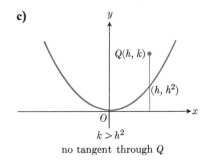

$k > h^2$

no tangent through Q

Figure 8–7

Since $Q(h, k)$ is *on this line*, its coordinates must satisfy the equation

$$k - y_1 = 2x_1(h - x_1). \tag{10a}$$

Also, since (x_1, y_1) is *on the curve*, its coordinates must satisfy the equation

$$y_1 = x_1^2. \tag{10b}$$

Now in reality, h and k are known to us but x_1 and y_1 are not. We therefore have two equations, (10a) and (10b), for two unknowns, x_1 and y_1. We eliminate y_1 between them and obtain

$$k - x_1^2 = 2hx_1 - 2x_1^2$$

or

$$x_1^2 - 2hx_1 + k = 0.$$

If we solve this for x_1 by means of the quadratic formula, we obtain

$$x_1 = h \pm \sqrt{h^2 - k}. \tag{10c}$$

Only real values of x_1 correspond to points P_1 on the curve; hence no tangent may be drawn if $h^2 - k$ is negative, which is the same condition as saying k is greater than h^2. If $h^2 = k$, then the two roots in (10c) coincide and give only one point, namely $x_1 = h$, $y_1 = k = h^2$, to which the tangent can be drawn. But if $k < h^2$, the two roots in (10c) are distinct and each root gives a value of x_1 which with $y_1 = x_1^2$ determines a point P_1 such that the line QP_1 is tangent to the curve, so that two tangents may be drawn.

Angle between Two Curves

Let C_1 and C_2 be two curves that intersect at a point P. Then the angle between C_1 and C_2 at P is, by definition, the angle β between their tangents at P (Fig. 8–8). If these tangents are, respectively, L_1 and L_2, they have slopes

$$m_1 = \tan \phi_1, \qquad m_2 = \tan \phi_2.$$

Then $\tan \beta$ can be found from m_1 and m_2 as follows. Since

$$\beta = \phi_2 - \phi_1,$$

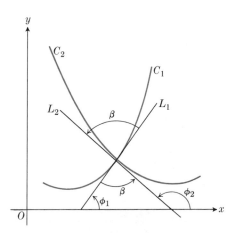

8–8 The angle between two smooth curves C_1 and C_2 at a point of intersection is the angle β between their tangents there. It is measured counterclockwise from C_1 to C_2.

we have

$$\tan \beta = \tan (\phi_2 - \phi_1) = \frac{\tan \phi_2 - \tan \phi_1}{1 + \tan \phi_2 \tan \phi_1} = \frac{m_2 - m_1}{1 + m_2 m_1}. \tag{11}$$

Here β is measured in the counterclockwise direction from L_1 to L_2.

We recall that the lines L_1 and L_2 are perpendicular if $m_2 = -1/m_1$. In this case we say that the curves C_1 and C_2 are *orthogonal*.

EXAMPLE 5.   Show that every curve of the family

$$xy = a, \qquad a \neq 0, \tag{12a}$$

is orthogonal to every curve of the family

$$x^2 - y^2 = b, \qquad b \neq 0. \tag{12b}$$

Solution.   The two families of curves are sketched in Fig. 8–9. At a point $P(x, y)$ on any curve of (12a), the slope is

$$\frac{dy}{dx} = -\frac{y}{x}, \tag{13a}$$

and on any curve of (12b) the slope is

$$\frac{dy}{dx} = \frac{x}{y}. \tag{13b}$$

At a point of intersection, the values of x and y in (13b) are the same as in (13a), and the two curves are orthogonal because these slopes are negative reciprocals of each other. The cases $x = 0$ or $y = 0$ cannot occur in Eqs. (13) if (x, y) is a point of intersection of any curve (12a) and a curve (12b), since a and b are restricted to be constants different from zero. That every curve in (12a) does in fact intersect every curve in (12b) follows from the fact that the equation

$$x^2 - \frac{a^2}{x^2} = b,$$

which results from eliminating y between (12a) and (12b), has real roots for every pair of nonzero real constants a and b.

The curves in (12b) are called *orthogonal trajectories* of the curves in (12a). Such mutually orthogonal systems of curves are of particular importance in physical problems related to electrical potential, where the curves in one family correspond to lines of flow and those in the other family correspond to lines of constant potential. They also occur in hydrodynamics and in heat-flow problems.

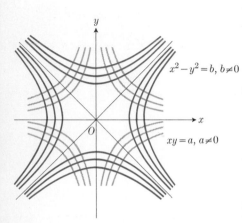

$x^2 - y^2 = b,\ b \neq 0$

$xy = a,\ a \neq 0$

8–9   Each curve is orthogonal to every curve it meets in the other family.

PROBLEMS

1. Find the tangent to the curve $y^2 - 2x - 4y - 1 = 0$ at the point $(-2, 1)$.

2. Find the normal to the curve $xy + 2x - 5y - 2 = 0$ at the point $(3, 2)$.

3. Find the tangents to the curve $y = x^3 - 6x + 2$ that are parallel to the line $y = 6x - 2$.

4. Find the normals to the curve $xy + 2x - y = 0$ that are parallel to the line $2x + y = 0$.

5. Show that the two lines that are drawn from $(\frac{3}{2}, 0)$ tangent to the curve $x^2 - 4y + 4 = 0$ are perpendicular.

6. There are three normals through the point $(\frac{3}{4}, 0)$ to the curve $y^2 = x$. One of them is the x-axis. Show that the other two are perpendicular.

7. Does the line that is tangent to the curve $y = x^3$ at the point $(1, 1)$ intersect the curve at any other point? If so, find the point.

8. A line is drawn from the point $P_0(1, 5)$ tangent to the curve $y = x^3$ at a point $P_1(x_1, y_1)$ on it. Find the coordinates of P_1. Is there more than one possibility for the point P_1? Why?

9. Find all lines that can be drawn normal to the curve $x^2 - y^2 = 5$ and parallel to the line $2x + 3y = 10$. Sketch the curve and the lines.

10. Find all lines that can be drawn tangent to the curve $4xy = 1$ from the point $P(-1, 2)$. Sketch the curve and the lines.

11. The line that is normal to the curve $y = x^2 + 2x - 3$ at $(1, 0)$ intersects the curve at what other point?

12. If l represents the distance between a fixed point $P_1(x_1, y_1)$ and a variable point $P(x, y)$ on a curve $y = f(x)$ (Fig. 8–10), then

$$l^2 = (x - x_1)^2 + [f(x) - y_1]^2.$$

Show that the derivative $d(l^2)/dx$ is equal to zero when $x = x_2$ if and only if the line $P_1 P_2$ is normal to the curve at $P_2[x_2, f(x_2)]$.

13. Show that the curve $2x^2 + 3y^2 = 5$ and the curve $y^2 = x^3$ intersect at right angles.

14. Let $P_1(x_1, y_1)$ and $P_2(x_2, y_2)$ be any two points on the curve

$$y = ax^2 + bx + c, \qquad a \neq 0.$$

If a line is drawn tangent to the curve at (x_0, y_0) and is parallel to the chord $P_1 P_2$, show that $x_0 = (x_1 + x_2)/2$.

15. For what values of b is the line $y = 12x + b$ tangent to the curve $y = x^3$?

16. For what values of m is the line $y = mx$ tangent to the curve

$$y^2 + x^2 - 4x + 3 = 0?$$

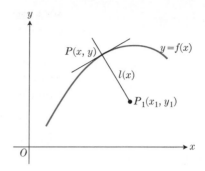

8–10 The values of x where the line P_1P is normal to the curve are critical values of the function $l(x)$.

17. Find the interior angles of the triangle whose vertices are $A(1, 1)$, $B(3, -1)$, and $C(5, 2)$.

18. Find the slope of the line that bisects the angle ACB in the previous problem.

19. Let A, B, C be the interior angles of a triangle in which no angle is a right angle. By calculating $\tan (A + B + C)$ and observing that

$$A + B + C = 180°,$$

show that the equation

$$\tan A + \tan B + \tan C = \tan A \tan B \tan C$$

must be satisfied.

20. Calculate the interior angles of the triangle whose vertices are $A(1, 2)$, $B(2, -1)$, and $C(-1, 1)$, and check your results by showing that they satisfy the equation

$$\tan A + \tan B + \tan C = \tan A \tan B \tan C.$$

(See Problem 19, above.)

21. Find the angles between the following pairs of curves:

a) $3x + y = 5, \quad 2x - y = 4,$

b) $y = x^2, \quad xy = 1,$

c) $x^2 + y^2 = 16, \quad y^2 = 6x,$

d) $x^2 + xy + y^2 = 7, \quad y = 2x.$

It is at once apparent from Fig. 8–11 and the theorem of Pythagoras that the distance d between the two points $P_1(x_1, y_1)$ and $P_2(x_2, y_2)$ is given by

$$d = \sqrt{(x_2 - x_1)^2 + (y_2 - y_1)^2}. \qquad \textbf{(1)}$$

This formula is particularly useful in finding the equation of a curve whose geometric character depends upon one or more distances, as in the example below.

8–3

DISTANCE BETWEEN TWO POINTS. EQUATIONS

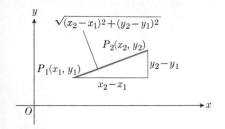

8–11 The distance between two points P_1 and P_2 is computed from their coordinates.

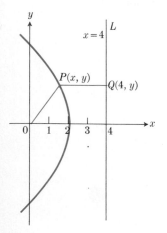

8–12 The curve traced by a point P that stays equidistant from point O and from line L.

EXAMPLE 1. Find an equation for the set of points $P(x, y)$ that are equidistant from the origin O and the line $L: x = 4$.

Solution. The distance between P and L is the perpendicular distance PQ between $P(x, y)$ and the point $Q(4, y)$ on L that has the same ordinate as P. (See Fig. 18–12.) Thus,

$$PQ = \sqrt{(4 - x)^2 + (y - y)^2} = |4 - x|.$$

The distance OP is

$$OP = \sqrt{x^2 + y^2}.$$

The condition to be satisfied by P is $OP = PQ$, or

$$\sqrt{x^2 + y^2} = |4 - x|. \tag{2}$$

If (2) holds, so does the equation we get by squaring:

$$x^2 + y^2 = 16 - 8x + x^2$$

or

$$y^2 = 16 - 8x. \tag{3}$$

That is, if a point is equidistant from O and L, then its coordinates must satisfy Eq. (3). The converse is also true, for if Eq. (3) holds, then

$$\sqrt{x^2 + y^2} = \sqrt{x^2 + (16 - 8x)}$$
$$= \sqrt{(x - 4)^2}$$
$$= |x - 4|$$
$$= |4 - x|,$$

and hence

$$OP = PQ.$$

Therefore Eq. (3) expresses both the necessary and sufficient condition on the coordinates of $P(x, y)$ for P to be equidistant from O and L.

PROBLEMS

In Problems 1–8, use the distance formula to derive equations for the sets of points $P(x, y)$ that satisfy the specified conditions. Analyze each equation and sketch its graph.

1. P is equidistant from the two points $A(-2, 1)$ and $B(2, -3)$.

2. The distance from P to $F_1(-1, 0)$ is twice its distance to $F_2(2, 0)$.

3. The product of its distances from $F_1(-2, 0)$ and $F_2(2, 0)$ is 4.

4. The sum of the distances from P to $F_1(1, 0)$ and $F_2(0, 1)$ is constant and the curve passes through the origin.

5. The distance of P from the line $x = -2$ is 2 times its distance from the point $(2, 0)$.

6. The distance of P from the point $(-3, 0)$ is 4 more than its distance from the point $(3, 0)$.

7. The distance of P from the line $y = 1$ is 3 less than its distance from the origin.

8. P is 3 units from the point $(2, 3)$.

9. Find a point that is equidistant from the three points $A(0, 1)$, $B(1, 0)$, $C(4, 3)$. What is the radius of the circle through A, B, and C?

10. Find the distance between the point $P_1(x_1, y_1)$ and the straight line $Ax + By + C = 0$.

8–4

THE CIRCLE

Definition. *A circle is the set of points in a plane whose distance from a given fixed point in the plane is a constant.*

Equation of a Circle

Let $C(h, k)$ be the given fixed point, the *center* of the circle. Let r be the constant distance, the *radius* of the circle. Let $P(x, y)$ be a point on the circle (Fig. 8–13). Then

$$\overline{CP} = r, \tag{1}$$

or

$$\sqrt{(x - h)^2 + (y - k)^2} = r,$$

or

$$(x - h)^2 + (y - k)^2 = r^2. \tag{2}$$

If (1) is satisfied, so is (2), and conversely. Therefore (2) is an equation for the circle.

EXAMPLE 1. Find an equation for the circle with center at the origin and with radius r.

8–13 $(x - h)^2 + (y - k)^2 = r^2$.

Solution. If $h = k = 0$, Eq. (2) becomes

$$x^2 + y^2 = r^2. \tag{3}$$

EXAMPLE 2. Find the circle through the origin with center at $C(2, -1)$.

Solution. Its equation, (2), is of the form

$$(x - 2)^2 + (y + 1)^2 = r^2.$$

Since the circle goes through the origin, $x = y = 0$ must satisfy the equation. Hence

$$(0 - 2)^2 + (0 + 1)^2 = r^2$$

or

$$r^2 = 5.$$

The equation is

$$(x - 2)^2 + (y + 1)^2 = 5.$$

EXAMPLE 3. What points $P(x, y)$ satisfy the inequality

$$(x - h)^2 + (y - k)^2 < r^2? \tag{4}$$

Solution. The left side of (4) is the square of the distance CP from $C(h, k)$ to $P(x, y)$. The inequality is satisfied if and only if

$$\overline{CP} < r;$$

that is, if P lies inside the circle of radius r with center at $C(h, k)$, Fig. 8–14.

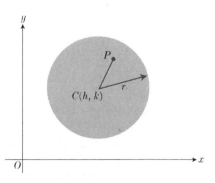

8–14   The region $(x - h)^2 + (y - k)^2 < r^2$ is the interior of the circle with center $C(h, k)$ and radius r.

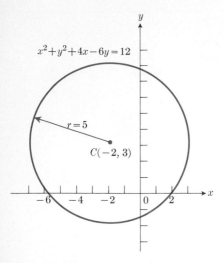

$$x^2 + y^2 + 4x - 6y = 12$$

$r = 5$

$C(-2, 3)$

8–15 The graph of
$x^2 + y^2 + 4x - 6y = 12.$

EXAMPLE 4. Analyze the equation

$$x^2 + y^2 + 4x - 6y = 12.$$

Solution. We complete the squares in the x terms and y terms and get

$$(x^2 + 4x + 4) + (y^2 - 6y + 9) = 12 + 4 + 9$$

or

$$(x + 2)^2 + (y - 3)^2 = 25.$$

This is of the same form as Eq. (2); therefore it represents a circle with center $C(-2, 3)$ and radius $r = 5$. Its graph is shown in Fig. 8–15.

REMARK 1. An equation of the form

$$Ax^2 + Ay^2 + Dx + Ey + F = 0, \qquad A \neq 0, \tag{5}$$

can often be reduced to the form of Eq. (2) by completing the squares as we did in Example 4. More specifically, we may divide (5) by A and write

$$\left(x^2 + \frac{D}{A}x\right) + \left(y^2 + \frac{E}{A}y\right) = -\frac{F}{A}. \tag{6}$$

To complete the squares for x, add $(D/2A)^2 = D^2/(4A^2)$; and for y add $(E/2A)^2 = E^2/(4A^2)$. Of course we must add to both sides of Eq. (6), thus obtaining

$$\left(x + \frac{D}{2A}\right)^2 + \left(y + \frac{E}{2A}\right)^2 = -\frac{F}{A} + \frac{D^2 + E^2}{4A^2}$$

$$= \frac{D^2 + E^2 - 4AF}{4A^2}. \tag{7}$$

Equation (7) is like Eq. (2), with

$$r^2 = \frac{D^2 + E^2 - 4AF}{4A^2}, \tag{8}$$

provided this expression is positive. Then (5) represents a circle with center at $(-D/2A, -E/2A)$ and radius $r = \sqrt{(D^2 + E^2 - 4AF)/(4A^2)}$.

If (8) is equal to zero, the curve reduces to a single point, and if it is negative, there are no points (with real coordinates) that satisfy Eq. (7) or Eq. (5).

We recommend that you apply the method of Example 4, and not use formulas, to handle problems of this type. The thing to remember is that an equation like (5), which is *quadratic in x and in y, with equal coefficients of* x^2 *and* y^2*, and with no xy term, represents a circle* (or a single point, or no real locus).

REMARK 2. Equation (5) can be divided by A and be replaced by an equation of the form

$$x^2 + y^2 + C_1x + C_2y + C_3 = 0, \tag{9}$$

where C_1, C_2, C_3 are three constants. The three coefficients in (9) can often be determined so as to satisfy three prescribed conditions. Typical conditions might be that the circle go through three given (noncollinear) points; or be tangent to three given nonconcurrent lines; or be tangent to two lines and pass through a given point not on either line.

EXAMPLE 5.　Find the circle through the three points $A(1, 0)$, $B(0, 1)$, and $C(2, 2)$.

Solution.　Let Eq. (9) be the equation of the circle. Then substitute for x and y the coordinates of A, B, and C, since these points are to be on the circle.

Point	$x^2 + y^2 +$	$C_1 x +$	$C_2 y +$	$C_3 = 0$
$A(1, 0)$	1	$+ C_1$		$+ C_3 = 0$
$B(0, 1)$	1		$+ C_2$	$+ C_3 = 0$
$C(2, 2)$	$4 + 4$	$+ 2C_1$	$+ 2C_2$	$+ C_3 = 0$

$$(10)$$

Equations (10) are three equations for the three unknowns. We solve them for C_1, C_2, and C_3. Subtract the second equation from the first to get

$$C_2 = C_1.$$

Substitute C_1 for C_2 in the third equation:

$$8 + 4C_1 + C_3 = 0.$$

Subtract the first equation from this:

$$7 + 3C_1 = 0.$$

Hence

$$C_2 = C_1 = -\tfrac{7}{3}$$

and

$$C_3 = -1 - C_1 = \tfrac{4}{3}.$$

Therefore, the equation of the circle through C_1, C_2, and C_3 is

$$x^2 + y^2 - \tfrac{7}{3}x - \tfrac{7}{3}y + \tfrac{4}{3} = 0$$

or

$$3x^2 + 3y^2 - 7x - 7y + 4 = 0.$$

Of course this example could equally well have been solved starting with Eq. (2), which contains the three unknowns h, k, and r. Or we could have found the center Q of the circle by locating the point of intersection of the perpendicular bisectors of the segments AB and BC. The radius is the distance from the center Q to any one of the three points A, B, or C.

PROBLEMS

In each of the following problems (1 through 4), find the equation of the circle having the given center $C(h, k)$ and radius r.

1. $C(0, 2)$, $r = 2$ **2.** $C(-2, 0)$, $r = 3$

3. $C(3, -4)$, $r = 5$ **4.** $C(1, 1)$, $r = \sqrt{2}$

5. Write an inequality that describes the points that lie inside the circle with center $C(-2, -1)$ and radius $r = \sqrt{6}$.

6. Write an inequality that describes the points that lie outside the circle with center $C(-4, 2)$ and radius $r = 4$.

In each of the following problems (7 through 10), find the center and radius of the given circle.

7. $x^2 + y^2 - 2y = 3$ **8.** $x^2 + y^2 + 2x = 8$

9. $3x^2 + 3y^2 + 6x = 1$ **10.** $2x^2 + 2y^2 + x + y = 0$

What points satisfy the inequalities in Problems 11 and 12?

11. $x^2 + y^2 + 2x - 4y + 5 \leq 0$

12. $x^2 + y^2 + 4x + 4y + 9 \geq 0$

13. The center of a circle is $C(2, 2)$. The circle goes through the point $A(4, 5)$. Find its equation.

14. The center of a circle is $C(-1, 1)$. The circle is tangent to the line $x + 2y = 4$. Find its equation.

15. A circle passes through the points $A(2, -2)$ and $B(3, 4)$. Its center is on the line $x + y = 2$. Find its equation.

16. Show geometrically that the lines that are drawn from the exterior point $P_1(x_1, y_1)$ tangent to the circle $(x - h)^2 + (y - k)^2 = r^2$ have length l given by

$$l^2 = (x_1 - h)^2 + (y_1 - k)^2 - r^2.$$

17. Find the equation of the circle that passes through the three points, $A(2, 3)$, $B(3, 2)$, and $C(-4, 3)$.

18. Find an equation for the coordinates of the point $P(x, y)$ if the sum of the squares of its distances from the two points $(-5, 2)$ and $(1, 4)$ is always 52. Identify and sketch the curve.

19. Is the point $(0.1, 3.1)$ inside, outside, or on the circle

$$x^2 + y^2 - 2x - 4y + 3 = 0?$$

Why?

20. If the distance from $P(x, y)$ to the point $(6, 0)$ is twice its distance from the point $(0, 3)$, show that P lies on a circle and find the center and radius.

21. Find the circle inscribed in the triangle whose sides are the lines $4x + 3y = 24$, $3x - 4y = 18$, $4x - 3y + 32 = 0$. [*Hint.* The distance between the point (h, k) and the line $ax + by = c$ is

$$\frac{|ah + bk - c|}{\sqrt{a^2 + b^2}}$$

by the answer to Problem 10, Article 8–3.]

22. Let P be a point outside a given circle C. Let PT be tangent to C at T. Let the line PN from P through the center of C intersect C at M and N. Prove that $PM \cdot PN = (PT)^2$.

23. It is known that any angle inscribed in a semicircle is a right angle. Prove the converse: i.e., if for every choice of the point $P(x, y)$ on a curve C joining O and A, the angle OPA is a right angle, then the curve is a circle or a semicircle having OA as diameter.

24. Suppose that Eqs. (2) and (9) represent the same circle. (a) Express C_1, C_2, and C_3 in terms of h, k, and r. (b) Express h, k, and r in terms of C_1, C_2, and C_3.

THE PARABOLA

Definition. *A parabola is the set of points in a plane that are equidistant from a given fixed point and fixed line in the plane.*

The Equation of a Parabola

The fixed point is called the *focus* of the parabola and the fixed line the *directrix*. If the focus F lies on the directrix L, then the parabola is nothing more than the line through F perpendicular to L. (We consider this to be a degenerate case.) If F does not lie on L, then we may choose a coordinate system that results in a simple equation for the parabola by taking the y-axis through F perpendicular to L, and taking the origin halfway between F and L. If the distance between F and L is $2p$, we may assign F coordinates $(0, p)$ and the equation of L is $y = -p$, as in Fig. 8–16. Then a point $P(x, y)$ lies on the parabola if and only if the distances PF and PQ are equal:

$$PF = PQ, \tag{1}$$

where $Q(x, -p)$ is the foot of the perpendicular from P to L. From the distance formula,

$$PF = \sqrt{x^2 + (y - p)^2} \quad \text{and} \quad PQ = \sqrt{(y + p)^2}.$$

When we equate these two expressions, square, and simplify, we get

$$x^2 = 4py. \tag{2}$$

This equation must be satisfied by any point on the parabola. Conversely, if (2) is satisfied, then

$$\begin{aligned} PF &= \sqrt{x^2 + (y - p)^2} \\ &= \sqrt{4py + (y^2 - 2py + p^2)} \\ &= \sqrt{(y + p)^2} \\ &= PQ, \end{aligned}$$

and $P(x, y)$ is on the parabola.

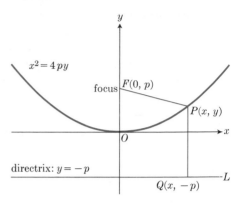

8–16 The parabola $x^2 = 4py$.

DISCUSSION.   In Eq. (2) assume p is positive. Then y cannot be negative, for real x, and the curve lies above the x-axis. It is symmetric about the y-axis, since x appears only to an even power.

The axis of symmetry of the parabola is also called the "axis of the parabola." The point on this axis midway between the focus and the directrix is on the parabola, since it is equidistant from the focus and the directrix. It is called the *vertex* of the parabola. The origin is the vertex of the parabola in Fig. 8–16. The tangent to a parabola at its vertex is parallel to the directrix. From Eq. (2) we find the slope of the tangent at any point is $dy/dx = x/2p$, and this is zero at the origin. The second derivative is $d^2y/dx^2 = 1/2p$, which is positive, so the curve is concave upward.

EXAMPLE 1. Find the focus and directrix of the parabola

$$x^2 = 8y. \tag{3}$$

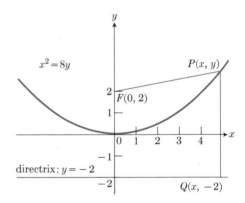

8–17 The parabola $x^2 = 8y$.

Solution. Equation (3) matches (2) if we take $4p = 8$, $p = 2$. The focus is on the axis of symmetry (the y-axis), p units from the vertex, that is, at $F(0, 2)$. The directrix is the line $y = -2$. Every point on the graph of (3) is equidistant from $F(0, 2)$ and the line $y = -2$ (Fig. 8–17).

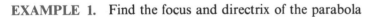

REMARK 1.   Suppose the parabola opens downward, as in Fig. 8–18, with its focus $F(0, -p)$ and directrix the line $y = p$. The effect is to change the sign of p in Eq. (2), which now becomes

$$x^2 = -4py. \tag{4}$$

We may also interchange the roles of x and y in Eqs. (2) and (4). The resulting equations

$$y^2 = 4px \tag{5a}$$

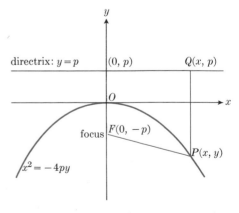

8–18 The parabola $x^2 = -4py$.

and

$$y^2 = -4px \tag{5b}$$

also represent parabolas, but now they are symmetric about the x-axis because y appears only to an even power. The *vertex* is still at the origin. The directrix is perpendicular to the axis of symmetry, and p units from the vertex. The focus is on the axis of symmetry, also p units from the vertex, and "inside" the curve. If we assume that p is positive in Eqs. (5), then (5a) opens toward the right, because x must be greater than or equal to zero, while (5b) opens toward the left. Figure 8–19 shows graphs of parabolas of these two types.

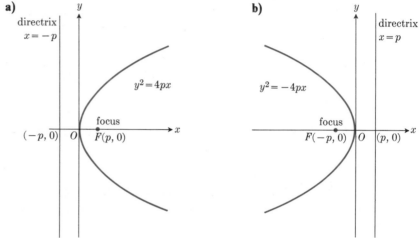

8–19   (a) The parabola $y^2 = 4px$.
(b) The parabola $y^2 = -4px$.

Translation of Axes

If the vertex of the parabola is at the point $V(h, k)$, Eqs. (2), (4), and (5) no longer apply in those forms. However, it is easy to determine what the appropriate equation is, by introducing a new coordinate system, with its origin O' at V, and axes parallel to the original axes. Every point P in the plane then has two sets of coordinates, say x and y in the original system, and x', y' in the new. To go from O to P, we have a horizontal displacement x and a vertical displacement y. The abscissa may be resolved into two horizontal displacements: h from O to O' and x' from O' to P (Fig. 8–20). Similarly, the ordinate is the resultant of two vertical displacements: k from O to O' and y' from O' to P. Thus the two sets of coordinates are related as follows:

$$\left.\begin{aligned} x &= x' + h \\ y &= y' + k \end{aligned}\right\} \tag{6a}$$

or

$$\left.\begin{aligned} x' &= x - h \\ y' &= y - k \end{aligned}\right\}. \tag{6b}$$

8–20   Translation of axes.

Equations (6) are called the equations for *translation of axes*, because the new coordinate axes may be obtained by moving the old axes to the position of the new ones in a motion known as a pure translation without rotation.

Suppose, now, we consider a parabola, with vertex $V(h, k)$ and opening upward as in Fig. 8–21. In terms of $x'y'$-coordinates, Eq. (2) provides us with the equation of the parabola in the form

$$(x')^2 = 4py'. \tag{7}$$

By using Eqs. (6), we may express this in xy-coordinates by the equation

$$(x - h)^2 = 4p(y - k). \tag{8a}$$

The axis of symmetry of the parabola in (8a) is the line $x = h$. The equation of this line is obtained by setting the quadratic term $(x - h)^2$ in (8a) equal to zero. When p is positive, $y - k$ must be greater than or equal to zero in (8a), for real $x - h$, and therefore the graph opens upward. The focus is on the axis of symmetry, p units above the vertex at $x = h$, $y = k + p$. The directrix is p units below the vertex and perpendicular to the axis of symmetry.

Other forms of equations of parabolas are:

$$(x - h)^2 = -4p(y - k), \tag{8b}$$

$$(y - k)^2 = 4p(x - h), \tag{8c}$$

$$(y - k)^2 = -4p(x - h). \tag{8d}$$

Equation (8b) has a graph symmetric about $x = h$, opening downward; (8c) symmetric about $y = k$ and opening to the right $(x \geq h)$; (8d) symmetric about $y = k$ and opening to the left $(x \leq h)$.

EXAMPLE 2. Discuss the parabola

$$y = x^2 + 4x. \tag{9}$$

Solution. We complete the square in the x terms by adding 4 to both sides of Eq. (9):

$$y + 4 = x^2 + 4x + 4 = (x + 2)^2.$$

This has the form

$$(x - h)^2 = 4p(y - k)$$

with

$$h = -2, \qquad k = -4,$$

$$4p = 1, \qquad p = \tfrac{1}{4}.$$

The vertex of the parabola is $V(-2, -4)$; its axis of symmetry $(x + 2)^2 = 0$; and it opens upward because $y \geq -4$ for real x. The graph is shown in Fig. 8–22. The focus is on the axis of symmetry, $\tfrac{1}{4}$ unit above the vertex, at $F(-2, -3\tfrac{3}{4})$. The directrix is parallel to the x-axis, $\tfrac{1}{4}$ unit below the vertex. Its equation is $y = -4\tfrac{1}{4}$.

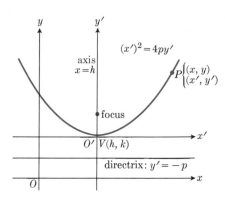

8–21 Parabola with vertex at $V(h, k)$.

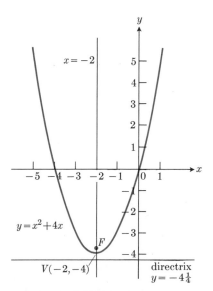

8–22 The parabola $y = x^2 + 4x$.

The key feature of an equation of a parabola is that it is quadratic in one of the coordinates and linear in the other. Whenever we have such an equation we may reduce it to one of the standard forms (8a, b, c, d) by completing the square in the coordinate that appears quadratically. We then put the linear terms in the form $\pm 4p(x - h)$ or $\pm 4p(y - k)$. Then the information about vertex, distance from vertex to focus, axis of symmetry, and direction the curve opens can all be read from the equation in this standard form.

EXAMPLE 3. Discuss the equation

$$2x^2 + 5y - 3x + 4 = 0.$$

Solution. This equation is quadratic in x, linear in y. We divide by 2, the coefficient of x^2, and collect all the x terms on one side of the equation:

$$x^2 - \tfrac{3}{2}x = -\tfrac{5}{2}y - 2.$$

Now we complete the square by adding $\left(-\tfrac{3}{4}\right)^2 = \tfrac{9}{16}$ to both sides:

$$\left(x - \tfrac{3}{4}\right)^2 = -\tfrac{5}{2}y - 2 + \tfrac{9}{16}$$

$$= -\tfrac{5}{2}y - \tfrac{23}{16}.$$

To get the y terms in the form $-4p(y - k)$, we factor out $-\tfrac{5}{2}$, and write

$$\left(x - \tfrac{3}{4}\right)^2 = -\tfrac{5}{2}\left(y + \tfrac{23}{40}\right).$$

This has the form

$$(x - h)^2 = -4p(y - k)$$

with

$$h = \tfrac{3}{4}, \qquad k = -\tfrac{23}{40}, \qquad 4p = \tfrac{5}{2}.$$

Hence the vertex is $V\left(\tfrac{3}{4}, -\tfrac{23}{40}\right)$. The axis of symmetry is $\left(x - \tfrac{3}{4}\right)^2 = 0$, or $x = \tfrac{3}{4}$; and the distance from the vertex to the focus is

$$p = \tfrac{5}{8}.$$

Since $y - k$ must here be ≤ 0 for real x, the curve opens downward, and the focus is p units below the vertex at $F\left(\tfrac{3}{4}, -\tfrac{6}{5}\right)$. The graph is shown in Fig. 8–23.

REMARK 3. In Fig. 8–24, $T'PT$ is tangent to the parabola, F is the focus, and PL is parallel to the axis of the parabola. The angles $\alpha = \angle L'PT$ and $\beta = \angle T'PF$ are equal (see Problem 31). This accounts for the property of a parabolic reflector that rays originating from the focus are reflected parallel to the axis, or rays coming into the reflector parallel to the axis are reflected to the focus. This property is used in parabolic mirrors of telescopes and in parabolic radar antennas.

EXAMPLE 4. The equation $x + 6p = 20$ gives the relation between the wholesale price p of coffee (dollars per pound) and the number of pounds x consumed per person in the United States from 1960 through 1974. The

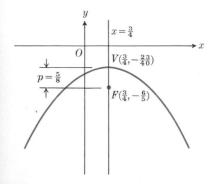

8–23 The parabola $2x^2 + 5y - 3x + 4 = 0$.

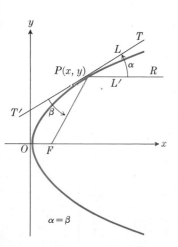

8–24 In a parabolic reflector, the angles α and β are equal.

number x is called the *demand* for the coffee, and the equation $x + 6p = 20$ is called the *demand law*. (See Problem 19, Article 1–5.) The revenue from coffee sales under this demand law is

$$R = xp = (20 - 6p)p = 20p - 6p^2 \quad \text{dollars per person.}$$

The graph of the revenue function is a parabola (Fig. 8–25), but only the portion in the first quadrant is meaningful in the present economic context. When we complete the square in p, we find

$$p^2 - \frac{10}{3}p = -\frac{R}{6},$$

$$p^2 - \frac{10}{3}p + \frac{25}{9} = -\frac{R}{6} + \frac{25}{9},$$

$$(p - \tfrac{5}{3})^2 = -\tfrac{1}{6}(R - \tfrac{50}{3}).$$

The vertex is $V(\frac{5}{3}, \frac{50}{3})$ and the axis of symmetry is the line $p = \frac{5}{3}$.

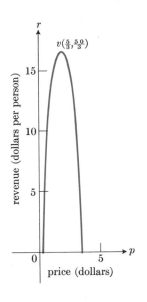

8–25   Revenue vs. price for the coffee demand law of Example 4.

Construction

A parabola can be constructed with straightedge and compass in the following way (Fig. 8–26):

a) Construct a family of lines parallel to the directrix L.

b) Set a compass to measure the distance d from the directrix to one of these lines L'. With the focus as center, construct an arc of radius d intersecting L' in points A' and B'.

c) Repeat the process with other lines L'', L''', and so on, constructing points A'', B'', A''', B''', and so on. The points constructed this way are all equidistant from L and F.

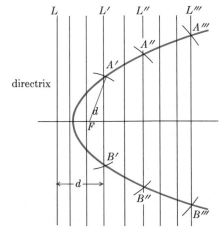

8–26   Construction of points on a parabola with focus F and directrix L.

PROBLEMS

In each of the following problems (1 through 6), the vertex V and focus F of a parabola are given. Find the equation of the parabola and of its directrix. Sketch the graph showing the focus, vertex, and directrix.

  1. $V(0, 0)$, $F(0, 2)$ **2.** $V(0, 0)$, $F(-2, 0)$

  3. $V(-2, 3)$, $F(-2, 4)$ **4.** $V(0, 3)$, $F(-1, 3)$

  5. $V(-3, 1)$, $F(0, 1)$ **6.** $V(1, -3)$, $F(1, 0)$

In each of the following problems (7 through 12), the vertex V and directrix L of a parabola are given. Find the equation of the parabola and its focus. Sketch the graph showing the focus, vertex, and directrix.

  7. $V(2, 0)$; L is the y-axis.

  8. $V(1, -2)$; L is the x-axis.

  9. $V(-3, 1)$; L is the line $x = 1$.

10. $V(-2, -2)$; L is the line $y = -3$.

11. $V(0, 1)$; L is the line $x = -1$.

12. $V(0, 1)$; L is the line $y = 2$.

In each of the following problems (13 through 22), find the vertex, axis of symmetry, focus, and directrix of the given parabola. Sketch the curve, showing these features.

13. $x^2 + 8y - 2x = 7$ **14.** $x^2 - 2y + 8x + 10 = 0$

15. $y^2 + 4x = 8$ **16.** $x^2 - 8y = 4$

17. $x^2 + 2x - 4y - 3 = 0$ **18.** $y^2 + x + y = 0$

19. $4y^2 - 8y + 3x - 2 = 0$ **20.** $y^2 + 6y + 2x + 5 = 0$

21. $3x^2 - 8y - 12x = 4$ **22.** $3x - 2y^2 - 4y + 7 = 0$

23. What points satisfy the inequality $x^2 < 8y$? Sketch.

24. (a) Do Problem 19 of Article 1–5 if you have not done so already. (b) At what price is the revenue from coffee sales under the demand law of Example 4 the greatest? What per capita consumption does the demand law give for this price?

25. A clothing-store chain has found that the daily revenue R from sales of a particular style of shirt is related to the dollar price p per shirt by the equation $R = -(\frac{1}{3})p^3 + 125p$. (a) Express the daily demand x as a function of p (see Example 4). Graph x as a function of p in the first quadrant. (b) At what price is the revenue R the greatest?

26. Find the length of the chord perpendicular to the axis of the parabola $y^2 = 4px$ and passing through the focus. (This chord is called the "latus rectum" of the parabola.)

27. Find the equation of the parabolic arch of base b and altitude h in Fig. 8–27.

28. Given the three points $(-1, 2)$, $(1, -1)$, and $(2, 1)$. (a) Find a parabola passing through the given points and having its axis parallel to the x-axis. (b) Find a parabola passing through the given points and having its axis parallel to the y-axis.

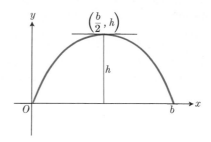

8–27 The parabolic arch of Problem 27.

29. Suppose a and b are positive numbers. Sketch the parabolas

$$y^2 = 4a^2 - 4ax \qquad \text{and} \qquad y^2 = 4b^2 + 4bx$$

in the same diagram. Show that they have a common focus, the same for any a and b. Show that they intersect at $(a - b, \pm 2\sqrt{ab})$, and that each "a-parabola" is orthogonal to every "b-parabola." (Using different values of a and b, we obtain families of confocal parabolas. Each family is a set of orthogonal trajectories of the other family. See Article 8–2.)

30. What points satisfy the equation

$$(2x + y - 3)(x^2 + y^2 - 4)(x^2 - 8y) = 0?$$

Give a reason for your answer.

31. Prove that the angles α and β in Fig. 8–24 are equal.

32. Prove that the tangent to the parabola $y^2 = 4px$ at $P_1(x_1, y_1)$ intersects the axis of symmetry x_1 units to the left of the vertex. (This provides a simple method for constructing the tangent to a parabola at any point on it.)

33. Show that the area of a parabolic segment of altitude h and base b is $\frac{2}{3}bh$ (see Problem 27).

34. Show that the volume generated by rotating the area bounded by the parabola $y = (4h/b^2)x^2$ and the line $y = h$ about the y-axis is equal to one and one-half times the volume of the corresponding inscribed cone.

35. The condition for equilibrium of the section OP of a cable that supports a weight of w pounds per foot measured along the horizontal (Fig. 8–28) is

$$\frac{dy}{dx} = \frac{wx}{H} \left(= \frac{T \sin \phi}{T \cos \phi} \right),$$

where the origin O is taken at the low point of the cable and H is the horizontal tension at O. Show that the curve in which the cable hangs is a parabola.

36. (*Reflective property of parabolas*) Assume, from optics, that when a ray of light is reflected by a mirror the angle of

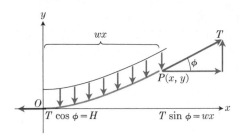

8–28 Diagram of a cable supporting a load of w pounds per horizontal foot.

incidence is equal to the angle of reflection. If a mirror is formed by rotating a parabola about its axis and silvering the resulting surface, show that a ray of light emanating from the focus of the parabola is reflected parallel to the axis.

37. Construct the graph of the parabola with focus $F(2, 2)$ and directrix the line $x + y = 0$.

38. Find the equation of the parabola of Problem 37. [Assume that the distance between a point (x, y) and the line $Ax + By + C = 0$ is $|Ax + By + C|/\sqrt{A^2 + B^2}$.]

Definition.   *An ellipse is the set of points in a plane whose distances from two fixed points in the plane have a constant sum.*

8–6

THE ELLIPSE

The Equation of an Ellipse

If the two fixed points, called *foci*, are taken at $F_1(-c, 0)$ and $F_2(c, 0)$ (Fig. 8–29), and the sum of the distances $PF_1 + PF_2$ is denoted by $2a$, then the coordinates of a point $P(x, y)$ on the ellipse must satisfy the equation

$$\sqrt{(x + c)^2 + y^2} + \sqrt{(x - c)^2 + y^2} = 2a.$$

To simplify this expression, we transpose the second radical to the right side of the equation, square, and simplify, to obtain

$$a - \frac{c}{a}x = \sqrt{(x - c)^2 + y^2}.$$

Again we square and simplify, and obtain

$$\frac{x^2}{a^2} + \frac{y^2}{a^2 - c^2} = 1. \qquad (1)$$

Since the sum $PF_1 + PF_2 = 2a$ of two sides of the triangle $F_1 F_2 P$ is greater than the third side $F_1 F_2 = 2c$, the term $(a^2 - c^2)$ in (1) is positive and has a real positive square root, which we denote by b:

$$b = \sqrt{a^2 - c^2}. \qquad (2)$$

Then (1) takes the more compact form

$$\frac{x^2}{a^2} + \frac{y^2}{b^2} = 1, \qquad (3)$$

from which it is readily seen that the curve is symmetric about both axes and lies inside the rectangle bounded by the lines $x = a, x = -a, y = b, y = -b$. The intercepts of the curve are at $(\pm a, 0)$ and $(0, \pm b)$. The curve intersects each axis at an angle of 90°, since

$$\frac{dy}{dx} = \frac{-b^2 x}{a^2 y}$$

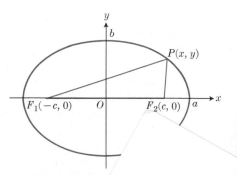

8–29 The ellipse $(x^2/a^2) + (y^2/b^2)$

is zero at $x = 0$, $y = \pm b$ and is infinite at $y = 0$, $x = \pm a$.

We have shown that the coordinates of P must satisfy (1) if P satisfies the geometric condition $PF_1 + PF_2 = 2a$. Conversely, if x and y satisfy the algebraic equation (1) with $0 < c < a$, then

$$y^2 = (a^2 - c^2)\frac{a^2 - x^2}{a^2},$$

and substituting this in the radicals below, we find that

$$PF_1 = \sqrt{(x + c)^2 + y^2} = \left| a + \frac{c}{a}x \right| \tag{4a}$$

and

$$PF_2 = \sqrt{(x - c)^2 + y^2} = \left| a - \frac{c}{a}x \right|. \tag{4b}$$

Since x is restricted to the range $-a \le x \le a$, the value of $(c/a)x$ lies between $-c$ and c, so that both $a + (c/a)x$ and $a - (c/a)x$ are positive, both being between $a + c$ and $a - c$. Hence the absolute values in (4a) and (4b) yield

$$PF_1 = a + \frac{c}{a}x, \qquad PF_2 = a - \frac{c}{a}x, \tag{5}$$

and, adding these, we see that $PF_1 + PF_2$ has a value $2a$ independent of the position of P on the curve. Thus the *geometric property* and *algebraic equation* are equivalent.

In Eq. (3), $b^2 = a^2 - c^2$ is less than a^2. The *major axis* of the ellipse is the segment of length $2a$ between the x-intercepts $(\pm a, 0)$. The *minor axis* is the segment of length $2b$ between the y-intercepts $(0, \pm b)$. The numbers a and b are also referred to respectively as *semimajor axis* and *semiminor axis*. If these semiaxes are $a = 4$, $b = 3$, then Eq. (3) is

$$\frac{x^2}{16} + \frac{y^2}{9} = 1. \tag{6a}$$

On the other hand, if we interchange the roles of x and y in (6a), we get the equation

$$\frac{x^2}{9} + \frac{y^2}{16} = 1, \tag{6b}$$

which must also represent an ellipse, but one with its major axis vertical rather than horizontal. Graphs of Eqs. (6a) and (6b) are given in Fig. 8–30 (a) and (b).

There is never any need for confusion in analyzing equations like (6a) and (6b). We simply find the intercepts on the axes of symmetry; then we know which way the major axis runs. The foci are always on the major axis. And if we use the letters a, b, and c to represent the lengths of semimajor axis, semiminor axis, and half-distance between foci, then Eq. (2) tells us that

$$b^2 = a^2 - c^2$$

or

$$a^2 = b^2 + c^2. \tag{7}$$

a)

b)

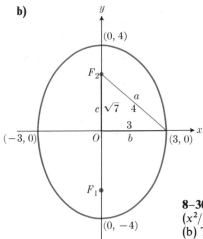

8–30 (a) The major axis of $(x^2/16) + (y^2/9) = 1$ is horizontal. (b) The major axis of $(x^2/9) + (y^2/16) = 1$ is vertical.

Hence a is the hypotenuse of a right triangle of sides b and c, as in Fig. 8–30. When we start with an equation like (6a) or (6b), we can read off a^2 and b^2 from it at once. Then Eq. (7) determines c^2 as their difference. So in either of Eqs. (6a) and (6b) we have

$$c^2 = 16 - 9 = 7.$$

Therefore the foci are $\sqrt{7}$ units from the center of the ellipse as shown.

Center not at the Origin

The *center* of an ellipse is defined as the point of intersection of its axes of symmetry. If the center is at $C(h, k)$, and the axes of the ellipse are parallel to the x- and y-axes, then we may introduce new coordinates

$$x' = x - h, \qquad y' = y - k, \tag{8}$$

using C as origin O' of $x'y'$-coordinates. The equation of the ellipse in the new coordinates is either

$$\frac{x'^2}{a^2} + \frac{y'^2}{b^2} = 1 \tag{9a}$$

or

$$\frac{x'^2}{b^2} + \frac{y'^2}{a^2} = 1, \tag{9b}$$

depending upon which way the major axis runs.

EXAMPLE 1. Analyze the equation $9x^2 + 4y^2 + 36x - 8y + 4 = 0$.

Solution. In order to complete the squares, we collect the x terms and the y terms separately, thus

$$9(x^2 + 4x) + 4(y^2 - 2y) = -4,$$

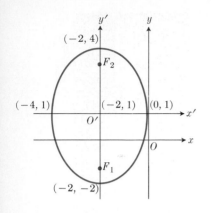

8–31   The ellipse
$9x^2 + 4y^2 + 36x - 8y + 4 = 0$.

and then complete the square in each set of parentheses to obtain

$$9(x^2 + 4x + 4) + 4(y^2 - 2y + 1) = -4 + 36 + 4.$$

We now divide both sides by 36 and write

$$\frac{(x + 2)^2}{4} + \frac{(y - 1)^2}{9} = 1.$$

Setting

$$x' = x + 2, \qquad y' = y - 1,$$

we see that the new origin $x' = 0$, $y' = 0$, is the same as the point $x = -2$, $y = 1$. In terms of the new coordinates, the equation is

$$\frac{x'^2}{4} + \frac{y'^2}{9} = 1,$$

which represents an ellipse with intercepts at $(0, \pm 3)$ on the y'-axis and $(\pm 2, 0)$ on the x'-axis (Fig. 8–31). To locate the foci, we use the relation

$$b = \sqrt{a^2 - c^2}$$

to find

$$c = \sqrt{a^2 - b^2}.$$

Here

$$a^2 = 9, \qquad b^2 = 4,$$

so

$$c = \sqrt{5}.$$

The foci are at the points $(0, \pm\sqrt{5})$ on the y'-axis or at $(-2, 1 \pm \sqrt{5})$ in terms of the original coordinates.

We recall (Fig. 8–29) that the essential *geometric* property of an ellipse is that the sum of the distances from any point on it to the two foci is a constant, namely,

$$PF_1 + PF_2 = 2a.$$

The essential *algebraic* property of its equation, when written in the form of a quadratic without a cross-product term, is that the x^2 and y^2 terms have the same sign.

In order to discuss the properties of the ellipse in more detail, we shall assume that its equation has been reduced to the form

$$\frac{x^2}{a^2} + \frac{y^2}{b^2} = 1, \qquad a > b > 0. \tag{10}$$

Although the distance c from the center of the ellipse to a focus does not appear in its equation, we may still determine c as in the examples above from the equation

$$c^2 = a^2 - b^2, \tag{11}$$

which simply comes from rewriting Eq. (7).

8–32   The eccentricity of an ellipse describes its shape.

Eccentricity

If we keep a fixed and vary c over the range $0 \le c \le a$, the resulting ellipses will vary in shape. They are circular when $c = 0$ (so that $a = b$), and become flatter as c increases, until in the extreme case $c = a$, the "ellipse" reduces to the line segment $F_1 F_2$ joining the two foci (Fig. 8–32). The ratio

$$e = \frac{c}{a}, \tag{12}$$

called the *eccentricity* of the ellipse, varies from 0 to 1 and indicates the degree of departure from circularity.

The planets in the solar system revolve around the sun in elliptical orbits with the sun at one focus. Most of the planets, including the earth, have orbits that are nearly circular, as can be seen from the eccentricities in Table 8–1. Pluto, however, has a fairly eccentric orbit, with $e = 0.25$, as does Mercury, with $e = 0.21$. Other members of the solar system have orbits that are even more eccentric. Icarus, an asteroid about one mile wide that revolves around the sun every 409 earth days, has an orbital eccentricity of 0.83 (Fig. 8–33).

Table 8–1.   Eccentricities of planetary orbits

Mercury	0.21	Saturn	0.06
Venus	0.01	Uranus	0.05
Earth	0.02	Neptune	0.01
Mars	0.09	Pluto	0.25
Jupiter	0.05		

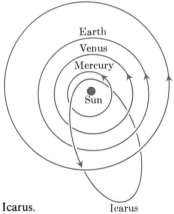

8–33   The orbit of the asteroid Icarus.

8–34   The orbit of Comet Kohoutek, shown approximately to scale. The small circle shows the outer limit of the orbit of Pluto.

EXAMPLE 2.   The dimensions of the orbit of the comet Kohoutek (Fig. 8–34) are approximately 44 astronomical units wide by 3,600 astronomical units long. (One astronomical unit (AU) is the earth's mean distance from the sun, about 92,600,000 miles.) Find the eccentricity of the orbit.

Solution

$$e = \frac{\sqrt{a^2 - b^2}}{a} = \frac{\sqrt{(1800)^2 - (22)^2}}{1800} \approx 0.99993.$$

We recall that a parabola has one focus and one directrix. Each ellipse has two foci and two directrices. The directrices are lines perpendicular to the major axis of the ellipse at distances $\pm a/e$ from its center. The *parabola* has the property that

$$PF = 1 \cdot PD \tag{13}$$

for any point P on it, where F is the focus and D is the point nearest P on the directrix. For an *ellipse*, it is not difficult to show that the equations which take the place of (13) are

$$PF_1 = e \cdot PD_1, \qquad PF_2 = e \cdot PD_2. \tag{14}$$

Here e is the eccentricity, P is any point on the ellipse, F_1 and F_2 are the foci, and D_1 and D_2 are the points nearest P on the two directrices. In Eq. (14), the corresponding directrix and focus must be used; that is, if one uses the distance from P to the focus F_1, one must also use the distance from P to the directrix at the same end of the ellipse (see Fig. 8–35). We thus associate the directrix $x = -a/e$ with the focus $F_1(-c, 0)$, and the directrix $x = a/e$ with the focus $F_2(c, 0)$. In terms of the semimajor axis a and eccentricity $e < 1$, as one goes away from the center along the major axis, one finds successively

> a *focus* at distance ae from the center,
>
> a *vertex* at distance a from the center,
>
> a *directrix* at distance a/e from the center.

The "focus-and-directrix" property furnishes a common bond uniting the parabola, ellipse, and hyperbola. Namely, if a point $P(x, y)$ is such that its distance PF from a fixed point (the focus) is proportional to its distance PD from a fixed line (the directrix), that is, so that

$$PF = e \cdot PD, \tag{15}$$

where e is a constant of proportionality, then the locus of P is

a) a *parabola* if $e = 1$,
b) an *ellipse* of eccentricity e if $e < 1$, and
c) a *hyperbola* of eccentricity e if $e > 1$.

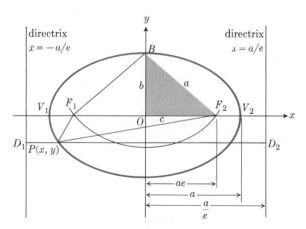

8–35   The ellipse $(x^2/a^2) + (y^2/b^2) = c^2$.

Constructions

There are several ways to construct an ellipse. One of these uses the definition directly. The two ends of a string of length $2a$ are held fixed at the foci F_1 and F_2 and a pencil traces the curve as it is held taut against the string (see Fig. 8–36).

A second method uses a straightedge AB of length $a + b$. Place point A on the y-axis and B on the x-axis, and on the graph paper, make a dot at $P(x, y)$ at distance a from A (see Fig. 8–37). In terms of the angle θ that line AB makes with the (negative) x-axis, we have

$$x = a \cos \theta, \qquad y = b \sin \theta, \tag{16}$$

and hence

$$\frac{x^2}{a^2} + \frac{y^2}{b^2} = \cos^2 \theta + \sin^2 \theta = 1.$$

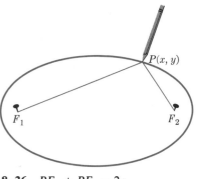

8–36 $PF_1 + PF_2 = 2a.$

Therefore $P(x, y)$ is on the ellipse, Eq. (10).

8–37 As B moves out from the origin, and A slides downward, the point P traces out part of an ellipse.

A third method is to construct two concentric circles of radii a and b (Fig. 8–38). A line making an angle θ with the horizontal is drawn from the center cutting the two circles in points A and B respectively. The vertical line through A and the horizontal line through B intersect in a point P whose coordinates also satisfy (16). By varying the angle θ from 0 to 2π, we may obtain as many points on the ellipse as we desire.

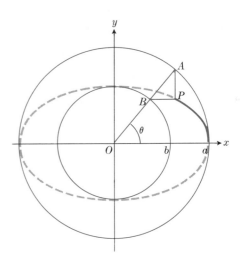

8–38 As θ increases from 0 to 2π, the point P at the intersection of the vertical line through A and the horizontal line through B traces out an ellipse.

PROBLEMS

In each of the following problems (1 through 5), find the equation of an ellipse having the given center C, focus F, and semimajor axis a. Sketch the graph and give the eccentricity of each ellipse.

  1. $C(0, 0)$, $F(0, 2)$, $a = 4$

  2. $C(0, 0)$, $F(-3, 0)$, $a = 5$

  3. $C(0, 2)$, $F(0, 0)$, $a = 3$

  4. $C(-3, 0)$, $F(-3, -2)$, $a = 4$

  5. $C(2, 2)$, $F(-1, 2)$, $a = \sqrt{10}$

6. The endpoints of the major and minor axes of an ellipse are $(1, 1)$, $(3, 4)$, $(1, 7)$, and $(-1, 4)$. Sketch the ellipse, give its equation, and find its foci.

7. Find the center, vertices, and foci of the ellipse

$$25x^2 + 9y^2 - 100x + 54y - 44 = 0.$$

Sketch the curve.

8. Sketch each of the following ellipses:

  a) $9x^2 + 4y^2 = 36$ **b)** $4x^2 + 9y^2 = 144$

c) $\dfrac{(x-1)^2}{16} + \dfrac{(y+2)^2}{4} = 1$

d) $4x^2 + y^2 = 1$

e) $16(x-2)^2 + 9(y+3)^2 = 144$

9. Find the equation of the ellipse that passes through the origin and has foci at $(-1, 1)$ and $(1, 1)$.

10. Find the eccentricity and the directrices of the ellipse $(x^2/7) + (y^2/16) = 1$.

11. Find the volume generated by rotating an ellipse of semi-axes a and b $(a > b)$ about its major axis.

12. Set up the integrals that give (a) the area of a quadrant of the circle $x^2 + y^2 = a^2$, (b) the area of a quadrant of the ellipse $b^2x^2 + a^2y^2 = a^2b^2$. Show that the integral in (b) is b/a times the integral in (a), and deduce the area of the ellipse from the known area of the circle.

13. (*Reflective property of ellipses*) An ellipsoid is generated by rotating an ellipse about its major axis. The inside surface of the ellipsoid is silvered to produce a mirror. Show that a ray of light emanating from one focus will be reflected to the other focus. (Sound waves also follow such paths, and this property of ellipsoids accounts for phenomena in certain "whispering galleries.")

14. Find the length of the chord perpendicular to the major axis of the ellipse $b^2x^2 + a^2y^2 = a^2b^2$ and passing through a focus. (This chord is called the "latus rectum" of the ellipse.)

15. Find the equation of an ellipse of eccentricity $\frac{2}{3}$ if the line $x = 9$ is one directrix and the corresponding focus is at $(4, 0)$.

16. Find the values of the constants A, B, and C if the ellipse

$$4x^2 + y^2 + Ax + By + C = 0$$

is to be tangent to the x-axis at the origin and to pass through the point $(-1, 2)$.

17. Show that the line tangent to the ellipse $(x^2/a^2) + (y^2/b^2) = 1$ at the point $P_1(x_1, y_1)$ on it is

$$\frac{xx_1}{a^2} + \frac{yy_1}{b^2} = 1.$$

In Problems 18–20, graph the sets of points whose coordinates satisfy the given inequality or equation.

18. $9x^2 + 16y^2 < 144$.

19. $(x^2 + 4y)(2x - y - 3)(x^2 + y^2 - 25)(x^2 + 4y^2 - 4) = 0$.

20. $(x^2 + y^2 - 1)(9x^2 + 4y^2 - 36) < 0$.

21. Draw an ellipse of eccentricity $\frac{4}{5}$.

22. Draw the orbit of Pluto to scale.

23. (*Calculator*) The orbit of Halley's Comet (expected to return in 1986) is about 9.12 AU wide and 36.18 AU long. Find its eccentricity. (See Example 2.)

24. (*Calculator*) The equations $x = a \cos \theta$, $y = b \sin \theta$, $0 \le \theta \le 2\pi$, are parametric equations for an ellipse.

a) Show that $(x^2/a^2) + (y^2/b^2) = 1$.

b) Show that the total length (perimeter) of the ellipse is

$$4a \int_0^{\pi/2} \sqrt{1 - e^2 \cos^2 \theta}\, d\theta,$$

where e is the eccentricity of the ellipse.

c) The integral in (b) is called an *elliptic integral*. It has no elementary antiderivative. Estimate the length of the ellipse when $a = 1$ and $e = \frac{1}{2}$ by the trapezoidal rule with $n = 10$.

d) The absolute value of the second derivative of $f(\theta) = \sqrt{1 - e^2 \cos^2 \theta}$ is less than one. Based on this, what estimate does Eq. (3), Article 4–9, give of the error in the approximation in (c)?

25. Problem 39, Article 6–1, considered a rope with a ring at one end looped over two pegs in a horizontal line. The free end of the rope passed through the ring to a weight that pulled the rope taut. It was assumed that the rope, which slipped freely over the pegs and through the ring, would come to rest in a configuration symmetric with respect to the line of the vertical part of the rope.

a) Show that for each fixed position of the ring on the rope the possible locations of the ring in space lie on an ellipse with foci at the pegs.

b) Justify the original symmetry assumption by combining the result in (a) with the assumption that the rope and weight will take a rest position of minimal potential energy.

8–7

THE HYPERBOLA

Definition. *A hyperbola is the set of points in a plane whose distances from two fixed points in the plane have a constant difference.*

The Equation of a Hyperbola

If we take the two fixed points, called *foci*, at $F_1(-c, 0)$ and $F_2(c, 0)$ and the constant equal to $2a$ (see Fig. 8–39), then a point $P(x, y)$ lies on the hyperbola if and only if

$$\sqrt{(x + c)^2 + y^2} - \sqrt{(x - c)^2 + y^2} = 2a$$

or

$$\sqrt{(x - c)^2 + y^2} - \sqrt{(x + c)^2 + y^2} = 2a.$$

The second equation is like the first, with $2a$ replaced by $-2a$. Hence we write the first one with $\pm 2a$, transpose one radical to the right side of the equation, square, and simplify. One radical still remains. We isolate it and square again. We then obtain the equation

$$\frac{x^2}{a^2} + \frac{y^2}{a^2 - c^2} = 1. \qquad \textbf{(1)}$$

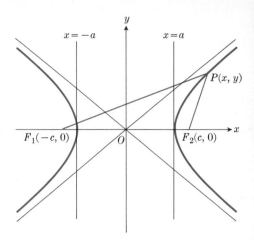

8–39 $PF_1 - PF_2 = 2a.$

So far, this is just like the equation for an ellipse. But now $a^2 - c^2$ is negative, because the *difference* in two sides of the triangle $F_1 F_2 P$ is less than the third side:

$$2a < 2c.$$

So in this case $c^2 - a^2$ is positive and has a real positive square root, which we call b:

$$b = \sqrt{c^2 - a^2}, \qquad \textbf{(2a)}$$

or

$$a^2 - c^2 = -b^2. \qquad \textbf{(2b)}$$

The equation of the hyperbola now becomes

$$\frac{x^2}{a^2} - \frac{y^2}{b^2} = 1, \qquad \textbf{(3)}$$

which is analogous to the equation of an ellipse. The only differences are the minus sign in the equation of the hyperbola, and the new relation among a, b, and c given by Eq. (2b). The hyperbola, like the ellipse, is symmetric with respect to both axes and the origin, but it has no real y-intercepts and in fact no portion of the curve lies between the lines $x = a$ and $x = -a$.

If we start with a point $P(x, y)$ whose coordinates satisfy Eq. (3), the distances PF_1 and PF_2 will be given by

$$PF_1 = \sqrt{(x + c)^2 + y^2} = \left| a + \frac{c}{a} x \right|, \qquad \textbf{(4a)}$$

$$PF_2 = \sqrt{(x - c)^2 + y^2} = \left| a - \frac{c}{a} x \right|, \qquad \textbf{(4b)}$$

as for the ellipse. But now c is greater than a, and P is either to the right of the line $x = a$, that is

$$x > a,$$

or else P is to the left of the line $x = -a$, and then

$$x < -a.$$

The absolute values in Eqs. (4) work out to be

$$PF_1 = a + \frac{c}{a}x \Big\}$$
$$PF_2 = \frac{c}{a}x - a \Big\} \quad \text{if } x > a \tag{5a}$$

and

$$PF_1 = -\left(a + \frac{c}{a}x\right) \Big\}$$
$$PF_2 = a - \frac{c}{a}x \Big\} \quad \text{if } x < -a. \tag{5b}$$

Thus, when P is to the right of the line $x = a$, the condition $PF_1 - PF_2 = 2a$ is satisfied, while if P is to the left of $x = -a$, the condition $PF_2 - PF_1 = 2a$ is fulfilled (Fig. 8–39). In either case, *any point P that satisfies the geometric conditions must satisfy Eq. (3). Conversely, any point that satisfies Eq. (3) also satisfies the geometric conditions.*

Asymptotes

The left side of (3) can be factored and the equation written in the form

$$\left(\frac{x}{a} - \frac{y}{b}\right)\left(\frac{x}{a} + \frac{y}{b}\right) = 1$$

or

$$\frac{x}{a} - \frac{y}{b} = \frac{ab}{bx + ay}. \tag{6a}$$

Analysis of (3) shows that one branch of the curve lies in the first quadrant and has infinite extent. If the point P moves along this branch so that x and y both become infinite, then the right side of (6a) tends to zero; hence the left side must do likewise. That is

$$\lim_{\substack{x \to \infty \\ y \to \infty}} \left(\frac{x}{a} - \frac{y}{b}\right) = 0, \tag{6b}$$

which leads us to speculate that the straight line

$$\frac{x}{a} - \frac{y}{b} = 0 \tag{7a}$$

may be an asymptote of the curve. To see that this is definitely so, we investigate the vertical distance $(y_2 - y_1)$ between the curve and the line where we take

$$y_2 = \frac{b}{a}x$$

on the line, and

$$y_1 = \frac{b}{a}\sqrt{x^2 - a^2}$$

on the curve (Fig. 8–40). We then multiply both sides of Eq. (6b) by b, and see that

$$\lim_{x \to \infty} (y_2 - y_1) = 0.$$

Since this vertical distance tends to zero, certainly the perpendicular distance from the line to the curve also approaches zero, and the line in Eq. (7a) is an asymptote of the hyperbola.

By symmetry, the line

$$\frac{x}{a} + \frac{y}{b} = 0 \qquad\qquad \textbf{(7b)}$$

is also an asymptote of the hyperbola. Both asymptotes may be obtained by replacing the "one" on the right side of (3) by a zero and then factoring. In sketching a hyperbola (Fig. 8–41), it is convenient to mark off distances a to the right and to the left of the origin along the x-axis and distances b above and below the origin along the y-axis, and to construct a rectangle whose sides pass through these points, parallel to the coordinate axes. The diagonals of this rectangle, extended, are the asymptotes of the hyperbola. The semidiagonal

$$c = \sqrt{a^2 + b^2}$$

can also be used as the radius of a circle that will cut the x-axis in two points, $F_1(-c, 0)$ and $F_2(c, 0)$, which are the foci of the hyperbola.

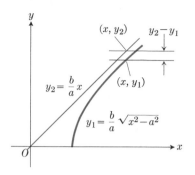

8–40   As $x \to \infty$, the point (x, y_1) rises on the hyperbola toward the asymptote $y_2 = (b/a)x$.

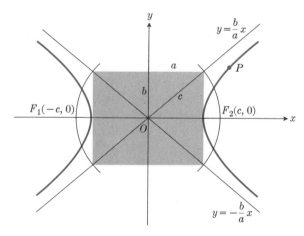

8–41   The hyperbola $(x^2/a^2) - (y^2/b^2) = 1$.

If we interchange x and y in Eq. (3), the new equation

$$\frac{y^2}{a^2} - \frac{x^2}{b^2} = 1 \qquad\qquad \textbf{(8)}$$

represents a hyperbola with foci on the y-axis. Its graph is shown in Fig. 8–42.

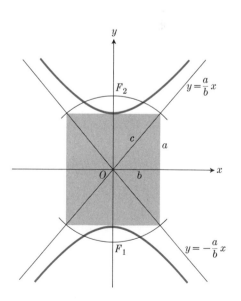

8–42   The hyperbola $(y^2/a^2) - (x^2/b^2) = 1$.

Center not at the Origin

The *center* of a hyperbola is the point of intersection of its axes of symmetry. If the center is $C(h, k)$, we may introduce a translation to new coordinates

$$x' = x - h, \qquad y' = y - k \tag{9}$$

with origin O' at the center. In terms of the new coordinates, the equation of the hyperbola is either

$$\frac{x'^2}{a^2} - \frac{y'^2}{b^2} = 1 \tag{10a}$$

or

$$\frac{y'^2}{a^2} - \frac{x'^2}{b^2} = 1. \tag{10b}$$

EXAMPLE 1. Analyze the equation $x^2 - 4y^2 + 2x + 8y - 7 = 0$.

Solution. We complete the squares in the x and y terms separately and reduce to standard form:

$$(x^2 + 2x) - 4(y^2 - 2y) = 7,$$

$$(x^2 + 2x + 1) - 4(y^2 - 2y + 1) = 7 + 1 - 4,$$

$$\frac{(x + 1)^2}{4} - (y - 1)^2 = 1.$$

The translation of axes

$$x' = x + 1, \qquad y' = y - 1$$

reduces the equation to

$$\frac{x'^2}{4} - \frac{y'^2}{1} = 1,$$

which represents a hyperbola with center at $x' = 0, y' = 0$, or $x = -1, y = 1$, having

$$a^2 = 4, \qquad b^2 = 1, \qquad c^2 = a^2 + b^2 = 5$$

and asymptotes

$$\frac{x'}{2} - y' = 0, \qquad \frac{x'}{2} + y' = 0.$$

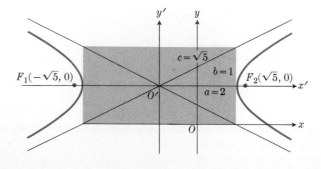

8–43 The xy-equation of the hyperbola shown to the right is $x^2 - 4y^2 + 2x + 8y - 7 = 0$. The $x'y'$-equation is $(x'^2/4) - (y'^2/1) = 1$.

The foci have coordinates $(\pm\sqrt{5}, 0)$ relative to the new axes or, since

$$x = x' - 1, \qquad y = y' + 1,$$

the coordinates relative to the original axes are $(-1 \pm \sqrt{5}, 1)$. The curve is sketched in Fig. 8–43.

EXAMPLE 2

$$x^2 - 4y^2 - 2x + 8y - 2 = 0.$$

Proceeding as before, we obtain

$$(x - 1)^2 - 4(y - 1)^2 = 2 + 1 - 4 = -1.$$

The standard form requires a plus one on the right side of the equation, so we change signs and have

$$4(y - 1)^2 - (x - 1)^2 = 1.$$

Comparison with (10) indicates that we should write the first term of this equation as $(y - 1)^2$ divided by 0.25:

$$\frac{(y - 1)^2}{0.25} - \frac{(x - 1)^2}{1} = 1.$$

The translation $x' = x - 1$, $y' = y - 1$ replaces this by

$$\frac{y'^2}{0.25} - \frac{x'^2}{1} = 1,$$

which represents a hyperbola with center at $x' = y' = 0$, or $x = y = 1$. The curve has intercepts at $(0, \pm 0.5)$ on the y'-axis but does not cross the x'-axis. Here (10b) applies, with

$$a^2 = 0.25, \qquad b^2 = 1, \qquad c^2 = a^2 + b^2 = 1.25.$$

The lines (Fig. 8–44)

$$\frac{y'}{0.5} - x' = 0, \qquad \frac{y'}{0.5} + x' = 0$$

are the asymptotes, while the foci are at $(0, \pm\sqrt{1.25})$ on the y'-axis.

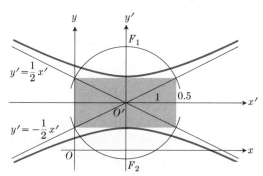

8–44   The hyperbola $(y'^2/0.25) - (x'^2/1) = 1$.

There is no restriction $a > b$ for the hyperbola as there is for the ellipse, and the direction in which the hyperbola opens is controlled by the *signs* rather than by the relative *sizes* of the coefficients of the quadratic terms.

In our further discussion of the hyperbola, we shall assume that it has been referred to axes through its center and that its equation has the form

$$\frac{x^2}{a^2} - \frac{y^2}{b^2} = 1. \tag{11}$$

Then

$$b = \sqrt{c^2 - a^2}$$

and

$$c^2 = a^2 + b^2. \tag{12}$$

As for the ellipse, we define the *eccentricity e* to be

$$e = \frac{c}{a}.$$

Since $c \geq a$, the eccentricity of a hyperbola is never less than one. The lines

$$x = \frac{a}{e}, \qquad x = -\frac{a}{e}$$

are the *directrices*.

We shall now verify that a point $P(x, y)$ whose coordinates satisfy Eq. (11) also has the property that

$$PF_1 = e \cdot PD_1 \tag{13a}$$

and

$$PF_2 = e \cdot PD_2, \tag{13b}$$

where $F_1(-c, 0)$ and $F_2(c, 0)$ are the foci while $D_1(-a/e, y)$ and $D_2(a/e, y)$ are the points nearest P on the directrices.

We shall content ourselves with establishing the results (13a, b) for any point P on the right branch of the hyperbola; the method is the same when P is on the left branch. Reference to Eqs. (5a) then shows that

$$PF_1 = \frac{c}{a}x + a = e\left(x + \frac{a}{e}\right),$$

$$PF_2 = \frac{c}{a}x - a = e\left(x - \frac{a}{e}\right), \tag{14a}$$

while we see from Fig. 8–45 that

$$PD_1 = x + \frac{a}{e}, \qquad PD_2 = x - \frac{a}{e}. \tag{14b}$$

These results combine to establish the "focus-and-directrix" properties of the hyperbola expressed in Eqs. (13a, b). Conversely, if Eqs. (14a) are satisfied, it is also true that

$$PF_1 - PF_2 = 2a;$$

that is, P satisfies the requirement that the difference of its distances from the two foci is constant.

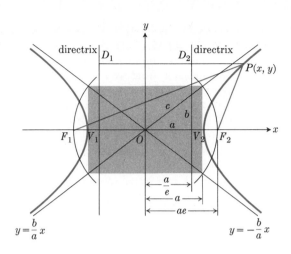

8–45 $PF_1 = e \cdot PD_1$ and $PF_2 = e \cdot PD_2$.

Construction

There are various schemes for sketching hyperbolas. One of them (see Fig. 8–46) exploits the equation

$$PF_1 = 2a + PF_2$$

as follows: Construct a circle of radius r centered at F_2 and a circle of radius $(2a + r)$ centered at F_1. The points P, P', where the two circles cross, are points on the hyperbola. By varying r, we may obtain as many points on the hyperbola as desired. Interchanging the roles of the two foci F_1 and F_2 will give points on the other branch.

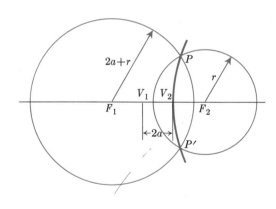

8–46   The points P and P' are on the hyperbola $PF_1 = 2a + PF_2$.

PROBLEMS

1. Sketch each of the following hyperbolas:

a) $\dfrac{x^2}{9} - \dfrac{y^2}{16} = 1,$ **b)** $\dfrac{x^2}{16} - \dfrac{y^2}{9} = 1,$

c) $\dfrac{y^2}{9} - \dfrac{x^2}{16} = 1,$ **d)** $\dfrac{x^2}{9} - \dfrac{y^2}{16} = -1.$

In each of the following problems (2 through 8), find the center, vertices, foci, and asymptotes of the given hyperbola.

Sketch the curve.

2. $9(x - 2)^2 - 4(y + 3)^2 = 36$

3. $4(x - 2)^2 - 9(y + 3)^2 = 36$

4. $4(y + 3)^2 - 9(x - 2)^2 = 1$

5. $5x^2 - 4y^2 + 20x + 8y = 4$

6. $4x^2 = y^2 - 4y + 8$

7. $4y^2 = x^2 - 4x$

8. $4x^2 - 5y^2 - 16x + 10y + 31 = 0$

9. Show that the line tangent to the hyperbola $b^2x^2 - a^2y^2 = a^2b^2$ at a point $P(x_1, y_1)$ on it has an equation that may be written in the form $b^2xx_1 - a^2yy_1 = a^2b^2$.

10. Find the volume generated when the area bounded by the hyperbola $b^2x^2 - a^2y^2 = a^2b^2$ and the line $x = c$, through its focus $(c, 0)$, is rotated about the y-axis.

11. Show that the equation

$$\frac{x^2}{9 - C} + \frac{y^2}{5 - C} = 1$$

represents (a) an ellipse if C is any constant less than 5, (b) a hyperbola if C is any constant between 5 and 9, (c) no real locus if C is greater than 9. Show that each ellipse in (a) and each hyperbola in (b) has foci at the two points $(\pm 2, 0)$, independent of the value of C.

12. Find the equation of the hyperbola with foci at $(0, 0)$ and $(0, 4)$ if it is required to pass through the point $(12, 9)$.

13. One focus of a hyperbola is located at the point $(1, -3)$ and the corresponding directrix is the line $y = 2$. Find the equation of the hyperbola if its eccentricity is $\frac{3}{2}$.

14. Find out what you can about the DECCA system of air navigation. [See *Time*, Feb. 23, 1959, p. 87, or the reference in Problem 15.]

15. A radio signal was sent simultaneously from towers A and B located several hundred miles apart on the California coast. A ship offshore received the signal from A 1400 microseconds before it received the signal from B.

a) Assume that the radio signals traveled at 980 ft per microsecond. What can be said about the approximate location of the ship relative to the two towers?

b) Find out what you can about LORAN and other hyperbolic radio-navigation systems. [See, for example, Nathaniel Bowditch's *American Practical Navigator*, Vol. I, U.S. Defense Mapping Agency Hydrographic Center, Publication No. 9, 1977, Chapter XLIII.]

16. (*Reflective property of hyperbolas*) Show that a ray of light directed toward one focus of a hyperbolic mirror, as in Fig. 8–47, is reflected toward the other focus. [*Hint.* Show that the tangent to the hyperbola at the point P in Fig. 8–47 bisects the angle made by the segments PF_1 and PF_2.]

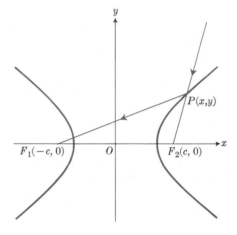

8–47 Reflective property of hyperbolas.

8–8

SECOND DEGREE CURVES

The equations of the circle, parabola, ellipse, and hyperbola are special cases of the general second degree equation

$$Ax^2 + Bxy + Cy^2 + Dx + Ey + F = 0, \tag{1}$$

in which the coefficients A, B, and C are not all zero. For example, the circle

$$(x - h)^2 + (y - k)^2 = r^2$$

may be obtained from Eq. (1) by taking

$$A = C = 1, \qquad B = 0, \qquad D = -2h,$$
$$E = -2k, \qquad F = h^2 + k^2 - r^2,$$

and the parabola

$$x^2 = 4py$$

is obtained by taking

$$A = 1, \qquad E = -4p, \qquad B = C = D = F = 0.$$

In fact, even the straight line is a special case of (1) with $A = B = C = 0$, but this reduces (1) to a *linear* equation instead of maintaining its status as a second degree equation. The terms Ax^2, Bxy, and Cy^2 are the second degree, or quadratic terms, and we shall presently investigate the nature of the curve represented by Eq. (1) when at least one of these quadratic terms is present.

The so-called "cross-product" term, Bxy, has not appeared in the equations we found in Articles 8–4 to 8–7. This is a consequence of the way in which we chose coordinate axes, namely, such that at least one of them is parallel to an axis of symmetry of the curve in question. However, suppose we seek to find the equation of a hyperbola with foci at $F_1(-a, -a)$ and $F_2(a, a)$, for example, and with $|PF_1 - PF_2| = 2a$ (Fig. 8–48). Then

$$\sqrt{(x + a)^2 + (y + a)^2} - \sqrt{(x - a)^2 + (y - a)^2} = \pm 2a,$$

and when we transpose one radical, square, solve for the radical that still appears, and square again, this reduces to

$$2xy = a^2, \tag{2}$$

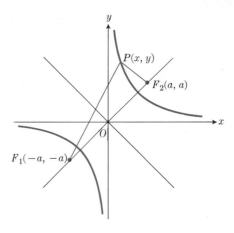

8–48 The hyperbola $2xy = a^2$.

which is a special case of Eq. (1) in which the cross-product term is present. The asymptotes of the hyperbola in Eq. (2) are the x- and y-axes, and the transverse axis of the hyperbola (the axis of symmetry on which the foci lie) makes an angle of 45° with the coordinate axes. In fact, the cross-product term is present only in some similar circumstance, where the axes of the conic are tilted.

Rotation of Axes

The equation of a curve can be modified by referring it to $x'y'$-axes by a rotation through an angle α in the counterclockwise direction. In the notation of Fig. 8–49, we have

$$x = OM = OP \cos (\theta + \alpha),$$
$$y = MP = OP \sin (\theta + \alpha), \tag{3a}$$

while

$$x' = OM' = OP \cos \theta,$$
$$y' = M'P = OP \sin \theta. \tag{3b}$$

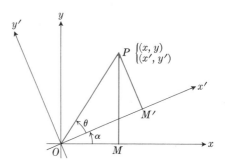

8–49 A counterclockwise rotation through angle α.

Using the relationships

$$\cos (\theta + \alpha) = \cos \theta \cos \alpha - \sin \theta \sin \alpha,$$
$$\sin (\theta + \alpha) = \sin \theta \cos \alpha + \cos \theta \sin \alpha,$$

in (3a) and taking account of (3b), we find

Equations for Rotation of Axes

$$x = x' \cos \alpha - y' \sin \alpha,$$
$$y = x' \sin \alpha + y' \cos \alpha. \tag{4}$$

EXAMPLE 1. The x- and y-axes are rotated $\alpha = 45°$ about the origin. Find the equation of the hyperbola of Eq. (2) in terms of the new coordinates.

Solution. Since $\cos 45° = \sin 45° = \sqrt{\frac{1}{2}}$, we substitute

$$x = \frac{x' - y'}{\sqrt{2}}, \qquad y = \frac{x' + y'}{\sqrt{2}}$$

into Eq. (2) and obtain

$$(x')^2 - (y')^2 = a^2,$$

which is equivalent to Eq. (3), Article 8–7, with $b = a$.

If we apply the equations for rotation of axes (4) to the general quadratic equation (1), we obtain a new quadratic equation of the form

$$A'x'^2 + B'x'y' + Cy'^2 + D'x' + E'y' + F' = 0. \tag{5}$$

The new coefficients are related to the old as follows:

$$\left.\begin{aligned}
A' &= A\cos^2 \alpha + B\cos \alpha \sin \alpha + C\sin^2 \alpha, \\
B' &= B(\cos^2 \alpha - \sin^2 \alpha) + 2(C - A)\sin \alpha \cos \alpha, \\
C' &= A\sin^2 \alpha - B\sin \alpha \cos \alpha + C\cos^2 \alpha, \\
D' &= D\cos \alpha + E\sin \alpha, \\
E' &= -D\sin \alpha + E\cos \alpha, \\
F' &= F.
\end{aligned}\right\} \tag{6}$$

If we start with an equation for a curve in which the cross-product term is present $(B \neq 0)$, we can always find an angle of rotation α such that the cross-product term does not appear in the new equation $(B' \neq 0)$. To find the angle α that eliminates the cross-product term, we put $B' = 0$ in the second equation in (6) and solve for α. It is easier to do this if we note that

$$\cos^2 \alpha - \sin^2 \alpha = \cos 2\alpha,$$

$$2 \sin \alpha \cos \alpha = \sin 2\alpha,$$

so that

$$B' = B\cos 2\alpha + (C - A)\sin 2\alpha.$$

Hence B' will vanish if we choose α so that

$$\cot 2\alpha = \frac{A - C}{B}. \tag{7}$$

EXAMPLE 2. The coordinate axes are to be rotated through an angle α so that the new equation for the curve

$$x^2 + xy + y^2 = 3 \tag{8}$$

has no cross-product term. Find α and the new equation.

Solution. The equation (8) has $A = B = C = 1$. Choose α according to Eq. (7):

$$\cot 2\alpha = 0, \qquad 2\alpha = 90°, \qquad \alpha = 45°.$$

Substitute this value for α into Eq. (4) to obtain

$$x = \frac{x' - y'}{\sqrt{2}}, \qquad y = \frac{x' + y'}{\sqrt{2}}.$$

When these values are substituted in the original equation (8), we find that

$$3(x')^2 + (y')^2 = 6.$$

This is the equation of an ellipse with foci on the new y'-axis.

Since axes may always be rotated to eliminate the cross-product term, there is no loss in generality in assuming that this has been done. Then the quadratic equation (5), with $B' = 0$, will look like Eq. (1), with $B = 0$:

$$Ax^2 + Cy^2 + Dx + Ey + F = 0. \tag{9}$$

Equation (9) represents:

a) A straight line if $A = C = 0$, and not both D and E vanish.

b) A circle if $A = C \neq 0$. In special cases the locus may reduce to a single point, or no real locus.

c) A parabola if (9) is quadratic in one variable, linear in the other.

d) An ellipse if A and C are both positive or both negative. In special cases the locus may reduce to a single point, or no real locus.

e) A hyperbola if A and C are of opposite signs, both different from zero. In special cases the locus may reduce to a pair of intersecting straight lines. (For example: $x^2 - y^2 = 0$.)

We have already seen how to reduce (9) to the standard form for the equation of a circle, parabola, ellipse, or hyperbola by completing the squares (as needed) and translating to new axes.

Summary

Any second degree equation in x and y represents a circle, parabola, ellipse, or hyperbola (except for certain special cases in which the locus may reduce to a point, a line, a pair of lines, or fail to exist, as noted above). Conversely, any of these curves has an equation of the second degree. To find the curve, given its equation, we

FIRST. Rotate axes (if necessary) to eliminate the cross-product term,

SECOND. Translate axes (if desired) to reduce the equation to a standard form that we recognize.

PROBLEMS

Transform each of the following equations by a rotation of axes into an equation that has no cross-product term.

1. $xy = 2$

2. $x^2 + xy + y^2 = 1$

3. $2y^2 + \sqrt{3}\,xy - x^2 = 2$

4. $3x^2 + 2xy + 3y^2 = 19$

5. $x^2 - 3xy + y^2 = 5$

6. $3x^2 + 4\sqrt{3}\,xy - y^2 = 7$

7. Use the definition of an ellipse to write an equation for the ellipse with foci at $F_1(-1, 0)$ and $F_2(0, \sqrt{3})$ if it passes through the point $(1, 0)$. Through what angle α should the axes be rotated to eliminate the cross-product term from the equation found? (Do not carry out the rotation.)

8. Show that the equation $x^2 + y^2 = r^2$ becomes $x'^2 + y'^2 = r^2$ for every choice of the angle α in the equations for rotation of axes.

9. Show that $A' + C' = A + C$ for every choice of the angle α in Eqs. (6).

10. Show that $B'^2 - 4A'C' = B^2 - 4AC$ for every choice of the angle α in Eqs. (6).

11. Show that a rotation of the axes through 45° will eliminate the cross-product term from Eq. (1) whenever $A = C$.

12. Find the equation of the curve $x^2 + 2xy + y^2 = 1$ after a rotation of axes which makes $A' = 0$ in Eq. (6).

INVARIANTS AND THE DISCRIMINANT

The equation

$$Ax^2 + Bxy + Cy^2 + Dx + Ey + F = 0 \tag{1}$$

is a quadratic equation when at least one of the coefficients A, B, and C is different from zero. There is a criterion we may apply to tell whether the curve represented by such a quadratic equation is a parabola, an ellipse, or a hyperbola, without first performing a rotation of axes to eliminate the cross-product term. Our discussion has shown that if $B \neq 0$ then a rotation of axes through an angle α determined by

$$\cot 2\alpha = \frac{A - C}{B} \tag{2}$$

will transform the equation to the equivalent form

$$A'x'^2 + B'x'y' + C'y'^2 + D'x' + E'y' + F' = 0 \tag{3}$$

with new coefficients $A', \ldots, F'$ related to the old as in Eq. (6), Article 8–8, and with $B' = 0$ for the particular choice of α satisfying Eq. (2) above.

Now the nature of the curve whose equation is (3) with cross-product term removed is determined as follows:

a) a *parabola* if A' or $C' = 0$, that is, if $A'C' = 0$;
b) an *ellipse* if A' and C' have the same sign, that is, if $A'C' > 0$; and
c) a *hyperbola* if A' and C' have opposite signs, that is, if $A'C' < 0$.

But it has been discovered and can easily be verified by use of Eq. (6), Article 8–8, that the coefficients A, B, C, and A', B', C' satisfy the following condition:

$$B^2 - 4AC = B'^2 - 4A'C' \tag{4}$$

for *any* rotation of axes. That is, the quantity $B^2 - 4AC$ is *invariant* under a rotation of axes. But when the particular rotation is performed that makes $B' = 0$, the right side of (4) becomes simply $-4A'C'$. The criteria above, expressed in terms of A' and C', can now be expressed in terms of the *discriminant*:

$$\text{Discriminant} = B^2 - 4AC. \tag{5}$$

Namely, the curve is

a)   a *parabola* if $B^2 - 4AC = 0$,

b)   an *ellipse* if $B^2 - 4AC < 0$,

c)   a *hyperbola* if $B^2 - 4AC > 0$,

with the understanding that certain degenerate cases may arise.

Another invariant associated with Eqs. (1) and (3) is the sum of the coefficients of the squared terms. For it is evident from Eq. (6), Article 8–8, that

$$A' + C' = A(\cos^2 \alpha + \sin^2 \alpha) + C(\sin^2 \alpha + \cos^2 \alpha)$$

or

$$A' + C' = A + C, \tag{6}$$

since

$$\sin^2 \alpha + \cos^2 \alpha = 1 \qquad \text{for any angle } \alpha.$$

The two invariants (4) and (6) may be used as a check against numerical errors in performing a rotation of axes of a quadratic equation. They may also be used to find the new coefficients of the quadratic terms

$$A'x'^2 + B'x'y' + C'y'^2,$$

with

$$B' = 0,$$

as in the following example.

EXAMPLE.   Determine the equation to which

$$x^2 + xy + y^2 = 1$$

reduces when the axes are rotated to eliminate the cross-product term.

Solution.   From the original equation we find

$$B^2 - 4AC = -3, \qquad A + C = 2.$$

Then, taking $B' = 0$, we have from (4) and (6),

$$-4A'C' = -3, \qquad A' + C' = 2.$$

Substituting $C' = 2 - A'$ from the second of these into the first, we obtain the quadratic equation

$$4A'^2 - 8A' + 3 = 0,$$

which factors into

$$(2A' - 3)(2A' - 1) = 0$$

and gives

$$A' = \tfrac{3}{2} \qquad \text{or} \qquad A' = \tfrac{1}{2}.$$

The corresponding values of C' are

$$C' = \tfrac{1}{2} \quad \text{or} \quad C' = \tfrac{3}{2}.$$

The equation therefore is

$$\tfrac{3}{2}x'^2 + \tfrac{1}{2}y'^2 = 1$$

or

$$\tfrac{1}{2}x'^2 + \tfrac{3}{2}y'^2 = 1$$

in the new coordinates. Hence the curve is an ellipse.

It should be noted that when no first-power terms are present in the original equation, they will also be absent in the new equation. This is due to the fact that a rotation of axes preserves the algebraic degree of each term of the equation; or we may refer to Eq. (6), Article 8–8, which shows that D' and E' are both zero if D and E are zero.

PROBLEMS

Use the discriminant and classify each of the following second degree equations as representing a circle, an ellipse, a parabola, or a hyperbola.

1. $x^2 + y^2 + xy + x - y = 3$
2. $2x^2 - y^2 + 4xy - 2x + 3y = 6$
3. $x^2 + 4xy + 4y^2 - 3x = 6$
4. $x^2 + y^2 + 3x - 2y = 10$
5. $xy + y^2 - 3x = 5$
6. $3x^2 + 6xy + 3y^2 - 4x + 5y = 12$
7. $x^2 - y^2 = 1$
8. $2x^2 + 3y^2 - 4x = 7$
9. $x^2 - 3xy + 3y^2 + 6y = 7$

10. When $B^2 - 4AC$ is negative, the equation
$$Ax^2 + Bxy + Cy^2 = 1$$
represents an ellipse. If the semiaxes have lengths a and b, the area of the ellipse is πab. Show that the area of the ellipse given above is $2\pi/\sqrt{4AC - B^2}$

11. Show, by reference to Eq. (6), Article 8–8, that
$$D'^2 + E'^2 = D^2 + E^2$$
for every angle of rotation α.

12. If $C = -A$ in Eq. (1), show that there is a rotation of axes for which $A' = C' = 0$ in the resulting Eq. (3). Find the angle α that makes $A' = C' = 0$ in this case. [*Hint.* Since $A' + C' = 0$, one need only make the further requirement that $A' = 0$ in Eq. (3).]

SECTIONS OF A CONE

The circle, parabola, ellipse, and hyperbola are known as *conic* sections because each may be obtained by cutting a cone by a plane. If the cutting plane is perpendicular to the axis of the cone, the section is a circle.

In general, suppose the cutting plane makes an angle α with the axis of the cone and let the generating angle of the cone be β (see Fig. 8–50). Then the section is

   i) a circle, if $\alpha = 90°$;
   ii) an ellipse, if $\beta < \alpha < 90°$;
   iii) a parabola, if $\alpha = \beta$;
   iv) a hyperbola, if $0 \le \alpha < \beta$.

The connection between these curves as we have defined them and the sections from a cone is readily made by reference to Fig. 8–51. The figure is

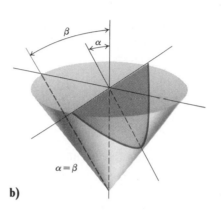

8–50   Plane intersecting a cone in (a) an ellipse, (b) a parabola, (c) a hyperbola.

drawn to illustrate the case of an ellipse, but the argument holds for the other cases as well.

A sphere is inscribed tangent to the cone along a circle C, and tangent to the cutting plane at a point F. Point P is any point on the conic section. We shall see that F is a focus, and that the line L, in which the cutting plane and the plane of the circle C intersect, is a directrix of the curve. To this end let Q be the point where the line through P parallel to the axis of the cone intersects the plane of C, let A be the point where the line joining P to the vertex of the cone touches C, and let PD be perpendicular to line L at D. Then PA and PF are two lines tangent to the same sphere from a common point P and hence have the same length:

$$PA = PF.$$

Also, from the right triangle PQA, we have

$$PQ = PA \cos \beta;$$

and from the right triangle PQD, we find that

$$PQ = PD \cos \alpha.$$

Hence

$$PA \cos \beta = PD \cos \alpha,$$

or

$$\frac{PA}{PD} = \frac{\cos \alpha}{\cos \beta}.$$

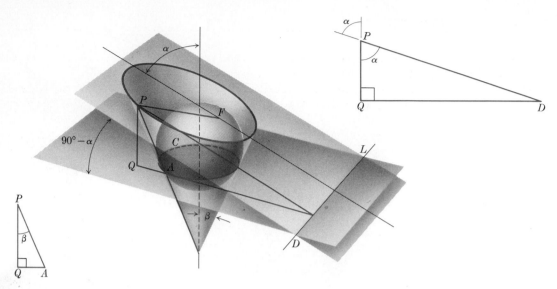

8–51   The line L is the directrix that corresponds to the focus F of the ellipse.

But since $PA = PF$, this means that

$$\frac{PF}{PD} = \frac{\cos \alpha}{\cos \beta}. \tag{1}$$

Since α and β are constant for a given cone and a given cutting plane, Eq. (1) has the form

$$PF = e \cdot PD.$$

This characterizes P as belonging to a parabola, an ellipse, or a hyperbola, with focus at F and directrix L, accordingly as $e = 1, e < 1,$ or $e > 1$, respectively, where

$$e = \frac{\cos \alpha}{\cos \beta}$$

is thus identified with the eccentricity.

PROBLEMS

1. Sketch a figure similar to Fig. 8–51 when the conic section is a parabola, and carry through the argument of this article on the basis of such a figure.

2. Sketch a figure similar to Fig. 8–51 when the conic section is a hyperbola and carry through the argument of this article on the basis of such a figure.

3. Which parts of the construction described in this article become impossible when the conic section is a circle?

4. Let one directrix be the line $x = -p$ and take the corresponding focus at the origin. Using Eq. (15) of Article 8–6, derive the equation of the general conic section of eccentricity e. If e is neither 0 nor 1, show that the center of the conic section has coordinates

$$\left(\frac{pe^2}{1 - e^2}, 0 \right).$$

REVIEW QUESTIONS AND EXERCISES

1. Discuss criteria for symmetry of a curve with respect to: (a) the x-axis, (b) the y-axis, (c) the origin, (d) the line $y = x$.

2. Define *asymptote*. How do you find vertical and horizontal asymptotes of a curve if its equation is given in the form $y = f(x)/g(x)$?

3. How do you find the extent of a curve (or, alternatively, strips of the plane from which the curve is excluded)?

4. Name the conic sections.

5. What kind of equation characterizes the conic sections?

6. If the equation of a conic section is given, and it contains no xy-term, how can you tell by inspection whether it is a parabola, circle, ellipse, or hyperbola? How can you tell what the curve is if there is an xy-term in the equation?

7. What are the equations of transformation of coordinates:

a) for a translation of axes? **b)** for a rotation of axes?

Illustrate with diagrams.

8. What two quantities that are associated with the equation of a conic section remain invariant under a rotation of axes?

9. Sketch a parabola and label its vertex, focus, axis, and directrix. What is the definition of a parabola? What is the equation of your parabola?

10. Sketch an ellipse and label its vertices, foci, axes, and directrices. What is the definition of an ellipse? What is the equation of your ellipse?

11. Sketch a hyperbola and label its vertices, foci, axes, asymptotes, and directrices. What is the definition of a hyperbola? What is the equation of your hyperbola?

12. A ripple tank is made by bending a strip of tin around the perimeter of an ellipse for the wall of the tank and soldering a flat bottom onto this. An inch or two of water is put in the tank and the experimenter pokes a finger into it, right at one focus of the ellipse. Ripples radiate outward through the water, reflect from the strip around the edge of the tank, and (in a short time) a drop of water spurts up at the second focus. Why?

MISCELLANEOUS PROBLEMS

In Problems 1 through 9, determine the following properties of the curves whose equations are given: (A) symmetry, (B) extent, (C) intercepts, (D) asymptotes, (E) slope at intercepts. Use this information in sketching the curves.

1. a) $y^2 = x(4 - x)$ **b)** $y^2 = x(x - 4)$

   c) $y^2 = \dfrac{x}{4 - x}$

2. a) $y = x + \dfrac{1}{x^2}$ **b)** $y^2 = x + \dfrac{1}{x^2}$

   c) $y = x^2 + \dfrac{1}{x}$

3. a) $y = x(x + 1)(x - 2)$ **b)** $y^2 = x(x + 1)(x - 2)$

4. a) $y = \dfrac{8}{4 + x^2}$ **b)** $y = \dfrac{8}{4 - x^2}$ **c)** $y = \dfrac{8x}{4 + x^2}$

5. a) $xy = x^2 + 1$ **b)** $y = \dfrac{x^2}{x - 1}$

6. a) $y^2 = x^4 - x^2$ **b)** $y^2 = \dfrac{x - 1}{x - 2}$

7. $x^2 y - y = 4(x - 2)$ **8.** $y = \dfrac{x^2 + 1}{x^2 - 1}$

9. $x^2 + xy + y^2 = 3$

10. Let C be the curve in Problem 9. Let $P(x, y)$ be a point on C. Let $P'(kx, ky)$ be a point on the line OP from the origin to P. If k is held constant, what is the equation of the curve described by P' as P traces out the curve C?

11. Sketch the graph whose equation is
$$(y - x + 2)(2y + x - 4) = 0.$$

12. A certain graph has an equation of the form
$$ay^2 + by = \frac{cx + d}{ex^2 + fx + g},$$
where $a, b, c, d, e, f,$ and g are constants whose value in each case is either 0 or 1. From the following information about the graph, determine the constants and give a reason for your choice in each case:

Extent. The curve does not exist for $x < -1$. All values of y are permissible.

Symmetry. The curve is symmetric about the x-axis.

Intercepts. No y-intercept; x-intercept at $(-1, 0)$.

Asymptotes. Both axes; no others.

Sketch the graph.

13. Each of the following inequalities describes one or more regions of the xy-plane. Sketch first the curve obtained by replacing the inequality sign by an equal sign; then indicate the region that contains the points whose coordinates satisfy the given inequality.

a) $x < 3$ **b)** $x < y$ **c)** $x^2 < y$

d) $x^2 + y^2 > 4$ **e)** $x^2 + xy + y^2 < 3$

f) $x^2 + xy + y^2 > 3$ **g)** $y^2 < \dfrac{x}{4 - x}$

14. Write an equation of the tangent, at $(2, 2)$, to the curve

$$x^2 - 2xy + y^2 + 2x + y - 6 = 0.$$

15. Sketch the curves $xy = 2$ and $x^2 - y^2 = 3$ in one diagram, and show that they intersect orthogonally.

16. Find equations of the lines that are tangent to the curve

$$y = x^3 - 6x + 2$$

and are parallel to the line $y = 6x - 2$.

17. Prove that if a line is drawn tangent to the curve $y^2 = kx$ at a point $P(x, y)$ not at the origin, then the portion of the tangent that lies between the x-axis and P is bisected by the y-axis.

18. Through the point $P(x, y)$ on the curve $y^2 = kx$, lines are drawn parallel to the axes. The rectangular area bounded by these two lines and the axes is divided into two portions by the given curve. (a) If these two areas are rotated about the y-axis, show that they generate two solids whose volumes are in the ratio of four to one. (b) What is the ratio of the volumes of the solids generated when these areas are rotated about the x-axis?

19. Show that the curves $2x^2 + 3y^2 = a^2$ and $ky^2 = x^3$ are orthogonal for all values of the constants a and k ($a \neq 0$, $k \neq 0$). Sketch the four curves corresponding to $a = 2$, $a = 4$, $k = \frac{1}{2}$, $k = -2$ in one diagram.

20. Show, analytically, that an angle inscribed in a semicircle is a right angle.

21. Two points P, Q are called symmetric with respect to a circle if P and Q lie on the same ray through the center and if the product of their distances from the center is equal to the square of the radius. Given that Q describes the straight line $x + 2y - 5 = 0$, find the locus of the point P that is symmetric to Q with respect to the circle $x^2 + y^2 = 4$.

22. A point $P(x, y)$ moves so that the ratio of its distances from two fixed points is a constant k. Show that the point traces a circle if $k \neq 1$, and a straight line if $k = 1$.

23. Show that the centers of all chords of the parabola $x^2 = 4py$ with slope m lie on a straight line, and find its equation.

24. The line through the focus F and the point $P(x_1, y_1)$ on the parabola $y^2 = 4px$ intersects the parabola in a second point $Q(x_2, y_2)$. Find the coordinates of Q in terms of y_1 and p. If O is the vertex and PO cuts the directrix at R, prove that QR is parallel to the axis of the parabola.

25. Find the point (or points) on the curve $x^2 = y^3$ nearest the point $P(0, 4)$. Sketch the curve and the shortest line from P to the curve.

26. Prove that every line through the center of the circle

$$(x - h)^2 + (y - k)^2 = r^2$$

is orthogonal to the circle.

27. Find all points on the curve $x^2 + 2xy + 3y^2 = 3$, where the tangent line is perpendicular to the line $x + y = 1$.

28. A line PT is drawn tangent to the curve $xy = x + y$ at the point $P(-2, \frac{2}{3})$. Find equations of two lines that are normal to the curve and perpendicular to PT.

29. Graph each of the following equations:
   a) $(x + y)(x^2 + y^2 - 1) = 0$;
   b) $(x + y)(x^2 + y^2 - 1) = 1$.
[*Hint.* In part (b), consider intersections of the curve with the line $x + y = k$ for different values of the constant k.]

30. Find the center and radius of the circle through the two points $A(2, 0)$ and $B(6, 0)$ and tangent to the curve $y = x^2$.

31. Find the center of the circle that passes through the point $(0, 1)$ and is tangent to the curve $y = x^2$ at $(2, 4)$.

32. Let L_1, L_2, L_3 be three straight lines, no two of which are parallel. Let $E_i = a_i x + b_i y + c_i = 0$, $i = 1, 2, 3$, be the equation of the line L_i.
   a) Describe the graph of the equation $E_1 E_2 + h E_2 E_3 + k E_1 E_3 = 0$, assuming h and k are constants.
   b) Use the method of part (a) and determine h and k so that the equation represents a circle through the points of intersection of the lines

$$x + y - 2 = 0, \qquad x - y + 2 = 0, \qquad y - 2x = 0.$$

   c) Find a parabola, axis vertical, through the points of intersection of the lines in (b).

33. A comet moves in a parabolic orbit with the sun at the focus. When the comet is 4×10^7 miles from the sun, the line from the sun to it makes an angle of $60°$ with the axis of the orbit (drawn in the direction in which the orbit opens). How near does the comet come to the sun?

34. Sketch in one diagram the curves $y^2 = 4x + 4$, $y^2 = 64 - 16x$, and find the angles at which they intersect.

35. Find an equation of the curve such that the distance from any point $P(x, y)$ on the curve to the line $x = 3$ is the same as its distance to the point $(4, 0)$. Sketch the curve.

36. Two radar stations lying along an east–west line are separated by 20 mi. Choose a coordinate system such that their positions are $(-10, 0)$ and $(10, 0)$. A low-flying plane traveling from west to east is known to have a speed of v_0 mi/sec. At $t = 0$ a signal is sent from the station at $(-10, 0)$, bounces off the plane, and is received at $(10, 0)$ $30/c$ sec later (c is the velocity of the signal). When $t = 10/v_0$, another signal is sent out from the station at $(-10, 0)$, reflects off the plane, and is once again received $30/c$ sec later by the other station. What is the position of the plane when it reflects the second signal, providing that one assumes $v_0 \ll c$ (that is, v_0 is much less than c)?

37. A line is drawn tangent to the parabola $y^2 = 4px$ at a point $P(x, y)$ on the curve. Let A be the point where this tangent line crosses the axis of the parabola, let F be the focus, and let PD be the line parallel to the axis of the parabola and intersecting the directrix at D. Prove that $AFPD$ is a rhombus.

38. Find the equation of the locus of a point $P(x, y)$ if the distance from P to the vertex is twice the distance from P to the focus of the parabola $x^2 = 8y$. Name the locus.

39. Prove that the tangent to a parabola at a point P cuts the axis of the parabola at a point whose distance from the vertex equals the distance from P to the tangent at the vertex.

40. Discuss and sketch the graph of the equation $x^4 - (y^2 - 9)^2 = 0$.

41. Show that the curve $C: x^4 - (y^2 - 9)^2 = 1$ approaches part of the curve $x^4 - (y^2 - 9)^2 = 0$ as the point $P(x, y)$ moves farther and farther away from the origin. Sketch. Do any points of C lie inside the circle $x^2 + y^2 = 9$? Give a reason for your answer.

42. The ellipse $(x^2/a^2) + (y^2/b^2) = 1$ divides the plane into two regions; one inside the ellipse, the other outside. Show that points in one of these regions have coordinates that satisfy the inequality $(x^2/a^2) + (y^2/b^2) < 1$, while in the other, $(x^2/a^2) + (y^2/b^2) > 1$. (Consider the effect of replacing x, y in the given equation by $x' = kx$, $y' = ky$, with $k < 1$ in one case and $k > 1$ in the other.)

43. Find an equation of an ellipse with foci at $(1, 0)$ and $(5, 0)$, and one vertex at the origin.

44. Let $F_1 = (3, 0)$, $F_2 = (0, 5)$, $P = (-1, 3)$. (a) Find the distances $F_1 P$ and $F_2 P$. (b) Does the origin O lie inside or outside the ellipse that has F_1 and F_2 as its foci and that passes through the point P? Why?

45. Find the greatest area of a rectangle inscribed in the ellipse $(x^2/a^2) + (y^2/b^2) = 1$, with sides parallel to the coordinate axes.

46. Show that the line $y = mx + c$ is tangent to the conic section $Ax^2 + y^2 = 1$ if and only if the constants A, m, and c satisfy the condition $A(c^2 - 1) = m^2$.

47. Starting from the general equation for the conic, find the equation of the conic with the following properties: (a) it is symmetric with respect to the origin; (b) it passes through the point $(1, 0)$; (c) the tangent to it at the point $(-2, 1)$ on it is the line $y = 1$.

48. Find an ellipse with one vertex at the point $(3, 1)$, the nearer focus at the point $(1, 1)$, and eccentricity $\frac{2}{3}$.

49. By a suitable rotation of axes, show that the equation $xy - x - y = 1$ represents a hyperbola. Sketch.

50. Find an equation of a hyperbola with eccentricity equal to $\sqrt{2}$ and with vertices at the points $(2, 0)$ and $(-2, 0)$.

51. Sketch the conic $\sqrt{2}\, y - 2xy = 3$. Locate its center and find its eccentricity.

52. If c is a fixed positive constant, then

$$\frac{x^2}{t^2} + \frac{y^2}{t^2 - c^2} = 1 \qquad (c^2 < t^2)$$

defines a family of ellipses, any member of which is characterized by a particular value of t. Show that every member of the family

$$\frac{x^2}{t^2} - \frac{y^2}{c^2 - t^2} = 1 \qquad (t^2 < c^2)$$

intersects any member of the first family at right angles.

53. Graph the equation $|x| + |y| = 1$ and find the area it encloses.

54. Show that if the tangent to a curve at a point $P(x, y)$ passes through the origin, then $dy/dx = y/x$ at the point. Hence show that no tangent can be drawn from the origin to the hyperbola $x^2 - y^2 = 1$.

55. (a) Find the coordinates of the center and the foci, the lengths of the axes, and the eccentricity of the ellipse $x^2 + 4y^2 - 4x + 8y - 1 = 0$. (b) Do likewise with the hyperbola $3x^2 - y^2 + 12x - 3y = 0$, and in addition find equations of its asymptotes.

56. If the ends of a line segment of constant length move along perpendicular lines, show that a point P on the segment, at distances a and b from the ends, describes an ellipse.

57. Sketch the curves:

a) $(9x^2 + 4y^2 - 36)(4x^2 + 9y^2 - 36) = 0$,

b) $(9x^2 + 4y^2 - 36)(4x^2 + 9y^2 - 36) = 1$.

Is the curve in (b) bounded or does it extend to points arbitrarily far from the origin? Give a reason for your answer.

58. Let p, q be positive numbers such that $q < p$. If r is a third number, prove that the equation $[x^2/(p - r)] + [y^2/(q - r)] = 1$ represents (a) an ellipse if $r < q$, (b) a hyperbola if $q < r < p$, (c) nothing if $p < r$. Prove that all these ellipses and hyperbolas have the same foci, and find these foci.

59. Find the eccentricity of the hyperbola $xy = 1$.

60. On a level plane the sound of a rifle and that of the bullet striking the target are heard at the same instant. What is the location of the hearer?

61. Show that any tangent to the hyperbola $xy = a^2$ determines with its asymptotes a triangle of area $2a^2$.

62. Given the hyperbola $9x^2 - 4y^2 - 18x - 16y + 29 = 0$. Find the coordinates of the center and foci, and the equations of the asymptotes. Sketch.

63. By an appropriate rotation, eliminate the xy-term from the equation,

$$7x^2 - 8xy + y^2 = 9.$$

64. Show that the tangent to the conic section

$$Ax^2 + Bxy + Cy^2 + Dx + Ey + F = 0$$

at a point (x_1, y_1) on it has an equation that may be written in the form

$$Axx_1 + B\left(\frac{x_1 y + x y_1}{2}\right) + Cyy_1$$

$$+ D\left(\frac{x + x_1}{2}\right) + E\left(\frac{y + y_1}{2}\right) + F = 0.$$

65. a) Find the eccentricity and center of the conic

$$x^2 + 12y^2 - 6x - 48y + 9 = 0.$$

b) Find the vertex of the conic

$$x^2 - 6x - 12y + 9 = 0.$$

c) Sketch the conics in one diagram.

66. Find an equation of the circle passing through the three points common to the conics of Problem 65.

67. Two vertices A, B of a triangle are fixed and the vertex $C(x, y)$ moves in such a way that $\angle A = 2(\angle B)$. Find the path traced by C.

68. Find the equation into which $x^{1/2} + y^{1/2} = a^{1/2}$ is transformed by a rotation of axes through 45° and elimination of radicals.

69. Show that $dx^2 + dy^2$ is invariant under any rotation of axes about the origin.

70. Show that $x\,dy - y\,dx$ is invariant under any rotation of axes about the origin.

71. Graph the equation $x^{2n} + y^{2n} = a^{2n}$ for the following values of n: (a) 1, (b) 2, (c) 100. In each instance find where the curve cuts the line $y = x$.

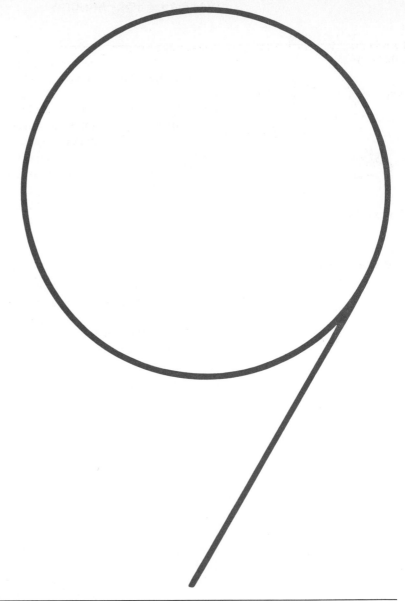

HYPERBOLIC FUNCTIONS

9–1

INTRODUCTION

In this chapter we shall consider certain combinations of the exponentials e^x and e^{-x} that are called "hyperbolic functions." There are two reasons why we study these functions. One reason is that they are used to solve engineering problems. For example, the tension at any point in a cable, suspended by its ends and hanging under its own weight (such as an electric transmission line) may be computed with hyperbolic functions. We shall investigate the hanging cable in some detail in Article 9–6. A second reason for studying the hyperbolic functions is that they are useful in solving differential equations.

9–2

DEFINITIONS AND IDENTITIES

The combinations $\frac{1}{2}(e^u + e^{-u})$ and $\frac{1}{2}(e^u - e^{-u})$ occur so frequently that it has been found convenient to give special names to them. It may not be clear at this particular time why the names about to be introduced are especially appropriate. But it will become apparent as we proceed that these functions are related to each other by rules that are very much like the rules that relate the functions cos u and sin u. And just as cos u and sin u may be identified with the point (x, y) on the unit circle $x^2 + y^2 = 1$, the functions

$$\cosh u = \tfrac{1}{2}(e^u + e^{-u}),$$
$$\sinh u = \tfrac{1}{2}(e^u - e^{-u}),$$

$$(1)$$

may be identified with the coordinates of the point (x, y) on the *unit hyperbola* $x^2 - y^2 = 1$.

Equations (1) are the *definitions* of the *hyperbolic cosine* and *hyperbolic sine* of u (cosh u is often pronounced to rhyme with "gosh you," and sinh u pronounced as though it were spelled "cinch u").

To check that the point (x, y) with $x = \cosh u$ and $y = \sinh u$ lies on the unit hyperbola, we substitute the defining relations (1) into the equation of the hyperbola:

$$x^2 - y^2 = 1,$$
$$\cosh^2 u - \sinh^2 u \stackrel{?}{=} 1,$$
$$\tfrac{1}{4}(e^{2u} + 2 + e^{-2u}) - \tfrac{1}{4}(e^{2u} - 2 + e^{-2u}) \stackrel{?}{=} 1,$$
$$\tfrac{1}{4}(e^{2u} + 2 + e^{-2u} - e^{2u} + 2 - e^{-2u}) \stackrel{?}{=} 1,$$
$$\tfrac{1}{4}(4) \stackrel{?}{=} 1. \quad \text{(Yes!)}$$

Actually, if we let

$$x = \cosh u = \tfrac{1}{2}(e^u + e^{-u}),$$
$$y = \sinh u = \tfrac{1}{2}(e^u - e^{-u}),$$

$$(2)$$

then when u varies from $-\infty$ to $+\infty$, the point $P(x, y)$ describes the right-hand branch of the hyperbola $x^2 - y^2 = 1$. The sense in which the curve is described is shown by the arrows in Fig. 9–1. Since e^u is always positive and $e^{-u} = 1/e^u$ is also positive, it follows that $x = \cosh u = \tfrac{1}{2}(e^u + e^{-u})$ is positive

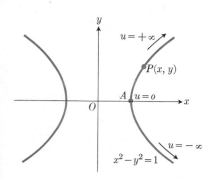

9–1 The equations $x = \cosh u$, $y = \sinh u$, $-\infty < u < \infty$, are parametric equations for the righthand branch of the unit hyperbola $x^2 - y^2 = 1$.

for all real values of u, $-\infty < u < +\infty$. Hence the point (x, y) remains always to the right of the y-axis.

The first bit of hyperbolic trigonometry that we have just established is the basic identity

$$\cosh^2 u - \sinh^2 u = 1. \tag{3}$$

This is analogous to, but not the same as the ordinary trigonometric identity, $\cos^2 u + \sin^2 u = 1$.

The remaining hyperbolic functions are *defined* in terms of $\sinh u$ and $\cosh u$ as follows:

$$\tanh u = \frac{\sinh u}{\cosh u} = \frac{e^u - e^{-u}}{e^u + e^{-u}},$$

$$\coth u = \frac{\cosh u}{\sinh u} = \frac{e^u + e^{-u}}{e^u - e^{-u}},$$

$$\operatorname{sech} u = \frac{1}{\cosh u} = \frac{2}{e^u + e^{-u}}, \tag{4}$$

$$\operatorname{csch} u = \frac{1}{\sinh u} = \frac{2}{e^u - e^{-u}}.$$

If we divide the identity (3) by $\cosh^2 u$, we get

$$1 - \tanh^2 u = \operatorname{sech}^2 u, \tag{5a}$$

and if we divide it by $\sinh^2 u$, we get

$$\coth^2 u - 1 = \operatorname{csch}^2 u. \tag{5b}$$

Since from (1) we find

$$\cosh u + \sinh u = e^u, \tag{6a}$$

$$\cosh u - \sinh u = e^{-u}, \tag{6b}$$

it is apparent that *any* combination of the exponentials e^u and e^{-u} can be replaced by a combination of $\sinh u$ and $\cosh u$, and conversely. Also, since e^{-u} is positive, (6b) shows that $\cosh u$ is always greater than $\sinh u$. But for large values of u, e^{-u} is small, and $\cosh u \approx \sinh u$.

The graphs of the hyperbolic functions are shown in Fig. 9–2(a) through (d).

At $x = 0$, $\cosh x = 1$ and $\sinh x = 0$, so the hyperbolic functions all have the same values at 0 that the corresponding trigonometric functions have. The hyperbolic cosine is an *even function*, that is,

$$\cosh (-x) = \cosh x, \tag{7}$$

and the hyperbolic sine is an *odd function*, that is,

$$\sinh (-x) = -\sinh x; \tag{8}$$

a)

b)

c)

d)

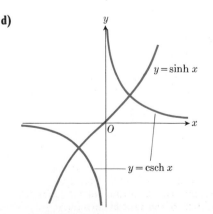

9–2 Graphs of the six hyperbolic functions.

so one curve is symmetric about the y-axis and the other is symmetric with respect to the origin. Here again the hyperbolic functions behave like the ordinary trigonometric (or circular) functions.

Certain major differences between the hyperbolic and the circular functions should be noted. For example, the circular functions are periodic: $\sin (x + 2\pi) = \sin x$, $\tan (x + \pi) = \tan x$, etc. But *the hyperbolic functions are not periodic.* Again, they differ greatly in the range of values they assume:

$\sin x$ varies between -1 and $+1$, oscillates;
$\sinh x$ varies from $-\infty$ to $+\infty$, steadily increases;

$\cos x$ varies between -1 and $+1$, oscillates;
$\cosh x$ varies from $+\infty$ to $+1$ to $+\infty$;

$|\sec x|$ is never less than unity;
$\operatorname{sech} x$ is never greater than unity, is always positive;

$\tan x$ varies from $-\infty$ to $+\infty$;
$\tanh x$ varies from -1 to $+1$.

Another difference lies in the behavior of the functions as $x \to \pm \infty$. We can say nothing very specific about the behavior of the circular functions $\sin x$, $\cos x$, $\tan x$, etc., for large values of x. But the hyperbolic functions behave very much like $e^x/2$, $e^{-x}/2$, unity, or zero, as follows:

For x large and positive:	**For x negative, $|x|$ large:**
$\cosh x \approx \sinh x \approx \frac{1}{2}e^x$	$\cosh x \approx -\sinh x \approx \frac{1}{2}e^{-x}$
$\tanh x \approx \coth x \approx 1$	$\tanh x \approx \coth x \approx -1$
$\operatorname{sech} x \approx \operatorname{csch} x \approx 2e^{-x} \approx 0$	$\operatorname{sech} x \approx -\operatorname{csch} x \approx 2e^x \approx 0$ **(9)**

Additional analogies will be apparent when we study the calculus of hyperbolic functions in the next article. We conclude this article with a number of formulas that are easily checked.

It requires only the definitions in (1) and a bit of routine algebra to produce the identities

$$\sinh (x + y) = \sinh x \cosh y + \cosh x \sinh y$$

$$\cosh (x + y) = \cosh x \cosh y + \sinh x \sinh y \qquad \textbf{(10)}$$

These in turn give

$$\sinh 2x = 2 \sinh x \cosh x, \qquad \textbf{(11a)}$$

$$\cosh 2x = \cosh^2 x + \sinh^2 x, \qquad \textbf{(11b)}$$

when we take $y = x$. The second of these leads to useful "half-angle" formulas when we combine it with the basic identity

$$1 = \cosh^2 x - \sinh^2 x. \qquad \textbf{(3)}$$

For if we add (11b) and (3), we have

$$\cosh 2x + 1 = 2 \cosh^2 x, \qquad \textbf{(12a)}$$

while if we subtract (3) from (11b), we get

$$\cosh 2x - 1 = 2 \sinh^2 x. \qquad \textbf{(12b)}$$

PROBLEMS

1. Show that $x = -\cosh u$, $y = \sinh u$ represents a point on the left branch of the hyperbola $x^2 - y^2 = 1$.

2. Using the definitions of $\cosh u$ and $\sinh u$ given by Eq. (1), show that $\cosh(-u) = \cosh u$ and $\sinh(-u) = -\sinh u$.

3. Verify Eqs. (10) for $\sinh(x + y)$ and $\cosh(x + y)$.

4. Show that $(\cosh x + \sinh x)^n = \cosh nx + \sinh nx$.

5. Let L be the line tangent to the hyperbola $x^2 - y^2 = 1$ at the point $P_1(x_1, y_1)$, where $x_1 = \cosh u$, $y_1 = \sinh u$. Show that L cuts the x-axis at the point $(\operatorname{sech} u, 0)$ and the y-axis at $(0, -\operatorname{csch} u)$.

6. In each of the following problems, one of the six hyperbolic functions of u is given; determine the remaining five.

a) $\sinh u = -\frac{3}{4}$,   **b)** $\cosh u = \frac{17}{15}$,

c) $\tanh u = -\frac{7}{25}$,   **d)** $\coth u = \frac{13}{12}$,

e) $\operatorname{sech} u = \frac{3}{5}$,   **f)** $\operatorname{csch} u = \frac{5}{12}$.

7. Show that the distance r from the origin O to the point $P(\cosh u, \sinh u)$ on the hyperbola $x^2 - y^2 = 1$ is $r = \sqrt{\cosh 2u}$.

8. Show that the line tangent to the hyperbola at its vertex A in Fig. 9–1 intersects the line OP in the point $(1, \tanh u)$. This gives a geometric representation of $\tanh u$.

9. If θ lies in the interval $-\pi/2 < \theta < \pi/2$ and $\sinh x = \tan \theta$, show that $\cosh x = \sec \theta$, $\tanh x = \sin \theta$, $\coth x = \csc \theta$, $\operatorname{csch} x = \cot \theta$, and $\operatorname{sech} x = \cos \theta$.

Let u be a differentiable function of x and differentiate

$$\sinh u = \tfrac{1}{2}(e^u - e^{-u}), \qquad \cosh u = \tfrac{1}{2}(e^u + e^{-u}), \qquad \text{(1)}$$

9–3

DERIVATIVES AND INTEGRALS

with respect to x. Applying the formulas

$$\frac{de^u}{dx} = e^u \frac{du}{dx}, \qquad \frac{de^{-u}}{dx} = e^{-u} \frac{d(-u)}{dx} = -e^{-u} \frac{du}{dx},$$

we get

$$\frac{d(\sinh u)}{dx} = \cosh u \frac{du}{dx}, \qquad\qquad \text{XXI}$$

$$\frac{d(\cosh u)}{dx} = \sinh u \frac{du}{dx}. \qquad\qquad \text{XXII}$$

Then, if we let

$$y = \tanh u = \frac{\sinh u}{\cosh u}$$

and differentiate as a fraction, we get

$$\frac{d(\tanh u)}{dx} = \frac{\cosh u [d(\sinh u)/dx] - \sinh u [d(\cosh u)/dx]}{\cosh^2 u}$$

$$= \frac{\cosh^2 u (du/dx) - \sinh^2 u (du/dx)}{\cosh^2 u}$$

$$= \frac{(\cosh^2 u - \sinh^2 u)(du/dx)}{\cosh^2 u} = \frac{1}{\cosh^2 u} \frac{du}{dx}$$

$$= \operatorname{sech}^2 u \frac{du}{dx}.$$

In a similar manner, we may establish the rest of the formulas in the following list:

$$\frac{d(\tanh u)}{dx} = \operatorname{sech}^2 u \frac{du}{dx}, \qquad\qquad \text{XXIII}$$

$$\frac{d(\coth u)}{dx} = -\operatorname{csch}^2 u \frac{du}{dx}, \qquad\qquad \text{XXIV}$$

$$\frac{d(\operatorname{sech} u)}{dx} = -\operatorname{sech} u \tanh u \frac{du}{dx}, \qquad\qquad \text{XXV}$$

$$\frac{d(\operatorname{csch} u)}{dx} = -\operatorname{csch} u \coth u \frac{du}{dx}. \qquad\qquad \text{XXVI}$$

Aside from the pattern of algebraic signs, these formulas are the exact analogs of the formulas for the corresponding circular functions. Exactly half of them have minus signs, but we no longer attach the minus signs to the derivatives of the cofunctions. The first three, sinh u, cosh u, tanh u, have positive derivatives and the last three have negative derivatives.

Each of these derivative formulas has a matching differential formula. These in turn may be integrated at once to produce the following integration formulas:

1. $$\int \sinh u \, du = \cosh u + C.$$

2. $$\int \cosh u \, du = \sinh u + C.$$

3. $$\int \operatorname{sech}^2 u \, du = \tanh u + C.$$

$$(2)$$

4. $$\int \operatorname{csch}^2 u \, du = -\coth u + C.$$

5. $$\int \operatorname{sech} u \tanh u \, du = -\operatorname{sech} u + C.$$

6. $$\int \operatorname{csch} u \coth u \, du = -\operatorname{csch} u + C.$$

EXAMPLE 1. Show that $y = a \cosh (x/a)$ satisfies the differential equation

$$\frac{d^2y}{dx^2} = \frac{w}{H} \sqrt{1 + \left(\frac{dy}{dx}\right)^2}, \qquad\qquad (3)$$

provided $a = H/w$, where H and w are constants.

Solution. By differentiating $y = a \cosh (x/a)$, we find

$$\frac{dy}{dx} = a\left(\sinh \frac{x}{a}\right)\frac{1}{a} = \sinh \frac{x}{a}, \qquad \frac{d^2y}{dx^2} = \left(\cosh \frac{x}{a}\right)\frac{1}{a}.$$

We substitute these into (3) and obtain

$$\frac{1}{a}\cosh\frac{x}{a} \overset{?}{=} \frac{w}{H}\sqrt{1 + \sinh^2\frac{x}{a}} \qquad \textbf{(a)}$$

$$= \frac{w}{H}\sqrt{\cosh^2\frac{x}{a}} \qquad \textbf{(b)}$$

$$= \frac{w}{H}\cosh\frac{x}{a}, \qquad \textbf{(c)}$$

which is a true equation provided $a = H/w$.

REMARK 1.   In going from (a) to (b) above, we used the fundamental identity

$$\cosh^2 u - \sinh^2 u = 1$$

in the form

$$1 + \sinh^2 u = \cosh^2 u.$$

In going from (b) to (c), we used the fact that $\cosh u$ is always positive, and hence

$$\sqrt{\cosh^2 u} = |\cosh u| = \cosh u.$$

REMARK 2.   The differential equation (3) expresses the condition for equilibrium of forces acting on a section AP of a hanging cable (Fig. 9–3). We imagine the rest of the cable as having been removed and the section AP from the lowest point A to the representative point $P(x, y)$ as being in equilibrium under the forces

1. H = horizontal tension pulling on the cable at A,
2. T = tangential tension pulling on the cable at P,
3. $W = ws$ = weight of s feet of the cable at w pounds per foot of length from A to P.

Then equilibrium of the cable requires that the horizontal and vertical components of T just balance H and W:

$$T\cos\phi = H, \qquad T\sin\phi = W = ws. \qquad \textbf{(4)}$$

By division, we get

$$\frac{T\sin\phi}{T\cos\phi} = \tan\phi = \frac{W}{H}$$

or

$$\frac{dy}{dx} = \frac{ws}{H}, \qquad \textbf{(5)}$$

since $\tan\phi = dy/dx$. The arc length s in Eq. (5) would be found by integrating

$$ds = \sqrt{1 + \left(\frac{dy}{dx}\right)^2}\, dx$$

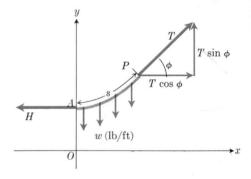

9–3 Forces acting on a section AP of a flexible hanging cable weighing w lb/ft. The load on the cable is uniform along the cable but is not uniform per horizontal foot.

from A to P. But instead of doing so, we may differentiate Eq. (5) with respect to x:

$$\frac{d^2y}{dx^2} = \frac{w}{H}\frac{ds}{dx},$$

and then substitute $\sqrt{1 + (dy/dx)^2}$ in place of ds/dx to obtain Eq. (3) above.

REMARK 3. In Example 1, above, we pulled the equation $y = a \cosh(x/a)$ out of the hat, so to speak, and showed by substitution that it satisfies the differential equation (3). In Article 9–6, we shall adopt the more straightforward approach of simply solving Eq. (3) subject to the initial conditions

$$\frac{dy}{dx} = 0 \quad \text{and} \quad y = y_0 \quad \text{when} \quad x = 0.$$

By choosing the origin so that $y_0 = a = H/w$, we shall find that the solution is indeed the one given above, namely,

$$y = a \cosh \frac{x}{a} \quad \text{with} \quad a = \frac{H}{w}. \tag{6}$$

EXAMPLE 2. Suppose that the height $y(0)$ of the curve $y = a \cosh(x/a)$ above the x-axis is chosen to be $y(0) = H/w$. (This can be done by letting $a = H/w$.) Show that the tension in the cable at $P(x, y)$ in Fig. 9–3 is

$$T = wy.$$

Solution. We make use of the fact that

$$\frac{dy}{dx} = \tan \phi,$$

since T acts along the tangent, and

$$T = \frac{H}{\cos \phi} = H \sec \phi,$$

by Eq. (4a). Then, differentiating (6), we have

$$\tan \phi = \frac{dy}{dx} = \sinh \frac{x}{a}$$

and

$$\sec \phi = \sqrt{\sec^2 \phi} = \sqrt{1 + \tan^2 \phi} = \sqrt{1 + \left(\frac{dy}{dx}\right)^2}$$

$$= \sqrt{1 + \sinh^2 \frac{x}{a}} = \sqrt{\cosh^2 \frac{x}{a}} = \cosh \frac{x}{a}.$$

Therefore

$$T = H \sec \phi = H \cosh \frac{x}{a}, \tag{7a}$$

where

$$a = \frac{H}{w} \quad \text{or} \quad H = wa. \tag{7b}$$

Combining (7a) and (7b), we have

$$T = wa \cosh \frac{x}{a}$$

or, when we take account of Eq. (6),

$$T = wy.$$

This means that the tension at P is equal to the weight of y feet of the cable. Thus if the end of the cable to the right of P is allowed to hang down over a smooth peg while the cable is held at P so that it does not slip, and if the cable is then cut off at the point Q where it crosses the x-axis (Fig. 9–4), it may then be released at P and the weight wy of the section of cable PQ will be just sufficient to prevent the cable from slipping. If this is carried out at two different points P and P', the cable may be draped over two smooth pegs without slipping, provided the free ends reach just to the x-axis. The curve $y = a \cosh (x/a)$ is called a *catenary* from the Latin word *catena*, meaning chain. The x-axis is called the directrix of the catenary.

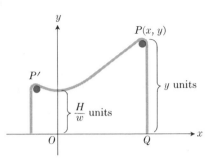

9–4 If the axes are positioned so that the lowest point of the uniform cable is H/w units above the x-axis, then the tension at each point $P(x, y)$ on the cable is exactly equal to the weight of a piece of cable y units long.

PROBLEMS

1. Establish the validity of the formulas XXIV–XXVI.

Find dy/dx in each of the following:

2. $y = \sinh 3x$

3. $y = \cosh^2 5x$

4. $y = \cosh^2 5x - \sinh^2 5x$

5. $y = \tanh 2x$

6. $y = \coth (\tan x)$

7. $y = \operatorname{sech}^3 x$

8. $y = 4 \operatorname{csch} (x/4)$

9. $\sinh y = \tan x$

Integrate each of the following:

10. $\int \cosh (2x + 1) \, dx$

11. $\int \tanh x \, dx$

12. $\int \dfrac{\sinh x}{\cosh^4 x} \, dx$

13. $\int \dfrac{4 \, dx}{(e^x + e^{-x})^2}$

14. $\int \dfrac{e^x - e^{-x}}{e^x + e^{-x}} \, dx$

15. $\int \tanh^2 x \, dx$

16. $\int \dfrac{\sinh \sqrt{x}}{\sqrt{x}} \, dx$

17. $\int \cosh^2 3x \, dx$

18. $\int \sqrt{\cosh x - 1} \, dx$

19. Find the area of the hyperbolic sector AOP bounded by the arc AP and the lines OA, OP through the origin, in Fig. 9–1.

20. Find the length of $y = \cosh x$, $0 \le x \le 1$.

21. (*Calculator*) The line $y = (x/2) + 1$ crosses the catenary $y = \cosh x$ at the point $(0, 1)$. Experiment with a calculator to collect evidence for the fact that the line also crosses the catenary approximately at the point $(0.9308, 1.4654)$.

22. (*Calculator*) Two successive poles supporting an electric power line are 100 feet apart, the supporting members being at the same level. If the wire dips 25 feet at the center,

(a) find the length of the wire between supports, and (b) find the tension in the wire at its lowest point if its weight is $w = 0.3$ lb/ft. [*Hint.* First approximate a from the equation $(25/a) + 1 = \cosh (50/a)$, which can be related to Problem 21 with $x = 50/a$.]

23. The equation $\sinh x = \tan \theta$, $-\pi/2 < \theta < \pi/2$, defines θ as a function of x:

$$\theta = \tan^{-1} (\sinh x),$$

to which the name "gudermannian of x" has been attached, written

$$\theta = \operatorname{gd} x.$$

Show that

$$\frac{d\theta}{dx} = \frac{1}{\cosh x} = \frac{1}{\sec \theta},$$

so that $\sec \theta \, d\theta = dx$ and

$$\int \sec \theta \, d\theta = \operatorname{gd}^{-1} \theta + C = \sinh^{-1} (\tan \theta) + C.$$

24. Sketch the curve $\theta = \operatorname{gd} x$ (see Problem 23) by the following procedure: First sketch the curves $y = \sinh x$ and $y = \tan \theta \, (-\pi/2 < \theta < \pi/2)$ on separate xy- and θy-planes. Starting in the xy-plane with any value of x, $-\infty < x < +\infty$, determine the corresponding value of y from the curve $y = \sinh x$. Transfer this y reading to the y-axis in the θy-plane and determine the corresponding value of θ from the curve $y = \tan \theta$. Use this value of θ as ordinate and the original value of x as abscissa to plot a point on the curve $\theta = \operatorname{gd} x$.

25. Show that the curve $\theta = \operatorname{gd} x$ (see Problems 23 and 24) has the lines $\theta = \pm\pi/2$ as horizontal asymptotes, is always rising (from left to right), has a point of inflection at the origin, and is symmetric with respect to the origin.

*9–4

GEOMETRIC SIGNIFICANCE OF THE HYPERBOLIC RADIAN

We are now in a position to illustrate the meaning of the variable u in the equations

$$x = \cosh u, \qquad y = \sinh u \tag{1}$$

as they relate to the point $P(x, y)$ on the unit hyperbola

$$x^2 - y^2 = 1. \tag{2}$$

Before we do so, however, we shall find the analogous meaning of the variable θ in the equations

$$x = \cos \theta, \qquad y = \sin \theta \tag{3}$$

as they relate to the point $P(x, y)$ on the unit circle

$$x^2 + y^2 = 1. \tag{4}$$

The most familiar interpretation of θ is, of course, that it is the radian measure of the angle AOP in Fig. 9–5, that is

$$\theta = \frac{\text{arc } AP}{\text{radius } OA}.$$

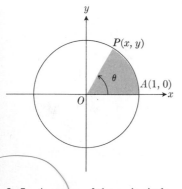

9–5 A sector of the unit circle $x^2 + y^2 = 1$. The number θ is twice the number of units of shaded area.

But we also recall that the area of a circular sector of radius r and central angle θ (radians) is given by $(\frac{1}{2})r^2\theta$. Since we are here dealing with a unit circle, this says that

$$\text{Area of sector } AOP = \tfrac{1}{2}\theta$$

or, if we solve this for θ,

$$\theta = \text{twice the area of the sector } AOP. \tag{5}$$

Of course we must realize that θ is a pure (dimensionless) number and Eq. (5) really says that the value of θ which Eqs. (3) associate with the point $P(x, y)$ on the unit circle is twice the *number* of square units of area that the radius vector OP sweeps out as P moves along the circle from A to its final position P. Thus when the area of the sector AOP is one-half the area of a square having OA as a side, then $\theta = 1$ and the coordinates of P represent $\cos 1$ and $\sin 1$. Negative values of θ would be interpreted as corresponding to areas swept over in a *clockwise* rotation of OP.

Now for the unit hyperbola,

$$x^2 - y^2 = 1,$$

we shall find an analogous interpretation for the variable u in the equations

$$x = \cosh u, \qquad y = \sinh u.$$

To see that this is indeed the case, we shall calculate the area of the sector AOP in Fig. 9–6. This area is clearly equal to the area of the triangle OQP minus the area AQP bounded above by the curve, below by the x-axis, and

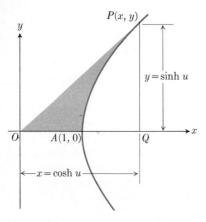

9–6 A "sector" of the unit hyperbola $x^2 - y^2 = 1$. The number u is twice the number of units of shaded area. (The text explains why.)

---

*   Starred sections may be omitted without loss of continuity.

on the right by the vertical line QP. But this area is simply

$$\text{area } AQP = \int_A^P y \, dx = \int_A^P \sinh u \, d(\cosh u)$$

$$= \int_A^P \sinh^2 u \, du = \tfrac{1}{2} \int_A^P (\cosh 2u - 1) \, du \qquad \begin{matrix}[\text{Eq. (12b),} \\ \text{Article 9–2}]\end{matrix}$$

$$= \tfrac{1}{2}[\tfrac{1}{2} \sinh 2u - u]_{A(u=0)}^{P(u=u)}$$

$$= \tfrac{1}{4} \sinh 2u - \tfrac{1}{2}u = \tfrac{1}{2} \sinh u \cosh u - \tfrac{1}{2}u.$$

Hence,

$$\text{Area of sector } AOP = \text{Area of } OQP - \text{Area of } AQP$$

$$= \tfrac{1}{2} \sinh u \cosh u - (\tfrac{1}{2} \sinh u \cosh u - \tfrac{1}{2}u)$$

$$= \tfrac{1}{2}u,$$

or, solving for u,

$$u = \text{twice the area of the sector } AOP. \qquad (6)$$

As for the circle, a positive value of u is associated with an area above the x-axis and a negative value with an area below the x-axis, and areas are to be measured in terms of the unit square having OA as side. The term *hyperbolic radian* is sometimes used in connection with the variable u in Eq. (6), but here again, u is just a dimensionless real number. For example, cosh 2 and sinh 2 may be interpreted as the coordinates of P when the area of the sector AOP is just equal to the area of a square having OA as side.

If we start with

$$x = \sinh y, \qquad (1)$$

then as y varies continuously from $-\infty$ to $+\infty$, x does likewise. Graphically, this means that we may start with any real value on the y-axis in Fig. 9–7(a) and draw a horizontal line to the curve. Then a vertical line to the x-axis locates exactly one value of x such that the point (x, y) is on the curve. On the other hand, we could equally well reverse these steps and start with any real value x on the x-axis, go along a vertical line to the curve, then on a horizontal line to the y-axis. This latter procedure gives us y as a function of x, and the notation we use is

$$y = \sinh^{-1} x. \qquad (2)$$

Here we have no problem about principal values, as we did in the case of the inverses of the circular functions, since the correspondence between the real numbers x and the real numbers y in Eq. (1) is one-to-one. Equation (1) says exactly the same thing as Eq. (2).

$$y = \sinh^{-1} x \qquad \text{means} \qquad x = \sinh y. \qquad (3)$$

9–5

THE INVERSE HYPERBOLIC FUNCTIONS

a)

b)

c)

d)

e)

f)

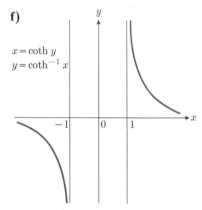

9–7 Graphs of the inverse hyperbolic functions.

The inverse hyperbolic cosine, however, is double-valued and it is desirable to prescribe a principal branch. For if we start with the equation

$$x = \cosh\ y,$$

then y and $-y$ both give the same value of x; that is, the correspondence between y-values and x-values is two-to-one, so that if x is considered the independent variable, there are *two* corresponding values of y. This is analogous to the situation surrounding the equation $x = y^2$, which defines x as a single-valued function of y; but when x is given and we ask for y, the result is $y = \pm\sqrt{x}$. In the case of the inverse hyperbolic cosine, we take the positive values of y as the principal branch:

$$y = \cosh^{-1} x \qquad \text{means} \quad x = \cosh\ y, \quad y \geq 0, \quad x \geq 1. \tag{4}$$

Thus in Fig. 9–7(b) the equation $x = \cosh\ y$ represents the entire curve, but $y = \cosh^{-1} x$ represents only that portion above the x-axis, while the portion below the x-axis is given by $y = -\cosh^{-1} x$.

Reference to Fig. 9–2 shows that the only other double-valued inverse is the inverse hyperbolic secant, and again we select the positive branch. That is,

$$y = \text{sech}^{-1} x, \qquad y > 0, \qquad 0 < x \leq 1 \tag{5}$$

defines the principal branch and the numbers x and y satisfy

$$x = \text{sech}\ y. \tag{6}$$

Since

$$\text{sech } y = \frac{1}{\cosh y},$$

Eq. (6) is equivalent to

$$\cosh y = \frac{1}{x}$$

and the restriction $y > 0$ defines the same branch as in (5), so that

$$y = \cosh^{-1} \frac{1}{x}.$$

That is,

$$\text{sech}^{-1} x = \cosh^{-1} \frac{1}{x}.$$

Similarly, we see that

$$y = \text{csch}^{-1} x = \sinh^{-1} \frac{1}{x} \qquad \text{means} \quad \text{csch } y = x. \tag{7}$$

Also,

$$y = \tanh^{-1} x \qquad \text{means} \quad x = \tanh y, \tag{8a}$$

and

$$y = \coth^{-1} x \qquad \text{means} \quad x = \coth y. \tag{8b}$$

The graphs of the inverse hyperbolic functions are given in Fig. 9–7. Numerical values of $\sinh^{-1} x$, $\cosh^{-1} x$, and $\tanh^{-1} x$ are given in tables such as *Handbook of Mathematical Functions* (formerly published by the National Bureau of Standards, now printed by Dover Publications), which gives their values to ten decimal places. They are also given by many scientific calculators to eight or ten places.

When hyperbolic function keys are not available on a calculator, it is still possible to evaluate the inverse hyperbolic functions by expressing them in terms of logarithms, as illustrated below for $\tanh^{-1} x$. Let $y = \tanh^{-1} x$; then $\tanh y = x$ or

$$x = \frac{\sinh y}{\cosh y} = \frac{\frac{1}{2}(e^y - e^{-y})}{\frac{1}{2}(e^y + e^{-y})} = \frac{e^y - (1/e^y)}{e^y + (1/e^y)} = \frac{e^{2y} - 1}{e^{2y} + 1}.$$

We now solve this equation for e^{2y}:

$$xe^{2y} + x = e^{2y} - 1$$

or

$$1 + x = e^{2y}(1 - x),$$

and

$$e^{2y} = \frac{1 + x}{1 - x}.$$

Hence

$$y = \tanh^{-1} x = \frac{1}{2} \ln \frac{1+x}{1-x}, \qquad |x| < 1. \tag{9}$$

The variable x in Eq. (9) is restricted to the domain $|x| < 1$, since $x = \tanh y$ lies in this interval for all real values of y, $-\infty < y < +\infty$.

EXAMPLE 1

$$\tanh^{-1} 0.25 = \frac{1}{2} \ln \frac{1.25}{0.75} = \frac{1}{2} \ln \frac{5}{3}$$

$$= \tfrac{1}{2}(\ln 5 - \ln 3) \approx 0.25541.$$

The expressions for the other inverse hyperbolic functions in terms of logarithms are found in a similar manner. They are:

$$\sinh^{-1} x = \ln (x + \sqrt{x^2 + 1}), \quad -\infty < x < \infty,$$

$$\cosh^{-1} x = \ln (x + \sqrt{x^2 - 1}), \quad x \geq 1,$$

$$\operatorname{sech}^{-1} x = \ln \left(\frac{1 + \sqrt{1 - x^2}}{x} \right) = \cosh^{-1} \left(\frac{1}{x} \right), \quad 0 < x \leq 1,$$

$$\operatorname{csch}^{-1} x = \ln \left(\frac{1}{x} + \frac{\sqrt{1 + x^2}}{|x|} \right) = \sinh^{-1} \left(\frac{1}{x} \right), \quad x \neq 0,$$

$$\coth^{-1} x = \frac{1}{2} \ln \frac{x+1}{x-1} = \tanh^{-1} \left(\frac{1}{x} \right), \quad |x| > 1. \tag{10}$$

These logarithmic expressions are, on the whole, rather cumbersome, and the inverse hyperbolic functions provide a useful shorthand wherever these expressions arise.

The chief merit of the inverse hyperbolic functions lies in their usefulness in integration. This will easily be understood after we have derived the following formulas for their derivatives:

$$\frac{d(\sinh^{-1} u)}{dx} = \frac{1}{\sqrt{1 + u^2}} \frac{du}{dx}, \qquad \text{XXVII}$$

$$\frac{d(\cosh^{-1} u)}{dx} = \frac{1}{\sqrt{u^2 - 1}} \frac{du}{dx}, \qquad \text{XXVIII}$$

$$\frac{d(\tanh^{-1} u)}{dx} = \frac{1}{1 - u^2} \frac{du}{dx}, \quad |u| < 1, \qquad \text{XXIX}$$

$$\frac{d(\coth^{-1} u)}{dx} = \frac{1}{1 - u^2} \frac{du}{dx}, \quad |u| > 1, \qquad \text{XXX}$$

$$\frac{d(\operatorname{sech}^{-1} u)}{dx} = \frac{-du/dx}{u\sqrt{1 - u^2}}, \qquad \text{XXXI}$$

$$\frac{d(\operatorname{csch}^{-1} u)}{dx} = \frac{-du/dx}{|u|\sqrt{1 + u^2}}. \qquad \text{XXXII}$$

The proofs of these all follow the same method. We illustrate the case of $\cosh^{-1} u$. To this end, let

$$y = \cosh^{-1} u;$$

then

$$\cosh y = u,$$

$$\sinh y \frac{dy}{dx} = \frac{du}{dx},$$

and

$$\frac{dy}{dx} = \frac{1}{\sinh y} \frac{du}{dx}.$$

But

$$\cosh^2 y - \sinh^2 y = 1,$$

$$\cosh y = u,$$

so that

$$\sinh y = \pm \sqrt{\cosh^2 y - 1}$$

$$= \pm \sqrt{u^2 - 1}$$

and

$$\frac{dy}{dx} = \frac{1}{\pm \sqrt{u^2 - 1}} \frac{du}{dx}.$$

The ambiguous sign will be $+$ if we restrict attention to the principal value, $y = \cosh^{-1} u$, $y \geq 0$, for then $\sinh y \geq 0$ and the ambiguous sign is the same as the sign of $\sinh y$. Thus **XXVIII** is established. The identities (5a) and (5b) of Article 9–2, with y in place of u, will be found to be useful in proving formulas **XXIX** to **XXXII**. The derivation is straightforward.

The restrictions $|u| < 1$ and $|u| > 1$ in **XXIX** and **XXX**, respectively, are due to the fact that if

$$y = \tanh^{-1} u,$$

then

$$u = \tanh y,$$

and since

$$-1 < \tanh y < 1,$$

this means $|u| < 1$. Similarly,

$$y = \coth^{-1} u, \qquad u = \coth y$$

requires $|u| > 1$. The distinction becomes important when we invert the formulas to get integration formulas, since otherwise we would be unable to tell whether we should write $\tanh^{-1} u$ or $\coth^{-1} u$ for

$$\int \frac{du}{1 - u^2}.$$

The following integration formulas follow at once from the differential formulas XXVII′ to XXXII′, that are obtained by multiplying both sides of XXVII to XXXII by dx:

1.
$$\int \frac{du}{\sqrt{1 + u^2}} = \sinh^{-1} u + C,$$

2.
$$\int \frac{du}{\sqrt{u^2 - 1}} = \cosh^{-1} u + C,$$

3.
$$\int \frac{du}{1 - u^2} = \begin{Bmatrix} \tanh^{-1} u + C & \text{if } |u| < 1 \\ \coth^{-1} u + C & \text{if } |u| > 1 \end{Bmatrix} = \frac{1}{2} \ln \left| \frac{1 + u}{1 - u} \right| + C, \quad \textbf{(11)}$$

4.
$$\int \frac{du}{u\sqrt{1 - u^2}} = -\operatorname{sech}^{-1} |u| + C = -\cosh^{-1} \left(\frac{1}{|u|} \right) + C,$$

5.
$$\int \frac{du}{u\sqrt{1 + u^2}} = -\operatorname{csch}^{-1} |u| + C = -\sinh^{-1} \left(\frac{1}{|u|} \right) + C.$$

PROBLEMS

1. Solve the equation $x = \sinh y = \frac{1}{2}(e^y - e^{-y})$ for e^y in terms of x, and thus show that $y = \ln (x + \sqrt{1 + x^2})$. (This equation expresses $\sinh^{-1} x$ as a logarithm.)

2. Express $\cosh^{-1} x$ in terms of logarithms by using the method of Problem 1.

3. Establish formula XXVII.

4. Establish formula XXIX.

5. Establish formula XXXI.

Find dy/dx in each of the following:

6. $y = \sinh^{-1} (2x)$ **7.** $y = \tanh^{-1} (\cos x)$

8. $y = \cosh^{-1} (\sec x)$ **9.** $y = \coth^{-1} (\sec x)$

10. $y = \operatorname{sech}^{-1} (\sin 2x)$

Evaluate each of the following integrals:

11. $\displaystyle\int \frac{dx}{\sqrt{1 + 4x^2}}$ **12.** $\displaystyle\int \frac{dx}{\sqrt{4 + x^2}}$ **13.** $\displaystyle\int_0^{0.5} \frac{dx}{1 - x^2}$

14. $\displaystyle\int_{5/4}^{2} \frac{dx}{1 - x^2}$ **15.** $\displaystyle\int \frac{dx}{x\sqrt{4 + x^2}}$

16. (*Retarded free fall*) If a body of mass m falling from rest under the action of gravity encounters an air resistance proportional to the square of the velocity, then the velocity v at time t satisfies the differential equation

$$m\left(\frac{dv}{dt} \right) = mg - kv^2,$$

where k is a constant of proportionality and $v = 0$ when $t = 0$. Show that

$$v = \sqrt{\frac{mg}{k}} \tanh \left(\sqrt{\frac{gk}{m}}\, t \right),$$

and hence deduce that the body approaches a "limiting velocity" equal to $\sqrt{mg/k}$ as $t \to \infty$.

*9–6

THE HANGING CABLE

We conclude this chapter by deriving the solution of the differential equation

$$\frac{d^2 y}{dx^2} = \frac{w}{H} \sqrt{1 + \left(\frac{dy}{dx} \right)^2}, \qquad \textbf{(1)}$$

which is the equation of equilibrium of forces on a hanging cable discussed in Article 9–3, Example 1. Since Eq. (1) involves the second derivative, we shall require two conditions to determine the constants of integration. By choosing the y-axis to be the vertical line through the lowest point of the cable (Fig. 9–8), one condition becomes

$$\frac{dy}{dx} = 0 \qquad \text{when} \quad x = 0. \tag{2a}$$

Then we may still move the x-axis up or down to suit our convenience. That is, we let

$$y = y_0 \qquad \text{when} \quad x = 0, \tag{2b}$$

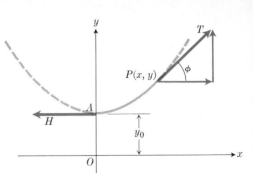

9–8   A section of hanging cable.

and we may choose y_0 so as to give us the simplest form in our final answer.

It is customary, when solving an equation such as (1), to introduce a single letter to represent dy/dx. The letter p is most often used. Thus we let

$$\frac{dy}{dx} = p, \tag{3a}$$

and then we may write

$$\frac{d^2y}{dx^2} = \frac{dp}{dx}, \tag{3b}$$

so that Eq. (1) takes the form

$$\frac{dp}{dx} = \frac{w}{H}\sqrt{1 + p^2}.$$

We may now separate the variables to get

$$\frac{dp}{\sqrt{1 + p^2}} = \frac{w}{H}\,dx$$

or

$$\int \frac{dp}{\sqrt{1 + p^2}} = \frac{w}{H}x + C_1. \tag{4a}$$

The integral on the left is of the same form, with p in place of u, as the first formula in (11), Article 9–5. Hence (4a) becomes

$$\sinh^{-1} p = \frac{w}{H}x + C_1. \tag{4b}$$

Since $p = dy/dx = 0$ when $x = 0$, we determine the constant of integration

$$\sinh^{-1} 0 = C_1,$$

from which (see Fig. 9–7)

$$C_1 = 0.$$

Hence

$$\sinh^{-1} p = \frac{w}{H}x$$

or

$$p = \sinh\left(\frac{w}{H}x\right). \tag{5a}$$

We substitute $p = dy/dx$, multiply by dx, and have

$$dy = \sinh\left(\frac{w}{H}x\right)dx$$

or

$$y = \int \sinh\left(\frac{w}{H}x\right)dx$$

$$= \frac{H}{w}\int \sinh\left(\frac{w}{H}x\right)d\left(\frac{w}{H}x\right)$$

$$= \frac{H}{w}\cosh\left(\frac{w}{H}x\right) + C_2. \tag{5b}$$

The condition $y = y_0$ when $x = 0$ determines C_2:

$$y_0 = \frac{H}{w}\cosh 0 + C_2,$$

$$C_2 = y_0 - \frac{H}{w}, \tag{5c}$$

and hence

$$y = \frac{H}{w}\cosh\left(\frac{w}{H}x\right) + y_0 - \frac{H}{w}. \tag{5d}$$

Clearly, this equation will have a simpler form if we choose y_0 so that

$$y_0 = \frac{H}{w}.$$

We do so. The answer then takes the form

$$y = \frac{H}{w}\cosh\left(\frac{w}{H}x\right)$$

or

$$y = a\cosh\frac{x}{a} \quad \text{with} \quad a = \frac{H}{w}. \tag{6}$$

PROBLEMS

1. Find the length of arc of the catenary $y = a\cosh x/a$ from $A(0, a)$ to $P_1(x_1, y_1)$, $x_1 > 0$.

2. Show that the area bounded by the x-axis, the catenary $y = a\cosh x/a$, the y-axis, and the vertical line through $P_1(x_1, y_1)$, $x_1 > 0$, is the same as the area of a rectangle of altitude a and base s, where s is the length of the arc from $A(0, a)$ to P_1. (See Problem 1.)

3. The catenary $y = a\cosh x/a$ is revolved about the x-axis. Find the surface area generated by the portion of the curve between the points $A(0, a)$ and $P_1(x_1, y_1)$, $x_1 > 0$. (Incidentally, of all continuously differentiable curves $y = f(x)$, $f(x) > 0$, from $A(0, a)$ to $P(x_1, y_1)$, the catenary generates the surface of revolution of least area.)

4. Find the center of gravity of the arc of the catenary

$y = a \cosh x/a$ between two symmetrically located points $P_0(-x_1, y_1)$ and $P_1(x_1, y_1)$.

5. Find the volume generated when the area of Problem 2 is revolved about the x-axis.

6. The length of the arc AP (Fig. 9–8) is $s = a \sinh x/a$. (See Problem 1.)

a) Show that the coordinates of $P(x, y)$ may be expressed as functions of the arc length s, as follows:

$$x = a \sinh^{-1} \frac{s}{a}, \qquad y = \sqrt{s^2 + a^2}.$$

b) Calculate dx/ds and dy/ds from part (a) above and verify that $(dx/ds)^2 + (dy/ds)^2 = 1$.

7. (*Calculator or tables*) A cable 32 feet long and weighing 2 pounds per foot has its ends fastened at the same level to two posts 30 feet apart.

a) Show that the constant a in Eq. (6) must satisfy the equation

$$\sinh u = \frac{16}{15} u, \qquad u = \frac{15}{a}. \qquad \text{(See Problem 6a.)}$$

b) Sketch graphs of the curves $y_1 = \sinh u$, $y_2 = (16/15)u$ and show (with the aid of a calculator or tables) that they intersect at $u = 0$ and $u = \pm 0.6$ (approximately).

c) Using the results of part (b), find the dip in the cable at its center.

d) Using the results of part (b), find the tension in the cable at its lowest point.

REVIEW QUESTIONS AND EXERCISES

1. Define each of the hyperbolic functions.

2. State three trigonometric identities [such as formulas for $\sin (A + B)$, $\cos (A - B)$, $\cos^2 A + \sin^2 A = 1$, etc.]. What are the corresponding hyperbolic identities? Verify them.

3. Develop formulas for derivatives of the six hyperbolic functions.

4. What is the domain of the hyperbolic sine? What is its range?

5. What are the domain and range of the hyperbolic

cosine? Of the hyperbolic tangent?

6. State some differences between the graphs of the trigonometric functions and their hyperbolic counterparts (for example, sine and sinh, cosine and cosh, tangent and tanh).

7. If $y = A \sin (at) + B \cos (at)$, then $y'' = -a^2 y$. What is the corresponding differential equation satisfied by $y = A \sinh (at) + B \cosh (at)$?

8. Define $\sinh^{-1}$ and $\cosh^{-1}$ functions. What are their domains? What are their ranges? What are their derivatives?

MISCELLANEOUS PROBLEMS

1. Prove the hyperbolic identity $\cosh 2x = \cosh^2 x + \sinh^2 x$.

2. Verify that $\tanh x = \sinh 2x/(1 + \cosh 2x)$.

3. Sketch the curves $y = \cosh x$ and $y = \sinh x$ in one diagram. To each positive value of x corresponds a point P on $y = \sinh x$ and a point Q on $y = \cosh x$. Calculate the limit of the distance PQ as x becomes infinitely large.

4. If $\cosh x = \frac{5}{4}$, find $\sinh x$ and $\tanh x$.

5. If $\operatorname{csch} x = -\frac{9}{40}$, find $\cosh x$ and $\tanh x$.

6. If $\tanh x > \frac{5}{13}$, show that $\sinh x > 0.4$ and $\operatorname{sech} x < 0.95$.

7. Let $P(x, y)$ be a point on the curve $y = \tanh x$ (Fig. 9–2(b)). Let AB be the vertical line segment through P with A and B on the asymptotes of the curve. Let C be a semicircle with AB as diameter. Let L be a line through P perpendicular to AB and cutting C in a point Q. Show that $PQ = \operatorname{sech} x$.

8. Prove that $\sinh 3u = 3 \sinh u + 4 \sinh^3 u$.

9. Find equations of the asymptotes of the hyperbola represented by the equation $y = \tanh (\frac{1}{2} \ln x)$.

10. A particle moves along the x-axis according to one of the following laws: (a) $x = a \cos kt + b \sin kt$, (b) $x = a \cosh kt + b \sinh kt$. In both cases, show that the acceleration is proportional to x, but that in the first case it is always directed toward the origin while in the second case it is directed away from the origin.

11. Show that $y = \cosh x, \sinh x, \cos x$, and $\sin x$ all satisfy the relationship $d^4 y/dx^4 = y$.

Find dy/dx in each of Problems 12–21.

12. $y = \sinh^2 3x$

13. $\tan x = \tanh^2 y$

14. $\sin^{-1} x = \operatorname{sech} y$

15. $\sinh y = \sec x$

16. $\tan^{-1} y = \tanh^{-1} x$

17. $y = \tanh (\ln x)$

18. $x = \cosh (\ln y)$

19. $y = \sinh (\tan^{-1} e^{3x})$

20. $y = \sinh^{-1} (\tan x)$

21. $y^2 + x \cosh y + \sinh^2 x = 50$

Evaluate each of the following integrals, Problems 22–31:

22. $\int \dfrac{d\theta}{\sinh \theta + \cosh \theta}$

23. $\int \dfrac{\cosh \theta \, d\theta}{\sinh \theta + \cosh \theta}$

24. $\int \sinh^3 x \, dx$

25. $\int e^x \sinh 2x \, dx$

26. $\int \dfrac{e^{2x} - 1}{e^{2x} + 1} dx$

27. $\int_0^1 \dfrac{dx}{4 - x^2}$

28. $\int_3^5 \dfrac{dx}{4 - x^2}$

29. $\int \dfrac{e^t \, dt}{\sqrt{1 + e^{2t}}}$

30. $\int \dfrac{\sin x \, dx}{1 - \cos^2 x}$

31. $\int \dfrac{\sec^2 \theta \, d\theta}{\sqrt{\tan^2 \theta - 1}}$

Sketch the following curves, Problems 32–34:

32. $y = \dfrac{1}{2} \ln \dfrac{1 + \tanh x}{1 - \tanh x}$

33. $y = \tan \left(\dfrac{\pi}{2} \tanh x \right)$

34. $\cosh y = 1 + \dfrac{x^2}{2}$

35. If the arc s of the catenary $y = a \cosh (x/a)$ is measured from the lowest point, show that $dy/dx = s/a$.

36. A body starting from rest falls under the attraction of gravity but encounters resistance proportional to the square of its velocity. Show that if the body could continue to fall indefinitely under these same conditions, its velocity would approach a limiting value, and find the distance it would fall in time t.

37. Evaluate the limit, as $x \to \infty$, of $\cosh^{-1} x - \ln x$.

38. Evaluate

$$\lim_{x \to \infty} \int_1^x \left(\frac{1}{\sqrt{1 + t^2}} - \frac{1}{t} \right) dt.$$

POLAR COORDINATES

THE POLAR COORDINATE
SYSTEM

We know that a point can be located in a plane by giving its abscissa and ordinate relative to a given coordinate system. Such x- and y-coordinates are called *cartesian* coordinates, in honor of the French mathematician-philosopher René Descartes* (1596–1650), who is credited with discovering this method of describing the position of a point in a plane.

Another useful way to locate a point in a plane is by *polar coordinates*, Fig. 10–1. First, we fix an *origin O* and an *initial ray*† from O. The point P has polar coordinates r, θ, with

$$r = \text{Directed distance from } O \text{ to } P, \tag{1a}$$

and

$$\theta = \text{Directed angle from initial ray to } OP. \tag{1b}$$

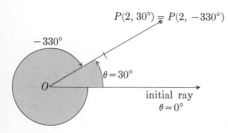

10–1 Polar coordinates.

As in trigonometry, the angle θ is *positive* when measured counterclockwise and negative when measured clockwise (Fig. 10–1). But the angle associated with a given point is not unique (Fig. 10–2). For instance, the point 2 units from the origin, along the ray θ = 30°, has polar coordinates r = 2, θ = 30°. It also has coordinates r = 2, θ = −330°, or r = 2, θ = 390°.

There are occasions when we wish to allow r to be negative. That is why we say "directed distance" in Eq. (1a). The ray θ = 30° and the ray θ = 210° together make up a complete line through O (Fig. 10–3). The point P(2, 210°) two units from O on the ray θ = 210° has polar coordinates r = 2, θ = 210°. It can be reached by standing at O and facing out along the initial ray, if you first turn 210° counterclockwise, and then go forward two units. You would reach the same point by turning only 30° counterclockwise from the initial ray and then going *backward* two units. So we say that the point also has polar coordinates r = −2, θ = 30°.

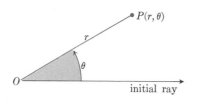

10–2 The ray θ = 30° is the same as the ray θ = −330°.

10–3 The rays θ = 30° and θ = 210° make a line.

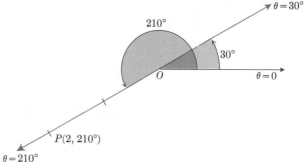

Whenever the angle between two rays is 180°, the rays actually make a straight line. We then say that each ray is the negative of the other. Points on the ray θ = α have polar coordinates (r, α) with r ≥ 0. Points on the

---

* For an interesting biographical account, together with an excerpt from Descartes' own writings, see *World of Mathematics*, Vol. 1, pp. 235–253.

† A *ray* is a half-line consisting of a vertex and points of a line on one side of the vertex. For example, the origin and positive x-axis make up a ray. The set of points on the line y = 2x + 3 with x ≥ 1 is another ray; its vertex is (1, 5).

negative ray, $\theta = \alpha + 180°$, have coordinates (r, α) with $r \leq 0$. The origin is $r = 0$. (See Fig. 10–4 for the ray $\theta = 30°$ and its negative. *Caution.* The "negative" of the ray $\theta = 30°$ is the ray $\theta = 30° + 180° = 210°$ and *not* the ray $\theta = -30°$. "Negative" refers to the directed distance r.)

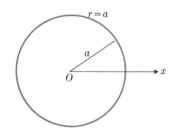

10–4   The terminal ray $\theta = \pi/6$ and its negative.

There is a great advantage in being able to use both polar and cartesian coordinates. To do this, we use a common origin and take the initial ray as the positive x-axis, the ray $\theta = 90°$ as the positive y-axis. The coordinates (Fig. 10–5) are then related by the equations

$$x = r \cos \theta, \qquad y = r \sin \theta. \qquad \textbf{(2)}$$

These are the equations that define $\sin \theta$ and $\cos \theta$ when r is positive. They are also valid if r is negative, because $\cos (\theta + 180°) = -\cos \theta$, $\sin (\theta + 180°) = -\sin \theta$, so positive r's on the ray $\theta + 180°$ correspond to negative r's associated with the ray θ. When $r = 0$, then $x = y = 0$, and P is the origin.

If we impose the condition

$$r = a \qquad (a \text{ constant}), \qquad \textbf{(3)}$$

then the locus of P is a circle with center O, radius a, and P describes the circle once as θ varies from 0 to 360° (Fig. 10–6). On the other hand, if we let r vary and hold θ fixed, say

$$\theta = 30°, \qquad \textbf{(4)}$$

the locus of P is the straight line shown in Fig. 10–4.

We adopt the convention that r may be any real number, $-\infty < r < \infty$. Then $r = 0$ corresponds to $x = 0$, $y = 0$ in Eqs. (2), regardless of θ. That is,

$$r = 0, \qquad \theta \text{ any value} \qquad \textbf{(5)}$$

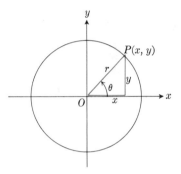

10–5   Polar and cartesian coordinates.

is the origin. Positive values of r with θ fixed give points on the terminal side of the angle θ; *negative* values of r give points on the negative ray.

The same point may be represented in several different ways in polar coordinates. For example, the point $(2, 30°)$, or $(2, \pi/6)$, has the following representations:

$$(2, 30°), \qquad (2, -330°), \qquad (-2, 210°), \qquad (-2, -150°).$$

These and all others are summarized in the two formulas

$$(2, 30° + n360°), \qquad (-2, 210° + n360°) \qquad [n = 0, \pm 1, \pm 2, \ldots]$$

10–6   The polar equation for the circle shown above is $r = a$.

or, if we measure the angles in radians,

$$\left(2, \frac{\pi}{6} + 2n\pi\right), \qquad \left(-2, \frac{7\pi}{6} + 2n\pi\right) \qquad [n = 0, \pm 1, \pm 2, \ldots].$$

The fact that the same point may be represented in several different ways in polar coordinates makes added care necessary in certain situations. For example, the point $(2a, \pi)$ is on the curve

$$r^2 = 4a^2 \cos \theta \tag{6}$$

even though its coordinates as given do not satisfy the equation, because the same point is represented by $(-2a, 0)$ and these coordinates do satisfy the equation. The same point $(2a, \pi)$ is on the curve

$$r = a(1 - \cos \theta), \tag{7}$$

and hence this point should be included among the points of intersection of the two curves represented by Eqs. (6) and (7). But if we solve the equations simultaneously by substituting $\cos \theta = r^2/4a^2$ from (6) into (7) and then solving the resulting quadratic equation

$$\left(\frac{r}{a}\right)^2 + 4\left(\frac{r}{a}\right) - 4 = 0$$

for

$$\frac{r}{a} = -2 \pm 2\sqrt{2}, \tag{8}$$

we do *not* obtain the point $(2a, \pi)$ as a point of intersection. The reason is simple enough; namely, the point is not on the curves "simultaneously" in the sense of being reached at the same value of θ, since it is reached in the one case when $\theta = 0$ and in the other case when $\theta = \pi$. It is as though two ships describe paths that intersect at a point, but the ships do not collide because they reach the point of intersection at different times! The curves represented by Eqs. (6) and (7) are shown in Fig. 10–10(c), and they are seen to intersect at the four points

$$(0, 0), \qquad (2a, \pi), \qquad (r_1, \theta_1), \qquad (r_1, -\theta_1), \tag{9a}$$

where

$$r_1 = (-2 + 2\sqrt{2})a,$$
$$\cos \theta_1 = 1 - \frac{r_1}{a} = 3 - 2\sqrt{2}. \tag{9b}$$

Only the last two of these points are found from the simultaneous solution; the first two are disclosed only by graphing the curves.

REMARK.   Karl von Frisch has advanced the following theory about how bees communicate information about newly discovered sources of food. A scout returning to the hive from a flower bed gives away samples of the food and then, if the bed is more than about a hundred yards away, performs a dance to show where the flowers are. The bee runs straight ahead for a centimeter or so, waggling from side to side, and circles back to the starting place. The bee then repeats the straight run, circling back in the opposite direction (Fig. 10–7). The dance continues this way in regular alternation. Exceptionally excited bees have been observed to dance for more than three and a half hours.

If the dance is performed outside the hive, the straight run points to the flowers. If the dance is performed inside, it is performed on the vertical wall of a honeycomb, with gravity substituting for the sun's position. A vertical straight run means that the food is in the direction of the sun. A run 30° to the right of vertical means that the food is 30° to the right of the sun, and so on. Distance (more accurately, the amount of energy required to reach the food) is communicated by the duration of the straight-run portions of the dance. Straight runs lasting three seconds each are typical for distances of about a half-mile from the hive. Straight runs that last five seconds each mean about two miles. (See E. O. Wilson's *The Insect Societies*, Belknap Press of Harvard University Press, Cambridge, MA, 1971, for details.)

10–7 The waggle dance of a scout bee.

PROBLEMS

1. Plot the following points, given in polar form, and find *all* polar coordinates of each point:

a) $(3, \pi/4)$ **b)** $(-3, \pi/4)$ **c)** $(3, -\pi/4)$ **d)** $(-3, -\pi/4)$

In Problems 2–9, graph the set of points $P(r, \theta)$ whose polar coordinates satisfy the given equation, inequality or inequalities.

2. $r = 2$

3. $0 \leq r \leq 2$

4. $r > 1$

5. $1 < r < 2$

6. $0° \leq \theta \leq 30°, \quad r \geq 0$

7. $\theta = 120°, \quad r \leq -2$

8. $\theta = 60°, \quad -1 \leq r \leq 3$

9. $\theta = 495°, \quad r \geq -1$

10. Find cartesian coordinates for the points in Problem 1.

In Problems 11–14, use Eq. (2) to write cartesian equations equivalent to the given polar equations. Then graph the equations.

11. $r \cos \theta = 2$

12. $r \sin \theta = -1$

13. $r \cos \theta + r \sin \theta = 1$

14. $r \sin \theta = r \cos \theta$

In Problems 15–18, use the trigonometric formulas in Eqs. (11a–e) of Article 2–9 to expand the left side of each equation. Then replace the resulting polar equation by an equivalent cartesian equation, and sketch the graph.

15. $r \cos (\theta - 60°) = 3$

16. $r \sin (\theta + 45°) = 4$

17. $r \sin (45° - \theta) = \sqrt{2}$

18. $r \cos (30° - \theta) = 0$

19. Show that $(2, \frac{3}{4}\pi)$ is on the curve $r = 2 \sin 2\theta$.

20. Show that $(\frac{1}{2}, \frac{3}{2}\pi)$ is on the curve $r = -\sin (\theta/3)$.

21. Show that the equations $r = \cos \theta + 1$, $r = \cos \theta - 1$, represent the same curve.

Find some intersections of the following pairs of curves (a = constant):

22. $r^2 = 2a^2 \sin 2\theta$, $\quad r = a$ **23.** $r = a \sin \theta$, $\quad r = a \cos \theta$

24. $r = a(1 + \cos \theta)$, $\quad r = a(1 - \sin \theta)$

25. $r = a(1 + \sin \theta)$, $\quad r = 2a \cos \theta$

26. $r = a \cos 2\theta$, $\quad r = a(1 + \cos \theta)$

10–2

GRAPHS OF POLAR EQUATIONS

The graph of an equation

$$F(r, \theta) = 0$$

consists of all those points whose coordinates (in some form) satisfy the equation. Frequently the equation gives r explicitly in terms of θ, as

$$r = f(\theta).$$

As many points as desired may then be obtained by substituting values of θ and calculating the corresponding values of r. In particular, it is desirable to plot the points where r is a maximum or a minimum and to find the values of θ when the curve passes through the origin, if that occurs.

Certain types of *symmetry* are readily detected. For example, the curve is:

a) symmetric about the origin if the equation is unchanged when r is replaced by $-r$;

b) symmetric about the x-axis if the equation is unchanged when θ is replaced by $-\theta$;

c) symmetric about the y-axis if the equation is unchanged when θ is replaced by $\pi - \theta$.

These and certain other tests for symmetry are readily verified by considering the symmetrically located points in Fig. 10–8.

a)

about the origin

b)

about the x-axis

c)

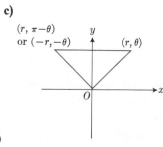

about the y-axis

10–8 Some of the polar coordinate tests for symmetry.

EXAMPLE 1. Discuss and sketch the curve $r = a(1 - \cos \theta)$, where a is a positive constant.

Discussion. Since $\cos(-\theta) = \cos \theta$, the equation is unaltered when θ is replaced by $-\theta$; hence the curve is symmetric about the x-axis (Fig. 10–8b). Also, since

$$-1 \le \cos \theta \le 1,$$

the values of r vary between 0 and $2a$. The minimum value, $r = 0$, occurs at $\theta = 0$, and the maximum value, $r = 2a$, occurs at $\theta = \pi$. Moreover, as θ varies from 0 to π, $\cos \theta$ decreases from 1 to -1; hence $1 - \cos \theta$ increases from 0 to 2. That is, r increases from 0 to $2a$ as the radius vector OP swings from $\theta = 0$ to $\theta = \pi$. We make a table of values (Table 10–1) and plot the corresponding points.

Table 10–1. Values of $r = a(1 - \cos \theta)$ for selected values of θ

θ:	0	60°	90°	120°	180°
r:	0	$a/2$	a	$3a/2$	$2a$

Now we sketch a smooth curve through them (Fig. 10–9) in such a way that r increases as θ increases, since

$$\frac{dr}{d\theta} = a \sin \theta$$

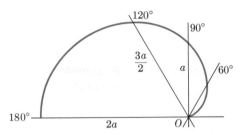

10–9 A smooth curve sketched through the points from Table 10–1.

is positive for $0 < \theta < \pi$. Then we exploit the symmetry of the curve and reflect this portion across the x-axis. The result is the curve shown in Fig. 10–10(a), which is called a *cardioid* because of its heart-shaped appearance. Its behavior at the origin and the angles between its tangents and the coordinate axes at the other intercepts are more easily discussed at a later time. However, we may investigate the slope of the cardioid at the origin as follows: Let P be a point on the curve in the first quadrant, where P is

10–10 (a) $r = a(1 - \cos \theta)$. (b) $r^2 = 4a^2 \cos \theta$. (c) The four points of intersection of the curves in (a) and (b). Only two of the four (A and B) can be found by simultaneous solution. The intersections at O and C are disclosed only by graphing.

a)

b)

c)

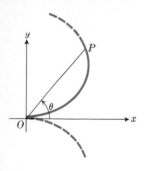

10–11   As $P \to O$ along the cardioid, $\theta \to 0$. At the origin, the cardioid has a horizontal tangent.

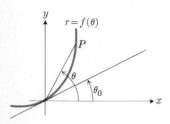

10–12   If the curve $r = f(\theta)$ passes through the origin at $\theta = \theta_0$, and if f has a derivative at $\theta = \theta_0$, then the line $\theta = \theta_0$ is tangent to the curve at the origin.

destined to approach O along the curve (see Fig. 10–11). Then, as $P \to O$, the slope of OP ($= \tan \theta$) approaches the slope of the tangent at O. Since $P \to O$ as $\theta \to 0$,

$$\lim_{\theta \to 0} (\text{slope of } OP) = \lim_{\theta \to 0} \tan \theta = 0.$$

That is, the slope of the tangent to the curve at the origin is zero.

The process by which we found the tangent to the cardioid at the origin at the end of Example 1 works for any smooth curve through the origin. If the curve passes through the origin when $\theta = \theta_0$, then the discussion in Example 1 would be modified only to the extent of saying that $P \to O$ along the curve as $\theta \to \theta_0$, and hence

$$\left(\frac{dy}{dx}\right)_{\theta = \theta_0} = \lim_{\theta \to \theta_0} (\tan \theta) = \tan \theta_0.$$

But $(dy/dx)_{\theta = \theta_0}$ is also the tangent of the angle between the x-axis and the curve at this point. Hence the line $\theta = \theta_0$ is tangent to the curve at the origin. In other words, whenever a curve passes through the origin for a value θ_0 of θ and the derivative $dr/d\theta$ exists at that point, it does so *tangent* to the line $\theta = \theta_0$. See Fig. 10–12.

EXAMPLE 2. $r^2 = 4a^2 \cos \theta$. This curve is symmetric about the origin. Two values,

$$r = \pm 2a\sqrt{\cos \theta},$$

correspond to each value of θ for which $\cos \theta > 0$, namely,

$$-\frac{\pi}{2} < \theta < \frac{\pi}{2}.$$

Furthermore, the curve is symmetric about the x-axis, since θ may be replaced by $-\theta$ without altering the value of $\cos \theta$. The curve passes through the origin at $\theta = \pi/2$ and is tangent to the y-axis at this point. Since $\cos \theta$ never exceeds unity, the maximum value of r is $2a$, which occurs at $\theta = 0$. As θ increases from 0 to $\pi/2$, $|r|$ decreases from $2a$ to 0. The curve is sketched in Fig. 10–10(b).

EXAMPLE 3. $r\theta = a$, where a is a positive constant. When $\theta = 0$ the equation becomes $0 = a$, which is not true. That is, there is no point on the curve for $\theta = 0$. However, suppose θ is a *small* positive angle. Then from $r = a/\theta$, we see that r is large and positive. Consider the situation in Fig. 10–13. No matter how small the positive angle θ may be, if r is sufficiently large the point P may be far above the x-axis. In fact, we need to see what happens to

$$y = r \sin \theta = \frac{a}{\theta} \sin \theta$$

for small positive values of θ. We know, of course, that

$$\lim_{\theta \to 0} \frac{\sin \theta}{\theta} = 1;$$

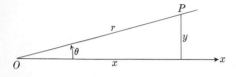

10–13   As $\theta \to 0$, P can be kept away from the axis by increasing r.

hence

$$\lim_{\theta \to 0} y = \lim_{\theta \to 0} a \frac{\sin \theta}{\theta} = a.$$

This shows that the line $y = a$ is an asymptote of this curve. So we think of the curve being traced by a point P that starts far out near the line $y = a$ for $\theta = 0^+$ and moves in the direction indicated by the arrows in Fig. 10–14(a) as θ increases and r decreases. As the radius vector OP continues to rotate about the origin, it shrinks in length, and P describes a spiral, which coils around the origin with r tending to zero as θ increases indefinitely.

When r and θ are replaced by $-r$ and $-\theta$, respectively, the equation is unaltered. Hence for every point (r_1, θ_1) on the curve in Fig. 10–14(a), there is a point $(-r_1, -\theta_1)$ symmetrically located with respect to the y-axis, also on the curve $r\theta = a$. We therefore reflect the curve in Fig. 10–14(a) in the y-axis, obtaining another spiral which coils around the origin in the clockwise sense as θ approaches minus infinity. The complete curve is indicated in Fig. 10–14(b). It is called a *hyperbolic spiral*, the adjective "hyperbolic" being used because the equation $r\theta = a$ is analogous to the equation $xy = a$, which represents a hyperbola in cartesian coordinates.

a)

b)

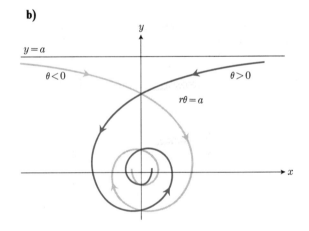

10–14   The hyperbolic spiral $r\theta = a$.

PROBLEMS

1. Find the polar form of the equation of the line $3x + 4y = 5$.

2. If the polar coordinates (r, θ) of a point P satisfy the equation $r = 2a \cos \theta$, what equation is satisfied by the cartesian coordinates (x, y) of P?

Discuss and sketch each of the following curves;

3. $r = a(1 + \cos \theta)$ **4.** $r = a(1 - \sin \theta)$

5. $r = a \sin 2\theta$ **6.** $r^2 = 2a^2 \cos 2\theta$

7. $r = a(2 + \sin \theta)$ **8.** $r = a(1 + 2 \sin \theta)$

9. $r = \theta$ **10.** $r = a \sin \theta/2$

11. Find the points on the curve $r = a(1 + \cos \theta)$, where the tangent is (a) parallel to the x-axis, (b) parallel to the y-axis. [*Hint.* Express x and y in terms of θ. Then calculate dy/dx.]

12. Sketch the curves $r = a(1 + \cos \theta)$ and $r = 3a \cos \theta$ in one diagram and find the angle between their tangents at the point of intersection that lies in the first quadrant.

13. What kind of symmetry occurs in the graph of $r = f(\theta)$ if the equation is unaltered when r and θ are replaced by $-r$ and $-\theta$, respectively?

**POLAR EQUATIONS OF
THE CONIC SECTIONS
AND OTHER CURVES**

The relationships given in Article 10–1 between cartesian and polar coordinates enable us to change any cartesian equation into a polar equation for the same curve.

For example, the circle

$$x^2 + y^2 - 2ax = 0, \qquad (1)$$

with center at $(a, 0)$ and radius a (Fig. 10–15a) becomes

$$(r \cos \theta)^2 + (r \sin \theta)^2 - 2a(r \cos \theta) = 0,$$

which reduces to

$$r(r - 2a \cos \theta) = 0.$$

The graph obtained by putting the first factor equal to zero, $r = 0$, is just one point, the origin. The other factor vanishes when

$$r = 2a \cos \theta. \qquad (2)$$

This includes the origin among its points and hence represents the entire graph of Eq. (1).

The example illustrates one method of finding the polar equation for a curve, namely by transforming its cartesian equation into polar form. An alternative method is to derive the polar equation directly from some geometric property. For example, take the circle in Fig. 10–15(b) and let $P(r, \theta)$ be a representative point on the circle. Then angle OPA is a right angle (why?) and from the right triangle OPA, we read

$$\frac{r}{2a} = \cos \theta \qquad \text{or} \qquad r = 2a \cos \theta,$$

which is the same equation obtained above.

We shall apply this second method to obtain equations of various curves in the following examples.

EXAMPLE 1. Find the polar equation of the circle of radius a with center at (b, β).

Solution. We let $P(r, \theta)$ be a representative point on the circle and apply the law of cosines to the triangle OCP (Fig. 10–16) to obtain

$$a^2 = b^2 + r^2 - 2br \cos (\theta - \beta). \qquad (3)$$

If the circle passes through the origin, then $b = a$ and the equation takes the simpler form

$$r[r - 2a \cos (\theta - \beta)] = 0$$

or

$$r = 2a \cos (\theta - \beta). \qquad (4)$$

10–15 The circle $r = 2a \cos \theta$.

10–16 To find an equation for the circle shown above, apply the law of cosines to triangle OCP.

In particular, if $\beta = 0$, Eq. (4) reduces to the result we have obtained before, while if $\beta = 90°$, so that the center of the circle lies on the y-axis (Fig. 10-17), Eq. (4) reduces to

$$r = 2a \sin \theta. \tag{5}$$

EXAMPLE 2.   The normal from the origin to the line L intersects L at the point $N(p, \beta)$. Find the polar equation of L.

Solution.   We let $P(r, \theta)$ be a representative point on the line L in Fig. 10-18 and, from the right triangle ONP, read the result

$$r \cos (\theta - \beta) = p. \tag{6}$$

This equation is simply a more general form of the equation

$$r \cos \theta = p, \tag{7}$$

which is the polar form of the line

$$x = p.$$

In fact, if we perform a rotation of axes as in Fig. 10-19, the new polar coordinates (r', θ') are related to the old polar coordinates as follows:

$$r' = r, \qquad \theta' = \theta - \beta. \tag{8}$$

If we apply this rotation to Eq. (6), we get

$$r' \cos \theta' = p.$$

But

$$r' \cos \theta' = x',$$

so the equation is the same as

$$x' = p,$$

which represents a straight line p units from and parallel to the y'-axis.

EXAMPLE 3.   Find a polar equation for the path of a point P that moves in such a way that the product of its distances from the two points $F_1(a, \pi)$ and $F_2(a, 0)$ is a constant, say b^2.

Solution.   We let $P(r, \theta)$ be a representative point on the locus and determine the equation satisfied by the coordinates r and θ in order to fulfill the requirement

$$d_1 d_2 = b^2, \tag{9}$$

where $d_1 = PF_1$ and $d_2 = PF_2$ (Fig. 10-20). We apply the law of cosines twice: once to the triangle OPF_2,

$$d_2^2 = r^2 + a^2 - 2ar \cos \theta,$$

and again to the triangle OPF_1,

$$d_1^2 = r^2 + a^2 - 2ar \cos (\pi - \theta).$$

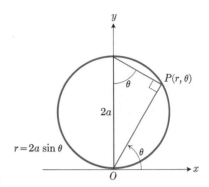

10-17 $r = 2a \sin \theta$ is the equation of a circle through the origin with its center on the positive y-axis.

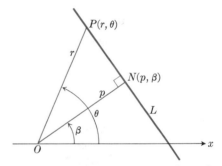

10-18   The relation $p/r = \cos (\theta - \beta)$ can be read from the triangle ONP.

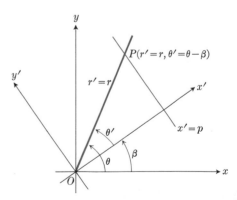

10-19   Another equation of the line L of Fig. 10-18 is $x' = p$.

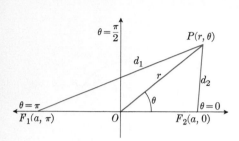

10–20 Example 3 shows that if P is constrained to move so that $PF_1 \cdot PF_2 = b^2$ (a positive constant), then P traces out the curve $b^4 = a^4 + r^4 - 2a^2r^2 \cos 2\theta$.

But

$$\cos (\pi - \theta) = -\cos \theta,$$

so that

$$d_1^2 = r^2 + a^2 + 2ar \cos \theta.$$

Hence

$$d_1^2 d_2^2 = (r^2 + a^2)^2 - (2ar \cos \theta)^2$$

or

$$b^4 = a^4 + r^4 + 2a^2r^2(1 - 2 \cos^2 \theta).$$

The trigonometric identity $\cos 2\theta = 2 \cos^2 \theta - 1$ enables us to put our equation in the form

$$b^4 = a^4 + r^4 - 2a^2r^2 \cos 2\theta. \tag{10}$$

One special case allows the locus to pass through the origin, namely, if $b = a$. Then the equation simplifies still further to the form

$$r^2 = 2a^2 \cos 2\theta. \tag{11}$$

The graphs of the curves represented by (10) for different values of $PF_1 \cdot PF_2$ are shown in Fig. 10–21(a)–(c). The curves in both (a) and (b) are called lemniscates, and the curve in (c) consists of two separate closed portions known as "ovals of Cassini."

Figure 10–21

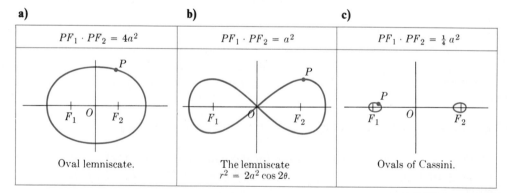

a)	b)	c)
$PF_1 \cdot PF_2 = 4a^2$	$PF_1 \cdot PF_2 = a^2$	$PF_1 \cdot PF_2 = \frac{1}{4} a^2$
Oval lemniscate.	The lemniscate $r^2 = 2a^2 \cos 2\theta$.	Ovals of Cassini.

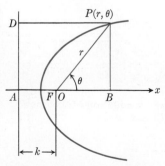

10–22 If $PF = e \cdot PD$, then $r = e(k + r \cos \theta)$.

EXAMPLE 4. Find the polar equation of the conic section of eccentricity e if the focus is at the origin and the associated directrix is the line $x = -k$.

Solution. We adopt the notation of Fig. 10–22 and use the focus-and-directrix property

$$PF = e \cdot PD, \tag{12}$$

which allows us to handle the parabola, ellipse, and hyperbola all at the same time.

By taking the origin at the focus F, we have

$$PF = r,$$

while

$$PD = AB$$

and

$$AB = AF + FB = k + r \cos \theta.$$

Then Eq. (12) is the same as

$$r = e(k + r \cos \theta).$$

If we solve this equation for r, we get

$$r = \frac{ke}{1 - e \cos \theta}. \tag{13}$$

Typical special cases of (13) are obtained by taking

$$e = 1, \qquad r = \frac{k}{1 - \cos \theta} = \frac{k}{2} \csc^2 \frac{\theta}{2}, \tag{14a}$$

which represents a *parabola*;

$$e = \frac{1}{2}, \qquad r = \frac{k}{2 - \cos \theta}, \tag{14b}$$

which represents an *ellipse*; and

$$e = 2, \qquad r = \frac{2k}{1 - 2 \cos \theta}, \tag{14c}$$

which represents a *hyperbola*.

It is worth noting that the denominator in Eq. (14b) for the ellipse can never vanish, so that r remains finite for all values of θ. But r becomes infinite as θ approaches 0 in (14a) and as θ approaches $\pi/3$ in (14c).

By replacing the constant ke in Eq. (13) by its equivalent value

$$ke = a(1 - e^2)$$

when $e < 1$, we may let $e \rightarrow 0$ and get

$$r = a$$

in the limit. That is, the circle of radius a and center at O is a limiting case of the curves represented by Eq. (13).

PROBLEMS

1. A line segment of length $2a$ slides with its ends on the x- and y-axes. Find the polar equation of the locus described by the point $P(r, \theta)$ in which the perpendicular from the origin intersects the moving line. Sketch the curve.

2. OA is a diameter of a circle of radius a, AC is tangent to the circle, and OC intersects the circle at B. On OC the point $P(r, \theta)$ is found such that $OP = BC$. With O as origin, OA as x-axis, and angle AOP as θ, find the polar equation of the locus of P and sketch the curve. Show that the line $x = 2a$ is

an asymptote. The curve is called a "cissoid," meaning "ivy-like."

In Problems 3–7 determine the polar equation and sketch the given curve.

3. $x^2 + y^2 - 2ay = 0$

4. $(x^2 + y^2)^2 + 2ax(x^2 + y^2) - a^2 y^2 = 0$

5. $x \cos \alpha + y \sin \alpha = p$ (α, p constants)

6. $y^2 = 4ax + 4a^2$ **7.** $(x^2 + y^2)^2 = x^2 - y^2$

In Problems 8–13 determine the cartesian equation and sketch the given curve.

8. $r = 4 \cos \theta$ **9.** $r = 6 \sin \theta$

10. $r = \sin 2\theta$ **11.** $r^2 = 2a^2 \cos 2\theta$

12. $r = 8/(1 - 2 \cos \theta)$ **13.** $r = a(1 + \sin \theta)$

14. Sketch the following curves:

a) $r = 2 \cos (\theta + 45°)$,   **b)** $r = 4 \csc (\theta - 30°)$,

c) $r = 5 \sec (60° - \theta)$,   **d)** $r = 3 \sin (\theta + 30°)$,

e) $r = a + a \cos (\theta - 30°)$,   **f)** $0 \le r \le 2 - 2 \cos \theta$.

Each of the graphs in Problems 15–22 is the graph of exactly one of the equations (a)–(l) in the list below. Find the equation for each graph.

a) $r = \cos 2\theta$ **g)** $r = 1 + \cos \theta$

b) $r \cos \theta = 1$ **h)** $r = 1 - \sin \theta$

c) $r = \dfrac{6}{1 - 2 \cos \theta}$ **i)** $r = \dfrac{2}{1 - \cos \theta}$

d) $r = \sin 2\theta$ **j)** $r^2 = \sin 2\theta$

e) $r = \theta$ **k)** $r = -\sin \theta$

f) $r^2 = \cos 2\theta$ **l)** $r = 2 \cos \theta + 1$

20.   **21.**

22.

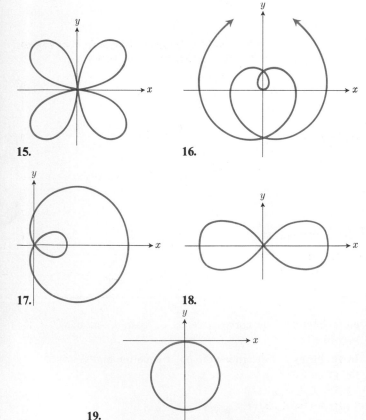

15.   **16.**

17.   **18.**

19.

Figure 10–23

23. (a) How can the angle β and the distance p [see Fig. 10–18 and Eq. (6)] be determined from the cartesian equation $ax + by = c$ for a straight line? (b) Specifically, find p, β, and the polar equation for the straight line $\sqrt{3}\,x + y = 6$.

24. The focus of a parabola is at the origin and its directrix is the line $r \cos \theta = -4$. Find the polar equation of the parabola.

25. One focus of a hyperbola of eccentricity $\frac{5}{4}$ is at the origin and the corresponding directrix is the line $r \cos \theta = 9$. Find the polar coordinates of the second focus. Also determine the polar equation of the hyperbola and sketch.

26. One focus of an ellipse of eccentricity $\frac{1}{4}$ is at the origin. The corresponding directrix is the line $r \cos \theta = 8$. Find the coordinates of the other focus. Write a polar equation for the ellipse, and sketch.

27. Find the maximum and minimum values of r that satisfy Eq. (10), first in terms of a and b, and then specifically for the cases $b = 2a$, $b = a$, and $b = a/2$.

28. Determine the slopes of the lines that are tangent to the lemniscate $r^2 = 2a^2 \cos 2\theta$ at the origin.

29. Equation (14b), $r = k/(2 - \cos \theta)$, represents an ellipse with one focus at the origin. Sketch the curve and its directrices for the case $k = 2$ and locate the center of the ellipse.

30. In the case $e > 1$, Eq. (13) represents a hyperbola. From the polar form of the equation, determine the slopes of the asymptotes of the hyperbola of eccentricity e.

In cartesian coordinates, when we want to discuss the direction of a curve at a point, we use the angle ϕ from the positive x-axis to the tangent line. In polar coordinates, it is more convenient to make use of the angle ψ (psi) from the *radius vector* to the tangent line. Then the relationship

$$\phi = \theta + \psi, \qquad (1)$$

which can be read from Fig. 10–24, makes it a simple matter to find ϕ if that angle is desired instead of ψ.

Suppose the equation of the curve is given in the form $r = f(\theta)$, where $f(\theta)$ is a differentiable function of θ. Then from

$$x = r \cos \theta, \qquad y = r \sin \theta, \qquad (2)$$

we see that x and y are differentiable functions of θ with

$$\frac{dx}{d\theta} = -r \sin \theta + \cos \theta \frac{dr}{d\theta},$$

$$\frac{dy}{d\theta} = r \cos \theta + \sin \theta \frac{dr}{d\theta}. \qquad (3)$$

Since $\psi = \phi - \theta$ from (1),

$$\tan \psi = \tan (\phi - \theta) = \frac{\tan \phi - \tan \theta}{1 + \tan \phi \tan \theta},$$

while

$$\tan \phi = \frac{dy/d\theta}{dx/d\theta}, \qquad \tan \theta = \frac{y}{x}.$$

Hence

$$\tan \psi = \frac{\dfrac{dy/d\theta}{dx/d\theta} - \dfrac{y}{x}}{1 + \dfrac{y}{x}\dfrac{dy/d\theta}{dx/d\theta}} = \frac{x\dfrac{dy}{d\theta} - y\dfrac{dx}{d\theta}}{x\dfrac{dx}{d\theta} + y\dfrac{dy}{d\theta}}. \qquad (4)$$

The numerator in the last expression in Eq. (4) is found by substitution from Eqs. (2) and (3) to be

$$x\frac{dy}{d\theta} - y\frac{dx}{d\theta} = r^2.$$

Similarly, the denominator is

$$x\frac{dx}{d\theta} + y\frac{dy}{d\theta} = r\frac{dr}{d\theta}.$$

When we substitute these into Eq. (4), we obtain the very simple final result

$$\tan \psi = \frac{r}{dr/d\theta}. \qquad (5)$$

**THE ANGLE ψ BETWEEN
THE RADIUS VECTOR
AND THE TANGENT LINE**

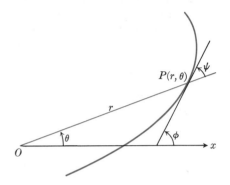

10–24 The angle ψ between the tangent vector and the radius vector.

REMARK.   This formula for $\tan \psi$ is much simpler than the formula

$$\tan \phi = \frac{r \cos \theta + (\sin \theta) \, dr/d\theta}{-r \sin \theta + (\cos \theta) \, dr/d\theta}, \tag{6}$$

that one obtains by calculating

$$\frac{dy}{dx} = \frac{dy/d\theta}{dx/d\theta}$$

from (3). This is why it is usually preferable to work with the angle ψ rather than with ϕ in the case of polar coordinates.

One may obtain a simple expression for the differential element of arc length ds by squaring and adding the differentials

$$dx = -r \sin \theta \, d\theta + \cos \theta \, dr,$$

$$dy = r \cos \theta \, d\theta + \sin \theta \, dr.$$

We find that

$$ds^2 = dx^2 + dy^2 = r^2 \, d\theta^2 + dr^2.$$

This result and the result for $\tan \psi$ are both easily remembered in the form

$$\tan \psi = \frac{r \, d\theta}{dr}, \tag{7a}$$

$$ds^2 = r^2 \, d\theta^2 + dr^2 \tag{7b}$$

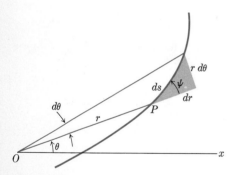

10–25   Arc length: $ds^2 = r^2 \, d\theta^2 + dr^2$.

if we refer to the "differential triangle" shown in Fig. 10–25. We simply treat dr and $r \, d\theta$ as the two legs and ds as the hypotenuse of an ordinary right triangle with the angle ψ opposite the side $r \, d\theta$. If we realize that certain terms of higher order are being neglected, we may think of dr as the component of displacement along the radius vector and $r \, d\theta$ as the component at right angles to this produced by the displacement ds along the curve. The relationships (7) may be read at once from this triangle. We should realize, of course, that the *proof* of these equations did not depend upon any such "differential triangle" and that the latter is only a mnemonic device.

To find the angle ψ, we use the first equation in (7). To find the length of a polar curve, we find ds from the second equation in (7) and integrate between appropriate limits as in the following examples.

EXAMPLE 1.   Find the angle ψ for the cardioid (Fig. 10–26),

$$r = a(1 - \cos \theta). \tag{8a}$$

Solution.   From the equation of the curve, we get

$$dr = a \sin \theta \, d\theta, \tag{8b}$$

so that

$$\tan \psi = \frac{r \, d\theta}{dr} = \frac{a(1 - \cos \theta) \, d\theta}{a \sin \theta \, d\theta} = \tan \frac{\theta}{2}.$$

As θ varies from 0 to 2π, the angle ψ varies from 0 to π according to the equation $\psi = \theta/2$. Thus at the y-intercepts the tangent line makes an angle of

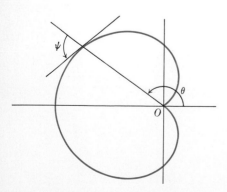

10–26   Cardioid: $r = a(1 - \cos \theta)$.

45° with the vertical, at the origin the curve is tangent to the *x*-axis, and at $(2a, \pi)$ the tangent line makes an angle of 90° with the negative *x*-axis.

Suppose we ask for the points on the cardioid where the tangent line is vertical. Denoting the inclination angle of the tangent line by ϕ and recalling that

$$\phi = \psi + \theta \quad \text{and} \quad \psi = \tfrac{1}{2}\theta,$$

we get

$$\phi = \tfrac{3}{2}\theta.$$

Since the tangent is vertical when

$$\phi = \frac{\pi}{2} + n\pi,$$

the values of θ satisfy

$$\theta = \frac{2}{3}\phi = \frac{\pi}{3} + \frac{2}{3}n\pi.$$

Taking $n = 0, -1, 1, -2, 2, \ldots$, we obtain

$$\theta = \frac{\pi}{3}, \quad \frac{-\pi}{3}, \quad \pi, \quad -\pi, \quad \tfrac{5}{3}\pi, \quad \ldots$$

These lead to three distinct points, namely,

$$\left(\frac{a}{2}, \pm\frac{\pi}{3}\right) \quad \text{and} \quad (2a, \pi),$$

whose radius vectors are spaced 120° apart. (See Fig. 10–27.)

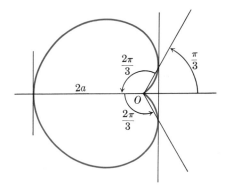

10–27 Vertical tangents to the cardioid $r = a(1 - \cos \theta)$.

EXAMPLE 2. Find the length of the cardioid $r = a(1 - \cos \theta)$.

Solution. Substituting dr and r from (8b, a) into the second equation in (7), we have

$$ds^2 = a^2\, d\theta^2[\sin^2 \theta + (1 - \cos \theta)^2]$$
$$= 2a^2\, d\theta^2(1 - \cos \theta)$$

and

$$ds = a\sqrt{2}\,\sqrt{1 - \cos \theta}\, d\theta.$$

To integrate the expression on the right, we substitute

$$1 - \cos \theta = 2 \sin^2 \frac{\theta}{2}$$

so that

$$ds = 2a \left| \sin \frac{\theta}{2} \right| d\theta.$$

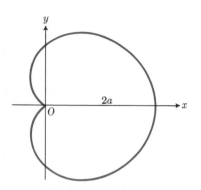

10–28   Cardioid: $r = a(1 + \cos \theta)$.

Since $\sin \theta/2$ is not negative when θ varies from 0 to 2π, we obtain

$$s = \int_0^{2\pi} 2a \sin \frac{\theta}{2} \, d\theta$$

$$= -4a \cos \frac{\theta}{2} \Big]_0^{2\pi} = 8a.$$

In letting θ range from 0 to 2π, we start at the cusp at the origin, go once around the smooth portion of the cardioid and return to the cusp. In doing this we do not pass *across* the cusp (Fig. 10–26). If, on the other hand, we take the cardioid $r = a(1 + \cos \theta)$, the appropriate procedure for avoiding the cusp (Fig. 10–28) is to let θ increase from $-\pi$ to π, or we may use the symmetry of the curve and calculate half of the total length by letting θ vary from 0 to π.

EXAMPLE 3.   The lemniscate

$$r^2 = 2a^2 \cos 2\theta$$

is revolved about the y-axis. Find the area of the surface generated.

Solution.   An element of arc length ds (Fig. 10–29) generates a portion of surface area

$$dS = 2\pi x \, ds,$$

where

$$x = r \cos \theta, \qquad ds = \sqrt{dr^2 + r^2 \, d\theta^2}.$$

That is,

$$dS = 2\pi r \cos \theta \sqrt{dr^2 + r^2 \, d\theta^2} = 2\pi \cos \theta \sqrt{r^2 \, dr^2 + r^4 \, d\theta^2}.$$

From the equation of the curve, we get

$$r \, dr = -2a^2 \sin 2\theta \, d\theta.$$

Then

$$(r^2 \, dr^2 + r^4 \, d\theta^2) = (2a^2 \, d\theta)^2 (\sin^2 2\theta + \cos^2 2\theta)$$

and

$$dS = 4\pi a^2 \cos \theta \, d\theta.$$

10–29   Lemniscate: $r^2 = 2a^2 \cos 2\theta$.

The total surface area is generated by the loop of the lemniscate to the right of the y-axis between $\theta = -\pi/4$ and $\theta = +\pi/4$, so that

$$S = \int_{-\pi/4}^{\pi/4} 4\pi a^2 \cos\theta \, d\theta = 4\pi a^2 \sqrt{2}.$$

PROBLEMS

1. For the hyperbolic spiral $r\theta = a$ show that $\psi = 135°$ when $\theta = 1$ radian, and that $\psi \to 90°$ as the spiral winds around the origin. Sketch the curve and indicate ψ for $\theta = 1$ radian.

2. Show, by reference to a figure, that the angle β between the tangents to two curves at a point of intersection may be found from the formula

$$\tan\beta = \frac{\tan\psi_2 - \tan\psi_1}{1 + \tan\psi_2 \tan\psi_1}.$$

When will the two curves intersect orthogonally?

3. Find a point of intersection of the parabolas

$$r = \frac{1}{1 - \cos\theta} \quad \text{and} \quad r = \frac{3}{1 + \cos\theta}$$

and find the angle between the tangents to these curves at this point.

4. Find points on the cardioid $r = a(1 + \cos\theta)$ where the tangent line is horizontal.

5. Find the length of the cardioid $r = a(1 + \cos\theta)$. [*Hint.* $\int \sqrt{1 + \cos\theta} \, d\theta = \int \sqrt{2} \, |\cos\theta/2| \, d\theta.$]

6. A thin, uniform wire is bent into the shape of the cardioid $r = a(1 + \cos\theta)$. Find its center of gravity $(\bar{x}, \bar{y})$. [*Hint.* $\int \cos\theta \cos\theta/2 \, d\theta$ can be evaluated by substituting $\cos\theta = 1 - 2\sin^2\theta/2$ and then letting $u = \sin\theta/2$.]

7. The lemniscate $r^2 = 2a^2 \cos 2\theta$ is rotated about the x-axis. Find the area of the surface generated.

8. Find the length of the curve $r = a\sin^2\theta/2$ from $\theta = 0$ to $\theta = \pi$. Sketch the curve.

9. Find the length of the parabolic spiral $r = a\theta^2$ between $\theta = 0$ and $\theta = \pi$. Sketch the curve.

10. Find the length of the curve $r = a\sin^3\theta/3$ between $\theta = 0$ and $\theta = \pi$. Sketch the curve.

11. Find the surface area generated by rotating the curve $r = 2a\cos\theta$ about the line $\theta = \pi/2$. Sketch.

The area AOB in Fig. 10–30 is bounded by the rays $\theta = \alpha$, $\theta = \beta$, and the curve $r = f(\theta)$. We imagine the angle AOB as being divided into n parts

$$\Delta\theta = \frac{\beta - \alpha}{n},$$

10–5

PLANE AREAS IN POLAR COORDINATES

10–30　To derive a formula for the area swept out by the radius vector OP as P moves from A to B along the curve, the area is divided into sectors.

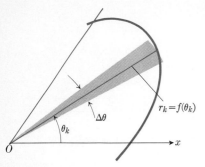

10–31   For some θ_k between θ and $\theta + \Delta\theta$, the area of the shaded circular sector just equals the area of the sector *POQ* bounded by the curve shown in Fig. 10–30.

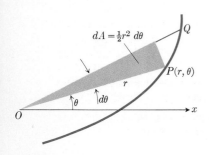

10–32   The area of the sector *POQ* is approximated by the area of the shaded circular sector.

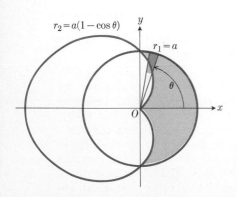

10–33   The shaded area is obtained from the integral $\int_{-\pi/2}^{\pi/2} \frac{1}{2}(r_1^2 - r_2^2)\, d\theta$.

and we approximate the area in a typical sector *POQ* by the area of a *circular sector* of radius *r* and central angle $\Delta\theta$ (Fig. 10–31). That is,

$$\text{Area of } POQ \approx \tfrac{1}{2}r^2\, \Delta\theta,$$

and hence the entire area *AOB* is approximately

$$\sum_{\theta=\alpha}^{\beta} \tfrac{1}{2}r^2\, \Delta\theta.$$

In fact, if the function $r = f(\theta)$ which represents the polar curve is a continuous function of θ for $\alpha \le \theta \le \beta$, then there is a θ_k between θ and $\theta + \Delta\theta$ such that the circular sector of radius

$$r_k = f(\theta_k)$$

and central angle $\Delta\theta$ gives the *exact* area of *POQ* (Fig. 10–31). Then the entire area is given exactly by

$$A = \sum \tfrac{1}{2}r_k^2\, \Delta\theta = \sum \tfrac{1}{2}[f(\theta_k)]^2\, \Delta\theta.$$

If we let $\Delta\theta \to 0$, we may apply the Fundamental Theorem of the integral calculus and obtain

$$A = \lim_{\Delta\theta \to 0} \sum \tfrac{1}{2}[f(\theta_k)]^2\, \Delta\theta = \tfrac{1}{2}\int_{\alpha}^{\beta} [f(\theta)]^2\, d\theta,$$

or

$$A = \int_{\alpha}^{\beta} \tfrac{1}{2}r^2\, d\theta. \qquad (1)$$

This result may also be remembered as the integral of the differential element of area (Fig. 10–32):

$$dA = \tfrac{1}{2}r^2\, d\theta,$$

taken between the appropriate limits on θ.

EXAMPLE.   Find the area that is inside the circle $r = a$ and outside the cardioid $r = a(1 - \cos\theta)$. (See Fig. 10–33.)

Solution.   We take a representative element of area

$$dA = dA_1 - dA_2,$$

where

$$dA_1 = \tfrac{1}{2}r_1^2\, d\theta, \qquad dA_2 = \tfrac{1}{2}r_2^2\, d\theta$$

with

$$r_1 = a, \qquad r_2 = a(1 - \cos\theta).$$

Such elements of area belong to the region inside the circle and outside the cardioid provided θ lies between

$$-\frac{\pi}{2} \quad \text{and} \quad +\frac{\pi}{2},$$

where the curves intersect. Hence

$$A = \int_{-\pi/2}^{\pi/2} \tfrac{1}{2}(r_1^2 - r_2^2) \, d\theta$$

$$= \int_{-\pi/2}^{\pi/2} \frac{a^2}{2} (2 \cos \theta - \cos^2 \theta) \, d\theta$$

$$= a^2 \int_{-\pi/2}^{\pi/2} \cos \theta \, d\theta - \frac{a^2}{2} \int_{-\pi/2}^{\pi/2} \frac{1 + \cos 2\theta}{2} \, d\theta$$

$$= a^2 \left(2 - \frac{\pi}{4} \right).$$

As a check against gross errors, we observe that this is roughly 80 percent of the area of a semicircle of radius a, and this seems reasonable when we look at the area in Fig. 10–33.

PROBLEMS

[*Note.* The trigonometric identities

$$\sin^2 \theta = \tfrac{1}{2}(1 - \cos 2\theta), \qquad \cos^2 \theta = \tfrac{1}{2}(1 + \cos 2\theta)$$

should be used to evaluate $\int \sin^2 \theta \, d\theta$ and $\int \cos^2 \theta \, d\theta$ in certain of the problems that follow.]

1. Find the total area inside the cardioid $r = a(1 + \cos \theta)$.

2. Find the total area inside the circle $r = 2a \sin \theta$.

3. Find the total area inside the lemniscate $r^2 = 2a^2 \cos 2\theta$.

4. Find that portion of the area inside the lemniscate $r^2 = 2a^2 \cos 2\theta$ that is not included in the circle $r = a$. Sketch.

5. Find the area inside the curve $r = a(2 + \cos \theta)$.

6. Find the area common to the circles $r = 2a \cos \theta$ and $r = 2a \sin \theta$. Sketch.

7. Find the area inside the circle $r = 3a \cos \theta$ and outside the cardioid $r = a(1 + \cos \theta)$.

8. Since the center of gravity of a triangle is located on a median at a distance $\tfrac{2}{3}$ of the way from a vertex to the opposite base, the lever arm for the moment about the x-axis of the area of triangle POQ in Fig. 10–30 is $\tfrac{2}{3}r \sin \theta + \epsilon$, where $\epsilon \to 0$ as $\Delta\theta \to 0$. Deduce that the center of gravity of the area AOB in the figure is given by

$$\bar{y} = \frac{\int \tfrac{2}{3} r \sin \theta \cdot \tfrac{1}{2} r^2 \, d\theta}{\int \tfrac{1}{2} r^2 \, d\theta}$$

and similarly,

$$\bar{x} = \frac{\int \tfrac{2}{3} r \cos \theta \cdot \tfrac{1}{2} r^2 \, d\theta}{\int \tfrac{1}{2} r^2 \, d\theta},$$

with limits $\theta = \alpha$ to $\theta = \beta$ on all integrals.

9. Use the results of Problem 8 to find the center of gravity of the area bounded by the cardioid $r = a(1 + \cos \theta)$.

10. Use the results of Problem 8 to find the center of gravity of the area of a semicircle of radius a.

REVIEW QUESTIONS AND EXERCISES

1. Make a diagram to show the standard relations between cartesian coordinates (x, y) and polar coordinates (r, θ). Express each set of coordinates in terms of the other kind.

2. If a point has polar coordinates (r_1, θ_1), what other polar coordinates represent the same point?

3. What is the expression for area between curves in polar coordinates?

4. What is the expression for length of arc of a curve in polar coordinates? For area of a surface of revolution?

5. What are some criteria for symmetry of a curve if its polar coordinates satisfy the equation $r = f(\theta)$? Illustrate your discussion with specific examples.

6. An artificial satellite is in an orbit that passes over the North and South Poles of the earth. When it is over the North Pole it is at the highest point of its orbit, 1000 miles above the earth's surface. Above the South Pole it is at the lowest point of its orbit, 300 miles above the earth's surface. (a) Assuming that the orbit (with reference to the earth) is an ellipse with one focus at the center of the earth, find its eccentricity. (Take the diameter of the earth to be 8000 miles.) (b) Using the north–south axis of the earth as polar axis, and the center of the earth as origin, find a polar equation of the orbit.

MISCELLANEOUS PROBLEMS

Discuss and sketch each of the curves in Problems 1–13 (where a is a positive constant).

1. $r = a\theta$
2. $r = a(1 + \cos 2\theta)$
3. a) $r = a \sec \theta$ b) $r = a \csc \theta$
   c) $r = a \sec \theta + a \csc \theta$
4. $r = a \sin \left(\theta + \dfrac{\pi}{3}\right)$
5. $r^2 + 2r(\cos \theta + \sin \theta) = 7$
6. $r = a \cos \theta - a \sin \theta$ 7. $r \cos \dfrac{\theta}{2} = a$
8. $r^2 = a^2 \sin \theta$ 9. $r^2 = 2a^2 \sin 2\theta$
10. $r = a(1 - 2 \sin 3\theta)$ 11. a) $r = \cos 2\theta$
    b) $r^2 = \cos 2\theta$
12. a) $r = 1 + \cos \theta$ b) $r = \dfrac{1}{1 + \cos \theta}$
13. a) $r = \dfrac{2}{1 - \cos \theta}$ b) $r = \dfrac{2}{1 + \sin \theta}$

14. Sketch and discuss the graph whose equation in polar coordinates is

$$r = 1 - \tan^2 \theta.$$

Show that it has no vertical asymptotes.

Sketch each of the pairs of curves in Problems 15–20, and find all points of intersection and the angle between their tangents at each point of intersection.

15. $r = a, \quad r = 2a \sin \theta$
16. $r = a, \quad r = a(1 - \sin \theta)$
17. $r = a \sec \theta, \quad r = 2a \sin \theta$
18. $r = a \cos \theta, \quad r = a(1 + \cos \theta)$
19. $r = a(1 + \cos 2\theta), \quad r = a \cos 2\theta$
20. $r^2 = 4 \cos 2\theta, \quad r^2 = \sec 2\theta$

21. Find the equation, in polar coordinates, of a parabola whose focus is at $r = 0$ and whose vertex is at $r = 1, \theta = 0$.

22. Find the polar equation of the straight line with intercepts a and b on the lines $\theta = 0, \theta = \pi/2$.

23. Find the equation of a circle with center on the line $\theta = \pi$, of radius a, and passing through the origin.

24. Find the polar equation of a parabola with focus at the origin and vertex at $(a, \pi/4)$.

25. Find the polar equation of an ellipse with one focus at the origin, the other at $(2, 0)$, and a vertex at $(4, 0)$.

26. Find the polar equation of a hyperbola with one focus at the origin, center at $(2, \pi/2)$, and vertex at $(1, \pi/2)$.

27. Three LORAN stations are located (in polar coordinates) at $(a, 0)$, $(0, 0)$, and $(a, \pi/4)$. Radio signals are sent out from the three stations simultaneously. A ship receiving the signals notes that the signals from the second and third stations arrive $a/2v$ sec later than that from the first. If v is the velocity of a radio signal, what is the location of the ship in polar coordinates?

28. Show that the parabolas $r = a/(1 + \cos \theta)$, $r = b/(1 - \cos \theta)$ are orthogonal at each point of intersection $(ab \neq 0)$.

29. Find the angle between the line $\theta = \pi/2$ and the cardioid $r = a(1 - \cos \theta)$ at their intersection.

30. Find the angle between the line $r = 3 \sec \theta$ and the curve $r = 4(1 + \cos \theta)$ at one of their intersections.

31. Find the slope of the tangent line to the curve $r = a \tan (\theta/2)$ at $\theta = \pi/2$.

32. Check that the two curves $r = 1/(1 - \cos \theta)$ and $r = 3/(1 + \cos \theta)$ intersect at the point $(2, \pi/3)$. Find the angle between the tangents to these curves at this point.

33. The equation $r^2 = 2 \csc 2\theta$ represents a curve in polar coordinates. (a) Sketch the curve. (b) Find the equation of the curve in rectangular coordinates. (c) Find the angle at which the curve intersects the line $\theta = \pi/4$.

34. A given curve cuts all rays $\theta = $ constant at the constant angle α.

a) Show that the area bounded by the curve and two rays $\theta = \theta_1, \theta = \theta_2$, is proportional to $r_2^2 - r_1^2$, where (r_1, θ_1) and (r_2, θ_2) are polar coordinates of the ends of the arc of the curve between these rays. Find the factor of proportionality.

b) Show that the length of the arc of the curve in part (a) is proportional to $r_2 - r_1$ and find the proportionality constant.

35. The cardioid $r = a(1 - \cos \theta)$ is rotated about the initial line.

a) Find the area of the surface generated. [*Hint.* You may use the fact that $\sin \theta = 2 \sin (\theta/2) \cos (\theta/2)$, and $1 - \cos \theta = 2 \sin^2 (\theta/2)$ to evaluate your integral.]
b) Set up the definite integral (or integrals) that would be used to find the centroid of the area in part (a).
c) Find the centroid of the area in part (a).

36. Let P be a point on the hyperbola $r^2 \sin 2\theta = 2a^2$. Show that the triangle formed by OP, the tangent at P, and the initial line is isosceles.

37. Verify that the formula for finding the length of a curve in polar form gives the correct result for the circumference of the circles (a) $r = a$, (b) $r = a \cos \theta$, (c) $r = a \sin \theta$.

38. If $r = a \cos^3 (\theta/3)$, show that $ds = a \cos^2 (\theta/3) d\theta$ and determine the perimeter of the curve.

39. Find the area that lies inside the curve $r = 2a \cos 2\theta$ and outside the curve $r = a\sqrt{2}$.

40. Sketch the curves

$$r = 2a \cos^2 (\theta/2) \quad \text{and} \quad r = 2a \sin^2 (\theta/2),$$

and find the area they have in common.

Find the total area enclosed by each of the curves in Problems 41–47.

41. $r^2 = a^2 \cos 2\theta$ **42.** $r = a(2 - \cos \theta)$

43. $r = a(1 + \cos 2\theta)$ **44.** $r = 2a \cos \theta$

45. $r = 2a \sin 3\theta$ **46.** $r^2 = 2a^2 \sin 3\theta$

47. $r^2 = 2a^2 \cos^2 (\theta/2)$

48. Find the area that is inside the cardioid $r = a(1 + \sin \theta)$ and outside the circle $r = a \sin \theta$.

VECTORS AND PARAMETRIC EQUATIONS

11–1

VECTOR COMPONENTS AND THE UNIT VECTORS i AND j

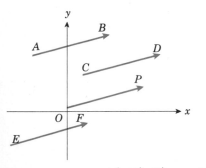

11–1 The arrows $\overrightarrow{AB}$, $\overrightarrow{CD}$, $\overrightarrow{OP}$, and $\overrightarrow{EF}$ shown here have the same direction and the same length. They all represent the same vector, and we write $\overrightarrow{AB} = \overrightarrow{CD} = \overrightarrow{OP} = \overrightarrow{EF}$.

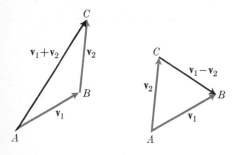

11–2 The sum (a) and difference (b) of two vectors, v_1 and v_2.

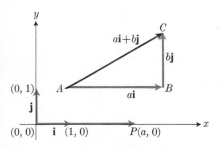

11–3 The vector $\overrightarrow{AC}$ expressed as a multiple of **i** plus a multiple of **j**.

Some physical quantities, like length and mass, are completely determined when their magnitudes are given in terms of specific units. Such quantities are called *scalars*. Other quantities, like forces and velocities, in which the direction as well as the magnitude is important, are called *vectors*. It is customary to represent a vector by a directed line segment whose direction represents the direction of the vector and whose length, in terms of some chosen unit, represents its magnitude.

We shall ordinarily deal with "free vectors," meaning that a vector is free to move about under parallel displacements. We say that two vectors are *equal* if they have the same direction and the same magnitude. See Fig. 11–1.

Addition

Two vectors, v_1 and v_2, may be added geometrically by drawing a representative of v_1, say from A to B as in Fig. 11–2(a), and then a vector equal to v_2 starting from the terminal point of v_1.* In Fig. 11–2(a), $v_2 = \overrightarrow{BC}$. The sum $v_1 + v_2$ is then the vector from the starting point A of v_1 to the terminal point C of v_2. That is, if

$$v_1 = \overrightarrow{AB}, \qquad \text{and} \qquad v_2 = \overrightarrow{BC},$$

then

$$v_1 + v_2 = \overrightarrow{AB} + \overrightarrow{BC} = \overrightarrow{AC}.$$

The most satisfactory algebra of vectors is based on a representation of each vector in terms of its components parallel to the axes of a cartesian coordinate system. This is accomplished by using the same unit of length on the two axes, with vectors of unit length along the axes used as basic vectors in terms of which the other vectors in the plane may be expressed. Along the x-axis we choose the vector **i** from $(0, 0)$ to $(1, 0)$, as in Fig. 11–3. Along the y-axis we choose the vector **j** from $(0, 0)$ to $(0, 1)$. Then a**i**, a being a scalar, represents a vector parallel to the x-axis, having magnitude $|a|$ and pointing to the right if a is positive, to the left if a is negative. Similarly, b**j** is a vector parallel to the y-axis and having the same direction as **j** if b is positive, or the opposite direction if b is negative.

The equality of two vectors may be expressed algebraically by saying that

$$a\mathbf{i} + b\mathbf{j} = a'\mathbf{i} + b'\mathbf{j} \quad \text{if and only if} \quad a = a' \text{ and } b = b'.$$

That is, two vectors are equal if and only if their corresponding *components* are equal. Thus, in Fig. 11–3, the vector $\overrightarrow{AB}$ and the vector $\overrightarrow{OP}$ from $(0, 0)$ to $(a, 0)$ are both equal to a**i**.

Vectors may be added algebraically by adding their components in the following way. In Fig. 11–3, we see that $a\mathbf{i} + b\mathbf{j}$ is the vector hypotenuse of a right triangle whose vector sides are a**i** and b**j**. If two vectors v_1 and v_2 are given in terms of components,

---

* Vectors are indicated in print by bold-faced Roman letters. In handwritten work, however, it is customary to indicate vectors by drawing small arrows over the letters that represent them.

$$\mathbf{v}_1 = a_1\mathbf{i} + b_1\mathbf{j}, \qquad \mathbf{v}_2 = a_2\mathbf{i} + b_2\mathbf{j},$$

then

$$\mathbf{v}_1 + \mathbf{v}_2 = (a_1 + a_2)\mathbf{i} + (b_1 + b_2)\mathbf{j} \qquad (1)$$

has x- and y-components obtained by adding the x- and y-components of $\mathbf{v}_1$ and $\mathbf{v}_2$. See Fig. 11–4.

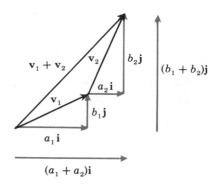

11–4 If $\mathbf{v}_1 = a_1\mathbf{i} + b_1\mathbf{j}$ and $\mathbf{v}_2 = a_2\mathbf{i} + b_2\mathbf{j}$, then $\mathbf{v}_1 + \mathbf{v}_2 = (a_1 + a_2)\mathbf{i} + (b_1 + b_2)\mathbf{j}$.

Subtraction

To *subtract* one vector $\mathbf{v}_2$ from another vector $\mathbf{v}_1$ geometrically, we draw them both from a common initial point and then draw the vector from the tip of $\mathbf{v}_2$ to the tip of $\mathbf{v}_1$. Thus in Fig. 11–2(b), we have

$$\mathbf{v}_1 = \overrightarrow{AB}, \qquad \mathbf{v}_2 = \overrightarrow{AC},$$

and

$$\mathbf{v}_1 - \mathbf{v}_2 = -\mathbf{v}_2 + \mathbf{v}_1 = \overrightarrow{CA} + \overrightarrow{AB} = \overrightarrow{CB}.$$

In terms of components, vector subtraction follows the simple algebraic law

$$\mathbf{v}_1 - \mathbf{v}_2 = (a_1 - a_2)\mathbf{i} + (b_1 - b_2)\mathbf{j}, \qquad (2)$$

which says that corresponding components are subtracted.

Length of a Vector

The length of the vector $\mathbf{v} = a\mathbf{i} + b\mathbf{j}$ is usually denoted by $|\mathbf{v}|$, which may be read "the magnitude of v." Figure 11–3 shows that $\mathbf{v}$ is the hypotenuse of a right triangle whose legs have lengths $|a|$ and $|b|$. Hence we may apply the theorem of Pythagoras to obtain

$$|\mathbf{v}| = |a\mathbf{i} + b\mathbf{j}| = \sqrt{a^2 + b^2}.$$

Multiplication by Scalars

The algebraic operation of multiplying a vector $\mathbf{v} = a\mathbf{i} + b\mathbf{j}$ by a scalar c is also simple, namely

$$c(a\mathbf{i} + b\mathbf{j}) = (ca)\mathbf{i} + (cb)\mathbf{j}.$$

Note how the unit vectors $\mathbf{i}$ and $\mathbf{j}$ allow us to keep the components separated from one another when we operate on vectors algebraically. Geometrically, $c\mathbf{v}$ is a vector whose length is $|c|$ times the length of $\mathbf{v}$:

$$|c\mathbf{v}| = |(ca)\mathbf{i} + (cb)\mathbf{j}| = \sqrt{(ca)^2 + (cb)^2} = |c|\sqrt{a^2 + b^2} = |c|\,|\mathbf{v}|. \qquad (3)$$

The direction of $c\mathbf{v}$ agrees with that of $\mathbf{v}$ if c is positive, and is opposite to that of $\mathbf{v}$ if c is negative (Fig. 11–5). If $c = 0$, the vector $c\mathbf{v}$ has no direction.

11–5 Scalar multiples of $\mathbf{v}$.

Zero Vector

Any vector whose length is zero is called the *zero vector*, **0**. The vector

$$a\mathbf{i} + b\mathbf{j} = \mathbf{0}, \qquad \text{if and only if} \quad a = b = 0.$$

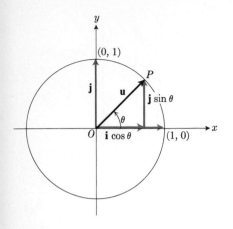

11-6 $\mathbf{u} = \mathbf{i} \cos \theta + \mathbf{j} \sin \theta$.

Unit Vector

Any vector $\mathbf{u}$ whose length is equal to the unit of length used along the coordinate axes is called a *unit vector*. If $\mathbf{u}$ is the unit vector obtained by rotating $\mathbf{i}$ through an angle θ in the positive direction, then (Fig. 11-6) $\mathbf{u}$ has a horizontal component

$$u_x = \cos \theta$$

and a vertical component

$$u_y = \sin \theta,$$

so that

$$\mathbf{u} = \mathbf{i} \cos \theta + \mathbf{j} \sin \theta. \tag{4}$$

If we allow the angle θ in Eq. (4) to vary from 0 to 2π, then the point P in Fig. 11-6 traces the unit circle $x^2 + y^2 = 1$ once in the counterclockwise direction. Every unit vector in the plane is described by Eq. (4) for some value of θ.

To find a unit vector in the direction of a given nonzero vector $\mathbf{v}$, we divide $\mathbf{v}$ by its own length, $|\mathbf{v}|$. This amounts to multiplying $\mathbf{v}$ by the scalar $1/|\mathbf{v}|$. The result has length 1 because

$$\left| \frac{\mathbf{v}}{|\mathbf{v}|} \right| = \frac{1}{|\mathbf{v}|} |\mathbf{v}| = 1. \tag{5}$$

Two vectors are said to be *parallel* if the line segments representing them are parallel. Similarly, a vector is parallel to a line if the segments that represent the vector are parallel to the line. When we talk of a vector's being *tangent* or *normal* to a curve at a point, we mean that the vector is parallel to the line that is tangent or normal to the curve at the point. The next example shows how such a vector may be found.

EXAMPLE 1. Find unit vectors tangent and normal to the curve $y = \frac{1}{2}x^3 + \frac{1}{2}$ at the point $(1, 1)$.

Solution. The slope of the line tangent to the curve at the point $(1, 1)$ is

$$y' = \frac{3x^2}{2} \bigg|_{x=1} = \frac{3}{2}.$$

We find a unit vector with this slope. The vector $\mathbf{v} = 2\mathbf{i} + 3\mathbf{j}$ has slope $\frac{3}{2}$ (Fig. 11-7), as does every nonzero multiple of $\mathbf{v}$. To find a multiple of $\mathbf{v}$ that is a unit vector, we divide $\mathbf{v}$ by its length,

$$|\mathbf{v}| = \sqrt{2^2 + 3^2} = \sqrt{13}.$$

This produces the unit vector

$$\mathbf{u} = \frac{\mathbf{v}}{|\mathbf{v}|} = \frac{2}{\sqrt{13}}\mathbf{i} + \frac{3}{\sqrt{13}}\mathbf{j}.$$

The vector $\mathbf{u}$ is tangent to the curve at $(1, 1)$ because it has the same direction as $\mathbf{v}$. Of course, the vector

$$-\mathbf{u} = -\frac{2}{\sqrt{13}}\mathbf{i} - \frac{3}{\sqrt{13}}\mathbf{j},$$

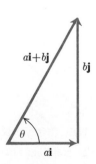

11-7 If $a \neq 0$, the vector $a\mathbf{i} + b\mathbf{j}$ has slope $b/a = \tan \theta$.

which points in the direction opposite to **u**, is also tangent to the curve at (1, 1). Without some additional requirement, there is no reason to prefer one of these vectors to the other.

To find unit vectors normal to the curve at (1, 1), we look for unit vectors whose slopes are the negative reciprocal of the slope of **u**. This is quickly done by interchanging the components of **u** and changing the sign of one of them. We obtain

$$\mathbf{n} = \frac{3}{\sqrt{13}}\mathbf{i} - \frac{2}{\sqrt{13}}\mathbf{j}, \quad \text{and} \quad -\mathbf{n} = -\frac{3}{\sqrt{13}}\mathbf{i} + \frac{2}{\sqrt{13}}\mathbf{j}.$$

Again, either one will do. Both are normal to the curve at the point (1, 1).

PROBLEMS

In Problems 1–10 express each of the vectors in the form $a\mathbf{i} + b\mathbf{j}$. Indicate all quantities graphically.

1. $\overrightarrow{P_1 P_2}$ if P_1 is the point (1, 3) and P_2 is the point (2, −1).

2. $\overrightarrow{OP_3}$ if O is the origin and P_3 is the midpoint of the vector $\overrightarrow{P_1 P_2}$ joining $P_1(2, -1)$ and $P_2(-4, 3)$.

3. The vector from the point $A(2, 3)$ to the origin.

4. The sum of the vectors $\overrightarrow{AB}$ and $\overrightarrow{CD}$, given the four points $A(1, -1)$, $B(2, 0)$, $C(-1, 3)$, and $D(-2, 2)$.

5. A unit vector making an angle of 30° with the positive x-axis.

6. The unit vector obtained by rotating **j** through 120° in the clockwise direction.

7. A unit vector having the same direction as the vector $3\mathbf{i} - 4\mathbf{j}$.

8. A unit vector tangent to the curve $y = x^2$ at the point (2, 4).

9. A unit vector normal to the curve $y = x^2$ at the point $P(2, 4)$ and pointing from P toward the concave side of the curve (that is, an "inner" normal).

10. A unit vector tangent to the unit circle. [*Hint.* See Eq. (4).]

Find the lengths of each of the following vectors and the angle that each makes with the positive x-axis.

11. $\mathbf{i} + \mathbf{j}$ **12.** $2\mathbf{i} - 3\mathbf{j}$ **13.** $\sqrt{3}\,\mathbf{i} + \mathbf{j}$
14. $-2\mathbf{i} + 3\mathbf{j}$ **15.** $5\mathbf{i} + 12\mathbf{j}$ **16.** $-5\mathbf{i} - 12\mathbf{j}$

17. Let A, B, C, D be the vertices, in order, of a quadrilateral. Let A', B', C', D' be the midpoints of the sides AB, BC, CD, and DA, in order. Prove that $A'B'C'D'$ is a parallelogram. [*Hint.* First show that $\overrightarrow{A'B'} = \overrightarrow{D'C'} = \frac{1}{2}\overrightarrow{AC}$.]

18. Using vectors, show that the diagonals of a parallelogram bisect each other. [*Method.* Let A be one vertex and let M and N be the midpoints of the diagonals. Then show that $\overrightarrow{AM} = \overrightarrow{AN}$.]

In newtonian mechanics, the motion of a particle in a plane is usually described by a pair of differential equations

$$F_x = \frac{d(mv_x)}{dt}, \qquad F_y = \frac{d(mv_y)}{dt} \tag{1}$$

that express Newton's second law of motion

$$\mathbf{F} = \frac{d(m\mathbf{v})}{dt} \tag{2}$$

11-2

PARAMETRIC EQUATIONS IN KINEMATICS

in parametric form. Here, **F** is a vector that represents a force acting on a particle of mass m at time t. The vector **v** is the velocity vector of the particle

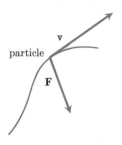

The force and velocity vectors of the motion of a particle in a plane might look like this at a particular time t.

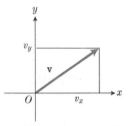

The components v_x and v_y of $\mathbf{v}$

The components F_x and F_y of $\mathbf{F}$

11–8 Motion of a particle in a plane.

at time t (Fig. 11–8). The quantities F_x and F_y are the x- and y-components of $\mathbf{F}$, while v_x and v_y are the components of $\mathbf{v}$.

If we know the position and velocity of the particle at some given instant, then the position of the particle at all later instants can usually be found by integrating Eqs. (1) with respect to time. The constants of integration are determined from given initial conditions. The result is another pair of parametric equations

$$x = f(t), \qquad y = g(t) \tag{3}$$

that give the coordinates x and y of the particle as functions of t.

The equations in (3) contain more information about the motion of the particle than the cartesian equation

$$y = F(x) \tag{4}$$

that we get from (3) by eliminating t. The parametric equations tell where the particle goes and *when* it gets to any given place, whereas the cartesian equation only tells the curve along which the particle travels. (Sometimes, too, a parametric representation of a curve is all that is possible; that is, a parameter cannot always be eliminated in practice.)

EXAMPLE 1. A projectile is fired with an initial velocity v_0 ft/sec at an angle of elevation α. Assuming that gravity is the only force acting on the projectile, find its motion.

Solution. We introduce coordinate axes with the origin at the point where the projectile begins its motion (Fig. 11–9). The distance traveled by the projectile over the ground is measured along the x-axis, and the height of the projectile above the ground is measured along the y-axis. At any time t, the projectile's position is given by a coordinate pair $x(t)$, $y(t)$, that we assume to be differentiable functions of t. If we measure distance in feet and time in seconds, with $t = 0$ at the instant the projectile is fired, then the initial conditions for the projectile's motion are

$$t = 0 \text{ sec}, \qquad x = 0 \text{ ft}, \qquad y = 0 \text{ ft},$$

$$v_x(0) = \frac{dx}{dt}(0) = v_0 \cos \alpha \quad \text{ft/sec}, \qquad v_y(0) = \frac{dy}{dt}(0) = v_0 \sin \alpha \quad \text{ft/sec}. \tag{5}$$

11–9 Ideal projectiles move along parabolas. The schematic figure here shows the lengths of the velocity vector and its components, first at time $t = 0$, and then later in the flight.

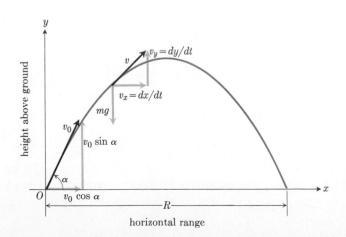

If the projectile is to travel only a few miles, and not go very high, it will cause no serious error to model the force of gravity with a constant vector $\mathbf{F}$ that points straight down. Its x- and y-components are

$$F_x = 0 \text{ lb}, \qquad F_y = -mg \text{ lb},$$

where m is the mass of the projectile and g is the acceleration of gravity. With these values for F_x and F_y, the equations in (1) become

$$0 = m\frac{d^2x}{dt^2}, \qquad -mg = m\frac{d^2y}{dt^2}. \qquad \textbf{(6)}$$

To solve these equations for x and y, we integrate each one twice. This introduces four constants of integration, which may be evaluated by using the initial conditions (5). From the first equation in (6), we get

$$\frac{d^2x}{dt^2} = 0 \text{ ft/sec}^2, \qquad \frac{dx}{dt} = c_1 \text{ ft/sec}, \qquad x = c_1 t + c_2 \text{ ft}, \qquad \textbf{(7a)}$$

and from the second equation in (6),

$$\frac{d^2y}{dt^2} = -g \text{ ft/sec}^2, \qquad \frac{dy}{dt} = -gt + c_3 \text{ ft/sec}, \qquad y = -\tfrac{1}{2}gt^2 + c_3 t + c_4 \text{ ft}. \qquad \textbf{(7b)}$$

From the initial conditions, we find

$$c_1 = v_0 \cos \alpha \text{ ft/sec}, \qquad c_2 = 0 \text{ ft}, \qquad c_3 = v_0 \sin \alpha \text{ ft/sec}, \qquad c_4 = 0 \text{ ft}. \qquad \textbf{(7c)}$$

The position of the projectile t seconds after firing is

$$x = (v_0 \cos \alpha)\, t \text{ ft}, \qquad y = -\tfrac{1}{2}gt^2 + (v_0 \sin \alpha)t \text{ ft}. \qquad \textbf{(8)}$$

For a given angle of elevation α and a given muzzle velocity v_0, the position of the projectile at any time may be determined from the parametric equations in (8). These equations may be used to answer such questions as:

1. How high does the projectile rise?
2. How far away does the projectile land, and how does the horizontal range R vary with the angle of elevation?
3. What angle of elevation gives the maximum range?

First, the projectile will reach its highest point when its y-(vertical) velocity component is zero, that is, when

$$\frac{dy}{dt} = -gt + v_0 \sin \alpha = 0 \text{ ft/sec}$$

or

$$t = t_m = \frac{v_0 \sin \alpha}{g} \text{ sec}.$$

For this value of t, the value of y is

$$y_{\text{max}} = -\frac{1}{2} g(t_m)^2 + (v_0 \sin \alpha)t_m = \frac{(v_0 \sin \alpha)^2}{2g} \text{ ft}.$$

Second, to find R we first find the time when the projectile strikes the ground. That is, we find the value of t for which $y = 0$. We then find the value of x for this value of t:

$$y = t(-\tfrac{1}{2}gt + v_0 \sin \alpha) = 0 \text{ ft}$$

when

$$t = 0 \quad \text{or} \quad t = \frac{2v_0 \sin \alpha}{g} = 2t_m \text{ sec.}$$

Since $t = 0$ is the instant when the projectile is fired, $t = 2t_m$ is the time when the projectile hits the ground. The corresponding value of x is

$$R = (v_0 \cos \alpha)(2t_m) = v_0 \cos \alpha \frac{2v_0 \sin \alpha}{g} = \frac{v_0^2}{g} \sin 2\alpha \text{ ft.}$$

Finally, the formula just given for R shows that the maximum range for a given muzzle velocity is obtained when $\sin 2\alpha = 1$, or $\alpha = 45°$.

The cartesian equation of the path of the projectile is readily obtained from (8). We need only substitute

$$t = \frac{x}{v_0 \cos \alpha}$$

from the first into the second equation of (8) to eliminate t and obtain

$$y = -\left(\frac{g}{2v_0^2 \cos^2 \alpha}\right)x^2 + (\tan \alpha)x. \tag{9}$$

Since this equation is linear in y and quadratic in x, it represents a *parabola*. Thus the path of a projectile (neglecting air resistance) is a parabola.

Differential equations that take air resistance into account are usually too complicated for straightforward integration. The M.I.T. differential analyzers were used to solve such equations during War II to build up "range tables." In following moving targets, keeping track of *time* is of great importance, so that equations or tables that give x and y in terms of t are preferred over other forms.

PROBLEMS

In Problems 1–4, the projectile is assumed to obey the laws of motion discussed above, in which air resistance is neglected.

1. Find two values of the angle of elevation that will enable a projectile to reach a target on the same level as the gun and 25,000 feet distant from it if the initial velocity is 1000 ft/sec. Determine the times of flight corresponding to these two angles.

2. Show that doubling the initial velocity of a projectile multiplies both the maximum height and the range by a factor of four.

3. Show that a projectile attains three-quarters of its maximum height in one-half the time required to reach that maximum.

4. Suppose a target moving at the constant rate of a ft/sec is level with and b ft away from a gun at the instant the gun is fired. If the target moves in a horizontal line directly away from the gun, show that the muzzle velocity v_0 and angle of elevation α must satisfy the equation

$$v_0^2 \sin 2\alpha - 2av_0 \sin \alpha - bg = 0$$

if the projectile is to strike the target.

In Problems 5–7, find parametric equations and sketch the curve described by the point $P(x, y)$ for $t \geq 0$ if its coordinates satisfy the given differential equations and initial conditions.

5. $\dfrac{dx}{dt} = x, \quad \dfrac{dy}{dt} = -x^2; \quad t = 0, \quad x = 1, \quad y = -4.$

[*Hint.* Solve for x first.]

6. $\dfrac{dx}{dt} = y, \quad \dfrac{dy}{dt} = y^2; \quad t = 0, \quad x = 0,$
$$y = 1.$$

7. $\dfrac{dx}{dt} = \sqrt{1 - x^2}, \quad \dfrac{dy}{dt} = x^2; \quad t = 0, \quad x = 0,$
$$y = 1.$$

The solutions of differential equations of motion are not the only ways in which parametric equations arise. For example, we have already used the equations

$$x = a \cos \theta, \qquad y = a \sin \theta, \qquad 0 \leq \theta \leq 2\pi, \tag{1}$$

to represent the circle of radius a whose center is at the origin (Fig. 11–10). Similarly, the equations

$$x = a \cos \phi, \qquad y = b \sin \phi, \qquad 0 \leq \phi \leq 2\pi, \tag{2}$$

are parametric equations for the ellipse whose cartesian equation is

$$\frac{x^2}{a^2} + \frac{y^2}{b^2} = 1.$$

EXAMPLE 1. Find parametric equations for the parabola

$$y^2 = 4px. \tag{3}$$

Solution. The parabola can be parametrized in several ways. One way is to use the slope

$$t = \frac{dy}{dx}$$

of the tangent to the curve at (x, y) as a parameter (Fig. 11–11(a)). Since

$$2y \frac{dy}{dx} = 4p \qquad \text{or} \qquad \frac{dy}{dx} = \frac{2p}{y},$$

11-3

PARAMETRIC EQUATIONS IN ANALYTIC GEOMETRY

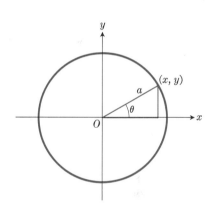

11–10 $x = a \cos \theta, y = a \sin \theta.$

11–11 Parametrizations of the parabola $y^2 = 4px.$

a)

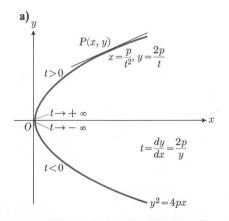

parameter t: slope of the tangent at P

b)

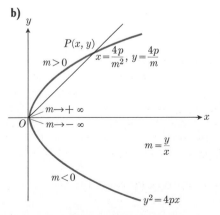

parameter m: slope of OP

the parametric equations in this case are

$$y = \frac{2p}{t}, \qquad x = \frac{p}{t^2}. \tag{4}$$

If we use the parameter

$$m = \frac{y}{x},$$

(Fig.11–11(b)), which is the slope of the line joining the origin to the point $P(x, y)$ on the parabola, we have

$$y^2 = m^2 x^2 \qquad \text{and} \qquad y^2 = 4px,$$

which lead to

$$x = \frac{4p}{m^2}, \qquad y = \frac{4p}{m} \tag{5}$$

as the parametric equations.

Sometimes the parametric equations of a curve and the cartesian equation are not coextensive.

EXAMPLE 2.   Suppose the parametric equations of a curve are

$$x = \cosh \theta, \qquad y = \sinh \theta. \tag{6}$$

Then the hyperbolic identity

$$\cosh^2 \theta - \sinh^2 \theta = 1$$

enables us to eliminate θ and write

$$x^2 - y^2 = 1 \tag{7}$$

as a cartesian equation of the curve. Closer scrutiny, however, shows that Eq. (7) *includes too much*, for $x = \cosh \theta$ is always positive. The parametric equations represent a curve lying wholly to the right of the y-axis, whereas the cartesian equation (7) represents both the right- and lefthand branches of the hyperbola (Fig. 11–12). The lefthand branch could be excluded by taking only positive values of x. That is,

$$x = \sqrt{1 + y^2} \tag{8}$$

does represent the curve given by (6).

EXAMPLE 3.   The curve whose parametric equations are

$$x = \cos 2\theta, \qquad y = \cos \theta, \tag{9}$$

lies within the square $-1 \le x \le 1,\ -1 \le y \le 1$. We may eliminate θ as follows:

$$x = \cos 2\theta = 2\cos^2 \theta - 1 = 2y^2 - 1.$$

Thus every point on the graph of (9) also lies on the curve

$$x = 2y^2 - 1. \tag{10}$$

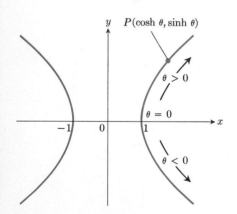

11–12   The parametric equations $x = \cosh \theta,\ y = \sinh \theta,\ -\infty < \theta < \infty$, give only the right branch of the hyperbola $x^2 - y^2 = 1$, because $\cosh \theta \ge 1$.

If we omit the restrictions

$$|x| \le 1, \qquad |y| \le 1,$$

then Eq. (10) represents the complete parabola

$$y^2 = \tfrac{1}{2}(x + 1)$$

shown in Fig. 11–13. The parametric equations, however, represent only the arc ABC. From (9), we see that the point starts at $A(1, 1)$ when $\theta = 0$, moves along AB to $B(-1, 0)$ as θ varies from 0 to $\pi/2$, and continues to $C(1, -1)$ as θ increases to π. As θ varies from π to 2π, the point traverses the arc CBA back to A. Since both x and y are periodic, x of period π and y of period 2π, further variations in θ result in retracing the same portion of the parabola.

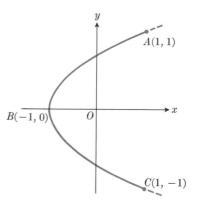

11–13 $x = \cos 2\theta$, $y = \cos \theta$.

EXAMPLE 4.   A wheel of radius a rolls along a horizontal straight line without slipping. Find the curve traced by a point P on a spoke of the wheel b units from its center. Such a curve is called a *trochoid* (one Greek word for wheel is *trochos*). When $b = a$, P is on the circumference and the curve is called a *cycloid*. This is like the path traveled by the head of a nail in a tire.

Solution.   In Fig. 11–14 we take the x-axis to be the line the wheel rolls along, with the y-axis through a low point of the trochoid. It is customary to use the angle ϕ through which CP has rotated as the parameter. Since the circle rolls without slipping, the distance OM that the wheel has moved horizontally is just equal to the circular arc $MN = a\phi$. (Roll the wheel back. Then N will fall at the origin O.) The xy-coordinates of C are therefore

$$h = a\phi, \qquad k = a. \tag{11}$$

11–14   Trochoid: $x = a\phi - b \sin \phi$, $y = a - b \cos \phi$.

We now introduce $x'y'$-axes parallel to the xy-axes and having their origin at C (Fig. 11–15). The xy- and $x'y'$-coordinates of P are related by the equations

$$x = h + x', \qquad y = k + y'. \tag{12}$$

From Fig. 11–15 we may immediately read

$$x' = b \cos \theta, \qquad y' = b \sin \theta,$$

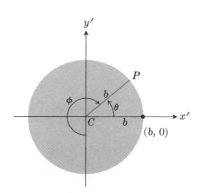

11–15   The $x'y'$-coordinates of P are $x' = b \cos \theta$, $y = b \sin \theta$.

or, since

$$\theta = \frac{3\pi}{2} - \phi,$$

$$x' = -b \sin \phi, \qquad y' = -b \cos \phi. \tag{13}$$

We substitute these results and Eqs. (12) into (11) and obtain

$$x = a\phi - b \sin \phi,$$

$$y = a - b \cos \phi \tag{14}$$

as parametric equations of the trochoid.

The cycloid (Fig. 11–16(a)),

$$x = a(\phi - \sin \phi), \qquad y = a(1 - \cos \phi), \tag{15}$$

obtained from (14) by taking $b = a$, is the most important special case.

Brachistochrones and Tautochrones

If we reflect both the cycloid and the y-axis across the x-axis, Eqs. (15) still apply, and the resulting curve (Fig. 11–16(b)) has several interesting properties, one of which we shall now discuss without proof. The proofs belong to a branch of mathematics known as the calculus of variations. Much of the fundamental theory of this subject is attributed to the Bernoulli brothers, John and James, who were friendly rivals and stimulated each other with mathematical problems in the form of challenges. One of these, the brachisto-chrone problem, was: Among all smooth curves joining two given points, to find that one along which a bead, subject only to the force of gravity, might slide *in the shortest time.*

The two points, labeled P_0 and P_1 in Fig. 11–17, may be taken to lie in a vertical plane at the origin and at (x_1, y_1), respectively. We can formulate the problem in mathematical terms as follows. The kinetic energy of the bead at the start is zero, since its velocity is zero. The work done by gravity in moving the particle from $(0, 0)$ to any point (x, y) is mgy and this must be equal to the change in kinetic energy; that is,

$$mgy = \tfrac{1}{2}mv^2 - \tfrac{1}{2}m(0)^2.$$

Thus the velocity

$$v = ds/dt$$

that the particle has when it reaches $P(x, y)$ is

$$v = \sqrt{2gy}.$$

That is,

$$\frac{ds}{dt} = \sqrt{2gy} \qquad \text{or} \qquad dt = \frac{ds}{\sqrt{2gy}} = \frac{\sqrt{1 + \left(\dfrac{dy}{dx}\right)^2}\, dx}{\sqrt{2gy}}.$$

a)

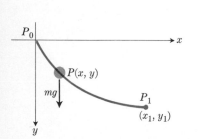

b)

11–16 Cycloid: $x = a(\phi - \sin \phi)$, $y = a(1 - \cos \phi)$.

11–17 A bead sliding down a cycloid.

The time t_1 required for the bead to slide from P_0 to P_1 depends upon the particular curve $y = f(x)$ along which it moves and is given by

$$t_1 = \int_0^{x_1} \sqrt{\frac{1 + (f'(x))^2}{2gf(x)}} \, dx. \tag{16}$$

The problem is *to find the curve* $y = f(x)$ that passes through the points $P_0(0, 0)$ and $P_1(x_1, y_1)$ and minimizes the value of the integral in Eq. (16). (*Brachistochrone* is derived from two Greek words that together mean "shortest time.")

At first sight, one might guess that the straight line joining P_0 and P_1 would also yield the shortest time, but a moment's reflection will cast some doubt on this conjecture, for there may be some gain in time by having the particle start to fall vertically at first, thereby building up its velocity more quickly than if it were to slide along an inclined path. With this increased velocity, one may be able to afford to travel over a longer path and still reach P_1 in a shorter time. The solution of the problem is beyond the present book, but the brachistochrone curve is actually an arc of a cycloid through P_0 and P_1, having a cusp at the origin.

If we write Eq. (16) in the equivalent form

$$t_1 = \int \sqrt{\frac{dx^2 + dy^2}{2gy}}$$

and then substitute Eqs. (15) into this, we obtain

$$t_1 = \int_{\phi=0}^{\phi_1} \sqrt{\frac{a^2(2 - 2\cos\phi)}{2ga(1 - \cos\phi)}} \, d\phi = \phi_1 \sqrt{\frac{a}{g}}$$

as the time required for the particle to slide from P_0 to P_1. The time required to reach the bottom of the arc is obtained by taking $\phi_1 = \pi$. Now it is a remarkable fact, which we shall soon demonstrate, that the time required to slide along the cycloid from $(0, 0)$ to the lowest point $(a\pi, 2a)$ is the same as the time required for the particle, starting from rest, to slide from *any intermediate point* of the arc, say (x_0, y_0), to $(a\pi, 2a)$. For the latter case, one has

$$v = \sqrt{2g(y - y_0)}$$

as the velocity at $P(x, y)$, and the time required is

$$T = \int_{\phi_0}^{\pi} \sqrt{\frac{a^2(2 - 2\cos\phi)}{2ag(\cos\phi_0 - \cos\phi)}} \, d\phi = \sqrt{\frac{a}{g}} \int_{\phi_0}^{\pi} \sqrt{\frac{1 - \cos\phi}{\cos\phi_0 - \cos\phi}} \, d\phi$$

$$= \sqrt{\frac{a}{g}} \int_{\phi_0}^{\pi} \sqrt{\frac{2\sin^2(\phi/2)}{[2\cos^2(\phi_0/2) - 1] - [2\cos^2(\phi/2) - 1]}} \, d\phi$$

$$= 2\sqrt{\frac{a}{g}} \left[-\sin^{-1}\frac{\cos(\phi/2)}{\cos(\phi_0/2)} \right]_{\phi_0}^{\pi} = 2\sqrt{\frac{a}{g}}(-\sin^{-1}0 + \sin^{-1}1) = \pi\sqrt{\frac{a}{g}}.$$

11-18 Beads released on the cycloid at
O, A, and B will take the same amount
of time to reach C.

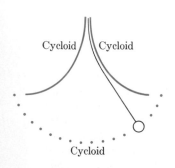

11-19 A flexible pendulum constrained
by cycloids swings in a cycloid.

Since this answer is independent of the value of ϕ_0, it follows that the same length of time is required to reach the lowest point on the cycloid no matter where on the arc the particle is released from rest. Thus, in Fig. 11-18, three particles which start at the same time from O, A, and B will reach C simultaneously. In this sense, the cycloid is also a *tautochrone* (meaning "the same time") as well as being a brachistochrone.

Pendulum Clocks

One trouble with pendulum clocks is that the rate at which the pendulum swings changes with the size of the swing. The wider the swing, the longer it takes the pendulum to return. This would create no problem if clocks never ran down, but they do. As the spring unwinds, the force exerted on the pendulum decreases, the pendulum swings through increasingly shorter arcs, and the clock speeds up. The ticks come faster as the clock winds down. Christiaan Huygens, a seventeenth-century Dutch mathematician, physicist and astronomer, needed an accurate clock to make careful astronomical measurements. In 1673 he published the first description of an ideal pendulum clock whose bob swings in a cycloid. The period of the swing of Huygens' clock did not depend on the amplitude, and would not change as the clock wound down.

How does one make a pendulum bob swing in a cycloid? Hang it from a fine wire constrained by "cheeks" (Fig. 11-19), which cause the bob to draw up as it swings to the side. And what is the shape of the cheeks? They are cycloids.

PROBLEMS

In each of Problems 1-10, sketch the graph of the curve described by the point $P(x, y)$ as the parameter t varies over the domain given. Also find a cartesian equation of the curve in each case.

1. $x = \cos t$, $y = \sin t$, $0 \le t \le 2\pi$
2. $x = \cos 2t$, $y = \sin t$, $0 \le t \le 2\pi$
3. $x = \sec t$, $y = \tan t$, $-\pi/2 < t < \pi/2$
4. $x = 2 + 4 \sin t$, $y = 3 - 2 \cos t$, $0 \le t \le 2\pi$
5. $x = 2t + 3$, $y = 4t^2 - 9$, $-\infty < t < \infty$
6. $x = \cosh t$, $y = 2 \sinh t$, $0 \le t < \infty$
7. $x = 2 + 1/t$, $y = 2 - t$, $0 < t < \infty$
8. $x = t + 1$, $y = t^2 + 4$, $0 \le t < \infty$
9. $x = t^2 + t$, $y = t^2 - t$, $-\infty < t < \infty$
10. $x = 3 + 2 \operatorname{sech} t$, $y = 4 - 3 \tanh t$, $-\infty < t < \infty$
11. Find parametric equations of the semicircle
$$x^2 + y^2 = a^2, \qquad y > 0,$$
using as parameter the slope $t = dy/dx$ of the tangent to the curve at (x, y).

12. Find parametric equations of the semicircle
$$x^2 + y^2 = a^2, \qquad y > 0,$$
using as parameter the variable θ defined by the equation $x = a \tanh \theta$.

13. Find parametric equations of the circle
$$x^2 + y^2 = a^2,$$
using as parameter the arc length s measured counterclockwise from the point $(a, 0)$ to the point (x, y).

14. Find parametric equations of the catenary $y = a \cosh x/a$, using as parameter the length of arc s from the point $(0, a)$ to the point (x, y), with the sign of s taken to be the same as the sign of x.

15. If a string wound around a fixed circle is unwound while held taut in the plane of the circle, its end traces an *involute* of the circle (Fig. 11-20). Let the fixed circle be located with its center at the origin O and have radius a. Let the initial position of the tracing point P be $A(a, 0)$ and let the unwound portion of the string PT be tangent to the

circle at *T*. Derive parametric equations of the involute, using the angle *AOT* as the parameter *t*.

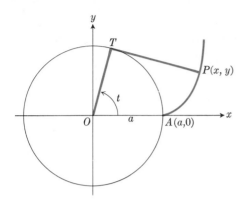

11–20 Involute of a circle.

16. When a circle rolls externally on the circumference of a second, fixed circle, any point *P* on the circumference of the rolling circle describes an *epicycloid* (Fig. 11–21). Let the fixed circle have its center at the origin *O* and have radius *a*. Let the radius of the rolling circle be *b* and let the initial position of the tracing point *P* be *A*(*a*, 0). Determine parametric equations of the epicycloid, using as parameter the angle θ from the positive *x*-axis to the line of centers.

18. Find the length of one arch of the cycloid

$$x = a(\phi - \sin \phi),$$
$$y = a(1 - \cos \phi).$$

19. Show that the slope of the cycloid

$$x = a(\phi - \sin \phi),$$
$$y = a(1 - \cos \phi)$$

is $dy/dx = \cot \phi/2$. In particular, the tangent to the cycloid is vertical when ϕ is 0 or 2π.

20. Show that the slope of the trochoid

$$x = a\phi - b \sin \phi, \qquad y = a - b \cos \phi$$

is always finite if $b < a$.

21. The *witch of Maria Agnesi* is a bell-shaped curve that may be constructed as follows: Let *C* be a circle of radius *a* having its center at (0, *a*) on the *y*-axis (Fig. 11–23). The variable line *OA* through the origin *O* intersects the line $y = 2a$ in the point *A* and intersects the circle in the point *B*. A point *P* on the witch is now located by taking the intersection of lines through *A* and *B* parallel to the *y*- and *x*-axes, respectively. (a) Find parametric equations of the witch, using as parameter the angle θ from the *x*-axis to

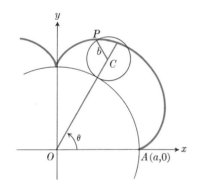

11–21 Epicycloid, with $b = a/4$.

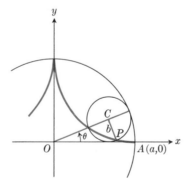

11–22 Hypocycloid, with $b = a/4$.

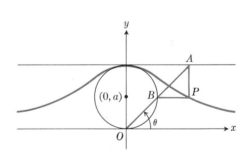

11–23 The witch of Maria Agnesi.

17. When a circle rolls on the inside of a fixed circle any point *P* on the circumference of the rolling circle describes a *hypocycloid*. Let the fixed circle be $x^2 + y^2 = a^2$, let the radius of the rolling circle be *b*, and let the initial position of the tracing point *P* be *A*(*a*, 0). Use the angle θ from the positive *x*-axis to the line of centers as parameter and determine parametric equations of the hypocycloid. In particular, if $b = a/4$, as in Fig. 11–22, show that

$$x = a \cos^3 \theta, \qquad y = a \sin^3 \theta.$$

the line *OA*.
(b) Also find the cartesian equation for the witch.

22. (*Calculator*) An automobile tire of radius 1 ft has a pebble stuck in the tread. Estimate to the nearest foot how far the pebble travels when the car goes one mile. Start by finding the ratio of the length of one arch of a cycloid to its base length.

11-4

THE DERIVATIVE OF A VECTOR FUNCTION

Let $\mathbf{i}$ and $\mathbf{j}$ be the unit vectors along the x- and y-axes in the plane. Then a function

$$\mathbf{F}(t) = \mathbf{i}x(t) + \mathbf{j}y(t), \tag{1}$$

where $x(t)$ and $y(t)$ are real valued functions of the real variable t, is a vector function of t. We shall be interested primarily in using such functions to describe the motion of a particle in the plane.

EXAMPLE 1. Suppose that the position of a particle in the xy-plane at time t is given by

$$x = e^t, \qquad y = te^t.$$

Let

$$\mathbf{R}(t) = \mathbf{i}x + \mathbf{j}y = \mathbf{i}e^t + \mathbf{j}te^t.$$

Where is the particle at time $t = 0$? How fast is it moving then, and in what direction?

Solution. At $t = 0$, we have $x = 1$ and $y = 0$, so

$$\mathbf{R}(0) = \mathbf{i}.$$

This is the vector from the origin to the position P of the particle at time $t = 0$. Next, how can we find the speed and direction of motion? Think where the particle might be a short time after $t = 0$: Both x and y will have increased somewhat, and there will be a vector to the new position. The vector between the two positions is

$$\Delta\mathbf{R} = \mathbf{i}\,\Delta x + \mathbf{j}\,\Delta y.$$

For a small Δt, this vector gives, approximately, the direction of motion. Also, $|\Delta\mathbf{R}/\Delta t|$ gives the speed, approximately. Now, for small values of Δt, we know that

$$\Delta x \approx \frac{dx}{dt}\,\Delta t \qquad \text{and} \qquad \Delta y \approx \frac{dy}{dt}\,\Delta t.$$

Therefore,

$$\Delta\mathbf{R} \approx \mathbf{i}\frac{dx}{dt}\,\Delta t + \mathbf{j}\frac{dy}{dt}\,\Delta t = \left(\mathbf{i}\frac{dx}{dt} + \mathbf{j}\frac{dy}{dt}\right)\Delta t,$$

which leads to the conclusion that

$$\frac{\Delta\mathbf{R}}{\Delta t} \approx \mathbf{i}\frac{dx}{dt} + \mathbf{j}\frac{dy}{dt}.$$

From this line of reasoning (which we shall make more precise in the next article), it seems reasonable to use the vector

$$\mathbf{i}\frac{dx}{dt} + \mathbf{j}\frac{dy}{dt} = \mathbf{i}(e^t) + \mathbf{j}(te^t + e^t),$$

evaluated at $t = 0$, as the vector whose magnitude gives the speed, and whose direction gives the direction of motion at the instant $t = 0$. When $t = 0$, this vector is $\mathbf{i} + \mathbf{j}$, so

$$\text{Speed} = |\mathbf{i} + \mathbf{j}| = \sqrt{2},$$

$$\text{Direction} = \frac{\mathbf{i} + \mathbf{j}}{\sqrt{2}}.$$

Naturally, the vector $\mathbf{i} + \mathbf{j}$ is called the *velocity vector* at $t = 0$. Its components are just the derivatives of the components of the position vector $\mathbf{R} = \overrightarrow{OP}$ at $t = 0$. (See Fig. 11-24.)

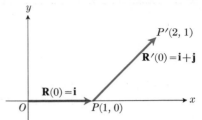

11-24 At $t = 0$, the position vector of the motion described in Example 1 is $\mathbf{R} = \mathbf{i}$, and the velocity vector is $\mathbf{R}' = \mathbf{i} + \mathbf{j}$.

It is clear that we shall want to define the derivative of a vector function $\mathbf{R}(t)$. This in turn means that we need to define a limit such as

$$\lim_{h \to a} \mathbf{F}(h),$$

where $\mathbf{F}(h)$ is a *vector function* of h. For this definition, we assume that

$$\mathbf{F}(t) = \mathbf{i}f_1(t) + \mathbf{j}f_2(t),$$

where the components $f_1(t)$ and $f_2(t)$ are functions whose domains include all the points of some open interval about a, except perhaps the point a itself. We then restrict h to lie in the intersection of these open intervals, and say that $\mathbf{F}$ has a limit, as $h \to a$, if and only if the two components of $\mathbf{F}$ have limits. If, as $h \to a$,

$$\lim f_1(t) = L_1 \qquad \text{and} \qquad \lim f_2(t) = L_2, \tag{2a}$$

then we *define the limit* of $\mathbf{F}(h)$ to be the vector

$$\lim_{h \to a} \mathbf{F}(h) = \mathbf{i}L_1 + \mathbf{j}L_2. \tag{2b}$$

EXAMPLE 2. Let

$$\mathbf{F}(h) = \mathbf{i}e^h + \mathbf{j}\frac{\sin h}{h}.$$

Then, as $h \to 0$,

$$\lim e^h = e^0 = 1, \quad \lim \frac{\sin h}{h} = 1,$$

and

$$\lim_{h \to 0} \mathbf{F}(h) = \mathbf{i} + \mathbf{j}.$$

Continuity

The vector function $\mathbf{F}$ is *continuous* at a if and only if its two components are continuous there. This is equivalent to the ε, δ-requirement stated in the following definition.

Definition.   *The vector function* $\mathbf{F}(t) = \mathbf{i}f_1(t) + \mathbf{j}f_2(t)$ *is said to be continuous at* $h = a$ *if and only if, to each* $\varepsilon > 0$, *there corresponds a* $\delta > 0$ *such that*

$$|\mathbf{F}(h) - \mathbf{F}(a)| < \varepsilon \qquad \text{when} \qquad |h - a| < \delta. \tag{3}$$

The following inequalities enables us to show that this is equivalent to requiring both components of $\mathbf{F}$ to be continuous at $h = a$:

$$|f_i(h) - f_i(a)| = \sqrt{[f_i(h) - f_i(a)]^2}$$

$$\leq \sqrt{[f_1(h) - f_1(a)]^2 + [f_2(h) - f_2(a)]^2} \tag{4}$$

$$= |\mathbf{F}(h) - \mathbf{F}(a)|.$$

Also,

$$|\mathbf{F}(h) - \mathbf{F}(a)| = \sqrt{[f_1(h) - f_1(a)]^2 + [f_2(h) - f_2(a)]^2}$$

$$\leq |f_1(h) - f_1(a)| + |f_2(h) - f_2(a)|. \tag{5}$$

The first inequality holds in turn for each of the components f_1 and f_2, because the squares under the radical are both nonnegative, so their sum is greater than or equal to either one of them. The second inequality has the form

$$\sqrt{a^2 + b^2} \leq |a| + |b|. \tag{6}$$

This latter inequality can be proved by squaring both sides and then taking square roots.

Now let us suppose that each component of $\mathbf{F}$ is a continuous function at $h = a$. Then, given $\varepsilon > 0$, there corresponds to each integer $j = 1, 2$, a positive number δ_j such that

$$|f_j(h) - f_j(a)| < \varepsilon/2 \qquad \text{when} \qquad |h - a| < \delta_j.$$

If $\delta = \min\{\delta_1, \delta_2\}$, then both terms in the summation in (5) are less than $\varepsilon/2$ when $|h - a| < \delta$. This means that their sum is less than ε, so condition (3) is satisfied. Conversely, suppose that we had started with condition (3). Then the inequality in (4) would say that each of the two components of $\mathbf{F}$ satisfies the condition

$$|f_i(h) - f_i(a)| < \varepsilon \qquad \text{when} \qquad |h - a| < \delta.$$

Hence, f_1 and f_2 are both continuous at $h = a$.

Working rule. A vector function is continuous at a point of its domain at which *both* of its components are continuous.

Derivative of a Vector Function

We shall define the derivative of $\mathbf{F}$ by the same type of limit equation we used for scalar functions:

$$\mathbf{F}'(c) = \lim_{h \to 0} \frac{\mathbf{F}(c + h) - \mathbf{F}(c)}{h}, \tag{7}$$

provided that this limit exists. The following theorem provides a statement of the necessary and sufficient condition.

Theorem. *Let*

$$\mathbf{F}(t) = \mathbf{i}f_1(t) + \mathbf{j}f_2(t)$$

be a vector function whose component functions are defined in some neighborhood of c. Then **F** *is differentiable at c if and only if both of its components are differentiable there. If this condition is met, then*

$$\mathbf{F}'(c) = \mathbf{i}f'_1(c) + \mathbf{j}f'_2(c). \tag{8}$$

Proof. The difference quotient we need to consider is

$$\frac{\mathbf{F}(c + h) - \mathbf{F}(c)}{h} = \mathbf{i}\left(\frac{f_1(c + h) - f_1(c)}{h}\right) + \mathbf{j}\left(\frac{f_2(c + h) - f_2(c)}{h}\right). \tag{9}$$

The left side of this equation has a limit as $h \to 0$ if and only if each component on the right side has a limit as $h \to 0$. The first component on the right has a limit if and only if f_1 is differentiable at c. Likewise, the second component on the right has a limit if and only if f_2 is differentiable at c. If the two components are differentiable at c, then, as $h \to 0$ and we pass to the limit in Eq. (9), we get Eq. (8). This concludes the proof.

EXAMPLE 2. At what values of t is the vector function

$$\mathbf{F}(t) = \mathbf{i} \sin t + \mathbf{j} \ln t$$

differentiable? What is its derivative at these values?

Solution. The first component, $\sin t$, is differentiable at every value of t, and its derivative is $\cos t$. The second component, $\ln t$, is differentiable for $t > 0$, and its derivative is $1/t$. Hence the vector function is differentiable for $t > 0$, and its derivative is

$$\mathbf{F}'(t) = \mathbf{i} \cos t + \mathbf{j}\frac{1}{t}, \qquad t > 0.$$

PROBLEMS

In Problems 1 through 5, find the derivative of the given vector function and state the domain of the derived function.

1. $\mathbf{i}e^{2t} + \mathbf{j}te^{-t}$

2. $\mathbf{i} \ln \sqrt{1 + t} + \mathbf{j}\sqrt{1 - t^2}$

3. $\mathbf{i} \sin^{-1} 2t + \mathbf{j} \tan 3t$

4. $\mathbf{i} \sec^{-1} 3x + \mathbf{j} \cosh 2x$

5. $\mathbf{i}\left(\frac{2t - 1}{2t + 1}\right) + \mathbf{j} \ln(1 - 4t^2)$

6. Show that the inequality $\sqrt{a^2 + b^2} \le |a| + |b|$ holds for any real numbers a and b.

11–5

VELOCITY AND ACCELERATION

We shall be interested in applications of vectors to problems in physics. For applications to *statics*, we need only a knowledge of the *algebra* of vectors. But for applications to *dynamics*, we also require a knowledge of the *calculus* of vectors. In this article we shall study motion of a particle in a plane, for simplicity, but most of the ideas can easily be extended to motion in space.

Position Vector

Suppose the point P moves along a curve in the xy-plane, and suppose we know its position at any time t. This means that the motion of P is described by a pair of functions f and g:

$$x = f(t), \qquad y = g(t). \tag{1}$$

The vector from the origin to P is customarily called the *position vector* of P, although it might be appropriate to call it the "radar" vector. This vector is a function of t given by

$$\mathbf{R} = \mathbf{i}x + \mathbf{j}y, \tag{2a}$$

or

$$\mathbf{R} = \mathbf{i}f(t) + \mathbf{j}g(t). \tag{2b}$$

Velocity Vector

We now ask what physical meaning we might attach to the *derivative* of $\mathbf{R}$ with respect to t. Mathematically, we have already *defined* the derivative to be

$$\frac{d\mathbf{R}}{dt} = \lim_{\Delta t \to 0} \frac{\Delta \mathbf{R}}{\Delta t}, \tag{3}$$

where $\mathbf{R}$ is given by (2a) and

$$\mathbf{R} + \Delta \mathbf{R} = \mathbf{i}(x + \Delta x) + \mathbf{j}(y + \Delta y). \tag{4}$$

Here $P(x, y)$ represents the position of the particle at time t, while $Q(x + \Delta x, y + \Delta y)$ gives its position at time $t + \Delta t$. By subtracting (2a) from (4), we obtain

$$\Delta \mathbf{R} = \mathbf{i}\,\Delta x + \mathbf{j}\,\Delta y, \tag{5}$$

which is the vector $\overrightarrow{PQ}$ in Fig. 11–25. The remaining calculations needed to give $d\mathbf{R}/dt$ proceed as follows:

$$\frac{\Delta \mathbf{R}}{\Delta t} = \mathbf{i}\frac{\Delta x}{\Delta t} + \mathbf{j}\frac{\Delta y}{\Delta t},$$

$$\lim_{\Delta t \to 0} \frac{\Delta \mathbf{R}}{\Delta t} = \lim_{\Delta t \to 0} \left(\mathbf{i}\frac{\Delta x}{\Delta t} + \mathbf{j}\frac{\Delta y}{\Delta t} \right)$$

$$= \mathbf{i} \lim_{\Delta t \to 0} \frac{\Delta x}{\Delta t} + \mathbf{j} \lim_{\Delta t \to 0} \frac{\Delta y}{\Delta t},$$

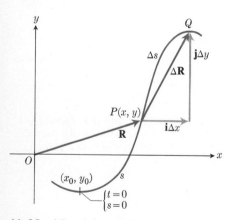

11–25 $\Delta \mathbf{R} = \mathbf{i}\,\Delta x + \mathbf{j}\,\Delta y.$

As $\Delta s \to 0$ and $Q \to P$, the direction of the chord through P and Q approaches the direction of the *tangent* to the curve at P. Thus the limiting direction of $\Delta \mathbf{R}/\Delta s$, in other words the *direction of $d\mathbf{R}/ds$*, is along the *tangent to the curve at P*, and its sense is that which points in the direction of increasing arc length s. It points away from P_0 when s is positive, and toward P_0 when s is negative.

Whichever way it points, the vector

$$\frac{d\mathbf{R}}{ds} = \mathbf{T} \tag{3}$$

is a *unit vector, tangent to the curve at P* (Fig. 11–29(c)).

If we let $\Delta s \to 0$ in Eq. (1), we find that

$$\frac{d\mathbf{R}}{ds} = \mathbf{i} \frac{dx}{ds} + \mathbf{j} \frac{dy}{ds}, \tag{4}$$

and this may be used to find $\mathbf{T}$ at any point of a curve whose equation is given. However, the natural parametrization of a motion in many cases is likely to be time and not arc length. If $\mathbf{R} = x(t)\mathbf{i} + y(t)\mathbf{j}$ and t is not arc length, then the best way to find $\mathbf{T}$ is to normalize $\mathbf{v} = d\mathbf{R}/dt$. That is, first find $\mathbf{v}$ and then divide $\mathbf{v}$ by $|\mathbf{v}|$ to obtain

$$\mathbf{T} = \frac{\mathbf{v}}{|\mathbf{v}|}.$$

This works in all cases, except when $\mathbf{v} = \mathbf{0}$ at a point.

EXAMPLE 1. Find $\mathbf{T}$ for the motion

$$\mathbf{R} = (\cos t + t \sin t)\mathbf{i} + (\sin t - t \cos t)\mathbf{j}, \qquad t \geq 0.$$

Solution

$$\mathbf{v} = \frac{d\mathbf{R}}{dt} = (-\sin t + t \cos t + \sin t)\mathbf{i} + (\cos t + t \sin t - \cos t)\mathbf{j}$$

$$= (t \cos t)\mathbf{i} + (t \sin t)\mathbf{j};$$

$$|\mathbf{v}| = \sqrt{t^2 \cos^2 t + t^2 \sin^2 t} = t;$$

$$\mathbf{T} = \frac{\mathbf{v}}{|\mathbf{v}|} = (\cos t)\mathbf{i} + (\sin t)\mathbf{j}.$$

EXAMPLE 2. For the counterclockwise motion

$$\mathbf{R} = \mathbf{i} \cos \theta + \mathbf{j} \sin \theta$$

around the unit circle, we find that

$$\mathbf{v} = (-\sin \theta)\mathbf{i} + (\cos \theta)\mathbf{j}$$

is already a unit vector, so that $\mathbf{v} = \mathbf{T}$. In fact, $\mathbf{T}$ is $\mathbf{R}$ rotated 90° counterclockwise (Fig. 11–30).

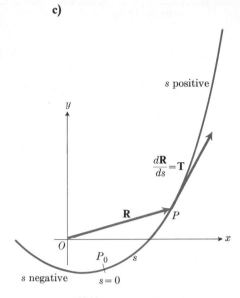

c)

11–29 The direction of $\Delta \mathbf{R}/\Delta s$ (parts a and b) and of $\mathbf{T} = d\mathbf{R}/ds$ (part c), is determined by how we decide to measure s, as well as by the geometry of the curve.

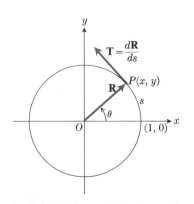

11–30 $\mathbf{R} = \mathbf{i} \cos \theta + \mathbf{j} \sin \theta$.

PROBLEMS

In each of the following problems (1 through 8), $\mathbf{R} = \mathbf{i}x + \mathbf{j}y$ is the vector from the origin O to $P(x, y)$. For each of these motions, find the unit tangent vector $\mathbf{T} = d\mathbf{R}/ds$.

1. $\mathbf{R} = 2\mathbf{i} \cos t + 2\mathbf{j} \sin t$

2. $\mathbf{R} = e^t\mathbf{i} + t^2\mathbf{j}$

3. $\mathbf{R} = (\cos^3 t)\mathbf{i} + (\sin^3 t)\mathbf{j}$

4. $\mathbf{R} = \mathbf{i}x + \mathbf{j}x^2$

5. $\mathbf{R} = (\cos 2t)\mathbf{i} + (2 \cos t)\mathbf{j}$

6. $\mathbf{R} = \dfrac{t^3}{3}\mathbf{i} + \dfrac{t^2}{2}\mathbf{j}$

7. $\mathbf{R} = (e^t \cos t)\mathbf{i} + (e^t \sin t)\mathbf{j}$

8. $\mathbf{R} = \cosh t\,\mathbf{i} + t\mathbf{j}$

11–7

CURVATURE AND NORMAL VECTORS

11–31　The value of $|d\phi/ds|$ at P is called the curvature of the curve at P.

Our next step is to consider the rate of change of the unit tangent vector $\mathbf{T}$ as P moves along the curve. Of course, the length of $\mathbf{T}$ is constant, always being equal to one. But the direction of $\mathbf{T}$ changes, since it is tangent to the curve and the tangent changes direction from point to point except where the curve is straight.

Motion in a Plane

If P moves along a curve in the xy-plane, we measure the direction of $\mathbf{T}$ by the angle ϕ from the positively directed x-axis to $\mathbf{T}$ (Fig. 11–31). We may then measure the rate at which $\mathbf{T}$ turns to one side or the other as we move along the curve by keeping track of the change in ϕ. The absolute value of the derivative $d\phi/ds$ of ϕ with respect to arc length (measured in radians per unit of length) is called the *curvature function* of the curve, and its value at any given point is called the curvature at that point. The usual notation for curvature is the Greek letter κ (kappa):

$$\kappa = \left| \frac{d\phi}{ds} \right|, \tag{1}$$

where

$$\tan \phi = \frac{dy}{dx}$$

and

$$ds = \pm\sqrt{dx^2 + dy^2}.$$

One may derive a formula for κ from the equations above in a straightforward manner. Namely,

$$\phi = \tan^{-1} \frac{dy}{dx},$$

$$\frac{d\phi}{dx} = \frac{d^2y/dx^2}{1 + (dy/dx)^2},$$

and

$$\frac{ds}{dx} = \pm\sqrt{1 + (dy/dx)^2},$$

so that

$$\kappa = \left| \frac{d\phi}{ds} \right| = \left| \frac{d\phi/dx}{ds/dx} \right| = \frac{|d^2y/dx^2|}{[1 + (dy/dx)^2]^{3/2}}. \tag{2a}$$

We may arrive at a formula for κ in terms of dx/dy and d^2x/dy^2 if we use

$$\phi = \cot^{-1}\frac{dx}{dy}$$

and

$$\kappa = \left|\frac{d\phi}{ds}\right| = \left|\frac{d\phi/dy}{ds/dy}\right|.$$

The result, which corresponds to (2a), is

$$\kappa = \frac{|d^2x/dy^2|}{[1 + (dx/dy)^2]^{3/2}}. \tag{2b}$$

If the equation of the curve is given in parametric form,

$$x = f(t), \qquad y = g(t),$$

then

$$\phi = \tan^{-1}\left(\frac{dy/dt}{dx/dt}\right),$$

and if we use

$$\kappa = \left|\frac{d\phi/dt}{ds/dt}\right|,$$

the calculations are as follows:

$$\frac{d\phi}{dt} = \frac{1}{1 + \left(\dfrac{dy/dt}{dx/dt}\right)^2}\frac{\dfrac{dx}{dt}\dfrac{d^2y}{dt^2} - \dfrac{dy}{dt}\dfrac{d^2x}{dt^2}}{\left(\dfrac{dx}{dt}\right)^2}$$

$$= \frac{\dot{x}\ddot{y} - \dot{y}\ddot{x}}{\dot{x}^2 + \dot{y}^2} \qquad \left[\dot{x} = \frac{dx}{dt}, \ddot{x} = \frac{d^2x}{dt^2}\right]$$

and

$$\frac{ds}{dt} = \pm\sqrt{\dot{x}^2 + \dot{y}^2},$$

so that

$$\kappa = \frac{|\dot{x}\ddot{y} - \dot{y}\ddot{x}|}{[\dot{x}^2 + \dot{y}^2]^{3/2}}. \tag{2c}$$

EXAMPLE 1. *The curvature of a straight line is* 0.

On a straight line, ϕ is constant. Therefore $d\phi/ds$ in Eq. (2a) is zero.

EXAMPLE 2. *The curvature of a circle of radius a is* $1/a$.

We place the center of the circle at the origin to make its equation simple (Fig. 12–11).

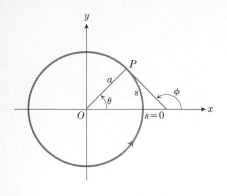

11–32 $P: x = a \cos \theta,\ y = a \sin \theta.$

METHOD 1.   Parametrize the circle with the equations

$$x = a \cos \theta, \qquad y = a \sin \theta.$$

Then,

$$\dot{x} = -a \sin \theta, \qquad \dot{y} = a \cos \theta,$$

$$\ddot{x} = -a \cos \theta, \qquad \ddot{y} = -a \sin \theta.$$

From Eq. (2c) we have

$$\kappa = \frac{\left| (-a \sin \theta)(-a \sin \theta) - (a \cos \theta)(-a \cos \theta) \right|}{[a^2 \sin^2 \theta + a^2 \cos^2 \theta]^{3/2}}$$

$$= \frac{a^2}{a^3} = \frac{1}{a}.$$

METHOD 2.   (Special to the circle) The geometry of Fig. 11–32 allows s and ϕ to be expressed in terms of θ as follows:

$$s = a\theta, \qquad \phi = \theta + \frac{\pi}{2}. \tag{3}$$

Equation (1) then gives

$$\kappa = \left| \frac{d\phi}{ds} \right| = \left| \frac{d\theta}{a\,d\theta} \right| = \frac{1}{a}.$$

The curvature of a circle is equal to the reciprocal of its radius. The smaller the circle, the greater its curvature. To "turn on a dime" indicates a more rapid change of direction per unit of arc length than does to turn on a silver dollar!

Circle and Radius of Curvature

The circle that is tangent to a plane curve at P, whose center lies on the concave side of the curve and that has the same curvature as the curve has at P, is called the *circle of curvature*. Its radius is $1/\kappa$, from Example 2. We define the *radius of curvature* ρ at P to be

$$\rho = \frac{1}{\kappa} = \frac{[1 + (dy/dx)^2]^{3/2}}{|d^2y/dx^2|}. \tag{4}$$

The center of the circle of curvature is called the center of curvature. The circle of curvature has its first and second derivatives equal, respectively, to the first and second derivatives of the curve itself at this point. For this reason it has a higher degree of contact with the curve at P than has any other circle, so it is also called the *osculating* circle! (See Fig. 11–33.) Since velocity and acceleration involve only the first and second time derivatives of the coordinates of P, it is natural to anticipate that the instantaneous velocity and acceleration of a particle moving on any curve may be expressed in terms of instantaneous velocity and acceleration of an associated particle moving on the osculating circle. This will be investigated in the next article.

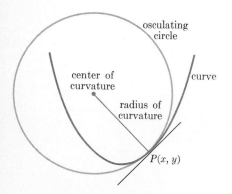

11–33   The osculating circle or circle of curvature at $P(x, y)$.

Unit Normal Vector

We return once more to the question of the rate of change of the unit vector **T** as P moves along the curve. In terms of the slope angle ϕ (Fig. 11–34), we may write

$$\mathbf{T} = \mathbf{i} \cos \phi + \mathbf{j} \sin \phi, \tag{5}$$

and then the derivative

$$\frac{d\mathbf{T}}{d\phi} = -\mathbf{i} \sin \phi + \mathbf{j} \cos \phi \tag{6}$$

has magnitude

$$\left| \frac{d\mathbf{T}}{d\phi} \right| = \sqrt{\sin^2 \phi + \cos^2 \phi} = 1.$$

The slope of the derivative is

$$\frac{\cos \phi}{-\sin \phi} = \frac{-1}{\tan \phi}$$

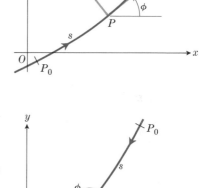

(recall Fig. 11–7), which is the negative reciprocal of the slope of **T**. Therefore, $d\mathbf{T}/d\phi$ is perpendicular to **T**. In fact, if we replace $-\sin \phi$ by $\cos(\phi + 90°)$, and $\cos \phi$ by $\sin(\phi + 90°)$, in the formula for $d\mathbf{T}/d\phi$, we see that

$$\frac{d\mathbf{T}}{d\phi} = \mathbf{i} \cos(\phi + 90°) + \mathbf{j} \sin(\phi + 90°). \tag{7}$$

This is the unit vector that is obtained by rotating **T** counterclockwise by 90°. We call this vector **N**: thus

$$\mathbf{N} = \frac{d\mathbf{T}}{d\phi} = -\mathbf{i} \sin \phi + \mathbf{j} \cos \phi, \tag{8}$$

and it is the *unit normal vector* to the curve (Fig. 11–34). Equation (8) gives us a way to calculate **N** if we know **T**: we interchange the components of **T**, and change the sign of the new first component.

11–34   Turn **T** counterclockwise 90° to get **N**.

EXAMPLE 3. Find **N** for the curve traced by $\mathbf{R} = (2t + 3)\mathbf{i} + (t^2 - 1)\mathbf{j}$.

Solution. We first find **T**:

$$\mathbf{v} = 2\mathbf{i} + 2t\mathbf{j},$$

$$|\mathbf{v}| = \sqrt{4 + 4t^2} = 2\sqrt{1 + t^2},$$

$$\mathbf{T} = \frac{\mathbf{v}}{|\mathbf{v}|} = \frac{1}{\sqrt{1 + t^2}}\mathbf{i} + \frac{t}{\sqrt{1 + t^2}}\mathbf{j}.$$

We then interchange the components of **T** and change the sign of the new first component, to get

$$\mathbf{N} = -\frac{t}{\sqrt{1 + t^2}}\mathbf{i} + \frac{1}{\sqrt{1 + t^2}}\mathbf{j}.$$

From the chain rule we have

$$\frac{d\mathbf{T}}{ds} = \frac{d\mathbf{T}}{d\phi}\frac{d\phi}{ds} = \mathbf{N}\frac{d\phi}{ds} = \mathbf{N}(\pm\kappa), \tag{9}$$

where κ is the curvature at P. We draw two conclusions about κ, $\mathbf{N}$, and $\mathbf{T}$ from Eq. (9). The first conclusion is that κ measures the length of $d\mathbf{T}/ds$, for

$$\left|\frac{d\mathbf{T}}{ds}\right| = |\pm\kappa\mathbf{N}| = \kappa. \tag{10}$$

The second conclusion has to do with the ambiguous sign in Eq. (9). If we can direct the curve so that ϕ increases with s, then $d\phi/ds$ is positive and equals $+\kappa$, and Eq. (9) reduces to

$$\frac{d\mathbf{T}}{ds} = \kappa\mathbf{N}. \tag{11}$$

PROBLEMS

Find the curvature of each of the curves in Problems 1–12.

1. $y = a \cosh (x/a)$

2. $y = \ln (\cos x)$

3. $y = e^{2x}$

4. $x = a \cos^3 t, \quad y = a \sin^3 t$

5. $x = a(\cos \theta + \theta \sin \theta),$ $\quad y = a(\sin \theta - \theta \cos \theta)$

6. $x = a(\theta - \sin \theta),$ $\quad y = a(1 - \cos \theta)$

7. $x = \ln \sec y$

8. $x = \frac{1}{3}(y^2 + 2)^{3/2}$

9. $x = \frac{y^4}{4} + \frac{1}{8y^2}$

10. $x = 2t + 3, \quad y = 5 - t^2$

11. $x = \frac{t^3}{3}, \quad y = \frac{t^2}{2}$

12. $x = e^t \cos t, \quad y = e^t \sin t$

In Problems 13 through 16, find the unit normal vector $\mathbf{N}$ to each curve.

13. The curve of Problem 5, for a and θ positive.

14. The curve of Problem 10.

15. The curve of Problem 11:
  a) for $t > 0$.   **b)** for $t < 0$.

16. The curve of Problem 12.

17. Find the equation of the osculating circle associated with the curve $y = e^x$ at the point $(0, 1)$. By calculating dy/dx and d^2y/dx^2 at the point $(0, 1)$ from the equation of this circle, verify that these derivatives have the same values there as do the corresponding derivatives for the curve $y = e^x$. Sketch the curve and the osculating circle.

18. Show that when x and y are considered as functions of arc length s, the unit vectors $\mathbf{T}$ and $\mathbf{N}$ may be expressed as follows:

$$\mathbf{T} = \mathbf{i}\frac{dx}{ds} + \mathbf{j}\frac{dy}{ds}, \qquad \mathbf{N} = -\mathbf{i}\frac{dy}{ds} + \mathbf{j}\frac{dx}{ds},$$

where $dx/ds = \cos \phi$, $dy/ds = \sin \phi$, and ϕ is the angle from the positive x-axis to the tangent line.

11–8

TANGENTIAL AND NORMAL COMPONENTS OF THE VELOCITY AND ACCELERATION VECTORS

In mechanics it is useful to be able to discuss the motion of a particle P in terms of its instantaneous speed ds/dt, acceleration along its path d^2s/dt^2, and the curvature of the path. This is easy if we refer the velocity and acceleration vectors to the unit vectors $\mathbf{T}$ and $\mathbf{N}$.

In Article 11–5 we found the velocity vector to be given by

$$\mathbf{v} = \frac{d\mathbf{R}}{dt}, \tag{1}$$

where $\mathbf{R} = \mathbf{i}x + \mathbf{j}y$ is the position vector $\overrightarrow{OP}$. We may also write this in the form

$$\mathbf{v} = \frac{d\mathbf{R}}{dt} = \frac{d\mathbf{R}}{ds}\frac{ds}{dt}$$

or

$$\mathbf{v} = \mathbf{T}\frac{ds}{dt} \qquad (2)$$

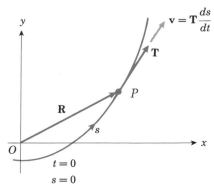

11–35 Divide **v** by ds/dt to get **T**.

if we use the result of Eq. (3), Article 11–6. This is in keeping with our earlier remark that the velocity vector is tangent to the curve and has magnitude $|\mathbf{v}| = |ds/dt|$. (See Fig. 11–35.)

To obtain the acceleration vector, we differentiate Eq. (2) with respect to t:

$$\mathbf{a} = \frac{d\mathbf{v}}{dt} = \frac{d}{dt}\left(\mathbf{T}\frac{ds}{dt}\right) = \mathbf{T}\frac{d^2s}{dt^2} + \frac{d\mathbf{T}}{dt}\frac{ds}{dt}.$$

From the chain rule and Eq. (11), Article 11–7,

$$\frac{d\mathbf{T}}{dt} = \frac{d\mathbf{T}}{ds}\frac{ds}{dt} = \mathbf{N}\kappa\frac{ds}{dt},$$

so that

$$\mathbf{a} = \mathbf{T}\frac{d^2s}{dt^2} + \mathbf{N}\kappa\left(\frac{ds}{dt}\right)^2. \qquad (3)$$

Equation (3) expresses the acceleration vector in terms of its tangential and normal components. The *tangential component*, $a_T = d^2s/dt^2$, is simply the derivative of the speed ds/dt of the particle in its path. The *normal component* $a_N = \kappa(ds/dt)^2$ is directed toward the concave side of the curve and has magnitude

$$a_N = \kappa\left(\frac{ds}{dt}\right)^2 = \frac{(ds/dt)^2}{\rho} = \frac{v^2}{\rho},$$

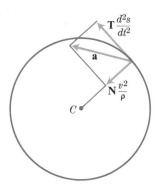

11–36 Tangential and normal components of an acceleration vector.

where v is the instantaneous speed of the particle and ρ is the radius of curvature of the path at the point in question. This explains why a large normal force, which must be supplied by friction between the tires and the roadway, is required to hold an automobile on a level road if it makes a sharp turn (small ρ) or a moderate turn at high speed (large v^2).

If the particle is moving in a circle with *constant* speed $v = ds/dt$, then d^2s/dt^2 is zero, and the only acceleration is the normal acceleration v^2/ρ toward the center of the circle. If the speed is not constant, the acceleration vector **a** is the resultant of the tangential and normal components, as in Fig. 11–36.

The following example illustrates how the tangential and normal components of velocity and acceleration may be computed when the equations of motion are known. In particular, it should be noted that the equation

$$|\mathbf{a}|^2 = a_x^2 + a_y^2 = a_T^2 + a_N^2 \qquad (4)$$

is used to determine the normal component of acceleration

$$a_N = \sqrt{|\mathbf{a}|^2 - a_T^2}. \qquad (5)$$

Equation (5) gives a way to find a_N without having to find κ first.

EXAMPLE 1. The coordinates of a moving particle at time t are given by

$$x = \cos t + t \sin t,$$

$$y = \sin t - t \cos t.$$

Find the velocity and acceleration vectors, the speed ds/dt, and the normal and tangential components of acceleration.

Solution

$$\mathbf{v} = \mathbf{i}\frac{dx}{dt} + \mathbf{j}\frac{dy}{dt}$$

$$= \mathbf{i}[-\sin t + t \cos t + \sin t] + \mathbf{j}[\cos t + t \sin t - \cos t]$$

$$= \mathbf{i}t \cos t + \mathbf{j}t \sin t$$

and

$$\mathbf{a} = \frac{d\mathbf{v}}{dt} = \mathbf{i}[-t \sin t + \cos t] + \mathbf{j}[t \cos t + \sin t].$$

Now the tangential component of velocity is

$$\frac{ds}{dt} = |\mathbf{v}| = \sqrt{(t \cos t)^2 + (t \sin t)^2} = t$$

and the tangential component of acceleration is

$$a_T = \frac{d^2 s}{dt^2} = \frac{d}{dt}\left(\frac{ds}{dt}\right) = \frac{d}{dt}(t) = 1.$$

We use Eq. (5) to determine the normal component of acceleration:

$$a_N = \sqrt{|\mathbf{a}|^2 - a_T^2} = \sqrt{(-t \sin t + \cos t)^2 + (t \cos t + \sin t)^2 - 1} = t.$$

Here the tangential acceleration has constant magnitude and the normal acceleration starts with zero magnitude at $t = 0$ and increases with time. The equations of motion are the same as the parametric equations for the *involute* of a circle of unit radius. This is the path of the endpoint P of a string that is held taut as it is unwound from the circle. To get the parametrization, the origin is taken as the center of the circle (Fig. 11–37), with $(1, 0)$ being the position where P starts. The angle t is measured from the positively directed x-axis counterclockwise to the ray from O to the point of tangency Q.

We can find the radius of curvature from the equation $a_N = v^2/\rho$, since $v^2 = |\mathbf{v}|^2 = t^2$ and $a_N = t$ and hence

$$\rho = \frac{v^2}{a_N} = \frac{t^2}{t} = t.$$

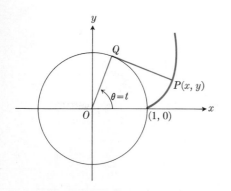

11–37 Involute of a circle.

PROBLEMS

1. With the book closed, derive vector expressions for the velocity and acceleration in terms of tangential and normal components. Check your derivations with those given in the text.

In Problems 2 through 6, find the velocity and acceleration vectors, and then find the speed ds/dt and the tangential and normal components of acceleration.

2. $\mathbf{R} = \mathbf{i} \cosh 2t + \mathbf{j} \sinh 2t$

3. $\mathbf{R} = (2t + 3)\mathbf{i} + (t^2 - 1)\mathbf{j}$

4. $\mathbf{R} = (a \cos \omega t)\mathbf{i} + (a \sin \omega t)\mathbf{j}$, a and ω positive constants

5. $\mathbf{R} = \mathbf{i} \ln (t^2 + 1) + \mathbf{j}(t - 2 \tan^{-1} t)$

6. $\mathbf{R} = \mathbf{i}e^t \cos t + \mathbf{j}e^t \sin t$

7. Deduce from Eq. (11) that a particle will move in a straight line if the normal component of acceleration is identically zero.

8. Show that the radius of curvature of a plane curve is given by

$$\rho = \frac{(\dot{x}^2 + \dot{y}^2)}{\sqrt{\ddot{x}^2 + \ddot{y}^2 - \ddot{s}^2}},$$

where

$$\dot{x} = \frac{dx}{dt}, \qquad \ddot{x} = \frac{d^2x}{dt^2}, \qquad \dot{y} = \frac{dy}{dt}, \qquad \ddot{y} = \frac{d^2y}{dt^2},$$

and

$$\ddot{s} = \frac{d}{dt}(\sqrt{\dot{x}^2 + \dot{y}^2}).$$

9. If a particle moves in a curve with constant speed, show that the force is always directed along the normal.

10. If the force acting on a particle is at all times perpendicular to the direction of motion, show that the speed remains constant.

When a particle P moves on a curve whose equation is given in polar coordinates, it is convenient to express the velocity and acceleration vectors in terms of the unit vectors

$$\mathbf{u}_r = \mathbf{i} \cos \theta + \mathbf{j} \sin \theta, \qquad \mathbf{u}_\theta = -\mathbf{i} \sin \theta + \mathbf{j} \cos \theta. \tag{1}$$

11-9

POLAR COORDINATES

The vector $\mathbf{u}_r$ points along the radius vector $\overrightarrow{OP}$, and $\mathbf{u}_\theta$ points at right angles to $\overrightarrow{OP}$ and in the direction of increasing θ, as shown in Fig. 11–38. From (1), we find that

$$\frac{d\mathbf{u}_r}{d\theta} = -\mathbf{i} \sin \theta + \mathbf{j} \cos \theta = \mathbf{u}_\theta,$$

$$\frac{d\mathbf{u}_\theta}{d\theta} = -\mathbf{i} \cos \theta - \mathbf{j} \sin \theta = -\mathbf{u}_r. \tag{2}$$

This says that differentiating either $\mathbf{u}_r$ or $\mathbf{u}_\theta$ with respect to θ is equivalent to rotating that vector 90° counterclockwise.

Since the vectors $\mathbf{R} = \overrightarrow{OP}$ and $r\mathbf{u}_r$ have the same direction, and the length of $\mathbf{R}$ is the absolute value of the polar coordinate r of $P(r, \theta)$, we have

$$\mathbf{R} = r\mathbf{u}_r. \tag{3}$$

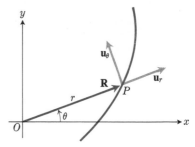

11–38   The unit vectors $\mathbf{u}_r$ and $\mathbf{u}_\theta$.

We differentiate this equation with respect to t to obtain the velocity, remembering that both r and $\mathbf{u}_r$ may be variables. From (2) and the chain rule we get

$$\frac{d\mathbf{u}_r}{dt} = \frac{d\mathbf{u}_r}{d\theta}\frac{d\theta}{dt} = \mathbf{u}_\theta \frac{d\theta}{dt}, \qquad \frac{d\mathbf{u}_\theta}{dt} = \frac{d\mathbf{u}_\theta}{d\theta}\frac{d\theta}{dt} = -\mathbf{u}_r \frac{d\theta}{dt}. \tag{4}$$

11–39 $\mathbf{u}_r \dfrac{dr}{dt} + \mathbf{u}_\theta r \dfrac{d\theta}{dt}$ is the velocity vector.

Hence,

$$\mathbf{v} = \frac{d\mathbf{R}}{dt} = \mathbf{u}_r \frac{dr}{dt} + r \frac{d\mathbf{u}_r}{dt}$$

becomes

$$\mathbf{v} = \mathbf{u}_r \frac{dr}{dt} + \mathbf{u}_\theta r \frac{d\theta}{dt}. \tag{5}$$

Of course this velocity vector is tangent to the curve at P and has magnitude

$$|\mathbf{v}| = \sqrt{(dr/dt)^2 + r^2(d\theta/dt)^2} = |ds/dt|.$$

In fact, if the three sides of the "differential triangle" of sides dr, $r\,d\theta$, and ds are all divided by dt (Fig. 11–39), the result will be a similar triangle having sides dr/dt, $r\,d\theta/dt$, and ds/dt, which illustrates the vector equation

$$\mathbf{v} = \mathbf{T}\frac{ds}{dt} = \mathbf{u}_r \frac{dr}{dt} + \mathbf{u}_\theta r \frac{d\theta}{dt}.$$

The acceleration vector is found by differentiating the velocity vector in (5) as follows:

$$\mathbf{a} = \frac{d\mathbf{v}}{dt} = \left(\mathbf{u}_r \frac{d^2 r}{dt^2} + \frac{d\mathbf{u}_r}{dt}\frac{dr}{dt} \right) + \left(\mathbf{u}_\theta r \frac{d^2\theta}{dt^2} + \mathbf{u}_\theta \frac{dr}{dt}\frac{d\theta}{dt} + \frac{d\mathbf{u}_\theta}{dt} r \frac{d\theta}{dt} \right).$$

When Eqs. (4) are used to evaluate the derivatives of $\mathbf{u}_r$ and $\mathbf{u}_\theta$ and the components are separated, the result becomes

$$\mathbf{a} = \mathbf{u}_r \left[\frac{d^2 r}{dt^2} - r\left(\frac{d\theta}{dt}\right)^2 \right] + \mathbf{u}_\theta \left[r\frac{d^2\theta}{dt^2} + 2\frac{dr}{dt}\frac{d\theta}{dt} \right]. \tag{6}$$

11–40 $\mathbf{F}$ is a central force if it points toward a fixed point (here the origin) no matter how P moves.

The polar form is particularly convenient in discussing the motion of a particle in what is called a "central force field." By this we mean that the force acting on the particle is always directed toward a single point, the center of force, which we choose as origin (Fig. 11–40). Then from $\mathbf{F} = m\mathbf{a}$, we see that the $\mathbf{u}_\theta$ component of acceleration must vanish. That is, in any central force field,

$$r\frac{d^2\theta}{dt^2} + 2\frac{dr}{dt}\frac{d\theta}{dt} = 0, \tag{7}$$

where the origin is at the center of force. (For instance, the sun would be chosen as the origin in discussing the gravitational attraction between the sun and a planet.) To integrate (7), let

$$u = \frac{d\theta}{dt}.$$

Then

$$r\frac{du}{dt} + 2u\frac{dr}{dt} = 0,$$

or

$$r \, du = -2u \, dr, \qquad \frac{du}{u} = -2\frac{dr}{r},$$

$$\ln |u| = -2 \ln |r| + c_1, \qquad \ln |ur^2| = c_1, \qquad |ur^2| = e^{c_1} = C,$$

or

$$r^2 \frac{d\theta}{dt} = \pm C. \tag{8}$$

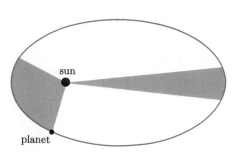

The left side of this equation is $2 \, dA/dt$, where $dA = \frac{1}{2}r^2 \, d\theta$ is the area swept over as the radius vector $\overrightarrow{OP}$ rotates through a small angle $d\theta$. Hence, Eq. (8) says that the radius vector *sweeps over area at a constant rate* in a central force field. Kepler's second law of planetary motion is thus a consequence of the fact that the field of gravitational attraction of the sun for the planets is a central force field (Fig. 11–41).

11–41 The line joining a planet and its sun sweeps over equal areas in equal times.

PROBLEMS

1. With the book closed, derive vector expressions for the velocity and acceleration in terms of components along and at right angles to the radius vector. Check your derivations with those given in the text.

In Problems 2–6, find the velocity and acceleration vectors in terms of $\mathbf{u}_r$ and $\mathbf{u}_\theta$.

2. $r = a(1 - \cos \theta)$ and $\dfrac{d\theta}{dt} = 3$

3. $r = a \sin 2\theta$ and $\dfrac{d\theta}{dt} = 2t$

4. $r = e^{a\theta}$ and $\dfrac{d\theta}{dt} = 2$

5. $r = a(1 + \sin t)$ and $\theta = 1 - e^{-t}$

6. $r = 2 \cos 4t$ and $\theta = 2t$

7. If a particle moves in an ellipse whose polar equation is $r = c/(1 - e \cos \theta)$ and the force is directed toward the origin, show that the magnitude of the force is proportional to $1/r^2$.

REVIEW QUESTIONS AND EXERCISES

1. When are two vectors equal?

2. How are two vectors added? Subtracted?

3. If a vector is multiplied by a scalar, how is the result related to the original vector? In your discussion include all possible values of the scalar: positive, negative, and zero.

4. Define the derivative of a vector function.

5. Develop formulas for the derivatives, with respect to θ, of the unit vectors $\mathbf{u}_r$ and $\mathbf{u}_\theta$.

6. Develop vector formulas for velocity and acceleration of a particle moving in a plane curve:

a) in terms of Cartesian coordinates,

b) in terms of polar coordinates,

c) in terms of distance traveled along the curve and unit vectors tangent and normal to the curve.

7. a) Define curvature of a plane curve.

b) Define radius of curvature.

c) Define center of curvature.

d) Define osculating circle.

8. Develop a formula for the curvature of a curve whose parametric equations are $x = f(t)$, $y = g(t)$.

9. In what way does the curvature of a curve affect the acceleration of a particle moving along the curve? In particular, discuss the case of constant-speed motion along a curve.

10. State and derive Kepler's second law concerning motion in a central force field.

11. Give examples of two ways in which parametric equations of a curve may arise.

12. What is the relation between a path represented by parametric equations and the path represented by the Cartesian equations that we may get when we eliminate the parameter? Illustrate with an example.

MISCELLANEOUS PROBLEMS

In Problems 1 through 10, find parametric equations for the path traced by the point $P(x, y)$ for the given data.

1. $\dfrac{dx}{dt} = x^2$, $\dfrac{dy}{dt} = x$; $t = 0$, $x = 1$, $y = 1$

2. $\dfrac{dx}{dt} = \cos^2 x$, $\dfrac{dy}{dt} = x$; $t = 0$, $x = \dfrac{\pi}{4}$, $y = 0$

3. $\dfrac{dx}{dt} = e^t$, $\dfrac{dy}{dt} = xe^x$; $t = 0$, $x = 1$, $y = 0$

4. $\dfrac{dx}{dt} = 6 \sin 2t$, $\dfrac{dy}{dt} = 4 \cos 2t$; $t = 0$, $x = 0$, $y = 4$

5. $\dfrac{dx}{dt} = 1 - \cos t$, $\dfrac{dy}{dt} = \sin t$; $t = 0$, $x = 0$, $y = 0$

6. $\dfrac{dx}{dt} = \sqrt{1 + y}$, $\dfrac{dy}{dt} = y$; $t = 0$, $x = 0$, $y = 1$

7. $\dfrac{dx}{dt} = \operatorname{sech} x$, $\dfrac{dy}{dt} = x$; $t = 0$, $x = 0$, $y = 0$

8. $\dfrac{dx}{dt} = \cosh \dfrac{t}{2}$, $\dfrac{dy}{dt} = x$; $t = 0$, $x = 2$, $y = 0$

9. $\dfrac{dx}{dt} = y$, $\dfrac{dy}{dt} = -x$; $t = 0$, $x = 0$, $y = 4$

10. $\dfrac{d^2x}{dt^2} = -\dfrac{dx}{dt}$, $\dfrac{dy}{dt} = x$; $t = 0$, $x = 1$, $y = 1$, $\dfrac{dx}{dt} = 1$

11. A particle is projected with velocity v at an angle α to the horizontal from a point that is at the foot of a hill inclined at an angle ϕ to the horizontal, where

$$0 < \phi < \alpha < (\pi/2).$$

Show that it reaches the ground at a distance

$$\frac{2v^2 \cos \alpha}{g \cos^2 \phi} \sin (\alpha - \phi)$$

measured up the face of the hill. Hence show that the greatest range achieved for a given v is when $\alpha = (\phi/2) + (\pi/4)$.

12. A wheel of radius 4 in. rolls along the x-axis with angular velocity 2 rad/sec. Find the locus described by a point on a spoke and 2 in. from the center of the wheel if it starts from the point $(0, 2)$ at time $t = 0$.

13. OA is the diameter of a circle of radius a. AN is tangent to the circle at A. A line through O making angle θ with diameter OA intersects the circle at M and tangent line at N. On ON a point P is located so that $OP = MN$. Taking O as origin, OA along the y-axis, and angle θ as parameter, find parametric equations of the locus described by P.

14. Let a line AB be the x-axis of a system of rectangular coordinates. Let the point C be the point $(0, 1)$. Let the line DE through C intersect AB at F. Let P and P' be the points on DE such that $PF = P'F = a$. Find parametric equations of the loci of P and P' in terms of the angle $\theta = \angle CFB$.

15. For the curve

$$x = a(t - \sin t), \quad y = a(1 - \cos t),$$

find the following quantities.

a) The area bounded by the x-axis and one loop of the curve

b) The length of one loop

c) The radius of curvature

d) The area of the surface of revolution obtained by rotating one loop about the x-axis

e) The coordinates of the centroid of the area in (a).

16. In Fig. 11–42, D is the midpoint of side AB and E is one-third of the way between C and B. *Using vectors*, prove that F is the midpoint of the line CD.

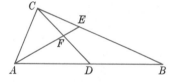

Figure 11–42

17. The vectors $2\mathbf{i} + 3\mathbf{j}$, $4\mathbf{i} + \mathbf{j}$, and $5\mathbf{i} + y\mathbf{j}$ have their initial points at the origin. Find the value of y so that the vectors terminate on one straight line.

18. $\mathbf{A}$ and $\mathbf{B}$ are vectors from the origin to the two points A and B. The point P is determined by the vector $\overrightarrow{OP} = x\mathbf{A} + y\mathbf{B}$, where x and y are positive quantities, neither of which is zero, and whose sum is equal to one. Prove that P lies on the line segment AB.

19. Using vector methods, prove that the segment joining the midpoints of two sides of a triangle is parallel to, and half the length of, the third side.

20. Let ABC be a triangle and let M be the midpoint of AB. Let P be the point on CM that is two-thirds of the way from C to M. Let O be any point in space.

a) Show that

$$\overrightarrow{OP} = \left(\frac{\overrightarrow{OA} + \overrightarrow{OB} + \overrightarrow{OC}}{3} \right).$$

b) Show how the result in (a) leads to the conclusion that the medians of a triangle meet in a point.

21. A, B, C are the vertices of a triangle and a, b, c are the midpoints of the opposite sides. Show that

$$\vec{Aa} + \vec{Bb} + \vec{Cc} = \mathbf{0}.$$

Interpret the result geometrically.

22. Vectors are drawn from the center of a regular polygon to its vertices. Show that their sum is zero.

23. Let $\mathbf{A}$, $\mathbf{B}$, $\mathbf{C}$ be vectors from a common point O to points A, B, C.

a) If A, B, C are collinear, show that three constants x, y, z (not all zero) exist such that

$$x + y + z = 0 \quad \text{and} \quad x\mathbf{A} + y\mathbf{B} + z\mathbf{C} = \mathbf{0}.$$

b) Conversely, if three constants x, y, z (not all zero) exist such that

$$x + y + z = 0 \quad \text{and} \quad x\mathbf{A} + y\mathbf{B} + z\mathbf{C} = \mathbf{0},$$

show that A, B, C are collinear.

24. A particle moves in the xy-plane according to the time law

$$x = 1/\sqrt{1 + t^2}, \quad y = t/\sqrt{1 + t^2}.$$

a) Compute the velocity vector and acceleration vector when $t = 1$.

b) At what time is the speed of the particle a maximum?

25. A circular wheel with unit radius rolls along the x-axis uniformly, rotating one half-turn per second (Fig. 11–43). The position of a point P on the circumference is given by the formula

$$\vec{OP} = \mathbf{R} = \mathbf{i}(\pi t - \sin \pi t) + \mathbf{j}(1 - \cos \pi t).$$

a) Determine the velocity (*vector*) $\mathbf{v}$ and the acceleration (*vector*) $\mathbf{a}$ at time t.

b) Determine the slopes (as functions of t) of the two straight lines PC and PQ joining P to the center C of the wheel and to the point Q that is topmost at the instant.

c) Show that the directions of the vectors $\mathbf{v}$ and $\mathbf{a}$ can be expressed in terms of the straight lines described in (b).

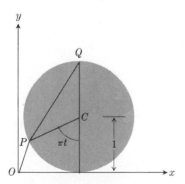

Figure 11–43

26. The motion of a particle in the xy-plane is given by

$$\mathbf{R} = \mathbf{i}at \cos t + \mathbf{j}at \sin t.$$

Find the speed, and the tangential and normal components of the acceleration.

27. A particle moves in such a manner that the derivative of the position vector is always perpendicular to the position vector. Show that the particle moves on a circle with center at the origin.

28. The position of a point at time t is given by the formulas $x = e^t \cos t$, $y = e^t \sin t$.

a) Show that $\mathbf{a} = 2\mathbf{v} - 2\mathbf{r}$.

b) Show that the angle between the radius vector $\mathbf{r}$ and the acceleration vector $\mathbf{a}$ is constant, and find this angle.

29. Given the instantaneous velocity $\mathbf{v} = a\mathbf{i} + b\mathbf{j}$ and acceleration $\mathbf{a} = c\mathbf{i} + d\mathbf{j}$ of a particle at a point P on its path of motion, determine the curvature of the path at P.

30. Find the parametric equations, in terms of the parameter θ, of the locus of the center of curvature of the cycloid

$$x = a(\theta - \sin \theta), \quad y = a(1 - \cos \theta).$$

31. Find the point on the curve $y = e^x$ for which the radius of curvature is a minimum.

32. a) Given a closed curve having the property that every line parallel to the x-axis or the y-axis has at most two points in common with the curve. Let

$$x = x(t), \quad y = y(t), \quad \alpha \le t \le \beta,$$

be equations of the curve. Prove that if dx/dt and dy/dt are continuous, then the area bounded by the curve is

$$\frac{1}{2} \left| \int_{\alpha}^{\beta} \left[x(t) \frac{dy}{dt} - y(t) \frac{dx}{dt} \right] dt \right|.$$

b) Use the result of (a) to find the area inside the ellipse

$$x = a \cos \phi, \quad y = b \sin \phi, \quad 0 \le \phi \le 2\pi.$$

What does the answer become when $a = b$?

33. For the curve defined by the equations

$$x = \int_0^\theta \cos \left(\tfrac{1}{2}\pi t^2 \right) dt, \quad y = \int_0^\theta \sin \left(\tfrac{1}{2}\pi t^2 \right) dt,$$

calculate the curvature κ as a function of the length of arc s, where s is measured from $(0, 0)$.

34. The curve for which the length of the tangent intercepted between the point of contact and the y-axis is always equal to 1 is called the *tractrix*. Find its equation. Show that the radius of curvature at each point of the curve is inversely proportional to the length of the normal intercepted between the point on the curve and the y-axis. Calculate the length of arc of the tractrix, and find the parametric equations in terms of the length of arc.

35. Let $x = x(t)$, $y = y(t)$ be a closed curve. A constant length p is measured off along the normal to the curve. The extremity of this segment describes a curve which is called a *parallel curve* to the original curve. Find the length of arc, the radius of curvature, and the area enclosed by the parallel curve.

36. Given the curve represented by the parametric equations

$$x = 32t, \quad y = 16t^2 - 4.$$

 a) Calculate the radius of curvature of the curve at the point where $t = 3$.

 b) Find the length of the curve between the points where $t = 0$ and $t = 1$.

37. Find the velocity, acceleration, and speed of a particle whose position at time t is

$$x = 3 \sin t, \quad y = 2 \cos t.$$

Also find the tangential and normal components of the acceleration.

38. The position of a particle at time t is given by the equations

$$x = 1 + \cos 2t, \quad y = \sin 2t.$$

Find

 a) the normal and tangential components of acceleration at time t;

 b) the radius of curvature of the path;

 c) the equation of the path in polar coordinates, using the x-axis as the line $\theta = 0$ and the y-axis as the line $\theta = \pi/2$.

39. A particle moves so that its position at time t has the polar coordinates $r = t$, $\theta = t$. Find the velocity $\mathbf{v}$, the acceleration $\mathbf{a}$, and the curvature κ at any time t.

40. Find an expression for the curvature of the curve whose equation in polar coordinates is $r = f(\theta)$.

41. a) Find the equation in *polar coordinates* of the curve

$$x = e^{2t} \cos t, \quad y = e^{2t} \sin t.$$

 b) Find the length of this curve from $t = 0$ to $t = 2\pi$.

42. Express the velocity vector in terms of $\mathbf{u}_r$ and $\mathbf{u}_\theta$ for a point moving in the xy-plane according to the law

$$\mathbf{r} = (t + 1)\mathbf{i} + (t - 1)\mathbf{j}.$$

43. The polar coordinates of a particle at time t are

$$r = e^{\omega t} + e^{-\omega t}, \quad \theta = t,$$

where ω is a constant. Find the acceleration vector when $t = 0$.

44. A slender rod, passing through the fixed point O, is rotating about O in a plane at the constant rate of 3 rad/min. An insect is crawling along the rod toward O at the constant rate of 1 in/min. Use polar coordinates in the plane, with point O as the origin, and assume that the insect starts at the point $r = 2$, $\theta = 0$.

 a) Find, in polar form, the vector velocity and vector acceleration of the insect when it is halfway to the origin.

 b) What will be the length of the path, in the plane, that the insect has traveled when it reaches the origin?

45. A smooth ball rolls inside a long hollow tube while the tube rotates with constant angular velocity ω about an axis perpendicular to the axis of the tube. Assuming no friction between the ball and the sides of the tube, show that the distance r from the axis of rotation to the ball satisfies the differential equation

$$d^2r/dt^2 - \omega^2 r = 0.$$

If at time $t = 0$ the ball is at rest (relative to the tube) at $r = a > 0$, find r as a function of t.

46. Find the orbit of a planet relative to the sun, assuming the sun to be fixed at the origin and the force acting on the planet to be directed toward the sun with magnitude $\gamma mM/r^2$ where γ is the universal gravitational constant, M is the mass of the sun, m is the mass of the planet, and r is its distance from the sun. Choose the initial line to pass through the perihelion point of the orbit, and assume the velocity at perihelion is v_0. Show that the path is a circle, ellipse, parabola, or hyperbola according as $v_0^2 r_0/\gamma M$ equals one, lies between one and two, equals two, or is greater than two.

12
INFINITE SERIES

12-1

INTRODUCTION

The division of $1 - x^{n+1}$ by $1 - x$ results in the equation

$$\frac{1 - x^{n+1}}{1 - x} = 1 + x + x^2 + \cdots + x^n. \tag{1}$$

But when $|x|$ is small enough for x^{n+1} to be omitted from the numerator on the left without disturbing the results of some practical application, we may replace the equality (1) by the approximation

$$\frac{1}{1 - x} \approx 1 + x + x^2 + \cdots + x^n. \tag{2}$$

When $|x| < 1$, this approximation can be used in computing, as an alternative to division by $1 - x$.

Just how reliable this approximation is depends on how small x is and on how large we take n. In general, when $|x| < 1$, the more terms we add the better the approximation becomes, and it is natural to ask what would happen if we could just keep on adding. As long as we kept $|x| < 1$, so that the successive powers of x in (2) became smaller and smaller, couldn't we actually write

$$\frac{1}{1 - x} = 1 + x + x^2 + \cdots + x^n + \cdots? \tag{3}$$

The answer is "Yes." For functions like $1/(1 - x)$ that have derivatives of all orders, we can write equalities like the one in (3) as long as we are careful about the domain of x and about what we mean by the sum of infinitely many terms.

The study of such sums, of what functions they represent on what domains, of how we can compute with them, and of what we can do with such sums that we could not do before we had them, is what this chapter is about. We will see why, for example, the approximation

$$\sin x \approx x - \frac{x^3}{6} \tag{4}$$

underestimates $\sin x$ by less than 0.0003 when $0 \leq x \leq 0.5$. And we will at last be able to find convenient expressions for estimating integrals like $\int_0^1 \sin x^2 \, dx$.

The way we proceed is to define an infinite sum like

$$1 + x + x^2 + x^3 + \cdots \tag{5}$$

for each x to be the limiting value of a sequence of partial sums

$$\begin{array}{cccc} \text{First} & \text{Second} & \text{Third} & \\ 1 + x, & 1 + x + x^2, & 1 + x + x^2 + x^3, & \dots. \end{array} \tag{6}$$

The additions within the partial sums pose no problem because there are only finitely many of them at each stage, so that it only remains to make clear what we mean by the limit of a sequence of such sums. This is best done by studying sequences in their own right. In the next article, therefore, we address the questions of what we mean by a sequence and the limit of a sequence, and of how to tell when a sequence has a limit.

We begin our study of sequences with a definition.

Definition 1. *A **sequence** is a function whose domain is the set of positive integers.*

Sequences are defined by rules the way other functions are, typical rules being

$$a(n) = n - 1, \qquad a(n) = 1 - \frac{1}{n}, \qquad a(n) = \frac{\ln n}{n^2}. \qquad \textbf{(1)}$$

To signal the fact that the domains are restricted to the set of positive integers, it is conventional to use a letter like n from the middle of the alphabet for the independent variable instead of the x, y, z, and t used so widely in other contexts. The formulas in the defining rules, however, like the ones above, are often valid for domains much larger than the set of positive integers. This can prove to be an advantage, as we shall see at the end of this article.

The numbers in the range of a sequence are called the *terms* of the sequence, the number $a(n)$ being called the *nth term*, or the term with *index n*. For example, if $a(n) = (n + 1)/n$, then the terms are:

First term　　Second term　Third term　　　　　　　　*nth* term

$$a(1) = 2, \qquad a(2) = \frac{3}{2}, \qquad a(3) = \frac{4}{3}, \qquad \ldots, \qquad a(n) = \frac{n + 1}{n}, \qquad \ldots \qquad \textbf{(2)}$$

When we use the simpler notation a_n for $a(n)$, the sequence in (2) becomes

$$a_1 = 2, \qquad a_2 = \tfrac{3}{2}, \qquad a_3 = \tfrac{4}{3}, \qquad \ldots, \qquad a_n = \frac{n + 1}{n}, \qquad \ldots \qquad \textbf{(3)}$$

To describe sequences, we often write the first few terms as well as a formula for the nth term.

EXAMPLE 1

We write:	For the sequence whose defining rule is:
$0, \quad 1, \quad 2, \quad \ldots, \quad n - 1, \quad \ldots$	$a_n = n - 1$
$1, \quad \dfrac{1}{2}, \quad \dfrac{1}{3}, \quad \ldots, \quad \dfrac{1}{n}, \quad \ldots$	$a_n = \dfrac{1}{n}$
$1, \quad -\dfrac{1}{2}, \quad \dfrac{1}{3}, \quad -\dfrac{1}{4}, \quad \ldots, \quad (-1)^{n+1}\dfrac{1}{n}, \quad \ldots$	$a_n = (-1)^{n+1}\dfrac{1}{n}$
$0, \quad \dfrac{1}{2}, \quad \dfrac{2}{3}, \quad \dfrac{3}{4}, \quad \ldots, \quad 1 - \dfrac{1}{n}, \quad \ldots$	$a_n = 1 - \dfrac{1}{n}$
$0, \quad -\dfrac{1}{2}, \quad \dfrac{2}{3}, \quad -\dfrac{3}{4}, \quad \ldots, \quad (-1)^{n+1}\left(1 - \dfrac{1}{n}\right), \quad \ldots$	$a_n = (-1)^{n+1}\left(1 - \dfrac{1}{n}\right)$
$3, \quad 3, \quad 3, \quad \ldots, \quad 3, \quad \ldots$	$a_n = 3$

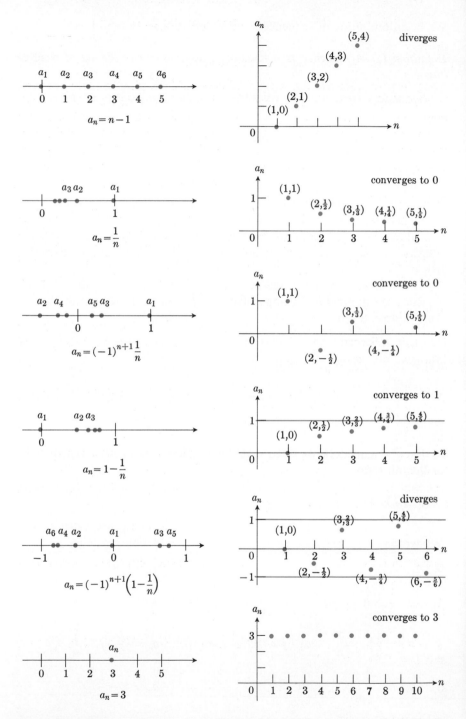

12–1 The sequences of Example 1 are graphed here in two different ways: by plotting the numbers a_n on a horizontal axis, and by plotting the points (n, a_n) in the coordinate plane.

We can, of course, use set notation to describe sequences, writing:

$\{(n, a_n)\}$　　　The sequence whose ordered pairs are (n, a_n)

or even

$\{a_n\}$　　　The sequence a_n

when such an abbreviation will not cause trouble. Both choices of notation lead to graphs. We can either plot the ordered pairs (n, a_n) in the coordinate plane, or plot the numbers a_n on a single axis (shown as a horizontal axis in Fig. 12–1). Plotting just the number a_n has the advantage of simplicity. A potential disadvantage, however, is the fact that several a_n's may turn out to be the same for different values of n, as they are in the sequence defined by the rule $a_n = 3$, in which every term is 3. The points (n, a_n) are distinct for different values of n.

As Fig. 12–1 shows, the sequences of Example 1 exhibit different kinds of behavior. The sequences $\{1/n\}$, $\{(-1)^{n+1}(1/n)\}$, and $\{1 - 1/n\}$ seem to approach single limiting values as n increases, and the sequence $\{3\}$ is already at a limiting value from the very first. On the other hand, terms of the sequence $\{(-1)^{n+1}(1 - 1/n)\}$ seem to accumulate near two different values, -1 and 1, while the terms of $\{n - 1\}$ get larger and larger and do not accumulate anywhere.

To distinguish sequences that approach a unique limiting value L, as n increases, from those that do not, we say that they *converge*, according to the following definition.

Definition 2.　*The sequence $\{(n, a_n)\}$ converges to the number L if to every positive number ϵ there corresponds an index N such that*

$$|a_n - L| < \epsilon \qquad \text{for all} \quad n > N. \tag{4}$$

In other words, $\{(n, a_n)\}$ converges to L if, for every positive ϵ, there is an index N such that all the terms after the Nth lie within ϵ of L. (See Fig. 12–2, and look once more at the sequences in Fig. 12–1.) We indicate the fact that $\{(n, a_n)\}$ converges to L by writing

$$\lim_{n \to \infty} a_n = L \qquad \text{or} \qquad a_n \to L \quad \text{as } n \to \infty,$$

and we call L the *limit* of the sequence $\{a_n\}$. If no such limit exists, we say that $\{a_n\}$ *diverges*.

EXAMPLE 2.　$\{1/n\}$ converges to 0.

To see why, we begin by writing down the inequality (4), with $a_n = 1/n$ and $L = 0$. This gives

$$|a_n - L| = \left| \frac{1}{n} - 0 \right| = \frac{1}{n} < \epsilon, \tag{5}$$

and therefore we seek an integer N such that

$$\frac{1}{n} < \epsilon \qquad \text{for all} \quad n > N. \tag{6}$$

12–2　$a_n \to L$ if L is a horizontal asymptote of $\{(n, a_n)\}$. In this figure, all the a_n's after a_N are within ϵ of L.

Certainly

$$\frac{1}{n} < \epsilon \qquad \text{for all} \quad n > \frac{1}{\epsilon}, \tag{7}$$

but there is no reason to expect $1/\epsilon$ to be an integer. This minor difficulty is easily overcome: We just choose any integer $N > 1/\epsilon$. Then every index n greater than N will automatically be greater than $1/\epsilon$. In short, for this choice of N we can guarantee (6). The criterion set forth in Definition 2 for convergence to 0 is satisfied.

EXAMPLE 3.   If k is any number, then the constant sequence $\{k\}$, defined by $a_n = k$ for all n, converges to k.

When we take both $a_n = k$ and $L = k$ on the left of the inequality in (4), we find

$$|a_n - L| = |k - k| = 0, \tag{8}$$

which is less than every positive ϵ for every $n \geq 1$.

EXAMPLE 4.   The sequence $\{(-1)^{n+1}(1 - 1/n)\}$ diverges. To see why, pick a positive ϵ smaller than 1 so that the bands shown in Fig. 12–3 about the lines $y = 1$ and $y = -1$ do not overlap. Any $\epsilon < 1$ will do. Convergence to 1 would require every point of the graph from some index on to lie inside the upper band, but this will never happen. As soon as a point (n, a_n) lies in the upper band, every alternate point starting with $(n + 1, a_{n+1})$ will lie in the lower band. Likewise, the sequence cannot converge to -1. On the other hand, because the terms of the sequence get increasingly close to 1 and -1 alternately, they never accumulate near any other value.

$$a_n = (-1)^{n+1}\left(1 - \frac{1}{n}\right)$$

Neither the ϵ interval about 1 nor the ϵ interval about -1 contains a complete tail of the sequence.

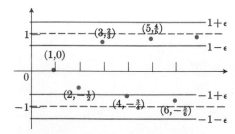

12–3   The sequence $\{(-1)^{n+1}[1 - (1/n)]\}$ diverges.

Neither of the ϵ bands shown here contains all the points (n, a_n) from some index onward.

REMARK 1. A *tail* of a sequence $\{a_n\}$ is the collection of all the terms whose indices are greater than some index N; in other words, one of the sets $\{a_n \mid n > N\}$. Another way to say $a_n \to L$ is to say that every ϵ-interval about L contains a tail. As Example 4 suggests, a sequence cannot have more than one limit. There cannot be two different numbers with the property that every ϵ-interval about each one contains a complete tail.

REMARK 2. The behavior of the sequence $\{(-1)^{n+1}(1 - 1/n)\}$ is qualitatively different from that of $\{n - 1\}$, which diverges because it outgrows every real number L. We describe the behavior of $\{n - 1\}$ by writing

$$\lim_{n \to \infty} (n - 1) = \infty.$$

In speaking of infinity as a limit of a sequence $\{a_n\}$, we do not mean that the difference between a_n and infinity becomes small as n increases. We mean that a_n becomes numerically large as n increases.

REMARK 3. Some sequences are defined *iteratively*, by giving a rule for computing the nth term from earlier terms in the sequence, and stating how to start the sequence. For example, Newton's method for finding a solution of an equation $f(x) = 0$ is to guess a first approximation x_1 and then to use the formula

$$x_{n+1} = x_n - \frac{f(x_n)}{f'(x_n)}$$

to generate, by iteration, a sequence $\{x_n\}$. In favorable circumstances, the sequence converges to a number L which satisfies the equation $f(L) = 0$. As a second example, setting

$$a_1 = 1, \qquad a_2 = 1,$$

and

$$a_n = a_{n-1} + a_{n-2} \qquad \text{for} \quad n \geq 3$$

defines a Fibonacci sequence:

$$1, \quad 1, \quad 2, \quad 3, \quad 5, \quad 8, \quad 13, \quad 21, \quad \ldots.$$

REMARK 4. Iteration is used as a method for solving many kinds of problems by computer. The technique is to start with a first approximation, use that to compute a second approximation, use the second to get a third, and so on. The idea is to generate a sequence whose terms approximate the solution with increasing accuracy.

The study of limits of sequences would be a cumbersome business if every question about convergence had to be answered by applying Definition 2 directly, as we have had to do so far. Fortunately there are three theorems that will make this process largely unnecessary from now on. The first two are the ones with which we began the study of limits of functions in Chapter 1. We restate them here in the notation of sequences.

Theorem 1.   *If $A = \lim_{n \to \infty} a_n$ and $B = \lim_{n \to \infty} b_n$ both exist and are finite, then*

i) $\lim \{a_n + b_n\} = A + B$,

ii) $\lim \{ka_n\} = kA$ (*k any number*),

iii) $\lim \{a_n \cdot b_n\} = A \cdot B$,

iv) $\lim \left\{ \dfrac{a_n}{b_n} \right\} = \dfrac{A}{B}$,   *provided $B \neq 0$ and b_n is never 0,*

it being understood that all of the limits are to be taken as $n \to \infty$.

By combining Theorem 1 with Examples 2 and 3, we can proceed immediately to

$$\lim_{n \to \infty} -\frac{1}{n} = -1 \cdot \lim_{n \to \infty} \frac{1}{n} = -1 \cdot 0 = 0,$$

$$\lim_{n \to \infty} \left(1 - \frac{1}{n} \right) = \lim_{n \to \infty} 1 - \lim_{n \to \infty} \frac{1}{n} = 1 - 0 = 1,$$

$$\lim_{n \to \infty} \frac{5}{n^2} = 5 \cdot \lim_{n \to \infty} \frac{1}{n} \cdot \lim_{n \to \infty} \frac{1}{n} = 5 \cdot 0 \cdot 0 = 0,$$

$$\lim_{n \to \infty} \frac{4 - 7n^6}{n^6 + 3} = \lim_{n \to \infty} \frac{(4/n^6) - 7}{1 + (3/n^6)} = \frac{0 - 7}{1 + 0} = -7.$$

A corollary of Theorem 1 that will be useful later on is that every nonzero multiple of a divergent sequence is divergent.

Corollary.   *If the sequence $\{a_n\}$ diverges, and if c is any number different from 0, then the sequence $\{ca_n\}$ diverges.*

Proof of the corollary.   Suppose, on the contrary, that $\{ca_n\}$ converges. Then, by taking $k = 1/c$ in part (ii) of Theorem 1, we see that the sequence

$$\left\{ \frac{1}{c} \cdot ca_n \right\} = \{a_n\}$$

converges. Thus $\{ca_n\}$ cannot converge unless $\{a_n\}$ converges. If $\{a_n\}$ does not converge, then $\{ca_n\}$ does not converge.   Q.E.D.

The next theorem is the sequence version of the *Sandwich Theorem* of Article 1–10.

Theorem 2.   *If $a_n \leq b_n \leq c_n$ for all n beyond some index N, and if $\lim a_n = \lim c_n = L$, then $\lim b_n = L$ also.*

An immediate consequence of Theorem 2 is that, if $|b_n| \leq c_n$ and $c_n \to 0$, then $b_n \to 0$ because $-c_n \leq b_n \leq c_n$. We use this fact in the next example.

EXAMPLE 5

$$\frac{\cos n}{n} \to 0 \qquad \text{because} \quad 0 \leq \left| \frac{\cos n}{n} \right| = \frac{|\cos n|}{n} \leq \frac{1}{n}.$$

EXAMPLE 6

$$\frac{1}{2^n} \to 0 \qquad \text{because} \quad 0 \le \frac{1}{2^n} \le \frac{1}{n}.$$

EXAMPLE 7

$$(-1)^n \frac{1}{n} \to 0 \qquad \text{because} \quad 0 \le \left| (-1)^n \frac{1}{n} \right| \le \frac{1}{n}.$$

The application of Theorems 1 and 2 is broadened by a theorem that says that the result of applying a continuous function to a convergent sequence is again a convergent sequence. We state the theorem without proof.

Theorem 3. *If $a_n \to L$ and if f is a function that is continuous at L and defined at all the a_n's, then $f(a_n) \to f(L)$.*

EXAMPLE 8. Because $\sqrt{x}$ is continuous at 1 and $(n+1)/n \to 1$,

$$\sqrt{\frac{n+1}{n}} \to \sqrt{1} = 1.$$

EXAMPLE 9. Because 2^x is continuous at 0 and $1/n \to 0$,

$$\sqrt[n]{2} = 2^{1/n} \to 2^0 = 1.$$

L'Hôpital's rule can be used to determine the limits of some sequences. The next example shows how.

EXAMPLE 10. Find $\lim_{n \to \infty} (\ln n)/n$.

Solution. The function $(\ln x)/x$ is defined for all $x \ge 1$ and agrees with the given sequence on the positive integers. Therefore $\lim_{n \to \infty} (\ln n)/n$ will equal $\lim_{x \to \infty} (\ln x)/x$ if the latter exists. A single application of l'Hôpital's rule shows that

$$\lim_{x \to \infty} \frac{\ln x}{x} = \lim_{x \to \infty} \frac{1/x}{1} = \frac{0}{1} = 0.$$

We conclude that $\lim_{n \to \infty} (\ln n)/n = 0$.

When we use l'Hôpital's rule to find the limit of a sequence, we often treat n as a continuous real variable, and differentiate directly with respect to n. This saves us from having to rewrite the formula for a_n as we did in Example 10.

EXAMPLE 11. Find $\lim_{n \to \infty} (2^n/5n)$.

Solution. By l'Hôpital's rule,

$$\lim_{n \to \infty} \frac{2^n}{5n} = \lim_{n \to \infty} \frac{2^n \cdot \ln 2}{5} = \infty.$$

PROBLEMS

Write a_1, a_2, a_3, and a_4 for each of the following sequences $\{a_n\}$. Determine which of the sequences converge and which diverge. Find the limit of each sequence that converges.

1. $a_n = \dfrac{1 - n}{n^2}$ 　　　 **2.** $a_n = \dfrac{n}{2^n}$

3. $a_n = \left(\dfrac{1}{3}\right)^n$ 　　　 **4.** $a_n = \dfrac{1}{n!}$

5. $a_n = \dfrac{(-1)^{n+1}}{2n - 1}$ 　 **6.** $a_n = 2 + (-1)^n$

7. $a_n = \cos \dfrac{n\pi}{2}$ 　　 **8.** $a_n = 8^{1/n}$

9. $a_n = \dfrac{(-1)^{n-1}}{\sqrt{n}}$ 　 **10.** $a_n = \sin^2 \dfrac{1}{n} + \cos^2 \dfrac{1}{n}$

Determine which of the following sequences $\{a_n\}$ converge and which diverge. Find the limit of each sequence that converges.

11. $a_n = \dfrac{1}{10n}$ 　　　 **12.** $a_n = \dfrac{n}{10}$

13. $a_n = 1 + \dfrac{(-1)^n}{n}$ 　 **14.** $a_n = \dfrac{1 + (-1)^n}{n}$

15. $a_n = (-1)^n \left(1 - \dfrac{1}{n}\right)$ 　 **16.** $a_n = 1 + (-1)^n$

17. $a_n = \dfrac{2n + 1}{1 - 3n}$ 　 **18.** $a_n = \dfrac{n^2 - n}{2n^2 + n}$

19. $a_n = \sqrt{\dfrac{2n}{n + 1}}$ 　 **20.** $a_n = \dfrac{\sin n}{n}$

21. $a_n = \sin \pi n$ 　　 **22.** $a_n = \sin \left(\dfrac{\pi}{2} + \dfrac{1}{n}\right)$

23. $a_n = n\pi \cos n\pi$ 　 **24.** $a_n = \dfrac{\sin^2 n}{2^n}$

25. $a_n = \dfrac{n^2}{(n + 1)^2}$ 　 **26.** $a_n = \dfrac{\sqrt{n - 1}}{\sqrt{n}}$

27. $a_n = \dfrac{1 - 5n^4}{n^4 + 8n^3}$ 　 **28.** $a_n = \sqrt[n]{3^{2n+1}}$

29. $a_n = \tanh n$ 　　 **30.** $a_n = \dfrac{\ln n}{\sqrt{n}}$

31. $a_n = \dfrac{2(n + 1) + 1}{2n + 1}$ 　 **32.** $a_n = \dfrac{(n + 1)!}{n!}$

33. $a_n = 5$ 　　　 **34.** $a_n = 5^n$

35. $a_n = (0.5)^n$ 　　 **36.** $a_n = \dfrac{10^{n+1}}{10^n}$

37. $a_n = \dfrac{n^n}{(n + 1)^{n+1}}$ 　 **38.** $a_n = (0.03)^{1/n}$

39. $a_n = \sqrt{2 - \dfrac{1}{n}}$ 　 **40.** $a_n = 2 + (0.1)^n$

41. $a_n = \dfrac{3^n}{n^3}$ 　　 **42.** $a_n = \dfrac{\ln (n + 1)}{n + 1}$

43. $a_n = \ln n - \ln (n + 1)$ 　 **44.** $a_n = \dfrac{1 - 2^n}{2^n}$

45. $a_n = \dfrac{n^2 - 2n + 1}{n - 1}$ 　 **46.** $a_n = \dfrac{n + (-1)^n}{n}$

47. $a_n = \left(-\dfrac{1}{2}\right)^n$ 　 **48.** $a_n = \dfrac{\ln n}{\ln 2n}$

49. $a_n = \tan^{-1} n$ 　　 **50.** $a_n = \sinh (\ln n)$

51. $a_n = n \sin \dfrac{1}{n}$ 　 **52.** $a_n = \dfrac{2n + \sin n}{n + \cos 5n}$

53. $a_n = \dfrac{n^2}{2n - 1} \sin \dfrac{1}{n}$ 　 **54.** $a_n = n\left(1 - \cos \dfrac{1}{n}\right)$

55. Show that $\lim_{n \to \infty} (n!/n^n) = 0$.

[*Hint.* Expand the numerator and denominator and compare the quotient with $1/n$.]

56. (*Calculator*) The formula $x_{n+1} = (x_n + a/x_n)/2$ is the one produced by Newton's method to generate a sequence of approximations to the positive solution of $x^2 - a = 0$, $a > 0$. Starting with $x_1 = 1$ and $a = 3$, use the formula to calculate successive terms of the sequence until you have approximated $\sqrt{3}$ as accurately as your calculator permits.

57. (*Calculator*) If your calculator has a square-root key, enter $x = 10$ and take successive square roots to approximate the terms of the sequence $10^{1/2}$, $10^{1/4}$, $10^{1/8}$, ..., continuing as far as your calculator permits. Repeat, with $x = 0.1$. Try other positive numbers above and below 1. When you have enough evidence, guess the answers to these questions: Does $\lim_{n \to \infty} x^{1/n}$ exist when $x > 0$? Does it matter what x is?

58. (*Calculator*) If you start with a reasonable value of x_1, then the rule $x_{n+1} = x_n + \cos x_n$ will generate a sequence that converges to $\pi/2$. Figure 12-4 shows why. The convergence is rapid. With $x_1 = 1$, calculate x_2, x_3, and x_4. Find out what happens when you start with $x_1 = 5$. Remember to use radians.

59. Suppose that $f(x)$ is defined for all $0 \le x \le 1$, that f is differentiable at $x = 0$, and that $f(0) = 0$. Define a sequence $\{a_n\}$ by the rule $a_n = nf(1/n)$. Show that $\lim a_n = f'(0)$.

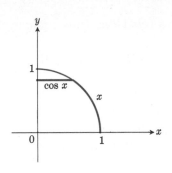

12–4 The length $\pi/2$ of the circular arc is approximated by $x + \cos x$.

Use the result of Problem 59 to find the limits of the sequences in Problems 60 and 61.

60. $a_n = n \tan^{-1} \dfrac{1}{n}$ **61.** $a_n = n(e^{1/n} - 1)$

62. Prove that a sequence $\{a_n\}$ cannot have two different limits L and L'. [*Hint.* Take $\epsilon = \frac{1}{2}|L - L'|$ in Eq. (4).]

63. Prove that, if f is a function that is defined for $x > 0$, and if $\lim_{x\to\infty} f(x) = L$, then $\lim_{n\to\infty} f(n) = L$. [*Hint.* If $|f(x) - L| < \epsilon$ for all x beyond some x_0, then $|f(x) - L| < \epsilon$ for all x beyond some integer $N > x_0$.]

64. Prove Theorem 2.

65. Prove Theorem 3.

Some limits arise so frequently that they are worth special attention. In this article we investigate these limits and look at examples in which they occur.

12-3

LIMITS THAT ARISE FREQUENTLY

1. $\displaystyle\lim_{n\to\infty} \frac{\ln n}{n} = 0$ **2.** $\displaystyle\lim_{n\to\infty} \sqrt[n]{n} = 1$

3. $\displaystyle\lim_{n\to\infty} x^{1/n} = 1$ $(x > 0)$ **4.** $\displaystyle\lim_{n\to\infty} x^n = 0$ $(|x| < 1)$

5. $\displaystyle\lim_{n\to\infty} \left(1 + \frac{x}{n}\right)^n = e^x$ (any x)   **6.** $\displaystyle\lim_{n\to\infty} \frac{x^n}{n!} = 0$ (any x)

Calculation of the Limits

1. $\displaystyle\lim_{n\to\infty} \frac{\ln n}{n} = 0$

This limit was calculated in Example 10 of Article 12–2.

2. $\displaystyle\lim_{n\to\infty} \sqrt[n]{n} = 1$

Let $a_n = n^{1/n}$. Then

$$\ln a_n = \ln n^{1/n} = \frac{1}{n}\ln n \to 0, \tag{1}$$

so that, by applying Theorem 3 of Article 12–2 to $f(x) = e^x$, we have

$$a_n = n^{1/n} = e^{\ln a_n} \to e^0 = 1. \tag{2}$$

3. $\displaystyle\lim_{n\to\infty} x^{1/n} = 1$, if $x > 0$

Let $a_n = x^{1/n}$. Then

$$\ln a_n = \ln x^{1/n} = \frac{1}{n}\ln x \to 0, \tag{3}$$

because x remains fixed while n gets large. Thus, again by Theorem 3, with $f(x) = e^x$,

$$a_n = x^{1/n} = e^{\ln a_n} \to e^0 = 1. \tag{4}$$

4. $\lim\limits_{n \to \infty} x^n = 0$, if $|x| < 1$

Our scheme here is to show that the criteria of Definition 2 of Article 12–2 are satisfied, with $L = 0$. That is, we will show that to each $\epsilon > 0$ there corresponds an index N so large that

$$|x^n| < \epsilon \quad \text{for} \quad n > N. \tag{5}$$

Since $\epsilon^{1/n} \to 1$, while $|x| < 1$, there is an index N for which

$$|x| < \epsilon^{1/N}. \tag{6}$$

In other words,

$$|x^N| = |x|^N < \epsilon. \tag{7}$$

This is the index we seek, because

$$|x^n| < |x^N| \quad \text{for} \quad n > N. \tag{8}$$

Combining (7) and (8) produces

$$|x^n| < |x^N| < \epsilon \quad \text{for} \quad n > N, \tag{9}$$

which is just what we needed to show.

5. $\lim\limits_{n \to \infty} \left(1 + \dfrac{x}{n}\right)^n = e^x$ (any x)

Let

$$a_n = \left(1 + \frac{x}{n}\right)^n.$$

Then

$$\ln a_n = \ln\left(1 + \frac{x}{n}\right)^n = n \ln\left(1 + \frac{x}{n}\right) \to x,$$

as we can see by the following application of l'Hôpital's rule, in which we differentiate with respect to n:

$$\lim_{n \to \infty} n \ln\left(1 + \frac{x}{n}\right) = \lim_{n \to \infty} \frac{\ln\left(1 + x/n\right)}{1/n}$$

$$= \lim_{n \to \infty} \frac{\left(\dfrac{1}{1 + x/n}\right) \cdot \left(-\dfrac{x}{n^2}\right)}{-1/n^2}$$

$$= \lim_{n \to \infty} \frac{x}{1 + x/n} = x.$$

Thus,

$$a_n = \left(1 + \frac{x}{n}\right)^n = e^{\ln a_n} \to e^x.$$

6. $\displaystyle\lim_{n \to \infty} \frac{x^n}{n!} = 0$ **(any** x**)**

Since

$$-\frac{|x|^n}{n!} \le \frac{x^n}{n!} \le \frac{|x|^n}{n!},$$

all we really need to show is that $|x|^n/n! \to 0$. The first step is to choose an integer $M > |x|$, so that

$$\frac{|x|}{M} < 1 \quad \text{and} \quad \left(\frac{|x|}{M}\right)^n \to 0.$$

We then restrict our attention to values of $n > M$. For these values of n, we can write

$$\frac{|x|^n}{n!} = \frac{|x|^n}{1 \cdot 2 \cdots M \cdot \underbrace{(M+1)(M+2) \cdots n}_{(n-M)\text{ factors}}}$$

$$\le \frac{|x|^n}{M! \, M^{n-M}} = \frac{|x|^n M^M}{M! \, M^n} = \frac{M^M}{M!}\left(\frac{|x|}{M}\right)^n.$$

Thus,

$$0 \le \frac{|x|^n}{n!} \le \frac{M^M}{M!}\left(\frac{|x|}{M}\right)^n.$$

Now, the constant $M^M/M!$ does not change with n. Thus the Sandwich Theorem tells us that

$$\frac{|x|^n}{n!} \to 0 \quad \text{because} \quad \left(\frac{|x|}{M}\right)^n \to 0. \qquad \text{Q.E.D.}$$

A large number of limits can be found directly from the six limits we have just calculated.

EXAMPLES

1. If $|x| < 1$, then $x^{n+4} = x^4 \cdot x^n \to x^4 \cdot 0 = 0$.

2. $\sqrt[n]{2n} = \sqrt[n]{2}\,\sqrt[n]{n} \to 1 \cdot 1 = 1$.

3. $\left(1 + \dfrac{1}{n}\right)^{2n} = \left[\left(1 + \dfrac{1}{n}\right)^n\right]^2 \to e^2$.

4. $\dfrac{100^n}{n!} \to 0$

5. $\dfrac{x^{n+1}}{(n+1)!} = \dfrac{x}{(n+1)} \cdot \dfrac{x^n}{n!} \to 0 \cdot 0 = 0.$

Still other limits can be calculated by using logarithms or l'Hôpital's rule, as in the calculations of limits (2), (3), and (5) at the beginning of this article.

EXAMPLE 6. Find $\lim_{n \to \infty} (\ln (3n + 5))/n$.

Solution. By l'Hôpital's rule,

$$\lim_{n \to \infty} \frac{\ln (3n + 5)}{n} = \lim_{n \to \infty} \frac{3/(3n + 5)}{1} = 0.$$

EXAMPLE 7. Find $\lim_{n \to \infty} \sqrt[n]{3n + 5}$.

Solution. Let

$$a_n = \sqrt[n]{3n + 5} = (3n + 5)^{1/n}.$$

Then,

$$\ln a_n = \ln (3n + 5)^{1/n} = \frac{\ln (3n + 5)}{n} \to 0,$$

as in Example 6. Therefore,

$$a_n = e^{\ln a_n} \to e^0 = 1,$$

by Theorem 3 of Article 12–2.

PROBLEMS

Determine which of the following sequences $\{a_n\}$ converge and which diverge. Find the limit of each sequence that converges.

1. $a_n = \dfrac{1 + \ln n}{n}$

2. $a_n = \dfrac{\ln n}{3n}$

3. $a_n = \dfrac{(-4)^n}{n!}$

4. $a_n = \sqrt[n]{10n}$

5. $a_n = (0.5)^n$

6. $a_n = \dfrac{1}{(0.9)^n}$

7. $a_n = \left(1 + \dfrac{7}{n}\right)^n$

8. $a_n = \left(\dfrac{n + 5}{n}\right)^n$

9. $a_n = \dfrac{\ln (n + 1)}{n}$

10. $a_n = \sqrt[n]{n + 1}$

11. $a_n = \dfrac{n!}{10^{6n}}$

12. $a_n = \dfrac{1}{\sqrt{2^n}}$

13. $a_n = \sqrt[2n]{n}$

14. $a_n = (n + 4)^{1/(n + 4)}$

15. $a_n = \dfrac{1}{3^{2n-1}}$

16. $a_n = \ln \left(1 + \dfrac{1}{n}\right)^n$

17. $a_n = \left(\dfrac{n}{n + 1}\right)^n$

18. $a_n = \left(1 + \dfrac{1}{n}\right)^{-n}$

19. $a_n = \dfrac{\ln (2n + 1)}{n}$

20. $a_n = \sqrt[n]{2n + 1}$

21. $a_n = \sqrt[n]{\dfrac{x^n}{2n + 1}}, \quad x > 0$

22. $a_n = \sqrt[n]{n^2}$

23. $a_n = \sqrt[n]{n^2 + n}$

24. $a_n = \dfrac{3^n \cdot 6^n}{2^{-n} \cdot n!}$

25. $a_n = \left(\dfrac{3}{n}\right)^{1/n}$

26. $a_n = \sqrt[n]{4^n n}$

27. $a_n = \left(1 - \dfrac{1}{n}\right)^n$

28. $a_n = \left(1 - \dfrac{1}{n^2}\right)^n$

29. $a_n = \dfrac{1}{n} \displaystyle\int_1^n \dfrac{1}{x}\,dx$ **30.** $a_n = \displaystyle\int_1^n \dfrac{1}{x^p}\,dx, \quad p > 1$ **33.** $\dfrac{2^n}{n!} < 10^{-9}$

[*Hint.* If you do not have a factorial key, then write

(*Calculator*) In Problems 31–33, use a calculator to find a value of N such that the given inequality is satisfied for $n \ge N$.

$$\frac{2^n}{n!} = \left(\frac{2}{1}\right)\left(\frac{2}{2}\right) \cdots \left(\frac{2}{n}\right).$$

That is, calculate successive terms by multiplying by 2 and dividing by the next value of n.]

31. $\left|\sqrt[n]{0.5} - 1\right| < 10^{-3}$ **32.** $\left|\sqrt[n]{n} - 1\right| < 10^{-3}$

Infinite series are sequences of a special kind.

12-4
INFINITE SERIES

Definition

1. *If $\{a_n\}$ is a sequence, and*

$$s_n = a_1 + a_2 + \cdots + a_n,$$

*then the sequence $\{s_n\}$ is called an **infinite series**.*

2. *Instead of $\{s_n\}$ we usually use the notation*

$$\sum_{n=1}^{\infty} a_n$$

for the series, because it shows how the sums s_n are to be constructed.

3. *The number a_n is called the nth* term *of the series (it is still the nth term of the sequence $\{a_n\}$) and the number s_n is the nth **partial sum** of the series.*

4. *If the sequence $\{s_n\}$ of partial sums converges to a finite limit L, we say that the series $\sum_{n=1}^{\infty} a_n$ **converges** to L or that its **sum** is L, and we write*

$$\sum_{n=1}^{\infty} a_n = L \qquad or \qquad a_1 + a_2 + \cdots + a_n + \cdots = L.$$

*If no such limit exists, that is if $\{s_n\}$ diverges, we say that the series $\sum_{n=1}^{\infty} a_n$ **diverges**.*

We shall illustrate the method of finding the sum of an infinite series with the repeating decimal

$$0.3333\ldots = \frac{3}{10} + \frac{3}{100} + \frac{3}{1000} + \frac{3}{10{,}000} + \cdots$$

$$s_1 = \frac{3}{10},$$

$$s_2 = \frac{3}{10} + \frac{3}{10^2},$$

$$\vdots$$

$$s_n = \frac{3}{10} + \frac{3}{10^2} + \cdots + \frac{3}{10^n}.$$

We can obtain a simple expression for s_n in closed form as follows: We multiply both sides of the equation for s_n by $\frac{1}{10}$ and obtain

$$\frac{1}{10}s_n = \frac{3}{10^2} + \frac{3}{10^3} + \cdots + \frac{3}{10^n} + \frac{3}{10^{n+1}}.$$

When we subtract this from s_n, we have

$$s_n - \frac{1}{10}s_n = \frac{3}{10} - \frac{3}{10^{n+1}} = \frac{3}{10}\left(1 - \frac{3}{10^n}\right).$$

Therefore,

$$\frac{9}{10}s_n = \frac{3}{10}\left(1 - \frac{1}{10^n}\right),$$

$$s_n = \frac{3}{9}\left(1 - \frac{1}{10^n}\right).$$

As $n \to \infty$, $\left(\frac{1}{10}\right)^n \to 0$ and

$$\lim_{n \to \infty} s_n = \frac{3}{9} = \frac{1}{3}.$$

We therefore say that the sum of the infinite series

$$\frac{3}{10^1} + \frac{3}{10^2} + \frac{3}{10^3} + \cdots + \frac{3}{10^n} + \cdots$$

is $\frac{1}{3}$, and we write

$$\sum_{n=1}^{\infty} \frac{3}{10^n} = \frac{1}{3}.$$

A repeating decimal is a special kind of *geometric series*.

Definition.   *A series of the form*

$$a + ar + ar^2 + ar^3 + \cdots + ar^{n-1} + \cdots \tag{1}$$

*is called a **geometric series**. The ratio of any term to the one before it is r.*

The ratio r can be positive, as in

$$1 + \frac{1}{2} + \frac{1}{4} + \cdots + \frac{1}{2^{n-1}} + \cdots, \tag{2}$$

or negative, as in

$$1 - \frac{1}{3} + \frac{1}{9} - \cdots + (-1)^n \frac{1}{3^{n-1}} + \cdots. \tag{3}$$

The sum of the first n terms of (1) is

$$s_n = a + ar + ar^2 + \cdots + ar^{n-1}. \tag{4}$$

Multiplying both sides of (4) by r gives

$$rs_n = ar + ar^2 + \cdots + ar^{n-1} + ar^n. \tag{5}$$

When we subtract (5) from (4), nearly all the terms cancel on the right side, leaving

$$s_n - rs_n = a - ar^n,$$

or

$$(1 - r)s_n = a(1 - r^n). \tag{6}$$

If $r \neq 1$, we may divide (6) by $(1 - r)$ to obtain

$$s_n = \frac{a(1 - r^n)}{1 - r}, \qquad r \neq 1. \tag{7a}$$

On the other hand, if $r = 1$ in (4), we get

$$s_n = na, \qquad r = 1. \tag{7b}$$

We are interested in the limit as $n \to \infty$ in Eqs. (7a) and (7b). Clearly, (7b) has no finite limit if $a \neq 0$. If $a = 0$, the series (1) is just

$$0 + 0 + 0 + \cdots,$$

which converges to the sum zero.

If $r \neq 1$, we use (7a). In the right side of (7a), n appears only in the expression r^n. This approaches zero as $n \to \infty$ if $|r| < 1$. Therefore,

$$\lim_{n \to \infty} s_n = \lim_{n \to \infty} \frac{a(1 - r^n)}{1 - r}$$

$$= \frac{a}{1 - r}, \qquad \text{if} \quad |r| < 1. \tag{8}$$

If $|r| > 1$, then $|r^n| \to \infty$, and (1) diverges.

The remaining case is where $r = -1$. Then $s_1 = a$, $s_2 = a - a = 0$, $s_3 = a$, $s_4 = 0$, and so on. If $a \neq 0$, this sequence of partial sums has no limit as $n \to \infty$, and the series (1) diverges.

We have thus proved the following theorem.

Theorem 1.   The geometric series theorem. *If $|r| < 1$, the geometric series*

$$a + ar + ar^2 + \cdots + ar^{n-1} + \cdots$$

converges to $a/(1 - r)$. If $|r| \geq 1$, the series diverges unless $a = 0$. If $a = 0$, the series converges to 0.

EXAMPLE 1.   A ball is dropped from a meters above a flat surface. Each time the ball hits after falling a distance h, it rebounds a distance rh, where r is a positive number less than one. Find the total distance the ball travels up and down.

Solution.   (See Fig. 12–5.) The distance is given by the series

$$s = a + 2ar + 2ar^2 + 2ar^3 + \cdots$$

The terms following the first term form a geometric series of sum $2ar/(1 - r)$.

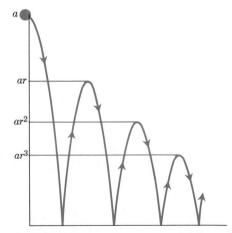

12–5 The height of each rebound is reduced by the factor r.

Hence the distance is

$$s = a + \frac{2ar}{1 - r} = a\frac{1 + r}{1 - r}.$$

For instance, if a is 6 meters and $r = \frac{2}{3}$, the distance is

$$s = 6\frac{1 + \frac{2}{3}}{1 - \frac{2}{3}} = 30 \text{ m}.$$

EXAMPLE 2.   If we take $a = 1$ and $r = x$ in the geometric series theorem, we obtain

$$\frac{1}{1 - x} = 1 + x + x^2 + \cdots + x^{n-1} + \cdots, \qquad |x| < 1, \tag{9}$$

which is the result we sought in Article 12–1.

To find the sum of the geometric series of Theorem 1, we first found a closed expression for s_n and then used our experience with sequences to find $\lim_{n \to \infty} s_n$. We use the same procedure in the next example.

EXAMPLE 3.   Determine whether $\sum_{n=1}^{\infty} [1/(n(n + 1))]$ converges. If it does, find the sum.

Solution.   We begin by looking for a pattern in the sequence of partial sums that might lead us to a closed expression for s_k. The key to success here, as in the integration

$$\int \frac{dx}{x(x + 1)} = \int \frac{dx}{x} - \int \frac{dx}{x + 1},$$

is the use of partial fractions:

$$\frac{1}{k(k + 1)} = \frac{1}{k} - \frac{1}{k + 1}.$$

This permits us to write the partial sum

$$\sum_{n=1}^{k} \frac{1}{n(n + 1)} = \frac{1}{1 \cdot 2} + \frac{1}{2 \cdot 3} + \cdots + \frac{1}{k \cdot (k + 1)}$$

as

$$s_k = \left(\frac{1}{1} - \frac{1}{2}\right) + \left(\frac{1}{2} - \frac{1}{3}\right) + \cdots + \left(\frac{1}{k} - \frac{1}{k + 1}\right).$$

By removing parentheses on the right, and combining terms, we find that

$$s_k = 1 - \frac{1}{k + 1} = \frac{k}{k + 1}. \tag{10}$$

From this formulation of s_k, we see immediately that $s_k \to 1$. Therefore the series does converge, and

$$\sum_{n=1}^{\infty} \frac{1}{n(n+1)} = 1. \tag{11}$$

There are, of course, other series that diverge besides geometric series with $|r| \geq 1$.

EXAMPLE 4. The series

$$\sum_{n=1}^{\infty} n^2 = 1 + 4 + 9 + \cdots + n^2 + \cdots$$

diverges because the partial sums grow beyond every number L. The number $s_n = 1 + 4 + 9 + \cdots + n^2$ is greater than or equal to n^2 at each stage.

EXAMPLE 5. The series

$$\sum_{n=1}^{\infty} \frac{n+1}{n} = \frac{2}{1} + \frac{3}{2} + \frac{4}{3} + \cdots + \frac{n+1}{n} + \cdots$$

diverges. The sequence of partial sums eventually outgrows every preassigned number: each term is greater than 1, so the sum of n terms is greater than n.

A series can diverge without its partial sums ever becoming large. For instance, the partial sums may oscillate between two extremes, as they do in the next example.

EXAMPLE 6. $\sum_{n=1}^{\infty} (-1)^{n+1}$ diverges because its partial sums alternate between 1 and 0:

$$s_1 = (-1)^2 = 1,$$
$$s_2 = (-1)^2 + (-1)^3 = 1 - 1 = 0,$$
$$s_3 = (-1)^2 + (-1)^3 + (-1)^4 = 1 - 1 + 1 = 1,$$

and so on.

The next theorem provides a quick way to detect the kind of divergence that occurred in Examples 4, 5, and 6.

Theorem 2. *The nth-term test for divergence. If* $\lim_{n \to \infty} a_n \neq 0$, *or if* $\lim_{n \to \infty} a_n$ *fails to exist, then* $\sum_{n=1}^{\infty} a_n$ *diverges.*

When we apply Theorem 2 to the series in Examples 4, 5, and 6, we find that:

$$\sum_{n=1}^{\infty} n^2 \qquad \text{diverges because } n^2 \to \infty;$$

$$\sum_{n=1}^{\infty} \frac{n+1}{n} \qquad \text{diverges because } \frac{n+1}{n} \to 1 \neq 0;$$

$$\sum_{n=1}^{\infty} (-1)^{n+1} \qquad \text{diverges because } \lim_{n \to \infty} (-1)^{n+1} \text{ does not exist.}$$

Proof of the theorem. We prove Theorem 2 by showing that if $\sum a_n$ converges, then $\lim_{n\to\infty} a_n = 0$. Let

$$s_n = a_1 + a_2 + \cdots + a_n,$$

and suppose that $\sum a_n$ converges to S; that is $s_n \to S$. Then, corresponding to any preassigned number $\epsilon > 0$, there is an index N such that all the terms of the sequence $\{s_n\}$ after the Nth one lie between $S - (\epsilon/2)$ and $S + (\epsilon/2)$. Hence, no two of them may differ by as much as ϵ. That is, if m and n are both greater than N, then

$$|s_n - s_m| < \epsilon.$$

In particular, this inequality holds if $m = n - 1$ and $n > N + 1$, so that

$$|s_n - s_{n-1}| = |a_n| < \epsilon \qquad \text{when} \quad n > N + 1.$$

Since ϵ was any positive number whatsoever, this means that

$$\lim_{n \to \infty} a_n = 0. \qquad\qquad \text{Q.E.D.}$$

Because of how it is proved, Theorem 2 is often stated in the following shorter way.

Theorem 3. *If $\sum_{n=1}^{\infty} a_n$ converges, then $a_n \to 0$.*

A word of caution. Theorem 3 does *not* say that if $a_n \to 0$ then $\sum a_n$ converges. A series $\sum a_n$ may diverge even though $a_n \to 0$. Thus, the condition $\lim a_n = 0$ is a necessary, but not a sufficient condition for the series $\sum a_n$ to converge.

EXAMPLE 7. The series

$$1 + \underbrace{\frac{1}{2} + \frac{1}{2}}_{2 \text{ terms}} + \underbrace{\frac{1}{4} + \frac{1}{4} + \frac{1}{4} + \frac{1}{4}}_{4 \text{ terms}} + \underbrace{\frac{1}{8} + \frac{1}{8} + \cdots + \frac{1}{8}}_{8 \text{ terms}} + \cdots \\ + \underbrace{\frac{1}{2^n} + \frac{1}{2^n} + \cdots + \frac{1}{2^n}}_{2^n \text{ terms}} + \cdots$$

diverges even though its terms form a sequence that converges to 0.

Whenever we have two convergent series we can add them, subtract them, and multiply them by constants, to make other convergent series. The next theorem gives the details.

Theorem 4. *If $A = \sum_{n=1}^{\infty} a_n$ and $B = \sum_{n=1}^{\infty} b_n$ both exist and are finite, then*

i) $\sum_{n=1}^{\infty} (a_n + b_n) = A + B;$

ii) $\sum_{n=1}^{\infty} ka_n = k \sum_{n=1}^{\infty} a_n = kA$ *(k any number).*

Proof of the theorem.   Let

$$A_n = a_1 + a_2 + \cdots + a_n, \qquad B_n = b_1 + b_2 + \cdots + b_n.$$

Then the partial sums of $\sum_{n=1}^{\infty} (a_n + b_n)$ are:

$$S_n = (a_1 + b_1) + (a_2 + b_2) + \cdots + (a_n + b_n)$$
$$= (a_1 + \cdots + a_n) + (b_1 + \cdots + b_n)$$
$$= A_n + B_n.$$

Since $A_n \to A$ and $B_n \to B$, we have $S_n \to A + B$. The partial sums of $\sum_{n=1}^{\infty} (ka_n)$ are:

$$S_n = ka_1 + ka_2 + \cdots + ka_n$$
$$= k(a_1 + a_2 + \cdots + a_n)$$
$$= kA_n,$$

which converge to kA.   Q.E.D.

REMARK 1.   If you think there should be two more parts of Theorem 4 to match those of Theorem 1, Article 12–2, see Problems 44–46. Also, see Problem 41, Article 12–5, and Problem 39, Article 12–7.

Part (ii) of Theorem 4 says that every multiple of a convergent series converges. Then, when we take $k = 1/c$ in part (ii) of Theorem 4, we find that *nonzero* multiple of a divergent series diverges.

Corollary. *If $\sum_{n=1}^{\infty} a_n$ diverges, and if c is any number different from 0, then the series of multiples $\sum_{n=1}^{\infty} ca_n$ diverges.*

Proof of the corollary.   Suppose, to the contrary, that $\sum_{n=1}^{\infty} ca_n$ actually converges. Then, when we take $k = 1/c$ in part (ii) of Theorem 4, we find that

$$\frac{1}{c} \cdot \sum_{n=1}^{\infty} ca_n = \sum_{n=1}^{\infty} \frac{1}{c} \cdot ca_n = \sum_{n=1}^{\infty} a_n$$

converges. That is, $\sum_{n=1}^{\infty} ca_n$ cannot converge unless $\sum_{n=1}^{\infty} a_n$ also converges. Thus, if $\sum_{n=1}^{\infty} a_n$ diverges, then $\sum_{n=1}^{\infty} ca_n$ must diverge.   Q.E.D.

REMARK 2. An immediate consequence of Theorem 4 is that, if $A = \sum_{n=1}^{\infty} a_n$ and $B = \sum_{n=1}^{\infty} b_n$, then

$$\sum (a_n - b_n) = \sum a_n + \sum (-1)b_n = \sum a_n - \sum b_n = A - B. \qquad (12)$$

The series $\sum_{n=1}^{\infty} (a_n - b_n)$ is called the *difference* of $\sum_{n=1}^{\infty} a_n$ and $\sum_{n=1}^{\infty} b_n$, while $\sum_{n=1}^{\infty} (a_n + b_n)$ is called their *sum*.

EXAMPLE 8

a) $\sum_{n=1}^{\infty} \dfrac{4}{2^{n-1}} = 4 \sum_{n=1}^{\infty} \dfrac{1}{2^{n-1}} = 4 \dfrac{1}{1 - \frac{1}{2}} = 8;$

b) $\sum_{n=0}^{\infty} \dfrac{3^n - 2^n}{6^n} = \sum_{n=0}^{\infty} \left(\dfrac{1}{2^n} - \dfrac{1}{3^n} \right)$

$$= \sum_{n=0}^{\infty} \frac{1}{2^n} - \sum_{n=0}^{\infty} \frac{1}{3^n}$$

$$= \frac{1}{1 - \frac{1}{2}} - \frac{1}{1 - \frac{1}{3}}$$

$$= 2 - \tfrac{3}{2}$$

$$= \tfrac{1}{2}.$$

REMARK 3. A finite number of terms can always be deleted from or added to a series without altering its convergence or divergence. If $\sum_{n=1}^{\infty} a_n$ converges and k is an index greater than 1, then $\sum_{n=k}^{\infty} a_n$ converges, and

$$\sum_{n=1}^{\infty} a_n = a_1 + a_2 + \cdots + a_{k-1} + \sum_{n=k}^{\infty} a_n. \qquad (13)$$

Conversely, if $\sum_{n=k}^{\infty} a_n$ converges for any $k > 1$, then $\sum_{n=1}^{\infty} a_n$ converges and the sums continue to be related as in Eq. (13). Thus, for example,

$$\sum_{n=1}^{\infty} \frac{1}{5^n} = \frac{1}{5} + \frac{1}{25} + \frac{1}{125} + \sum_{n=4}^{\infty} \frac{1}{5^n} \qquad (14)$$

and

$$\sum_{n=4}^{\infty} \frac{1}{5^n} = \sum_{n=1}^{\infty} \frac{1}{5^n} - \frac{1}{5} - \frac{1}{25} - \frac{1}{125}. \qquad (15)$$

Note that while the addition or removal of a finite number of terms from a series has no effect on the convergence or divergence of the series, these operations can change the *sum* of a convergent series.

REMARK 4. The indexing of the terms of a series can be changed without altering convergence of the series. For example, the geometric series that starts with

$$1 + \frac{1}{2} + \frac{1}{4} + \cdots$$

can be described as

$$\sum_{n=0}^{\infty} \frac{1}{2^n} \quad \text{or} \quad \sum_{n=-4}^{\infty} \frac{1}{2^{n+4}} \quad \text{or} \quad \sum_{n=5}^{\infty} \frac{1}{2^{n-5}}. \qquad (16)$$

The partial sums remain the same no matter what indexing is chosen, so that we are free to start indexing with whatever integer we want. Preference is usually given to an indexing that leads to a simple expression. In Example 8(b) we chose to start with $n = 0$ instead of $n = 1$, because this allowed us to describe the series we had in mind as:

$$\sum_{n=0}^{\infty} \frac{3^n - 2^n}{6^n} \quad \text{instead of} \quad \sum_{n=1}^{\infty} \frac{3^{n-1} - 2^{n-1}}{6^{n-1}}. \qquad (17)$$

PROBLEMS

In Problems 1 through 8, find a closed expression for the sum s_n of the first n terms of each series. Then compute the sum of the series if the series converges.

1. $\dfrac{1}{2 \cdot 3} + \dfrac{1}{3 \cdot 4} + \dfrac{1}{4 \cdot 5} + \cdots + \dfrac{1}{(n+1)(n+2)} + \cdots$

2. $\ln \dfrac{1}{2} + \ln \dfrac{2}{3} + \ln \dfrac{3}{4} + \cdots + \ln \dfrac{n}{n+1} + \cdots$

3. $1 + e^{-1} + e^{-2} + \cdots + e^{-(n-1)} + \cdots$

4. $1 - \dfrac{1}{2} + \dfrac{1}{4} - \dfrac{1}{8} + \cdots + (-1)^{n-1} \dfrac{1}{2^{n-1}} + \cdots$

5. $1 - 2 + 4 - 8 + \cdots + (-1)^{n-1} 2^{n-1} + \cdots$

6. $2 + \dfrac{2}{3} + \dfrac{2}{9} + \dfrac{2}{27} + \cdots + \dfrac{2}{3^{n-1}} + \cdots$

7. $\dfrac{9}{100} + \dfrac{9}{100^2} + \dfrac{9}{100^3} + \cdots + \dfrac{9}{100^n} + \cdots$

8. $1 + 2 + 3 + \cdots + n + \cdots$

9. The series in Problem 1 can be described as

$$\sum_{n=1}^{\infty} \frac{1}{(n+1)(n+2)}.$$

It can also be described as a summation beginning with $n = -1$:

$$\sum_{n=-1}^{\infty} \frac{1}{(n+3)(n+4)}.$$

Describe the series as a summation beginning with
a) $n = -2$ **b)** $n = 0$ **c)** $n = 5$.

10. A ball is dropped from a height of 4 m. Each time it strikes the pavement after falling from a height of h meters, it rebounds to a height of $0.75h$ meters. Find the total distance traveled up and down by the ball.

In Problems 11 through 14, write out the fourth partial sum of each series. Then find the sum of the series.

11. $\displaystyle\sum_{n=0}^{\infty} \frac{1}{4^n}$ **12.** $\displaystyle\sum_{n=2}^{\infty} \frac{1}{4^n}$

13. $\displaystyle\sum_{n=1}^{\infty} \frac{7}{4^n}$ **14.** $\displaystyle\sum_{n=0}^{\infty} (-1)^n \frac{5}{4^n}$

Find the sum of each series.

15. $\displaystyle\sum_{n=0}^{\infty} \left(\frac{5}{2^n} + \frac{1}{3^n} \right)$ **16.** $\displaystyle\sum_{n=0}^{\infty} \left(\frac{5}{2^n} - \frac{1}{3^n} \right)$

17. $\displaystyle\sum_{n=0}^{\infty} \left(\frac{2^n}{5^n} \right)$ **18.** $\displaystyle\sum_{n=0}^{\infty} \left(\frac{2^{n+1}}{5^n} \right)$

Use partial fractions to find the sum of each series.

19. $\displaystyle\sum_{n=1}^{\infty} \frac{4}{(4n-3)(4n+1)}$ **20.** $\displaystyle\sum_{n=1}^{\infty} \frac{1}{(4n-3)(4n+1)}$

21. $\displaystyle\sum_{n=3}^{\infty} \frac{4}{(4n-3)(4n+1)}$ **22.** $\displaystyle\sum_{n=1}^{\infty} \frac{2n+1}{n^2(n+1)^2}$

23. a) Express the repeating decimal

$$0.234 \; 234 \; 234 \ldots$$

as an infinite series, and give the sum as a ratio p/q of two integers.
b) Is it true that *every* repeating decimal is a rational number p/q? Give a reason for your answer.

24. Express the decimal number

$$1.24 \; 123 \; 123 \; 123 \ldots,$$

which begins to repeat after the first three figures, as a rational number p/q.

In Problems 25 through 38, determine whether each series converges or diverges. If it converges, find the sum.

25. $\displaystyle\sum_{n=0}^{\infty} \left(\frac{1}{\sqrt{2}}\right)^n$

26. $\displaystyle\sum_{n=1}^{\infty} \ln \frac{1}{n}$

27. $\displaystyle\sum_{n=1}^{\infty} (-1)^{n+1} \frac{3}{2^n}$

28. $\displaystyle\sum_{n=1}^{\infty} (\sqrt{2})^n$

29. $\displaystyle\sum_{n=0}^{\infty} \cos n\pi$

30. $\displaystyle\sum_{n=0}^{\infty} \frac{\cos n\pi}{5^n}$

31. $\displaystyle\sum_{n=0}^{\infty} e^{-2n}$

32. $\displaystyle\sum_{n=1}^{\infty} \frac{n^2 + 1}{n}$

33. $\displaystyle\sum_{n=1}^{\infty} (-1)^{n+1} n$

34. $\displaystyle\sum_{n=1}^{\infty} \frac{2}{10^n}$

35. $\displaystyle\sum_{n=0}^{\infty} \frac{2^n - 1}{3^n}$

36. $\displaystyle\sum_{n=1}^{\infty} \left(1 - \frac{1}{n}\right)^n$

37. $\displaystyle\sum_{n=0}^{\infty} \frac{n!}{1000^n}$

38. $\displaystyle\sum_{n=0}^{\infty} \frac{1}{x^n}, \qquad |x| > 1$

In Problems 39 and 40, the equalities are instances of Theorem 1. Give the value of a and of r in each case.

39. $\displaystyle\frac{1}{1+x} = \sum_{n=0}^{\infty} (-1)^n x^n, \qquad |x| < 1$

40. $\displaystyle\frac{1}{1+x^2} = \sum_{n=0}^{\infty} (-1)^n x^{2n}, \qquad |x| < 1$

41. Figure 12–6 shows the first five of an infinite series of squares. The outermost square has an area of 4, and each of the other squares is obtained by joining the midpoints of the sides of the square before it. Find the sum of the areas of all the squares.

42. Find a closed-form expression for the nth partial sum of the series $\sum_{n=1}^{\infty} (-1)^{n+1}$.

43. Show by example that the term-by-term sum of two divergent series may converge.

44. Find convergent geometric series $A = \sum_{n=1}^{\infty} a_n$ and $B = \sum_{n=1}^{\infty} b_n$ that illustrate the fact that $\sum_{n=1}^{\infty} a_n \cdot b_n$ may converge without being equal to $A \cdot B$.

45. Show by example that $\sum_{n=1}^{\infty} (a_n/b_n)$ may diverge even though $\sum_{n=1}^{\infty} a_n$ and $\sum_{n=1}^{\infty} b_n$ converge and no $b_n = 0$.

46. Show by example that $\sum_{n=1}^{\infty} (a_n/b_n)$ may converge to something other than A/B even when $A = \sum_{n=1}^{\infty} a_n$, $B = \sum_{n=1}^{\infty} b_n \neq 0$, and no $b_n = 0$.

47. Show that if $\sum_{n=1}^{\infty} a_n$ converges, and $a_n \neq 0$ for all n, then $\sum_{n=1}^{\infty} (1/a_n)$ diverges.

48. a) Verify by long division that

$$\frac{1}{1+t} = 1 - t + t^2 - t^3 + \cdots + (-1)^n t^n + \frac{(-1)^{n+1} t^{n+1}}{1+t}.$$

b) By integrating both sides of the equation in part (a) with respect to t, from 0 to x, show that

$$\ln(1+x) = x - \frac{x^2}{2} + \frac{x^3}{3} - \frac{x^4}{4} + \cdots + (-1)^n \frac{x^{n+1}}{n+1} + R,$$

where

$$R = (-1)^{n+1} \int_0^x \frac{t^{n+1}}{1+t} \, dt.$$

c) If $x > 0$, show that

$$|R| \leq \int_0^x t^{n+1} \, dt = \frac{x^{n+2}}{n+2}.$$

[*Hint.* As t varies from 0 to x, $1 + t \geq 1$.]

d) If $x = \frac{1}{2}$, how large should n be in part (c) above if we want to be able to guarantee that $|R| < 0.001$? Write a polynomial that approximates $\ln(1+x)$ to this degree of accuracy for $0 \leq x \leq \frac{1}{2}$.

e) If $x = 1$, how large should n be in part (c) above if we want to be able to guarantee that $|R| < 0.001$?

49. (*Calculator*) The concentration in the blood resulting from a single dose of a drug normally decreases with time as the drug is eliminated from the body. Doses may therefore be repeated to keep the concentration of the drug from falling below some desired level. One model for the effect of repeated doses gives the residual concentration just before the $(n+1)$st dose as: $R_n = C_0 e^{-kt_0} + C_0 e^{-2kt_0} + \cdots + C_0 e^{-nkt_0}$, where $C_0 =$ the change in concentration achievable by a single dose (mg/ml), $k =$ the *elimination constant* (hr^{-1}), and $t_0 =$ time between doses (hr). See Fig. 12–7.

12–7 One possible effect of repeated doses on the concentration of a drug in the bloodstream.

Figure 12–6

12–8 Safe and effective concentrations of a drug. C_0 is the change in concentration produced by one dose; t_0 is the time between doses.

a) Write R_n in closed form as a single fraction, and find $R = \lim_{n \to \infty} R_n$.

b) Calculate R_1 and R_{10} for $C_0 = 1$ mg/ml, $k = 0.1$ hr^{-1}, and $t_0 = 10$ hr. How good an estimate of R is R_{10}?

c) If $k = 0.01$ hr^{-1} and $t_0 = 10$ hr, find the smallest n such that $R_n > \frac{1}{2}R$.

d) If a drug is known to be ineffective below a concentration C_L and harmful above some higher concentration C_H, one needs to find values of C_0 and t_0 that will produce a concentration that is safe (not above C_H) but effective (not below C_L). See Fig. 12–8. We therefore want to find values of C_0 and t_0 for which $R = C_L$ and $C_0 + R = C_H$.

Thus $C_0 = C_H - C_L$. Show that, when these values are substituted in the equation for R obtained in (a), the resulting equation simplifies to:

$$t_0 = \frac{1}{k} \ln \frac{C_H}{C_L}.$$

To reach an effective level rapidly, one might administer a "loading" dose that would produce a concentration of C_H mg/ml. This could be followed every t_0 hours by a dose that raises the concentration by $C_0 = C_H - C_L$ mg/ml.

e) If $k = 0.05$ hr^{-1} and the highest safe concentration is e times the lowest effective concentration, find the length of time between doses that will assure safe and effective concentrations.

f) Given $C_H = 2$ mg/ml, $C_L = 0.5$ mg/ml, and $k = 0.02$ hr^{-1}, determine a scheme for administering the drug.

g) Suppose that $k = 0.2$ hr^{-1} and that the smallest effective concentration is 0.03 mg/ml. A single dose that produces a concentration of 0.1 mg/ml is administered. About how long will the drug remain effective?

(This problem was adapted from Horelick and Koont's *Prescribing Safe and Effective Dosage*, Project UMAP, Education Development Center, Newton, MA, 1977.)

In this article we will study series that do not have negative terms. The reason for this restriction is that the partial sums of these series always form increasing sequences, and increasing sequences that are bounded above always converge, as we will see. Thus, to show that a series of nonnegative terms converges, we need only show that there is some number beyond which the partial sums never go.

It may at first seem to be a drawback that this approach establishes the fact of convergence without actually producing the sum of the series in question. Surely it would be better to compute sums of series directly from nice formulas for their partial sums. But in most cases such formulas are not available, and in their absence we have to turn instead to a two-step procedure of first establishing convergence and then approximating the sum. In this article and the next, we focus on the first of these two steps.

Surprisingly enough it is not a severe restriction to begin our study of convergence with the temporary exclusion of series that have one or more negative terms, for it is a fact, as we shall see in the next article, that a series $\sum_{n=1}^{\infty} a_n$ will converge whenever the corresponding series of absolute values $\sum_{n=1}^{\infty} |a_n|$ converges. Thus, once we know that

$$\sum_{n=1}^{\infty} \frac{1}{n^2} = 1 + \frac{1}{4} + \frac{1}{9} + \frac{1}{16} + \frac{1}{25} + \cdots \tag{1}$$

12–5

TESTS FOR CONVERGENCE OF SERIES WITH NONNEGATIVE TERMS

converges, we will know that *all* of the series like

$$1 - \frac{1}{4} + \frac{1}{9} - \frac{1}{16} + \frac{1}{25} + \cdots \tag{2}$$

and

$$-1 - \frac{1}{4} + \frac{1}{9} + \frac{1}{16} - \frac{1}{25} - \cdots, \tag{3}$$

that can be obtained from (1) by changing the sign of one or more terms, also converge! We might not know at first what they converge to, but at least we know they converge, and that is a first and necessary step towards estimating their sums.

Suppose now that $\sum_{n=1}^{\infty} a_n$ is an infinite series that has no negative terms. That is, $a_n \geq 0$ for every n. Then, when we calculate the partial sums s_1, s_2, s_3, and so on, we see that each one is greater than or equal to its predecessor because $s_{n+1} = s_n + a_n$. That is,

$$s_1 \leq s_2 \leq s_3 \leq \cdots \leq s_n \leq s_{n+1} \leq \cdots. \tag{4}$$

A sequence $\{s_n\}$ like the one in (4), with the property that $s_n \leq s_{n+1}$ for every n, is called an *increasing* sequence. The cardinal principle governing increasing sequences is contained in the following theorem.

Theorem 1.   *Let $s_1, s_2, s_3, \ldots$ be an increasing sequence of real numbers. Then one or the other of the following alternatives must hold:*

A. *The terms of the sequence are all less than or equal to some finite constant M. In this case, the sequence has a finite limit L which is also less than or equal to M.*

B. *The sequence diverges to plus infinity; that is, the numbers in the sequence $\{s_n\}$ ultimately exceed every preassigned number, no matter how large.*

When all of the terms of a sequence $\{s_n\}$ are less than or equal to some finite constant M, we say that the sequence is *bounded from above*, and we call the number M an *upper bound* for the sequence. In these terms, Theorem 1 says:

A. Every increasing sequence that is bounded from above converges.

B. Every increasing sequence that is *not* bounded from above becomes infinite.

Note that the theorem does not tell us how to find the limit L when it exists.

We shall not prove Theorem 1, but we may gain an intuitive appreciation of the result by plotting the points $(1, s_1)$, $(2, s_2)$, $\ldots$, (n, s_n), $\ldots$, in the xy-plane (Fig. 12–9). Then if there is a line $y = M$ such that *none* of the points (n, s_n) lies above this line, it is intuitively clear that there is a *lowest* such line. That is, there is a line

$$y = L$$

such that none of the points lies above it but such that there are points (n, s_n) that lie above any *lower* line

$$y = L - \epsilon,$$

where ϵ is any positive number. Analytically, this means that the number L

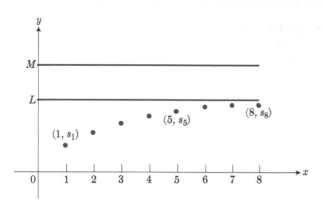

12–9 When the terms of an increasing sequence have an upper bound M, they have a limit $L \leq M$.

has the properties (a) $s_n \leq L$ for *all* values of n, (b) given any $\epsilon > 0$, there exists at least one integer N such that

$$s_N > L - \epsilon.$$

Then the fact that $\{s_n\}$ is an increasing sequence tells us further that

$$s_n \geq s_N > L - \epsilon \qquad \text{for all} \quad n \geq N.$$

This means that *all* the numbers s_n, beyond the Nth one in the sequence, lie within ϵ distance of L. This is precisely the condition for L to be the limit of the sequence s_n,

$$L = \lim_{n \to \infty} s_n.$$

Alternative B of the theorem is what happens when there are points (n, s_n) above any given line $y = M$, no matter how large M may be.

Let us now apply Theorem 1 to the convergence of infinite series of nonnegative numbers. If $\sum a_n$ is such a series, its sequence of partial sums $\{s_n\}$ is an increasing sequence. Therefore, $\{s_n\}$, and hence $\sum a_n$, will converge if and only if the numbers s_n have an upper bound. The question is how to find out in any particular instance whether the s_n's do have an upper bound.

Sometimes we can show that the s_n's are bounded above by showing that each one is less than or equal to the corresponding partial sum of a series that is already known to converge. The next example shows how this can happen.

EXAMPLE 1

$$\sum_{n=0}^{\infty} \frac{1}{n!} = 1 + \frac{1}{1!} + \frac{1}{2!} + \frac{1}{3!} + \cdots \tag{5}$$

converges because its terms are all positive and less than or equal to the corresponding terms of

$$1 + \sum_{n=0}^{\infty} \frac{1}{2^n} = 1 + 1 + \frac{1}{2} + \frac{1}{2^2} + \cdots. \tag{6}$$

To see how this relationship between these two series leads to an upper bound for the partial sums of $\sum_{n=0}^{\infty} (1/n!)$, let

$$s_n = 1 + \frac{1}{1!} + \frac{1}{2!} + \cdots + \frac{1}{n!},$$

and observe that, for each n,

$$s_n \leq 1 + 1 + \frac{1}{2} + \frac{1}{2^2} + \cdots + \frac{1}{2^n} < 1 + \sum_{n=0}^{\infty} \frac{1}{2^n} = 1 + \frac{1}{1 - \frac{1}{2}} = 3. \quad (7)$$

Thus the partial sums of $\sum_{n=0}^{\infty} (1/n!)$ are all less than 3. Therefore, $\sum_{n=0}^{\infty} (1/n!)$ converges.

Just because 3 is an upper bound for the partial sums of $\sum_{n=0}^{\infty} (1/n!)$ we cannot conclude that the series converges to 3. The series actually converges to $e = 2.71828 \ldots$.

We established the convergence of the series in Example 1 by comparing it with a series that was already known to converge. This kind of comparison is typical of a procedure called the *comparison test* for convergence of series of nonnegative terms.

Comparison Test for Series of Nonnegative Terms

Let $\sum_{n=1}^{\infty} a_n$ be a series that has no negative terms.

A. *Test for* **convergence** *of $\sum a_n$. The series $\sum a_n$ converges if there is a convergent series of nonnegative terms $\sum c_n$ with $a_n \leq c_n$ for all n.*

B. *Test for* **divergence** *of $\sum a_n$. The series $\sum a_n$ diverges if there is a divergent series of nonnegative terms $\sum d_n$ with $a_n \geq d_n$ for all n.*

To see why the test works, we need only observe that in (A) the partial sums of $\sum a_n$ are bounded above by $M = \sum c_n$, while in (B) the partial sums of $\sum a_n$, being greater than or equal to the corresponding partial sums of a divergent series of nonnegative terms, eventually exceed every preassigned number.

To apply the comparison test to a series, we do not have to include the early terms of the series. We can start the test with any index N, provided we include all the terms of the series being tested from there on.

EXAMPLE 2. The convergence of the series

$$5 + \frac{2}{3} + 1 + \frac{1}{7} + \frac{1}{2} + \frac{1}{3!} + \frac{1}{4!} + \cdots + \frac{1}{k!} + \cdots$$

can be established by ignoring the first four terms and comparing the remainder of the series from the fifth term on (the fifth term is $\frac{1}{2}$) with the convergent series

$$\sum_{n=1}^{\infty} \frac{1}{2^n} = \frac{1}{2} + \frac{1}{4} + \frac{1}{8} + \cdots$$

To apply the comparison test we need to have on hand a list of series that are known to converge and a list of series that are known to diverge. Our next example adds a divergent series to the list.

EXAMPLE 3. The *harmonic series*

$$\sum_{n=1}^{\infty} \frac{1}{n} = 1 + \frac{1}{2} + \frac{1}{3} + \frac{1}{4} + \cdots$$

diverges.

To see why, we represent the terms of the series as the areas of rectangles each of base unity and having altitudes $1, \frac{1}{2}, \frac{1}{3}, \ldots$, as in Fig. 12–10. The sum of the first n terms of the series,

$$s_n = 1 + \frac{1}{2} + \frac{1}{3} + \cdots + \frac{1}{n},$$

represents the sum of n rectangles each of which is somewhat greater than the area underneath the corresponding portion of the curve $y = 1/x$. Thus s_n is greater than the area under this curve between $x = 1$ and $x = n + 1$:

$$s_n > \int_1^{n+1} \frac{dx}{x} = \ln (n + 1).$$

Therefore $s_n \to +\infty$ because $\ln (n + 1) \to +\infty$. The series

$$1 + \frac{1}{2} + \frac{1}{3} + \cdots + \frac{1}{n} + \cdots$$

diverges to plus infinity.

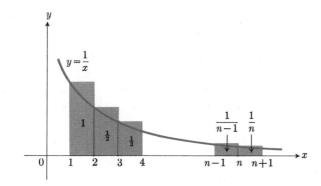

12–10 $1 + \dfrac{1}{2} + \dfrac{1}{3} + \cdots + \dfrac{1}{n} > \displaystyle\int_1^{n+1} \dfrac{1}{x}\, dx = \ln (n + 1).$

REMARK 1. The harmonic series $\sum_{n=1}^{\infty} (1/n)$ is another series whose divergence cannot be detected by the nth-term test for divergence. The series diverges in spite of the fact that $1/n \to 0$.

REMARK 2. We know that every nonzero multiple of a divergent series diverges (Corollary of Theorem 4 in the preceding article). Therefore, the divergence of the harmonic series implies the divergence of series like

$$\sum_{n=1}^{\infty} \frac{1}{2n} = \frac{1}{2} + \frac{1}{4} + \frac{1}{6} + \frac{1}{8} + \cdots$$

and

$$\sum_{n=1}^{\infty} \frac{1}{100n} = \frac{1}{100} + \frac{1}{200} + \frac{1}{300} + \frac{1}{400} + \cdots.$$

In Example 3 we deduced the divergence of the harmonic series by comparing its sequence of partial sums with a divergent sequence of integrals. This comparison is a special case of a general comparison process called the *integral test*, a test that gives criteria for convergence as well as for divergence of series whose terms are positive.

The Integral Test

Let the function $y = f(x)$, obtained by introducing the continuous variable x in place of the discrete variable n in the nth term of the positive series

$$\sum_{n=1}^{\infty} a_n,$$

be a decreasing function of x for $x \geq 1$. Then the series and the integral

$$\int_{1}^{\infty} f(x)\, dx$$

both converge or both diverge.

a)

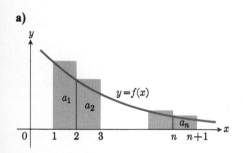

Proof. We start with the assumption that f is a decreasing function with $f(n) = a_n$ for every n. This leads us to observe that the rectangles in Fig. 12–11(a), which have areas $a_1, a_2, \ldots, a_n$, collectively enclose more area than that under the curve $y = f(x)$ from $x = 1$ to $x = n + 1$. That is,

$$\int_{1}^{n+1} f(x)\, dx \leq a_1 + a_2 + \cdots + a_n.$$

b)

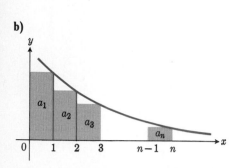

In Fig. 12–11(b) the rectangles have been faced to the left instead of to the right. If we momentarily disregard the first rectangle, of area a_1, we see that

$$a_2 + a_3 + \cdots + a_n \leq \int_{1}^{n} f(x)\, dx.$$

If we include a_1, we have

$$a_1 + a_2 + \cdots + a_n \leq a_1 + \int_{1}^{n} f(x)\, dx.$$

12–11 $\displaystyle\int_{1}^{n+1} f(x)\, dx \leq a_1 + a_2 + \cdots + a_n$

$$\leq a_1 + \int_{1}^{n} f(x)\, dx.$$

Combining these results, we have

$$\int_{1}^{n+1} f(x)\, dx \leq a_1 + a_2 + \cdots + a_n \leq a_1 + \int_{1}^{n} f(x)\, dx. \qquad \textbf{(8)}$$

If the integral $\int_{1}^{\infty} f(x)\, dx$ is finite, the righthand inequality shows that

$$\sum_{n=1}^{\infty} a_n$$

is also finite. But if $\int_1^\infty f(x)\,dx$ is infinite, then the lefthand inequality shows that the series is also infinite. Hence the series and the integral are both finite or both infinite.

EXAMPLE 4.   *The p-series.* If p is a real constant, the series

$$\sum_{n=1}^\infty \frac{1}{n^p} = \frac{1}{1^p} + \frac{1}{2^p} + \frac{1}{3^p} + \cdots + \frac{1}{n^p} + \cdots$$

converges if $p > 1$ and diverges if $p \le 1$. To prove this, let

$$f(x) = \frac{1}{x^p}.$$

Then, if $p > 1$, we have

$$\int_1^\infty x^{-p}\,dx = \lim_{b \to \infty} \frac{x^{-p+1}}{-p+1} \Big|_1^b = \frac{1}{p-1},$$

which is finite. Hence the p-series converges if p is greater than one.

If $p = 1$, we have

$$1 + \frac{1}{2} + \frac{1}{3} + \cdots + \frac{1}{n} + \cdots,$$

which we already know diverges. Or, by the integral test,

$$\int_1^\infty x^{-1}\,dx = \lim_{b \to \infty} \ln x \Big|_1^b = +\infty,$$

and, since the integral diverges, the series does likewise.

Finally, if $p < 1$, then the terms of the p-series are greater than the corresponding terms of the divergent harmonic series. Hence the p-series diverges, by the comparison test.

Thus, we have convergence for $p > 1$, but divergence for every other value of p.

Estimation of Remainders by Integrals

The difference $R_n = L - s_n$ between the sum of a convergent series and its nth partial sum is called a *remainder* or a *truncation error*. Since R_n itself is given as an infinite series, which, in principle, is as difficult to evaluate as the original series, you might think that there would be no advantage in singling out R_n for attention. But sometimes even a crude estimate for R_n can lead to an estimate of L that is closer to L than s_n is.

Suppose, for example, that we are interested in learning the numerical value of the series

$$\sum_{k=1}^\infty \frac{1}{k^2} = \frac{1}{1^2} + \frac{1}{2^2} + \frac{1}{3^2} + \cdots$$

This is a p-series with $p = 2$, and hence is known to converge. This means that the sequence of partial sums

$$s_n = \frac{1}{1^2} + \frac{1}{2^2} + \cdots + \frac{1}{n^2}$$

has a limit L. If we want to know L to a couple of decimal places, we might try to find an integer n such that the corresponding *finite* sum s_n differs from L by less, say, than 0.005. Then we would use this s_n in place of L, to two decimals. If we write

$$L = \sum_{k=1}^{\infty} \frac{1}{k^2} = \frac{1}{1^2} + \frac{1}{2^2} + \cdots + \frac{1}{n^2} + \frac{1}{(n+1)^2} + \cdots,$$

we see that

$$R_n = L - s_n = \frac{1}{(n+1)^2} + \cdots.$$

We estimate the error R_n by comparing it with the area under the curve

$$y = \frac{1}{x^2}$$

from $x = n$ to ∞.

From Fig. 12–12 we see that

$$R_n < \int_n^{\infty} \frac{1}{x^2}\, dx = \frac{1}{n},$$

which tells us that, by taking 200 terms of the series, we can be sure that the difference between the sum L of the entire series and the sum s_{200} of these 200 terms will be less than 0.005.

A somewhat closer estimate of R_n results from using the trapezoidal rule to approximate the area under the curve in Fig. 12–12. Let us write u_k for $1/k^2$ and consider the trapezoidal approximation

$$T_n = \sum_{k=n}^{\infty} \tfrac{1}{2}(u_k + u_{k+1}) = \tfrac{1}{2}(u_n + u_{n+1}) + \tfrac{1}{2}(u_{n+1} + u_{n+2}) + \cdots$$

$$= \tfrac{1}{2}u_n + u_{n+1} + u_{n+2} + \cdots = \tfrac{1}{2}u_n + R_n.$$

Now since the curve $y = 1/x^2$ is concave upward,

$$T_n > \int_n^{\infty} \frac{1}{x^2}\, dx = \frac{1}{n},$$

and we have

$$R_n = T_n - \frac{1}{2}u_n > \frac{1}{n} - \frac{1}{2n^2}.$$

12–12 The rectilinear area R_n is

$$\frac{1}{(n+1)^2} + \frac{1}{(n+2)^2} + \frac{1}{(n+3)^2} + \cdots < \int_n^{\infty} \frac{dx}{x^2}.$$

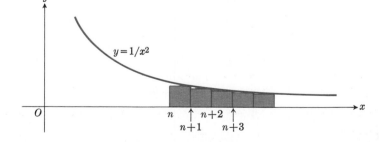

We now know that

$$\frac{1}{n} > R_n > \frac{1}{n} - \frac{1}{2n^2},$$

and $L = s_n + R_n$ may be estimated as follows:

$$s_n + \frac{1}{n} > L > s_n + \frac{1}{n} - \frac{1}{2n^2}. \tag{9}$$

Thus, by using $s_n + 1/n$ in place of s_n to estimate L, we shall be making an error which is numerically less than $1/(2n^2)$. By taking $n \geq 10$, this error is then made less than 0.005. The difference in time required to compute the sum of 10 terms versus 200 terms is sufficiently great to make this sharper analysis of practical importance.

What we have done in the case of this specific example may be done in any case where the graph of the function $y = f(x)$ is concave upward as in Fig. 12–12. We find that when $\int_n^\infty f(x)\,dx$ exists,

$$u_1 + u_2 + \cdots + u_n + \int_n^\infty f(x)\,dx \tag{10}$$

tends to overestimate the value of the series, but by an amount that is less than $u_n/2$.

Ratio Test and Root Test

It is not always possible to tell whether a particular series converges by using the comparison test. We might not be able to find a series to compare it with. Nor is it always possible to use the integral test to answer whatever questions of convergence then remain unanswered. The terms of the series might not decrease as n increases, or we might not find a formula for the nth term that we can integrate. What we really need is an intrinsic test for convergence, one that can be applied to the series without outside help, so to speak. The next two tests are intrinsic in this sense. They are also easy to apply, and they succeed on a wide variety of series. The first of these is the *ratio test*, for series with positive terms.

The Ratio Test

Let $\sum a_n$ be a series with positive terms, and suppose that

$$\lim_{n \to \infty} \frac{a_{n+1}}{a_n} = \rho \qquad \text{(Greek letter rho)}.$$

Then,

a) *the series **converges** if $\rho < 1$;*
b) *the series **diverges** if $\rho > 1$;*
c) *the series **may converge or it may diverge** if $\rho = 1$.*

Proof.   **a)** Assume first that $\rho < 1$ and let r be a number between ρ and 1. Then the number

$$\epsilon = r - \rho$$

is positive. Since

$$\frac{a_{n+1}}{a_n} \to \rho,$$

a_{n+1}/a_n must lie within ϵ of ρ when n is large enough, say, for all $n \geq N$. In particular,

$$\frac{a_{n+1}}{a_n} < \rho + \epsilon = r, \qquad \text{when } n > N.$$

That is,

$$a_{N+1} < ra_N,$$

$$a_{N+2} < ra_{N+1} < r^2 a_N,$$

$$a_{N+3} < ra_{N+2} < r^3 a_N,$$

$$\vdots$$

$$a_{N+m} < ra_{N+m-1} < r^m a_N,$$

and

$$\sum_{n=1}^{\infty} a_n = a_1 + a_2 + \cdots + a_{N-1} + a_N + a_{N+1} + \cdots$$

$$< a_1 + a_2 + \cdots + a_{N-1} + a_N(1 + r + r^2 + \cdots). \qquad \textbf{(11)}$$

Since $|r|$ is less than one, the geometric series $1 + r + r^2 + \cdots$ converges and the right side of the inequality (11) is finite. Therefore the series on the left converges, by the comparison test.

b) Next, suppose $\rho > 1$. Then, from some index M on, we have

$$\frac{a_{n+1}}{a_n} > 1$$

or

$$a_M < a_{M+1} < a_{M+2} < \cdots.$$

Hence, the terms of the series do not approach 0 as n becomes infinite, and the series diverges, by the nth-term test.

c) Finally, the two series

$$\sum_{n=1}^{\infty} \frac{1}{n} \qquad \text{and} \qquad \sum_{n=1}^{\infty} \frac{1}{n^2}$$

show that, when $\rho = 1$, some other test for convergence must be used.

For $\displaystyle\sum_{n=1}^{\infty} \frac{1}{n}$: $\rho = \dfrac{1/(n+1)}{1/n} = \dfrac{n}{n+1} \to 1;$

For $\displaystyle\sum_{n=1}^{\infty} \frac{1}{n^2}$: $\rho = \dfrac{1/(n+1)^2}{1/n^2} = \left(\dfrac{n}{n+1}\right)^2 \to 1^2 = 1.$

In both cases $\rho = 1$, yet the first series diverges while the second converges.   Q.E.D.

EXAMPLE 5. For the series $\sum_{n=0}^{\infty} (2^n + 5)/3^n$,

$$\frac{a_{n+1}}{a_n} = \frac{(2^{n+1} + 5)/3^{n+1}}{(2^n + 5)/3^n} = \frac{1}{3} \cdot \frac{2^{n+1} + 5}{2^n + 5} = \frac{1}{3} \cdot \left(\frac{2 + 5 \cdot 2^{-n}}{1 + 5 \cdot 2^{-n}} \right) \to \frac{1}{3} \cdot \frac{2}{1} = \frac{2}{3}.$$

The series converges because $\rho = \frac{2}{3}$ is less than 1.

This does *not* mean that $\frac{2}{3}$ is the sum of the series. In fact,

$$\sum_{n=0}^{\infty} \frac{2^n + 5}{3^n} = \sum_{n=0}^{\infty} \left(\frac{2}{3}\right)^n + \sum_{n=0}^{\infty} \frac{5}{3^n} = \frac{1}{1 - \frac{2}{3}} + \frac{5}{1 - \frac{1}{3}} = 10\frac{1}{2}.$$

EXAMPLE 6. For what values of x does the series

$$x + \frac{x^3}{3} + \frac{x^5}{5} + \frac{x^7}{7} + \cdots + \frac{x^{2n-1}}{2n - 1} + \cdots \tag{12}$$

converge?

Solution. The nth term of the series is

$$a_n = \frac{x^{2n-1}}{2n - 1}.$$

We consider first the case where x is positive. Then the series is a positive series and

$$\frac{a_{n+1}}{a_n} = \frac{(2n - 1)x^2}{(2n + 1)} \to x^2.$$

The ratio test therefore tells us that the series converges if x is positive and less than one and diverges if x is greater than one.

Since only odd powers of x occur in the series, we see that the series simply changes sign when x is replaced by $-x$. Therefore the series also converges for $-1 < x \leq 0$ and diverges for $x < -1$. The series converges to zero when $x = 0$.

We know, thus far, that the series

$$\text{converges for } |x| < 1,$$

$$\text{diverges for } \quad |x| > 1,$$

but we don't know what happens when $|x| = 1$. To test at $x = 1$, we apply the integral test to the series

$$1 + \frac{1}{3} + \frac{1}{5} + \frac{1}{7} + \cdots + \frac{1}{2n - 1} + \cdots,$$

which we get by taking $x = 1$ in the series (12). The companion integral is

$$\int_1^{\infty} \frac{dx}{2x - 1} = \frac{1}{2} \ln (2x - 1) \Big|_1^{\infty} = \infty.$$

Hence the series diverges to $+\infty$ when $x = 1$. It diverges to $-\infty$ when $x = -1$. Therefore the only values of x for which the given series converges are $-1 < x < 1$.

REMARK.   When $\rho < 1$, the ratio test is also useful in estimating the truncation error that results from using

$$s_N = a_1 + a_2 + \cdots + a_N$$

as an approximation to the sum of a convergent series of positive terms

$$S = a_1 + a_2 + \cdots + a_N + (a_{N+1} + \cdots);$$

for, if we know that

$$r_1 \leq \frac{a_{n+1}}{a_n} \leq r_2 \qquad \text{for} \quad n \geq N, \tag{13}$$

where r_1 and r_2 are constants that are both less than one, then the inequalities

$$r_1 a_n \leq a_{n+1} \leq r_2 a_n \qquad (n = N, N+1, N+2, \ldots)$$

enable us to deduce that

$$a_N(r_1 + r_1^2 + r_1^3 + \cdots) \leq \sum_{n=N+1}^{\infty} a_n \leq a_N(r_2 + r_2^2 + r_2^3 + \cdots). \tag{14}$$

The two geometric series have sums

$$r_1 + r_1^2 + r_1^3 + \cdots = \frac{r_1}{1 - r_1},$$

$$r_2 + r_2^2 + r_2^3 + \cdots = \frac{r_2}{1 - r_2}.$$

Hence, the error

$$R_N = \sum_{n=N+1}^{\infty} a_n$$

lies between

$$a_N \frac{r_1}{1 - r_1} \qquad \text{and} \qquad a_N \frac{r_2}{1 - r_2}.$$

That is,

$$a_N \frac{r_1}{1 - r_1} \leq S - s_n \leq a_N \frac{r_2}{1 - r_2} \tag{15}$$

if

$$0 \leq r_1 \leq \frac{a_{n+1}}{a_n} \leq r_2 < 1 \qquad \text{for} \quad n \geq N.$$

The second of the two intrinsic tests we referred to earlier is called the *root test*.

The Root Test

Let $\sum a_n$ be a series with no negative terms, and suppose that

$$\sqrt[n]{a_n} \to \rho.$$

Then,

a) *the series **converges** if $\rho < 1$*
b) *the series **diverges** if $\rho > 1$*
c) *the test is **not conclusive** if $\rho = 1$.*

Proof.   **a)** Suppose that $\rho < 1$, and choose an $\epsilon > 0$ so small that $\rho + \epsilon < 1$ also. Since $\sqrt[n]{a_n} \to \rho$, the terms $\sqrt[n]{a_n}$ eventually get closer than ϵ to ρ. In other words,

$$\sqrt[n]{a_n} < \rho + \epsilon$$

for n sufficiently large, or

$$a_n < (\rho + \epsilon)^n \qquad \text{for} \quad n \geq N.$$

Now,

$$\sum_{n=N}^{\infty} (\rho + \epsilon)^n,$$

a geometric series with ratio $(\rho + \epsilon) < 1$, converges. By comparison,

$$\sum_{n=N}^{\infty} a_n$$

converges, from which it follows that

$$\sum_{n=1}^{\infty} a_n = a_1 + \cdots + a_{N-1} + \sum_{n=N}^{\infty} a_n$$

converges.

b) Suppose that $\rho > 1$. Then, for all indices beyond some index M, we have

$$\sqrt[n]{a_n} > 1,$$

so that

$$a_n > 1 \qquad \text{for} \quad n > M,$$

and the terms of the series do not converge to 0. The series therefore diverges by the nth-term test.

c) The series $\sum_{n=1}^{\infty} (1/n)$ and $\sum_{n=1}^{\infty} (1/n^2)$ show that the test is not conclusive when $\rho = 1$. The first series diverges and the second converges, but in both cases $\sqrt[n]{a_n} \to 1$.   Q.E.D.

EXAMPLE 7.   For the series $\sum_{n=1}^{\infty} (1/n^n)$,

$$\sqrt[n]{\frac{1}{n^n}} = \frac{1}{n} \to 0.$$

The series converges.

EXAMPLE 8.   For the series $\sum_{n=1}^{\infty} (2^n/n^2)$,

$$\sqrt[n]{\frac{2^n}{n^2}} = \frac{2}{\sqrt[n]{n^2}} = \frac{2}{(\sqrt[n]{n})^2} \to \frac{2}{1^2} = 2.$$

The series diverges.

EXAMPLE 9. For the series $\sum_{n=1}^{\infty} (1 - 1/n)^n = 0 + \frac{1}{4} + \frac{8}{27} + \cdots,$

$$\sqrt[n]{\left(1 - \frac{1}{n}\right)^n} = \left(1 - \frac{1}{n}\right) \to 1.$$

Because $\rho = 1$, the root test is not conclusive. However, if we apply the nth-term test for divergence, we find that

$$\left(1 - \frac{1}{n}\right)^n = \left(1 + \frac{-1}{n}\right)^n \to e^{-1} = \frac{1}{e}.$$

The series diverges.

We now have five tests for divergence and convergence of infinite series:

1. The nth-term test for divergence (applies to all series).
2. **A)** The comparison test for convergence (nonnegative series);
   B) The comparison test for divergence (nonnegative series).
3. The integral test (positive decreasing series).
4. The ratio test (positive series).
5. The root test (nonnegative series).

These tests can be applied to settle questions about the convergence or divergence of series of nonpositive or negative terms. Just factor -1 from the series in question, and test the resulting series of nonnegative or positive terms.

EXAMPLE 10

$$\sum_{n=1}^{\infty} -\frac{1}{n} = -1 \cdot \sum_{n=1}^{\infty} \frac{1}{n} \quad \text{diverges.}$$

EXAMPLE 11

$$\sum_{n=0}^{\infty} -\frac{1}{2^n} = -1 \cdot \sum_{n=0}^{\infty} \frac{1}{2^n} = -1 \cdot 2 = -2.$$

PROBLEMS

In each of the following problems, determine whether the given series converges or diverges. In each case, give a reason for your answer.

1. $\sum_{n=1}^{\infty} \frac{1}{10^n}$

2. $\sum_{n=1}^{\infty} \frac{n}{n+2}$

3. $\sum_{n=1}^{\infty} \frac{\sin^2 n}{2^n}$

4. $\sum_{n=1}^{\infty} \frac{5}{n}$

5. $\sum_{n=1}^{\infty} \frac{n^3}{2^n}$

6. $\sum_{n=1}^{\infty} -\frac{1}{8^n}$

7. $\sum_{n=1}^{\infty} \frac{\ln n}{n}$

8. $\sum_{n=1}^{\infty} \frac{1}{n\sqrt{n}}$

9. $\sum_{n=1}^{\infty} \frac{2^n}{3^n}$

10. $\sum_{n=0}^{\infty} \frac{-2}{n+1}$

11. $\sum_{n=1}^{\infty} \frac{1}{1 + \ln n}$

12. $\sum_{n=1}^{\infty} \frac{1}{\sqrt{n+1}}$

13. $\sum_{n=1}^{\infty} \frac{2^n}{n+1}$

14. $\sum_{n=1}^{\infty} \left(\frac{n}{3n+1}\right)^n$

15. $\sum_{n=1}^{\infty} -\frac{n^2}{2^n}$

16. $\sum_{n=1}^{\infty} \frac{1}{\sqrt{n}}$

17. $\sum_{n=1}^{\infty} \frac{1}{\sqrt{n^3 + 2}}$

18. $\sum_{n=1}^{\infty} \frac{1}{\sqrt[n]{2}}$

19. $\displaystyle\sum_{n=1}^{\infty} \frac{(n+1)(n+2)}{n!}$

20. $\displaystyle\sum_{n=1}^{\infty} \frac{\sqrt{n}}{n^2+1}$

21. $\displaystyle\sum_{n=1}^{\infty} \frac{n}{n^2+1}$

22. $\displaystyle\sum_{n=1}^{\infty} n^2 e^{-n}$

23. $\displaystyle\sum_{n=1}^{\infty} \left(1+\frac{1}{n}\right)^n$

24. $\displaystyle\sum_{n=1}^{\infty} \frac{1}{3^{n-1}+1}$

25. $\displaystyle\sum_{n=1}^{\infty} \frac{(n+3)!}{3!\,n!\,3^n}$

26. $\displaystyle\sum_{n=2}^{\infty} \frac{1}{n \ln n}$

27. $\displaystyle\sum_{n=1}^{\infty} \frac{1}{(2n+1)!}$

28. $\displaystyle\sum_{n=1}^{\infty} \frac{1}{(\ln 2)^n}$

29. $\displaystyle\sum_{n=1}^{\infty} \frac{n!}{n^n}$

30. $\displaystyle\sum_{n=1}^{\infty} \frac{1-n}{n \cdot 2^n}$

31. Show that the series

$$\sum_{n=1}^{\infty} \frac{1}{2n-1} = 1 + \frac{1}{3} + \frac{1}{5} + \cdots$$

diverges. [*Hint.* Compare the series with a multiple of the harmonic series.]

In Problems 32 through 34, find all values of x for which the given series converge. Begin with the ratio test or the root test, and then apply other tests as needed.

32. $\displaystyle\sum_{n=1}^{\infty} \left(\frac{x^2+1}{3}\right)^n$

33. $\displaystyle\sum_{n=1}^{\infty} \frac{x^{2n+1}}{n^2}$

34. $\displaystyle\sum_{n=1}^{\infty} \left(\frac{1}{|x|}\right)^n$

35. (*Calculator*) Use Inequality (9) of this article to estimate $\sum_{n=1}^{\infty} (1/n^2)$ with an error less than 0.005. Compare your result with the value given in Problem 36.

36. (*Calculator*) Euler discovered that

$$\sum_{n=1}^{\infty} \frac{1}{n^2} = \sum_{n=1}^{\infty} \frac{3[(n-1)!]^2}{(2n)!} = \frac{\pi^2}{6}.$$

Compute s_6 for each series. To 10 decimal places, $\pi^2/6 = 1.6449340668$.

37. (*Calculator*) Use the expression in (10) of this article to find the value of $\sum_{n=1}^{\infty} (1/n^4) = (\pi^4/90)$ with an error less than 10^{-6}.

38. (*Calculator*) To estimate partial sums of the divergent harmonic series, Inequality (8) with $f(x) = 1/x$ tells us that

$$\ln n < 1 + \frac{1}{2} + \cdots + \frac{1}{n} < 1 + \ln n.$$

Suppose that the summation started with $s_1 = 1$ thirteen billion years ago (one estimate of the age of the universe) and that a new term has been added every *second* since then. How large would you expect s_n to be today?

39. There are no values of x for which $\sum_{n=1}^{\infty} (1/nx)$ converges. Why?

40. Show that if $\sum_{n=1}^{\infty} a_n$ is a convergent series of nonnegative numbers then the series $\sum_{n=1}^{\infty} (a_n/n)$ converges.

41. Show that if $\sum a_n$ and $\sum b_n$ are convergent series with $a_n \geq 0$ and $b_n \geq 0$, then $\sum a_n b_n$ converges. [*Hint.* From some index on, $a_n b_n < a_n + b_n$.]

42. A sequence of numbers

$$s_1 \geq s_2 \geq \cdots \geq s_n \geq s_{n+1} \geq \cdots,$$

in which $s_n \geq s_{n+1}$ for every n, is called a *decreasing sequence*. A sequence $\{s_n\}$ is *bounded from below* if there is a finite constant M with $M \leq s_n$ for every n. Such a number M is called a *lower bound* for the sequence. Deduce from Theorem 1 that a decreasing sequence that is bounded from below converges, and that a decreasing sequence that is not bounded from below diverges.

43. The *Cauchy condensation test* says:

Let $\{a_n\}$ be a decreasing sequence ($a_n \geq a_{n+1}$, all n) of positive terms that converges to 0. Then,

$$\sum a_n \text{ converges} \quad \text{if and only if} \quad \sum 2^n a_{2^n} \text{ converges.}$$

For example, $\sum (1/n)$ diverges because $\sum 2^n \cdot (1/2^n) = \sum 1$. Show why the test works.

44. Use the Cauchy condensation test of Problem 43 to show that

a) $\displaystyle\sum_{n=2}^{\infty} \frac{1}{n \ln n}$ diverges.

b) $\displaystyle\sum_{n=1}^{\infty} \frac{1}{n^p}$ converges if $p > 1$ and diverges if $p \leq 1$.

45. Pictures like the one in Fig. 12–10 suggest that, as n increases, there is very little change in the difference between the sum

$$1 + \frac{1}{2} + \cdots + \frac{1}{n}$$

and the integral

$$\ln n = \int_1^n \frac{1}{x}\,dx.$$

To explore this idea, carry out the following steps.

a) By taking $f(x) = (1/x)$ in inequality (8), show that

$$\ln n < 1 + \frac{1}{2} + \cdots + \frac{1}{n} < 1 + \ln n.$$

or

$$0 < 1 + \frac{1}{2} + \cdots + \frac{1}{n} - \ln n < 1.$$

Thus, the sequence

$$a_n = 1 + \frac{1}{2} + \cdots + \frac{1}{n} - \ln n$$

is bounded from below.

b) Show that

$$\frac{1}{n+1} < \int_n^{n+1} \frac{1}{x}\,dx = \ln(n+1) - \ln n,$$

so that the sequence $\{a_n\}$ in part (a) is decreasing.

Since a decreasing sequence that is bounded from below converges (Problem 42) the numbers a_n defined in (a)

converge:

$$1 + \frac{1}{2} + \cdots + \frac{1}{n} - \ln n \to \gamma.$$

The number γ, whose value is $0.5772\ldots$, is called *Euler's constant*. In contrast to other special numbers like π and e, no other expression with a simple law of formulation has ever been found for γ.

12-6

ABSOLUTE CONVERGENCE

We now extend to series that have both positive and negative terms the techniques that we have developed for answering questions about the convergence of series of nonnegative numbers. The extension is made possible by a theorem that says that, if a series converges after all its negative terms have been made positive, then the unaltered series converges also.

Theorem.   *If $\sum_{n=1}^{\infty} |a_n|$ converges, then $\sum_{n=1}^{\infty} a_n$ converges.*

Proof of the theorem.   For each n,

$$-|a_n| \le a_n \le |a_n|,$$

so that

$$0 \le a_n + |a_n| \le 2|a_n|.$$

If $\sum_{n=1}^{\infty} |a_n|$ converges, then $\sum_{n=1}^{\infty} 2|a_n|$ converges and, by the comparison test, the nonnegative series

$$\sum_{n=1}^{\infty} (a_n + |a_n|)$$

converges. The equality $a_n = (a_n + |a_n|) - |a_n|$ now lets us express $\sum_{n=1}^{\infty} a_n$ as the difference of two convergent series:

$$\sum_{n=1}^{\infty} a_n = \sum_{n=1}^{\infty} (a_n + |a_n| - |a_n|) = \sum_{n=1}^{\infty} (a_n + |a_n|) - \sum_{n=1}^{\infty} |a_n|.$$

Therefore, $\sum_{n=1}^{\infty} a_n$ converges.

Definition.   *A series $\sum_{n=1}^{\infty} a_n$ is said to **converge absolutely** if $\sum_{n=1}^{\infty} |a_n|$ converges.*

Our theorem says that if a series converges absolutely, then it converges when the absolute value signs are removed. In other words, *every absolutely convergent series converges*. We will see in the next article, however, that the converse of this statement is false. Many convergent series do not converge absolutely. That is, there are many series whose convergence depends on the presence of negative terms. Here are some examples of how the theorem can and cannot be used to determine convergence.

EXAMPLE 1. For $\sum_{n=1}^{\infty} (-1)^{n+1} \frac{1}{n^2} = 1 - \frac{1}{4} + \frac{1}{9} - \frac{1}{16} + \cdots$,

the corresponding series of absolute values is

$$\sum_{n=1}^{\infty} \frac{1}{n^2} = 1 + \frac{1}{4} + \frac{1}{9} + \frac{1}{16} + \cdots,$$

which converges because it is a p-series with $p = 2 > 1$ (Article 12–5). Therefore

$$\sum_{n=1}^{\infty} (-1)^{n+1} \frac{1}{n^2}$$

converges absolutely. Therefore

$$\sum_{n=1}^{\infty} (-1)^{n+1} \frac{1}{n^2}$$

converges.

EXAMPLE 2. For $\sum_{n=1}^{\infty} \frac{\sin n}{n^2} = \frac{\sin 1}{1} + \frac{\sin 2}{4} + \frac{\sin 3}{9} + \cdots$,

the corresponding series of absolute values is

$$\sum_{n=1}^{\infty} \left| \frac{\sin n}{n^2} \right| = \frac{|\sin 1|}{1} + \frac{|\sin 2|}{4} + \cdots,$$

which converges by comparison with $\sum_{n=1}^{\infty} (1/n^2)$, because $|\sin n| \leq 1$ for every n. The original series converges absolutely; therefore it converges.

EXAMPLE 3. For $\sum_{n=1}^{\infty} (-1)^{n+1} \frac{1}{n} = 1 - \frac{1}{2} + \frac{1}{3} - \frac{1}{4} + \cdots$,

the corresponding series of absolute values is

$$\sum_{n=1}^{\infty} \frac{1}{n} = 1 + \frac{1}{2} + \frac{1}{3} + \frac{1}{4} + \cdots,$$

which diverges. *We can draw no conclusion from this about the convergence or divergence of the original series.* Some other test must be found. In fact, the original series converges, but we will have to wait until the next article to see why.

EXAMPLE 4. The series

$$\sum_{n=1}^{\infty} (-1)^n \frac{n}{5n+1} = -\frac{1}{6} + \frac{2}{11} - \frac{3}{16} + \frac{4}{21} - \cdots$$

does not converge, by the nth term test. Therefore, the series does not converge absolutely.

REMARK. We know that $\sum a_n$ converges if $\sum |a_n|$ converges, but the two series will generally not converge to the same sum. For example,

$$\sum_{n=0}^{\infty} \left| \frac{(-1)^n}{2^n} \right| = \sum_{n=0}^{\infty} \frac{1}{2^n} = \frac{1}{1 - \frac{1}{2}} = 2,$$

while

$$\sum_{n=0}^{\infty} \frac{(-1)^n}{2^n} = \frac{1}{1+\frac{1}{2}} = \frac{2}{3}.$$

In fact, when a series $\sum a_n$ converges absolutely, we can expect $\sum a_n$ to equal $\sum |a_n|$ only if none of the numbers a_n is negative.

PROBLEMS

Determine whether the following series converge absolutely. In each case give a reason for the convergence or divergence of the corresponding series of absolute values.

1. $\sum_{n=1}^{\infty} \frac{1}{n^2}$

2. $\sum_{n=1}^{\infty} \frac{1}{(-n)^3}$

3. $\sum_{n=1}^{\infty} \frac{1-n}{n^2}$

4. $\sum_{n=1}^{\infty} \left(-\frac{1}{5}\right)^n$

5. $\sum_{n=1}^{\infty} \frac{-1}{n^2+2n+1}$

6. $\sum_{n=1}^{\infty} \frac{(-1)^n}{2n}$

7. $\sum_{n=1}^{\infty} \frac{\cos n\pi}{n\sqrt{n}}$

8. $\sum_{n=1}^{\infty} \frac{-10}{n}$

9. $\sum_{n=0}^{\infty} \frac{(-1)^n}{(2n)!}$

10. $\sum_{n=0}^{\infty} \frac{(-1)^n}{(2n+1)!}$

11. $\sum_{n=2}^{\infty} (-1)^n \frac{n}{n+1}$

12. $\sum_{n=1}^{\infty} \frac{-n}{2^n}$

13. $\sum_{n=1}^{\infty} (5)^{-n}$

14. $\sum_{n=1}^{\infty} \left(\frac{1}{2^n} - 1\right)$

15. $\sum_{n=1}^{\infty} \frac{(-100)^n}{n!}$

16. $\sum_{n=2}^{\infty} (-1)^n \frac{\ln n}{\ln n^2}$

17. $\sum_{n=1}^{\infty} \frac{2-n}{n^3}$

18. $\sum_{n=1}^{\infty} \left(\frac{1}{2^n} - \frac{1}{3^n}\right)$

19. Show that if $\sum_{n=1}^{\infty} a_n$ diverges, then $\sum_{n=1}^{\infty} |a_n|$ diverges.

20. Show that if $\sum_{n=1}^{\infty} a_n$ converges absolutely, then

$$\left|\sum_{n=1}^{\infty} a_n\right| \le \sum_{n=1}^{\infty} |a_n|.$$

21. Show that if $\sum_{n=1}^{\infty} a_n$ and $\sum_{n=1}^{\infty} b_n$ both converge absolutely, then so does

a) $\sum (a_n + b_n)$ b) $\sum (a_n - b_n)$
c) $\sum ka_n$ (k any number)

12-7

ALTERNATING SERIES. CONDITIONAL CONVERGENCE

When some of the terms of a series $\sum a_n$ are positive and others are negative, the series converges if $\sum |a_n|$ converges. Thus we may apply any of our tests for convergence of nonnegative series, provided we apply them to the series of absolute values. But we do not know, when the series of absolute values *diverges*, whether the *original* series diverges or converges. If it converges, but not absolutely, we say that it *converges conditionally*.

We shall discuss one simple case of series with mixed signs, namely, series that take the form

$$a_1 - a_2 + a_3 - a_4 + \cdots (-1)^{n+1}a_n + \cdots, \tag{1}$$

with all a's > 0. Such series are called *alternating series* because successive terms have alternate signs. Examples of alternating series are:

$$1 - \tfrac{1}{2} + \tfrac{1}{3} - \tfrac{1}{4} + \tfrac{1}{5} - \tfrac{1}{6} + \cdots, \tag{2}$$

$$\frac{1}{\ln 2} - \frac{1}{\ln 3} + \frac{1}{\ln 4} - \frac{1}{\ln 5} + \cdots \tag{3}$$

$$1 - \sqrt{2} + \sqrt{3} - \sqrt{4} + \cdots. \tag{4}$$

The series

$$1 - \frac{1}{2} - \frac{1}{4} + \frac{1}{6} - \frac{1}{8} - \frac{1}{10} + \frac{1}{12} \cdots \qquad (5)$$

is *not* an alternating series. The signs of its terms do not alternate.

Definition.   *A sequence $\{a_n\}$ is called a **decreasing sequence** if $a_n \geq a_{n+1}$ for every n.*

Examples of decreasing sequences are

$$1, \quad \frac{1}{2}, \quad \frac{1}{3}, \quad \frac{1}{4}, \quad \ldots,$$

$$1, \quad 1, \quad 1, \quad 1, \quad \ldots.$$

The sequence

$$\frac{1}{3}, \quad \frac{1}{2}, \quad \frac{1}{6}, \quad \frac{1}{4}, \quad \ldots, \quad \frac{1}{3n}, \quad \frac{1}{2n}, \quad \cdots$$

is *not* a decreasing sequence even though it converges to 0 from above.

One reason for selecting alternating series for study is that every alternating series whose numbers a_n form a decreasing sequence with limit 0 converges. Another reason is that whenever an alternating series converges, it is easy to estimate its sum. This fortunate combination of assured convergence and easy estimation gives us an opportunity to see how a wide variety of series behave. We look first at the convergence.

Theorem 1.   Leibniz's Theorem. $\sum_{n=1}^{\infty} (-1)^{n+1} a_n$ *converges if all three of the following conditions are satisfied:*

1. *The a_n's are all positive;*
2. $a_n \geq a_{n+1}$ *for every n;*
3. $a_n \to 0$.

Proof.   If n is an even integer, say $n = 2m$, then the sum of the first n terms is

$$s_{2m} = (a_1 - a_2) + (a_3 - a_4) + \cdots + (a_{2m-1} - a_{2m})$$

$$= a_1 - (a_2 - a_3) - (a_4 - a_5) - \cdots - (a_{2m-2} - a_{2m-1}) - a_{2m}.$$

The first equality exhibits s_{2m} as the sum of m nonnegative terms, since each expression in parentheses is positive or zero. Hence $s_{2m+2} \geq s_{2m}$, and the sequence $\{s_{2m}\}$ is increasing. The second equality shows that $s_{2m} \leq a_1$. Since $\{s_{2m}\}$ is increasing and bounded from above it has a limit, say

$$\lim_{n \to \infty} s_{2m} = L. \qquad (6)$$

If n is an odd integer, say $n = 2m + 1$, then the sum of the first n terms is

$$s_{2m+1} = s_{2m} + a_{2m+1}.$$

Since $a_n \to 0$,

$$\lim_{m \to \infty} a_{2m+1} = 0.$$

Hence, as $m \to \infty$,

$$s_{2m+1} = s_{2m} + a_{2m+1} \to L + 0 = L. \qquad (7)$$

Finally, we may combine (6) and (7) and say simply

$$\lim_{n \to \infty} s_n = L. \qquad\qquad \text{Q.E.D.}$$

Here are some examples of what Theorem 1 can do.

EXAMPLE 1. The *alternating harmonic* series

$$\sum_{n=1}^{\infty} (-1)^{n+1} \frac{1}{n} = 1 - \frac{1}{2} + \frac{1}{3} - \frac{1}{4} + \cdots$$

satisfies the three requirements of the theorem; therefore it converges. It converges conditionally because the corresponding series of absolute values is the harmonic series, which diverges.

EXAMPLE 2. The series

$$\sum_{n=1}^{\infty} (-1)^{n+1} \sqrt{n} = 1 - \sqrt{2} + \sqrt{3} - \sqrt{4} + \cdots$$

diverges by the *n*th-term test.

EXAMPLE 3. Theorem 1 gives no information about

$$\frac{2}{1} - \frac{1}{1} + \frac{2}{2} - \frac{1}{2} + \frac{2}{3} - \frac{1}{3} + \cdots + \frac{2}{n} - \frac{1}{n} + \cdots .$$

The sequence $\frac{2}{1}, \frac{1}{1}, \frac{2}{2}, \frac{1}{2}, \frac{2}{3}, \frac{1}{3}, \ldots$ is not a decreasing sequence. Some other test must be found. When we group the terms of the series in consecutive pairs

$$\left(\frac{2}{1} - \frac{1}{1} \right) + \left(\frac{2}{2} - \frac{1}{2} \right) + \left(\frac{2}{3} - \frac{1}{3} \right) + \cdots + \left(\frac{2}{n} - \frac{1}{n} \right) + \cdots ,$$

we see that the 2*n*th partial sum of the given series is the same number as the *n*th partial sum of the harmonic series. Thus the sequence of partial sums, and hence the series, diverges.

We use the following graphical interpretation of the partial sums to gain added insight into the way in which an alternating series converges to its limit L when the three conditions of the theorem are satisfied. Starting from the origin O on a scale of real numbers (Fig. 12–13), we lay off the positive distance

$$s_1 = a_1.$$

To find the point corresponding to

$$s_2 = a_1 - a_2$$

we must back up a distance equal to a_2. Since $a_2 \le a_1$, we do not back up any farther than O at most. Next we go forward a distance a_3 and mark the point corresponding to

$$s_3 = a_1 - a_2 + a_3.$$

12–13 The partial sums of an alternating series that satisfies the hypotheses of Leibniz's theorem straddle their limit.

Since $a_3 \leq a_2$, we go forward by an amount that is no greater than the previous backward step; that is, s_3 is less than or equal to s_1. We continue in this seesaw fashion, backing up or going forward as the signs in the series demand. But each forward or backward step is shorter than (or at most the same size as) the preceding step, because $a_{n+1} \leq a_n$. And since the nth term approaches zero as n increases, the size of step we take forward or backward gets smaller and smaller. We thus oscillate across the limit L, but the amplitude of oscillation continually decreases and approaches zero as its limit. The even-numbered partial sums $s_2, s_4, s_6, \ldots, s_{2m}$ continually increase toward L, while the odd-numbered sums $s_1, s_3, s_5, \ldots, s_{2m+1}$ continually decrease toward L. The limit L is between any two successive sums s_n and s_{n+1} and hence differs from s_n by an amount less than a_{n+1}.

It is because

$$|L - s_n| < a_{n+1} \qquad \text{for every } n \tag{8}$$

that we can make useful estimates of the sums of convergent alternating series.

Theorem 2. The Alternating Series Estimation Theorem. *If*

$$\sum_{n=1}^{\infty} (-1)^{n+1} a_n$$

is an alternating series that satisfies the three conditions of Theorem 1, then

$$s_n = a_1 - a_2 + \cdots + (-1)^{n+1} a_n$$

approximates the sum L of the series with an error whose absolute value is less than a_{n+1}, the numerical value of the first unused term. Furthermore, the remainder, $L - s_n$, has the same sign as the first unused term.

We will leave the determination of the sign of the remainder as an exercise.

EXAMPLE 4. Let us first try the estimation theorem on an alternating series whose sum we already know, namely, the geometric series:

$$\sum_{n=0}^{\infty} (-1)^n \frac{1}{2^n} = 1 - \frac{1}{2} + \frac{1}{4} - \frac{1}{8} + \frac{1}{16} - \frac{1}{32} + \frac{1}{64} - \frac{1}{128} + \frac{1}{256} - \cdots$$

Theorem 2 says that, when we truncate the series after the eighth term, we throw away a total that is positive and less than $\frac{1}{256}$. A rapid calculation shows that the sum of the first eight terms is

$$0.6640625.$$

The sum of the series is

$$\frac{1}{1 - (-\frac{1}{2})} = \frac{1}{3/2} = \frac{2}{3}. \tag{9}$$

The difference,

$$\frac{2}{3} - 0.6640625 = 0.0026041666\ldots,$$

is positive and less than

$$\tfrac{1}{256} = 0.00390625.$$

The series

$$\ln (1 + x) = x - \frac{x^2}{2} + \frac{x^3}{3} - \cdots + (-1)^{n+1} \frac{x^n}{n} \cdots \tag{10}$$

may be used to compute $\ln (1 + x)$ when $|x| < 1$. For $0 < x < 1$, this series satisfies all three conditions of Theorem 1, and we may use the estimation theorem to see how good an approximation of $\ln (1 + x)$ we get from the first few terms of the series.

EXAMPLE 5.   Calculate $\ln 1.1$ with the approximation

$$\ln (1 + x) \approx x - \frac{x^2}{2}, \tag{11}$$

and estimate the error involved. Is $x - (x^2/2)$ too large, or too small in this case?

Solution

$$\ln (1.1) \approx (0.1) - \frac{(0.1)^2}{2} = 0.095.$$

This approximation differs from the exact value of $\ln 1.1$ by less than

$$\frac{(0.1)^3}{3} = 0.000333\ldots.$$

Since the sign of this, the first unused term, is positive, the remainder is positive. That is, 0.095 underestimates $\ln 1.1$.

EXAMPLE 6.   How many terms of the series (10) do we need to use in order to be sure of calculating $\ln (1.2)$ with an error of less than 10^{-6}?

Solution

$$\ln (1.2) = (0.2) - \frac{(0.2)^2}{2} + \frac{(0.2)^3}{3} - \cdots$$

We find by trial that the eighth term

$$-\frac{(0.2)^8}{8} = -3.2 \times 10^{-7}$$

is the first term in the series whose absolute value is less than 10^{-6}. Therefore the sum of the first *seven* terms will give ln 1.2 with an error of less than 10^{-6}. The use of more terms would give an approximation that is even better, but seven terms are enough to guarantee the accuracy we wanted. Note also that we have not shown that six terms would *not* provide that accuracy.

PROBLEMS

In Problems 1 through 10, determine which of the following alternating series converge and which diverge.

1. $\displaystyle\sum_{n=1}^{\infty} (-1)^{n+1} \frac{1}{n^2}$ **2.** $\displaystyle\sum_{n=2}^{\infty} (-1)^{n+1} \frac{1}{\ln n}$

3. $\displaystyle\sum_{n=1}^{\infty} (-1)^{n+1}$ **4.** $\displaystyle\sum_{n=1}^{\infty} (-1)^{n+1} \frac{10^n}{n^{10}}$

5. $\displaystyle\sum_{n=1}^{\infty} (-1)^{n+1} \frac{\sqrt{n+1}}{n+1}$ **6.** $\displaystyle\sum_{n=1}^{\infty} (-1)^{n+1} \frac{\ln n}{n}$

7. $\displaystyle\sum_{n=1}^{\infty} (-1)^{n+1} \frac{1}{n^{3/2}}$ **8.** $\displaystyle\sum_{n=1}^{\infty} (-1)^{n+1} \frac{\ln n}{\ln n^2}$

9. $\displaystyle\sum_{n=1}^{\infty} (-1)^{n} \ln\left(1 + \frac{1}{n}\right)$ **10.** $\displaystyle\sum_{n=1}^{\infty} (-1)^{n+1} \frac{3\sqrt{n+1}}{\sqrt{n+1}}$

In Problems 11 through 28, determine whether the following series are absolutely convergent, conditionally convergent, or divergent.

11. $\displaystyle\sum_{n=1}^{\infty} (-1)^{n+1}(0.1)^n$ **12.** $\displaystyle\sum_{n=1}^{\infty} (-1)^{n+1} \frac{1}{\sqrt{n}}$

13. $\displaystyle\sum_{n=1}^{\infty} (-1)^{n+1} \frac{n}{n^3+1}$ **14.** $\displaystyle\sum_{n=1}^{\infty} \frac{n!}{2^n}$

15. $\displaystyle\sum_{n=1}^{\infty} (-1)^{n} \frac{1}{n+3}$ **16.** $\displaystyle\sum_{n=1}^{\infty} (-1)^{n} \frac{\sin n}{n^2}$

17. $\displaystyle\sum_{n=1}^{\infty} (-1)^{n+1} \frac{3+n}{5+n}$ **18.** $\displaystyle\sum_{n=2}^{\infty} (-1)^{n} \frac{1}{\ln n^3}$

19. $\displaystyle\sum_{n=1}^{\infty} (-1)^{n+1} \frac{1+n}{n^2}$ **20.** $\displaystyle\sum_{n=1}^{\infty} \frac{(-2)^{n+1}}{n+5^n}$

21. $\displaystyle\sum_{n=1}^{\infty} n^2(\tfrac{2}{3})^n$ **22.** $\displaystyle\sum_{n=1}^{\infty} (-1)^{n+1}(\sqrt[n]{10})$

23. $\displaystyle\sum_{n=1}^{\infty} (-1)^{n} \frac{\tan^{-1} n}{n^2+1}$ **24.** $\displaystyle\sum_{n=2}^{\infty} (-1)^{n+1} \frac{1}{n \ln n}$

25. $\displaystyle\sum_{n=1}^{\infty} \left(\frac{1}{n} - \frac{1}{2n}\right)$ **26.** $\displaystyle\sum_{n=1}^{\infty} (-1)^{n+1} \frac{(0.1)^n}{n}$

27. $\displaystyle\sum_{n=1}^{\infty} (-1)^{n+1}(\sqrt{n+1} - \sqrt{n})$ **28.** $\displaystyle\sum_{n=1}^{\infty} \frac{(-1)^{n+1}(n!)^2}{(2n)!}$

In Problems 29 through 32, estimate the magnitude of the error if the first four terms are used to approximate the series.

29. $\displaystyle\sum_{n=1}^{\infty} (-1)^{n+1} \frac{1}{n}$ **30.** $\displaystyle\sum_{n=1}^{\infty} (-1)^{n+1} \frac{1}{10^n}$

31. $\ln(1.01) = \displaystyle\sum_{n=1}^{\infty} (-1)^{n+1} \frac{(0.01)^n}{n}$

32. $\dfrac{1}{1+t} = \displaystyle\sum_{n=0}^{\infty} (-1)^{n}t^n, \qquad 0 < t < 1$

Approximate the following two sums to five decimal places (magnitude of the error less than 5×10^{-6}).

33. $\displaystyle\sum_{n=0}^{\infty} (-1)^{n} \frac{1}{(2n)!}$

(This is cos 1, the cosine of one radian.)

34. $\displaystyle\sum_{n=0}^{\infty} (-1)^{n} \frac{1}{n!}$ (This is $1/e$.)

35. a) The series

$$\frac{1}{3} - \frac{1}{2} + \frac{1}{9} - \frac{1}{4} + \frac{1}{27} - \frac{1}{8} + \cdots + \frac{1}{3^n} - \frac{1}{2^n} + \cdots$$

does not meet one of the conditions of Theorem 1. Which one?

b) Find the sum of the series in (a).

36. The limit L of an alternating series that satisfies the conditions of Theorem 1 lies between the values of any two consecutive partial sums. This suggests using the average

$$\frac{s_n + s_{n+1}}{2} = s_n + \frac{1}{2} a_{n+1}$$

to estimate L. Compute

$$s_{20} + \tfrac{1}{2} \cdot \tfrac{1}{21}$$

as an approximation to the sum of the alternating harmonic series. The exact sum is ln 2.

37. Show that whenever an alternating series is approximated by one of its partial sums, if the three conditions of Leibniz's theorem are satisfied, then the *remainder* (sum of the unused terms) has the same sign as the first unused term. [*Hint.* Group the terms of the remainder in consecutive pairs.]

38. Prove the "zipper" theorem for sequences: If $\{a_n\}$ and $\{b_n\}$ both converge to L, then the sequence

$$a_1, \quad b_1, \quad a_2, \quad b_2, \quad \ldots, \quad a_n, \quad b_n, \quad \ldots$$

also converges to L.

39. Show by example that $\sum_{n=1}^{\infty} a_n b_n$ may diverge even though $\sum_{n=1}^{\infty} a_n$ and $\sum_{n=1}^{\infty} b_n$ both converge.

12–8

POWER SERIES FOR FUNCTIONS

The rational operations of arithmetic are addition, subtraction, multiplication, and division. Using only these simple operations, we can evaluate any rational function of x. But other functions, such as $\sqrt{x}$, ln x, cos x, and so on, cannot be evaluated so simply. These functions occur so frequently, however, that their values have been printed in mathematical tables, and many calculators and computers have been programmed to produce them on demand. One may wonder where the values in the tables came from, and how a calculator produces the number it displays. By and large, these numbers come from calculating partial sums of power series.

Definition.   *A **power series** is a series of the form*

$$\sum_{n=0}^{\infty} a_n x^n = a_0 + a_1 x + a_2 x^2 + \cdots.$$

In this article we shall show how a power series can arise when we seek to approximate a function

$$y = f(x) \tag{1}$$

by a sequence of polynomials $f_n(x)$ of the form

$$f_n(x) = a_0 + a_1 x + a_2 x^2 + \cdots + a_n x^n. \tag{2}$$

We shall be interested, at least at first, in making the approximation for values of x near 0, because we want the term $a_n x^n$ to decrease as n increases. Hence we focus our attention on a portion of the curve $y = f(x)$ near the point $A(0, f(0))$, as shown in Fig. 12–14.

1. The graph of the polynomial $f_0(x) = a_0$ of degree zero will pass through $(0, f(0))$ if we take

$$a_0 = f(0).$$

2. The graph of the polynomial $f_1(x) = a_0 + a_1 x$ will pass through $(0, f(0))$ and have the same slope as the given curve at that point if we choose

$$a_0 = f(0) \qquad \text{and} \qquad a_1 = f'(0).$$

3. The graph of the polynomial $f_2(x) = a_0 + a_1 x + a_2 x^2$ will pass through $(0, f(0))$ and have the same slope and curvature as the given curve at that point if

$$a_0 = f(0), \qquad a_1 = f'(0), \qquad \text{and } a_2 = \frac{f''(0)}{2}.$$

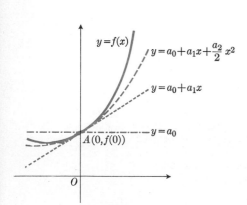

12–14 $f(x)$ is approximated near $x = 0$ by polynomials whose derivatives at $x = 0$ match the derivatives of f.

4. In general, the polynomial $f_n(x) = a_0 + a_1 x + a_2 x^2 + \cdots + a_n x^n$, which we choose to approximate $y = f(x)$ near $x = 0$, is the one whose graph passes through $(0, f(0))$ and whose first n derivatives match the derivatives of $f(x)$ at $x = 0$. To match the derivatives of f_n to those of f at $x = 0$, we merely have to choose the coefficients a_0 through a_n properly. To see how this may be done, we write down the polynomial and its derivatives as follows:

$$f_n(x) = a_0 + a_1 x + a_2 x^2 + a_3 x^3 + \cdots + a_n x^n$$
$$f'_n(x) = a_1 + 2a_2 x + 3a_3 x^2 + \cdots + na_n x^{n-1}$$
$$f''_n(x) = 2a_2 + 3 \cdot 2a_3 x + \cdots + n(n-1)a_n x^{n-2}$$
$$\vdots$$
$$f_n^{(n)}(x) = (n!)a_n.$$

When we substitute 0 for x in the array above, we find that

$$a_0 = f(0), \qquad a_1 = f'(0), \qquad a_2 = \frac{f''(0)}{2!}, \qquad \ldots, \qquad a_n = \frac{f^{(n)}(0)}{n!}.$$

Thus,

$$f_n(x) = f(0) + f'(0)x + \frac{f''(0)}{2!}x^2 + \cdots + \frac{f^{(n)}(0)}{n!}x^n \tag{3}$$

is the polynomial we seek. Its graph passes through the point $(0, f(0))$, and its first n derivatives match the first n derivatives of $y = f(x)$ at $x = 0$. It is called the nth-degree *Taylor polynomial of f at $x = 0$*.

EXAMPLE 1. Find the Taylor polynomials $f_n(x)$ for the function $f(x) = e^x$.

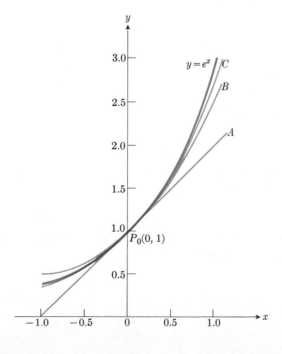

12–15 The graph of the function $y = e^x$, and graphs of three approximating polynomials, (*A*) a straight line, (*B*) a parabola, and (*C*) a cubic curve.

Solution. Expressed in terms of x, the given function and its derivatives are

$$f(x) = e^x, \qquad f'(x) = e^x, \qquad \ldots, \qquad f^{(n)}(x) = e^x,$$

so that

$$f(0) = e^0 = 1, \qquad f'(0) = 1, \qquad \ldots, \qquad f^{(n)}(0) = 1,$$

and

$$f_n(x) = 1 + x + \frac{x^2}{2!} + \frac{x^3}{3!} + \cdots + \frac{x^n}{n!}.$$

See Fig. 12–15.

EXAMPLE 2. Find the Taylor polynomials $f_n(x)$ for $f(x) = \cos x$.

Solution. The cosine and its derivatives are

$$
\begin{array}{llll}
f(x) & = & \cos x, & f'(x) & = & -\sin x, \\
f''(x) & = & -\cos x, & f^{(3)}(x) & = & \sin x, \\
\vdots & & & \vdots & & \\
f^{(2k)}(x) = (-1)^k \cos x, & & & f^{(2k+1)}(x) = (-1)^{k+1} \sin x.
\end{array}
$$

When $x = 0$, the cosines are 1 and the sines are 0, so that

$$f^{(2k)}(0) = (-1)^k, \qquad f^{(2k+1)}(0) = 0.$$

The Taylor polynomials have only even-powered terms, and for $n = 2k$ we have

$$f_{2k}(x) = 1 - \frac{x^2}{2!} + \frac{x^4}{4!} - \cdots + (-1)^k \frac{x^{2k}}{(2k)!}. \tag{4}$$

Figure 12–16 shows how well these polynomials can be expected to approximate $y = \cos x$ near $x = 0$. Only the righthand portions of the graphs are shown because the graphs are symmetric about the y-axis.

12–16 The polynomials $c_n(x) = \sum_{k=0}^{n} [(-1)^k x^{2k}/(2k)!]$ converge to $\cos x$ as $n \to \infty$. (Adapted from Helen M. Kammerer, *American Mathematical Monthly*, 43(1936), 293–294.)

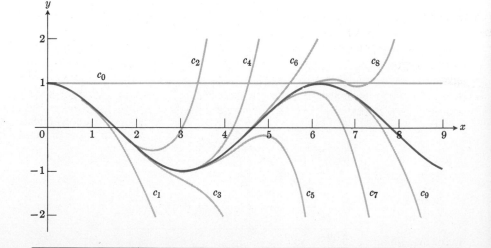

The degrees of the Taylor polynomials of a given function are limited by the degree of differentiability of the function at $x = 0$. But if $f(x)$ has derivatives of all orders at the origin, it is natural to ask whether, for a fixed value of x, the values of these approximating polynomials converge to $f(x)$ as $n \to \infty$. Now, these polynomials are precisely the partial sums of a series known as the *Maclaurin series* for f:

The Maclaurin series for f

$$f(0) + f'(0)x + \frac{f''(0)}{2!}x^2 + \cdots + \frac{f^{(n)}(0)}{n!}x^n + \cdots. \tag{5}$$

Thus, the question just posed is equivalent to asking whether the Maclaurin series for f converges to $f(x)$ as a sum. It certainly has the correct value, $f(0)$, at $x = 0$, but how far away from $x = 0$ may we go and still have convergence? And if the series does converge away from $x = 0$, does it still converge to $f(x)$? The graphs in Figs. 12–15 and 12–16 are encouraging, and the next few articles will confirm that we can normally expect a Maclaurin series to converge to its function in an interval about the origin. For many functions, this interval is the entire x-axis.

If, instead of approximating the values of f near zero, we are concerned with values of x near some other point a, we write our approximating polynomials in powers of $(x - a)$:

$$f_n(x) = a_0 + a_1(x - a) + a_2(x - a)^2 + \cdots + a_n(x - a)^n. \tag{6}$$

When we now determine the coefficients $a_0, a_1, \ldots, a_n$, so that the polynomial and its first n derivatives agree with the given function and its derivatives at $x = a$, we are led to a series that is called the *Taylor series expansion of f about $x = a$*, or simply the *Taylor series for f at $x = a$*.

The Taylor series for f at $x = a$

$$f(a) + f'(a)(x - a) + \frac{f''(a)}{2!}(x - a)^2 + \cdots + \frac{f^{(n)}(a)}{n!}(x - a)^n + \cdots. \tag{7}$$

There are two things to notice here. The first is that Maclaurin series are Taylor series with $a = 0$. The second is that a function cannot have a Taylor series expansion about $x = a$ unless it has finite derivatives of all orders at $x = a$. For instance, $f(x) = \ln x$ does not have a Maclaurin series expansion, since the function itself, to say nothing of its derivatives, does not have a finite value at $x = 0$. On the other hand, it does have a Taylor series expansion in powers of $(x - 1)$, since $\ln x$ and all its derivatives are finite at $x = 1$.

Here are some examples of Taylor series.

EXAMPLE 3. From the formula derived for the Taylor polynomials of $\cos x$ in Example 2, it follows immediately that

$$\sum_{k=0}^{\infty} (-1)^k \frac{x^{2k}}{(2k)!} = 1 - \frac{x^2}{2!} + \frac{x^4}{4!} - \frac{x^6}{6!} + \cdots$$

is the Maclaurin series for $\cos x$.

EXAMPLE 4. Find the Taylor series expansion of $\cos x$ about the point $a = 2\pi$.

Solution. The values of $\cos x$ and its derivatives at $a = 2\pi$ are the same as their values at $a = 0$. Therefore,

$$f^{(2k)}(2\pi) = f^{(2k)}(0) = (-1)^k \quad \text{and} \quad f^{(2k+1)}(2\pi) = f^{(2k+1)}(0) = 0,$$

as in Example 2. The required series is

$$\sum_{k=0}^{\infty} (-1)^{2k} \frac{(x - 2\pi)^{2k}}{(2k)!} = 1 - \frac{(x - 2\pi)^2}{2!} + \frac{(x - 2\pi)^4}{4!} - \cdots.$$

REMARK. There is a convention about how formulas like

$$\frac{x^{2k}}{(2k)!} \quad \text{and} \quad \frac{(x - 2\pi)^{2k}}{(2k)!},$$

which arise in the power series of Examples 3 and 4, are to be evaluated when $k = 0$. Besides the usual agreement that $0! = 1$, we also assume that

$$\frac{x^0}{0!} = \frac{1}{1} = 1 \quad \text{and} \quad \frac{(x - 2\pi)^0}{0!} = \frac{1}{1} = 1, \quad \text{even when } x = 0 \text{ or } 2\pi.$$

The binomial series

One of the most celebrated series of all times, the *binomial series*, is the Maclaurin series for the function $f(x) = (1 + x)^m$. Newton used it to estimate integrals (we will, in Article 12–12) and it can be used to give accurate estimates of roots. To derive the series, we first list the function and its derivatives:

$$f(x) \quad = (1 + x)^m,$$
$$f'(x) \quad = m(1 + x)^{m-1},$$
$$f''(x) \quad = m(m - 1)(1 + x)^{m-2},$$
$$f'''(x) \quad = m(m - 1)(m - 2)(1 + x)^{m-3},$$
$$\vdots$$
$$f^{(k)}(x) = m(m - 1)(m - 2) \cdots (m - k + 1)(1 + x)^{m-k}.$$

We then substitute the values of these at $x = 0$ in the basic Maclaurin series (5) to obtain

$$1 + mx + \frac{m(m - 1)}{2!} x^2 + \cdots + \frac{m(m - 1)(m - 2) \cdots (m - k + 1)}{k!} x^k + \cdots. \quad \textbf{(8)}$$

If m is an integer, the series terminates after $(m + 1)$ terms, because the coefficients from $k = m + 1$ on are 0. But when k is not an integer, the series is infinite. (For a proof that the series converges to $(1 + x)^m$ when $|x| < 1$, see Courant and John's *Introduction to Calculus and Analysis*, Wiley-Interscience, 1974.)

EXAMPLE 5. Use the binomial series to estimate $\sqrt{1.25}$ with an error of less than 0.001.

Solution. We take $x = \frac{1}{4}$ and $m = \frac{1}{2}$ in (8) to obtain

$$(1 + \tfrac{1}{4})^{1/2} = 1 + \tfrac{1}{2}(\tfrac{1}{4}) + \frac{(\tfrac{1}{2})(-\tfrac{1}{2})}{2!}(\tfrac{1}{4})^2 + \frac{(\tfrac{1}{2})(-\tfrac{1}{2})(-\tfrac{3}{2})}{3!}(\tfrac{1}{4})^3 + \cdots$$

$$= 1 + \tfrac{1}{8} - \tfrac{1}{128} + \tfrac{1}{1024} - \tfrac{1}{32768} + \cdots$$

The series alternates after the first term, so that the approximation

$$\sqrt{1.25} \approx 1 + \tfrac{1}{8} - \tfrac{1}{128} \approx 1.117$$

is within $\tfrac{1}{1024}$ of the exact value and thus has the required accuracy.

PROBLEMS

In Problems 1 through 9, use Eq. (3) to write the Taylor polynomials $f_3(x)$ and $f_4(x)$ for each of the following functions $f(x)$. In each case, your first step should be to complete a table like the one shown below.

n	$f^{(n)}(x)$	$f^{(n)}(0)$
0		
1		
2		
3		
4		

1. e^{-x}
2. $\sin x$
3. $\cos x$
4. $\sin\left(x + \dfrac{\pi}{2}\right)$
5. $\sinh x$
6. $\cosh x$
7. $x^4 - 2x + 1$
8. $x^3 - 2x + 1$
9. $x^2 - 2x + 1$

In Problems 10 through 13, find the Maclaurin series for each function.

10. $\dfrac{1}{1 + x}$
11. x^2
12. $(1 + x)^2$
13. $(1 + x)^{3/2}$

14. Find the Maclaurin series for $f(x) = 1/(1 - x)$. Show that the series diverges when $|x| \geq 1$ and converges when $|x| < 1$.

In Problems 15–20, use Eq. (7) to write the Taylor series expansion of the given function about the given point a.

15. $f(x) = e^x, \quad a = 10$
16. $f(x) = x^2, \quad a = \frac{1}{2}$
17. $f(x) = \ln x, \quad a = 1$
18. $f(x) = \sqrt{x}, \quad a = 4$
19. $f(x) = \dfrac{1}{x}, \quad a = -1$
20. $f(x) = \cos x, \quad a = -\dfrac{\pi}{4}$

In Problems 21 and 22, write the sum of the first three terms of the Taylor series for the given function about the given point a.

21. $f(x) = \tan x, \quad a = \dfrac{\pi}{4}$
22. $f(x) = \ln \cos x, \quad a = \dfrac{\pi}{3}$

23. Use the binomial theorem to estimate $\sqrt{1.02}$ with an error of less than 0.001.

In the previous article, we asked when a Taylor series for a function can be expected to converge to the function. In this article, we answer the question with a theorem named after the English mathematician Brook Taylor (1685–1731). Unfortunately, although several proofs of the theorem are known, none of them seems to have an obvious point of departure.

The path we shall follow starts with the simple formula

$$\int_a^b f'(t)\, dt = f(t)\Big|_a^b = f(b) - f(a), \tag{1}$$

12–9

TAYLOR'S THEOREM WITH REMAINDER: SINES, COSINES, AND e^x

which we rewrite in the form

$$f(b) = f(a) + \int_a^b f'(t) \, dt. \tag{2}$$

We then apply the integration-by-parts formula

$$\int u \, dv = uv - \int v \, du$$

with

$$u = f'(t) \qquad \text{and} \qquad v = t - b,$$

where, in determining v from $dv = dt$, we introduce the constant of integration $-b$ for future convenience. As a result,

$$f(b) = f(a) + (t - b)f'(t)\Big|_a^b - \int_a^b (t - b)f''(t) \, dt$$

$$= f(a) + (b - a)f'(a) + \int_a^b (b - t)f''(t) \, dt.$$

A second integration by parts, with

$$u = f''(t), \qquad v = -\frac{(b - t)^2}{2},$$

leads to

$$f(b) = f(a) + (b - a)f'(a) - \frac{(b - t)^2}{2}f''(t)\Big|_a^b + \int_a^b \frac{(b - t)^2}{2}f'''(t) \, dt$$

$$= f(a) + (b - a)f'(a) + \frac{(b - a)^2}{2!}f''(a) + \int_a^b \frac{(b - t)^2}{2!}f'''(t) \, dt.$$

By continuing in this fashion, we find that

$$f(b) = f(a) + (b - a)f'(a) + \frac{(b - a)^2}{2!}f''(a) + \cdots$$

$$+ \frac{(b - a)^n}{n!}f^{(n)}(a) + \int_a^b \frac{(b - t)^n}{n!}f^{(n+1)}(t) \, dt.$$

Finally, we replace b by x, to obtain the formula of Taylor's theorem.

Theorem 1. Taylor's Theorem. *Let f be a function that is continuous together with its first $n + 1$ derivatives on an interval containing a and x. Then the value of the function at x is given by*

$$f(x) = f(a) + f'(a) \cdot (x - a) + \frac{f''(a)}{2!}(x - a)^2 + \frac{f'''(a)}{3!}(x - a)^3 + \cdots$$

$$+ \frac{f^{(n)}(a)}{n!}(x - a)^n + R_n(x, a), \tag{3}$$

where

$$R_n(x, a) = \int_a^x \frac{(x - t)^n}{n!}f^{(n+1)}(t) \, dt.$$

Equation (3) is often referred to as *Taylor's formula.*

The application of integration by parts n times in succession requires that the integral in Eq. (3) exist at each stage. This will indeed be the case provided the $(n + 1)$st derivative of the function exists and is continuous in some closed interval that includes the domain of integration from a to x.

The term $R_n(x, a)$ is called the *remainder* in the Taylor-series expansion for $f(x)$. If the remainder is omitted in Eq. (3), the right side becomes the Taylor polynomial approximation to $f(x)$. The error in this approximation is what is measured by $R_n(x, a)$. Hence, we can pursue the question of whether the series converges to $f(x)$ by investigating this remainder. The series will converge to $f(x)$ provided

$$\lim_{n \to \infty} R_n(x, a) = 0. \tag{4}$$

In other words, when this limit is 0,

$$f(x) = \sum_{k=0}^{\infty} \frac{f^{(k)}(a)}{k!} (x - a)^k.$$

EXAMPLE 1. Let $f(x) = e^x$. This function and all its derivatives are continuous at every point, so Taylor's theorem may be applied with any convenient value of a. We take $a = 0$, since the values of f and its derivatives are easy to compute there. Taylor's theorem leads to

$$e^x = 1 + x + \frac{x^2}{2!} + \frac{x^3}{3!} + \cdots + \frac{x^n}{n!} + R_n(x, 0), \tag{5}$$

with

$$R_n(x, 0) = \int_0^x \frac{(x - t)^n}{n!} e^t \, dt. \tag{6}$$

When x is positive, we may *estimate* the remainder (6) by observing that the integrand is positive for $0 < t < x$, and that $e^t < e^x < 3^x$. Therefore,

$$|R_n(x, 0)| \le \int_0^x \frac{(x - t)^n}{n!} 3^x \, dt = 3^x \int_0^x \frac{(x - t)^n}{n!} \, dt = 3^x \frac{x^{n+1}}{(n+1)!}, \qquad x > 0. \tag{7}$$

When x is negative, we merely replace x by $|x|$ on the right, and the inequality continues to hold. Therefore, for all real values of x, we have

$$|R_n(x, 0)| \le 3^{|x|} \frac{|x|^{n+1}}{(n+1)!}, \tag{8}$$

and since

$$\lim_{n \to \infty} 3^{|x|} \frac{|x|^{n+1}}{(n+1)!} = 3^{|x|} \lim_{n \to \infty} \frac{|x|^{n+1}}{(n+1)!} = 3^{|x|} \cdot 0 = 0, \tag{9}$$

we know that

$$R_n(x, 0) \to 0.$$

Therefore, the Taylor series for e^x converges to e^x for every x:

$$e^x = \sum_{n=0}^{\infty} \frac{x^n}{n!} = 1 + x + \frac{x^2}{2!} + \frac{x^3}{3!} + \cdots.$$

Estimating the Remainder

It is often possible to estimate $R_n(x, a)$ as we did in Example 1 without having to evaluate the integral for it. The basis for such estimates is the following theorem, although the reason may not be immediately apparent upon reading the Theorem. We first state and prove the theorem. Then we state a corollary of the theorem (we will call the corollary Theorem 3) that is formulated specifically for estimating remainders.

Theorem 2. *Let $g(t)$ and $h(t)$ be continuous for $a \leq t \leq b$, and suppose that $h(t)$ does not change sign in this interval. Then there exists a number c between a and b such that*

$$\int_a^b g(t)h(t) \, dt = g(c) \int_a^b h(t) \, dt. \tag{10}$$

Proof.   Let m and M be respectively the least and greatest values of $g(t)$ for $a \leq t \leq b$. Then

$$m \leq g(t_i) \leq M \tag{11}$$

for any t_i between a and b, inclusive. We form a subdivision

$$a = t_0 < t_1 < t_2 < \cdots < t_n = b$$

of the interval $a \leq t \leq b$ with

$$t_i - t_{i-1} = \Delta t = (b - a)/n, \qquad (i = 1, \ldots, n),$$

and multiply each term in the inequalities (11) by $h(t_i) \, \Delta t$. Since the sign of $h(t)$ does not change over the interval $a \leq t \leq b$, all the terms $h(t_i) \, \Delta t$ are of the same sign, say positive. [If they are all negative, replace $h(t)$ by $-h(t)$ in the argument that follows.] Then

$$mh(t_i) \, \Delta t \leq g(t_i)h(t_i) \, \Delta t \leq Mh(t_i) \, \Delta t,$$

and the order of inequality is preserved when we sum on i from 1 to n; that is,

$$\sum_{i=1}^n mh(t_i) \, \Delta t \leq \sum_{i=1}^n g(t_i)h(t_i) \, \Delta t \leq \sum_{i=1}^n Mh(t_i) \, \Delta t. \tag{12}$$

Finally, we let n increase indefinitely and recall that, because the functions involved are continuous on $[a, b]$, the sums converge to definite integrals:

$$m \int_a^b h(t) \, dt \leq \int_a^b g(t)h(t) \, dt \leq M \int_a^b h(t) \, dt,$$

or

$$m \leq \frac{\int_a^b g(t)h(t) \, dt}{\int_a^b h(t) \, dt} \leq M. \tag{13}$$

Since

$$Q = \frac{\int_a^b g(t)h(t) \, dt}{\int_a^b h(t) \, dt} \tag{14}$$

is a number between the least and greatest values taken on by $g(t)$ for $a \leq t \leq b$ and $g(t)$ is assumed to be continuous, there is a number c between *a* and *b* such that

$$Q = g(c).$$

This leads at once to the result in Eq. (10) and completes the proof of the theorem.   Q.E.D.

We now apply this theorem to the integral in Eq. (3) with

$$h(t) = \frac{(x - t)^n}{n!}, \qquad g(t) = f^{(n+1)}(t).$$

As *t* varies from *a* to *x*, $h(t)$ is continuous and does not change sign. Hence, if $f^{(n+1)}(t)$ is continuous, Eq. (10) applies, and we have

$$R_n(x, a) = f^{(n+1)}(c) \int_a^x \frac{(x - t)^n}{n!} \, dt$$

$$= f^{(n+1)}(c) \frac{(x - a)^{n+1}}{(n+1)!}.$$

This is known as *Lagrange's* form of the remainder:

Lagrange's Form of the Remainder

$$R_n(x, a) = f^{(n+1)}(c) \frac{(x - a)^{n+1}}{(n+1)!}, \qquad c \text{ between } a \text{ and } x.* \qquad \textbf{(15)}$$

In applying Lagrange's form we can, in general, only estimate $f^{(n+1)}(c)$ because we do not know *c* exactly. But we do know that if the values of $|f^{(n+1)}(t)|$ are bounded above by some constant *M* for all *t* between *a* and *x*, inclusive, then

$$|R_n(x, a)| = |f^{(n+1)}(c)| \frac{|x - a|^{n+1}}{(n+1)!} \le M \frac{|x - a|^{n+1}}{(n+1)!}. \qquad \textbf{(16)}$$

This was the estimate used in Example 1 when e^t in Eq. (6) was replaced by $M = 3^{|x|}$ to produce the inequality in (7), although the work was done in several steps there.

This method of estimation is so convenient that we state it as a theorem for future reference.

Theorem 3.   The Remainder Estimation Theorem. *If there is a positive constant M such that $|f^{(n+1)}(t)| \le M$ for all t between a and x, inclusive, then the remainder term $R_n(x, a)$ in Taylor's theorem satisfies the inequality*

$$|R_n(x, a)| \le M \frac{|x - a|^{n+1}}{(n+1)!}.$$

---

*   Another proof of Taylor's theorem, leading directly to the Lagrange form of the remainder, is outlined in Problem 74 (Extended Mean Value Theorem), in the miscellaneous problems at the end of Chapter 3.

We are now ready to look at some examples of how the Remainder Estimation Theorem and Taylor's Theorem can be used together to settle questions of convergence. As you will see, they can also be used to determine the accuracy with which a function is approximated by one of its Taylor polynomials.

EXAMPLE 2.　The Maclaurin series for $\sin x$ converges to $\sin x$ for all x.

Expressed in terms of x, the function and its derivatives are

$$
\begin{aligned}
f(x) &= \sin x, & f'(x) &= \cos x, \\
f''(x) &= -\sin x, & f'''(x) &= -\cos x, \\
&\ \vdots & &\ \vdots \\
f^{(2k)}(x) &= (-1)^k \sin x, & f^{(2k+1)}(x) &= (-1)^k \cos x,
\end{aligned}
$$

so that

$$
f^{(2k)}(0) = 0 \quad \text{and} \quad f^{(2k+1)}(0) = (-1)^k.
$$

The series has only odd-powered terms and, for $n = 2k + 1$, Taylor's formula gives

$$
\sin x = x - \frac{x^3}{3!} + \frac{x^5}{5!} - \cdots + \frac{(-1)^k x^{2k+1}}{(2k+1)!} + R_{2k+1}(x, 0).
$$

Now, since all the derivatives of $\sin x$ have absolute values less than or equal to 1, we can apply the Remainder Estimation Theorem with $M = 1$ to obtain

$$
|R_{2k+1}(x, 0)| \le 1 \cdot \frac{|x|^{2k+2}}{(2k+2)!}.
$$

Since $[\,|x|^{2k+2}/(2k+2)!\,] \to 0$ as $k \to \infty$, whatever the value of x,

$$
R_{2k+1}(x, 0) \to 0,
$$

and the Maclaurin series for $\sin x$ converges to $\sin x$ for every x:

$$
\sin x = \sum_{k=0}^{\infty} \frac{(-1)^k x^{2k+1}}{(2k+1)!} = x - \frac{x^3}{3!} + \frac{x^5}{5!} - \frac{x^7}{7!} + \cdots
$$

EXAMPLE 3.　The Maclaurin series for $\cos x$ converges to $\cos x$ for every value of x. We begin by adding the remainder term to the Taylor polynomial for $\cos x$ in Eq. (4) of the previous article, to obtain Taylor's formula for $\cos x$ with $n = 2k$:

$$
\cos x = 1 - \frac{x^2}{2!} + \frac{x^4}{4!} - \cdots + (-1)^k \frac{x^{2k}}{(2k)!} + R_{2k}(x, 0).
$$

Since the derivatives of the cosine have absolute value less than or equal to 1, we apply the Remainder Estimation Theorem with $M = 1$ to obtain

$$
|R_{2k}(x, 0)| \le 1 \cdot \frac{|x|^{2k+1}}{(2k+1)!}.
$$

For every value of x, $R_{2k} \to 0$ as $k \to \infty$. Therefore, the series converges to cos x for every value of x.

$$\cos x = \sum_{k=0}^{\infty} \frac{(-1)^k x^{2k}}{(2k)!} = 1 - \frac{x^2}{2!} + \frac{x^4}{4!} - \frac{x^6}{6!} + \cdots.$$

EXAMPLE 4. Find the Maclaurin series for cos $2x$ and show that it converges to cos $2x$ for every value of x.

Solution. The Maclaurin series for cos x converges to cos x for every value of x, and therefore converges for every value of $2x$:

$$\cos 2x = \sum_{k=0}^{\infty} \frac{(-1)^k (2x)^{2k}}{(2k)!} = 1 - \frac{(2x)^2}{2!} + \frac{(2x)^4}{4!} - \frac{(2x)^6}{6!} + \cdots$$

Taylor series can be added, subtracted, and multiplied by constants, just as other series can, and the results are once again Taylor series. The Taylor series for $f(x) + g(x)$ is the sum of the Taylor series for $f(x)$ and $g(x)$, because the nth derivative of $f(x) + g(x)$ is $f^{(n)}(x) + g^{(n)}(x)$, and so on. In the next example, we add the series for e^x and e^{-x} and divide by 2, to obtain the Taylor series for cosh x.

EXAMPLE 5. Find the Taylor series for cosh x.

Solution

$$e^x = 1 + x + \frac{x^2}{2!} + \frac{x^3}{3!} + \frac{x^4}{4!} + \frac{x^5}{5!} + \cdots,$$

$$e^{-x} = 1 - x + \frac{x^2}{2!} - \frac{x^3}{3!} + \frac{x^4}{4!} - \frac{x^5}{5!} + \cdots;$$

$$\cosh x = \frac{e^x + e^{-x}}{2} = 1 \quad + \frac{x^2}{2!} \quad + \frac{x^4}{4!} \quad + \cdots = \sum_{k=0}^{\infty} \frac{x^{2k}}{(2k)!}.$$

Here are some examples of how to use the Remainder Estimation Theorem to estimate truncation error.

EXAMPLE 6. Calculate e with an error of less than 10^{-6}.

Solution. By Taylor's Theorem,

$$e = e^1 = 1 + 1 + \frac{1}{2!} + \frac{1}{3!} + \cdots + \frac{1}{n!} + R_n(x, 0),$$

where

$$R_n(x, 0) = \int_0^1 \frac{(x - t)^n}{n!} e^t \, dt.$$

The interval of integration is $0 \le t \le 1$. Since $|e^t| < 3$ when $0 \le t \le 1$, the Remainder Estimation Theorem, with $M = 3$ and $x = 1$, gives

$$|R_n| \le 3 \cdot \frac{|1|^{n+1}}{(n+1)!} = \frac{3}{(n+1)!}.$$

By trial we find that $3/9! > 10^{-6}$, while $3/10! < 10^{-6}$. Thus we should take $(n + 1)$ to be at least 10, or n to be at least 9. With an error of less than 10^{-6},

$$e = 1 + 1 + \frac{1}{2} + \frac{1}{3!} + \cdots + \frac{1}{9!} \approx 2.718282.$$

EXAMPLE 7. For what values of x can $\sin x$ be replaced by $x - (x^3/3!)$ with an error of magnitude no greater than 3×10^{-4}?

Solution. Here we can take advantage of the fact that the Maclaurin series for $\sin x$ is an alternating series for every nonzero value of x. According to the Alternating Series Estimation Theorem in Article 12–7, the error in truncating

$$\sin x = x - \frac{x^3}{3!} + \frac{x^5}{5!} - \cdots$$

after $(x^3/3!)$ is no greater than

$$\left| \frac{x^5}{5!} \right| = \frac{|x|^5}{120}.$$

Therefore the error will be less than or equal to 3×10^{-4} if

$$\frac{|x|^5}{120} < 3 \times 10^{-4}$$

or

$$|x| < \sqrt[5]{360 \times 10^{-4}} \approx 0.514.$$

The Alternating Series Estimation Theorem tells us something that the Remainder Estimation Theorem does not: namely, that the estimate $x - (x^3/3!)$ for $\sin x$ is an underestimate when x is positive, because then $x^5/120$ is positive.

Figure 12–17 shows the graph of $\sin x$, along with the graphs of a number of its approximating Taylor polynomials. Note that the graph of $s_1 = x - (x^3/3!)$ is almost indistinguishable from the sine curve when $-1 \leq x \leq 1$. However, it crosses the x-axis at $\pm\sqrt{6} \approx \pm 2.45$, whereas the sine curve crosses the axis at $\pm\pi \approx \pm 3.14$.

One might wonder how the estimate given by the Remainder Estimation Theorem would compare with the one we just obtained from the Alternating Series Estimation Theorem. If we write

$$\sin x = x - \frac{x^3}{3!} + R_3,$$

then the Remainder Estimation Theorem gives

$$|R_3| \leq 1 \cdot \frac{|x|^4}{4!} = \frac{|x|^4}{24},$$

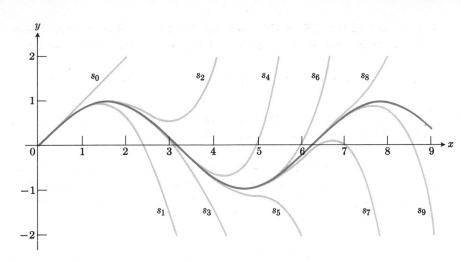

12–17 The polynomials
$s_n(x) = \sum_{k=0}^{n} [(-1)^k x^{2k+1}/(2k+1)!]$
converge to $\sin x$ as $n \to \infty$. (Adapted from Helen M. Kammerer, *American Mathematical Monthly*, 43(1936), 293–294.)

which is not very good. But, if we are clever, and write

$$\sin x = x - \frac{x^3}{3!} + 0 + R_4,$$

then the Remainder Estimation Theorem gives

$$|R_4| \leq 1 \cdot \frac{|x|^5}{5!} = \frac{|x|^5}{120},$$

which is just what we had from the Alternating Series Estimation Theorem.

Euler's formula: $e^{i\theta} = \cos\theta + i\sin\theta$.

Although we deal almost entirely with real numbers in this book, you are probably familiar with the symbol i for $\sqrt{-1}$ and with the system of complex numbers $a + ib$ where a and b are any real numbers. We usually meet these numbers for the first time when we study quadratic equations. There is an extensive branch of mathematics, called *complex analysis*, or *theory of functions of complex variables*, that extends the concepts of differentiation and integration to functions $f(z)$ where $z = x + iy$ is a complex variable. One of the standard ways of extending the domain of any one of the functions like $\sin x$, or $\cos x$, or e^x to the complex domain is to use the Taylor series for that function, in powers of x, and just see what happens when we replace x by $x + iy$, x^2 by $(x + iy)^2 = x^2 - y^2 + i(2xy)$, and so on, and then separating the real and imaginary parts of the series we get. We shall not do exactly that, but something that is simpler. (For a more extensive development, see the authors' *Calculus and Analytic Geometry*, 5th edition, Chapter 17, or books on Advanced Calculus or Theory of Functions.) It suffices for our purposes to look at the series for the cosine, sine, and exponential functions, as follows:

$$\cos\theta = 1 - \frac{\theta^2}{2!} + \frac{\theta^4}{4!} - \frac{\theta^6}{6!} + \cdots, \quad \sin\theta = \theta - \frac{\theta^3}{3!} + \frac{\theta^5}{5!} - \frac{\theta^7}{7!} + \cdots$$

$$e^{i\theta} = 1 + \frac{(i\theta)}{1!} + \frac{(i\theta)^2}{2!} + \frac{(i\theta)^3}{3!} + \frac{(i\theta)^4}{4!} + \frac{(i\theta)^5}{5!} + \frac{(i\theta)^6}{6!} + \frac{(i\theta)^7}{7!} + \cdots$$

$$= 1 + i\theta - \frac{\theta^2}{2!} - i\frac{\theta^3}{3!} + \frac{\theta^4}{4!} + i\frac{\theta^5}{5!} - \frac{\theta^6}{6!} - i\frac{\theta^7}{7!} + \cdots$$

$$= \left(1 - \frac{\theta^2}{2!} + \frac{\theta^4}{4!} - \frac{\theta^6}{6!} + \cdots\right) + i\left(\theta - \frac{\theta^3}{3!} + \frac{\theta^5}{5!} - \frac{\theta^7}{7!} + \cdots\right)$$

$$= \cos \theta + i \sin \theta.$$

The last result,

$$e^{i\theta} = \cos \theta + i \sin \theta, \tag{17}$$

is known as *Euler's formula*. If we replace θ by $-\theta$ in it, or in the earlier series, we get a companion formula

$$e^{-i\theta} = \cos \theta - i \sin \theta \tag{18}$$

because $\cos(-\theta) = \cos \theta$ and $\sin(-\theta) = -\sin \theta$. When we add and divide by 2, we find that we can write $\cos \theta$ in terms of the complex exponentials. Similarly, if we subtract and divide by $2i$, we can express $\sin \theta$ in terms of $e^{i\theta}$ and $e^{-i\theta}$. The results are as follows:

$$\cos \theta = \frac{e^{i\theta} + e^{-i\theta}}{2}, \qquad \sin \theta = \frac{e^{i\theta} - e^{-i\theta}}{2i}. \tag{19}$$

PROBLEMS

In Problems 1 through 6, write the Maclaurin series for each function.

1. $e^{x/2}$

2. $\sin 3x$

3. $5 \cos \dfrac{x}{\pi}$

4. $\sinh x$

5. $\dfrac{x^2}{2} - 1 + \cos x$

6. $\cos^2 2x = \dfrac{1 + \cos 2x}{2}$

7. Use series to verify that

a) $\cos(-x) = \cos x$

b) $\sin(-x) = -\sin x$

8. Show that

$$e^x = e^a \left[1 + (x - a) + \frac{(x - a)^2}{2!} + \cdots\right]$$

In Problems 9 through 11, write Taylor's formula (Eq. (3)), with $n = 2$ and $a = 0$, for the given function.

9. $\dfrac{1}{1 + x}$ **10.** $\ln(1 + x)$ **11.** $\sqrt{1 + x}$

12. Find the Taylor series for e^x at $a = 1$. Compare your series with the result in Problem 8.

13. For approximately what values of x can one replace $\sin x$ by $x - (x^3/6)$ with an error of magnitude no greater than 5×10^{-4}?

14. If $\cos x$ is replaced by $1 - (x^2/2)$ and $|x| < 0.5$, what estimate can be made of the error? Does $1 - (x^2/2)$ tend to be too large, or too small?

15. How close is the approximation $\sin x = x$ when $|x| < 10^{-3}$? For which of these values of x is $x < \sin x$?

16. The estimate $\sqrt{1 + x} = 1 + (x/2)$ is used when $|x|$ is small. Estimate the error when $|x| < 0.01$.

17. The approximation $e^x = 1 + x + (x^2/2)$ is used when x is small. Use the Remainder Estimation Theorem to estimate the error when $|x| < 0.1$.

18. When $x < 0$, the series for e^x is an alternating series. Use the Alternating Series Estimation Theorem to estimate the error that results from replacing e^x by $1 + x + (x^2/2)$ when $-0.1 < x < 0$. Compare with Problem 17.

19. Estimate the error in the approximation $\sinh x = x + (x^3/3!)$ when $|x| < 0.5$. [*Hint.* Use R_4, not R_3.]

20. When $0 \leq h \leq 0.01$, show that e^h may be replaced by $1 + h$ with an error of magnitude no greater than six-tenths of one percent of h. Use $e^{0.1} = 1.105$.

21. Let $f(x)$ and $g(x)$ have derivatives of all orders at $a = 0$. Show that the Maclaurin series for $f + g$ is

$$\sum_{n=0}^{\infty} \frac{f^{(n)}(0) + g^{(n)}(0)}{n!} x^n.$$

22. Each of the following sums is the value of an elementary function at some point. Find the function and the point.

a) $(0.1) - \dfrac{(0.1)^3}{3!} + \dfrac{(0.1)^5}{5!} - \cdots + \dfrac{(-1)^k(0.1)^{2k+1}}{(2k+1)!} + \cdots$

b) $1 - \dfrac{\pi^2}{4^2 \cdot 2!} + \dfrac{\pi^4}{4^4 \cdot 4!} - \cdots + \dfrac{(-1)^k(\pi)^{2k}}{4^{2k} \cdot (2k)!} + \cdots$

c) $1 + \dfrac{1}{2!} + \dfrac{1}{4!} + \cdots + \dfrac{1}{(2k)!} + \cdots$

23. Using Eq. (17) as the definition of $e^{i\theta}$, and trigonometric identities for $\cos(\theta_1 + \theta_2)$ and $\sin(\theta_1 + \theta_2)$, prove the law of addition of exponents:

$$e^{i\theta_1} \cdot e^{i\theta_2} = e^{i(\theta_1 + \theta_2)}.$$

24. In Eq. (19), let $\theta = ix$ and $i\theta = -x$ and deduce that

$$\cos(ix) = \cosh x \quad \text{and} \quad \sin(ix) = i \sinh x.$$

Remark: The (correct) identity $\cos^2(ix) + \sin^2(ix) = 1$ thus becomes the equally true identity $\cosh^2 x - \sinh^2 x = 1$.

The Taylor-series expansion

$$f(x) = f(a) + f'(a)(x - a) + \frac{f''(a)}{2!}(x - a)^2 + \cdots \tag{1}$$

$$+ \frac{f^{(n)}(a)}{n!}(x - a)^n + R_n(x, a)$$

12–10

FURTHER COMPUTATIONS, LOGARITHMS, ARCTANGENTS, AND π

expresses the value of the function at x in terms of its value and the values of its derivatives at a, plus a remainder term, which we hope is so small that it may safely be omitted. In applying series to numerical computations, it is therefore *necessary* that a be chosen so that $f(a), f'(a), f''(a), \ldots$ are known. In dealing with the trigonometric functions, for example, one might take $a = 0, \pm\pi/6, \pm\pi/4, \pm\pi/3, \pm\pi/2$, and so on. It is also clear that it is *desirable* to choose the value of a near to the value of x for which the function is to be computed, in order to make $(x - a)$ small, so that the terms of the series decrease rapidly as n increases.

EXAMPLE 1. What value of a might one choose in the Taylor series (1) to compute $\sin 35°$?

Solution. We could choose $a = 0$ and use the series

$$\sin x = x - \frac{x^3}{3!} + \frac{x^5}{5!} - \cdots + (-1)^n \frac{x^{2n+1}}{(2n+1)!} + 0 \cdot x^{2n+2} + R_{2n+2}(x, 0), \tag{2}$$

or we could choose $a = \pi/6$ (which corresponds to $30°$) and use the series

$$\sin x = \sin\frac{\pi}{6} + \cos\frac{\pi}{6}\left(x - \frac{\pi}{6}\right) - \sin\frac{\pi}{6}\frac{(x - \pi/6)^2}{2!} - \cos\frac{\pi}{6}\frac{(x - \pi/6)^3}{3!} + \cdots$$

$$+ \sin\left(\frac{\pi}{6} + n\frac{\pi}{2}\right)\frac{(x - \pi/6)^n}{n!} + R_n\left(x, \frac{\pi}{6}\right).$$

The remainder in the series (2) satisfies the inequality

$$|R_{2n+2}(x, 0)| \le \frac{|x|^{2n+3}}{(2n+3)!}, \tag{3}$$

which tends to zero as n becomes infinite, no matter how large $|x|$ may be.

We could therefore calculate sin 35° by placing

$$x = \frac{35\pi}{180} = 0.6108652$$

in the approximation

$$\sin x \approx x - \frac{x^3}{6} + \frac{x^5}{120} - \frac{x^7}{5040},$$

with an error of magnitude no greater than 3.3×10^{-8}, since

$$\left| R_8\left(\frac{35\pi}{180}, 0\right) \right| < \frac{(0.611)^9}{9!} < 3.3 \times 10^{-8}.$$

By using the series with $a = \pi/6$, we could obtain equal accuracy with a smaller exponent n, but at the expense of introducing $\cos \pi/6 = \sqrt{3}/2$ as one of the coefficients. In this series, with $a = \pi/6$, we would take

$$x = \frac{35\pi}{180},$$

but the quantity that appears raised to the various powers is

$$x - \frac{\pi}{6} = \frac{5\pi}{180} = 0.0872665,$$

which decreases rapidly when raised to high powers.

As a matter of fact, various trigonometric identities may be used, such as

$$\sin\left(\frac{\pi}{2} - x\right) = \cos x,$$

to facilitate the calculation of the sine or cosine of any angle with the Maclaurin series of the two functions. This method of finding the sine or cosine of an angle is used in computers.

Computation of Logarithms

Natural logarithms may be computed from series. The starting point is the series for $\ln(1 + x)$ in powers of x:

$$\ln(1 + x) = x - \frac{x^2}{2} + \frac{x^3}{3} - \cdots + (-1)^{n-1}\frac{x^n}{n} + \cdots$$

This series may be found directly from the Taylor-series expansion, Eq. (1), with $a = 0$. It may also be obtained by integrating the geometric series for $1/(1 + t)$ from $t = 0$ to $t = x$:

$$\int_0^x \frac{dt}{1+t} = \int_0^x (1 - t + t^2 - t^3 + \cdots)\, dt,$$

$$\ln(1+t)\Big]_0^x = t - \frac{t^2}{2} + \frac{t^3}{3} - \frac{t^4}{4} + \cdots \Big]_0^x,$$

$$\ln(1+x) = x - \frac{x^2}{2} + \frac{x^3}{3} - \frac{x^4}{4} + \cdots \tag{4}$$

The expansion (4) is valid for $|x| < 1$, since then the remainder, $R_n(x, 0)$, approaches zero as $n \to \infty$, as we shall now see. The remainder is given by the integral of the remainder in the geometric series, that is,

$$R_n(x, 0) = \int_0^x \frac{(-1)^n t^n}{1 + t}\, dt. \tag{5}$$

We now suppose that $|x| < 1$. For every t between 0 and x inclusive we have

$$|1 + t| \geq 1 - |x|$$

and

$$|(-1)^n t^n| = |t|^n,$$

so that

$$\left| \frac{(-1)^n t^n}{1 + t} \right| \leq \frac{|t|^n}{1 - |x|}.$$

Therefore,

$$|R_n(x, 0)| \leq \int_0^{|x|} \frac{t^n}{1 - |x|}\, dt = \frac{1}{n + 1} \cdot \frac{|x|^{n+1}}{1 - |x|}. \tag{6}$$

When $n \to \infty$, the right side of the inequality (6) approaches zero, and so must the left side. Thus (4) holds for $|x| < 1$.

If we replace x by $-x$, we obtain

$$\ln(1 - x) = -x - \frac{x^2}{2} - \frac{x^3}{3} - \cdots - \frac{x^n}{n} - \cdots, \tag{7}$$

which is also valid for $|x| < 1$. When we subtract (7) from (4), we get

$$\ln \frac{1 + x}{1 - x} = 2\left(x + \frac{x^3}{3} + \frac{x^5}{5} + \cdots + \frac{x^{2k-1}}{2k - 1} + \cdots \right), \tag{8}$$

which is true for $|x| < 1$. Equation (8) may be used to compute the natural logarithm of any positive number y by taking

$$y = \frac{1 + x}{1 - x} \qquad \text{or} \qquad x = \frac{y - 1}{y + 1}.$$

But the series converges most rapidly for values of x near zero, or when $(1 + x)/(1 - x)$ is near one. For this reason, the logarithms of the numbers

$$\frac{2}{1}, \quad \frac{3}{2}, \quad \frac{4}{3}, \quad \frac{5}{4}, \quad \cdots, \quad \frac{N + 1}{N}$$

are ordinarily computed first in forming a table of natural logarithms of the integers. Then it is a matter of simple arithmetic to compute

$$\ln 3 = \ln \tfrac{2}{1} + \ln \tfrac{3}{2},$$

$$\ln 4 = \ln 3 + \ln \tfrac{4}{3},$$

$$\ln 5 = \ln 4 + \ln \tfrac{5}{4},$$

$$\vdots$$

$$\ln(N + 1) = \ln N + \ln \frac{N + 1}{N}.$$

For this purpose, one may solve the equation

$$\frac{1 + x}{1 - x} = \frac{N + 1}{N}$$

for

$$x = \frac{1}{2N + 1}.$$

This may be substituted into Eq. (8), which becomes

$$\ln \frac{N + 1}{N} = 2 \left(\frac{1}{2N + 1} + \frac{1}{3(2N + 1)^3} + \frac{1}{5(2N + 1)^5} + \cdots \right). \qquad \textbf{(9)}$$

For example, to calculate $\ln 2$, we take $N = 1$, $x = \frac{1}{3}$, and calculate

$$x = 0.33333 \quad 33,$$

$$\frac{x^3}{3} = 0.01234 \quad 57,$$

$$\frac{x^5}{5} = 0.00082 \quad 30,$$

$$\frac{x^7}{7} = 0.00006 \quad 53,$$

$$\frac{x^9}{9} = 0.00000 \quad 56,$$

$$\frac{x^{11}}{11} = 0.00000 \quad 05,$$

$$\text{Sum} = 0.34657 \quad 34, \qquad \ln 2 \approx 0.69314 \quad 68.$$

Computation of π

Archimedes (287–212 B.C.) gave the approximation

$$3\tfrac{1}{7} > \pi > 3\tfrac{10}{71},$$

in the third century B.C. A French mathematician, Viéta (1540–1603), gave the formula

$$\frac{2}{\pi} = \sqrt{\tfrac{1}{2}} \times \sqrt{\left(\tfrac{1}{2} + \tfrac{1}{2}\sqrt{\tfrac{1}{2}}\right)} \times \sqrt{\left(\tfrac{1}{2} + \tfrac{1}{2}\sqrt{\left(\tfrac{1}{2} + \tfrac{1}{2}\sqrt{\tfrac{1}{2}}\right)}\right)} \times \cdots,$$

which Turnbull* calls "the first actual formula for the time-honoured number π." Other interesting formulas for π include†

$$\frac{\pi}{4} = \cfrac{1}{1 + \cfrac{1^2}{2 + \cfrac{3^2}{2 + \cfrac{5^2}{2 + \cdots}}}},$$

---

*   *World of Mathematics*, Vol. 1, p. 121.
†   *Ibid.*, p. 138.

which is credited to Lord Brouncker, an Irish peer;

$$\frac{\pi}{4} = \frac{2 \times 4 \times 4 \times 6 \times 6 \times 8 \times \cdots}{3 \times 3 \times 5 \times 5 \times 7 \times 7 \times \cdots},$$

discovered by the English mathematician Wallis; and

$$\frac{\pi}{4} = 1 - \frac{1}{3} + \frac{1}{5} - \frac{1}{7} + \cdots,$$

known as Leibniz's formula.

All of these formulas involve limits. To derive Viéta's formula, for example, we may begin with the trigonometric half-angle formulas:

$$\sin x = 2 \sin \frac{x}{2} \cos \frac{x}{2},$$

$$\sin \frac{x}{2} = 2 \sin \frac{x}{4} \cos \frac{x}{4}, \tag{10}$$

$$\sin \frac{x}{4} = 2 \sin \frac{x}{8} \cos \frac{x}{8},$$

$$\vdots \qquad \vdots$$

With these we write

$$\sin x = 2 \sin \frac{x}{2} \cos \frac{x}{2}$$

$$= 2^2 \sin \frac{x}{4} \cos \frac{x}{2} \cos \frac{x}{4} \tag{11}$$

$$= 2^3 \sin \frac{x}{8} \cos \frac{x}{2} \cos \frac{x}{4} \cos \frac{x}{8}$$

$$\vdots$$

Then, by induction on n,

$$\sin x = 2^n \sin \left(\frac{x}{2^n}\right) \cos \frac{x}{2} \cos \frac{x}{4} \cdots \cos \left(\frac{x}{2^n}\right).$$

Hence,

$$\frac{\sin x}{x} = \frac{\sin (x/2^n)}{(x/2^n)} \cos \frac{x}{2} \cos \frac{x}{4} \cdots \cos \left(\frac{x}{2^n}\right). \tag{12}$$

When $n \to \infty$,

$$\frac{\sin (x/2^n)}{(x/2^n)} \to 1,$$

while the left side of Eq. (12) remains unchanged. Therefore,

$$\frac{\sin x}{x} = \lim_{n \to \infty} \frac{\sin (x/2^n)}{(x/2^n)} \cos \frac{x}{2} \cos \frac{x}{4} \cdots \cos \frac{x}{2^n}$$

$$= 1 \cdot \cos \frac{x}{2} \cos \frac{x}{4} \cos \frac{x}{8} \cos \frac{x}{16} \cdots \tag{13}$$

Finally, substituting $x = \pi/2$ in Eq. (13) gives

$$\frac{2}{\pi} = \cos \frac{\pi}{4} \cos \frac{\pi}{8} \cos \frac{\pi}{16} \cos \frac{\pi}{32} \cdots \tag{14}$$

$$= \sqrt{\tfrac{1}{2}} \times \sqrt{\tfrac{1}{2}(1 + \sqrt{\tfrac{1}{2}})} \times \sqrt{\tfrac{1}{2}(1 + \sqrt{\tfrac{1}{2}(1 + \sqrt{\tfrac{1}{2}})})} \times \cdots, \tag{15}$$

which is Viéta's formula. The law of formation on the right is

$$\cos \frac{\pi}{4} = \sqrt{\tfrac{1}{2}}, \qquad \cos \frac{\theta}{2} = \sqrt{\tfrac{1}{2}(1 + \cos \theta)}.$$

Similarly, we could interpret the other formulas as expressing certain limits in terms of π. However, we now turn our attention to the series for $\tan^{-1} x$, since it leads to the Leibniz formula and others from which π has been computed to a great many decimal places.

Since

$$\tan^{-1} x = \int_0^x \frac{dt}{1 + t^2},$$

we integrate the geometric series, with remainder,

$$\frac{1}{1 + t^2} = 1 - t^2 + t^4 - t^6 + \cdots + (-1)^n t^{2n} + \frac{(-1)^{n+1} t^{2n+2}}{1 + t^2}. \tag{16}$$

Thus

$$\tan^{-1} x = x - \frac{x^3}{3} + \frac{x^5}{5} - \frac{x^7}{7} + \cdots + (-1)^n \frac{x^{2n+1}}{2n+1} + R,$$

where

$$R = \int_0^x \frac{(-1)^{n+1} t^{2n+2}}{1 + t^2} \, dt.$$

The denominator of the integrand is greater than or equal to 1; hence

$$|R| \le \int_0^{|x|} t^{2n+2} \, dt = \frac{|x|^{2n+3}}{2n+3}.$$

If $|x| \le 1$, the right side of this inequality approaches zero as $n \to \infty$. Therefore R also approaches zero and we have:

$$\tan^{-1} x = \sum_{n=0}^{\infty} \frac{(-1)^n x^{2n+1}}{2n+1},$$

or

$$\tan^{-1} x = x - \frac{x^3}{3} + \frac{x^5}{5} - \frac{x^7}{7} + \cdots, \qquad |x| \le 1. \tag{17}$$

Various trigonometric identities are useful if one wishes to use Eq. (17) to calculate π. For example, if

$$\alpha = \tan^{-1} \tfrac{1}{2} \qquad \text{and} \qquad \beta = \tan^{-1} \tfrac{1}{3},$$

then

$$\tan (\alpha + \beta) = \frac{\tan \alpha + \tan \beta}{1 - \tan \alpha \tan \beta} = \frac{\tfrac{1}{2} + \tfrac{1}{3}}{1 - \tfrac{1}{6}} = 1 = \tan \frac{\pi}{4}$$

and

$$\frac{\pi}{4} = \alpha + \beta = \tan^{-1} \tfrac{1}{2} + \tan^{-1} \tfrac{1}{3}. \tag{18}$$

Now Eq. (17) may be used with $x = \tfrac{1}{2}$ to evaluate $\tan^{-1} \tfrac{1}{2}$ and with $x = \tfrac{1}{3}$ to give $\tan^{-1} \tfrac{1}{3}$. The sum of these results, multiplied by 4, gives π.

In 1961, π was computed to more than 100,000 decimal places on an IBM 7090 computer. More recently, in 1973, Jean Guilloud and Martine Bouyer computed π to 1,000,000 decimal places on a CDC 7600 computer, by applying the arctangent series (17) to the formula

$$\pi = 48 \tan^{-1} \tfrac{1}{18} + 32 \tan^{-1} \tfrac{1}{57} - 20 \tan^{-1} \tfrac{1}{239}. \tag{19}$$

They checked their work with the formula

$$\pi = 24 \tan^{-1} \tfrac{1}{8} + 8 \tan^{-1} \tfrac{1}{57} + 4 \tan^{-1} \tfrac{1}{239}. \tag{20}$$

A number of current computations of π are being carried out with an algorithm discovered by Eugene Salamin (Problem 17). The algorithm produces sequences that converge to π even more rapidly than the sequence of partial sums of the arctangent series in Eqs. (19) and (20). [For a delightful account of attempts to compute, and even to *legislate*(!) the value of π, see Chapter 12 of David A. Smith's *Interface: Calculus and the Computer*, Houghton Mifflin Company, Boston, MA, 1976.]

REMARK. Two types of numerical error tend to occur in computing with series. One is the *truncation error*, which is the remainder $R_n(x, a)$ and consists of the sum of the infinite number of terms in the series that follow the term $(x - a)^n f^{(n)}(a)/n!$. This is the only error we have discussed so far.

The other is the *round-off error* that enters in calculating the sum of the finite number of terms

$$f(a) + f'(a)(x - a) + \cdots + \frac{f^{(n)}(a)(x - a)^n}{n!}$$

when we approximate each of these terms by a decimal number with only a finite number of decimal places. For example, taking 0.3333 in place of $\tfrac{1}{3}$ introduces a round-off error equal to $10^{-4}/3$. There are likely to be round-off errors associated with each term, some of these being positive and some negative. When the need for accuracy is paramount, it is important to control both the truncation error and the round-off errors. *Truncation* errors can be reduced by taking more terms of the series; *round-off* errors can be reduced by taking more decimal places.

PROBLEMS

In each of Problems 1 through 6, use a suitable series to calculate the indicated quantity to three decimal places. In each case, show that the remainder term does not exceed 5×10^{-4}.

1. $\cos 31°$

2. $\tan 46°$

3. $\sin 6.3$

4. $\cos 69$

5. $\ln 1.25$

6. $\tan^{-1} 1.02$

7. Find the Maclaurin series for $\ln(1 + 2x)$. For what values of x does the series converge?

8. For what values of x can one replace $\ln(1 + x)$ by x with an error of magnitude no greater than one percent of the absolute value of x?

Use series to evaluate the integrals in Problems 9 and 10 to three decimals.

9. $\displaystyle\int_0^{0.1} \frac{\sin x}{x}\, dx$ **10.** $\displaystyle\int_0^{0.1} e^{-x^2}\, dx$

11. Show that the ordinate of the catenary $y = a \cosh x/a$ deviates from the ordinate of the parabola $x^2 = 2a(y - a)$ by less than $0.003\,|a|$ over the range $|x/a| \le \frac{1}{3}$.

12. Construct a table of natural logarithms $\ln N$ for $N = 1, 2, 3, \ldots, 10$ by the method discussed in connection with Eq. (9), but taking advantage of the relationships

$$\ln 4 = 2 \ln 2, \qquad \ln 6 = \ln 2 + \ln 3, \qquad \ln 8 = 3 \ln 2,$$

$$\ln 9 = 2 \ln 3, \qquad \ln 10 = \ln 2 + \ln 5$$

to reduce the job to the calculation of relatively few logarithms by series. In fact, you may use $\ln 2$ as given in the text and calculate $\ln \frac{3}{2}$, $\ln \frac{5}{4}$, and $\ln \frac{7}{6}$ by series, and then combine these in suitable ways to get the logarithms of numbers N from 1 to 10.

13. Find the sum of the series

$$\tfrac{1}{2} - \tfrac{1}{2}(\tfrac{1}{2})^2 + \tfrac{1}{3}(\tfrac{1}{2})^3 - \tfrac{1}{4}(\tfrac{1}{2})^4 + \cdots$$

14. How many terms of the series for $\tan^{-1} 1$ would you have to add for the Alternating Series Estimation Theorem to guarantee a calculation of $\pi/4$ to two decimals?

15. (*Calculator*) Equations (17) and (19) yield a series that converges to $\pi/4$ fairly rapidly. Estimate π to three decimal places with this series. In contrast, the convergence of $\sum_{n=1}^{\infty}(1/n^2)$ to $\pi^2/6$ is so slow that even fifty terms will not yield two-place accuracy.

16. (*Calculator*) (a) Find π to two decimals with the formulas of Lord Brouncker and Wallis. (b) If your calculator is programmable, use Viéta's formula, Eqs. (14) or (15), to calculate π to five decimal places.

17. (*Calculator*) A special case of Salamin's algorithm for estimating π begins with defining sequences $\{a_n\}$ and $\{b_n\}$ by the rules

$$a_0 = 1, \qquad\qquad b_0 = \frac{1}{\sqrt{2}},$$

$$a_{n+1} = \frac{(a_n + b_n)}{2}, \qquad b_{n+1} = \sqrt{a_n b_n}.$$

Then the sequence $\{c_n\}$ defined by

$$c_n = \frac{4 a_n b_n}{1 - \sum_{j=1}^{n} 2^{j+1}(a_j^2 - b_j^2)}$$

converges to π. Calculate c_3. (E. Salamin, "Computation of

π using arithmetic–geometric mean," *Mathematics of Computation*, **30**, July, 1976, pp. 565–570.)

18. Show that the series in Eq. (17) for $\tan^{-1} x$ diverges for $|x| > 1$.

19. Show that

$$\int_0^x \frac{dt}{1 - t^2} = \int_0^x \left(1 + t^2 + t^4 + \cdots + t^{2n} + \frac{t^{2n+2}}{1 - t^2}\right) dt$$

or, in other words, that

$$\tanh^{-1} x = x + \frac{x^3}{3} + \frac{x^5}{5} + \cdots + \frac{x^{2n+1}}{2n+1} + R,$$

where

$$R = \int_0^x \frac{t^{2n+2}}{1 - t^2}\, dt.$$

20. Show that R in Problem 21 is no greater than

$$\frac{1}{1 - x^2} \cdot \frac{|x|^{2n+3}}{2n+3}, \qquad \text{if} \quad x^2 < 1.$$

21. a) Differentiate the identity

$$\frac{1}{1 - x} = 1 + x + x^2 + \cdots + x^n + \frac{x^{n+1}}{1 - x}$$

to obtain the expansion

$$\frac{1}{(1 - x)^2} = 1 + 2x + 3x^2 + \cdots + nx^{n-1} + R.$$

b) Prove that, if $|x| < 1$, then $R \to 0$ as $n \to \infty$.

c) In one throw of two dice, the probability of getting a score of 7 is $p = \frac{1}{6}$. If the dice are thrown repeatedly, the probability that a 7 will appear for the first time at the nth throw is $q^{n-1}p$, where $q = 1 - p = \frac{5}{6}$. The expected number of throws until a 7 first appears is $\sum_{n=1}^{\infty} nq^{n-1}p$. Evaluate this series numerically.

d) In applying statistical quality control to an industrial operation, an engineer inspects items taken at random from the assembly line. Each item sampled is classified as "good" or "bad." If the probability of a good item is p and of a bad item is $q = 1 - p$, the probability that the first bad item found is the nth inspected is $p^{n-1}q$. The average number inspected up to and including the first bad item found is $\sum_{n=1}^{\infty} np^{n-1}q$. Evaluate this series, assuming $0 < p < 1$.

22. In probability theory, a random variable X may assume the values $1, 2, 3, \ldots$, with probabilities $p_1, p_2, p_3, \ldots$, where p_k is the probability that X is equal to k ($k = 1, 2, \ldots$). It is customary to assume $p_k \ge 0$ and $\sum_{k=1}^{\infty} p_k = 1$. The *expected value* of X denoted by $E(X)$ is defined as $\sum_{k=1}^{\infty} kp_k$, provided this series converges. In each of the following cases, show that $\sum p_k = 1$ and find $E(X)$, if it exists. [*Hint.* See Problem 21.]

a) $p_k = 2^{-k}$ **b)** $p_k = \dfrac{5^{k-1}}{6^k}$

c) $p_k = \dfrac{1}{k(k+1)} = \dfrac{1}{k} - \dfrac{1}{k+1}$

In considering the ratio of two functions $f(x)$ and $g(x)$, we sometimes wish to know the value

$$\lim_{x \to a} \frac{f(x)}{g(x)} \qquad (1)$$

at a point a where $f(x)$ and $g(x)$ are both zero. L'Hôpital's rule is often a help, but the differentiation involved can be time-consuming, especially if the rule has to be applied several times to reach a determinate form. In many instances, the limit in (1) can be calculated more quickly if the functions involved have power series expansions about $x = a$. In fact, the ease and reliability of the kind of calculation we are about to illustrate contributed to the early popularity of power series. The theoretical justification of the technique is too long to discuss here, but the formal manipulations are worth learning by themselves.

Suppose, then, that the functions f and g both have series expansions in powers of $x - a$,

$$f(x) = f(a) + f'(a) \cdot (x - a) + \frac{f''(a)}{2!}(x - a)^2 + \cdots, \qquad \textbf{(2a)}$$

$$g(x) = g(a) + g'(a) \cdot (x - a) + \frac{g''(a)}{2!}(x - a)^2 + \cdots, \qquad \textbf{(2b)}$$

that are known to us and that converge in some interval $|x - a| < \delta$. We may then proceed to calculate the limit (1), provided the limit exists, in the manner shown by the following examples.

EXAMPLE 1. Evaluate $\lim_{x \to 1} [(\ln x)/(x - 1)]$.

Solution. Let $f(x) = \ln x$, $g(x) = x - 1$. The Taylor series for $f(x)$, with $a = 1$, is found as follows:

$$f(x) = \ln x, \qquad f(1) = \ln 1 = 0,$$
$$f'(x) = 1/x, \qquad f'(1) = 1,$$
$$f''(x) = -1/x^2, \qquad f''(1) = -1,$$

so that

$$\ln x = 0 + (x - 1) - \tfrac{1}{2}(x - 1)^2 + \cdots$$

Hence

$$\frac{\ln x}{x - 1} = 1 - \tfrac{1}{2}(x - 1) + \cdots$$

and

$$\lim_{x \to 1} \frac{\ln x}{x - 1} = \lim_{x \to 1} \left[1 - \tfrac{1}{2}(x - 1) + \cdots \right] = 1.$$

EXAMPLE 2. Evaluate $\lim_{x \to 0} [(\sin x - \tan x)/x^3]$.

Solution. The Maclaurin series for $\sin x$ and $\tan x$, to terms in x^5, are

$$\sin x = x - \frac{x^3}{3!} + \frac{x^5}{5!} - \cdots,$$

$$\tan x = x + \frac{x^3}{3} + \frac{2x^5}{15} + \cdots$$

Hence

$$\sin x - \tan x = -\frac{x^3}{2} - \frac{x^5}{8} - \cdots$$

$$= x^3 \left(-\frac{1}{2} - \frac{x^2}{8} - \cdots \right),$$

and

$$\lim_{x \to 0} \frac{\sin x - \tan x}{x^3} = \lim_{x \to 0} \left(-\frac{1}{2} - \frac{x^2}{8} - \cdots \right) = -\frac{1}{2}.$$

When we apply series to compute the limit $\lim_{x \to 0} (1/\sin x - 1/x)$ of Example 7, Article 3–9, we not only compute the limit successfully, but also discover a nice approximation formula for $\csc x$.

EXAMPLE 3.   Find

$$\lim_{x \to 0} \left(\frac{1}{\sin x} - \frac{1}{x} \right).$$

Solution

$$\frac{1}{\sin x} - \frac{1}{x} = \frac{x - \sin x}{x \sin x}$$

$$= \frac{x - \left[x - \dfrac{x^3}{3!} + \dfrac{x^5}{5!} - \cdots \right]}{x \cdot \left[x - \dfrac{x^3}{3!} + \dfrac{x^5}{5!} - \cdots \right]}$$

$$= \frac{x^3 \left[\dfrac{1}{3!} - \dfrac{x^2}{5!} + \cdots \right]}{x^2 \left[1 - \dfrac{x^2}{3!} + \cdots \right]} = x \, \frac{\dfrac{1}{3!} - \dfrac{x^2}{5!} + \cdots}{1 - \dfrac{x^2}{3!} + \cdots}.$$

Therefore,

$$\lim_{x \to 0} \left(\frac{1}{\sin x} - \frac{1}{x} \right) = \lim_{x \to 0} \left[x \, \frac{\dfrac{1}{3!} - \dfrac{x^2}{5!} + \cdots}{1 - \dfrac{x^2}{3!} + \cdots} \right] = 0.$$

In fact, from the series expressions above we can see that if $|x|$ is small, then

$$\frac{1}{\sin x} - \frac{1}{x} \approx x \cdot \frac{1}{3!} = \frac{x}{6}$$

or

$$\csc x \approx \frac{1}{x} + \frac{x}{6}.$$

PROBLEMS

Use series to evaluate the limits in Problems 1 through 20.

1. $\lim\limits_{h \to 0} \dfrac{\sin h}{h}$

2. $\lim\limits_{x \to 0} \dfrac{e^x - (1 + x)}{x^2}$

3. $\lim\limits_{t \to 0} \dfrac{1 - \cos t - \frac{1}{2}t^2}{t^4}$

4. $\lim\limits_{x \to \infty} x \sin \dfrac{1}{x}$

5. $\lim\limits_{x \to 0} \dfrac{x^2}{1 - \cosh x}$

6. $\lim\limits_{h \to 0} \dfrac{(\sin h)/h - \cos h}{h^2}$

7. $\lim\limits_{x \to 0} \dfrac{1 - \cos x}{\sin x}$

8. $\lim\limits_{x \to 0} \dfrac{\sin x}{e^x - 1}$

9. $\lim\limits_{z \to 0} \dfrac{\sin (z^2) - \sinh (z^2)}{z^6}$

10. $\lim\limits_{t \to 0} \dfrac{\cos t - \cosh t}{t^2}$

11. $\lim\limits_{x \to 0} \dfrac{\sin x - x + \dfrac{x^3}{6}}{x^5}$

12. $\lim\limits_{x \to 0} \dfrac{e^x - e^{-x} - 2x}{x - \sin x}$

13. $\lim\limits_{x \to 0} \dfrac{x - \tan^{-1} x}{x^3}$

14. $\lim\limits_{x \to 0} \dfrac{\tan x - \sin x}{x^3 \cos x}$

15. $\lim\limits_{x \to \infty} x^2(e^{-1/x^2} - 1)$

16. $\lim\limits_{x \to 0} \dfrac{\ln (1 + x^2)}{1 - \cos x}$

17. $\lim\limits_{x \to 0} \dfrac{\tan 3x}{x}$

18. $\lim\limits_{x \to 1} \dfrac{\ln x^2}{x - 1}$

19. $\lim\limits_{x \to \infty} \dfrac{x^{100}}{e^x}$

20. $\lim\limits_{x \to 0} \left(\dfrac{1}{2 - 2 \cos x} - \dfrac{1}{x^2} \right)$

21. a) Prove that $\int_0^x e^{t^2} \, dt \to +\infty$ as $x \to +\infty$.

b) Find $\lim_{x \to \infty} x \int_0^x e^{t^2 - x^2} \, dt$

22. Find values of r and s such that

$$\lim_{x \to 0} (x^{-3} \sin 3x + rx^{-2} + s) = 0.$$

23. (*Calculator*) The approximation for $\csc x$ in Example 3 leads to the approximation $\sin x \approx 6x/(6 + x^2)$. Evaluate both sides of this approximation for $x = \pm 1.0$, ± 0.1, and ± 0.01 radians. Try these values of x in the approximation $\sin x \approx x$. Which approximation appears to give better results?

We now know that some power series, like the Maclaurin series for $\sin x$, $\cos x$, and e^x, converge for all values of x, while others, like the series we derived for $\ln (1 + x)$ and $\tan^{-1} x$, converge only on finite intervals. But we learned all this by analyzing remainder formulas, and we have yet to face the question of how to investigate the convergence of a power series when there is no remainder formula to analyze. Moreover, all of the power series we have worked with have been Taylor series of functions for which we already had expressions in closed forms. What about other power series? Are they Taylor series, too, of functions otherwise unknown?

The first step in answering these questions is to note that a power series $\sum_{n=0}^{\infty} a_n x^n$ defines a function whenever it converges, namely, the function f whose value at each x is the number

$$f(x) = \sum_{n=0}^{\infty} a_n x^n. \tag{1}$$

12–12

CONVERGENCE OF POWER SERIES; INTEGRATION AND DIFFERENTIATION

We can then ask what kind of domain f has, how f is to be differentiated and integrated (if at all), whether f has a Taylor series, and, if it has, how its Taylor series is related to the defining series $\sum_{n=0}^{\infty} a_n x^n$.

The questions of what domain f has, and for what values the series (1) may be expected to converge, are answered by Theorem 1 and the discussion that follows it. We will prove Theorem 1, and then, after looking at examples, will proceed to Theorems 2 and 3, which answer the questions of whether f *can* be differentiated and integrated and *how* to do so when it can be. Theorem 3 also solves a problem that arose many chapters ago but that has remained unsolved until now: that of finding convenient expressions for evaluating integrals like

$$\int_0^1 \sin x^2 \, dx \qquad \text{and} \qquad \int_0^{0.5} \sqrt{1 + x^4} \, dx,$$

which frequently arise in applications. Finally, we will see that, in the interior of its domain of definition, the function f does have a Maclaurin series, and that this is none other than the defining series $\sum_{n=0}^{\infty} a_n x^n$.

Theorem 1. The convergence theorem for power series. *If a power series*

$$\sum_{n=0}^{\infty} a_n x^n = a_0 + a_1 x + a_2 x^2 + \cdots \tag{2}$$

converges for $x = c$ $(c \neq 0)$, then it converges absolutely for all $|x| < |c|$. If the series diverges for $x = d$, then it diverges for all $|x| > |d|$.

Proof. Suppose the series

$$\sum_{n=0}^{\infty} a_n c^n \tag{3}$$

converges. Then

$$\lim_{n \to \infty} a_n c^n = 0.$$

Hence, there is an index N such that

$$|a_n c^n| < 1 \qquad \text{for all} \quad n \geq N.$$

That is,

$$|a_n| < \frac{1}{|c|^n} \qquad \text{for} \quad n \geq N. \tag{4}$$

Now take any x such that $|x| < |c|$ and consider

$$|a_0| + |a_1 x| + \cdots + |a_{N-1} x^{N-1}| + |a_N x^N| + |a_{N+1} x^{N+1}| + \cdots$$

There is only a finite number of terms prior to $|a_N x^N|$ and their sum is finite. Starting with $|a_N x^N|$ and beyond, the terms are less than

$$\left|\frac{x}{c}\right|^N + \left|\frac{x}{c}\right|^{N+1} + \left|\frac{x}{c}\right|^{N+2} + \cdots \tag{5}$$

by virtue of the inequality (4). But the series in (5) is a geometric series with ratio $r = |x/c|$, which is less than one, since $|x| < |c|$. Hence the series (5) converges, so that the original series (3) converges absolutely. This proves the first half of the theorem.

The second half of the theorem involves nothing new. For if the series diverges at $x = d$ and converges at a value x_0 with $|x_0| > |d|$, we may take $c = x_0$ in the first half of the theorem and conclude that the series converges absolutely at d. But the series cannot both converge absolutely and diverge at one and the same time. Hence, if it diverges at d, it diverges for all $|x| > |d|$.   Q.E.D.

The significance of Theorem 1 is that a power series always behaves in exactly *one* of the following ways (Fig. 12–18):

1. It converges at $x = 0$ and diverges everywhere else.

2. There is a positive number c such that the series diverges for $|x| > c$ but converges absolutely for $|x| < c$. It may or may not converge at either of the endpoints $x = c$ and $x = -c$.

3. It converges absolutely for every x.

12–18 A power $\sum a_n x^u$ may converge only at $x = 0$, or it may converge absolutely for every value of x in some interval centered at $x = 0$, or it may converge absolutely for every value of x on the whole line.

In Case 2, the set of points at which the series converges is a finite interval. We know from past examples that this interval may be open, half open, or closed, depending on the series in question. But no matter which kind of interval it is, c is called the *radius of convergence* of the series, and the convergence is absolute at every point in the interior of the interval. The interval is called the *interval of convergence*. If a power series converges absolutely for all values of x, we say that its radius of convergence is infinite. If it converges only at $x = 0$, we say that its radius of convergence is 0.

As examples of power series whose radii of convergence are infinite, we have the Taylor series of $\sin x$, $\cos x$, and e^x. These series converge for every value of $c = 2x$, and therefore converge absolutely for every value of x.

As examples of series whose radii of convergence are finite we have:

Series	Interval of convergence
$\dfrac{1}{1-x} = 1 + x + x^2 + \cdots$	$-1 < x < 1$
$\ln (1 + x) = x - \dfrac{x^2}{2} + \dfrac{x^3}{3} - \dfrac{x^4}{4} + \cdots$	$-1 < x \le 1$
$\tan^{-1} x = x - \dfrac{x^3}{3} + \dfrac{x^5}{5} - \cdots$	$-1 \le x \le 1$

The interval of convergence of a power series

$$\sum_{n=0}^{\infty} a_n x^n$$

can often be found by applying the ratio test or the root test to the series of absolute values,

$$\sum_{n=0}^{\infty} |a_n x^n|.$$

Thus, if

$$\rho = \lim_{n \to \infty} \left| \frac{a_{n+1} x^{n+1}}{a_n x^n} \right|$$

or if

$$\rho = \lim_{n \to \infty} \sqrt[n]{|a_n x^n|},$$

then,

a) $\sum |a_n x^n|$ converges at all values of x for which $\rho < 1$;

b) $\sum |a_n x^n|$ diverges at all values of x for which $\rho > 1$;

c) $\sum |a_n x^n|$ may either converge or diverge at a value of x for which $\rho = 1$.

How do these three alternatives translate into statements about the series $\sum a_n x^n$? Case (a) says that $\sum a_n x^n$ converges absolutely at all values of x for which $\rho < 1$. Case (c) does not tell us anything more about the series $\sum a_n x^n$ than it does about the series $\sum |a_n x^n|$. Either series might converge or diverge at a value of x for which $\rho = 1$. In Case (b), we can actually conclude that $\sum a_n x^n$ diverges at all values of x for which $\rho > 1$. The argument goes like this: As you may recall from the discussions in Article 12–5, the fact that ρ is greater than 1 means that either

$$0 < |a_n x^n| < |a_{n+1} x^{n+1}| < |a_{n+2} x^{n+2}| < \cdots$$

or

$$\sqrt[n]{|a_n x^n|} > 1$$

for n sufficiently large. Thus the terms of the series do not approach 0 as n becomes infinite, and the series diverges *with or without absolute values*, by the nth-term test.

Therefore, the ratio and root tests, when successfully applied to $\sum |a_n x^n|$, lead us to the following conclusions about $\sum a_n x^n$:

A) $\sum a_n x^n$ converges absolutely for all values of x for which $\rho < 1$;

B) $\sum a_n x^n$ diverges at all values of x for which $\rho > 1$;

C) $\sum a_n x^n$ may either converge or diverge at a value of x for which $\rho = 1$.

In this case, another test is needed.

EXAMPLE 1. Find the interval of convergence of

$$\sum_{n=1}^{\infty} \frac{x^n}{n}. \tag{6}$$

Solution. We apply the ratio test to the series of absolute values, and find

$$\rho = \lim_{n \to \infty} \left| \frac{x^{n+1}}{n+1} \cdot \frac{n}{x^n} \right| = |x|.$$

Therefore the original series converges absolutely if $|x| < 1$ and diverges if $|x| > 1$. When $x = +1$, the series becomes

$$1 + \tfrac{1}{2} + \tfrac{1}{3} + \tfrac{1}{4} + \cdots,$$

which diverges. When $x = -1$, the series becomes

$$-(1 - \tfrac{1}{2} + \tfrac{1}{3} - \tfrac{1}{4} + \cdots),$$

which converges, by Leibnitz's Theorem. Therefore the series (6) converges for $-1 \le x < 1$ and diverges for all other values of x.

EXAMPLE 2.   For what values of x does the series

$$\sum_{n=1}^{\infty} \frac{(2x - 5)^n}{n^2}$$

converge?

Solution.   We treat the series as a power series in the variable $2x - 5$. An application of the root test to the series of absolute values yields

$$\rho = \lim_{n \to \infty} \sqrt[n]{\left| \frac{(2x - 5)^n}{n^2} \right|} = \lim_{n \to \infty} \frac{|2x - 5|}{\sqrt[n]{n^2}} = \frac{|2x - 5|}{1} = |2x - 5|.$$

The series converges absolutely for

$$|2x - 5| < 1 \qquad \text{or} \qquad -1 < 2x - 5 < 1$$

or

$$4 < 2x < 6 \qquad \text{or} \qquad 2 < x < 3.$$

When $x = 2$, the series is $\sum_{n=1}^{\infty} [(-1)^n/n^2]$, which converges.

When $x = 3$, the series is $\sum_{n=1}^{\infty} [(1)^n/n^2]$, which converges. Therefore, the interval of convergence is $2 \le x \le 3$.

Sometimes the comparison test does as well as any.

EXAMPLE 3.   For what values of x does

$$\sum_{n=1}^{\infty} \frac{\cos^n x}{n!}$$

converge?

Solution.   For every value of x,

$$\left| \frac{\cos^n x}{n!} \right| \le \frac{1}{n!}.$$

The series converges for every value of x.

The next theorem says that a function defined by a power series has derivatives of all orders at every point in the interior of its interval of convergence. The derivatives can be obtained as power series by differentiating the terms of the original series. The first derivative is obtained by differentiating the terms of the original series once:

$$\frac{d}{dx}\sum_{n=0}^{\infty}(a_n x^n) = \sum_{n=0}^{\infty}\frac{d}{dx}(a_n x^n) = \sum_{n=0}^{\infty} n a_n x^{n-1}.$$

For the second derivative, the terms are differentiated again, and so on. We state the theorem without proof, and go directly to the examples.

Theorem 2.　The term-by-term differentiation theorem. *If* $f(x) = \sum_{n=0}^{\infty} a_n x^n$ *converges on the open interval* $(-c, c)$, *then,*

1. $\displaystyle\sum_{n=0}^{\infty} n a_n x^{n-1}$ *converges on* $(-c, c)$;

2. $f(x)$ *is differentiable on* $(-c, c)$; *and*

3. $f'(x) = \displaystyle\sum_{n=0}^{\infty} n a_n x^{n-1}$ *on* $(-c, c)$.

Ostensibly, Theorem 2 mentions only f and f'. But note that f' has the same radius of convergence that f has, so that the theorem applies equally well to f', saying that it has a derivative f'' on $(-c, c)$. This in turn implies that f'' is differentiable on $(-c, c)$, and so on. Thus, if $f(x) = \sum_{n=0}^{\infty} a_n x^n$ converges on $(-c, c)$, it has derivatives of all orders at every point of $(-c, c)$.

EXAMPLE 4.　The relation $(d/dx)(\sin x) = \cos x$ is easily checked by differentiating the series for $\sin x$ term by term:

$$\sin x = x - \frac{x^3}{3!} + \frac{x^5}{5!} - \frac{x^7}{7!} + \cdots$$

$$\frac{d}{dx}(\sin x) = 1 - \frac{x^2}{2!} + \frac{x^4}{4!} - \frac{x^6}{6!} + \cdots$$

$$= \cos x.$$

Convergence at one or both endpoints of the interval of convergence of a power series may be lost in the process of differentiation. That is why Theorem 2 mentions only the *open* interval $(-c, c)$.

EXAMPLE 5.　The series $f(x) = \sum_{n=1}^{\infty}(x^n/n)$ of Example 1 converges for $-1 \le x < 1$. The series of derivatives

$$f'(x) = \sum_{n=1}^{\infty} x^{n-1} = 1 + x + x^2 + x^3 + \cdots$$

is a geometric series that converges only for $-1 < x < 1$. The series diverges at the endpoint $x = -1$, as well as at the endpoint $x = 1$.

Example 5 shows, however, that when the terms of a series are integrated, the resulting series may converge at an endpoint that was not a point of convergence before. The justification for term-by-term integration of a series is the following theorem, which we also state without proof.

Theorem 3. The term-by-term integration theorem. *If $f(x) = \sum_{n=0}^{\infty} a_n x^n$ converges on the open interval $(-c, c)$, then,*

1. $\sum_{n=0}^{n=\infty} \dfrac{a_n x^{n+1}}{n+1}$ *converges on* $(-c, c)$;

2. $\int f(x)\, dx$ *exists for x in* $(-c, c)$;

3. $\int f(x)\, dx = \sum_{n=0}^{n=\infty} \dfrac{a_n x^{n+1}}{n+1} + C$ *on* $(-c, c)$.

EXAMPLE 6. The series

$$\frac{1}{1+t} = 1 - t + t^2 - t^3 \cdots$$

converges on the open interval $-1 < t < 1$. Therefore,

$$\ln(1+x) = \int_0^x \frac{1}{1+t}\, dt = t - \frac{t^2}{2} + \frac{t^3}{3} - \frac{t^4}{4} + \cdots \Big|_0^x, \qquad -1 < x < 1,$$

$$= x - \frac{x^2}{2} + \frac{x^3}{3} - \frac{x^4}{4} + \cdots$$

As you know, the latter series also converges at $x = 1$, but that was not guaranteed by the theorem.

EXAMPLE 7. By replacing t by t^2 in the series of Example 6, we obtain

$$\frac{1}{1+t^2} = 1 - t^2 + t^4 - t^6 + \cdots, \qquad -1 < t < 1.$$

Therefore

$$\tan^{-1} x = \int_0^x \frac{1}{1+t^2}\, dt = t - \frac{t^3}{3} + \frac{t^5}{5} - \frac{t^7}{7} + \cdots \Big|_0^x$$

$$= x - \frac{x^3}{3} + \frac{x^5}{5} - \frac{x^7}{7} + \cdots, \qquad -1 < x < 1.$$

This is not as refined a result as the one we obtained in Article 12–10, where we were able to show that the interval of convergence was $-1 \le x \le 1$ by analyzing a remainder. But the result here is obtained more quickly.

EXAMPLE 8. Express

$$\int \sin x^2\, dx$$

as a power series.

Solution. From the series for $\sin x$ we obtain

$$\sin x^2 = x^2 - \frac{x^6}{3!} + \frac{x^{10}}{5!} - \frac{x^{14}}{7!} + \cdots, \qquad -\infty < x < \infty.$$

Therefore,

$$\int \sin x^2 \, dx = C + \frac{x^3}{3} - \frac{x^7}{7 \cdot 3!} + \frac{x^{11}}{11 \cdot 5!} - \frac{x^{15}}{15 \cdot 7!} + \cdots, \quad -\infty < x < \infty.$$

EXAMPLE 9. Estimate $\int_0^1 \sin x^2 \, dx$ with an error of less than 0.001.

Solution. From the indefinite integral in Example 8,

$$\int_0^1 \sin x^2 \, dx = \frac{1}{3} - \frac{1}{7 \cdot 3!} + \frac{1}{11 \cdot 5!} - \frac{1}{15 \cdot 7!} + \frac{1}{19 \cdot 9!} - \cdots$$

The series alternates, and we find by trial that

$$\frac{1}{11 \cdot 5!} \approx 0.00076$$

is the first term to be numerically less than 0.001. The sum of the preceding two terms gives

$$\int_0^1 \sin x^2 \, dx \approx \tfrac{1}{3} - \tfrac{1}{42} \approx 0.310.$$

With two more terms we could estimate

$$\int_0^1 \sin x^2 \, dx \approx 0.310268$$

with an error of less than 10^{-6}; and with only one term beyond that we have

$$\int_0^1 \sin x^2 \, dx \approx \tfrac{1}{3} - \tfrac{1}{42} + \tfrac{1}{1320} - \tfrac{1}{75600} + \tfrac{1}{6894720} \approx 0.310268303,$$

with an error of less than 10^{-9}. To guarantee this accuracy with the error formula for the trapezoid rule would require using about 13,000 subintervals.

EXAMPLE 10. Estimate $\int_0^{0.5} \sqrt{1 + x^4} \, dx$ with an error of less than 10^{-4}.

Solution. The binomial expansion of $(1 + x^4)^{1/2}$ is

$$(1 + x^4)^{1/2} = 1 + \tfrac{1}{2}x^4 - \tfrac{1}{8}x^8 + \cdots,$$

a series whose terms alternate in sign after the second term. Therefore,

$$\int_0^{0.5} \sqrt{1 + x^4} \, dx = x + \frac{1}{2 \cdot 5}x^5 - \frac{1}{8 \cdot 9}x^9 + \cdots \Big]_0^{0.5}$$

$$= 1 + 0.0031 - 0.00003 + \cdots$$

$$\approx 1.0031,$$

with an error of magnitude less than 0.00003.

At the beginning of this article we asked whether a function

$$f(x) = \sum_{n=0}^{\infty} a_n x^n$$

defined by a convergent power series has a Taylor series. We can now answer that a function defined by a power series with a radius of convergence $c > 0$ has a Maclaurin series that converges to the function at every point of $(-c, c)$. Why? Because the Maclaurin series for the function $f(x) = \sum_{n=0}^{\infty} a_n x^n$ is the series $\sum_{n=0}^{\infty} a_n x^n$ itself. To see this, we differentiate

$$f(x) = a_0 + a_1 x + a_2 x^2 + \cdots + a_n x^n + \cdots$$

term by term and substitute $x = 0$ in each derivative $f^{(n)}(x)$. This produces

$$f^{(n)}(0) = n! \, a_n \qquad \text{or} \qquad a_n = \frac{f^{(n)}(0)}{n!}$$

for every n. Thus,

$$f(x) = \sum_{n=0}^{\infty} a_n x^n = \sum_{n=0}^{\infty} \frac{f^{(n)}(0)}{n!} x^n, \qquad -c < x < c. \tag{7}$$

An immediate consequence of this is that series like

$$x \sin x = x^2 - \frac{x^4}{3!} + \frac{x^6}{5!} - \frac{x^8}{7!} + \cdots,$$

and

$$x^2 e^x = x^2 + x^3 + \frac{x^4}{2!} + \frac{x^5}{3!} + \cdots,$$

which are obtained by multiplying Maclaurin series by powers of x, as well as series obtained by integration and differentiation of power series, are themselves the Maclaurin series of the functions they represent.

Another consequence of (7) is that, if two power series $\sum_{n=0}^{\infty} a_n x^n$ and $\sum_{n=0}^{\infty} b_n x^n$ are equal for all values of x in an open interval that contains the origin $x = 0$, then $a_n = b_n$ for every n. For if

$$f(x) = \sum_{n=0}^{\infty} a_n x^n = \sum_{n=0}^{\infty} b_n x^n, \qquad -c < x < c,$$

then a_n and b_n are both equal to $f^{(n)}(0)/n!$.

PROBLEMS

In Problems 1–20, find the interval of absolute convergence. If the interval is finite, determine whether the series converges at each endpoint.

1. $\displaystyle\sum_{n=0}^{\infty} x^n$

2. $\displaystyle\sum_{n=0}^{\infty} n^2 x^n$

3. $\displaystyle\sum_{n=1}^{\infty} \frac{nx^n}{2^n}$

4. $\displaystyle\sum_{n=0}^{\infty} \frac{(2x)^n}{n!}$

5. $\displaystyle\sum_{n=0}^{\infty} \frac{(-1)^n x^{2n+1}}{(2n+1)!}$

6. $\displaystyle\sum_{n=1}^{\infty} (-1)^{n-1} \frac{(x-1)^n}{n}$

7. $\displaystyle\sum_{n=0}^{\infty} \frac{n^2}{2^n} (x+2)^n$

8. $\displaystyle\sum_{n=0}^{\infty} \frac{x^{2n+1}}{2n+1}$

9. $\displaystyle\sum_{n=0}^{\infty} (-1)^n \frac{x^{2n+1}}{2n+1}$

10. $\displaystyle\sum_{n=1}^{\infty} \frac{(x-2)^n}{n^2}$

11. $\displaystyle\sum_{n=0}^{\infty} \frac{\cos nx}{2^n}$

12. $\displaystyle\sum_{n=1}^{\infty} \frac{2^n x^n}{n^5}$

13. $\displaystyle\sum_{n=0}^{\infty} \frac{x^n e^n}{n+1}$

14. $\displaystyle\sum_{n=1}^{\infty} \frac{(\cos x)^n}{n^n}$

15. $\displaystyle\sum_{n=0}^{\infty} n^n x^n$

16. $\displaystyle\sum_{n=0}^{\infty} \frac{(3x+6)^n}{n!}$

17. $\displaystyle\sum_{n=1}^{\infty} (-2)^n (n+1)(x-1)^n$

18. $\displaystyle\sum_{n=1}^{\infty} \frac{(-1)^{n+1}(x-2)^n}{n \cdot 2^n}$

19. $\displaystyle\sum_{n=0}^{\infty} \left(\frac{x^2-1}{2}\right)^n$

20. $\displaystyle\sum_{n=1}^{\infty} \frac{(x+3)^{n-1}}{n}$

21. Find the sum of the series in Problem 16.

22. When the series of Problem 19 converges, to what does it converge?

23. Use series to verify that:

a) $\dfrac{d}{dx}(\cos x) = -\sin x$ **b)** $\displaystyle\int_0^x \cos t \, dt = \sin x$

c) $y = e^x$ is a solution of the equation $y' = y$.

24. Obtain the Maclaurin series for $1/(1 + x)^2$ from the series for $-1/(1 + x)$.

25. Use the Maclaurin series $1/(1 - x^2)$ to obtain a series for $2x/(1 - x^2)^2$.

26. Use the identity $\sin^2 x = (1 - \cos 2x)/2$ to obtain a series for $\sin^2 x$. Then differentiate this series to obtain a series for $2 \sin x \cos x$. Check that this is the series for $\sin 2x$.

(*Calculator*) In Problems 27 through 34, use series and a calculator to estimate each integral with an error of magnitude less than 0.001.

27. $\displaystyle\int_0^{0.2} \sin x^2 \, dx$ **28.** $\displaystyle\int_0^{0.1} \tan^{-1} x \, dx$

29. $\displaystyle\int_0^{0.1} x^2 e^{-x^2} \, dx$ **30.** $\displaystyle\int_0^{0.1} \dfrac{\tan^{-1} x}{x} \, dx$

31. $\displaystyle\int_0^{0.4} \dfrac{1 - e^{-x}}{x} \, dx$ **32.** $\displaystyle\int_0^{0.1} \dfrac{\ln(1 + x)}{x} \, dx$

33. $\displaystyle\int_0^{0.1} \dfrac{1}{\sqrt{1 + x^4}} \, dx$ **34.** $\displaystyle\int_0^{0.25} \sqrt[3]{1 + x^2} \, dx$

35. (*Calculator*)   **a)** Obtain a power series for
$$\sinh^{-1} x = \int_0^x \dfrac{dt}{\sqrt{1 + t^2}}.$$

b) Use the result of (a) to estimate $\sinh^{-1} 0.25$ to three decimal places.

36. (*Calculator*) Estimate $\int_0^1 \cos x^2 \, dx$ with an error of less than one millionth.

37. Show by example that there are power series that converge only at $x = 0$.

38. Show by examples that the convergence of a series at an endpoint of its interval of convergence may be either conditional or absolute.

39. Let r be any positive number. Use Theorem 1 to show that if $\sum_{n=0}^{\infty} a_n x^n$ converges for $-r < x < r$, then it converges absolutely for $-r < x < r$.

40. Use the ratio test to show that the binomial series converges for $|x| < 1$. (This still does not show that the series converges to $(1 + x)^m$.)

REVIEW QUESTIONS AND EXERCISES

1. Define "sequence," "series," "sequence of partial sums of a series."

2. Define "convergence" (a) of a sequence, (b) of an infinite series.

3. Which of the following statements are true, and which are false?

a) If a sequence does not converge, then it diverges.

b) If a sequence $\{n, f(n)\}$ does not converge, then $f(n)$ tends to infinity as n does.

c) If a series does not converge, then its nth term does not approach zero as n tends to infinity.

d) If the nth term of a series does not approach zero as n tends to infinity, then the series diverges.

e) If a sequence $\{n, f(n)\}$ converges, then there is a number L such that $f(n)$ lies within 1 unit of L (i) for all values of n, (ii) for all but a finite number of values of n.

f) If all partial sums of a series are less than some constant L, then the series converges.

g) If a series converges, then its partial sums s_n are bounded (that is, $m \le s_n \le M$ for some constants m and M).

4. List three tests for convergence (or divergence) of an infinite series.

5. Under what circumstances do you know that a bounded sequence converges?

6. Define "absolute convergence" and "conditional convergence." Give examples of series that are (a) absolutely convergent, (b) conditionally convergent.

7. State Taylor's theorem, with remainder, giving two different expressions for the remainder.

8. It can be shown (though not very simply) that the function f defined by

$$f(x) = \begin{cases} 0 & \text{when } x = 0, \\ e^{-1/x^2} & \text{when } x \ne 0 \end{cases}$$

is everywhere continuous, together with its derivatives of all orders. At 0, the derivatives are all equal to 0.

a) Write the Taylor series expansion of f in powers of x.

b) What is the remainder $R_n(x, 0)$ for this function? Does the Taylor series for f converge to $f(x)$ at some value of x different from zero? Give a reason for your answer.

9. If a Taylor series in powers of $x - a$ is to be used for the numerical evaluation of a function, what is necessary or desirable in the choice of a?

10. Describe a method that may be useful in finding $\lim_{x \to a} f(x)/g(x)$ if $f(a) = g(a) = 0$. Illustrate.

11. What tests may be used to find the interval of convergence of a power series? Do they also work at the endpoints of the interval? Illustrate with examples.

12. What test is usually used to decide whether a given alternating series converges? Give examples of convergent and divergent alternating series.

MISCELLANEOUS PROBLEMS

1. Find explicitly the nth partial sum of the series $\sum_{n=2}^{\infty} \ln (1 - 1/n^2)$, and thereby determine whether the series converges.

2. Evaluate $\sum_{k=2}^{\infty} 1/(k^2 - 1)$ by finding the nth partial sum and taking the limit as n becomes infinite.

3. Prove that the sequence $\{x_n\}$ and the series $\sum_{k=1}^{\infty} (x_{k+1} - x_k)$ both converge or both diverge.

4. In an attempt to find a root of the equation $x = f(x)$, a first approximation x_1 is estimated from the graphs of $y = x$ and $y = f(x)$. Then $x_2, x_3, \ldots, x_n, \ldots$ are computed successively from the formula $x_n = f(x_{n-1})$. If the points $x_1, x_2, \ldots, x_n, \ldots$ all lie on an interval $a \leq x \leq b$ on which $f(x)$ has a derivative such that $|f'(x)| < M < 1$, show that the sequence $\{x_n\}$ converges to a root of the given equation.

5. Assuming $|x| > 1$, show that

$$\frac{1}{1 - x} = -\frac{1}{x} - \frac{1}{x^2} - \frac{1}{x^3} - \cdots$$

6. (a) Find the expansion, in powers of x, of $x^2/(1 + x)$. (b) Does the series expansion of $x^2/(1 + x)$ in powers of x converge when $x = 2$? (Give a brief reason.)

7. Obtain the Maclaurin series expansion for $\sin^{-1} x$ by integrating the series for $(1 - t^2)^{-1/2}$ from 0 to x. Find the intervals of convergence of these series.

8. Obtain the Maclaurin series for $\ln (x + \sqrt{x^2 + 1}) = \sinh^{-1} x$ by integrating the series for $(1 + t^2)^{-1/2}$ from 0 to x. Find the intervals of convergence of these two series.

9. Obtain the first four terms in the Maclaurin series for $e^{\sin x}$ by substituting the series for $y = \sin x$ in the series for e^y.

10. Assuming $|x| > 1$, obtain the expansions

$$\tan^{-1} x = \frac{\pi}{2} - \frac{1}{x} + \frac{1}{3x^3} - \frac{1}{5x^5} + \cdots, \qquad x > 1,$$

$$\tan^{-1} x = -\frac{\pi}{2} - \frac{1}{x} + \frac{1}{3x^3} - \frac{1}{5x^5} + \cdots, \qquad x < -1,$$

by integrating the series

$$\frac{1}{1 + t^2} = \frac{1}{t^2} \cdot \frac{1}{1 + (1/t^2)} = \frac{1}{t^2} - \frac{1}{t^4} + \frac{1}{t^6} - \frac{1}{t^8} + \cdots$$

from x (> 1) to $+\infty$ or from $-\infty$ to x (< -1).

11. (a) Obtain the Maclaurin series, through the term in x^6, for $\ln (\cos x)$ by substituting the series for $y = 1 - \cos x$ in

the series for $\ln (1 - y)$. (b) Use the result of part (a) to estimate $\int_0^{0.1} \ln (\cos x) \, dx$ to five decimal places.

12. Compute $\int_0^1 [(\sin x)/x] \, dx$ to three decimal places.

13. Compute $\int_0^1 e^{-x^2} \, dx$ to three decimal places.

14. Expand the function $f(x) = \sqrt{1 + x^2}$ in powers of $(x - 1)$, obtaining three nonvanishing terms.

15. Expand the function $f(x) = 1/(1 - x)$ in powers of $(x - 2)$, and find the interval of convergence.

16. Find the first three nonvanishing terms of the Maclaurin series of $\tan x$.

17. Expand $f(x) = 1/(x + 1)$ in powers of $(x - 3)$.

18. Expand $\cos x$ in powers of $(x - \pi/3)$.

19. Find the first three terms of the Taylor series expansion of the function $1/x$ about the point π.

20. Let f and g be functions satisfying the following conditions: (a) $f(0) = 1$, (b) $f'(x) = g(x)$, $g'(x) = f(x)$, (c) $g(0) = 0$. Estimate $f(1)$ to three decimal places.

21. Suppose $f(x) = \sum_{n=0}^{\infty} a_n x^n$. Prove that (a) if $f(x)$ is an even function, then $a_1 = a_3 = a_5 = \cdots = 0$; (b) if $f(x)$ is an odd function, then $a_0 = a_2 = a_4 = \cdots = 0$.

22. Find the first four terms (up to x^3) of the Maclaurin series of $f(x) = e^{(e^x)}$.

23. Estimate the error involved in using $x - x^2/2$ as an approximation to $\ln (1 + x)$ for values of x between 0 and 0.2, inclusive.

24. If $(1 + x)^{1/3}$ is replaced by $1 + x/3$ and $0 \leq x \leq \frac{1}{10}$, what estimate can be given for the error?

25. Use series to find

$$\lim_{x \to 0} \frac{\ln (1 - x) - \sin x}{1 - \cos^2 x}.$$

26. Find $\lim_{x \to 0} [(\sin x)/x]^{1/x^2}$.

27. Does the series $\sum_{n=1}^{\infty} \operatorname{sech} n$ converge? Why?

28. Does $\sum_{n=1}^{\infty} (-1)^n \tanh n$ converge? Why?

Establish the convergence or divergence of the series whose nth terms are given in Problems 29–40.

29. $\dfrac{1}{\ln (n + 1)}$

30. $\dfrac{n}{2(n + 1)(n + 2)}$

31. $\dfrac{\sqrt{n + 1} - \sqrt{n}}{\sqrt{n}}$

32. $\dfrac{1}{n(\ln n)^2}, \qquad n \geq 2$

33. $\dfrac{1 + (-2)^{n-1}}{2^n}$

34. $\dfrac{n}{1000n^2 + 1}$

35. $e^n/n!$

36. $\dfrac{1}{n\sqrt{n^2+1}}$

37. $\dfrac{1}{n^{1+1/n}}$

38. $\dfrac{1\cdot 3\cdot 5\cdots(2n-1)}{2\cdot 4\cdot 6\cdots(2n)}$

39. $\dfrac{n^2}{n^3+1}$

40. $\dfrac{n+1}{n!}$

41. Find the sum of the convergent series

$$\sum_{n=1}^{\infty}\frac{1}{(n+1)(n+2)}.$$

42. (a) Suppose $a_1, a_2, a_3, \ldots, a_n$ are positive numbers satisfying the following conditions:

i) $a_1 \ge a_2 \ge a_3 \ge \cdots$;

ii) the series $a_2 + a_4 + a_8 + a_{16} + \cdots$ diverges.

Show that the series

$$\frac{a_1}{1}+\frac{a_2}{2}+\frac{a_3}{3}+\cdots$$

diverges. (b) Use the result above to show that

$$\sum_{n=2}^{\infty}\frac{1}{n\ln n}$$

diverges.

43. Given $a_n \ne 1$, $a_n > 0$, $\sum a_n$ converges. (a) Show that $\sum a_n^2$ converges. (b) Does $\sum a_n/(1-a_n)$ converge? (c) Does $\sum \ln(1+a_n)$ converge? Explain.

44. Show that $\sum_{n=2}^{\infty} 1/[n(\ln n)^k]$ converges for $k > 1$.

In Problems 45–52, find the interval of convergence of each series. Test for convergence at the endpoints if the interval is finite.

45. $1 + \dfrac{x+2}{3\cdot 1} + \dfrac{(x+2)^2}{3^2\cdot 2} + \cdots + \dfrac{(x+2)^n}{3^n\cdot n} + \cdots$

46. $1 + \dfrac{(x-1)^2}{2!} + \dfrac{(x-1)^4}{4!} + \cdots + \dfrac{(x-1)^{2n-2}}{(2n-2)!} + \cdots$

47. $\sum_{n=1}^{\infty}\dfrac{x^n}{n^n}$

48. $\sum_{n=1}^{\infty}\dfrac{n!\,x^n}{n^n}$

49. $\sum_{n=0}^{\infty}\dfrac{n+1}{2n+1}\dfrac{(x-3)^n}{2^n}$

50. $\sum_{n=0}^{\infty}\dfrac{n+1}{2n+1}\dfrac{(x-2)^n}{3^n}$

51. $\sum_{n=1}^{\infty}\dfrac{(-1)^{n-1}(x-1)^n}{n^2}$

52. $\sum_{n=1}^{\infty}\dfrac{x^n}{n}$

Determine *all* the values of x for which the following series converge:

53. $\sum_{n=1}^{\infty}\dfrac{(x-2)^{3n}}{n!}$,

54. $\sum_{n=1}^{\infty}\dfrac{2^n(\sin x)^n}{n^2}$,

55. $\sum_{n=1}^{\infty}\dfrac{1}{n}\left(\dfrac{x-1}{x}\right)^n$.

56. A function is defined by the power series

$$y = 1 + \frac{1}{6}x^3 + \frac{1}{180}x^6 + \cdots + \frac{1\cdot 4\cdot 7\cdots(3n-2)}{(3n)!}x^{3n} + \cdots$$

a) Find the interval of convergence of the series.

b) Show that there exist two constants a and b such that the function so defined satisfies a differential equation of the form $y'' = x^a y + b$.

57. If $a_n > 0$ and the series $\sum_{n=1}^{\infty} a_n$ converges, prove that $\sum_{n=1}^{\infty} a_n/(1+a_n)$ converges.

58. If $1 > a_n > 0$ and $\sum_{n=1}^{\infty} a_n$ converges, prove that $\sum_{n=1}^{\infty} \ln(1-a_n)$ converges. [*Hint.* First show that $|\ln(1-a_n)| \le a_n/(1-a_n)$; then apply the answer to Problem 43(b).]

59. An infinite product, indicated by $\prod_{n=1}^{\infty}(1+a_n)$, is said to converge if the series $\sum_{n=1}^{\infty} \ln(1+a_n)$ converges. (The series is the natural logarithm of the product.) Prove that the product converges if every $a_n > -1$ and $\sum_{n=1}^{\infty}|a_n|$ converges. [*Hint.* Show that

$$|\ln(1+a_n)| \le \frac{|a_n|}{1-|a_n|} < 2|a_n|$$

when $|a_n| < \frac{1}{2}$.]

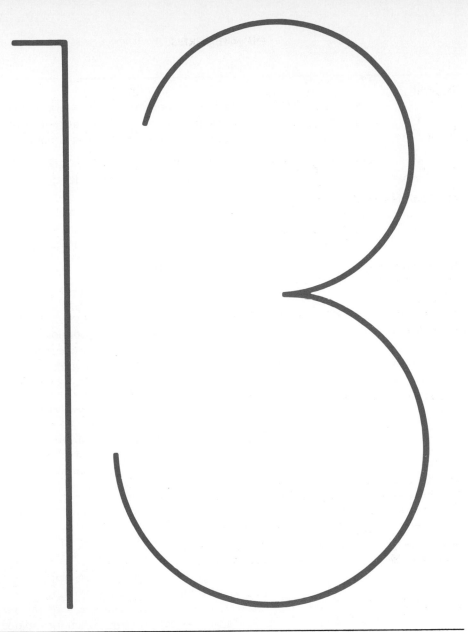

DIFFERENTIAL EQUATIONS

13–1

INTRODUCTION

As you know from your earlier work in Articles 4–2, 4–3, 6–11, and 11–2, equations that involve one or more derivatives or differentials are called differential equations. Differential equations are classified by

a) type (namely, *ordinary* or *partial*),

b) order (that of the highest order derivative that occurs in the equation), and

c) degree (the exponent of the highest power of the highest order derivative, after the equation has been cleared of fractions and radicals in the dependent variable and its derivatives).

For example,

$$\left(\frac{d^3y}{dx^3}\right)^2 + \left(\frac{d^2y}{dx^2}\right)^5 + \frac{y}{x^2+1} = e^x \tag{1}$$

is an ordinary differential equation, of order three and degree two.

Only "ordinary" derivatives occur when the dependent variable y is a function of a single independent variable x. On the other hand, if the dependent variable y is a function of two or more independent variables, say

$$y = f(x, t),$$

where x and t are independent variables, then partial derivatives of y, which are obtained by holding one variable fixed while we differentiate with respect to the other, may occur. For example,

$$\frac{\partial^2 y}{\partial t^2} = a^2 \frac{\partial^2 y}{\partial x^2} \tag{2}$$

is a partial differential equation, of order two and degree one. (It is the one-dimensional "wave equation." A systematic treatment of partial differential equations lies beyond the scope of this book. For a discussion of partial differential equations, including the wave equation, and solutions of associated physical problems, see Kaplan, *Advanced Calculus*, Chapter 10.)

Many physical problems, when formulated in mathematical terms, lead to differential equations. In Article 11–2, for example, we discussed and solved the system of differential equations

$$m\frac{d^2x}{dt^2} = 0, \qquad m\frac{d^2y}{dt^2} = -mg \tag{3}$$

which described the motion of a projectile (neglecting air resistance). Indeed, one of the chief sources of differential equations in mechanics is Newton's second law:

$$\mathbf{F} = \frac{d}{dt}(m\mathbf{v}), \tag{4}$$

where $\mathbf{F}$ is the resultant of the forces acting on a body of mass m and $\mathbf{v}$ is its velocity.

In the field of radiochemistry, the following situation is a typical simplification of what may happen. Suppose that, at time t, there are x, y, and z grams, respectively, of three substances, A, B, and C, that have the following properties:

i) A, through radioactive decomposition, transforms into B at a rate proportional to the amount of A present.

ii) B, in turn, transforms into C at a rate proportional to the amount of B present.

iii) Finally, C is caused to transform back into A at a rate proportional to the amount of C present; see Fig. 13–1.

If we call the proportionality factors k_1, k_2, and k_3, respectively, we have the following system of differential equations:

$$\frac{dx}{dt} = -k_1 x + k_3 z, \qquad \frac{dy}{dt} = k_1 x - k_2 y, \qquad \frac{dz}{dt} = k_2 y - k_3 z. \quad \textbf{(5)}$$

The first of these simply says that the amount of A present at time t, namely x, is decreasing at a rate $k_1 x$ through transformation into substance B, but is gaining at a rate $k_3 z$ from substance C. The other two equations have similar meanings. It is an immediate consequence of Eqs. (5) that

$$\frac{dx}{dt} + \frac{dy}{dt} + \frac{dz}{dt} = 0. \quad \textbf{(6)}$$

From Eq. (6), in turn, we readily deduce that

$$x + y + z = \text{constant}.$$

In other words, in the hypothetical case under consideration, the total amount of substances A, B, and C remains constant.

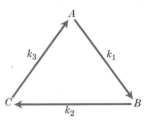

13–1 Three substances may transform in such a way that A changes into B, B into C, and C back into A.

A function

$$y = f(x)$$

is said to be a *solution* of a differential equation if the latter is satisfied when y and its derivatives are replaced throughout by $f(x)$ and its corresponding derivatives. For example, if C_1 and C_2 are any constants, then

$$y = C_1 \cos x + C_2 \sin x \quad \textbf{(1)}$$

is a solution of the differential equation

$$\frac{d^2 y}{dx^2} + y = 0. \quad \textbf{(2)}$$

13-2
SOLUTIONS

This may be checked by substituting y and its second derivative into the differential equation (2) to obtain

$$(-C_1 \cos x - C_2 \sin x) + (C_1 \cos x + C_2 \sin x) = 0.$$

A physical problem that translates into a differential equation usually involves additional conditions not expressed by the differential equation itself. When we determine the motion of a body in mechanics, for example, we usually know the initial position and velocity of the body as well as the forces whose relationships give rise to the differential equation. The differential equation, or equations, of motion will usually have solutions in which certain arbitrary constants occur, as in (1) above. Specific values are then assigned to these arbitrary constants to meet the prescribed initial conditions. (See the examples worked out in Articles 4–3, 6–11, and 11–2.)

A differential equation of order n will generally have a solution involving n arbitrary constants. (There is a more precise mathematical theorem, which we shall neither state nor prove.) This solution is called the *general* solution. Once this general solution is known, it is only a matter of algebra to determine specific values of the constants if initial conditions are also prescribed. Hence we shall devote our attention to the problem of finding the general solutions of certain types of differential equations.

The subject of differential equations is complex, and there are many textbooks on differential equations and advanced calculus where you can find a more extensive treatment than we shall present here. The field is also the subject of a great deal of current research; and, with the widespread availability of computers, numerical methods for solving differential equations play an important role.

In the remainder of this chapter, the following topics will be treated. Throughout, only *ordinary* differential equations will be considered.

1. First order.
   a) Variables separable.
   b) Homogeneous.
   c) Linear.
   d) Exact differentials.

2. Special types of second order.

3. Linear equations with constant coefficients.
   a) Homogeneous.
   b) Nonhomogeneous.

Several new terms occur in this list, and they will be defined in the appropriate places.

PROBLEMS

Show that each function is a solution of the accompanying differential equation.

1. $xy'' - y' = 0;$
a) $y = x^2 + 3;$
b) $y = C_1 x^2 + C_2$

2. $x^3 y''' + 4x^2 y'' + xy' + y = x;$ $y = \frac{1}{2}x$

3. $yy'' = 2(y')^2 - 2y';$
a) $y = C;$
b) $C_1 y = \tan(C_1 x + C_2)$

4. $y' + \frac{1}{x} y = 1;$ $y = \frac{C}{x} + \frac{x}{2}$

5. $2y' + 3y = e^{-x};$ $y = e^{-x} + Ce^{-(3/2)x}$

6. $(x \sin x)y' + (\sin x + x \cos x)y = e^x/x;$

$$y = \frac{1}{x \sin x} \int_{-1/2}^{x} \frac{e^t}{t} \, dt$$

A first order differential equation can be solved by integration if it is possible to collect all y terms with dy and all x terms with dx. That is, if it is possible to write the equation in the form

$$f(y)\, dy + g(x)\, dx = 0,$$

then the general solution is

$$\int f(y)\, dy + \int g(x)\, dx = C,$$

where C is an arbitrary constant.

13–3

FIRST ORDER: VARIABLES SEPARABLE

EXAMPLE. Solve the equation

$$(x + 1)\frac{dy}{dx} = x(y^2 + 1).$$

Solution. We change to differential form, separate the variables, and integrate:

$$(x + 1)\, dy = x(y^2 + 1)\, dx,$$

$$\frac{dy}{y^2 + 1} = \frac{x\, dx}{x + 1},$$

$$\tan^{-1} y = x - \ln |x + 1| + C.$$

Some models of population growth assume that the rate of change of the population at time t is proportional to the number y of individuals present at that time. This leads to the equation

$$\frac{dy}{dt} = ky, \tag{1}$$

where k is a constant that is positive if the population is increasing and negative if it is decreasing. To solve Eq. (1), we separate variables and integrate, to obtain

$$\int \frac{dy}{y} = \int k\, dt,$$

or

$$\ln y = kt + C_1$$

(remember that y is positive). It follows that

$$y = e^{kt + C_1}$$

$$= C e^{kt},$$

where $C = e^{C_1}$. If y_0 denotes the population when $t = 0$, then $C = y_0$ and

$$y = y_0 e^{kt}. \tag{2}$$

This equation is called the *law of exponential growth*.

PROBLEMS

Separate the variables and solve the following differential equations.

1. $x(2y - 3) dx + (x^2 + 1) dy = 0$

2. $x^2(y^2 + 1) dx + y\sqrt{x^3 + 1} dy = 0$

3. $\dfrac{dy}{dx} = e^{x-y}$

4. $\sqrt{2xy} \dfrac{dy}{dx} = 1$

5. $\sin x \dfrac{dx}{dy} + \cosh 2y = 0$

6. $\ln x \dfrac{dx}{dy} = \dfrac{x}{y}$

7. $xe^y dy + \dfrac{x^2 + 1}{y} dx = 0$

8. $y\sqrt{2x^2 + 3} dy + x\sqrt{4 - y^2} dx = 0$

9. $\sqrt{1 + x^2} dy + \sqrt{y^2 - 1} dx = 0$

10. $x^2 y \dfrac{dy}{dx} = (1 + x) \csc y$

11. *Growth of bacteria.* Suppose that the bacteria in a colony can grow unchecked, by the law of exponential growth. The colony starts with one bacterium, and doubles every half hour. How many bacteria will the colony contain at the end of 24 hours? (Under favorable laboratory conditions, the number of cholera bacteria can double every 30 minutes. Of course, in an infected person, many of the bacteria are destroyed, but this example helps to explain why a person who feels well in the morning may be dangerously ill by evening.)

12. *Discharging capacitor.* As a result of leakage, an electrical capacitor discharges at a rate proportional to the charge. If the charge Q has the value Q_0 at the time $t = 0$, find Q as a function of t.

13. *Electric current.* Ohm's law, $E = Ri$, requires modification in a circuit containing self-inductance, as in a coil. The modified form is

$$L\frac{di}{dt} + Ri = E$$

for the series circuit shown in Fig. 13–2. Here R denotes the resistance of the circuit in ohms, L is the inductance in henries, E is the impressed electromotive force in volts, i is the current in amperes, and t is the time in seconds. (See Sears, Zemansky, Young, *University Physics* (Fifth ed., 1976), Chapter 28.) (a) Solve the differential equation under the assumption that E is constant, and that $i = 0$ when $t = 0$. (b) Find the steady-state current $i_{ss} = \lim_{t \to \infty} i$. (See Fig. 13–3.)

14. *Radioactive decay.* The decay of a radioactive element can be described by Eq. (2), because the rate of decay is proportional to the number of radioactive nuclei present. The *half-life* of a radioactive element is the time required for half of the radioactive nuclei originally present in any sample to decay. Show that the half-life of a radioactive element is a constant that does not depend on the number of radioactive nuclei initially present in the sample.

15. *Carbon-14 dating.* The half-lives of radioactive elements (see Problem 14) can sometimes be used to date events from the earth's past. The ages of rocks more than 2 billion years old have been measured by the extent of the radioactive decay of uranium (half-life 4.5 billion years!). In a living organism, the ratio of radioactive carbon, carbon-14, to ordinary carbon stays fairly constant during the lifetime of the organism, being approximately equal to the ratio in the organism's surroundings at the time. After the organism's death, however, no new carbon is ingested, and the proportion of carbon-14 in the organism's remains decreases as the carbon-14 decays. Since the half-life of carbon-14 is known to be about 5700 years, it is possible to estimate the age of organic remains by comparing the proportion of carbon-14 they contain with the proportion assumed to have been in the organism's environment at the time it lived. Archeologists have dated shells (which contain $CaCO_3$), seeds, and wooden artifacts this way. The estimate of 15,500 years for the age of the cave paintings at Lascaux, France, is based on carbon-14 dating.

a) Find k in Eq. (2) for carbon-14.

b) What is the age of a sample of charcoal in which 90 percent of the carbon-14 has decayed?

c) The charcoal from a tree killed in the volcanic eruption that formed Crater Lake in Oregon contained $44\frac{1}{2}$ percent of the carbon-14 found in living matter. About how old is Crater Lake?

13–2 A simple series circuit.

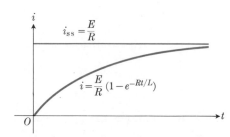

13–3 The current i in the circuit shown in Fig. 13–2 increases toward the steady-state value E/R.

Occasionally a differential equation whose variables cannot be separated can be transformed by a change of variable into an equation whose variables can be separated. This is the case with any equation that can be put into the form

$$\frac{dy}{dx} = F\left(\frac{y}{x}\right). \tag{1}$$

13–4

FIRST ORDER: HOMOGENEOUS

Such an equation is called *homogeneous*. For example, the equation

$$(x + y)\, dx - (x - y)\, dy = 0$$

is homogeneous because it can be rewritten as

$$\frac{dy}{dx} = \frac{x + y}{x - y} = \frac{1 + \left(\dfrac{y}{x}\right)}{1 - \left(\dfrac{y}{x}\right)}.$$

To transform Eq. (1) into an equation whose variables may be separated, we introduce the new independent variable

$$v = \frac{y}{x}. \tag{2}$$

Then

$$y = vx, \qquad \frac{dy}{dx} = v + x\frac{dv}{dx},$$

and (1) becomes

$$v + x\frac{dv}{dx} = F(v). \tag{3}$$

Equation (3) can be solved by separation of variables:

$$\frac{dx}{x} + \frac{dv}{v - F(v)} = 0. \tag{4}$$

After (4) is solved, the solution of the original equation is obtained when we replace v by y/x.

EXAMPLE. Show that the equation

$$(x^2 + y^2)\, dx + 2xy\, dy = 0$$

is homogeneous, and solve it.

Solution. From the given equation, we have

$$\frac{dy}{dx} = -\frac{x^2 + y^2}{2xy} = -\frac{1 + (y/x)^2}{2(y/x)}.$$

This has the form of Eq. (1), with

$$F(v) = -\frac{1 + v^2}{2v}, \qquad \text{where} \quad v = \frac{y}{x}.$$

Then Eq. (4) becomes

$$\frac{dx}{x} + \frac{dv}{v + \dfrac{1 + v^2}{2v}} = 0,$$

or

$$\frac{dx}{x} + \frac{2v\,dv}{1 + 3v^2} = 0.$$

When we integrate both sides of this equation, we obtain

$$\ln |x| + \tfrac{1}{3} \ln (1 + 3v^2) = C.$$

To eliminate the logarithms, we may write

$$3 \ln |x| + \ln (1 + 3v^2) = 3C,$$
$$\ln (|x^3|(1 + 3v^2)) = 3C,$$
$$|x^3|(1 + 3v^2) = e^{3C},$$
$$x^3(1 + 3v^2) = \pm e^{3C} = C_1.$$

In terms of y and x, this solution becomes

$$x(x^2 + 3y^2) = C_1,$$

where C_1 is an arbitrary constant.

PROBLEMS

Show that the following equations are homogeneous, and solve.

1. $(x^2 + y^2)\,dx + xy\,dy = 0$

2. $x^2\,dy + (y^2 - xy)\,dx = 0$

3. $(xe^{y/x} + y)\,dx - x\,dy = 0$

4. $(x + y)\,dy + (x - y)\,dx = 0$

5. $y' = \dfrac{y}{x} + \cos \dfrac{y - x}{x}$

6. $\left(x \sin \dfrac{y}{x} - y \cos \dfrac{y}{x}\right) dx + x \cos \dfrac{y}{x}\,dy = 0$

7. Solve the equation

$$(x + y + 1)\,dx + (y - x - 3)\,dy = 0$$

by making a change of variable of the form

$$x = r + a, \qquad y = s + b,$$

and choosing the constants a and b so that the resulting equation is

$$(r + s)\,dr + (r - s)\,ds = 0.$$

Then solve this equation and express its solution in terms of x and y.

8. Use the substitution $u = x + y$ to solve the equation $y' = (x + y)^2$.

Orthogonal trajectories. If every member of a family of curves is a solution of the differential equation

$$M(x, y)\,dx + N(x, y)\,dy = 0,$$

while every member of a second family of curves is a solution of the related equation

$$N(x, y)\,dx - M(x, y)\,dy = 0,$$

then each curve of the one family is orthogonal to every curve of the other family. Each family is said to be a family of *orthogonal trajectories* of the other. In Problems 9 and 10, find the family of solutions of the given differential equation and the family of orthogonal trajectories. Sketch both families.

9. $x\,dy - 2y\,dx = 0$

10. $2xy\,dy + (x^2 - y^2)\,dx = 0$

11. Find the orthogonal trajectories of the family of curves $xy = c$.

The complexity of a differential equation depends primarily upon the way in which the *dependent* variable and its derivatives occur. Of particular importance are those equations that are linear. In a linear differential equation, each term of the equation is of degree one or zero, where, in computing the degree of a term, we add the exponents of the dependent variable and of any of its derivatives that occur. Thus, for example, (d^2y/dx^2) is of the first degree, while $y(dy/dx)$ is of the second degree because we must add 1 for the exponent of y, and 1 for the exponent of dy/dx.

A differential equation of first order, which is also linear, can always be put into the standard form

$$\frac{dy}{dx} + Py = Q, \tag{1}$$

where P and Q are functions of x. For example, the equation

$$(4y - xe^x)\, dx + x\, dy = 0$$

can be rewritten in the form

$$x\frac{dy}{dx} + 4y - xe^x = 0$$

or

$$\frac{dy}{dx} + \frac{4}{x}y = e^x,$$

in which $P = 4/x$ and $Q = e^x$.

One way to solve Eq. (1) is to multiply both sides of the equation by a function $\rho = \rho(x)$ that is chosen so that the left side of the equation becomes the derivative of the product ρy. This enables us to find y by integrating both sides of the modified equation.

To find a formula for ρ, we multiply (1) by ρ to obtain

$$\rho\frac{dy}{dx} + \rho Py = \rho Q, \tag{1'}$$

and then try to impose upon ρ the condition that

$$\rho\frac{dy}{dx} + \rho Py = \frac{d}{dx}(\rho y). \tag{2}$$

When we expand the right side of (2) and cancel terms, we obtain, as the condition to be satisfied by ρ,

$$\frac{d\rho}{dx} = \rho P. \tag{3}$$

In Eq. (3), $P = P(x)$ is a known function, so we can separate the variables and solve for ρ:

$$\frac{d\rho}{\rho} = P\, dx,$$

$$\ln|\rho| = \int P\, dx + \ln C.$$

Therefore,

$$\rho = \pm Ce^{\int P\,dx}. \tag{4}$$

Since we do not require the most general function ρ, we may take $\pm C = 1$ in (4) and use

$$\rho = e^{\int P\,dx}. \tag{5}$$

This function is called an *integrating factor* for Eq. (1). With its help, (1') becomes

$$\frac{d}{dx}(\rho y) = \rho Q,$$

whose solution is

$$\rho y = \int \rho Q\,dx + C. \tag{6}$$

Since ρ is given by (5), while P and Q are known from the given differential equation (1), we have, in Eqs. (5) and (6), a summary of all that is required to solve (1).

EXAMPLE 1. Solve the equation

$$\frac{dy}{dx} + y = e^x.$$

Solution.

$$P = 1, \qquad Q = e^x,$$

$$\rho = e^{\int dx} = e^x,$$

$$e^x y = \int e^{2x}\,dx + C = \tfrac{1}{2}e^{2x} + C,$$

$$y = \tfrac{1}{2}e^x + Ce^{-x}.$$

EXAMPLE 2. Solve the equation

$$x\frac{dy}{dx} - 3y = x^2.$$

Solution. We put the equation in standard form,

$$\frac{dy}{dx} - \frac{3}{x}y = x,$$

and then read off

$$P = -\frac{3}{x}, \qquad Q = x.$$

Hence

$$\rho = e^{\int -(3/x)\,dx} = e^{-3\ln x} = \frac{1}{e^{3\ln x}} = \frac{1}{x^3},$$

and

$$\frac{1}{x^3} y = \int \frac{x}{x^3} dx + C = -\frac{1}{x} + C,$$

$$y = -x^2 + Cx^3.$$

REMARKS.   Note that whenever $\int P \, dx$ involves logarithms, as in Example 2, it is profitable to simplify the expression for $e^{\int P \, dx}$ before substituting into Eq. (6). To simplify the expression, we use the properties of the logarithmic and exponential functions:

$$e^{\ln A} = A, \qquad e^{m \ln A} = A^m, \qquad e^{n + m \ln A} = A^m e^n.$$

A differential equation that is linear in y and dy/dx may also be separable, or homogeneous. In such cases, we have a choice of methods of solution. Observe also that an equation that is linear in x and dx/dy can be solved by the technique of this article; one need only interchange the roles of x and y in Eqs. (1), (5), and (6).

PROBLEMS

Solve:

1. $\dfrac{dy}{dx} + 2y = e^{-x}$

2. $2\dfrac{dy}{dx} - y = e^{x/2}$

3. $x\dfrac{dy}{dx} + 3y = \dfrac{\sin x}{x^2}$

4. $x \, dy + y \, dx = \sin x \, dx$

5. $x \, dy + y \, dx = y \, dy$

6. $(x - 1)^3 \dfrac{dy}{dx} + 4(x - 1)^2 y = x + 1$

7. $\cosh x \, dy + (y \sinh x + e^x) \, dx = 0$

8. $e^{2y} \, dx + 2(xe^{2y} - y) \, dy = 0$

9. $(x - 2y) \, dy + y \, dx = 0$

10. $(y^2 + 1) \, dx + (2xy + 1) \, dy = 0$

11. *Blood sugar.* If glucose is fed intravenously at a constant rate, the change in the overall concentration $c(t)$ of glucose in the blood with respect to time may be described by the differential equation

$$\frac{dc}{dt} = \frac{G}{100V} - kc.$$

In this equation, G, V, and k are positive constants, G being the rate at which glucose is admitted, in milligrams per minute, and V the volume of blood in the body, in liters (around 5 liters for an adult). The concentration $c(t)$ is measured in milligrams per centiliter. The term $-kc$ is included because the glucose is assumed to be changing continually into other molecules at a rate proportional to its concentration. (a) Solve the equation for $c(t)$, using c_0 to denote $c(0)$. (b) Find the steady state concentration, $\lim_{t \to \infty} c(t)$.

An equation in the form

$$M(x, y) \, dx + N(x, y) \, dy = 0 \qquad \textbf{(1)}$$

is said to be *exact* if there is a function $f(x, y)$ such that

$$M(x, y) \, dx + N(x, y) \, dy = df. \qquad \textbf{(2)}$$

In this case, Eq. (1) becomes

$$df = 0,$$

13–6

FIRST ORDER: EXACT

and the solution of (1) is

$$f(x, y) = C,$$

where C is an arbitrary constant.

For example, the equation

$$2x \, dx + 2y \, dy = 0 \tag{3}$$

is exact, because

$$2x \, dx + 2y \, dy = d(x^2 + y^2). \tag{4}$$

Equation (3) therefore becomes

$$d(x^2 + y^2) = 0, \tag{5}$$

and the solution is

$$x^2 + y^2 = C. \tag{6}$$

Again, the equation

$$(2x + e^y) \, dx + xe^y \, dy = 0 \tag{7}$$

is exact because

$$(2x + e^y) \, dx + xe^y \, dy = d(x^2 + xe^y).$$

Equation (7) becomes

$$d(x^2 + xe^y) = 0,$$

and the solution is

$$x^2 + xe^y = C.$$

It can be proved that every first-order differential equation

$$P(x, y) \, dx + Q(x, y) \, dy = 0 \tag{8}$$

can be made exact by multiplication by a suitable *integrating factor* $\rho(x, y)$. That is, there is a function $\rho(x, y)$, which may sometimes be a function of x or y alone, such that the equation

$$\rho(x, y)P(x, y) \, dx + \rho(x, y)Q(x, y) \, dy = 0 \tag{9}$$

is exact. There are, in fact, a variety of integrating factors for any differential equation like (3), but it is not always easy to find one. There is no general technique by which even a single integrating factor can be produced for an arbitrary differential equation, and the search for one can be a frustrating experience. However, one can often recognize certain combinations of differentials that can be made exact by the use of "ingenious devices."

EXAMPLE 1. Solve the equation

$$x \, dy - y \, dx = xy^2 \, dx.$$

Solution. The combination $x \, dy - y \, dx$ may ring a bell in our memories and cause us to recall the formula

$$d\left(\frac{u}{v}\right) = \frac{v\,du - u\,dv}{v^2} = -\left[\frac{u\,dv - v\,du}{v^2}\right].$$

Therefore we might multiply the given equation by $1/x^2$, or change signs and multiply by $1/y^2$. The latter approach will be more profitable because it removes the factor of y^2 from the right side of the equation. We choose the integrating factor $-1/y^2$, and proceed as follows:

$$x\,dy - y\,dx = xy^2\,dx,$$

$$\frac{y\,dx - x\,dy}{y^2} = -x\,dx,$$

$$d\left(\frac{x}{y}\right) + x\,dx = 0,$$

$$\frac{x}{y} + \frac{x^2}{2} = C. \tag{10}$$

The same result would be obtained if we wrote our equation in the form

$$(xy^2 + y)\,dx - x\,dy = 0$$

and multiplied by the integrating factor $1/y^2$. This would give

$$\left(x + \frac{1}{y}\right)dx - \left(\frac{x}{y^2}\right)dy = 0,$$

$$d\left(\frac{x^2}{2} + \frac{x}{y}\right) = 0,$$

$$\frac{x^2}{2} + \frac{x}{y} = C,$$

which agrees with Eq. (10).

EXAMPLE 2. Solve the equation

$$(x + y)\,dx + (x + \cos y)\,dy = 0.$$

Solution. There are two kinds of terms:
1) Terms like $x\,dx$ and $\cos y\,dy$ in which the variables are separated, and
2) Terms like $y\,dx + x\,dy = d(xy)$ in which the variables can be combined in exact differentials but cannot be separated.

When we rewrite the equation in the form

$$x\,dx + \cos y\,dy + (y\,dx + x\,dy) = 0,$$

we see that it is the same as

$$d\left(\frac{x^2}{2} + \sin y + xy\right) = 0.$$

The solution is

$$\frac{x^2}{2} + \sin y + xy = C.$$

PROBLEMS

In Problems 1–3, use the given integrating factors to make differential equations exact. Then solve the equations.

1. $(x + 2y) dx - x dy = 0;$ $1/x^3$

2. $y dx + x dy = 0;$

a) $\dfrac{1}{xy}$ **b)** $\dfrac{1}{(xy)^2}$

3. $y dx - x dy = 0;$

a) $\dfrac{1}{y^2}$ **b)** $\dfrac{1}{x^2}$

c) $\dfrac{1}{xy}$ **d)** $\dfrac{1}{x^2 + y^2}$

Solve:

4. $(x + y) dx + (x + y^2) dy = 0$

5. $(2xe^y + e^x) dx + (x^2 + 1)e^y dy = 0$

6. $(2xy + y^2) dx + (x^2 + 2xy - y) dy = 0$

7. $(x + \sqrt{y^2 + 1}) dx - \left(y - \dfrac{xy}{\sqrt{y^2 + 1}}\right) dy = 0$

8. $x dy - y dx + x^3 dx = 0$

9. $x dy - y dx = (x^2 + y^2) dx$

10. $(x^2 + x - y) dx + x dy = 0$

11. $\left(e^x + \ln y + \dfrac{y}{x}\right) dx + \left(\dfrac{x}{y} + \ln x + \sin y\right) dy = 0$

12. $\left(\dfrac{y^2}{1 + x^2} - 2y\right) dx + (2y \tan^{-1} x - 2x + \sinh y) dy = 0$

13. $dy + \dfrac{y - \sin x}{x} dx = 0$

13-7

SPECIAL TYPES OF SECOND ORDER EQUATIONS

Certain types of second order differential equations, of which the general form is

$$F\left(x, y, \frac{dy}{dx}, \frac{d^2y}{dx^2}\right) = 0, \tag{1}$$

can be reduced to first order equations by a suitable change of variables.

Type 1. *Equations with dependent variable missing.* When Eq. (1) has the special form

$$F\left(x, \frac{dy}{dx}, \frac{d^2y}{dx^2}\right) = 0, \tag{2}$$

we can reduce it to a first order equation by substituting

$$p = \frac{dy}{dx}, \qquad \frac{d^2y}{dx^2} = \frac{dp}{dx}.$$

Then Eq. (2) takes the form

$$F\left(x, p, \frac{dp}{dx}\right) = 0,$$

which is of the first order in p. If this can be solved for p as a function of x, say

$$p = \phi(x, C_1);$$

then we can find y by one additional integration:

$$y = \int (dy/dx) dx = \int p dx = \int \phi(x, C_1) dx + C_2.$$

The differential equation

$$\frac{d^2y}{dx^2} = \frac{w}{H}\sqrt{1 + \left(\frac{dy}{dx}\right)^2}$$

was solved by this technique in Article 9–6.

Type 2. *Equations with independent variable missing.* When Eq. (1) does not contain x explicitly but has the form

$$F\left(y, \frac{dy}{dx}, \frac{d^2y}{dx^2}\right) = 0, \tag{3}$$

the substitutions to use are

$$p = \frac{dy}{dx} \quad \text{and} \quad \frac{d^2y}{dx^2} = p\frac{dp}{dy}.$$

Then Eq. (3) takes the form

$$F\left(y, p, p\frac{dp}{dy}\right) = 0,$$

which is of the first order in p. Its solution gives p in terms of y, and then a further integration gives the solution of Eq. (3).

EXAMPLE. Solve the equation

$$\frac{d^2y}{dx^2} + y = 0.$$

Solution. Let

$$\frac{dy}{dx} = p, \qquad \frac{d^2y}{dx^2} = \frac{dp}{dx} = \frac{dp}{dy}\frac{dy}{dx} = \frac{dp}{dy}p.$$

Then we proceed as follows:

$$p\frac{dp}{dy} + y = 0, \qquad p\,dp + y\,dy = 0,$$

$$\frac{p^2}{2} + \frac{y^2}{2} = \frac{C_1^2}{2}, \qquad p = \frac{dy}{dx} = \pm\sqrt{C_1^2 - y^2},$$

$$\frac{dy}{\sqrt{C_1^2 - y^2}} = \pm dx, \qquad \sin^{-1}\frac{y}{C_1} = \pm(x + C_2),$$

$$y = C_1 \sin\left[\pm(x + C_2)\right] = \pm C_1 \sin(x + C_2).$$

Since C_1 is arbitrary, there is no need for the $\pm$ sign, and we have

$$y = C_1 \sin(x + C_2)$$

as the general solution.

PROBLEMS

Solve:

1. $\dfrac{d^2y}{dx^2} + \dfrac{dy}{dx} = 0$ 2. $\dfrac{d^2y}{dx^2} + y\dfrac{dy}{dx} = 0$

3. $\dfrac{d^2y}{dx^2} + x\dfrac{dy}{dx} = 0$ 4. $x\dfrac{d^2y}{dx^2} + \dfrac{dy}{dx} = 0$

5. $\dfrac{d^2y}{dx^2} - y = 0$

6. $\dfrac{d^2y}{dx^2} + \omega^2 y = 0$ ($\omega = $ constant $\neq 0$)

7. $xy''' - 2y'' = 0$.   [*Hint.* Substitute $y'' = q$.]

8. $2y'' - (y')^2 + 1 = 0$

9. *Hooke's law.* A mass m is suspended from one end of a vertical spring whose other end is attached to a rigid support. The body is allowed to come to rest, and is then pulled down an additional slight amount A and released. Find its motion. [*Hint.* Assume Newton's second law of motion and Hooke's law, which says that the tension in the spring is proportional to the amount it is stretched. Let x denote the displacement of the body at time t, measured from the equilibrium position. Then $m(d^2x/dt^2) = -kx$, where k, the "spring constant," is the proportionality factor in Hooke's law.]

10. A man suspended from a parachute falls through space under the pull of gravity. If air resistance produces a retarding force proportional to the man's velocity and he starts from rest at time $t = 0$, find the distance he falls in time t.

13-8

LINEAR EQUATIONS WITH CONSTANT COEFFICIENTS

An equation of the form

$$\frac{d^n y}{dx^n} + a_1 \frac{d^{n-1}y}{dx^{n-1}} + a_2 \frac{d^{n-2}y}{dx^{n-2}} + \cdots + a_{n-1}\frac{dy}{dx} + a_n y = F(x), \qquad (1)$$

which is linear in y and its derivatives, is called a *linear* equation of order n. If $F(x)$ is identically zero, the equation is said to be *homogeneous*; otherwise it is called *nonhomogeneous*. The equation is called linear even when the coefficients $a_1, a_2, \ldots, a_n$ are functions of x. However, we shall consider only the case where these coefficients are *constants*.

It is convenient to introduce the symbol D to represent the operation of differentiation with respect to x. That is, we write $Df(x)$ to mean $(d/dx)f(x)$. Furthermore, we define powers of D to mean taking successive derivatives:

$$D^2 f(x) = D\{Df(x)\} = \frac{d^2 f(x)}{dx^2},$$

$$D^3 f(x) = D\{D^2 f(x)\} = \frac{d^3 f(x)}{dx^3},$$

and so on. A polynomial in D is to be interpreted as an operator which, when applied to $f(x)$, produces a linear combination of f and its successive derivatives. For example,

$$(D^2 + D - 2)f(x) = D^2 f(x) + Df(x) - 2f(x)$$

$$= \frac{d^2 f(x)}{dx^2} + \frac{df(x)}{dx} - 2f(x).$$

Such a polynomial in D is called a *linear differential operator* and may be denoted by the single letter L. If L_1 and L_2 are two such linear operators, their sum and product are defined by the equations

$$(L_1 + L_2)f(x) = L_1 f(x) + L_2 f(x),$$

$$L_1 L_2 f(x) = L_1(L_2 f(x)).$$

Linear differential operators that are polynomials in D with constant coefficients satisfy basic algebraic laws that make it possible to treat them like ordinary polynomials so far as addition, multiplication, and factoring are concerned. Thus,

$$(D^2 + D - 2)f(x) = (D + 2)(D - 1)f(x)$$

$$= (D - 1)(D + 2)f(x). \qquad (2)$$

Since Eq. (2) holds for any twice-differentiable function f, we also write the equality between operators:

$$D^2 + D - 2 = (D + 2)(D - 1) = (D - 1)(D + 2). \qquad (3)$$

Suppose, now, we wish to solve a differential equation of order two, say

$$\frac{d^2 y}{dx^2} + 2a\frac{dy}{dx} + by = 0, \qquad (1)$$

13-9

LINEAR, SECOND ORDER, HOMOGENEOUS EQUATIONS WITH CONSTANT COEFFICIENTS

where a and b are constants. In operator notation, this becomes

$$(D^2 + 2aD + b)y = 0. \qquad (1')$$

Associated with this differential equation is the algebraic equation

$$r^2 + 2ar + b = 0, \qquad (1'')$$

which we get by replacing D by r and suppressing y. This is called the *characteristic equation* of the differential equation. Suppose the roots of $(1'')$ are r_1 and r_2. Then

$$r^2 + 2ar + b = (r - r_1)(r - r_2)$$

and

$$D^2 + 2aD + b = (D - r_1)(D - r_2).$$

Hence Eq. $(1')$ is equivalent to

$$(D - r_1)(D - r_2)y = 0. \qquad (2)$$

If we now let

$$(D - r_2)y = u \qquad (3a)$$

and

$$(D - r_1)u = 0, \qquad (3b)$$

we can solve Eq. $(1')$ in two steps. From Eq. (3b), which is separable, we find

$$u = C_1 e^{r_1 x}.$$

We substitute this into (3a), which becomes

$$(D - r_2)y = C_1 e^{r_1 x}$$

or

$$\frac{dy}{dx} - r_2 y = C_1 e^{r_1 x}.$$

This equation is linear. Its integrating factor is

$$\rho = e^{-r_2 x},$$

(see Article 13–5), and its solution is

$$e^{-r_2 x}y = C_1 \int e^{(r_1 - r_2)x}\, dx + C_2. \tag{4}$$

How we proceed at this point depends on whether r_1 and r_2 are equal.

CASE 1.   If $r_1 \neq r_2$, the evaluation of the integral in Eq. (4) leads to

$$e^{-r_2 x}y = \frac{C_1}{r_1 - r_2} e^{(r_1 - r_2)x} + C_2$$

or

$$y = \frac{C_1}{r_1 - r_2} e^{r_1 x} + C_2 e^{r_2 x}.$$

Since C_1 is an arbitrary constant, so is $C_1/(r_1 - r_2)$, and the solution of Eq. (2) can be written simply as

$$y = C_1 e^{r_1 x} + C_2 e^{r_2 x}, \qquad \text{if} \quad r_1 \neq r_2. \tag{5}$$

CASE 2.   If $r_1 = r_2$, then $e^{(r_1 - r_2)x} = e^0 = 1$, and Eq. (4) reduces to

$$e^{-r_2 x}y = C_1 x + C_2$$

or

$$y = (C_1 x + C_2)e^{r_2 x}, \qquad \text{if} \quad r_1 = r_2. \tag{6}$$

EXAMPLE 1. Solve the equation

$$\frac{d^2 y}{dx^2} + \frac{dy}{dx} - 2y = 0.$$

Solution. The characteristic equation,

$$r^2 + r - 2 = (r - 1)(r + 2) = 0,$$

has roots

$$r_1 = 1, \qquad r_2 = -2.$$

Hence, by Eq. (5), the solution of the differential equation is

$$y = C_1 e^x + C_2 e^{-2x}.$$

EXAMPLE 2. Solve the equation

$$\frac{d^2 y}{dx^2} + 4\frac{dy}{dx} + 4y = 0.$$

Solution. The characteristic equation,

$$r^2 + 4r + 4 = (r + 2)^2 = 0,$$

has roots

$$r_1 = r_2 = -2.$$

Hence, by Eq. (6), the solution of the differential equation is

$$y = (C_1 x + C_2)e^{-2x}.$$

Imaginary Roots

If the coefficients a and b in Eq. (1) are real, the roots of the characteristic Eq. (1″) either will be real, or will be a pair of complex conjugate numbers:

$$r_1 = \alpha + i\beta, \qquad r_2 = \alpha - i\beta. \tag{7}$$

If $\beta \neq 0$, Eq. (5) applies, with the result

$$y = c_1 e^{(\alpha + i\beta)x} + c_2 e^{(\alpha - i\beta)x}$$

$$= e^{\alpha x}[c_1 e^{i\beta x} + c_2 e^{-i\beta x}]. \tag{8}$$

By Euler's formula, Eq. (17) of Article 12–9,

$$e^{i\beta x} = \cos \beta x + i \sin \beta x,$$

$$e^{-i\beta x} = \cos \beta x - i \sin \beta x.$$

Hence, Eq. (8) may be replaced by

$$y = e^{\alpha x}[(c_1 + c_2) \cos \beta x + i(c_1 - c_2) \sin \beta x]. \tag{9}$$

Finally, if we introduce new arbitrary constants

$$C_1 = c_1 + c_2, \qquad C_2 = i(c_1 - c_2),$$

Eq. (9) takes the form

$$y = e^{\alpha x}[C_1 \cos \beta x + C_2 \sin \beta x]. \tag{9'}$$

The arbitrary constants C_1 and C_2 in (9′) will be real provided the constants c_1 and c_2 in (9) are complex conjugates:

$$c_1 = \tfrac{1}{2}(C_1 - iC_2), \qquad c_2 = \tfrac{1}{2}(C_1 + iC_2).$$

To solve a problem where the roots of the characteristic equation are complex conjugates, we simply write down the appropriate version of Eq. (9′).

EXAMPLE 3. Solve the equation

$$\frac{d^2y}{dx^2} + 2\frac{dy}{dx} + 2y = 0.$$

Solution. The characteristic equation,

$$r^2 + 2r + 2 = 0,$$

has roots

$$r_1 = -1 + i, \qquad r_2 = -1 - i.$$

Hence, in Eq. (9′), we take

$$\alpha = -1, \qquad \beta = 1,$$

and obtain the solution

$$y = e^{-x}(C_1 \cos x + C_2 \sin x).$$

EXAMPLE 4. Solve the equation

$$\frac{d^2y}{dx^2} + \omega^2 y = 0, \qquad \omega \neq 0.$$

Solution. The characteristic equation,

$$r^2 + \omega^2 = 0,$$

has roots

$$r_1 = i\omega, \qquad r_2 = -i\omega.$$

Hence we take $\alpha = 0$, $\beta = \omega$ in Eq. (9′), and obtain the solution

$$y = C_1 \cos \omega x + C_2 \sin \omega x.$$

PROBLEMS

Solve:

1. $\dfrac{d^2y}{dx^2} + 2\dfrac{dy}{dx} = 0$ 2. $\dfrac{d^2y}{dx^2} + 5\dfrac{dy}{dx} + 6y = 0$ 7. $\dfrac{d^2y}{dx^2} + 6\dfrac{dy}{dx} + 9y = 0$ 8. $\dfrac{d^2y}{dx^2} - 6\dfrac{dy}{dx} + 10y = 0$

3. $\dfrac{d^2y}{dx^2} + 6\dfrac{dy}{dx} + 5y = 0$ 4. $\dfrac{d^2y}{dx^2} - 2\dfrac{dy}{dx} - 3y = 0$ 9. $\dfrac{d^2y}{dx^2} - 2\dfrac{dy}{dx} + 4y = 0$ 10. $\dfrac{d^2y}{dx^2} - 10\dfrac{dy}{dx} + 16y = 0$

5. $\dfrac{d^2y}{dx^2} + \dfrac{dy}{dx} + y = 0$ 6. $\dfrac{d^2y}{dx^2} - 4\dfrac{dy}{dx} + 4y = 0$

13-10

LINEAR, SECOND ORDER, NONHOMOGENEOUS EQUATIONS WITH CONSTANT COEFFICIENTS

In Article 13–9, we learned how to solve the homogeneous equation

$$\frac{d^2y}{dx^2} + 2a\frac{dy}{dx} + by = 0. \tag{1}$$

We can now describe a method for solving the nonhomogeneous equation

$$\frac{d^2y}{dx^2} + 2a\frac{dy}{dx} + by = F(x). \tag{2}$$

To solve Eq. (2), we first obtain the general solution of the related homogeneous Eq. (1) obtained by replacing $F(x)$ by zero. Denote this solution by

$$y_h = C_1 u_1(x) + C_2 u_2(x), \tag{3}$$

where C_1 and C_2 are arbitrary constants and $u_1(x)$, $u_2(x)$ are functions of one or more of the following forms:

$$e^{rx}, \quad xe^{rx}, \quad e^{\alpha x}\cos\beta x, \quad e^{\alpha x}\sin\beta x.$$

Now we might, by inspection or by inspired guesswork, be able to discover *one* particular function $y = y_p(x)$ that satisfies Eq. (2). In this case, we would be able to solve Eq. (2) completely, as

$$y = y_h(x) + y_p(x).$$

EXAMPLE 1.   Solve the equation

$$\frac{d^2y}{dx^2} + 2\frac{dy}{dx} - 3y = 6.$$

Solution. y_h satisfies

$$\frac{d^2y_h}{dx^2} + 2\frac{dy_h}{dx} - 3y_h = 0.$$

The characteristic equation is

$$r^2 + 2r - 3 = 0,$$

and its roots are

$$r_1 = -3, \qquad r_2 = 1.$$

Hence

$$y_h = C_1 e^{-3x} + C_2 e^{x}.$$

Now, to find a particular solution of the original equation, observe that $y = $ constant would do, provided $-3y = 6$. Hence,

$$y_p = -2$$

is one particular solution. The complete solution is

$$y = y_p + y_h = -2 + C_1 e^{-3x} + C_2 e^{x}.$$

Variation of Parameters

Fortunately, there is a general method for finding the solution of the nonhomogeneous Eq. (2) once the general solution of the corresponding homogeneous equation is known. The method is known as the method of *variation of parameters*. It consists in replacing the constants C_1 and C_2 in Eq. (3) by functions $v_1 = v_1(x)$ and $v_2 = v_2(x)$, and requiring (in a way to be explained) that the resulting expression satisfy Eq. (2). There are two functions to be determined, and requiring that Eq. (2) be satisfied is only one condition. As a second condition, we also require that

$$v_1' u_1 + v_2' u_2 = 0. \tag{4}$$

Then we have

$$y = v_1 u_1 + v_2 u_2,$$

$$\frac{dy}{dx} = v_1 u_1' + v_2 u_2',$$

$$\frac{d^2 y}{dx^2} = v_1 u_1'' + v_2 u_2'' + v_1' u_1' + v_2' u_2'.$$

If we substitute these expressions into the left side of Eq. (2), we obtain

$$v_1 \left[\frac{d^2 u_1}{dx^2} + 2a \frac{du_1}{dx} + bu_1 \right] + v_2 \left[\frac{d^2 u_2}{dx^2} + 2a \frac{du_2}{dx} + bu_2 \right] + v_1' u_1' + v_2' u_2' = F(x).$$

The two bracketed terms are zero, since u_1 and u_2 are solutions of the homogeneous Eq. (1). Hence Eq. (2) is satisfied if, in addition to Eq. (4), we require that

$$v_1' u_1' + v_2' u_2' = F(x). \tag{5}$$

Equations (4) and (5) may be solved together as a pair,

$$v_1' u_1 + v_2' u_2 = 0,$$

$$v_1' u_1' + v_2' u_2' = F(x),$$

for the unknown functions v_1' and v_2'. Cramer's rule gives

$$v_1' = \frac{\begin{vmatrix} 0 & u_2 \\ F(x) & u_2' \end{vmatrix}}{\begin{vmatrix} u_1 & u_2 \\ u_1' & u_2' \end{vmatrix}} = \frac{-u_2 F(x)}{D},$$

$$v_2' = \frac{\begin{vmatrix} u_1 & 0 \\ u_1' & F(x) \end{vmatrix}}{\begin{vmatrix} u_1 & u_2 \\ u_1' & u_2' \end{vmatrix}} = \frac{u_1 F(x)}{D}, \tag{6}$$

where

$$D = \begin{vmatrix} u_1 & u_2 \\ u_1' & u_2' \end{vmatrix}.$$

Now v_1 and v_2 can be found by integration.

In applying the method of variation of parameters to solve the equation

$$\frac{d^2 y}{dx^2} + 2a \frac{dy}{dx} + by = F(x), \tag{2}$$

we can work directly with the equations in (6). It is not necessary to rederive them. The steps we go through to solve (2) are:

1. Solve the associated homogeneous equation,

$$\frac{d^2 y}{dx^2} + 2a \frac{dy}{dx} + by = 0,$$

to find the functions u_1 and u_2.

2. Calculate D, v'_1, and v'_2 from (6).
3. Integrate v'_1 and v'_2 to find v_1 and v_2.
4. Write down the general solution of (2) as

$$y = v_1 u_1 + v_2 u_2.$$

EXAMPLE 2. Solve the equation

$$\frac{d^2y}{dx^2} + 2\frac{dy}{dx} - 3y = 6$$

of Example 1 by variation of parameters.

Solution. We first solve the associated homogeneous equation

$$\frac{d^2y}{dx^2} + 2\frac{dy}{dx} - 3y = 0$$

as in Example 1 to find

$$u_1(x) = e^{-3x}, \qquad u_2(x) = e^x.$$

Then, from the equations in (6), we have

$$D = \begin{vmatrix} e^{-3x} & e^x \\ -3e^{-3x} & e^x \end{vmatrix} = e^{-2x} + 3e^{-2x} = 4e^{-2x},$$

$$v'_1 = \frac{-6e^x}{4e^{-2x}} = -\tfrac{3}{2}e^{3x}, \qquad v'_2 = \frac{6e^{-3x}}{4e^{-2x}} = \tfrac{3}{2}e^{-x}. \tag{7}$$

Hence

$$v_1 = \int -\tfrac{3}{2}e^{3x}\,dx = -\tfrac{1}{2}e^{3x} + C_1,$$

$$v_2 = \int \tfrac{3}{2}e^{-x}\,dx = -\tfrac{3}{2}e^{-x} + C_2,$$

and

$$\begin{aligned} y &= v_1 u_1 + v_2 u_2 \\ &= \left(-\tfrac{1}{2}e^{3x} + C_1\right)e^{-3x} + \left(-\tfrac{3}{2}e^{-x} + C_2\right)e^x \\ &= -2 + C_1 e^{-3x} + C_2 e^x. \end{aligned}$$

Undetermined Coefficients

The method of variation of parameters is completely general, for it will produce a particular solution of the nonhomogeneous equation (2) for any continuous function $F(x)$. But the calculations involved can be complicated, and in special cases there may be easier methods to use. For instance, we do not need to use variation of parameters to find a particular solution of

$$\frac{d^2y}{dx^2} - \frac{dy}{dx} + 5y = 3, \tag{8}$$

if we can find the particular solution $y_p = 3/5$ by inspection first. And even for an equation like

$$\frac{d^2y}{dx^2} + 3y = e^x, \tag{9}$$

we might guess that there is a solution of the form

$$y_p = Ae^x,$$

and substitute $y_p = Ae^x$ and its second derivative into Eq. (9) to find A. If we do so, we find that

$$Ae^x + 3Ae^x = e^x,$$

$$4Ae^x = e^x,$$

$$4A = 1,$$

$$A = \tfrac{1}{4}.$$

The function $y_p = \tfrac{1}{4}e^x$ is a solution of Eq. (9).

Again, we might guess that the equation

$$\frac{d^2y}{dx^2} + y = 3x^2 + 4 \tag{10}$$

has a particular solution of the form

$$y_p = Cx^2 + Dx + E.$$

When we substitute this polynomial and its second derivative into Eq. (10) to see whether appropriate values for the constants C, D, and E can be found, Eq. (10) becomes

$$2C + (Cx^2 + Dx + E) = 3x^2 + 4,$$
$$Cx^2 + Dx + 2C + E = 3x^2 + 4. \tag{11}$$

This latter equation will hold for all values of x if its two sides are identical as polynomials in x; that is, if

$$C = 3, \quad D = 0, \quad \text{and} \quad 2C + E = 4, \tag{12}$$

or,

$$C = 3, \quad D = 0, \quad E = -2.$$

We conclude that

$$y_p = 3x^2 + 0x - 2 = 3x^2 - 2 \tag{13}$$

is a solution of Eq. (10).

In each of the foregoing examples, the particular solution we found resembled the function $F(x)$ on the right side of the given differential equation. This was no accident, for we guessed the form of the particular solution by looking at $F(x)$ first. The method of first guessing the form of the solution up to certain undetermined constants, and then determining the values of these constants by using the differential equation, is known as the *method of undetermined coefficients*. It depends for its success upon our ability to recognize the form of a particular solution, and for this reason, among others, it lacks the generality of the method of variation of parameters. Nevertheless, its simplicity makes it the method of choice in a number of special cases.

We shall limit our discussion of the method of undetermined coefficients to selected equations in which the function $F(x)$ in Eq. (2) is the sum of one or more terms like

$$e^{rx}, \quad \cos kx, \quad \sin kx, \quad ax^2 + bx + c.$$

Even so, we will find that the particular solutions of Eq. (2) do not always resemble $F(x)$ as closely as the ones we have seen.

EXAMPLE 3. Find a particular solution of

$$\frac{d^2y}{dx^2} - \frac{dy}{dx} = 2 \sin x. \tag{14}$$

Solution. If we try to find a particular solution of the form

$$y_p = A \sin x,$$

and substitute the derivatives of y_p in the given equation, we find that A must satisfy the equation

$$-A \sin x + A \cos x = 2 \sin x \tag{15}$$

for all values of x. Since this requires A to be equal to -2 and 0 at the same time, we conclude that Eq. (14) has no solution of the form $A \sin x$.

The fact that $\sin x$ appears among the derivatives of $\cos x$ might lead us to try

$$y_p = B \cos x.$$

But when we substitute the derivatives of $B \cos x$ in Eq. (14), we get

$$-B \cos x + B \sin x = 2 \sin x,$$

and we are no farther ahead than before.

It turns out that the required form is the sum

$$y_p = A \sin x + B \cos x. \tag{16}$$

The result of substituting the derivatives of this new candidate into Eq. (14) is

$$-A \sin x - B \cos x - (A \cos x - B \sin x) = 2 \sin x,$$

$$(B - A) \sin x - (A + B) \cos x = 2 \sin x. \tag{17}$$

Equation (17) will be an identity if

$$B - A = 2 \quad \text{and} \quad A + B = 0,$$

or,

$$A = -1, \quad B = 1.$$

Our particular solution is

$$y_p = \cos x - \sin x.$$

EXAMPLE 4. Find a particular solution of

$$\frac{d^2y}{dx^2} - 3\frac{dy}{dx} + 2y = 5e^x. \tag{18}$$

Solution. If we substitute

$$y_p = Ae^x$$

and its derivatives in Eq. (18), we find that

$$Ae^x - 3Ae^x + 2Ae^x = 5e^x,$$
$$0 = 5e^x.$$

The problem can be traced to the fact that $y = e^x$ is already a solution of the related homogeneous equation,

$$\frac{d^2y}{dx^2} - 3\frac{dy}{dx} + 2y = 0. \tag{19}$$

The characteristic equation of Eq. (19) is

$$r^2 - 3r + 2 = (r - 1)(r - 2) = 0,$$

which has $r = 1$ as a simple root. We may therefore expect Ae^x to "vanish" when substituted into the left side of (18).

The appropriate way to modify the trial solution in this case is to replace Ae^x by Axe^x. When we substitute

$$y_p = Axe^x$$

and its derivatives into (18), we obtain

$$(Axe^x + 2Ae^x) - 3(Axe^x + Ae^x) + 2Axe^x = 5e^x$$
$$-Ae^x = 5e^x$$
$$A = -5.$$

The function

$$y_p = -5xe^x.$$

is a particular solution of Eq. (19).

EXAMPLE 5. Find a particular solution of

$$\frac{d^2y}{dx^2} - 6\frac{dy}{dx} + 9y = e^{3x}. \tag{20}$$

Solution. The characteristic equation,

$$r^2 - 6r + 9 = (r - 3)^2 = 0,$$

has $r = 3$ as a *double* root. The appropriate choice for y_p in this case is neither Ae^{3x} nor Axe^{3x}, but Ax^2e^{3x}. When we substitute

$$y_p = Ax^2e^{3x}$$

and its derivatives in the given differential equation, we get

$$(9Ax^2e^{3x} + 12Axe^{3x} + 2Ae^{3x}) - 6(3Ax^2e^{3x} + 2Axe^{3x}) + 9Ax^2e^{3x} = e^{3x}.$$

$$2Ae^{3x} = e^{3x}$$

$$A = \tfrac{1}{2}.$$

The function

$$y_p = \tfrac{1}{2}x^2e^{3x}$$

is a solution of Eq. (20).

When we wish to find a particular solution of Eq. (2), and the function $F(x)$ is the sum of two or more terms, we choose a trial function for each term in $F(x)$, and add them.

EXAMPLE 6. Solve the equation

$$\frac{d^2y}{dx^2} - \frac{dy}{dx} = 5e^x - \sin 2x. \qquad (21)$$

Solution. We first check the characteristic equation, which is

$$r^2 - r = 0.$$

Its roots are

$$r_1 = 1, \qquad r_2 = 0,$$

so the general solution of the related homogeneous equation is

$$y_h = C_1 e^x + C_2.$$

We now seek a particular solution y_p; that is, a function that will produce $5e^x - \sin 2x$ when substituted into the left side of Eq. (21). One part of y_p is to produce $5e^x$, the other $-\sin 2x$.

Since any function of the form $C_1 e^x$ is a solution of the related homogeneous equation, we choose our trial y_p to be the sum

$$y_p = Axe^x + B \cos 2x + C \sin 2x,$$

including xe^x where we might otherwise have included e^x. When the derivatives of y_p are submitted in Eq. (21), the resulting equations are

$$(Axe^x + 2Ae^x - 4B \cos 2x - 4C \sin 2x)$$

$$- (Axe^x + Ae^x - 2B \sin 2x + 2C \cos 2x) = 5e^x - \sin 2x,$$

$$Ae^x - (4B + 2C) \cos 2x + (2B - 4C) \sin 2x = 5e^x - \sin 2x.$$

These equations will hold if

$$A = 5, \quad (4B + 2C) = 0, \quad (2B - 4C) = -1,$$

or,

$$A = 5, \quad B = -\tfrac{1}{10}, \quad C = \tfrac{1}{5}.$$

Our particular solution is

$$y_p = 5xe^x - \tfrac{1}{10}\cos 2x + \tfrac{1}{5}\sin 2x.$$

The complete solution of Eq. (21) is

$$y = y_h + y_p = C_1 e^x + C_2 + 5xe^x - \tfrac{1}{10}\cos 2x + \tfrac{1}{5}\sin 2x.$$

You may find the following table helpful in solving the problems at the end of this article.

Table 13–1. The method of undetermined coefficients for selected equations of the form

$$\frac{d^2y}{dx^2} + 2a\frac{dy}{dx} + by = F(x)$$

If $F(x)$ has a term that is a constant multiple of ...	And if	Then include this expression in the trial function for y_p.
e^{rx}	r is not a root of the characteristic equation	Ae^{rx}
	r is a single root of the characteristic equation	Axe^{rx}
	r is a double root of the characteristic equation	Ax^2e^{rx}
$\sin kx,\ \cos kx$	ki is not a root of the characteristic equation	$B\cos kx + C\sin kx$
$ax^2 + bx + c$	0 is not a root of the characteristic equation	$Dx^2 + Ex + F$ (chosen to match the degree of $ax^2 + bx + c$)
	0 is a single root of the characteristic equation	$Dx^3 + Ex^2 + Fx$ (degree one higher than the degree of $ax^2 + bx + c$)
	0 is a double root of the characteristic equation	$Dx^4 + Ex^3 + Fx^2$ (degree two higher than the degree of $ax^2 + bx + c$)

PROBLEMS

Solve the equations in Problems 1 through 12 by variation of parameters.

1. $\dfrac{d^2y}{dx^2} + \dfrac{dy}{dx} = x$

2. $\dfrac{d^2y}{dx^2} + y = \tan x, \quad -\dfrac{\pi}{2} < x < \dfrac{\pi}{2}$

3. $\dfrac{d^2y}{dx^2} + y = \sin x$

4. $\dfrac{d^2y}{dx^2} + 2\dfrac{dy}{dx} + y = e^x$

5. $\dfrac{d^2y}{dx^2} + 2\dfrac{dy}{dx} + y = e^{-x}$

6. $\dfrac{d^2y}{dx^2} - y = x$

7. $\dfrac{d^2y}{dx^2} - y = e^x$

8. $\dfrac{d^2y}{dx^2} - y = \sin x$

9. $\dfrac{d^2y}{dx^2} + 4\dfrac{dy}{dx} + 5y = 10$

10. $\dfrac{d^2y}{dx^2} - \dfrac{dy}{dx} = 2^x$

11. $\dfrac{d^2y}{dx^2} + y = \sec x, \quad -\dfrac{\pi}{2} < x < \dfrac{\pi}{2}$

12. $\dfrac{d^2y}{dx^2} - \dfrac{dy}{dx} = e^x \cos x, \quad x > 0$

Solve the equations in Problems 13 through 28 by the method of undetermined coefficients.

13. $\dfrac{d^2y}{dx^2} - 3\dfrac{dy}{dx} - 10y = -3$

14. $\dfrac{d^2y}{dx^2} - 3\dfrac{dy}{dx} - 10y = 2x - 3$

15. $\dfrac{d^2y}{dx^2} - \dfrac{dy}{dx} = \sin x$ **16.** $\dfrac{d^2y}{dx^2} + 2\dfrac{dy}{dx} + y = x^2$

17. $\dfrac{d^2y}{dx^2} + y = \cos 3x$ **18.** $\dfrac{d^2y}{dx^2} + y = e^{2x}$

19. $\dfrac{d^2y}{dx^2} - \dfrac{dy}{dx} - 2y = 20 \cos x$

20. $\dfrac{d^2y}{dx^2} + y = 2x + 3e^x$

21. $\dfrac{d^2y}{dx^2} - y = e^x + x^2$

22. $\dfrac{d^2y}{dx^2} + 2\dfrac{dy}{dx} + y = 6 \sin 2x$

23. $\dfrac{d^2y}{dx^2} - \dfrac{dy}{dx} - 6y = e^{-x} - 7 \cos x$

24. $\dfrac{d^2y}{dx^2} + 3\dfrac{dy}{dx} + 2y = e^{-x} + e^{-2x} - x$

25. $\dfrac{d^2y}{dx^2} + 5\dfrac{dy}{dx} = 15x^2$ **26.** $\dfrac{d^2y}{dx^2} - \dfrac{dy}{dx} = -8x + 3$

27. $\dfrac{d^2y}{dx^2} - 3\dfrac{dy}{dx} = e^{3x} - 12x$

28. $\dfrac{d^2y}{dx^2} + 7\dfrac{dy}{dx} = 42x^2 + 5x + 1$

In each of Problems 29 through 31, the given differential equation has a particular solution y_p of the form given. Determine the coefficients in y_p. Then solve the differential equation.

29. $\dfrac{d^2y}{dx^2} - 5\dfrac{dy}{dx} = xe^{5x}; \quad y_p = Ax^2e^{5x} + Bxe^{5x}$

30. $\dfrac{d^2y}{dx^2} - \dfrac{dy}{dx} = \cos x + \sin x; \quad y_p = A \cos x + B \sin x$

31. $\dfrac{d^2y}{dx^2} + y = 2 \cos x + \sin x; \quad y_p = Ax \cos x + Bx \sin x$

In Problems 32 through 35, solve the given differential equations (a) by variation of parameters; and (b) by the method of undetermined coefficients.

32. $\dfrac{d^2y}{dx^2} - 4\dfrac{dy}{dx} + 4y = 2e^{2x}$

33. $\dfrac{d^2y}{dx^2} - \dfrac{dy}{dx} = e^x + e^{-x}$

34. $\dfrac{d^2y}{dx^2} - 9\dfrac{dy}{dx} = 9e^{9x}$

35. $\dfrac{d^2y}{dx^2} - 4\dfrac{dy}{dx} - 5y = e^x + 4$

Solve the differential equations in Problems 36 through 45. Some of the equations can be solved by the method of undetermined coefficients, but others cannot.

36. $\dfrac{d^2y}{dx^2} + y = \csc x, \quad 0 < x < \pi$

37. $\dfrac{d^2y}{dx^2} + y = \cot x, \quad 0 < x < \pi$

38. $\dfrac{d^2y}{dx^2} + 4y = \sin x$ **39.** $\dfrac{d^2y}{dx^2} - 8\dfrac{dy}{dx} = e^{8x}$

40. $\dfrac{d^2y}{dx^2} + 4\dfrac{dy}{dx} + 5y = x + 2$ **41.** $\dfrac{d^2y}{dx^2} - \dfrac{dy}{dx} = x^3$

42. $\dfrac{d^2y}{dx^2} + 9y = 9x - \cos x$ **43.** $\dfrac{d^2y}{dx^2} + 2\dfrac{dy}{dx} = x^2 - e^x$

44. $\dfrac{d^2y}{dx^2} - 3\dfrac{dy}{dx} + 2y = e^x - e^{2x}$

45. $\dfrac{d^2y}{dx^2} + y = \sec x \tan x, \quad -\dfrac{\pi}{2} < x < \dfrac{\pi}{2}$

The method of undetermined coefficients can sometimes be used to solve first order ordinary differential equations. Use the method to solve the equations in Problems 46 through 49.

46. $\dfrac{dy}{dx} + 4y = x$ **47.** $\dfrac{dy}{dx} - 3y = e^x$

48. $\dfrac{dy}{dx} + y = \sin x$ **49.** $\dfrac{dy}{dx} - 3y = 5e^{3x}$

Solve the differential equations in Problems 50 and 51 subject to the given initial conditions.

50. $\dfrac{d^2y}{dx^2} + y = e^{2x}; \quad y(0) = 0, y'(0) = \frac{2}{5}$

51. $\dfrac{d^2y}{dx^2} + y = \sec^2 x, \quad -\dfrac{\pi}{2} < x < \dfrac{\pi}{2}; \quad y(0) = y'(0) = 1$

52. *Bernouilli's equation of order* 2. Solve the equation

$$\frac{dy}{dx} + y = (xy)^2$$

by carrying out the following steps: (1) divide both sides of the equation by y^2; (2) make the change of variable $u = y^{-1}$; (3) solve the resulting equation for u in terms of x; (4) let $y = u^{-1}$.

53. Solve the integral equation

$$y(x) + \int_0^x y(t)\, dt = x.$$

[*Hint.* Differentiate.]

VIBRATIONS

A spring of natural length L has its upper end fastened to a rigid support at A (Fig. 13–4). A weight W, of mass m, is suspended from the spring. The weight stretches the spring to a length $L + s$ when the system is allowed to come to rest in a new equilibrium position. By Hooke's law, the tension in the spring is ks, where k is the so-called spring constant. The force of gravity pulling down on the weight is $W = mg$. Equilibrium requires

$$ks = mg. \tag{1}$$

Suppose now that the weight is pulled down an additional amount a beyond the equilibrium position, and released. We shall discuss its motion.

Let x, positive direction downward, denote the displacement of the weight away from equilibrium at any time t after the motion has started. Then the forces acting upon the weight are

$$+mg, \text{ due to gravity,}$$

$$-k(s + x), \text{ due to the spring tension.}$$

The resultant of these forces is, by Newton's second law, also equal to

$$m\frac{d^2x}{dt^2}.$$

Therefore

$$m\frac{d^2x}{dt^2} = mg - ks - kx. \tag{2}$$

By Eq. (1), $mg - ks = 0$, so that (2) becomes

$$m\frac{d^2x}{dt^2} + kx = 0. \tag{3}$$

13–4 A spring stretched beyond its natural length by a weight.

In addition to the differential equation (3), the motion satisfies the initial conditions:

$$\text{At } t = 0: \quad x = a \quad \text{and} \quad \frac{dx}{dt} = 0. \tag{4}$$

Let $\omega = \sqrt{k/m}$. Then Eq. (3) becomes

$$\frac{d^2x}{dt^2} + \omega^2 x = 0$$

or

$$(D^2 + \omega^2)x = 0,$$

where

$$D = \frac{d}{dt}.$$

The roots of the characteristic equation

$$r^2 + \omega^2 = 0$$

are complex conjugates

$$r = \pm \omega i.$$

Hence

$$x = c_1 \cos \omega t + c_2 \sin \omega t \qquad (5)$$

is the general solution of the differential equation. To fit the initial conditions, we also compute

$$\frac{dx}{dt} = -c_1 \omega \sin \omega t + c_2 \omega \cos \omega t,$$

and then substitute from (4). This yields

$$a = c_1, \qquad 0 = c_2 \omega.$$

Therefore

$$c_1 = a, \qquad c_2 = 0,$$

and

$$x = a \cos \omega t \qquad (6)$$

describes the motion of the weight. Equation (6) represents simple harmonic motion of amplitude a and period $T = 2\pi/\omega$.

The two terms on the right side of Eq. (5) can be combined into a single term by using the trigonometric identity

$$\sin (\omega t + \phi) = \cos \omega t \sin \phi + \sin \omega t \cos \phi.$$

To apply the identity, we take

$$c_1 = C \sin \phi, \qquad c_2 = C \cos \phi, \qquad (7a)$$

where

$$C = \sqrt{c_1^2 + c_2^2}, \qquad \phi = \tan^{-1} \frac{c_1}{c_2}, \qquad (7b)$$

as in Fig. 13–5. Then Eq. (5) can be written in the alternative form

$$x = C \sin (\omega t + \phi). \qquad (8)$$

Here C and ϕ may be taken as two new arbitrary constants, replacing the two constants c_1 and c_2 of Eq. (5). Equation (8) represents simple harmonic motion of amplitude C and period $T = 2\pi/\omega$. The angle $\omega t + \phi$ is called the

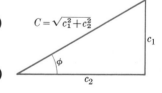

13–5 $c_1 = C \sin \phi$ and $c_2 = C \cos \phi$.

phase angle, and ϕ may be interpreted as the initial value of the phase angle. A graph of Eq. (8) is given in Fig. 13–6.

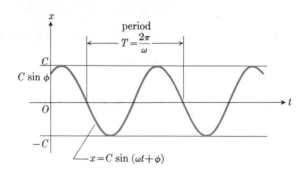

13–6   Undamped vibration.

Equation (3) assumes that there is no friction in the system. Next, consider the case where the motion of the weight is retarded by a friction force $c(dx/dt)$ proportional to the velocity, where c is a positive constant. Then the differential equation is

$$m\frac{d^2x}{dt^2} = -kx - c\frac{dx}{dt},$$

or

$$\frac{d^2x}{dt^2} + 2b\frac{dx}{dt} + \omega^2x = 0, \tag{9}$$

where

$$2b = \frac{c}{m} \quad \text{and} \quad \omega = \sqrt{\frac{k}{m}}.$$

If we introduce the operator $D = d/dt$, Eq. (9) becomes

$$(D^2 + 2bD + \omega^2)x = 0.$$

The characteristic equation is

$$r^2 + 2br + \omega^2 = 0$$

with roots

$$r = -b \pm \sqrt{b^2 - \omega^2}. \tag{10}$$

Three cases now present themselves, depending upon the relative sizes of b and ω.

CASE 1.   If $b = \omega$, the two roots in Eq. (10) are equal, and the solution of (9) is

$$x = (c_1 + c_2t)e^{-\omega t}. \tag{11}$$

As time goes on, x approaches zero. The motion is not oscillatory.

CASE 2.   If $b > \omega$, then the roots (10) are both real but unequal, and

$$x = c_1 e^{r_1 t} + c_2 e^{r_2 t}, \qquad (12)$$

where

$$r_1 = -b + \sqrt{b^2 - \omega^2} \quad \text{and} \quad r_2 = -b - \sqrt{b^2 - \omega^2}.$$

Here again the motion is not oscillatory. Both r_1 and r_2 are negative, and x approaches zero as time goes on.

CASE 3.   If $b < \omega$, let

$$\omega^2 - b^2 = \alpha^2.$$

Then

$$r_1 = -b + \alpha i, \qquad r_2 = -b - \alpha i$$

and

$$x = e^{-bt}[c_1 \cos \alpha t + c_2 \sin \alpha t]. \qquad (13a)$$

If we introduce the substitutions (7), we may also write Eq. (13a) in the equivalent form

$$x = C e^{-bt} \sin (\alpha t + \phi). \qquad (13b)$$

This equation represents damped vibratory motion. It is analogous to simple harmonic motion, of period $T = 2\pi/\alpha$, except that the amplitude is not constant but is given by $C e^{-bt}$. Since this tends to zero as t increases, the vibrations tend to die out as time goes on. Observe, however, that Eq. (13b) reduces to Eq. (8) in the absence of friction. The effect of friction is twofold:

1. $b = c/(2m)$ appears as a coefficient in the exponential *damping factor* e^{-bt}. The larger b is, the more quickly do the vibrations tend to become unnoticeable.

2. The period $T = 2\pi/\alpha = 2\pi/\sqrt{\omega^2 - b^2}$ is greater than the period $T_0 = 2\pi/\omega$ in the friction-free system.

Curves representing solutions of Eq. (9) in typical cases are shown in Figs. 13–6 and 13–7. The size of b, relative to ω, determines the kind of solution, and b also determines the rate of damping. It is therefore customary to say that there is

a) critical damping if $b = \omega$;   **c)** undercritical damping if $0 < b < \omega$;
b) overcritical damping if $b > \omega$;   **d)** no damping if $b = 0$.

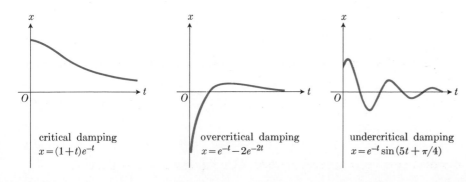

critical damping
$x = (1+t)e^{-t}$

overcritical damping
$x = e^{-t} - 2e^{-2t}$

undercritical damping
$x = e^{-t} \sin(5t + \pi/4)$

13–7   Three kinds of damping of vibration.

PROBLEMS

1. Suppose the motion of the weight in Fig. 18–4 is described by the differential equation (3). Find the motion if $x = x_0$ and $dx/dt = v_0$ at $t = 0$. Express the answer in two equivalent forms [Eqs. (5) and (8)].

2. A 5-lb weight is suspended from the lower end of a spring whose upper end is attached to a rigid support. The weight extends the spring by 2 in. If, after the weight has come to rest in its new equilibrium position, it is struck a sharp blow that starts it downward with a velocity of 4 ft/sec, find its subsequent motion, assuming there is no friction.

3. A simple electrical circuit shown in Fig. 13–8 contains a capacitor of capacitance C farads, a coil of inductance L henrys, a resistance of R ohms, and a generator which produces an electromotive force E volts, in series. If the current intensity at time t at some point of the circuit is I amperes, the differential equation describing the current I is

$$L\frac{d^2I}{dt^2} + R\frac{dI}{dt} + \frac{1}{C}I = \frac{dE}{dt}.$$

Find I as a function of t if

a) $R = 0$, $1/(LC) = \omega^2$, $E = $ constant,
b) $R = 0$, $1/(LC) = \omega^2$, $E = A \sin \alpha t$; $\alpha = $ constant $\neq \omega$,
c) $R = 0$, $1/(LC) = \omega^2$, $E = A \sin \omega t$,
d) $R = 50$, $L = 5$, $C = 9 \times 10^{-6}$, $E = $ constant.

13–8 A simple electrical circuit.

4. A simple pendulum of length l makes an angle θ with the vertical. As it swings back and forth, its motion, neglect-ing friction, is described by the differential equation

$$\frac{d^2\theta}{dt^2} = -\frac{g}{l}\sin\theta,$$

where g (the acceleration due to gravity, $g \approx 32$ ft/sec^2) is a constant. Solve the differential equation of motion, under the assumption that θ is so small that $\sin\theta$ may be replaced by θ without appreciable error. Assume that $\theta = \theta_0$ and $d\theta/dt = 0$ when $t = 0$.

5. A circular disk of mass m and radius r is suspended by a thin wire attached to the center of one of its flat faces. If the disk is twisted through an angle θ, torsion in the wire tends to turn the disk back in the opposite direction. The differential equation for the motion is

$$\tfrac{1}{2}mr^2\frac{d^2\theta}{dt^2} = -k\theta,$$

where k is the coefficient of torsion of the wire. Find the motion if $\theta = \theta_0$ and $d\theta/dt = v_0$ at $t = 0$.

6. A cylindrical spar buoy, diameter 1 foot, weight 100 lb, floats, partially submerged, in an upright position. When it is depressed slightly from its equilibrium position and released, it bobs up and down according to the differential equation

$$\frac{100}{g}\frac{d^2x}{dt^2} = -16\pi x - c\frac{dx}{dt}.$$

Here $c\,(dx/dt)$ is the frictional resistance of the water. Find c if the period of oscillation is observed to be 1.6 sec. (Take $g = 32$ ft/sec^2.)

7. Suppose the upper end of the spring in Fig. 13–4 is attached, not to a rigid support at A, but to a member which itself undergoes up and down motion given by a function of the time t, say $y = f(t)$. If the positive direction of y is downward, the differential equation of motion is

$$m\frac{d^2x}{dt^2} + kx = kf(t).$$

Let $x = x_0$ and $dx/dt = 0$ when $t = 0$, and solve for x:

a) if $f(t) = A \sin \alpha t$ and $\alpha \neq \sqrt{k/m}$,
b) if $f(t) = A \sin \alpha t$ and $\alpha = \sqrt{k/m}$.

REVIEW QUESTIONS AND EXERCISES

1. Review methods for solving ordinary first-order and first-degree differential equations

a) when the variables are separable,

b) when the equation is homogeneous,

c) when the equation is linear in one variable,

d) when the equation is exact.

Illustrate each with an example.

2. Review methods of solving second-order equations

a) with dependent variable missing,

b) with independent variable missing.

Illustrate each with an example.

3. Review methods for solving linear differential equations with constant coefficients

a) in the homogeneous case,

b) in the nonhomogeneous case.

Illustrate each with an example.

4. If an external force F acts on a system whose mass varies with time, Newton's law of motion is

$$\frac{d(mv)}{dt} = F + (v + u)\frac{dm}{dt}.$$

In this equation, m is the mass of the system at time t, v is its velocity, and $v + u$ is the velocity of the mass that is entering (or leaving) the system at the rate dm/dt. Suppose that a rocket of initial mass m_0 starts from rest, but is driven upward by firing some of its mass directly backward at the constant rate of $dm/dt = -b$ units per second and at constant speed relative to the rocket $u = -c$. The only external force acting on the rocket is $F = -mg$, due to gravity. Under these assumptions, show that the height of the rocket above the ground at the end of t seconds (t small compared to m_0/b) is

$$y = c\left(t + \frac{m_0 - bt}{b}\ln\frac{m_0 - bt}{m_0}\right) - \tfrac{1}{2}gt^2.$$

MISCELLANEOUS PROBLEMS

Solve the differential equations in Problems 1 through 30.

1. $y\ln y\,dx + (1 + x^2)\,dy = 0$

2. $\dfrac{dy}{dx} = \dfrac{y^2 - y - 2}{x^2 + x}$

3. $e^{x+2y}\,dy - e^{y-2x}\,dx = 0$

4. $\sqrt{1 + (dy/dx)^2} = ky$

5. $y\,dy = \sqrt{1 + y^4}\,dx$

6. $(2x + y)\,dx + (x - 2y)\,dy = 0$

7. $\dfrac{dy}{dx} = \dfrac{x^2 + y^2}{2xy}$

8. $x\dfrac{dy}{dx} = y + \sqrt{x^2 + y^2}$

9. $x\,dy = \left(y + x\cos^2\dfrac{y}{x}\right)dx$

10. $x(\ln y - \ln x)\,dy = y(1 + \ln y - \ln x)\,dx$

11. $x\,dy + (2y - x^2 - 1)\,dx = 0$

12. $\cos y\,dx + (x\sin y - \cos^2 y)\,dy = 0$

13. $\cosh x\,dy - (y + \cosh x)\sinh x\,dx = 0$

14. $(x + 1)\,dy + (2y - x)\,dx = 0$

15. $(1 + y^2)\,dx + (2xy + y^2 + 1)\,dy = 0$

16. $(x^2 + y)\,dx + (e^y + x)\,dy = 0$

17. $(x^2 + y^2)\,dx + (2xy + \cosh y)\,dy = 0$

18. $(e^x + \ln y)\,dx + \dfrac{x + y}{y}\,dy = 0$

19. $x(1 + e^y)\,dx + \tfrac{1}{2}(x^2 + y^2)e^y\,dy = 0$

20. $\left(\sin x + \tan^{-1}\dfrac{y}{x}\right)dx - (y - \ln\sqrt{x^2 + y^2})\,dy = 0$

21. $\dfrac{d^2y}{dx^2} - 2y\dfrac{dy}{dx} = 0$

22. $\dfrac{d^2x}{dy^2} + 4x = 0$

23. $\dfrac{d^2y}{dx^2} = 1 + \left(\dfrac{dy}{dx}\right)^2$

24. $\dfrac{d^2x}{dy^2} = 1 - \left(\dfrac{dx}{dy}\right)^2$

25. $x^2\dfrac{d^2y}{dx^2} + x\dfrac{dy}{dx} = 1$

26. $\dfrac{d^2y}{dx^2} - 4\dfrac{dy}{dx} + 3y = 0$

27. $\dfrac{d^3y}{dx^3} - 2\dfrac{d^2y}{dx^2} + \dfrac{dy}{dx} = 0$

28. $\dfrac{d^2y}{dx^2} + 4y = \sec 2x$

29. $\dfrac{d^2y}{dx^2} - \dfrac{dy}{dx} - 2y = e^{2x}$

30. $\dfrac{d^2y}{dx^2} - 2\dfrac{dy}{dx} + 5y = e^{-x}$

31. Find the *general solution* of the differential equation $4x^2y'' + 4xy' - y = 0$, given that there is a particular solution of the form $y = x^c$ for some constant c.

32. Show that the only plane curves that have constant curvature are circles and straight lines. (Assume that the appropriate derivatives exist and are continuous.)

33. Find the orthogonal trajectories of the family of curves $x^2 = Cy^3$. [*Caution.* The differential equation should not contain the arbitrary constant C.]

34. Find the orthogonal trajectories of the family of circles $(x - C)^2 + y^2 = C^2$.

35. Find the orthogonal trajectories of the family of parabolas $y^2 = 4C(C - x)$.

36. The equation $d^2y/dt^2 + 100y = 0$ represents a simple harmonic motion. Find the general solution of the equation and determine the constants of integration if $y = 10$, $dy/dt = 50$, when $t = 0$. Find the period and the amplitude of the motion.

In Problems 37 through 41, (a) find the general solution, and (b) find the solution that satisfies the given initial conditions.

37. a) $\dfrac{d^2y}{dx^2} + 16y = 0$

b) When $x = 0$: $y = 0$, $dy/dx = 5$.

38. a) $\dfrac{d^2y}{dx^2} - 16y = 0$

b) When $x = 0$: $y = 0$, $dy/dx = 5$.

39. a) $\dfrac{d^2x}{dt^2} - 2\dfrac{dx}{dt} - 3x = 0$

b) When $t = 0$: $x = 2$, $dx/dt = -2$.

40. a) $\dfrac{d^2y}{dt^2} + 2\dfrac{dy}{dt} + 5y = 0$

b) When $t = 0$: $y = 3$, $dy/dt = 5$.

41. a) $\dfrac{d^2y}{dx^2} - 4y = e^x$

b) When $x = 0$: $y = 0$, $dy/dx = 3$.

APPENDIX

FORMULAS FROM ELEMENTARY MATHEMATICS

ALGEBRA

1. Laws of Exponents

$$a^m a^n = a^{m+n}, \quad (ab)^m = a^m b^m, \quad (a^m)^n = a^{mn}, \quad a^{m/n} = \sqrt[n]{a^m}.$$

If $a \neq 0$,

$$\frac{a^m}{a^n} = a^{m-n}, \quad a^0 = 1, \quad a^{-m} = \frac{1}{a^m}.$$

2. Zero

$$a \cdot 0 = 0 \cdot a = 0 \text{ for any finite number } a.$$

If $a \neq 0$,

$$\frac{0}{a} = 0, \quad 0^a = 0, \quad a^0 = 1.$$

Division by zero is not defined.

3. Fractions

$$\frac{a}{b} + \frac{c}{d} = \frac{ad + bc}{bd}, \quad \frac{a}{b} \cdot \frac{c}{d} = \frac{ac}{bd}, \quad \frac{a/b}{c/d} = \frac{a}{b} \cdot \frac{d}{c}, \quad \frac{-a}{b} = -\frac{a}{b} = \frac{a}{-b}.$$

$$\frac{(a/b) + (c/d)}{(e/f) + (g/h)} = \frac{(a/b) + (c/d)}{(e/f) + (g/h)} \cdot \frac{bdfh}{bdfh} = \frac{(ad + bc)fh}{(eh + fg)bd}.$$

4. Binomial Theorem, for n = positive integer

$$(a + b)^n = a^n + na^{n-1}b + \frac{n(n-1)}{1 \cdot 2} a^{n-2}b^2$$

$$+ \frac{n(n-1)(n-2)}{1 \cdot 2 \cdot 3} a^{n-3}b^3 + \cdots + nab^{n-1} + b^n.$$

5. Proportionality Factor

If y is proportional to x, or y varies directly as x, then $y = kx$ for some constant k, called the *proportionality factor*. If $y = k/x$, we say that y is *inversely proportional* to x, or that y *varies inversely* as x.

6. Remainder Theorem and Factor Theorem

If the polynomial $f(x)$ is divided by $x - r$ until a remainder R independent of x is obtained, then $R = f(r)$. In particular, $x - r$ is a *factor* of $f(x)$ if and only if r is a *root* of the equation $f(x) = 0$.

7. Quadratic Formula

If $a \neq 0$, the roots of the equation $ax^2 + bx + c = 0$ are given by the formula

$$x = \frac{-b \pm \sqrt{b^2 - 4ac}}{2a}.$$

(A = area, B = area of base, C = circumference, S = lateral area or surface area, V = volume.)

B

GEOMETRY

1. Triangle

$$A = \tfrac{1}{2}bh.$$

2. Similar Triangles

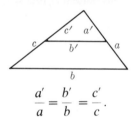

$$\frac{a'}{a} = \frac{b'}{b} = \frac{c'}{c}.$$

3. Theorem of Pythagoras

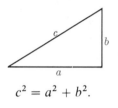

$$c^2 = a^2 + b^2.$$

4. Parallelogram

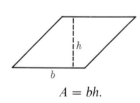

$$A = bh.$$

5. Trapezoid

$$A = \tfrac{1}{2}(a + b)h.$$

6. Circle

$$A = \pi r^2, \qquad C = 2\pi r.$$

7. Any Cylinder or Prism with Parallel Bases

$$V = Bh.$$

8. Right Circular Cylinder

$$V = \pi r^2 h, \qquad S = 2\pi rh.$$

9. Any Cone or Pyramid

$$V = \tfrac{1}{3}Bh.$$

10. Right Circular Cone

$$V = \tfrac{1}{3}\pi r^2 h, \qquad S = \pi rs.$$

11. Sphere

$$V = \tfrac{4}{3}\pi r^3, \qquad A = 4\pi r^2.$$

TRIGONOMETRY

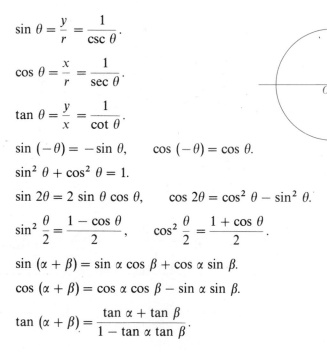

1. Definitions and Fundamental Identities

$$\sin \theta = \frac{y}{r} = \frac{1}{\csc \theta}.$$

$$\cos \theta = \frac{x}{r} = \frac{1}{\sec \theta}.$$

$$\tan \theta = \frac{y}{x} = \frac{1}{\cot \theta}.$$

$$\sin (-\theta) = -\sin \theta, \qquad \cos (-\theta) = \cos \theta.$$

$$\sin^2 \theta + \cos^2 \theta = 1.$$

$$\sin 2\theta = 2 \sin \theta \cos \theta, \qquad \cos 2\theta = \cos^2 \theta - \sin^2 \theta.$$

$$\sin^2 \frac{\theta}{2} = \frac{1 - \cos \theta}{2}, \qquad \cos^2 \frac{\theta}{2} = \frac{1 + \cos \theta}{2}.$$

$$\sin (\alpha + \beta) = \sin \alpha \cos \beta + \cos \alpha \sin \beta.$$

$$\cos (\alpha + \beta) = \cos \alpha \cos \beta - \sin \alpha \sin \beta.$$

$$\tan (\alpha + \beta) = \frac{\tan \alpha + \tan \beta}{1 - \tan \alpha \tan \beta}.$$

2. Angles and Sides of a Triangle

Law of cosines: $a^2 = b^2 + c^2 - 2bc \cos A.$

Law of sines: $\dfrac{\sin A}{a} = \dfrac{\sin B}{b} = \dfrac{\sin C}{c}.$

Area $= \tfrac{1}{2}bc \sin A = \tfrac{1}{2}ac \sin B = \tfrac{1}{2}ab \sin C.$

APPENDIX

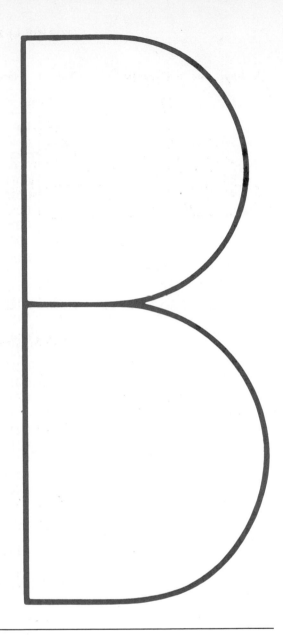

TABLES

Table 1. Natural trigonometric functions

Angle		Sine	Co-sine	Tan-gent	Angle		Sine	Co-sine	Tan-gent
De-gree	Ra-dian				De-gree	Ra-dian			
0°	0.000	0.000	1.000	0.000					
1°	0.017	0.017	1.000	0.017	46°	0.803	0.719	0.695	1.036
2°	0.035	0.035	0.999	0.035	47°	0.820	0.731	0.682	1.072
3°	0.052	0.052	0.999	0.052	48°	0.838	0.743	0.669	1.111
4°	0.070	0.070	0.998	0.070	49°	0.855	0.755	0.656	1.150
5°	0.087	0.087	0.996	0.087	50°	0.873	0.766	0.643	1.192
6°	0.105	0.105	0.995	0.105	51°	0.890	0.777	0.629	1.235
7°	0.122	0.122	0.993	0.123	52°	0.908	0.788	0.616	1.280
8°	0.140	0.139	0.990	0.141	53°	0.925	0.799	0.602	1.327
9°	0.157	0.156	0.988	0.158	54°	0.942	0.809	0.588	1.376
10°	0.175	0.174	0.985	0.176	55°	0.960	0.819	0.574	1.428
11°	0.192	0.191	0.982	0.194	56°	0.977	0.829	0.559	1.483
12°	0.209	0.208	0.978	0.213	57°	0.995	0.839	0.545	1.540
13°	0.227	0.225	0.974	0.231	58°	1.012	0.848	0.530	1.600
14°	0.244	0.242	0.970	0.249	59°	1.030	0.857	0.515	1.664
15°	0.262	0.259	0.966	0.268	60°	1.047	0.866	0.500	1.732
16°	0.279	0.276	0.961	0.287	61°	1.065	0.875	0.485	1.804
17°	0.297	0.292	0.956	0.306	62°	1.082	0.883	0.469	1.881
18°	0.314	0.309	0.951	0.325	63°	1.100	0.891	0.454	1.963
19°	0.332	0.326	0.946	0.344	64°	1.117	0.899	0.438	2.050
20°	0.349	0.342	0.940	0.364	65°	1.134	0.906	0.423	2.145
21°	0.367	0.358	0.934	0.384	66°	1.152	0.914	0.407	2.246
22°	0.384	0.375	0.927	0.404	67°	1.169	0.921	0.391	2.356
23°	0.401	0.391	0.921	0.424	68°	1.187	0.927	0.375	2.475
24°	0.419	0.407	0.914	0.445	69°	1.204	0.934	0.358	2.605
25°	0.436	0.423	0.906	0.466	70°	1.222	0.940	0.342	2.748
26°	0.454	0.438	0.899	0.488	71°	1.239	0.946	0.326	2.904
27°	0.471	0.454	0.891	0.510	72°	1.257	0.951	0.309	3.078
28°	0.489	0.469	0.883	0.532	73°	1.274	0.956	0.292	3.271
29°	0.506	0.485	0.875	0.554	74°	1.292	0.961	0.276	3.487
30°	0.524	0.500	0.866	0.577	75°	1.309	0.966	0.259	3.732
31°	0.541	0.515	0.857	0.601	76°	1.326	0.970	0.242	4.011
32°	0.559	0.530	0.848	0.625	77°	1.344	0.974	0.225	4.332
33°	0.576	0.545	0.839	0.649	78°	1.361	0.978	0.208	4.705
34°	0.593	0.559	0.829	0.675	79°	1.379	0.982	0.191	5.145
35°	0.611	0.574	0.819	0.700	80°	1.396	0.985	0.174	5.671
36°	0.628	0.588	0.809	0.727	81°	1.414	0.988	0.156	6.314
37°	0.646	0.602	0.799	0.754	82°	1.431	0.990	0.139	7.115
38°	0.663	0.616	0.788	0.781	83°	1.449	0.993	0.122	8.144
39°	0.681	0.629	0.777	0.810	84°	1.466	0.995	0.105	9.514
40°	0.698	0.643	0.766	0.839	85°	1.484	0.996	0.087	11.43
41°	0.716	0.656	0.755	0.869	86°	1.501	0.998	0.070	14.30
42°	0.733	0.669	0.743	0.900	87°	1.518	0.999	0.052	19.08
43°	0.750	0.682	0.731	0.933	88°	1.536	0.999	0.035	28.64
44°	0.768	0.695	0.719	0.966	89°	1.553	1.000	0.017	57.29
45°	0.785	0.707	0.707	1.000	90°	1.571	1.000	0.000	

Table 2. Exponential functions

x	e^x	e^{-x}	x	e^x	e^{-x}
0.00	1.0000	1.0000	2.5	12.182	0.0821
0.05	1.0513	0.9512	2.6	13.464	0.0743
0.10	1.1052	0.9048	2.7	14.880	0.0672
0.15	1.1618	0.8607	2.8	16.445	0.0608
0.20	1.2214	0.8187	2.9	18.174	0.0550
0.25	1.2840	0.7788	3.0	20.086	0.0498
0.30	1.3499	0.7408	3.1	22.198	0.0450
0.35	1.4191	0.7047	3.2	24.533	0.0408
0.40	1.4918	0.6703	3.3	27.113	0.0369
0.45	1.5683	0.6376	3.4	29.964	0.0334
0.50	1.6487	0.6065	3.5	33.115	0.0302
0.55	1.7333	0.5769	3.6	36.598	0.0273
0.60	1.8221	0.5488	3.7	40.447	0.0247
0.65	1.9155	0.5220	3.8	44.701	0.0224
0.70	2.0138	0.4966	3.9	49.402	0.0202
0.75	2.1170	0.4724	4.0	54.598	0.0183
0.80	2.2255	0.4493	4.1	60.340	0.0166
0.85	2.3396	0.4274	4.2	66.686	0.0150
0.90	2.4596	0.4066	4.3	73.700	0.0136
0.95	2.5857	0.3867	4.4	81.451	0.0123
1.0	2.7183	0.3679	4.5	90.017	0.0111
1.1	3.0042	0.3329	4.6	99.484	0.0101
1.2	3.3201	0.3012	4.7	109.95	0.0091
1.3	3.6693	0.2725	4.8	121.51	0.0082
1.4	4.0552	0.2466	4.9	134.29	0.0074
1.5	4.4817	0.2231	5	148.41	0.0067
1.6	4.9530	0.2019	6	403.43	0.0025
1.7	5.4739	0.1827	7	1096.6	0.0009
1.8	6.0496	0.1653	8	2981.0	0.0003
1.9	6.6859	0.1496	9	8103.1	0.0001
2.0	7.3891	0.1353	10	22026	0.00005
2.1	8.1662	0.1225			
2.2	9.0250	0.1108			
2.3	9.9742	0.1003			
2.4	11.023	0.0907			

Table 3. Natural logarithms of numbers

n	$\log_e n$	n	$\log_e n$	n	$\log_e n$
0.0	*	4.5	1.5041	9.0	2.1972
0.1	7.6974	4.6	1.5261	9.1	2.2083
0.2	8.3906	4.7	1.5476	9.2	2.2192
0.3	8.7960	4.8	1.5686	9.3	2.2300
0.4	9.0837	4.9	1.5892	9.4	2.2407
0.5	9.3069	5.0	1.6094	9.5	2.2513
0.6	9.4892	5.1	1.6292	9.6	2.2618
0.7	9.6433	5.2	1.6487	9.7	2.2721
0.8	9.7769	5.3	1.6677	9.8	2.2824
0.9	9.8946	5.4	1.6864	9.9	2.2925
1.0	0.0000	5.5	1.7047	10	2.3026
1.1	0.0953	5.6	1.7228	11	2.3979
1.2	0.1823	5.7	1.7405	12	2.4849
1.3	0.2624	5.8	1.7579	13	2.5649
1.4	0.3365	5.9	1.7750	14	2.6391
1.5	0.4055	6.0	1.7918	15	2.7081
1.6	0.4700	6.1	1.8083	16	2.7726
1.7	0.5306	6.2	1.8245	17	2.8332
1.8	0.5878	6.3	1.8405	18	2.8904
1.9	0.6419	6.4	1.8563	19	2.9444
2.0	0.6931	6.5	1.8718	20	2.9957
2.1	0.7419	6.6	1.8871	25	3.2189
2.2	0.7885	6.7	1.9021	30	3.4012
2.3	0.8329	6.8	1.9169	35	3.5553
2.4	0.8755	6.9	1.9315	40	3.6889
2.5	0.9163	7.0	1.9459	45	3.8067
2.6	0.9555	7.1	1.9601	50	3.9120
2.7	0.9933	7.2	1.9741	55	4.0073
2.8	1.0296	7.3	1.9879	60	4.0943
2.9	1.0647	7.4	2.0015	65	4.1744
3.0	1.0986	7.5	2.0149	70	4.2485
3.1	1.1314	7.6	2.0281	75	4.3175
3.2	1.1632	7.7	2.0412	80	4.3820
3.3	1.1939	7.8	2.0541	85	4.4427
3.4	1.2238	7.9	2.0669	90	4.4998
3.5	1.2528	8.0	2.0794	95	4.5539
3.6	1.2809	8.1	2.0919	100	4.6052
3.7	1.3083	8.2	2.1041		
3.8	1.3350	8.3	2.1163		
3.9	1.3610	8.4	2.1282		
4.0	1.3863	8.5	2.1401		
4.1	1.4110	8.6	2.1518		
4.2	1.4351	8.7	2.1633		
4.3	1.4586	8.8	2.1748		
4.4	1.4816	8.9	2.1861		

* Subtract 10 from $\log_e n$ entries for $n < 1.0$.

Table 4. A brief table of integrals

1. $\displaystyle\int u\,dv = uv - \int v\,du$

2. $\displaystyle\int a^u\,du = \frac{a^u}{\ln a} + C, \qquad a \neq 1, \qquad a > 0$

3. $\displaystyle\int \cos u\,du = \sin u + C$

4. $\displaystyle\int \sin u\,du = -\cos u + C$

5. $\displaystyle\int (ax+b)^n\,dx = \frac{(ax+b)^{n+1}}{a(n+1)} + C, \qquad n \neq -1$

6. $\displaystyle\int (ax+b)^{-1}\,dx = \frac{1}{a}\ln|ax+b| + C$

7. $\displaystyle\int x(ax+b)^n\,dx = \frac{(ax+b)^{n+1}}{a^2}\left[\frac{ax+b}{n+2} - \frac{b}{n+1}\right] + C, \qquad n \neq -1, -2$

8. $\displaystyle\int x(ax+b)^{-1}\,dx = \frac{x}{a} - \frac{b}{a^2}\ln|ax+b| + C$

9. $\displaystyle\int x(ax+b)^{-2}\,dx = \frac{1}{a^2}\left[\ln|ax+b| + \frac{b}{ax+b}\right] + C$

10. $\displaystyle\int \frac{dx}{x(ax+b)} = \frac{1}{b}\ln\left|\frac{x}{ax+b}\right| + C$

11. $\displaystyle\int (\sqrt{ax+b})^n\,dx = \frac{2}{a}\frac{(\sqrt{ax+b})^{n+2}}{n+2} + C, \qquad n \neq -2$

12. $\displaystyle\int \frac{\sqrt{ax+b}}{x}\,dx = 2\sqrt{ax+b} + b\int \frac{dx}{x\sqrt{ax+b}}$

13. (a) $\displaystyle\int \frac{dx}{x\sqrt{ax+b}} = \frac{2}{\sqrt{-b}}\tan^{-1}\sqrt{\frac{ax+b}{-b}} + C, \qquad \text{if} \quad b < 0$

   (b) $\displaystyle\int \frac{dx}{x\sqrt{ax+b}} = \frac{1}{\sqrt{b}}\ln\left|\frac{\sqrt{ax+b} - \sqrt{b}}{\sqrt{ax+b} + \sqrt{b}}\right| + C, \qquad \text{if} \quad b > 0$

14. $\displaystyle\int \frac{\sqrt{ax+b}}{x^2}\,dx = -\frac{\sqrt{ax+b}}{x} + \frac{a}{2}\int \frac{dx}{x\sqrt{ax+b}} + C$

15. $\displaystyle\int \frac{dx}{x^2\sqrt{ax+b}} = -\frac{\sqrt{ax+b}}{bx} - \frac{a}{2b}\int \frac{dx}{x\sqrt{ax+b}} + C$

16. $\displaystyle\int \frac{dx}{a^2+x^2} = \frac{1}{a}\tan^{-1}\frac{x}{a} + C$

17. $\displaystyle\int \frac{dx}{(a^2+x^2)^2} = \frac{x}{2a^2(a^2+x^2)} + \frac{1}{2a^3}\tan^{-1}\frac{x}{a} + C$

18. $\displaystyle\int \frac{dx}{a^2-x^2} = \frac{1}{2a}\ln\left|\frac{x+a}{x-a}\right| + C$

19. $\displaystyle\int \frac{dx}{(a^2-x^2)^2} = \frac{x}{2a^2(a^2-x^2)} + \frac{1}{2a^2}\int \frac{dx}{a^2-x^2}$

20. $\displaystyle\int \frac{dx}{\sqrt{a^2+x^2}} = \sinh^{-1}\frac{x}{a} + C = \ln|x+\sqrt{a^2+x^2}| + C$

21. $\displaystyle\int \sqrt{a^2 + x^2}\, dx = \frac{x}{2}\sqrt{a^2 + x^2} + \frac{a^2}{2}\sinh^{-1}\frac{x}{a} + C$

22. $\displaystyle\int x^2\sqrt{a^2 + x^2}\, dx = \frac{x(a^2 + 2x^2)\sqrt{a^2 + x^2}}{8} - \frac{a^4}{8}\sinh^{-1}\frac{x}{a} + C$

23. $\displaystyle\int \frac{\sqrt{a^2 + x^2}}{x}\, dx = \sqrt{a^2 + x^2} - a\sinh^{-1}\left|\frac{a}{x}\right| + C$

24. $\displaystyle\int \frac{\sqrt{a^2 + x^2}}{x^2}\, dx = \sinh^{-1}\frac{x}{a} - \frac{\sqrt{a^2 + x^2}}{x} + C$

25. $\displaystyle\int \frac{x^2}{\sqrt{a^2 + x^2}}\, dx = -\frac{a^2}{2}\sinh^{-1}\frac{x}{a} + \frac{x\sqrt{a^2 + x^2}}{2} + C$

26. $\displaystyle\int \frac{dx}{x\sqrt{a^2 + x^2}} = -\frac{1}{a}\ln\left|\frac{a + \sqrt{a^2 + x^2}}{x}\right| + C$

27. $\displaystyle\int \frac{dx}{x^2\sqrt{a^2 + x^2}} = -\frac{\sqrt{a^2 + x^2}}{a^2 x} + C$ 28. $\displaystyle\int \frac{dx}{\sqrt{a^2 - x^2}} = \sin^{-1}\frac{x}{a} + C$

29. $\displaystyle\int \sqrt{a^2 - x^2}\, dx = \frac{x}{2}\sqrt{a^2 - x^2} + \frac{a^2}{2}\sin^{-1}\frac{x}{a} + C$

30. $\displaystyle\int x^2\sqrt{a^2 - x^2}\, dx = \frac{a^4}{8}\sin^{-1}\frac{x}{a} - \frac{1}{8}x\sqrt{a^2 - x^2}\,(a^2 - 2x^2) + C$

31. $\displaystyle\int \frac{\sqrt{a^2 - x^2}}{x}\, dx = \sqrt{a^2 - x^2} - a\ln\left|\frac{a + \sqrt{a^2 - x^2}}{x}\right| + C$

32. $\displaystyle\int \frac{\sqrt{a^2 - x^2}}{x^2}\, dx = -\sin^{-1}\frac{x}{a} - \frac{\sqrt{a^2 - x^2}}{x} + C$

33. $\displaystyle\int \frac{x^2}{\sqrt{a^2 - x^2}}\, dx = \frac{a^2}{2}\sin^{-1}\frac{x}{a} - \frac{1}{2}x\sqrt{a^2 - x^2} + C$

34. $\displaystyle\int \frac{dx}{x\sqrt{a^2 - x^2}} = -\frac{1}{a}\ln\left|\frac{a + \sqrt{a^2 - x^2}}{x}\right| + C$ 35. $\displaystyle\int \frac{dx}{x^2\sqrt{a^2 - x^2}} = -\frac{\sqrt{a^2 - x^2}}{a^2 x} + C$

36. $\displaystyle\int \frac{dx}{\sqrt{x^2 - a^2}} = \cosh^{-1}\frac{x}{a} + C = \ln\left|x + \sqrt{x^2 - a^2}\right| + C$

37. $\displaystyle\int \sqrt{x^2 - a^2}\, dx = \frac{x}{2}\sqrt{x^2 - a^2} - \frac{a^2}{2}\cosh^{-1}\frac{x}{a} + C$

38. $\displaystyle\int \left(\sqrt{x^2 - a^2}\right)^n dx = \frac{x\left(\sqrt{x^2 - a^2}\right)^n}{n + 1} - \frac{na^2}{n + 1}\int \left(\sqrt{x^2 - a^2}\right)^{n-2} dx, \quad n \neq -1$

39. $\displaystyle\int \frac{dx}{\left(\sqrt{x^2 - a^2}\right)^n} = \frac{x\left(\sqrt{x^2 - a^2}\right)^{2-n}}{(2 - n)a^2} - \frac{n - 3}{(n - 2)a^2}\int \frac{dx}{\left(\sqrt{x^2 - a^2}\right)^{n-2}}, \quad n \neq 2$

40. $\displaystyle\int x\left(\sqrt{x^2 - a^2}\right)^n dx = \frac{\left(\sqrt{x^2 - a^2}\right)^{n+2}}{n + 2} + C, \quad n \neq -2$

41. $\displaystyle\int x^2\sqrt{x^2 - a^2}\, dx = \frac{x}{8}(2x^2 - a^2)\sqrt{x^2 - a^2} - \frac{a^4}{8}\cosh^{-1}\frac{x}{a} + C$

42. $\displaystyle\int \frac{\sqrt{x^2 - a^2}}{x}\, dx = \sqrt{x^2 - a^2} - a\sec^{-1}\left|\frac{x}{a}\right| + C$

43. $\displaystyle\int \frac{\sqrt{x^2 - a^2}}{x^2}\, dx = \cosh^{-1}\frac{x}{a} - \frac{\sqrt{x^2 - a^2}}{x} + C$

44. $\int \dfrac{x^2}{\sqrt{x^2 - a^2}}\, dx = \dfrac{a^2}{2} \cosh^{-1} \dfrac{x}{a} + \dfrac{x}{2}\sqrt{x^2 - a^2} + C$

45. $\int \dfrac{dx}{x\sqrt{x^2 - a^2}} = \dfrac{1}{a}\sec^{-1}\left|\dfrac{x}{a}\right| + C = \dfrac{1}{a}\cos^{-1}\left|\dfrac{a}{x}\right| + C$

46. $\int \dfrac{dx}{x^2\sqrt{x^2 - a^2}} = \dfrac{\sqrt{x^2 - a^2}}{a^2 x} + C$ 47. $\int \dfrac{dx}{\sqrt{2ax - x^2}} = \sin^{-1}\left(\dfrac{x - a}{a}\right) + C$

48. $\int \sqrt{2ax - x^2}\, dx = \dfrac{x - a}{2}\sqrt{2ax - x^2} + \dfrac{a^2}{2}\sin^{-1}\left(\dfrac{x - a}{a}\right) + C$

49. $\int (\sqrt{2ax - x^2})^n\, dx = \dfrac{(x - a)(\sqrt{2ax - x^2})^n}{n + 1} + \dfrac{na^2}{n + 1}\int (\sqrt{2ax - x^2})^{n-2}\, dx,$

50. $\int \dfrac{dx}{(\sqrt{2ax - x^2})^n} = \dfrac{(x - a)(\sqrt{2ax - x^2})^{2-n}}{(n - 2)a^2} + \dfrac{(n - 3)}{(n - 2)a^2}\int \dfrac{dx}{(\sqrt{2ax - x^2})^{n-2}}$

51. $\int x\sqrt{2ax - x^2}\, dx = \dfrac{(x + a)(2x - 3a)\sqrt{2ax - x^2}}{6} + \dfrac{a^3}{2}\sin^{-1}\dfrac{x - a}{a} + C$

52. $\int \dfrac{\sqrt{2ax - x^2}}{x}\, dx = \sqrt{2ax - x^2} + a\sin^{-1}\dfrac{x - a}{a} + C$

53. $\int \dfrac{\sqrt{2ax - x^2}}{x^2}\, dx = -2\sqrt{\dfrac{2a - x}{x}} - \sin^{-1}\left(\dfrac{x - a}{a}\right) + C$

54. $\int \dfrac{x\, dx}{\sqrt{2ax - x^2}} = a\sin^{-1}\dfrac{x - a}{a} - \sqrt{2ax - x^2} + C$

55. $\int \dfrac{dx}{x\sqrt{2ax - x^2}} = -\dfrac{1}{a}\sqrt{\dfrac{2a - x}{x}} + C$

56. $\int \sin ax\, dx = -\dfrac{1}{a}\cos ax + C$ 57. $\int \cos ax\, dx = \dfrac{1}{a}\sin ax + C$

58. $\int \sin^2 ax\, dx = \dfrac{x}{2} - \dfrac{\sin 2ax}{4a} + C$ 59. $\int \cos^2 ax\, dx = \dfrac{x}{2} + \dfrac{\sin 2ax}{4a} + C$

60. $\int \sin^n ax\, dx = \dfrac{-\sin^{n-1} ax \cos ax}{na} + \dfrac{n - 1}{n}\int \sin^{n-2} ax\, dx$

61. $\int \cos^n ax\, dx = \dfrac{\cos^{n-1} ax \sin ax}{na} + \dfrac{n - 1}{n}\int \cos^{n-2} ax\, dx$

62. (a) $\int \sin ax \cos bx\, dx = -\dfrac{\cos(a + b)x}{2(a + b)} - \dfrac{\cos(a - b)x}{2(a - b)} + C,\qquad a^2 \neq b^2$

   (b) $\int \sin ax \sin bx\, dx = \dfrac{\sin(a - b)x}{2(a - b)} - \dfrac{\sin(a + b)x}{2(a + b)},\qquad a^2 \neq b^2$

   (c) $\int \cos ax \cos bx\, dx = \dfrac{\sin(a - b)x}{2(a - b)} + \dfrac{\sin(a + b)x}{2(a + b)},\qquad a^2 \neq b^2$

63. $\int \sin ax \cos ax\, dx = -\dfrac{\cos 2ax}{4a} + C$

64. $\int \sin^n ax \cos ax\, dx = \dfrac{\sin^{n+1} ax}{(n + 1)a} + C,\qquad n \neq -1$

65. $\displaystyle\int \frac{\cos ax}{\sin ax}\, dx = \frac{1}{a}\ln|\sin ax| + C$

66. $\displaystyle\int \cos^n ax \sin ax\, dx = -\frac{\cos^{n+1} ax}{(n+1)a} + C, \qquad n \ne -1$

67. $\displaystyle\int \frac{\sin ax}{\cos ax}\, dx = -\frac{1}{a}\ln|\cos ax| + C$

68. $\displaystyle\int \sin^n ax \cos^m ax\, dx = -\frac{\sin^{n-1} ax \cos^{m+1} ax}{a(m+n)} + \frac{n-1}{m+n}\int \sin^{n-2} ax \cos^m ax\, dx,$
$$n \ne -m \qquad \text{(If } n = -m\text{, use No. 86.)}$$

69. $\displaystyle\int \sin^n ax \cos^m ax\, dx = \frac{\sin^{n+1} ax \cos^{m-1} ax}{a(m+n)} + \frac{m-1}{m+n}\int \sin^n ax \cos^{m-2} ax\, dx,$
$$m \ne -n \qquad \text{(If } m = -n\text{, use No. 87.)}$$

70. $\displaystyle\int \frac{dx}{b + c\sin ax} = \frac{-2}{a\sqrt{b^2 - c^2}}\tan^{-1}\left[\sqrt{\frac{b-c}{b+c}}\tan\left(\frac{\pi}{4} - \frac{ax}{2}\right)\right] + C, \qquad b^2 > c^2$

71. $\displaystyle\int \frac{dx}{b + c\sin ax} = \frac{-1}{a\sqrt{c^2 - b^2}}\ln\left|\frac{c + b\sin ax + \sqrt{c^2 - b^2}\cos ax}{b + c\sin ax}\right| + C, \qquad b^2 < c^2$

72. $\displaystyle\int \frac{dx}{1 + \sin ax} = -\frac{1}{a}\tan\left(\frac{\pi}{4} - \frac{ax}{2}\right) + C$

73. $\displaystyle\int \frac{dx}{1 - \sin ax} = \frac{1}{a}\tan\left(\frac{\pi}{4} + \frac{ax}{2}\right) + C$

74. $\displaystyle\int \frac{dx}{b + c\cos ax} = \frac{2}{a\sqrt{b^2 - c^2}}\tan^{-1}\left[\sqrt{\frac{b-c}{b+c}}\tan\frac{ax}{2}\right] + C, \qquad b^2 > c^2$

75. $\displaystyle\int \frac{dx}{b + c\cos ax} = \frac{1}{a\sqrt{c^2 - b^2}}\ln\left|\frac{c + b\cos ax + \sqrt{c^2 - b^2}\sin ax}{b + c\cos ax}\right| + C, \qquad b^2 < c^2$

76. $\displaystyle\int \frac{dx}{1 + \cos ax} = \frac{1}{a}\tan\frac{ax}{2} + C$

77. $\displaystyle\int \frac{dx}{1 - \cos ax} = -\frac{1}{a}\cot\frac{ax}{2} + C$

78. $\displaystyle\int x\sin ax\, dx = \frac{1}{a^2}\sin ax - \frac{x}{a}\cos ax + C$

79. $\displaystyle\int x\cos ax\, dx = \frac{1}{a^2}\cos ax + \frac{x}{a}\sin ax + C$

80. $\displaystyle\int x^n \sin ax\, dx = -\frac{x^n}{a}\cos ax + \frac{n}{a}\int x^{n-1}\cos ax\, dx$

81. $\displaystyle\int x^n \cos ax\, dx = \frac{x^n}{a}\sin ax - \frac{n}{a}\int x^{n-1}\sin ax\, dx$

82. $\displaystyle\int \tan ax\, dx = -\frac{1}{a}\ln|\cos ax| + C$

83. $\displaystyle\int \cot ax\, dx = \frac{1}{a}\ln|\sin ax| + C$

84. $\displaystyle\int \tan^2 ax\, dx = \frac{1}{a}\tan ax - x + C$

85. $\displaystyle\int \cot^2 ax\, dx = -\frac{1}{a}\cot ax - x + C$

86. $\displaystyle\int \tan^n ax\, dx = \frac{\tan^{n-1} ax}{a(n-1)} - \int \tan^{n-2} ax\, dx, \qquad n \ne 1$

87. $\displaystyle\int \cot^n ax\, dx = -\frac{\cot^{n-1} ax}{a(n-1)} - \int \cot^{n-2} ax\, dx, \qquad n \ne 1$

88. $\displaystyle\int \sec ax\, dx = \frac{1}{a}\ln|\sec ax + \tan ax| + C$

89. $\displaystyle\int \csc ax\, dx = -\frac{1}{a}\ln|\csc ax + \cot ax| + C$

90. $\displaystyle\int \sec^2 ax\, dx = \frac{1}{a}\tan ax + C$

91. $\displaystyle\int \csc^2 ax\, dx = -\frac{1}{a}\cot ax + C$

92. $\displaystyle\int \sec^n ax\, dx = \frac{\sec^{n-2} ax\tan ax}{a(n-1)} + \frac{n-2}{n-1}\int \sec^{n-2} ax\, dx, \qquad n \neq 1$

93. $\displaystyle\int \csc^n ax\, dx = -\frac{\csc^{n-2} ax\cot ax}{a(n-1)} + \frac{n-2}{n-1}\int \csc^{n-2} ax\, dx, \qquad n \neq 1$

94. $\displaystyle\int \sec^n ax\tan ax\, dx = \frac{\sec^n ax}{na} + C, \qquad n \neq 0$

95. $\displaystyle\int \csc^n ax\cot ax\, dx = -\frac{\csc^n ax}{na} + C, \qquad n \neq 0$

96. $\displaystyle\int \sin^{-1} ax\, dx = x\sin^{-1} ax + \frac{1}{a}\sqrt{1 - a^2 x^2} + C$

97. $\displaystyle\int \cos^{-1} ax\, dx = x\cos^{-1} ax - \frac{1}{a}\sqrt{1 - a^2 x^2} + C$

98. $\displaystyle\int \tan^{-1} ax\, dx = x\tan^{-1} ax - \frac{1}{2a}\ln(1 + a^2 x^2) + C$

99. $\displaystyle\int x^n \sin^{-1} ax\, dx = \frac{x^{n+1}}{n+1}\sin^{-1} ax - \frac{a}{n+1}\int \frac{x^{n+1}\, dx}{\sqrt{1 - a^2 x^2}}, \qquad n \neq -1$

100. $\displaystyle\int x^n \cos^{-1} ax\, dx = \frac{x^{n+1}}{n+1}\cos^{-1} ax + \frac{a}{n+1}\int \frac{x^{n+1}\, dx}{\sqrt{1 - a^2 x^2}}, \qquad n \neq -1$

101. $\displaystyle\int x^n \tan^{-1} ax\, dx = \frac{x^{n+1}}{n+1}\tan^{-1} ax - \frac{a}{n+1}\int \frac{x^{n+1}\, dx}{1 + a^2 x^2}, \qquad n \neq -1$

102. $\displaystyle\int e^{ax}\, dx = \frac{1}{a}e^{ax} + C$

103. $\displaystyle\int b^{ax}\, dx = \frac{1}{a}\frac{b^{ax}}{\ln b} + C, \qquad b > 0, \ b \neq 1$

104. $\displaystyle\int xe^{ax}\, dx = \frac{e^{ax}}{a^2}(ax - 1) + C$

105. $\displaystyle\int x^n e^{ax}\, dx = \frac{1}{a}x^n e^{ax} - \frac{n}{a}\int x^{n-1} e^{ax}\, dx$

106. $\displaystyle\int x^n b^{ax}\, dx = \frac{x^n b^{ax}}{a\ln b} - \frac{n}{a\ln b}\int x^{n-1} b^{ax}\, dx, \qquad b > 0, \ b \neq 1$

107. $\displaystyle\int e^{ax}\sin bx\, dx = \frac{e^{ax}}{a^2 + b^2}(a\sin bx - b\cos bx) + C$

108. $\displaystyle\int e^{ax}\cos bx\, dx = \frac{e^{ax}}{a^2 + b^2}(a\cos bx + b\sin bx) + C$

109. $\displaystyle\int \ln ax\, dx = x\ln ax - x + C$

110. $\displaystyle\int x^n \ln ax\, dx = \frac{x^{n+1}}{n+1}\ln ax - \frac{x^{n+1}}{(n+1)^2} + C, \qquad n \neq -1$

111. $\displaystyle\int x^{-1}\ln ax\, dx = \frac{1}{2}(\ln ax)^2 + C$

112. $\displaystyle\int \frac{dx}{x\ln ax} = \ln|\ln ax| + C$

113. $\displaystyle\int \sinh ax\, dx = \frac{1}{a}\cosh ax + C$

114. $\displaystyle\int \cosh ax\, dx = \frac{1}{a}\sinh ax + C$

115. $\displaystyle\int \sinh^2 ax\, dx = \frac{\sinh 2ax}{4a} - \frac{x}{2} + C$

116. $\displaystyle\int \cosh^2 ax\, dx = \frac{\sinh 2ax}{4a} + \frac{x}{2} + C$

117. $\displaystyle\int \sinh^n ax\, dx = \frac{\sinh^{n-1} ax\cosh ax}{na} - \frac{n-1}{n}\int \sinh^{n-2} ax\, dx, \qquad n \neq 0$

118. $\displaystyle\int \cosh^n ax\, dx = \frac{\cosh^{n-1} ax \sinh ax}{na} + \frac{n-1}{n} \int \cosh^{n-2} ax\, dx, \qquad n \neq 0$

119. $\displaystyle\int x \sinh ax\, dx = \frac{x}{a} \cosh ax - \frac{1}{a^2} \sinh ax + C$

120. $\displaystyle\int x \cosh ax\, dx = \frac{x}{a} \sinh ax - \frac{1}{a^2} \cosh ax + C$

121. $\displaystyle\int x^n \sinh ax\, dx = \frac{x^n}{a} \cosh ax - \frac{n}{a} \int x^{n-1} \cosh ax\, dx$

122. $\displaystyle\int x^n \cosh ax\, dx = \frac{x^n}{a} \sinh ax - \frac{n}{a} \int x^{n-1} \sinh ax\, dx$

123. $\displaystyle\int \tanh ax\, dx = \frac{1}{a} \ln(\cosh ax) + C$
    124. $\displaystyle\int \coth ax\, dx = \frac{1}{a} \ln|\sinh ax| + C$

125. $\displaystyle\int \tanh^2 ax\, dx = x - \frac{1}{a} \tanh ax + C$
    126. $\displaystyle\int \coth^2 ax\, dx = x - \frac{1}{a} \coth ax + C$

127. $\displaystyle\int \tanh^n ax\, dx = -\frac{\tanh^{n-1} ax}{(n-1)a} + \int \tanh^{n-2} ax\, dx, \qquad n \neq 1$

128. $\displaystyle\int \coth^n ax\, dx = -\frac{\coth^{n-1} ax}{(n-1)a} + \int \coth^{n-2} ax\, dx, \qquad n \neq 1$

129. $\displaystyle\int \operatorname{sech} ax\, dx = \frac{1}{a} \sin^{-1}(\tanh ax) + C$

130. $\displaystyle\int \operatorname{csch} ax\, dx = \frac{1}{a} \ln\left|\tanh \frac{ax}{2}\right| + C$
    131. $\displaystyle\int \operatorname{sech}^2 ax\, dx = \frac{1}{a} \tanh ax + C$

132. $\displaystyle\int \operatorname{csch}^2 ax\, dx = -\frac{1}{a} \coth ax + C$

133. $\displaystyle\int \operatorname{sech}^n ax\, dx = \frac{\operatorname{sech}^{n-2} ax \tanh ax}{(n-1)a} + \frac{n-2}{n-1} \int \operatorname{sech}^{n-2} ax\, dx, \qquad n \neq 1$

134. $\displaystyle\int \operatorname{csch}^n ax\, dx = -\frac{\operatorname{csch}^{n-2} ax \coth ax}{(n-1)a} - \frac{n-2}{n-1} \int \operatorname{csch}^{n-2} ax\, dx, \qquad n \neq 1$

135. $\displaystyle\int \operatorname{sech}^n ax \tanh ax\, dx = -\frac{\operatorname{sech}^n ax}{na} + C, \qquad n \neq 0$

136. $\displaystyle\int \operatorname{csch}^n ax \coth ax\, dx = -\frac{\operatorname{csch}^n ax}{na} + C, \qquad n \neq 0$

137. $\displaystyle\int e^{ax} \sinh bx\, dx = \frac{e^{ax}}{2}\left[\frac{e^{bx}}{a+b} - \frac{e^{-bx}}{a-b}\right] + C, \qquad a^2 \neq b^2$

138. $\displaystyle\int e^{ax} \cosh bx\, dx = \frac{e^{ax}}{2}\left[\frac{e^{bx}}{a+b} + \frac{e^{-bx}}{a-b}\right] + C, \qquad a^2 \neq b^2$

139. $\displaystyle\int_0^\infty x^{n-1} e^{-x}\, dx = \Gamma(n) = (n-1)!, \qquad n > 0.$

140. $\displaystyle\int_0^\infty e^{-ax^2}\, dx = \frac{1}{2}\sqrt{\frac{\pi}{a}}, \qquad a > 0$

141. $\displaystyle\int_0^{\pi/2} \sin^n x\, dx = \int_0^{\pi/2} \cos^n x\, dx = \begin{cases} \dfrac{1 \cdot 3 \cdot 5 \cdots (n-1)}{2 \cdot 4 \cdot 6 \cdots n} \cdot \dfrac{\pi}{2}, & \text{if } n \text{ is an even integer} \geq 2, \\[2ex] \dfrac{2 \cdot 4 \cdot 6 \cdots (n-1)}{3 \cdot 5 \cdot 7 \cdots n}, & \text{if } n \text{ is an odd integer} \geq 3 \end{cases}$

ANSWERS

CHAPTER 1

Article 1–2, pp. 4–5

1 to 13. If P is the point (x, y), then the other points are: $Q(x, -y)$, $R(-x, y)$, $S(-x, -y)$, $T(y, x)$. **14.** $45°$
15. Missing vertices: $(-1, 4)$, $(-1, -2)$, $(5, 2)$. See figure. **16. a)** $(-3, 0)$ **b)** $(-3, 3)$ **17.** $b = 2$

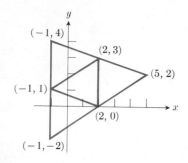

Article 1–3, p. 7

1. $(1, 1)$; 2; 1; $\sqrt{5}$ **2.** $(-1, 2)$; -2; -3; $\sqrt{13}$ **3.** $(-1, 2)$; 2; -4; $2\sqrt{5}$ **4.** $(-3, -2)$; -2; 4; $2\sqrt{5}$ **5.** $(-8, 1)$; -5; 0; 5
6. $(0, 4)$; 0; -6; 6 **7.** $x^2 + y^2 = 25$ **8.** $x^2 + y^2 - 10x = 0$ **9.** $x^2 + y^2 + 6x - 8y = 0$ **10.** $(x - h)^2 + (y - k)^2 = 25$
11. $B(3, -3)$ **12.** $(-2, -9)$ **13.** $A(u - h, v - k)$ **14.** $B(0, 11)$
15. $B(x, y) = B(x, x^2)$; $\Delta y = x^2 - 1 = (x - 1)(x + 1)$; $\Delta x = x - 1$; $\Delta y/\Delta x = x + 1$ if $x \neq 1$ (or $\Delta x \neq 0$)

Article 1–4, p. 10

1. 3; $-\frac{1}{3}$ **2.** $-\frac{1}{3}$; 3 **3.** -1; 1 **4.** 0; ∞ (vertical) **5.** 0; ∞ (vertical) **6.** ∞ (vertical); 0 **7.** 2; $-\frac{1}{2}$ **8.** $\frac{2}{3}$; $-\frac{3}{2}$
9. y/x; $-(x/y)$ **10.** 0; ∞ (vertical) **11.** ∞ (vertical); 0 **12.** $-(b/a)$; a/b **13.** Rectangle **14.** Rectangle **15.** No **16.** No
17. a) $-1/0.35 \approx -2.9$ **b)** $(9 - 68)/(4 - 0.4) \approx -16.4$ **c)** $(4 - 9)/(4.7 - 4) \approx -7.1$
18. Fiber glass is the best insulator (slope has greatest absolute value); gypsum wallboard is the poorest insulator (slope has least absolute value). **19.** $(1, 2)$ **20.** If $P(x, y)$ lies on L, then $(y - 0)/(x - 0) = -\frac{1}{2}$ or $y = -(x/2)$. **21.** Yes **22.** No
23. No **24.** $[(x_1 + x_2)/2, (y_1 + y_2)/2]$

Article 1–5, pp. 14–15

1. $2y = 3x$ **2.** $y = 1$ **3.** $x = 1$ **4.** $3x + 4y + 2 = 0$ **5.** $x = -2$ **6.** $x + y = 4$ **7.** $x/a + y/b = 1$ **8.** $y = 0$ **9.** $x = 0$
10. $x + y = 1$ **11.** Slope: 3; x-intercept: $(-\frac{5}{3}, 0)$; y-intercept: $(0, 5)$ **12.** $\frac{3}{2}$; $(-\frac{5}{3}, 0)$; $(0, \frac{5}{2})$ **13.** -1; $(2, 0)$; $(0, 2)$
14. 2; $(2, 0)$; $(0, -4)$ **15.** $\frac{1}{2}$; $(4, 0)$; $(0, -2)$ **16.** $-\frac{3}{4}$; $(4, 0)$; $(0, 3)$ **17.** $\frac{4}{3}$; $(3, 0)$; $(0, -4)$ **18.** $\frac{1}{2}$; $(-5, 0)$; $(0, \frac{5}{2})$
19. a) $x/20 + p/(10/3) = 1$ **b)** $\frac{10}{3}$ dollars/pound; 20 pounds/person **c)** 1.2 dollars/pound **d)** 12.2 dollars/person
20. $x + 2y = 5$ **21. a)** $x - 2y + 6 = 0$ **b)** $(\frac{2}{5}, \frac{16}{5})$ **c)** $6\sqrt{5}/5$ **22.** $y - 4 = \sqrt{3}(x - 1)$ **23.** $180° - \tan^{-1}(2) \approx 116° \, 34'$
24. a) $p = 0.1042d$ **b)** 5.21 atmospheres **25.** $y = x - 1$, $x \geq 1$ **26.** $70\ell - 0.16t = 2439.6$ (ℓ in feet, t in degrees F)

Article 1–6, pp. 27–28

1. $x \geq -4$, $y \geq 0$ **2.** $0 \leq x \leq 1$, $0 \leq y \leq 1$ **3.** $-\infty < x < \infty$, $0 \leq y < 1$ **4.** $x < -1$ or $x \geq 0$; $y \geq 0$, $y \neq 1$
5. $x \neq 0$, $-\infty < y < \infty$ **6.** $x \geq 0$, $y \geq 0$
7.

9.

10. (a), because value of y at $x = 0$ must be negative. **11.** (d), because value of y at $x = 1$ must be 0.

12. $y = \pm\sqrt{1 - x^2}$

13.

x	y
0	0
$\frac{1}{2}$	$\frac{1}{2}$
1	1
$\frac{3}{2}$	$\frac{1}{2}$
2	0

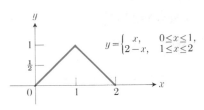

$y = \begin{cases} x, & 0 \le x \le 1, \\ 2 - x, & 1 \le x \le 2 \end{cases}$

14. $-2 < x < 2$ **15.** $x \le -2$ or $x \ge 2$ **16.** $-4 \le x \le 6$ **17.** $0 \le x \le 4$ **18.** $|x| \le 8$ **19.** $|x - 1| < 4$ **20.** $|x + 3| < 2$
21. $|1 - x| = 1 - x$ when $x \le 1$; $|1 - x| = x - 1$ when $x \ge 1$.

22.

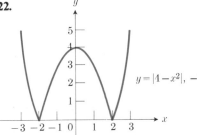

$y = |4 - x^2|, \ -3 \le x \le 3$

23.

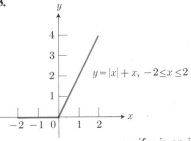

$y = |x| + x, \ -2 \le x \le 2$

24. $\pi/4$ **25.** $-(\pi/3)$ **26.** $\pi/2$
27. $2\pi/3$ **28.** $-(\pi/6)$ **29.** $-(3\pi/4)$
30. $60°$ **31.** $-30°$ **32.** $45°$
33. $120°$ **34.** $270°$ **35.** $-90°$
36. Odd **37.** Even **38.** Even
39. Odd **40.** Even **41.** Odd
42. $\frac{1}{2}$; $1/(x + 2)$; $-x/(4x + 8)$ **43.** 4
44. $\sqrt{x - 7}$ **45.** $3x + 6$ **46.** $\sqrt{x}$
47. x^2 **48.** 20,000 years

49. 21 mowers **50.** $\sqrt{2}$; 4 **51.** No closer than ≈ 52.02 km **52.** $[x] = \begin{cases} x \text{ if } x \text{ is an integer } < 0 \\ \text{integer part of decimal form } less\ one \\ \text{if } x < 0 \text{ is not an integer.} \end{cases}$

53.

$y = x - [x], \ -3 \le x \le 3$

54.

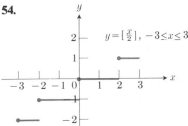

$y = [\frac{x}{2}], \ -3 \le x \le 3$

Article 1–7, p. 30

1. $2x - 2$ **2.** $4x - 1$ **3.** $-2x$ **4.** $2x - 4$ **5.** $2x - 4$ **6.** $2x + 4$ **7.** $1 - 2x$ **8.** $5 - 2x$ **9.** $2x + 3$ **10.** $-1 - 2x$
11. $6x^2 + 6x - 12$ **12.** $3x^2 - 3$ **13.** $3x^2 - 12$ **14.** $12x^2 + 6x$ **15.** $3x^2 - 6x$ **16.** ~ 18 flies.

Article 1–8, p. 37

1. $2x, 6, y = 6x - 9$ **2.** $3x^2, 27, y = 27x - 54$ **3.** $2, 2, y = 2x + 3$ **4.** $2x - 1, 5, y = 5x - 8$ **5.** $-(1/x^2), -\frac{1}{9}, x + 9y = 6$
6. $-(2/x^3), -\frac{2}{27}, 2x + 27y = 9$ **7.** $-2/(2x + 1)^2, -\frac{2}{49}, 2x + 49y = 13$ **8.** $+1/(x + 1)^2, \frac{1}{16}, x - 16y + 9 = 0$
9. $4x - 1, 11, y = 11x - 13$ **10.** $3x^2 - 12, 15, y = 15x - 43$ **11.** $4x^3, 108, y = 108x - 243$
12. $2ax + b, 6a + b, y = (6a + b)x - 9a + c$ **13.** $1 + (1/x^2), 1\frac{1}{9}, 10x - 9y = 6$ **14.** $a - (b/x^2), a - (b/9), 9y = (9a - b)x + 6b$
15. $1/\sqrt{2x}, 1/\sqrt{6}, \sqrt{6}y = x + 3$ **16.** $1/(2\sqrt{x + 1}), \frac{1}{4}, x - 4y + 5 = 0$ **17.** $1/\sqrt{2x + 3}, \frac{1}{3}, y = (x/3) + 2$
18. $-1/(2x\sqrt{x}), -1/6\sqrt{3}, x + 6\sqrt{3}y = 9$ **19.** $-1/(2x + 3)^{3/2}_{x}, -\frac{1}{27}, x + 27y = 12$
20. $x/\sqrt{x^2 + 1}, 3/\sqrt{10}, y = (3x/\sqrt{10}) + (1/\sqrt{10})$
21.
                                                                          22. 0, 0 **23.** 1700, 1250

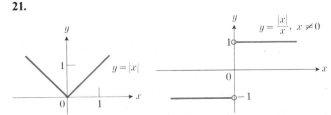

$y = |x|$

$y = \frac{|x|}{x}, \ x \ne 0$

Graph of $|x|/x$, $x \ne 0$, shows slope
of $|x|$ at any value $x \ne 0$

Article 1–9, p. 41–42

2. $4t + 5$ **3.** $gt + v_0$ **4.** 4   **5.** $2t - 3$ **6.** $-2 - 2t$ **7.** $8t + 12$ **8.** $2t - 4$ **9.** $-4t$ **10.** $64 - 32t$
11.

12. a) 1.23 mole/min   **b)** Rate $\approx$ 1.15 mole/min

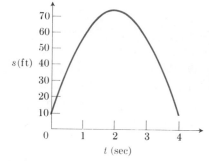

The data satisfy
$s = -16t^2 + 64t + 10$ ft
a) 32 ft/sec
b) -16 ft/sec
c) 0 ft/sec

13. 190 ft/sec   **14.** 2 sec   **15.** After 8 seconds; velocity was 0 ft/sec   **16.** At about $t = 11$ sec; falling at 95 ft/sec   **17.** 3 sec
18. a) 110 dollars/machine   **b)** 80 dollars/machine   **c)** (i) $f(101) - f(100) = 79.9$ dollars   **19. a)** 10^4 **b)** 0
c) -10^4 (Units are bacteria/hr)   **d)** $5(1 + \sqrt{41})$ hrs (≈ 37.02 hrs)   **20.** 8000 gal/min; 10,000 gal/min   **21. a)** $2\pi r + \pi \, \Delta r$
b) $2\pi r$ **22.** $4\pi r^2$ **23.** πh^2

Article 1–10, pp. 51–52

1. $\frac{5}{4}$ **2.** 2   **3.** 5   **4.** -1 **5.** -2 **6.** $\frac{1}{7}$ **7.** 0   **8.** $\frac{1}{2}$ **9. a)** $0 < x < 1$, $1 < x < 2$ (that is, $x \neq 0, 1, 2$)   **b)** $x = 2$ **c)** $x = 0$
10.

11. $\lim_{\Delta x \to 0^+} (|\Delta x|/\Delta x) = 1$; $\lim_{\Delta x \to 0^-} (|\Delta x|/\Delta x) = -1$
12. a) $|t - 3| < \frac{1}{80}$ will work   **b)** $|t - 3| < \frac{1}{800}$ will work
c) $|t - 3| \leq \min\{1, \epsilon/8\}$ **13.** $1/x^2$ increases most rapidly;
$1/\sqrt{x}$ increases least rapidly.   **14.** n **15.** $\frac{1}{4}$ **16.** 1   **17.** 0
18. 0   **19.** $\sqrt{4 + x}$; $\sin x$ **20.** $f(x) = x^2$ at $x = 1$, or $f(x) = (x + 1)^2$ at $x = 0$ **21.** $f(x) = |x|$ at $x = -1$, or $f(x) = |x - 1|$ at $x = 0$ **22.** 1

a) $x < -1$; $-1 < x < 1$; $x > 1$
b) None   **c)** None

Article 1–11, p. 55

1. a) $\lim_{t \to c} t = c$.   [*Proof.* Given $\epsilon > 0$, let $\delta = \epsilon$. Then $|t - c| < \epsilon$ when $|t - c| < \delta$.]   **b)** $\lim_{t \to c} k = k$, k constant.
[*Proof.* Given $\epsilon > 0$, let δ be anything greater than 0. Then $0 = |k - k| < \epsilon$ when $|t - c| < \delta$.]   **2.** Apply Theorem 1,
part (i), to F_1, F_2. Then apply again to $(F_1 + F_2), F_3$. In general, use induction argument.   **3.** Use an induction
argument, applying Theorem 1, part (iii).   **4.** $\lim_{t \to c} t^n = (\lim_{t \to c} t)^n = c^n$, for n a positive integer.   **5.** $\lim_{t \to c} a_i t^{n-i} =$
$a_i \lim_{t \to c} t^{n-i} = a_i c^{n-i}$, by Problems 1(b), 4, 1(a). Then $\lim_{t \to c} (a_0 t^n + a_1 t^{n-1} + \cdots + a_n) = a_0 c^n + a_1 c^{n-1} + \cdots + a_n$, by
Problem 2. So $\lim_{t \to c} f(t) = f(c)$ for polynomial functions $f(x)$.   **6.** $\lim_{t \to c} f(t) = f(c)$; $\lim_{t \to c} g(t) = g(c)$. If $g(c) \neq 0$,
Theorem 1, part (iv) implies $\lim_{t \to c} (f(t)/g(t)) = (f(c)/g(c))$.

Miscellaneous Problems Chapter 1, pp. 56–58

1. b) $-\frac{3}{2}, \frac{2}{3}, -\frac{3}{2}, \frac{2}{3}, 0, \infty$ **c)** $ABCD$ is a parallelogram (its opposite sides are parallel).   **d)** Yes, AEB **e)** Yes, CD **f)** $3x + 2y = 26$; $3x + 2y = 0$; $-2x + 3y = -13$; $y = 6$; $x = 2$

g)

L	AB	CD	AD	CE	BD
y-intercept	13	0	$-\frac{13}{3}$	6	None
x-intercept	$\frac{26}{3}$	0	$\frac{13}{2}$	None	2

2. a) $2x + 3y = -7$ **b)** $\sqrt{13}$
3. a) No   **b)** No   **c)** Outside   **d)** $(-2, -\frac{9}{7})$
4. $3x + 4y = 0$; $x = 0$

5. $[(x_1 + x_2)/2, (y_1 + y_2)/2]$ **7. a)** $-(a/b)$ **b)** $(0, -(c/b))$ **c)** $(-(c/a), 0)$ **d)** $-bx + ay = 0$
9. Four; centers $(0, \sqrt{5} - 2)$, $(0, -\sqrt{5} - 2)$, $(-\sqrt{5} - 1, 1)$, $(\sqrt{5} - 1, 1)$. Radii (in same order).
$(3\sqrt{2} - \sqrt{10})/2$, $(3\sqrt{2} + \sqrt{10})/2$, $(\sqrt{10} + \sqrt{2})/2$, $(\sqrt{10} - \sqrt{2})/2$.   **10.** $|b' - b|/\sqrt{1 + m^2}$

11. Straight line through point of intersection of the two given lines. **12.** $(\frac{17}{18}, \frac{23}{6})$ **13.** $x + 5y = \pm 5\sqrt{2}$
14. $x = \sqrt{(y+2)/(y-1)}$; $y \le -2, y > 1$ **15.** $A = \pi r^2, C = 2\pi r, A = C^2/4\pi$
16. a) $x < -1, x > -1$; $y < 0, y > 0$ **b)** All x; $0 < y \le 1$ **c)** $x \ge 0, 0 < y \le 1$ **17.** $-5 < x < 3$
18. For $y \le 4$, $x = y - 2$; for $y \ge 4$, $x = (y+2)/3$. **19.** $y > 2$, $x = (y+2)/2$ **20.** $x = (y \pm \sqrt{y^2 - 4})/2$, $|y| \ge 2$
21. a) $f(-2) = -3$, $f(-1) = -4$, $f(x_1) = x_1^2 + 2x_1 - 3$, $f(x_1 + \Delta x) = x_1^2 + 2x_1 \Delta x + (\Delta x)^2 + 2x_1 + 2 \Delta x - 3$
22. c) $(\frac{1}{2}, -\frac{3}{4})$

24. $m(a, b) = (a + b - |a - b|)/2$ **26.** Take $\phi_k(x) = g_k(x)/g_k(x_k)$ where $g_k(x)$ is
the product $(x - x_1)(x - x_2) \cdots (x - x_n)$ with the factor $(x - x_k)$ deleted.

23. Range:
$-2 \le y \le 6$

$y = |x+2| + x$
$-5 \le x \le 2$

$(2, 6)$

$(-5, -2)$ $(-2, -2)$

27. $f(d) = g(b)$ **29. a)** $1/(1-x)$ **b)** $x/(x+1)$ **c)** x **d)** $1-x$
30. a) $2/(x+1)^2$ **b)** $3\sqrt{x}/2$ **c)** $\frac{1}{3}x^{-(2/3)}$ **31. a)** $2x - 3$ **b)** $-1/(3x^2) + 2$
c) $1/(2\sqrt{t-4})$ **32. a)** 6 **b)** $(0, 2)$ **33. a)** $f(0) = 0, f(-1) = 1, f(1/x) =$
$2/(1 - x)$ **b)** $-2/(x - 1)(x + \Delta x - 1)$ **c)** $-2/(x - 1)^2$ **34.** $P(\frac{45}{8}, \frac{2025}{4})$
35. $v = 180 - 32t, t = \frac{45}{8}$ **36.** $t = 1$ sec, $s = 16$ ft **37. a)** $-1/(v(v + \Delta v))$ **b)** $-\frac{1}{4}$
38. 28 in^3/sec **39. a)** 0 **b)** $-\frac{1}{3}$ **c)** $f(-(1/x)) = -x(x + 1)/(5x^2 + 7x + 2)$,
$f(0) = -\frac{1}{5}$, $1/f(x) = 2x - 5$ **40.** $((c+1)/(3c+2), -1/(5(3c+2)))$, $(\frac{2}{5}, -\frac{1}{25})$
41. a) 0 **b)** $\frac{1}{2}$ **42.** δ less than or equal to min $\{1, \epsilon^2/3\}$ **43.** $M = 1 + (1/\epsilon)$

48. a) $a^2 = |a|^2, b^2 = |b|^2; a^2, b^2 \ge 0$. For nonnegative numbers, $f(x) = x^2$ and $g(x) = x^{1/2}$ are increasing functions (look at derivatives). **b)** $2ab \le 2|a||b|$, $a^2 + b^2 = |a|^2 + |b|^2$. So $a^2 + 2ab + b^2 \le |a|^2 + 2|a||b| + |b|^2$, $(a + b)^2 \le (|a| + |b|)^2$ and $(a + b) \le |a| + |b|$, by part (a). **c)** $|a| = |a - b + b| \le |a - b| + |b|$, so $|a - b| \ge |a| - |b|$; $|b| = |b - a + a| \le |b - a| + |a|$, so $|a - b| \ge |b| - |a|$. Hence, $|a - b| \ge ||a| - |b||$.
d) True for $n = 2$ by part (b). Assume for $n - 1$. $|a_1 + a_2 + \cdots + a_{n-1} + a_n| \le |a_1 + \cdots + a_{n-1}| + |a_n|$ by part (b); $\le |a_1| + \cdots + |a_{n-1}| + |a_n|$ by induction hypothesis. **e)** $|a_1| = |a_1 + \cdots + a_n - a_2 - \cdots - a_n| \le |a_1 + \cdots + a_n| + |a_2| + \cdots + |a_n|$ by (d). So $|a_1 + \cdots + a_n| \ge |a_1| - |a_2| - \cdots - |a_n|$.

49.

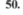

$|y| + |x| = 1$

I: $y = -x + 1, 0 \le x \le 1$;
II: $y = x + 1, -1 \le x \le 0$;
III: $y = -x - 1, -1 \le x \le 0$;
IV: $y = x - 1, 0 \le x \le 1$.

50.

$y = \sqrt{|x|}, -4 \le x \le 4$

CHAPTER 2

Article 2–2, p. 67

1. $v = 2t - 4, a = 2$ **2.** $v = 6t^2 - 10t + 4, a = 12t - 10$ **3.** $v = gt + v_0, a = g$ **4.** $v = 4 - 2t, a = -2$
5. $v = 8t + 12, a = 8$ **6.** $y' = 4x^3 - 21x^2 + 4x$; $y'' = 12x^2 - 42x + 4$ **7.** $y' = 15(x^2 - x^4)$; $y'' = 30(x - 2x^3)$
8. $y' = 8(x - 1)$; $y'' = 8$ **9.** $y' = x^3 - x^2 + x - 1$; $y'' = 3x^2 - 2x + 1$ **10.** $y' = 8(x^3 - x)$; $y'' = 8(3x^2 - 1)$
11. $y' = 2x^3 - 3x - 1$; $y'' = 6x^2 - 3$ **12.** $y' = 21(x^6 - x^2 + 2x)$; $y'' = 42(3x^5 - x + 1)$
13. $y' = 5x^4 - 2x$; $y'' = 20x^3 - 2$ **14.** $y' = 2x + 1$; $y'' = 2$ **15.** $y' = 12x + 13$; $y'' = 12$ **16. a)** 400 ft **b)** 96 ft/sec
17. $y = 8x - 5$ **18.** $y = 4x \pm 2$. Least slope is $+1$ at $(0, 0)$. **19.** $(-1, 27), (2, 0)$ **20.** Slope of $TP = 2x =$ slope of
tangent at P. **21.** $t = ((n - 1)/n)x_1 = x_1 - (x_1/n)$. Construct line L through $(0, n)$ and $(x_1, 0)$ and L' through $(0, n - 1)$
parallel to L. Then L' intersects the x-axis at T. Draw TP. **22.** x-intercept: $-\frac{4}{3}$; y-intercept: 16 **23.** $(2, 6)$
24. a) 2 **b)** $2\sqrt{5}/25 = 2/(5\sqrt{5})$ **c)** 0 **25.** $a = b = 1, c = 0$ **26.** $a = -3, b = 2, c = 1$ **27.** $c = \frac{1}{4}$

Article 2–3, p. 75

1. $x^2 - x + 1$ **2.** $(x - 1)^2(x + 2)^3(7x + 2)$ **3.** $10x(x^2 + 1)^4$ **4.** $12(x^2 - 1)(x^3 - 3x)^3$ **5.** $-2(2x^2 + 3x - 1)(x + 1)(x^2 + 1)^{-4}$
6. $-2(x^2 + x + 1)/(x^2 - 1)^2$ **7.** $-19/(3x - 2)^2$ **8.** $-4(x + 1)(x - 1)^{-3}$ **9.** $(1 - t^2)/(t^2 + 1)^2$ **10.** $6(2t + 3)^2$
11. $-2(2t - 1)(t^2 - t)^{-3}$ **12.** $(t^2 + 2t)(t + 1)^{-2}$ **13.** $(2 - 6t^2)/(3t^2 + 1)^2$ **14.** $2(t - t^{-3})$ **15.** $3(2t + 3)(t^2 + 3t)^2$
19. Increasing at 1%. **21.** $a_0 = f(1) = 2$, $a_1 = f'(1) = 1$, $a_2 = f''(1)/2 = 3$, $a_3 = f'''(1)/6 = 1$. Error is approximately
$a_2(x - 1)^2 = 3(x - 1)^2$. $\lim_{x \to 1} (f(x) - L_1(x))/(x - 1)^2 = a_2 = 3$.

Article 2–4, p. 79

1. $g(x) = \frac{1}{2}(x - 3)$; $g'(x) = \frac{1}{2} = 1/f'(x)$. **2.** $\frac{1}{3}(x - 1)^{-(2/3)}$ **3.** Slope at $P(a, 1/a)$: $-(1/a^2)$; slope at $P'(1/a, a)$: $-a^2$. They satisfy Rule 10 when $a \neq 0$. **4.** $db/da = (\frac{2}{3})a^{-(1/3)}$; $a \neq 0$. **5.** x-intercept: -4; y-intercept: 1.
6. $C_0 = \frac{5}{2}$; $C_1 = \frac{3}{16}$; $C_2 = -\frac{1}{256}$. Error estimate: $-(x - 4)^2/256$. At $x = 4.41$, estimate is: -0.00065664. Actual error is: -0.000684524. **7. b)** $y = x^{1/3}$ fails to have a derivative at $x = 0$. Slope of $y = x^3$ at $x = 0$ is 0. The y-axis is tangent to $y = x^{1/3}$ at $x = 0$. The x-axis is tangent to $y = x^3$ at $x = 0$.

Article 2–5, pp. 83–84

1. $-(x/y)$ **2.** $1/(y(x + 1)^2)$ **3.** $-(2x + y)/x$ **4.** $-(2xy + y^2)/(x^2 + 2xy)$ **5.** $3x^2/2y$ **6.** $-(y/x)^{1/3}$ **7.** $-(y/x)^{1/2}$
8. $(y - 3x^2)/(3y^2 - x)$ **9.** $(y/x) - (x + y)^2$ **10.** $(x^2 + 1)^{-(3/2)}$ **11.** $(2x^2 + 1)(x^2 + 1)^{-(1/2)}$ **12.** $(x^4 - 1)/x^3 y$
13. $(1 - 2y)/(2x + 2y - 1)$ **14.** $\frac{1}{2}x^{-(1/2)} + \frac{1}{3}x^{-(2/3)} + \frac{1}{4}x^{-(3/4)}$ **15.** $2x/(y(x^2 + 1)^2)$ **16.** $(2x^3 - 3x^2 - 3y^2)/(6xy - 2y^3)$
17. $5(3x + 7)^4/(2y^2)$ **18.** $(10x^2 + 30x - 8)(x + 5)^3(x^2 - 2)^2$ **19.** $-(y^2/x^2)$ **20.** $(6x + 15)(x^2 + 5x)^2$ **21.** $(2x - 1)/(2y)$
22. $x(y^2 - 1)/y(1 - x^2)$ **23.** $-(x^2 + 9)/[3x^2(x^2 + 3)^{2/3}]$ **25. a)** $-(x/y)$ **b)** $-(1/y^3)$ **26. a)** $-(x^2/y^2)$ **b)** $-(2x/y^5)$
27. a) $-x^{-(1/3)}y^{1/3}$ **b)** $\frac{1}{3}x^{-(4/3)}y^{-(1/3)}$ **28. a)** $-y(x + 2y)^{-1}$ **b)** $2(x + 2y)^{-3}$ **30. a)** $7x - 4y = 2$ **b)** $4x + 7y = 29$
31. a) $3x - 4y = 25$, $4x + 3y = 0$ **32. a)** $y = 3x + 6$ **b)** $x + 3y = 8$ **33. a)** $x = 3y$ **b)** $3x + y = 10$
34. a) $3x - 4y = 10$ **b)** $4x + 3y = 30$ **35.** x-intercepts: $x = \pm\sqrt{7}$. Slope of tangents: -2
36. a) $x = \pm\sqrt{\frac{7}{3}}$, $y = -2x$ **b)** $y = \pm\sqrt{\frac{7}{3}}$, $x = -2y$. At these points, $dx/dy = 0$. **37.** $y = (-x \pm (-3x^2 + 28)^{1/2})/2$; $-\frac{4}{5}$

Article 2–6, p. 85

1. a) $(2x + 2)\,\Delta x + (\Delta x)^2$ **b)** $(2x + 2)\,\Delta x$ **c)** $(\Delta x)^2$ **2. a)** $(4x + 4)\,\Delta x + 2(\Delta x)^2$ **b)** $(4x + 4)\,\Delta x$ **c)** $2(\Delta x)^2$
3. a) $(3x^2 - 1)\,\Delta x + 3x(\Delta x)^2 + (\Delta x)^3$ **b)** $(3x^2 - 1)\,\Delta x$ **c)** $3x(\Delta x)^2 + (\Delta x)^3$
4. a) $4x^3\,\Delta x + 6x^2(\Delta x)^2 + 4x(\Delta x)^3 + (\Delta x)^4$ **b)** $4x^3\,\Delta x$ **c)** $6x^2(\Delta x)^2 + 4x(\Delta x)^3 + (\Delta x)^4$
5. a) $-\Delta x/[x(x + \Delta x)]$ **b)** $-(\Delta x/x^2)$ **c)** $(\Delta x)^2/[x^2(x + \Delta x)]$ **6.** 2.13 **7.** 1.96 **8.** 0.48 **9.** 5.16 **10.** 0.58

Article 2–7, p. 88

1. 0.618 **2.** 0.682 **3.** 1.165 **4.** 1.189 **5.** -1.189 **6.** 3 **7.** $x_1 = x_2 = x_3$, etc. **8.** $m_1 = (q - 1)/q$, $m_2 = 1/q$
10. Yes, they may get worse.

Article 2–8, p. 93

1. $9y = (x - 1)^2$ **2.** $y^2 = x^3$ **3.** $y = (x/(1 + x))^2$ **4.** $y = x^2/(1 - x)$ **5.** -3 **6.** $8x + 10$ **7.** $1/2(x + 1)^2$
8. $4x/3(x^2 + 1)^{1/3}$ **9.** $18x + (1/3x^2)$ **10.** $12((3x + 2)^4 - 1)/(3x + 2)^3$

Article 2–9, pp. 100–101

1.

2.

3.

4.

5.

6.

7.

8.

9.

10. 37, 365, 101, 25   **11. a)** 62°, 193rd day   **b)** $-12°$, 10th day   **c)** 25°; average of $y = \sin x$ is zero, and shift is upward 25°.   **14.** $\cos^2 A + \sin^2 A = \cos 0 = 1$
15. $\sin 0 = 0$ **16.** $\tan (A - B) = (\tan A - \tan B)/(1 + \tan A \tan B)$
17. $\tan (A + B) = (\tan A + \tan B)/(1 - \tan A \tan B)$ **19.** Cosine and secant are even. Sine, tangent, cotangent, cosecant are odd.   **20.** $\cos 2A = \cos^2 A - \sin^2 A$, $\sin 2A = 2 \sin A \cos A$ **26.** $4n\pi \le \theta \le (4n + 2)\pi$, n integer   **27.** $(4n - 1)\pi \le \theta \le (4n + 1)\pi$, n integer

Article 2–10, p. 107

1. 1   **2.** 1   **3.** 2   **4.** $\frac{1}{3}$ **5.** 1   **6.** $\frac{1}{3}$ **7.** $\frac{5}{3}$ **8.** $\frac{1}{2}$ **9.** 0   **10.** 0   **11.** $\frac{1}{2}$ **12.** $\frac{2}{3}$ **13.** $\frac{3}{5}$ **14.** 1   **15.** 2π **16.** -2 **17.** $\frac{1}{2}$ **18.** 1
19. 2   **20.** $\cos a$ **21.** $-\sin a$ **22.** $\pi/4$ **23.** $3 \cos (3x + 4)$ **24.** $x \cos x + \sin x$ **25.** $(x \cos x - \sin x)/x^2$ **26.** $-5 \sin 5x$
27. $3x^2 \cos 3x + 2x \sin 3x$ **28.** $-\sin 2x/(2 + \cos 2x)^{1/2}$ **29.** 0   **30.** $6 \sin 3x/\cos^2 3x$ **31.** $6 \cos 2x + 8 \sin 2x$
32. $-24 \sin 2x \cos 2x$ or $-12 \sin 4x$ **33.** $2(\cos^2 x - \sin^2 x)$ or $2 \cos 2x$ **34.** $-\cos x/\sin^2 x$ **35.** $-3 \sin 6x$
36. $-1/\sin^2 x$ **37.** $4x \sin (x^2) \cos (x^2) = 2x \sin (2x^2)$ **38.** $(-x/\sqrt{x^2 + 1})[\sin (\sin \sqrt{x^2 + 1})][\cos \sqrt{x^2 + 1}]$
39. $(\sin 2y + 2y \sin 2x)/(\cos 2x - 2x \cos 2y)$ **40.** $-(\sin 8x)/y$ **41.** $y = mx$

Article 2–11, p. 117

1. b) Take δ less than or equal to the smaller of the two numbers 1 and $\epsilon/91$. Then $|x^2 + 5x + 25| < 91$ and $|x^3 - 5^3| < \epsilon$ when $|x - 5| < \delta$.   **2. a)** $x = -1$ **b)** $x = 1$ or 3   **3.** Continuous   **4.** Take $\delta \le \epsilon$ **5.** max = 1, min = 0
6. Neither a maximum nor a minimum since $f(x_2) > f(x_1)$ if $0 < x_1 < x_2 < 1$. Hence we can always find x_2 such that $f(x_2) > f(x_1)$, so $f(x_1)$ is *not* the maximum. This is true for any x_1 in the given domain. The same argument shows that no x_2 in the domain can give a minimum.   **7.** Take $a = 0$, $b = 1$, and $N = 0$ in Theorem 4.   **8.** Continuous but not differentiable.   **10.** 7.

Article 2–13, p. 121

1. $(3x^2 - 6x + 5) \, dx$ **2.** $(9x/2y)(3x^2 + 1)^{1/2} \, dx$ **3.** $-[(2xy + y^2)/(2xy + x^2)] \, dx$ **4.** $2(1 - x^2)(1 + x^2)^{-2} \, dx$
5. $[(1 - 2x^2)/\sqrt{1 - x^2}] \, dx$ **6.** $(6 - 2x - x^2)(x^2 - 2x + 4)^{-2} \, dx$ **7.** $3(1 - x)^2(2x - 1)(2 - 3x)^{-2} \, dx$
8. $(2 - 2x + x^2)(1 - x)^{-2} \, dx$ **9.** 12.04   **10.** 9.2   **11.** 2.03   **12.** 0.5013   **13.** 79.69   **14. c)** $5x - 3y = 8$ **15. c)** $15x - y = 20$
16. c) $11y = x + 16$ **17. c)** $9x + y = 6$ **18. c)** $4x + 2y = 9$ **19.** $-4t^3(t^2 - 1)^{-3}$ **20.** $2(t + 1)^3(t - 1)^{-3}$
22. If a changes by $m\%$ and b changes by $n\%$, then $A = ab$ changes by approximately $(m + n)\%$ (assuming m, n are small).

Miscellaneous Problems Chapter 2, pp. 123–124

1. $-4(x^2 - 4)^{-(3/2)}$ **2.** $(5 - 2x - y)/(x + 2y)$ **3.** $-y/(x + 2y)$ **4.** $(3x^2 + 4y)/(9y^2 - 4x)$ **5.** $-y(2x + y)/(x(2y + x))$
6. $-2(x + 1)(x^2 + 2x + 2)/(x^3(x + 2)^3)$ **7.** $2 \sin (1 - 2x)$ **8.** $-1/\sin^2 x$ **9.** $(x + 1)^{-2}$ **10.** $(2x + 1)^{-(1/2)}$
11. $(3x^3 - 2a^2x)/\sqrt{x^2 - a^2}$ **12.** $-4(2x - 1)^{-2}$ **13.** $2x(1 - x^2)^{-2}$ **14.** $3(x^2 + x + 1)^2(2x + 1)$ **15.** $10 \sin (5x)/\cos^3 (5x)$
16. $(\sin^2 x \cos x - \cos^2 x \sin x)/(\sin^3 x + \cos^3 x)^{2/3}$ **17.** $[(4x + 5)/2]\sqrt{2x^2 + 5x}$ **18.** $-(9/2)(4x + 5)(2x^2 + 5x)^{-(5/2)}$
19. $-(y/x)[(2y\sqrt{xy} + 1)/(4y\sqrt{xy} + 1)]$ **20.** $(2x - y)/(x + 2y)$ **21.** $-(y/x)^{1/3}$ **22.** $-\sqrt{y/x}$ **23.** $-(y/x)$
24. $-(y/x)$ **25.** $-\frac{1}{2}[(x + 2y + y^2)/(x + 2y + xy)]$ **26.** $(x^2 - 2x - 1)/(2(1 - x)^{1/2}(1 + x^2)^{3/2})$
27. $1/(2y(x + 1)^2)$ or $(x + 1)^{-2}/(2y)$ **28.** $(12x - 2xy - y^2)/(x^2 + 2xy - 12y)$ **29.** $-(y + 2)/(x + 3)$ **30.** 1
31. $(4x + 8)/\sqrt{4x^2 + 16x + 15}$ **32.** $2t(1 + t^2)^2/(1 - t^2)$ **33.** $2x[1 + ((1 - x^2)/(1 + x^2)^3)]$ **34.** $m = 1$, $y = x$ **35.** $2x + y = 6$
36. $c = 4$ **37.** $m = 2$, $y - 2x = -5$ **38.** $(2, 0)$ and $(-1, 27)$
39. a) $10(x^2 + 2x)^4(x + 1)$ **b)** $(3t - 1)/\sqrt{3t^2 - 2t}$ **c)** $r[(r^2 + 5)^{-(1/2)} + (r^2 - 5)^{-(1/2)}]$ **d)** $4x/(x^2 + 1)^2$ **40.** $x + 27y = 28$

41. $x + y = 3$ **42.** $(2x + 3)^{-(1/2)}$ **43.** $-6(2 - 3x), f(x) = (2 - 3x)^2$ **44.** $-\frac{8}{5}$
45. $6\pi(\Delta r)^2$; a shell around the can with thickness Δr.   **46.** $\pi x(20 - x)$ **47.** $x_1 = 40, p = 4\ (= 20\text{¢})$ **49.** $(x - 1)(2x - 1)$
50. $(2x + 1)/9$ **51.** 56 ft/sec   **52.** $-\frac{12}{5}$ **53. a)** $h + 2k = 5$ **b)** $h = -4, k = \frac{9}{2}, r = 5\sqrt{5/2}$ **54.** $2\sqrt{x^2 + 1}$
55. $2/[3(2y + 1)(2x + 1)\sqrt{x^2 + x}]$ **56.** $2x\sqrt{3x^4 - 1}$ **57.** $(3/(x + 1)^2)\sin[((2x - 1)/(x + 1))^2]$
58. $dy/du = (dy/dx)(dx/du) = 12u\cos(2u^2 + 2\pi)$. At $u = 0, dy/du = 0$.   **60.** $3(x - 2)/(2x - 3)^{3/2})$ **61.** $-\frac{3}{32}$ **62.** $y' = 2$,
$y'' = -2$ **64. a)** $3(2x - 1)^{-(5/2)}$ **b)** $-162(3x + 2)^{-4}$ **c)** $6a$ **66.** $\Delta y = 0.92$, principal part $= 0.9$
67. a) Length of each side $= 2r\sin(\pi/n)$ **b)** $2\pi r$; yes.   **68.** $dy/dx = -2x; d^2y/dx^2 = -2$ **69.** 14 ± 0.044 ft
70. a) $(x(x + 2)/(x + 1)^2)\,dx$ **b)** $(x/y)\,dx$ **c)** $(-y/(x + 2y))\,dx$
72. $\delta = \epsilon/4$; the function is uniformly continuous for $-2 \le x \le 2$.   **75.** $m = \frac{1}{2}, c = \sqrt{2}$

CHAPTER 3

Article 3–1, p. 127

1. Falling $x < \frac{1}{2}$, rising $x > \frac{1}{2}$. Low point at $(\frac{1}{2}, \frac{3}{4})$.   **2.** Rising $x < -1$, falling $-1 < x < 2$, rising $x > 2$. High point at $(-1, \frac{3}{2})$, low at $(2, -3)$.   **3.** Rising $x < 0$, falling $0 < x < 1$, rising $x > 1$. High at $(0, 3)$, low at $(1, 2)$.   **4.** Rising $x < -3$, falling $-3 < x < 3$, rising $x > 3$. High at $(-3, 90)$, low at $(3, -18)$.   **5.** Falling $x < -2$, rising $-2 < x < 0$, falling $0 < x < 2$, rising $x > 2$. Low points $(\pm 2, 0)$, high $(0, 16)$.   **6.** Defined on $x \ne 0$. Falling $x < 0$. Discontinuity at $x = 0$. Falling $x > 0$.   **7.** Rising $-(\pi/2) + 2\pi k < x < (\pi/2) + 2\pi k$. Falling $(\pi/2) + 2\pi k < x < (3\pi/2) + 2\pi k$. High points $((\pi/2) + 2\pi k, 1)$. Low points $((3\pi/2) + 2\pi k, -1)$. (k can be any integer.)   **8.** Discontinuous at $x = (\pi/2) + \pi k$. Rising $-(\pi/2) + \pi k < x < (\pi/2) + \pi k$. ($k$ can be any integer.)   **9.** Rising all x.

Article 3–2, pp. 131–132

1. $(dA/dt) = 2\pi r(dr/dt)$ **2.** $(dV/dt) = 4\pi r^2(dr/dt)$ **3.** $(8/5\pi)$ ft/min   **5.** $(ax + by)/\sqrt{x^2 + y^2}$ ft/sec   **6.** $(25/9\pi)$ ft/min
7. $10/\sqrt{21} \approx 2.2$ ft/sec   **8.** Increasing 33.7 ft/sec   **9.** $(125/144\pi)$ ft/min   **10.** $(dy/dt) = -x$. Clockwise.   **11.** 8 ft/sec toward the lamp post. Decreasing 3 ft/sec   **12.** Increasing 8.75 psi/sec   **13.** 1500 ft/sec   **14.** 20 ft/sec   **15.** Thickness decreasing at the rate of $(5/72\pi)$ in/min.   Area decreasing at the rate of $(10/3)$ in²/min.   **16.** $260/\sqrt{37}$ mi/hr.

Article 3–4, pp. 137–138

1. a) $x > 2$ **b)** $x < 2$ **c)** Always   **d)** Never $m(2, -1)$ **2. a)** Always   **b)** Never   **c)** $x < -1$ **d)** $x > -1$ **3. a)** $-1 < x < 1$ **b)** $x < -1, x > 1$ **c)** $x < 0$ **d)** $x > 0$ $M(1, 6); m(-1, 2); I(0, 4)$ **4. a)** $x < -2, x > 3$ **b)** $-2 < x < 3$
c) $x > \frac{1}{2}$ **d)** $x < \frac{1}{2}$ $M(-2, \frac{22}{3}); m(3, -\frac{27}{2}); I(\frac{1}{2}, -\frac{37}{12})$ **5. a)** $x < -2, x > 2$ **b)** $-2 < x < 2, x \ne 0$ **c)** $x > 0$ **d)** $x < 0$,
$M(-2, -4); m(2, 4)$ **6. a)** $-\pi + 2\pi k < x < 2\pi k$ **b)** $2\pi k < x < \pi + 2\pi k$ **c)** $(\pi/2) + 2\pi k < x < (3\pi/2) + 2\pi k$
d) $-(\pi/2) + 2\pi k < x < (\pi/2) + 2\pi k; M(2\pi k, 1); m(\pi + 2\pi k, -1); I((\pi/2) + \pi k, 0)$; k any integer   **9.** $M(-1, 7)$ **10.** $m(1, 1)$
11. $M(-2, 28); m(2, -4); I(0, 12)$ **12.** $M(0, 2); m(2, -2); I(1, 0)$
13. $M(0, 0)$ **14.** $m(2, 0)$ **15.** $(1, -1)$ **16.** $(16, -3), (-16, 1)$
17. $(2, 0), (1, \pm 1)$ **18.** $(3, 1)$ **21.** Concave downward because $f''(x) = -(1/x^2)$ is negative.   **23. a)** 3 times; near $x = -1.2, -0.4, +0.8$ **b)** Once; near $x = -1.8$ **c)** Once; near $x = 1.2$

24. $dy/dx = 1 + \cos x = 0$ at $x = \pi + 2\pi k$; elsewhere the slope is positive and the graph is rising.

Article 3–6, pp. 151–153

2. $(r\sqrt{2}) \times (r/\sqrt{2})$ **3.** 32   **4.** $\frac{5}{3} \times \frac{14}{3} \times \frac{35}{3}$ (inches)   **5.** Use one-half of the fence parallel to the river.
6. $\sqrt{A/3} \times \sqrt{A/3} \times \frac{1}{2}\sqrt{A/3}$, where $A =$ given amount of material.   **7.** $4'' \times 4'' \times 2''$ **8.** 4   **9.** 9 inches wide and 18 inches high
10. $V_{\max} = 2\pi h^3/(9\sqrt{3})$, $h =$ given hypotenuse   **11.** $(100 + c)/2$ **12.** $0.58L$
13. a) 16   **b)** -54 **c)** -1 **d)** $f'(x) = 0$ when $2x^3 = a$ and then $f''(x) = +6$ or $+2$, according as $a \ne 0$ or $a = 0$.

14. a) $a = -3, b = -9$ **b)** $a = -3, b = -24$ **15. a)** $4L/(4 + 3\sqrt{3})$ for the square, $3\sqrt{3}\,L/(4 + 3\sqrt{3})$ for the triangle
  b) Use it all for the square **16.** $(\frac{1}{2}, -\frac{1}{2})$ and $(-\frac{1}{2}, \frac{1}{2})$ **17. a)** $(c - \frac{1}{2}, \sqrt{c - \frac{1}{2}})$ **b)** $(0, 0)$ **18.** $\frac{32}{81}\pi r^3$ **19.** $\frac{4}{9}\pi r^3 \sqrt{3}$
21. Width $= 2r/\sqrt{3}$, depth $= 2r\sqrt{\frac{2}{3}}$ **22.** Width of beam = radius of log. **23.** $x/(c - x) = \sqrt[3]{a/b}$, where x is the distance from the source of strength a. **24.** Height of rectangle $= (4 + \pi)/8$ times diameter of semicircle **25.** $4/\pi$ **26.** Diameter = altitude of cylinder $= \sqrt[3]{3V/\pi}$, V = total volume **27. a)** Unity **b)** Zero **31.** Before tax: Production = 7,500; price = \$1.25; profit = \$5,425. After tax: Production = 7,000; price = \$1.30; profit = \$4,700. To maximize profit the company should absorb 5¢ of the tax and add 5¢ to the price. **32.** Still $Q = \sqrt{2KM/h}$. Of course the average weekly cost increases if $p > 0$. **35.** Maxima: $x = (\pi/4) + 2\pi k$, k any integer, $y = \sqrt{2}$. Minima: $x = (5\pi/4) + 2\pi k$, k any integer, $y = -\sqrt{2}$. [*Note.* $\sin x + \cos x = \sqrt{2} \sin [x + (\pi/4)]$.]

Article 3–7, p. 155

6. The function is not continuous on the closed interval $0 \le x \le 1$.

Article 3–8, pp. 159–160

1. $\frac{1}{2}$ **2.** $\sqrt{3}$ **3.** $\frac{8}{27}$ **4.** 1 **5.** $\frac{3}{2}$ **7. a)** $3\frac{1}{6}$ **b)** 4.012 **c)** 0.0101

Article 3–9, p. 165

1. $\frac{1}{4}$ **2.** 2 **3.** $\frac{5}{7}$ **4.** $\frac{3}{11}$ **5.** 0 **6.** -2 **7.** 5 **8.** $-\frac{1}{2}$ **9.** 1 **10.** $\frac{1}{4}$ **11.** $\frac{1}{6}$ **12.** $\frac{1}{2}$ **13.** $+\infty$ **14.** 3 **15.** $\cos a$ **16.** an
17. $+\infty$ **18.** $-\frac{1}{2}$ **19.** (b) is correct. L'Hôpital's rule does not apply because the limit of the denominator is finite and nonzero.
20. -1 **21.** $(a + b)/2$ **22.** $(-1 + \sqrt{37})/3 \approx 1.694$

Miscellaneous Problems Chapter 3, pp. 171–174

1. a) $x < \frac{9}{2}$ **b)** $x > \frac{9}{2}$ **c)** No values **d)** All values **2. a)** $x > 3, x < \frac{1}{3}$ **b)** $\frac{1}{3} < x < 3$ **c)** $x > \frac{5}{3}$ **d)** $x < \frac{5}{3}$
3. a) $x < 3$ **b)** $x > 3$ **c)** $0 < x < 2$ **d)** $x < 0, x > 2$ **4. a)** $|x| > \frac{1}{2}$ **b)** $|x| < \frac{1}{2}$ **c)** $x > 0$ **d)** $x < 0$
5. a) $x > \sqrt[3]{2}$ **b)** $x < \sqrt[3]{2}$ **c)** $x > 0, x < -\sqrt[3]{4}$ **d)** $-\sqrt[3]{4} < x < 0$ **6. a)** $x < 0, x > 2$ **b)** $0 < x < 2$ **c)** $x \ne 0$ **d)** Never
7. a) $x < 0$ **b)** $x > 0$ **c)** $x \ne 0$ **d)** Never **8. a)** $x \ne -1$ **b)** Never **c)** $x < -1$ **d)** $x > -1$ **9. a)** $x \ne 0$ **b)** Never
  c) $x < 0$ **d)** $x > 0$ **10. a)** $-1 < x < 0, x > 1$ **b)** $x < -1, 0 < x < 1$ **c)** $x < -1/\sqrt{3}, x > 1/\sqrt{3}$ **d)** $|x| < 1/\sqrt{3}$
11. a) $x < -2b/a, x > 0$ **b)** $-2b/a < x < 0$ **c)** $x > -b/a$ **d)** $x < -b/a$
12. a) $x < 1, x > 2$ **b)** $1 < x < 2$ **c)** $x > \frac{3}{2}$ **d)** $x < \frac{3}{2}$ **13. a)** $x < -1, x > \frac{1}{3}$ **b)** $-1 < x < \frac{1}{3}$ **c)** $x > -\frac{1}{3}$ **d)** $x < -\frac{1}{3}$
14. a) $0 < x < 4$ **b)** $x < 0, x > 4$ **c)** $x < 2$ **d)** $x > 2$
15. a) At $x = 1$; because y' goes from $+$ to $-$. **b)** At $x = 3$; because y' goes from $-$ to $+$.
17. If $v = k/\sqrt{s}$, then $dv/dt = -k^2/2s^2$ **18.** $k^2/2$ **19.** $\frac{1}{4}$ in/min **20.** $(3/400\pi)$ ft/min
21. $dr/dt = -(3/400)$ ft/min. $dA/dt = -\frac{6}{5}\pi$ ft²/min. $\Delta r \approx -(3/4000)$ ft; $\Delta A \approx -(3\pi/25)$ ft²
22. a) Approx. 606 mi/hr **b)** Approx. 0.83 mi **23.** $\frac{1}{2}\sqrt{3}$ **24.** $-480\sqrt{2}/7$ **25.** Yes, it will fill, because $dy/dt > 0.007$ for $y \le 10$.
26. $a = -gR^2/s^2$ **28.** $(\sqrt{3}/30)r$, increasing **29.** ≈ 18 mi/hr **30.** $(8/9\pi)$ ft/min **31.** $\frac{20}{3}$ and $\frac{40}{3}$ **32.** 10 **33.** 18 and 18. No.
34. $a = 1; b = -3; c = -9; d = 5$ **35.** $\frac{1}{2}$ **36.** $r = 25$ ft **37.** $t = 1, s = 16$ **38.** $r = 4, h = 4$ **39.** Diameter = height = 4 in
40. $4\sqrt{3}$ **41.** 276 (approx.) **42. a)** $(2, \pm\sqrt{3})$ **b)** and **c)** $(1, 0)$ **43. a)** $2\frac{1}{12}$ mi from A; **b)** $2\frac{1}{12}$ mi from A; **c)** at B
44. a) True **b)** False **c)** True **d)** False **45.** Each $= (P - b)/2$ **46.** Each $= \tan^{-1}(4k/b^2)$ **48.** $m = \frac{1}{4}$
50. Sides 100 m; radius of semicircular ends $100/\pi$ m **57.** 6×18 ft **58.** Approx. 16.4 in. **59.** $(h^{2/3} + w^{2/3})^{3/2}$ m
60. $v = \sqrt[n]{a/((n - 1)b)}$ **61.** $r = \sqrt{A}$, $\theta = 2$ rad **62.** Approx. 1.94 gal **63. a)** A decreasing 0.04π cm²/sec
  b) $t = (5b - 3a)/(a^2 - b^2)$ **64.** $t = (R - cr)/(ca - b)$, where $c = \sqrt{a/b}$ **66. a)** True **b)** Not necessarily true: $f(x) = g(x) = 5 + x + x^3$ for $|x| \le 1, a = 0$. **67.** $x = (1/n)\sum_{i=1}^{n} c_i$ **68.** $m = \frac{5}{7}$ **70.** Doesn't apply; derivative doesn't exist at $x = 0$. **72.** $c = \pm((b^{2/3} + a^{1/3}b^{1/3} + a^{2/3})/3)^{3/2}$ **73.** Root -0.67 **75. a)** $x = (c - b)/(2e)$ **b)** $P = \frac{1}{2}(b + c)$
  c) $-a + (c - b)^2/(4e)$ **d)** $P = \frac{1}{2}(b + t + c)$; that is, it adds $\frac{1}{2}t$ to its previous price. **76. a)** $\frac{10}{3}$ **b)** $\frac{5}{3}$ **c)** $\frac{1}{2}$ **d)** 0

CHAPTER 4

Article 4–2, p. 181

1. $y = (x^3/3) + x + C$ **2.** $y = -(1/x) + (x^2/2) + C$ **3.** $y^2 = x^2 + C$ **4.** $3y^{1/2} = x^{3/2} + C$ **5.** $y^{2/3} = x^{2/3} + C$ **6.** $-(1/y) = x^2 + C$ **7.** $y = x^3 - x^2 + 5x + C$ **8.** $s = t^3 + 2t^2 - 6t + C$ **9.** $r = (2z + 1)^4/8 + C$ **10.** $-u^{-1} = 2v^4 - 4v^{-2} + C$
11. $x^{1/2} = 4t + C$ **12.** $y = 4t^3/3 + 4t - t^{-1} + C$ **13.** $y = z^3/3 - z^{-1} + C$ **14.** $x^2 + 3x + C$ **15.** $(x^3/3) - (2x^{3/2}/3) + C$

16. $(3x - 1)^{235}/705 + C$ **17.** $-3(2 - 7t)^{5/3}/35 + C$ **18.** $2(2 + 5y)^{3/2}/15 + C$ **19.** $-1/(9x + 6) + C$ **20.** $-3\sqrt{1 - r^2} + C$
21. $(2x^2 + 1)^{3/2}/6 + C$ **22.** $\frac{1}{2}(1 + 2t^3)^{1/3} + C$ **23.** $\frac{1}{2}\sqrt{2y^2 + 1} + C$ **24.** $\frac{2}{3}x^{3/2} + 2x^{1/2} + C$ **25.** $\frac{3}{4}(z^2 + 2z + 2)^{2/3} + C$

Article 4-3, p. 184

1. $s = t^3 + s_0$ **2.** $s = t^2 + t + s_0$ **3.** $s = \frac{1}{3}(t + 1)^3 - \frac{1}{3} + s_0$ **4.** $s = \frac{1}{5}t^5 + \frac{2}{3}t^3 + t + s_0$ **5.** $s = -(t + 1)^{-1} + 1 + s_0$ **6.** $s = s_0$
$+ t\sqrt{2gs_0} + \frac{1}{2}gt^2$ **7.** $v = gt + v_0$; $s = \frac{1}{2}gt^2 + v_0 t + s_0$ **8.** $v = \frac{1}{2}t^2 + v_0$; $s = \frac{1}{6}t^3 + v_0 t + s_0$ **9.** $v = \frac{3}{8}(2t + 1)^{4/3} + v_0 - \frac{3}{8}$;
$s = \frac{9}{112}(2t + 1)^{7/3} + (v_0 - \frac{3}{8})t + s_0 - \frac{9}{112}$ **10.** $v = -\frac{1}{4}(2t + 1)^{-2} + v_0 + \frac{1}{4}$; $s = \frac{1}{8}(2t + 1)^{-1} + (v_0 + \frac{1}{4})t + s_0 - \frac{1}{8}$ **11.** $v = $
$\frac{1}{5}t^5 + \frac{2}{3}t^3 + t + v_0$; $s = \frac{1}{30}t^6 + \frac{1}{6}t^4 + \frac{1}{2}t^2 + v_0 t + s_0$ **13.** $y = 3x^3 - 2x^2 + 5x + 10$ **14.** $y = (x - 7)^4 + 9$
15. $y = \frac{2}{3}x^{3/2} + \frac{4}{5}x^{5/4} - 2$ **16.** $y = x - (1/x) + 1$ **17.** $4\sqrt{y} = x^2 + 4$ **18.** $-y^{-1} = x^2 - 2$ **19.** $(3y + 10)^2 = (1 + x^2)^3$
20. $(1 + y^2)^{-(1/2)} = (1/\sqrt{2}) - 4x$ **21. a)** $R(x) = 250\sqrt{x} + (100/x) - 101$ **b)** \$1,035.03

Article 4-4, pp. 187-188

1. $-\frac{1}{3}\cos 3x + C$ **2.** $\frac{1}{2}\sin (2x + 4) + C$ **3.** $-\frac{1}{4}\cos (2x^2) + C$ **4.** $2 \sin \sqrt{x} + C$ **5.** $-\frac{1}{2}\cos 2t + C$ **6.** $\frac{1}{3}\sin (3\theta - 1) + C$
7. $\frac{4}{3}\sin 3y + C$ **8.** $\sin^2 z + C$ **9.** $\frac{1}{3}\sin^3 x + C$ **10.** $-\frac{1}{6}\cos^3 2y + C$ **11.** $\frac{1}{3}\sin 3t - \frac{1}{9}\sin^3 3t + C$ **12.** $(1/\cos x) + C$
13. $-(1/\sin x) + C$ **14.** $\frac{2}{9}(2 + \sin 3t)^{3/2} + C$ **15.** $\sqrt{2 - \cos 2t} + C$ **16.** $\frac{1}{2}\sin^4 (y/2) + C$ **17.** $3 \sec [(z - 1)/3] + C$
18. $-\frac{1}{2}\cos^3 (2x/3) + C$ **19.** $\frac{1}{5}(1 + \sin 2t)^{5/2} + C$ **20.** $-\frac{3}{2}\cos 2x + \frac{4}{3}\sin 3x + C$ **21.** $\frac{1}{3}(\sin^3 t - \cos^3 t) + C$
22. $x \sin x + C$ **23.** $y^2 = (5x^2/2) + 3 \cos x - 3$ **24.** $y^{3/2} = \frac{3}{2}\sin \pi x - \frac{1}{2}$ **25.** Yes; from the identities $\cos^2 x + \sin^2 x = 1$,
$\cos 2x = \cos^2 x - \sin^2 x$, we find that the constants have to satisfy the relations: $C_2 = C_1 + 1, C_3 = C_1 + \frac{1}{2}$.

Article 4-5, p. 191

1. 1.75, 2.25   **2.** 0.25, 1.25   **3.** $\pi/(2\sqrt{2}) \approx 1.12$, $(\pi/2)(1 + (1/\sqrt{2})) \approx 2.68$ **4.** 0.6345, 0.7595   **5.** 4.146, 6.146   **6.** $\sum_{k=1}^{5} (1/k) =$
$\frac{1}{1} + \frac{1}{2} + \frac{1}{3} + \frac{1}{4} + \frac{1}{5}$ **7.** $\sum_{i=-1}^{3} 2^i = 2^{-1} + 2^0 + 2^1 + 2^2 + 2^3 = \frac{1}{2} + 1 + 2 + 4 + 8$ **8.** $\sum_{n=1}^{4} \cos n\pi x = \cos \pi x + \cos 2\pi x +$
$\cos 3\pi x + \cos 4\pi x$ **9.** $\frac{5}{3}$ **10.** $\frac{7}{6}$ **11.** 1

Article 4-7, p. 200

1. 12   **2.** 4   **3.** $8\frac{2}{3}$ **4.** 2   **5.** $\frac{1}{15}$ **6.** $57\frac{1}{3}$ **7.** 10   **8.** $4\frac{1}{3}$ **9.** 1   **10.** $\frac{2}{9}$ **11.** $\frac{1}{2}$ **12.** $10\frac{2}{3}$ **13.** 2   **14.** $\frac{2}{3}$ **15.** $\frac{4}{3}$ **16.** $\frac{2}{3}$
17. $\pi/6$ **18. b)** $\pi a^2/4$

Article 4-8, pp. 209-210

1. a) $c_k = \frac{1}{2}(x_k + x_{k-1})$ **b)** $c_k = \pm\sqrt{(x_{k-1}^2 + x_{k-1} x_k + x_k^2)/3}$, the sign being determined by the interval (x_{k-1}, x_k)
   c) $c_k = \sqrt[3]{(x_{k-1}^3 + x_{k-1}^2 x_k + x_{k-1} x_k^2 + x_k^3)/4}$ **d)** $c_k = ((\sqrt{x_{k-1}} + \sqrt{x_k})/2)^2$ **4.** $S_n = b^4/4$ **5.** $S_n = 2(\sqrt{b} - 1)$ **6.** 8   **7.** $\frac{7}{3}$
8. $\frac{8}{3}$ **9.** $\frac{13}{3}$ **10.** 2   **11.** 0   **12.** $\sqrt{2} - 1$ **13.** $\frac{1}{2}$ **14.** $\pi/2$ **15.** π/w **16.** $\frac{2}{9}$
17. a) $A = \lim_{n\to\infty} \sum_{k=1}^{n} (18 - 2x_k^2) \Delta x_k, (x_1 = -3, x_{n+1} = 3)$ **b)** $A = \int_{-3}^{3} (18 - 2x^2) dx = 72$ **18.** $\sqrt{1 + x^2}$ **19.** $1/x$
20. $-\sqrt{1 - x^2}$ **21.** $1/(1 + x^2)$ **22.** $2 \cos (4x^2)$ **23.** $2x/(1 + \sqrt{1 - x^2})$ **24.** $-\cos x/(2 + \sin x)$

Article 4-9, pp. 218-219

1. $\int_a^b f(x) dx = T - [(b - a)/12]f''(e)h^2$ **a)** Concave upward over $a < x < b$, then $f''(e) > 0$, $T > \int_a^b f(x) dx$ **b)** Concave
downward over $a < x < b$, then $f''(e) < 0$, $T < \int_a^b f(x) dx$ **2. a)** 2   **b)** 2   **c)** 2   **d)** 1 (smallest possible for trapezoidal
method)   **e)** 2 (smallest possible for Simpson's method)   **3. a)** $\frac{11}{4}$ **b)** $\frac{8}{3}$ **c)** $\frac{8}{3}$ **d)** 366   **e)** 2   **4. a)** $\frac{17}{4}$ **b)** 4   **c)** 4
d) 895   **e)** 2   **5. a)** ≈ 0.50899 **b)** ≈ 0.50042 **c)** $\frac{1}{2}$ (or 0.5)   **d)** 224   **e)** 18 (must be even)   **6. a)** ≈ 4.65509
b) ≈ 4.66622 **c)** $\frac{14}{3}$ (≈ 4.66667)   **d)** 238   **e)** 20   **7. a)** ≈ 1.89612 $((\pi/4)(1 + \sqrt{2}))$ **b)** ≈ 2.00456 $((\pi/6)(1 + 2\sqrt{2}))$
c) 2   **d)** 509   **e)** 22   **8. a)** $\frac{1}{4800} \leq |E_T| \leq \frac{1}{600}$ **b)** $4.1\overline{6} \times 10^{-6} \leq |E_S| \leq 1.\overline{3} \times 10^{-5}$ **9.** $n \geq 8$ (With $n = 8$, one gets
≈ 0.69315453. Compare with: $\ln 2 \approx 0.69314718$.)   **10.** milligram-seconds/liter   **12. a)** 40.25 lumen-milliseconds
b) 55.50 lumen-milliseconds

Article 4-10, p. 223

1. $\int_a^b f(t) dt = -\int_b^a f(t) dt$; $\int_a^c f(t) dt = \int_a^b f(t) dt + \int_b^c f(t) dt$; $(d/dx)\int_a^x f(t) dt = f(x)$; $\int_a^b f(t) dt = f(c) \cdot (b - a)$;
$\int_a^b f(t) dt = F(b) - F(a)$.   **2. a)** $(\pi - 4)/2\pi$ **b)** $\frac{55}{42}$ **3. a)** $\frac{1}{2}$, -1 **b)** $\sqrt{\frac{1}{2}}$, $(\frac{9}{2})^{-(1/3)}$ **c)** $\frac{2}{3}$, $-\frac{2}{5}$

Miscellaneous Problems Chapter 4, pp. 224-225

1. $x^2 y + 2 = cy$ **2.** $3\sqrt{y + 1} = (1 + x)^{3/2} + C$ **3.** $y^3 + 3y = x^3 - 3x + C$ **4.** $3(x^2 - y^2) + 4(x^{3/2} + y^{3/2}) = C$

5. $(2 + x)^{-1} = -(3 - y)^{-1} + C$ **6. a)** $y = \frac{1}{3}(x^2 - 4)^{3/2} + 3$ **b)** $y^2(1 - x^2) = 1$ **7.** Yes; $y = x$ is such a curve.

8. $y = x^3 + 2x - 4$ **9.** $(2\sqrt{2}/3)b^{3/4}$ **10. a)** $v = \frac{2}{3}t^{3/2} - 2\sqrt{t} + \frac{4}{3}$ **b)** $s = \frac{4}{15}t^{5/2} - \frac{4}{3}t^{3/2} + \frac{4}{3}t - \frac{4}{15}$

11. $v = t^2 + 3t + 4, \Delta s = 61\frac{1}{3}$ **12.** -8 ft/sec [*Note.* $d^2x/dt^2 = v(dv/dx)$, where $v = dx/dt$.]   **13.** $h(10) = h(0) = 5$

14. $(1 + y')(1 + y'^2) + y''(y - x) = 0$ **15. a)** $k = 38.72$ ft/sec^2 **b)** 25 ft   **16.** $3y = (1 + x^2)^{3/2} - 7$ **17.** $h = 96t - 16t^2$; 144 ft

19. a) ≈ 1.76 **b)** ≈ 1.73 **20. a)** 4 ft/sec   **b)** $\frac{64}{3}$ ft   **21.** $(x^2/2) - x^{-1} + C$ **22.** $\frac{1}{3}(y^2 + 1)^{3/2} + C$ **23.** $-\frac{1}{8}(1 + t^{4/3})^{-6} + C$

24. $\frac{4}{3}(1 + \sqrt{u})^{3/2} + C$ **25.** $-\frac{3}{5}(7 - 5r)^{1/3} + C$ **26.** $\frac{1}{4}\sin 4x + C$ **27.** $\frac{1}{9}\sin^3 3x + C$ **28.** $2\sqrt{\sin x} + C$ **29.** $\frac{1}{2}\sin(2x - 1) + C$

30. $-\frac{1}{4}\sqrt{25 - 4y^2} + C$ **31.** $-\sqrt{2/t} + C$ **32.** $\frac{1}{3}(x^3 - 2x^{3/2}) + C$ **33.** $\frac{1}{3}(2 - 3x)^{-1} + C$ **35.** $r\sqrt{2}/2$ ft   **37.** $|a|$

38. Yes; no; applies to identities, but not to equations.   **39.** 480π mi/hr   **40.** $|3a\omega \sin\theta \cos\theta|$ **41.** $f(x) = x/\sqrt{x^2 + 1}$

42. $\int_0^1 f(x)\,dx$ **43. a)** $\frac{1}{16}$ **b)** $\frac{2}{3}$ **c)** $2/\pi$ **d)** $\sqrt{1 + x^2} - x$ **e)** $x_1 f(x_1)$ **44.** $d^2y/dx^2 = 4y$

CHAPTER 5

Article 5–2, p. 230

1. a) $\lim_{\Delta y \to 0} \sum_a^b (f(y) - g(y))\,\Delta y$ **b)** $\int_a^b (f(y) - g(y))\,dy$ **2.** $\frac{4}{3}$ **3.** $\frac{1}{12}$ **4.** $\frac{32}{3}$ **5.** $\frac{32}{3}$ **6.** $\frac{1}{6}$ **7.** $\frac{4}{3}$ **8.** $\frac{128}{15}$ **9.** $\sqrt{2} - 1$

10. $\sqrt[3]{16} \approx 2.52$ **11.** $\frac{1}{6}$ **12.** $A \approx 3.141591$ (Actual area $= \pi$)

Article 5–3, pp. 233–234

1. 6 ft   **2.** $5\frac{1}{6}$ ft   **3.** $3\frac{2}{3}$ ft   **4.** 1 ft   **5.** 6 ft   **6.** 8 ft   **7.** $2\sqrt{2}$ ft   **8.** $2\frac{2}{3}$ ft   **9.** $6 - \sin 2 \approx 5.09$ ft   **10.** $1 + \cos 2 \approx 0.58$ ft

11. $2g$ **12.** $4\frac{29}{30}$ ft   **13.** $3\frac{1}{6}$ ft   **15.** 1.56 miles (using Simpson's rule with $n = 12$)

Article 5–4, p. 239

1. $8\pi/3$ **2.** $\pi^2/2$ **3.** $\pi/30$ **4.** $81\pi/10$ **5.** $16\pi/15$ **6.** $128\pi/7$ **7.** $\pi/9$ **8.** π **9. a)** $32\pi/5$ **b)** $8\pi/3$

10. a) $\pi r^2 h/3$ **b)** $2\pi h^2 r/3$ **11. a)** $\pi h^2(a - h/3)$ **b)** $0.1/12\pi$ ft/sec $= 6/\pi$ in/min   **12.** $\frac{4}{3}\pi ab^2$ **13.** $512\pi/15$ **14.** $16a^3/3$

15. $8a^3/3$ **16.** $8a^3/3$ **17.** $\pi\sqrt{3}/16$ **18.** 15,990 ft^3

Article 5–5, pp. 245–246

1. $8\pi/3$ **2.** $8\pi/3$ **3.** $56\pi/15$ **4.** $2\pi/3$ **5.** $256\pi/5$ **6.** $48\pi/5$ **7.** $117\pi/5$ **8.** $108\pi/5$ **9.** $\pi/3$ **10.** $64\pi/5$ **11. a)** $5\pi/3$ **b)** $4\pi/3$

12. $4\pi/15$ **13. a)** 8π **b)** $224\pi/15$ **14.** $\pi/2$ **15.** $4\pi/5$ **16.** $32\pi/3$ **17.** $2\pi^2$

18. a) 8π **b)** $512\pi/15$ **c)** $256\pi/5$ **d)** $1088\pi/15$ **e)** $128\pi/3$ **19.** $2\pi^2 a^2 b$

Article 5–7, pp. 254–255

1. 12   **2.** $\frac{8}{27}(10\sqrt{10} - 1)$ **3.** $\frac{14}{3}$ **4.** $\frac{53}{6}$ **5.** $\frac{123}{32}$ **6.** $\frac{4}{27}(10\sqrt{10} - 1)$ **7.** $a\pi^2/8$ **8.** 8   **9.** 12   **10.** $\frac{21}{2}$ **11.** 3.8202824

Article 5–8, p. 260

1. $99\pi/2$ **2.** $(\pi/27)(10\sqrt{10} - 1)$ **3.** $(\pi/6)(17\sqrt{17} - 1)$ **4.** $1823\pi/18$ **5.** $253\pi/20$ **6.** $(2\pi/3)(2\sqrt{2} - 1)$ **7.** $(\pi/6)(5\sqrt{5} - 1)$

8. $12\pi a^2/5$ **9.** $(2\pi/3)(26\sqrt{26} - 2\sqrt{2})$ **10.** $56\pi\sqrt{3}/5$

Article 5–9, pp. 263–264

1. a) $2/\pi$ **b)** 0   **2. a)** $\frac{1}{2}$ **b)** $\frac{1}{2}$ **3.** $\frac{49}{12}$ **4.** $\frac{1}{2}$ **5.** $\alpha((a + b)/2) + \beta$ **6.** $I_{av} = 300$; 6 dollars/day

7. $I_{av} = 200$; 1 dollar/day   **8.** 25°F   **9. a)** Average $= 67.25/60.00 \approx 1.12$ millions of lumens/millisecond   **b)** $t \approx 87.91$ seconds

10. $\pi a/2$ **11.** $4a/\pi$ **12.** $8a^2/3$ **13.** $2a^2$

Article 5–10, p. 270

1. $(4a/3\pi, 4a/3\pi)$ **2.** $(0, \frac{2}{5}h^2)$ **3.** $(2a/(3(4 - \pi)), 2a/(3(4 - \pi)))$ **4.** $(\pi/2, \pi/8)$ **5.** $(\frac{2}{5}, 1)$ **6.** $\frac{3}{7}h$ **7.** $\frac{3}{5}h$

8. On the axis, $(3h/4)$ from the vertex.   **9.** On the axis, $(3h/5)$ from the vertex.   **10.** On the axis, $(h/2)$ from the vertex.   **11.** $(0, \pi r/4)$

Article 5–11, pp. 273–274

1. $(0, 2c^2/5)$ **2.** $(\frac{16}{105}, \frac{8}{15})$ **3.** $(0, \frac{12}{5})$ **4.** $(1, -\frac{3}{5})$ **5.** $(\frac{3}{5}, 1)$ **6.** On the axis, $(3h/4)$ from the vertex.   **7.** $(0, \frac{8}{5})$ **8.** $(\frac{4}{5}, 0)$

9. On the axis, $(2h/3)$ from the vertex.   **10.** $(-r, 3r/(2 + \pi))$ **11.** $(17\sqrt{17} - 1)/12$ **12.** $(2r/\pi, 2r/\pi)$

Article 5–12, pp. 276–277

2. $(0, 2r/\pi)$ 3. $2\pi(\pi - 2)r^2$ 4. $[(3\pi + 4)/3]\pi r^3$ 5. $[(3\pi + 4)/3(\pi r^3/\sqrt{2})]$ 6. $\pi\sqrt{2}(\pi + 2)r^2$ 7. $2r^3/3$
8. $(4 + 3\pi)r^3/6$ 9. $(4 + 3\pi)r^3/(6\sqrt{2})$

Article 5–13, p. 280

1. 375 lb   2. $111\frac{1}{9}$ lb   3. $1666\frac{2}{3}$ lb   4. $116\frac{2}{3}$ lb   5. $41\frac{2}{3}$ lb   6. 975 tons   7. 8450 ton-ft

Article 5–14, pp. 284–285

1. $c = 5$ lb/in; 80 inch-lb   2. a) $c = 200$ lb/in   b) 400 inch-lb   c) 8 inches   3. a) 1250 inch-lb   b) 3750 inch-lb
4. a) $\frac{5}{2}$ ft-lb   b) 12 ft   5. $18\frac{3}{4}$ inch-lb; 300 lb   6. $c = (10/\sin 10°)$ lb; 78.5 inch-lb   7. $\frac{1}{2}k$, where k is the proportionality
factor   8. $\frac{1}{3}k$, k as above   9. $\frac{1}{2}mgR$ 10. 1944 ft-lb   12. (Work done *on* the gas) = −(Work done *by* the gas) =
$3164\frac{1}{16}$ ft-lb   13. $(200\pi/3)$ ft-tons   14. 27.2 ft-tons

Miscellaneous Problems Chapter 5, pp. 285–287

1. $\frac{9}{2}$ 2. $6\frac{3}{4}$ 3. 1   4. $(7 - 4\sqrt{2})/2$ 5. $\frac{9}{2}$ 6. $\frac{32}{3}$ 7. 18   8. $3^5/2^3$ 9. $a^2/6$ 10. $1 - \cos x_0 - (\sqrt{2}/4)x_0^2 \approx 0.137087$,
where $x_0 \approx 1.391557$ is the root of $\sin x = x/\sqrt{2}$, $x > 0$.   11. 8   12. $(\pi^2/32) + ((\sqrt{2}/2) - 1) \approx 0.015532$ 13. $\frac{13}{3}$ 14. $\frac{9}{8}$
15. $\frac{64}{3}$ 16. a) $0 \le x < 2$ b) $2 < x < 3$ c) $\frac{29}{2}$ ft   17. a) $\frac{3}{7}$ b) $\frac{3}{8}$ c) $y = 3/(2\sqrt{1 + 3x})$ d) $\frac{3}{7}$ 18. $f(x) = \sqrt{(2x - a)/\pi}$
19. a) $3^5\pi/5$ b) $189\pi/2$ c) $81\pi/2$ d) $2^9\pi/15$ e) $2^7\pi/3$ 20. $f(x) = \pm\sqrt{(2x + 1)/\pi}$ 21. $32\pi/3$ 22. a) $2\pi a^3$ b) $(\frac{16}{15})\pi a^3$
c) $(\frac{8}{5})\pi a^3$ 23. $V = 2\pi \int_0^2 x^2/\sqrt{x^3 + 8}\, dx = (8\pi/3)(2 - \sqrt{2})$ 24. $(\pi/15)(88\sqrt{2} + 107)$ 25. $112\pi a^3/15$ 26. $V = hs^2$
27. $(\frac{8}{3})r^3$ 28. $\pi^2/4$ 29. $28\pi/3$ 30. $72\pi/35$ 31. $2\sqrt{3}a^3$ 32. $\frac{19}{3}$ 33. $424\pi/15$ 34. $\frac{27}{20}$ 35. $153\pi/40$
36. $(a/3)(3\sqrt{3} - 1)$ 37. a) $\frac{2}{3}b^2$ b) $\frac{2}{3}b$ 38. a) $f(x) = a \pm x\sqrt{A^2 - 1}$, $|A| \ge 1$ b) No   39. a) $\bar{v} = 72$ b) $82\frac{2}{3}$ 40. Volume
401π; average area 40.1π 41. $(\frac{9}{10}, \frac{9}{5})$ 42. $(\frac{3}{2}, \frac{12}{5})$ 43. $(1, \frac{12}{5})$ 44. $(\frac{3}{4}, \frac{3}{10})$ 46. a) $(5a/7, 0)$ b) $(2a/3, 0)$ 47. a) $\bar{x} = \bar{y} = 4(a^2 + ab + b^2)/(3\pi(a + b))$ b) $(2a/\pi, 2a/\pi)$ 48. a) $(2a/5, 2a/5)$ b) $(0, 15\pi a/256)$ 49. 5 in., $7\frac{1}{2}$ in., $4\frac{8}{9}$ in.   50. 7000/3 lb
51. $5 \times 10^6/3$ lb   52. a) $2h/3$ below surface   b) $(a + h(4a + 3h))/(6a + 4h)$ below surface   53. $504d_1 + 72d_2$
54. $Mah + (h^2/a)$ 55. $k(b - a)/ab$ 56. $wr[1 - (r/2R)]$ ft-lb, R = radius of earth in feet   57. $(320w/3)(15\pi + 8)$ ft-lb

CHAPTER 6

Article 6–1, p. 294

13. $6x \sec^2 (3x^2)$ 14. $-2 \sin x \tan (\cos x) \sec^2 (\cos x)$ 15. $-3 \csc^2 (3x + 5)$ 16. $-\frac{1}{2}(\cot x)^{-(1/2)} \csc^2 x$ 17. 0
18. $\sec^3 x \tan x$ 19. $3(1 + \sec^2 3x)$ 20. $6 \sec^2 2x$ 21. $-\tan^2 x$ 22. $4 \sec^2 x \tan x$ 23. $-2 \csc x(\csc x + \cot x)^2$
24. $12 \sin 3x \cos 3x$, or $6 \sin 6x$ 25. $\frac{1}{2}(1 - \cos 2x)$, or $\sin^2 x$ 26. $\frac{1}{2}(1 + \cos 2x)$, or $\cos^2 x$ 27. $-\cos^3 (x/3)$
28. $-3 \cos (x/2) \sin (x/2)$, or $-\frac{3}{2} \sin x$ 29. $(x/2) \sin (x/2)$ 30. $2x/(\cos y + 2 \cos 2y)$ 31. $3(\sin^2 x \cos x - \cos 3x)$
32. $-5 \cos^3 5x$ 33. $-(\cos^2 (xy) + y)/x$ 34. 10 when $x = -\sin^{-1} (\frac{4}{5})$
35. max $y = \frac{3}{2}$ when $x = \pi/6$; min $y = 1$ when $x = 0$ or $\pi/2$.   36. 61°   38. 1.6π mi/sec   39. 120°   40. $-\frac{1}{3} \cos 3t + C$
41. $\frac{1}{2} \tan 2\theta + C$ 42. $\frac{1}{4} \tan^4 x + C$ 43. $\frac{1}{3} \sec^3 x + C$
44. $2 \sec (x/2) + C$ 45. $\frac{1}{2}y + \frac{1}{4} \sin 2y + C$ 46. $\tan \theta + C$ **54.**
47. $-3 \cot (\theta/3) + C$ 48. $\frac{3}{2}$ 49. $(\pi/4)(4 - \pi)$
50. $\frac{1}{3}$ 51. $\frac{1}{2}$ 52. 2   53. $\frac{1}{6}$

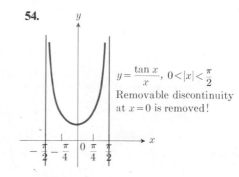

$y = \dfrac{\tan x}{x}$, $0 < |x| < \dfrac{\pi}{2}$
Removable discontinuity
at $x = 0$ is removed!

Article 6–2, p. 299

1. $\sqrt{3}/2, \sqrt{3}/3, 2\sqrt{3}/3, 2$ 2. $\sqrt{3}/2, -\sqrt{3}, -2, 2\sqrt{3}/3$ 3. π 4. $\pi/2$ 5. $-\pi/3$
8. a) 0.735   b) 0.6   c) 0.96   d) $\pi/3$ e) $2\pi/3$ f) $\pi/6$ 9. a) $\theta_2 = \sin^{-1} ((\sin \theta_1)/n_{12})$ b) If $n_{12} \le 1$, max $\theta_1 = \sin^{-1} n_{12}$.
If $n_{12} > 1$, then $0 \le \theta_1 < (\pi/2)$.   10. $c = \pi/4$

Article 6–3, pp. 302–303

5. $1/\sqrt{4-x^2}$ **6.** $1/(9+x^2)$ **7.** $1/(|x|\sqrt{25x^2-1})$ **8.** $-2/\sqrt{1-4x^2}$ **9.** $4/(4+x^2)$ **10.** $1/((x+1)\sqrt{x})$

11. $1/(x^2+1)$ **12.** $\sin^{-1} x$ **13.** $(\sin^{-1} x)^2$ **14.** $\cos^{-1} 2x$ **15.** $\sqrt{b(a+b)}$ ft   **16.** $\pi/6$ **17.** $\pi/2$ **18.** $\pi/12$ **19.** $-\pi/12$

20. $\frac{1}{2}\sin^{-1} 2x + C$ **21.** $\pi/6$ **22.** $y = \begin{cases} \sec^{-1}(2x) + 2 - (\pi/3), & x > \frac{1}{2} \\ -\sec^{-1}(2x) + ((2\pi/3) - 1), & x < -\frac{1}{2} \end{cases}$ **23. a)** 2   **b)** $\frac{6}{5}$ **c)** $\frac{1}{6}$ **d)** $-\frac{1}{3}$

24. $4_S = (7\pi/36) \approx 0.6109$; $A_T = (5\pi/24) \approx 0.6545$ **25.** $(\pi/2) - 1$

Article 6–4, pp. 304–305

1. 0.1826   **2.** 0.3369   **3.** 0.6938   **4.** -0.6956 **5. a)** Circumscribed   **b)** Inscribed   **6. a)** 0.0392   **b)** -0.0408

7. $\pi \ln 2 \approx 2.1776$ **8.** $0.18226 < \ln 1.2 < 0.18267$

Article 6–5, p. 307

1. $(2x+2)/(x^2+2x)$ **2.** $(3/x)(\ln x)^2$ **3.** $-\tan x$ **4.** $\sec x$ **5.** $(1/x) + x/(x^2+1)$ **6.** $(1/x) + 1/(2(x+2))$ **7.** $\ln x$

8. $3x^2 \ln (2x) + x^2$ **9.** $1/(1-x^2)$ **10.** $1/(x(1+x^3))$ **11.** $2/(x(2+3x))$ **12.** $-\tan^{-1}(x/2)$ **13.** $(\tan^{-1} x)/x^2$ **14.** $3(\ln x)^2$ $+ (\ln x)^3$ **15.** $2\cos(\ln x)$ **16.** $\sec^{-1} x$ **17.** $\ln(a^2+x^2)$ **18.** $1/(x \ln x)$ **19.** $\frac{1}{2}\ln|2x+3| + C$ **20.** $-\frac{1}{3}\ln|2-3x| + C$

21. $\frac{1}{8}\ln(4x^2+1) + C$ **22.** $\ln(2 - \cos x) + C$ **23.** $\ln|\sin x| + C$ **24.** $2x - 5\ln|x| + C$ **25.** $x - \ln|x+1| + C$

26. $-\frac{1}{3}\ln|4-x^3| + C$ **27.** $-\frac{1}{2}\ln|1-x^2| + C$ **28.** $2\ln(1+\sqrt{x}) + C$ **29.** $\frac{1}{3}(\ln x)^3 + C$ **30.** $-1/(4x+6) + C$

31. $-\ln|\cos x| + C$ **32.** $\ln|\ln x| + C$ **33.** $\frac{1}{2}(\ln x)^2 + C$ **34. a)** -2 **b)** 0   **c)** 0   **d)** 0   **35.** $\ln(1+\sqrt{2})$

Article 6–6, p. 309

1. $4a$ **2.** $2b/3$ **3.** $3a/2$ **4.** $-2a$ **5.** $2a - 2b$ **6.** $2a + b$ **7.** $2b - 3a$ **8.** $2a + 2b$ **9.** $2b - a$ **10.** $(3b - a)/2$

Article 6–7, p. 311

2. No inflection point since $y'' = 1/x$ is positive because x is positive.   **3.** Slope at $(x, y) = y$. Concave up because $y'' = y' = y$ is positive.   **7.** $\log_{10} N = (\ln N)/(\ln 10)$; 0.30103

Article 6–8, pp. 315–316

1. a) x **b)** x **c)** x^{-2} **d)** $-x^2$ **e)** $1/x$ **f)** $-x$ **g)** $1/x$ **h)** x **i)** $2x$ **j)** x^2 **k)** $x - x^2$ **l)** $-2x + 2\ln x$ **m)** xe^x **n)** x/y^2

2. $(x^2 + 2x)e^x$ **3.** $13e^{2x} \cos 3x$ **4.** $1/(1+e^x)$ **5.** $\frac{1}{2}(e^x + e^{-x})$ **6.** $\frac{1}{2}(e^x - e^{-x})$ **7.** $4/(e^x + e^{-x})^2$ **8.** $e^{\sin^{-1} x}/\sqrt{1-x^2}$

9. $-4xe^{-2x}$ **10.** $27x^2 e^{3x}$ **11.** xe^{ax} **12.** $-2xe^{-x^2}$ **13.** $2e^{-x^2}(x - x^3)$ **14.** $e^x(\ln x + (1/x))$ **15.** $e^x/(1 + e^{2x})$ **16.** $2/\sqrt{e^{4x} - 1}$

17. $\frac{2}{3}e^{2x} \sec(x + 3y) - \frac{1}{3}$ **18.** $-e^{1/x}/x^2$ **19.** $(\cos^2 y)(e^x + (1/x))$ **20. b)** $y = 3e^{-2t}$ **21. a)** $\frac{1}{2}$ **b)** ∞ **22.** $\frac{1}{2}e^{2x} + C$

23. $\frac{1}{2}e^{x^2} + C$ **24.** $e^{\sin x} + C$ **25.** $3e^{x/3} + C$ **26.** $(-4/3)e^{-3x} + C$ **27.** $\frac{1}{2}\ln|1 + 2e^x| + C$ **28.** $\ln 2$

29. $\ln|e^x + e^{-x}| + C$ **30.** $xe^x - e^x + C$ **32.** $M(e, 0.36788)$; $I(4.48, 0.335)$ **33.** $M(0, 1)$; $I(1, 0.736)$ **34.** Relative max $(7\pi/4, 0.003)$; $I(\pi, 0.0432)$; relative min $(3\pi/4, -0.067)$ **35.** $(\pi/2)(e^{-2} - 0.01) \approx 0.1969$ **36.** $\sqrt{2}(e^\pi - 1) \approx 31.312$

Article 6–9, pp. 320–321

1. $(y(2x+1)/(2x(x+1))$ **2.** $-2y/(3(x^2-1))$ **3.** $(y(4x^3 + 6x^2 + x + 3))/(3x(x+1)(x^2+1))$ **4.** $(y/3)[(1/x) + [1/(x+1)] + [1/(x-2)] - [2x/(x^2+1)] - [2/(2x+3)]]$ **5.** $y[(\sin x)/x + \cos x \cdot \ln x]$ **6.** $y[1 + \sec^2 x \cdot \ln(\sin x)]$

7. $y(\sec x \tan x) \ln 2$ **8.** $(2y \ln x)/x$ **11.** $\frac{3}{8}$ **12.** $(3^{1.2} - 1)/\ln 3 \approx 2.49$ **13.** $(4 \ln 4)^{-1} \approx 0.180$ **14.** $24/(50 \ln 5) \approx 0.298$

15. $(2 \ln 4)^{-1} \approx 0.360$ **18. c)** 0.485, 3.2124   **19.** 1, 2

Article 6–10, p. 323

1. a) 2   **b)** $\frac{5}{3}$ **c)** -2 **d)** -2 **2. a)** 2   **b)** $\frac{1}{2}$ **c)** $\frac{4}{3}$ **d)** $\frac{2}{5}$ **3.** $\log_{1.5} 2 = (\ln 2)/(\ln 1.5)$ **4.** 12   **6. a)** 1.30103, 2.30103; 9.30103 − 10, 8.30103 − 10   **b)** 2.99574, 5.29833; 8.39056 − 10, 6.08797 − 10   **7.** f_2 **8.** $m = 1/(\ln 10) \approx 0.43429$

9. a) $3^{\tan x} \sec^2 x \ln 3$ **b)** $y[(1/x) \ln(x^2 + 1) + [2x/(x^2+1)] \ln x]$ **c)** $-2t(\ln 2)2^{-t^2}$ **d)** $e^{-2\theta}(1 - 2\theta)$

Article 6–11, pp. 327–328

1. 17.67 years   **2.** 4.875%   **4.** $(mv_0/k)[1 - e^{-kt/m}]$ where k is a constant of proportionality.   **5.** $Q_0 e^{-kt}$ **6.** $N_0 e^{kt}$ **7.** 1, 3

8. $-1, 2$ **9.** $-5, -1$ **10.** $\pm 3, \pm 2$

Miscellaneous Problems Chapter 6, pp. 328–330

1. $2 \cos 2x$ **2.** $-8 \sin (2x + (\pi/4))$ **3.** $2 \cos x + 2 \cos 2x$ **4.** $(1 + \cos x)^{-1}$ **5.** $-\csc y$ **6.** $\cos^2 y$ **7.** $-2 \cos (x/2)$
8. $-\cos x$ **9.** $1 - \cos x$ **10.** $[(x \cos x - \sin x)/x^2]$ where $y \to 1$ as $x \to 0$ and $y \to 0$ as $x \to \infty$. **11.** $[(x \cos x - 2 \sin x)/x^3]$
where $y \to \infty$ as $x \to 0$ and $y \to 0$ as $x \to \infty$. **12.** $\sin (1/x) - (1/x) \cos (1/x)$ where $y \to 0$ as $x \to 0$ and $y \to 1$ as $x \to \infty$.
13. $2x \sin (1/x) - \cos (1/x)$ where $y \to 0$ as $x \to 0$ and $y \to \infty$ as $x \to \infty$. **14.** $(2/\pi) \cos^2 (\pi y/2)$ **15. a)** $\frac{1}{2}(e^x - e^{-x})$
b) $\frac{1}{2}(e^x + e^{-x})$ **c)** $4(e^x + e^{-x})^{-2}$ **16.** $e^{-x}(1 - x)$ **17. a)** $1 + \ln x$ **b)** $\frac{1}{2}x^{-(1/2)}(2 + \ln x)$ **18. a)** $x^{-2}(1 - \ln x)$
b) $\frac{1}{2}x^{-(3/2)}(2 - \ln x)$ **c)** $x^{-3}(1 - 2 \ln x)$ **19.** $e^{-x}(2 \cos 2x - \sin 2x)$ **20. a)** $2 - e^{2x}$ **b)** $(2 - e^{2x})e^{(2x - (1/2)e^{2x})}$
21. a) $1 - e^x$ **b)** $(1 - e^x)e^{(x - e^x)}$ **22.** $(1 + x^2)^{-(1/2)}$ **23.** $(1 - x^2)^{-1}$ **24.** $2x/(x^2 + 4)$ **25.** $\tan^{-1}(x/2) + 2x/(x^2 + 4)$
26. $8(e^{2x} + e^{-2x})^{-2}$ **27.** $2 \sec x$ **28.** $xe^{2x}(3x \cos 3x + 2x \sin 3x + 2 \sin 3x)$ **29.** $2x(1 - x^4)^{-(1/2)} - (2x^2 + 1)e^{x^2}$
30. $(4 + x^3)/(x(1 + x^3)) + \frac{2}{3}x^{-(1/3)}7^{x^{2/3}} \ln 7$ **31.** $2x(2 - x)(x^2 + 2)^{1-x} - (x^2 + 2)^{2-x} \ln (x^2 + 2)$ **32.** $x^{-1}e^{-x}(1 - x \ln x)$
33. $1/(x(x^2 + 1))$ **34.** $3/(3x - 4)$ **35.** $(6x + 4)/(3x^2 + 4x)$ **36.** $(\ln x)^2(\ln x + 3)$ **37.** $3(1 + \ln x)$ **38.** $x^2(1 + 3 \ln x)$
39. 1 **40.** $(x^2 + 2x)e^x$ **41.** e^x **42.** $1/(x \ln x)$ **43. a)** $(1 - x^2)/((1 + x^2)^2)$ **b)** $\frac{2}{3}(x^2 + x - 1)x^{-(2/3)}(x - 2)^{-(2/3)}(x^2 + 1)^{-(4/3)}$
44. $f(0) = 1; f'(0) = 5; f(0.01) \approx 1.05$ **45. a)** $a^{x^2 - x}(2x - 1) \ln a$ **b)** $(1 + e^x)^{-1}$ **c)** $\ln x$ **d)** $x^{(1 - 2x)/x}(1 - \ln x)$
48. $x = 1 + \sqrt{2}$ **49.** $(d^2y/dx^2) = 4(e^x + e^{-x})^{-2}$; $y = \ln (e^x + e^{-x}) + C$ **50.** $y = \ln |2x - 9|$ **52.** 0.88 **53.** $E = E_0 e^{-t/40}$,
$t = 92.1$ sec **54.** $y/y_1 = (x/x_1)^2$ **55.** $y = 1 - \frac{1}{2}(e^x - e^{-x})$
56. $t(\frac{1}{4}) = 1/\pi$; it will not reach $x = \frac{1}{2}$, because $t = (1/\pi) \tan (\pi x)$. **57.** $1 + 4 \ln \frac{3}{2} \approx 2.62$ **58.** $2\sqrt{2}$ **59.** $y = 2e^x/(2 - e^x)$
60. $N = N_0 e^{0.02t}$, $t = 34.7$ yr **62.** $(\pm a/\sqrt{2}, e^{-(1/2)})$ **63.** $\pi\sqrt{3}$ **64.** $(64a^2 + b^2 \ln 3)/8a$ **65.** $\pi(e^4 - 1)/2 \approx 84.2$
66. $(e - e^{-1})a^2 \approx 2.35a^2$ **67.** $y^2 = 4x$ **68.** $-\frac{1}{3} \ln |4 - 3x| + C$ **69.** $5 \ln |x - 3| + C$ **70.** $\frac{1}{2} \ln 3 \approx 0.550$ **71.** $\frac{1}{6}$
72. $x + \ln x + C$ **73.** $-\frac{1}{4} \ln |2x + 1| + (x/2) + C$ **74.** $\frac{1}{3} \ln 2 \approx 0.23$ **75.** $\frac{1}{2}(e^8 - e^{-1}) \approx 1490$ **76.** $\ln 3 \approx 1.10$
77. $\frac{1}{2} \ln 26 \approx 1.63$ **78.** e **79.** 585 lb **80.** $2000\pi(\frac{9}{10})^t$ ft^3
82. a) No, x could be 4. **b)** Yes; consider the graph of $y = (\ln x)/x$ for $x > 0$. **88.** $e - 1$

CHAPTER 7

Article 7–1, pp. 335–336

1. $\frac{1}{3}(2x + 3)^{3/2} + C$ **2.** $\frac{1}{3} \ln |3x + 5| + C$ **3.** $-1/(4x - 14) + C$ **4.** $\frac{1}{2} \ln |x^2 + 2x + 3| + C$ **5.** $-\ln |2 + \cos x| + C$
6. $\frac{1}{8} \tan^4 2x + C$ **7.** $-\frac{1}{4}\sqrt{1 - 4x^2} + C$ **8.** $\frac{1}{2}(x^{4/3} - 1)^{3/2} + C$ **9.** $\sin^{-1}(2x) + C$ **10.** $\sin^{-1}(v^2) + C$
11. $-1/(12(3x^2 + 4)^2) + C$ **12.** $\frac{2}{9}(x^3 + 5)^{3/2} + C$ **13.** $\frac{2}{3}(x^3 + 5)^{1/2} + C$ **14.** $\frac{1}{8} \ln (4x^2 + 1) + C$ **15.** $\frac{1}{2}e^{2x} + C$
16. $-e^{\cos x} + C$ **17.** $-\frac{1}{3}e^{-3x} + C$ **18.** $2e^{\sqrt{x+1}} + C$ **19.** $\tan^{-1}(e^x) + C$ **20.** $\frac{1}{3} \tan^{-1}(3t) + C$ **21.** $-\frac{1}{3} \cos^3 x + C$
22. $-\frac{1}{2} \csc^2 x + C$ **23.** $-\frac{1}{4} \cot^4 x + C$ **24.** $\frac{1}{6} \tan^2 3x + C$ **25.** $\frac{1}{2} \ln |e^{2x} - e^{-2x}| + C$ **26.** $-\frac{1}{6} \cos^3 2x + C$
27. $-\frac{1}{4}(1 + \cos \theta)^4 + C$ **28.** $-\frac{1}{2}e^{-t^2} + C$ **29.** $\sec^{-1} |2t| + C$ **30.** $\sec^{-1} |e^x| + C$ **31.** $\ln |\sin x| + C$
32. $\ln |1 + \sin x| + C$ **33.** $\frac{1}{3} \sec^3 x + C$ **34.** $-2\sqrt{1 + \cos \theta} + C$ **35.** $\frac{1}{3}e^{\tan 3x} + C$ **36.** $-\frac{1}{3}(4 - \sin 2t)^{3/2} + C$
37. $-\frac{1}{2}(\csc 2x + \cot 2x) + C$ **38.** $x - \frac{1}{2} \sin 2x + C$ **39.** $-\sqrt{1 + \cot 2t} + C$ **40.** $\frac{1}{3}e^{3x} + C$ **41.** $\frac{1}{2}e^{\tan^{-1} 2t} + C$
42. $-\frac{1}{2}e^{-x^2} + C$ **43.** $3^x/(\ln 3) + C$ **44.** $10^{2x}/(2 \ln 10) + C$ **45.** Yes. Constants C differ; $\cos^{-1}(-x) = (\pi/2) + \sin^{-1} x$
46. a) $\pi/2$ **b)** $\pi/2$ **47. a)** $-1; \frac{1}{2}(\ln x)^2 + C$ **b)** $2; \frac{1}{3}e^{x^3} + C$ **c)** $-\frac{1}{2}; -2 \cos \sqrt{x} + C$

Article 7–2, pp. 342–343

1. $\frac{2}{5}(\sin x)^{5/2} + C$ **2.** $-\frac{2}{3}(\cos x)^{3/2} + C$ **3.** $-\frac{2}{3}(1 + \cos t)^{3/2} + C$ **4.** $\ln |2 - \cos \theta| + C$ **5.** $\frac{1}{2} \ln |1 + \tan 2x| + C$
6. $-\frac{1}{3} \ln |\cos 3x| + C$ **7.** $\sin x - \frac{1}{3} \sin^3 x + C$ **8.** $\frac{1}{4} \tan 4\theta - \theta + C$ **9. a)** $\frac{1}{5} \cos^5 x - \frac{1}{3} \cos^3 x + C$ **b)** $\cos x + \sec x + C$
10. $((\sec^n x)/n) + C$ if $n \neq 0$; $\ln |\sec x| + C$ if $n = 0$ **11.** $[(\tan^{n+1} x)/(n + 1)] + C$ if $n \neq -1$; $\ln |\tan x| + C$ if $n = -1$
12. $[(\sin^{n+1} x)/(n + 1)] + C$ if $n \neq -1$; $\ln |\sin x| + C$ if $n = -1$ **13.** $[(-\cos^{n+1} x)/(n + 1)] + C$ if $n \neq -1$; $-\ln |\cos x| +$
C if $n = -1$ **14.** $\frac{1}{9} \sin^3 3x + C$ **15.** $-\frac{1}{8} \cos^4 2x + C$ **16.** $\frac{1}{12} \sec^4 3x + C$ **17.** $\frac{1}{9} \tan^3 3x + \frac{1}{3} \tan 3x + C$ **18.** $\frac{1}{2} \sin 2x$
$- \frac{1}{6} \sin^3 2x + C$ **19.** $\frac{1}{4} \tan^2 2x + \frac{1}{2} \ln |\cos 2x| + C$ **20.** $\frac{1}{3} \sec^3 x - \sec x + C$ **21.** $\frac{1}{3} \cos^3 x - \cos x + C$
22. $-1/(1 + \sin x) + C$ **23.** $\ln |2 + \tan x| + C$ **24.** $-\sin t - \csc t + C$ **25.** $\ln |1 + e^x| + C$ **26.** $[(\ln ax)^{n+1}/(n + 1)] +$
C if $n \neq -1$; $\ln |\ln ax| + C$ if $n = -1$ **27.** $\ln |\ln 3x| + C$ **28.** $-\ln |\sin x| - \frac{1}{2} \cot^2 x + C$ **29.** $-\frac{1}{6} \csc^3 2t + C$
30. $-\cot x - \frac{1}{3} \cot^3 x + C$ **31.** $\ln |\sec x + \tan x| + C$ **32.** $\ln |1 + \sqrt{2}| \approx 0.8814$ **33.** $-\ln |\csc \theta + \cot \theta| + C$
34. a) $25 \ln ((\sqrt{3} + \sqrt{6})/3) \approx 8.302$ cm **b)** $25 \ln ((2 + \sqrt{3})/(1 + \sqrt{2})) \approx 10.890$ cm **35.** $(2\pi/27)[(1 + 9\sqrt[3]{4})^{3/2} - 1] \approx 13.676$
36. $-(\cot^{n-1}(ax))/((n - 1)a) - \int \cot^{n-2}(ax) \, dx$; $-[(\cot^3 3x)/9] + [(\cot 3x)/3] + x + C$ **37.** $\ln (2 + \sqrt{3}) \approx 1.317$

Article 7–3, p. 345

1. $(x/8) - [(\sin 4x)/32] + C$ **2.** $(y/16) - [(\sin 4y)/64] - [(\sin^3 2y)/48] + C$ **3.** $(t/2) - \frac{1}{8} \sin 4t + C$ **4.** $(\theta/2) + \frac{1}{12} \sin 6\theta + C$
5. $\frac{3}{8}x - (1/4a) \sin 2ax + (1/32a) \sin 4ax + C$ **6.** $\tan x - \frac{3}{2}x + [(\sin 2x)/4] + C$ **7.** $\tan x + C$ **8.** $-\frac{1}{3} \cot^3 x - \cot x + C$

9. $-\frac{1}{6}\csc^3 2t + C$ **10.** $\frac{5}{16}x - \frac{1}{4}\sin 2x + \frac{3}{64}\sin 4x + \frac{1}{48}\sin^3 2x + C$ **11.** 4 **12.** $2\sqrt{2}$ **13.** 2/5 **14.** 8 **15.** $64\pi/3$ **16.** $\pi^2/2$

Article 7–4, p. 352

1. $0.2a$ **2.** $\frac{1}{2}\sin^{-1} 2x + C$ **3.** $\pi a^2/4$ **4.** $\sin^{-1}((x-1)/2) + C$ **5.** $\frac{1}{2}\ln|\sec 2t + \tan 2t| + C$ **6.** $\ln(1+\sqrt{2}) \approx 0.88$
7. $\pi/6$ **8.** $\sqrt{4+x^2} + C$ **9.** $\frac{1}{2}\ln 2$ **10.** $\pi/8$ **11.** $\frac{1}{4}\ln 3 = 0.2747$ **12.** $(2-\sqrt{2})/3$ **13.** $(1/a)\ln|x/(a+\sqrt{a^2+x^2})| + C$
14. $-\sqrt{4-x^2} + \sin^{-1}(x/2) + C$ **15.** $(1/\sqrt{5})\sin^{-1}(x\sqrt{\frac{5}{2}}) + C$ **16.** $\cos^{-1}((\cos\theta)/\sqrt{2}) + C$ **17.** $(1/|a|)\sec^{-1}|x/a| + C$
18. $(1/a)\ln|x/(a+\sqrt{a^2-x^2})| + C$ **19.** $(1/a^2)(x/\sqrt{a^2-x^2}) + C$ **20.** $(1/2a^3)(\tan^{-1}(x/a) + ax/(a^2+x^2)) + C$ **21.** $3\pi/4$
22. $2\sqrt{2}$ **23.** $\cos\theta = \sqrt{1-(u^2/4)} = \frac{1}{2}\sqrt{4-u^2}$; $\tan\theta = u/\sqrt{4-u^2}$ **24. a)** $u/\sqrt{a^2+u^2}$ **b)** a/u

Article 7–5, p. 355

1. $\pi/8$ **2.** $\sqrt{x^2-2x+5} + \ln|x-1+\sqrt{x^2-2x+5}| + C$ **3.** $2\sin^{-1}(x-1) - \sqrt{2x-x^2} + C$ **4.** $\sqrt{x^2-4x+3} +$
$\ln|x-2+\sqrt{x^2-4x+3}| + C$ **5.** $2\sin^{-1}[(x-2)/3] - \sqrt{5+4x-x^2} + C$ **6.** $\ln|x-1+\sqrt{x^2-2x-8}| + C$
7. $\sqrt{8+2x-x^2} + C$ **8.** $\sqrt{x^2+4x+5} - 2\ln|x+2+\sqrt{x^2+4x+5}| + C$
9. $\frac{1}{2}\ln(x^2+4x+5) - 2\tan^{-1}(x+2) + C$ **10.** $\frac{1}{4}\ln(4x^2+4x+5) + \frac{1}{2}\tan^{-1}(x+\frac{1}{2}) + C$

Article 7–6, pp. 362–363

1. $\frac{1}{2}\ln|(x+1)/(x-1)| + C$ **2.** $-[(\ln|\theta|)/2] + [(\ln|\theta+2|)/6] + [(\ln|\theta-1|)/3] + C$ **3.** $\frac{1}{6}\ln|(x+5)^5(x-1)| + C$
4. $\frac{3}{4}\ln|x-3| + \frac{1}{4}\ln|x+1| + C$ **5.** $\frac{2}{3}\ln|x+5| + \frac{1}{3}\ln|x-1| + C$ **6.** $x - 2\ln|x+1| - [1/(x+1)] + C$
7. $\ln|x/(x+1)| + [1/(x+1)] + C$ **8.** $\frac{1}{4}\ln[(x+1)^2/(x^2+1)] + \frac{1}{2}\tan^{-1} x + C$
9. $-\frac{3}{8}\ln|x| + \frac{1}{16}\ln|x+2| + \frac{5}{16}\ln|x-2| + C$ **10.** $-\frac{1}{5}\ln|\sin x + 3| + \frac{1}{5}\ln|\sin x - 2| + C$
11. $5x - 5\tan^{-1} x + C$ **12.** $(x^2/2) + 2x + 3\ln|x-1| - [1/(x-1)] + C$
13. $\frac{1}{2}\ln[x^2/(x^2+x+1)] - (1/\sqrt{3})\tan^{-1}((2x+1)/\sqrt{3}) + C$ **14.** $\frac{1}{3}\ln[(2+\cos\theta)/(1-\cos\theta)] + C$
15. $\ln[(1+e^t)/(2+e^t)] + C$ **16.** $\frac{1}{2}(\tan^{-1} x + [x/(1+x^2)]) + C$ **17.** $x - \frac{3}{2}\tan^{-1} x + \frac{1}{2}[x/(1+x^2)] + C$
18. $\ln|x+1| + \ln|x-1| + \ln|x-3| + \ln|x+3| + C$ **19.** Using first method, there is no equation for the coefficient of x^2.
Using Heaviside method, one gets $A = \frac{1}{2}$, $B = -\frac{1}{2}$, yet result is not equivalent to $x^2/(x^2-1)$.
20. If $a = b$: $x = a - (a-x_0)/[1 + kt(a-x_0)]$. If $a \neq b$: $\ln|(a-x)/(b-x)| = (a-b)kt + \ln|(a-x_0)/(b-x_0)|$.

Article 7–7, pp. 367–368

1. $(x^2/2)\ln x - (x^2/4) + C$ **2.** $[x^{n+1}/(n+1)]\ln ax - [x^{n+1}/((n+1)^2)] + C$ **3.** $[(x^2+1)/2]\tan^{-1} x - (x/2) + C$
4. $x\sin^{-1} ax + (1/a)\sqrt{1-a^2x^2} + C$ **5.** $(1/a^2)\sin ax - (1/a)x\cos ax + C$
6. $(2x/a^2)\cos ax - (2/a^3)\sin ax + (x^2/a)\sin ax + C$ **7.** $(x/a)\tan ax - (1/a^2)\ln|\sec ax| + C$
8. $[e^{ax}/(a^2+b^2)](a\sin bx - b\cos bx) + C$ **9.** $(x/2)[\sin(\ln x) - \cos(\ln x)] + C$ **10.** $(x/2)[\sin(\ln x) + \cos(\ln x)] + C$
11. $x\ln(a^2+x^2) - 2x + 2a\tan^{-1}(x/a) + C$ **12.** $(x/2)\sin(2x+1) + \frac{1}{4}\cos(2x+1) + C$
13. $((x^2/2) - \frac{1}{4})\sin^{-1} x + (x/4)\sqrt{1-x^2} + C$ **14.** $(4\pi - 3\sqrt{3})/6$ **15.** $(4\pi - 3\sqrt{3})/3$
16. $(x^3/3)\tan^{-1} x - (x^2/6) + \frac{1}{6}\ln(x^2+1) + C$ **17. b)** $(x^4/32)[8(\ln x)^2 - 4\ln x + 1] + C$ **18. b)** $\pi/16$
19. b) $(x^3 - 3x^2 + 6x - 6)e^x + C$ **20. b)** $\frac{1}{2}(\sec x \tan x + \ln|\sec x + \tan x|) + C$
c) $\frac{1}{2}(x\sqrt{x^2+a^2} + a^2\ln|x+\sqrt{x^2+a^2}|) + C$ **21.** $P(x) = 1 - 3x^2$ **22.** $\pi^2 - 2\pi$ **23.** $\bar{x} = (-2e+6)/(e-2)$;
$\bar{y} = (e^2-3)/[8(e-2)]$ **24.** $\bar{x} = (e^2-3)/4(e-2) \approx 1.53$; $\bar{y} = 1/2(e-2) \approx 0.696$ **25.** 2

Article 7–8, p. 371

1. 2 **2.** 1 **3.** $\tan x + \sec x + C$ **4.** $\pi/3\sqrt{3}$ **5.** $(4/\sqrt{3})\tan^{-1}(\sqrt{3}\tan(x/2)) - x + C$ **6.** $-\frac{2}{5}$ **7.** 0 **8.** π

Article 7–9, p. 374

1. $-x + 4\sqrt{x} - 4\ln|1+\sqrt{x}| + C$ **2.** $(2\sqrt{x}/b) - (2a/b^2)\ln|a+b\sqrt{x}| + C$ **3.** $[2(x+a)^{3/2}/105](15x^2 - 12ax + 8a^2)$
$+ C$ **4.** $2\sqrt{x-a} - 2\sqrt{b-a}\tan^{-1}\sqrt{(x-a)(b-a)} + C$
5. $[(b-a)/2](\ln|(u-1)/(u+1)| - 2u/(u^2-1)) + C$, where $u = \sqrt{(a+x)/(b+x)}$
6. $\frac{1}{2}\ln|x+\sqrt{x^2+a^2}| + [(x\sqrt{a^2+x^2} - x^2)/2a^2] + C$ **7.** $(3\sqrt{2}-4)/2$ **8.** $(1/nc)\ln|x^n/(ax^n+c)| + C$ **9.** $2 + 2\ln(\frac{3}{2})$
10. $3\ln|\sqrt[3]{x} - 1| + C$ **11.** $-1 + 4\ln(\frac{3}{2})$ **12.** $4\ln|\sqrt[4]{x}/(1-\sqrt[4]{x})| + C$
13. $\frac{3}{2}y^{2/3} + \ln|1+y^{1/3}| - \frac{1}{2}\ln|y^{2/3} - y^{1/3} + 1| - \sqrt{3}\tan^{-1}((2y^{1/3}-1)/\sqrt{3}) + C$ **14.** $\frac{2}{9}(z^3-2)\sqrt{z^3+1} + C$
15. $\frac{2}{3}(\sqrt{t^3-1} - \tan^{-1}\sqrt{t^3-1}) + C$ **16.** $\ln(\frac{4}{3})$ **17.** $2 + 4\ln(\frac{2}{3})$
18. $-\frac{1}{2}\ln|\sin x + \cos^2 x| - [1/(2\sqrt{5})]\ln|(2\sin x - 1 - \sqrt{5})/(2\sin x - 1 + \sqrt{5})| + C$
19. $\frac{1}{3}\ln|x+1| - \frac{1}{6}\ln|x^2-x+1| + (1/\sqrt{3})\tan^{-1}((2x-1)/\sqrt{3}) + C$
20. $-2y^{1/2} - 3y^{1/3} - 6y^{1/6} - 6\ln|y^{1/6} - 1| + C$

Article 7–10, p. 382

1. $\pi/2$ **2.** 2   **3.** 6   **4.** 1000   **5.** 4   **6.** $\pi/2$ **7.** $\frac{1}{2}$ **8.** 1000   **9.** Diverges   **10.** Converges   **11.** Converges   **12.** Diverges   **13.** Converges   **14.** Converges   **15.** Diverges   **16.** Diverges   **17.** Converges   **18.** Diverges   **19.** Converges   **20.** 0.88617   **21.** π **23.** 5000 dollars   **24.** $r = [(\ln(\frac{4}{3}))/5] \; (\approx 5.75\%)$ **25. a)** $100/(0.05 - \ln 0.95) \; (\approx 987.23)$ dollars   **b)** 2000 dollars

Miscellaneous Problems Chapter 7, pp. 383–386

1. $2\sqrt{1 + \sin x} + C$ **2.** $(\sin^{-1} x)^2/2 + C$ **3.** $(\tan^2 x)/2 + C$ **4.** $\tan x + \sec x + C$ **5.** $(2x^{3/2})/3 + C$ **6.** $2 \sin \sqrt{x} + C$

7. $\ln|x + 1 + \sqrt{x^2 + 2x + 2}| + C$ **8.** $\ln|(x - 2)(x - 3)/(x - 1)^2| + C$ **9.** $(x^2 - 2x + 2)e^x + C$ **10.** $\frac{1}{2}(\ln|x + \sqrt{x^2 + 1}| + x\sqrt{1 + x^2}) + C$ **11.** $\tan^{-1}(e^t) + C$ **12.** $\tan^{-1}(e^x) + C$ **13.** $2\sqrt{x} - 2\ln(1 + \sqrt{x}) + C$ **14.** $\frac{4}{3}(\sqrt{x} - 2)\sqrt{1 + \sqrt{x}} + C$ **15.** $\frac{9}{25}(t^{5/3} + 1)^{5/3} + C$ **16.** $\ln|\ln \sin x| + C$ **17.** $\ln[(\sqrt{1 + e^t} - 1)/(\sqrt{1 + e^t} + 1)] + C$ **18.** $t + 2\ln(1 + \sqrt{1 - e^{-t}}) + C$ **19.** $e^{\sec x} + C$ **20.** $\tan^{-1}(\sin x) + C$ **21.** $\sin^{-1}(x - 1) + C$ **22.** $\cot^{-1}(\cos x) + C$ **23.** $\frac{1}{2}\ln|1 + \sin 2t| + C$ **24.** $\ln|\tan x| + C$ **25.** $(-2 \cos x)/\sqrt{1 + \sin x} + C$ **26.** $(2 \cos x)/\sqrt{1 - \sin x} + C$

27. $x/(a^2\sqrt{a^2 - x^2}) + C$ **28.** $x/(a^2\sqrt{a^2 + x^2}) + C$ **29.** $\frac{1}{3}\ln[(1 - \cos x)/(4 - \cos x)] + C$ **30.** $\frac{3}{10}(2e^x - 3)(1 + e^x)^{2/3} + C$

31. $\sum_{k=0}^{m}[(-1)^k/(k!(m - k)!)]\ln|x + k| + C$ **32.** $\frac{1}{12}\ln[(x - 1)^2(x^2 - x + 1)/(x + 1)^2(x^2 + x + 1)] - (\sqrt{3}/6)\tan^{-1}(x\sqrt{3}/(1 - x^2)) + C$ **33.** $\frac{1}{3}[(2y^3 + 1)^{-1} + \ln|2y^3/(2y^3 + 1)|] + C$

34. $\frac{2}{3}x^{3/2} - x + 2x^{1/2} - 2\ln(1 + x^{1/2}) + C$ **35.** $\frac{1}{2}[\ln x^2 - \ln(1 + x^2) - x^2(1 + x^2)^{-1}] + C$ **36.** $(x - 1)\ln\sqrt{x - 1} - (x/2) + C$ **37.** $\ln|e^x - 1| - x + C$ **38.** $\frac{1}{4}\ln|(1 + \tan\theta)/(1 - \tan\theta)| + \frac{1}{2}\theta + C$ **39.** $x^{-1} + 2\ln|1 - x^{-1}| + C$

40. $\frac{1}{2}\ln|(x + 3)^3(x + 1)^{-1}| + C$ **41.** $-\frac{1}{2}[1/(e^{2u} - 1)] + C$ **42.** $\ln|x/\sqrt{x^2 + 4}| + C$ **43.** $\frac{1}{3}\tan^{-1}[(5x + 4)/3] + C$

44. $\sqrt{x^2 - a^2} - a\tan^{-1}(\sqrt{x^2 - a^2}/a) + C$ **45.** $e^x(\cos 2x + 2\sin 2x)/5 + C$ **46.** $\ln x - 2\ln(1 + 3\sqrt{x}) + C$

47. $\ln|x| - 3\ln|1 + \sqrt[3]{x}| + C$ **48.** $\ln|\sin\theta| - \frac{1}{2}\ln(1 + \sin^2\theta) + C$ **49.** $\frac{1}{15}(8 - 4z^2 + 3z^4)(1 + z^2)^{1/2} + C$ **50.** $\frac{3}{8}(e^{2t} - 3) \times (1 + e^{2t})^{1/3} + C$ **51.** $\frac{5}{2}(1 + x^{4/5})^{1/2} + C$ **52.** $x \tan x + \ln|\cos x| + C$ **53.** $\frac{1}{4}[(2x^2 - 1)\sin^{-1} x + x\sqrt{1 - x^2}] + C$

54. $(x^2/2) + \frac{4}{3}\ln|x + 2| + \frac{2}{3}\ln|x - 1| + C$ **55.** $x + \ln|(x - 1)/x| + C$ **56.** $\ln|x - 1| - (x - 1)^{-1} + C$ **57.** $\frac{2}{3}(3e^{2x} - 6e^x - 1)^{1/2} + (1/\sqrt{3})\ln|e^x - 1 + \sqrt{e^{2x} - 2e^x - \frac{1}{3}}| + C$ **58.** $\frac{3}{2}(x^2 + 2x - 3)^{1/3} + C$ **59.** $\tan^{-1}(2\sqrt{y^2 + y}) + C$

60. $-\sqrt{a^2 - x^2}/a^2x + C$ **61.** $\frac{3}{8}\sin^{-1} x + \frac{1}{8}(5x - 2x^3)\sqrt{1 - x^2} + C$ **62.** $x \ln(x + \sqrt{1 + x^2}) - \sqrt{1 + x^2} + C$ **63.** $x \tan x - (x^2/2) + \ln|\cos x| + C$ **64.** $-(\tan^{-1} x)/x + \ln|x| - \ln\sqrt{1 + x^2} + C$ **65.** $(x^2/4) + [(x \sin 2x)/4] + [(\cos 2x)/8] + C$

66. $-x^2 \cos x + 2x \sin x + 2 \cos x + C$ **67.** $(x^2/4) - [(x \sin 2x)/4] - [(\cos 2x)/8] + C$ **68.** $\frac{1}{2}\tan^{-1} t - [1/(2\sqrt{3})]\tan^{-1}(t/\sqrt{3}) + C$ **69.** $\frac{1}{12}[4u - 3\ln(1 + e^{2u}) + \ln(3 + e^{2u})] + C$ **70.** $\frac{1}{4}(x^2 - 4)\ln(x + 2) - x^2/8 + x/2 + C$ **71.** $(x^2 + 1)e^x + C$ **72.** $x \sec^{-1} x - \ln(|x| + \sqrt{x^2 - 1}) + C$ **73.** $-2x^{-2} + 2x^{-1} + \ln|x/(x + 2)| + C$ **74.** $\frac{1}{16}\ln|(x^2 - 4)/(x^2 + 4)| + C$ **75.** $2 - \sqrt{2}\ln(1 + \sqrt{2})$ **76.** $\ln|\cot x| + C$ **77.** $-\frac{1}{2}[1/(e^{2u} + 1)] + C$ **78.** $x - 2\sqrt{x} + (4/\sqrt{3})\tan^{-1}((1 + 2\sqrt{x})/\sqrt{3}) + C$ **79.** $\ln|\tan t - 2| - \ln|\tan t - 1| + C$ **80.** $-t + \sqrt{2}\tan^{-1}(\sqrt{2}\tan t) + C$ **81.** $(1/\sqrt{2})\tan^{-1}((\tan x)/\sqrt{2}) + C$ **82.** $e^t \sin(e^t) + \cos(e^t) + C$ **83.** $x \ln\sqrt{x^2 + 1} - x + \tan^{-1} x + C$ **84.** $\frac{1}{2}x^2 \ln(x^3 + x) - \frac{3}{4}x^2 + \frac{1}{2}\ln(x^2 + 1) + C$ **85.** $\frac{1}{2}(x^2 - 1)e^{x^2} + C$ **86.** $\ln|\sin x + \sqrt{3 + \sin^2 x}| + C$ **87.** $\sin^{-1}(3^{-(1/2)}\tan x) + C$ **88.** $(x^2 - 2)\cos(1 - x) + 2x \sin(1 - x) + C$ **89.** $\tan x - \sec x + C$ **90.** $3^{-(1/2)}[\ln|1 + 2\sin x| - \ln|2 + \sin x + \sqrt{3}\cos x|] + C$

91. $-\frac{1}{2}\cot x \csc x + \frac{1}{4}\ln[(1 - \cos x)/(1 + \cos x)] + C$ **92.** $\frac{1}{2}\tan^2 x + \ln|\cos x| + C$ **93.** $x(\sin^{-1} x)^2 - 2x + 2\sqrt{1 - x^2} \times \sin^{-1} x + C$ **94.** $\frac{1}{54}(9x^2 - 1)\ln|3x + 1| - x^2/12 + x/18 + C$ **95.** $\frac{1}{2}\ln(x^2 + 1) + \frac{1}{2}(x^2 + 1)^{-1} + C$ **96.** $-\frac{2}{3}(x + 2) \times \sqrt{1 - x} + C$ **97.** $\frac{1}{15}(3x - 1)(2x + 1)^{3/2} + C$ **98.** $x \ln(x + \sqrt{x^2 - 1}) - \sqrt{x^2 - 1} + C$ **99.** $x \ln(x - \sqrt{x^2 - 1}) + \sqrt{x^2 - 1} + C$ **100.** $\frac{1}{2}\ln|t - \sqrt{1 - t^2}| - \frac{1}{2}\sin^{-1} t + C$ **101.** $x - e^{-x}\tan^{-1}(e^x) - \frac{1}{2}\ln(1 + e^{2x}) + C$ **102.** $\frac{1}{2}(x - x^2)^{1/2} - \frac{1}{2}(1 - 2x)\sin^{-1}\sqrt{x} + C$ **103.** $x \ln(x + \sqrt{x}) - x + \sqrt{x} - \ln(1 + \sqrt{x}) + C$ **104.** $(x + 1)\tan^{-1}\sqrt{x} - \sqrt{x} + C$

105. $x \ln(x^2 + x) + \ln(x + 1) - 2x + C$ **106.** $(x + \frac{1}{2})\ln(\sqrt{x} + \sqrt{1 + x}) - \frac{1}{2}\sqrt{x^2 + x} + C$ **107.** $2\sqrt{x}\sin\sqrt{x} + 2\cos\sqrt{x} + C$ **108.** $-2\sqrt{x}\cos\sqrt{x} + 2\sin\sqrt{x} + C$ **109.** $(x + 2)\tan^{-1}\sqrt{x + 1} - \sqrt{x + 1} + C$

110. $\frac{1}{4}(\sin^{-1} x)^2 + \frac{1}{2}x\sqrt{1 - x^2}\sin^{-1} x - x^2/4 + C$ **111.** $\frac{1}{4}x^2 - \frac{1}{8}x \sin 4x - \frac{1}{32}\cos 4x + C$ **112.** $\sec x - \tan x + x + C$

113. $\ln(\sqrt{e^{2t} + 1} - 1) - t + C$ **114.** $\ln[(1 - \sin x)^{1/2}(1 + \sin x)^{-(1/18)}(2 - \sin x)^{-(4/9)}] + 1/(6 - 3\sin x) + C$

115. $(1/ac)\ln|e^{ct}/(a + be^{ct})| + C$ **116.** $-2\sin^{-1}[(\cos(x/2))/(\cos(\alpha/2))] + C$

117. $(1/\sqrt{2})\ln|\csc(x - (\pi/4)) - \cot(x - (\pi/4))| + C$

118. $x \ln\sqrt{1 + x^2} - x + \tan^{-1} x + C$ **119.** $x \ln(2x^2 + 4) + 2\sqrt{2}\tan^{-1}(x/\sqrt{2}) - 2x + C$ **120.** $-\frac{1}{3}(1 - x^2)^{1/2}(2 + x^2) + C$

121. $\ln|2 + \ln x| + C$ **122.** $x - \tan x + C$ **123.** $\frac{1}{3}\ln|x + 1| - \frac{1}{6}\ln(x^2 - x + 1) + (1/\sqrt{3})\tan^{-1}[(2x - 1)/\sqrt{3}] + C$

124. $\frac{4}{21}(e^x + 1)^{3/4}(3e^x - 4) + C$ **125.** $\tan^{-1}(e^x) + C$ **126.** $2e^{\sqrt{t}}(\sqrt{t} - 1) + C$ **127.** $-2\sqrt{x + 1}\cos\sqrt{x + 1} + 2\sin\sqrt{x + 1} + C$ **128.** $-2\sqrt{1 - x}\sin\sqrt{1 - x} - 2\cos\sqrt{1 - x} + C$ **129.** $\ln 2$ **130.** $2\sqrt{2} - 2$ **131.** $2/\pi$ **132.** $e - 1$

133. $\pi/4$ **134.** $2\ln 2 - 1$ **135.** $\pi/2$ **136.** $\frac{1}{2}$ **137.** -1 **139.** e^{-4} **140.** $4p^2(2\sqrt{2} - 1)/3$ **141.** Area $(\pi - 2)r^2/4$; centroid $2r\sqrt{2}/(3\pi - 6)$ from center.   **142.** $(1/(2e - 4), (e^2 - 3)/(4e - 8)) \approx (0.7, 1.5)$ **143.** $2\pi^2 kr^2$ **144.** $w(3e^8 - 20e^4 + 9)/4 \approx$ 123,000 lb   **145.** Integrals for A, V, and S converge. $A = 1$, $V = \pi/2$, $S = \pi[\sqrt{2} + \ln(1 + \sqrt{2})]$.   **146.** About 2

147. About 23 **148.** About 6.8 **149.** About 175 **150.** $2\pi[\sqrt{2} + \ln(1 + \sqrt{2})] \approx 14.4$ **151.** 1.9100989
152. $(0, 0.6)$ for arch $|x| \le \pi/2$ **153.** 2π **154.** $6a$ **155.** $12\pi a^2/5$ **156.** $(2a/5, 2a/5)$ for first-quadrant arch **157.** Converges, compare with $\int_1^{\infty} x^{-(3/2)}\, dx$ **158. c)** $1 - e^{-e^b}$ **d)** 1 **160.** Converges **161.** $x = a \cos kt$ **162.** $\frac{1}{2}$

CHAPTER 8

Article 8–1, p. 394

1.

a) About the x-axis
b) No curve for $0 < x < 2$
c) $(0, 0), (2, 0)$ **e)** ∞

2.

a) About the x-axis
b) No curve for $0 < x \le 2$
c) $(0, 0)$ **d)** $y = \pm 1$; $x = 2$
e) ∞

3.

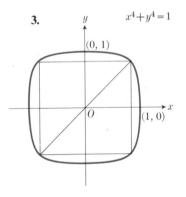

a) About both axes, the origin and the line $y = x$
b) Curve is inside the square $|x| \le 1$, $|y| \le 1$ **c)** $(0, \pm 1)$, $(\pm 1, 0)$ **e)** Slope is 0 at $(0, \pm 1)$, ∞ at $(\pm 1, 0)$

4.

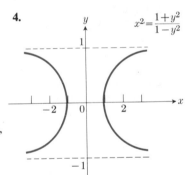

a) About both axes, and the origin. **b)** No curve for $|y| \ge 1$. No curve for $|x| < 1$ **c)** $(\pm 1, 0)$
d) $y = \pm 1$ **e)** ∞

5.

a) About both axes and the origin and $y = x$. **b)** No curve for $|y| \le 1$. No curve for $|x| \le 1$ **c)** No intercepts **d)** $x = \pm 1$; $y = \pm 1$

6.

a) About the origin **b)** No curve for $|y| < 2$ **c)** No intercepts **d)** $x = 0$; $y = x$ is also an asymptote
e) Low point at $(1, 2)$; high point at $(-1, -2)$

7.

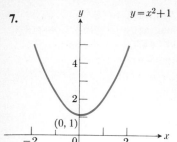

a) About the *y*-axis
b) Curve is confined to $y \geq 1$
c) $(0, 1)$
e) 0

8.

a) About the *y*-axis
b) $0 < y \leq 1$
c) $(0, 1)$
d) $y = 0$
e) 0

9.

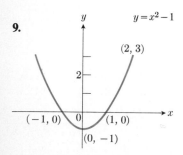

a) About the *y*-axis
b) $y \geq -1$
c) $(0, -1); (\pm 1, 0)$
e) $0; \pm 2$

10.

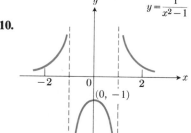

a) About the *y*-axis
b) No curve for $-1 < y$
≤ 0 c) $(0, -1)$ d) $x =$
$\pm 1; y = 0$ e) 0

Article 8–2, pp. 398–399

1. $x + y + 1 = 0$ **2.** $x + 2y = 7$ **3.** $6x - y = 14; y - 6x = 18$ **4.** $2x + y = \pm 3$ **5.** Lines are: $y = 2x - 3, y = -\frac{1}{2}x + \frac{3}{4}$
7. Yes, $(-2, -8)$ **8.** $(-1, -1)$. No, because $2x_1^3 - 3x_1^2 + 5 = 0$ and this equation has only one real root.
9. $2x + 3y = \pm 12$ **10.** $x + y = 1; 4x + y = -2$ **11.** $(-\frac{13}{4}, \frac{17}{16})$ **15.** ± 16 **16.** $\pm 1/\sqrt{3}$
17. $A = \tan^{-1}\left(\frac{5}{3}\right), B = \tan^{-1} 5, C = \tan^{-1}\left(\frac{10}{11}\right)$ **18.** $(-5 + \sqrt{221})/14 \approx 0.705$ **20.** $\tan A = 7, \tan B = \frac{7}{9}, \tan C = \frac{7}{4}$
21. a) $45°$ **b)** $\tan^{-1} 3$ **c)** $\tan^{-1}(5/\sqrt{3})$ **d)** $\tan^{-1}\left(\frac{14}{3}\right)$

Article 8–3, p. 400

1. $x - y = 1$ **2.** $x^2 + y^2 - 6x + 5 = 0$ **3.** $(x^2 + y^2)^2 + 8(y^2 - x^2) = 0$ **4.** $3x^2 + 3y^2 + 2xy - 4x - 4y = 0$
5. $3x^2 + 4y^2 - 20x + 12 = 0$ **6.** $5x^2 - 4y^2 = 20$ (right half only)
7. $x^2 = 10 - 2y + 6|y - 1|$; or $x^2 = 4y + 4$ when $y \geq 1$, and $x^2 = 16 - 8y$ when $y < 1$. **8.** $x^2 + y^2 - 4x - 6y + 4 = 0$
9. $(2, 2); \sqrt{5}$ **10.** $|Ax_1 + By_1 + C|/\sqrt{A^2 + B^2}$

Article 8–4, p. 404

1. $x^2 + y^2 - 4y = 0$ **2.** $x^2 + y^2 + 4x = 5$ **3.** $x^2 + y^2 - 6x + 8y = 0$ **4.** $x^2 + y^2 - 2x - 2y = 0$ **5.** $x^2 + y^2 + 4x + 2y < 1$
6. $x^2 + y^2 + 8x - 4y > -4$ **7.** $(0, 1); 2$ **8.** $(-1, 0); 3$ **9.** $(-1, 0); 2/\sqrt{3}$ **10.** $(-\frac{1}{4}, -\frac{1}{4}); 1/(2\sqrt{2})$ **11.** $(-1, 2)$
12. All points in cartesian plane. **13.** $x^2 + y^2 - 4x - 4y = 5$ **14.** $5x^2 + 5y^2 + 10x - 10y + 1 = 0$
15. $(x - 0.7)^2 + (y - 1.3)^2 = 12.58$ **17.** $x^2 + y^2 + 2x + 2y - 23 = 0$ **18.** Circle, with center $(-2, 3)$, and radius 4.
19. Center of circle is $(1, 2)$; radius $\sqrt{2}$. Distance of $(0.1, 3.1)$ from center is $\sqrt{2.02}$. Point is outside the circle.
20. Center $(-2, 4)$, radius $2\sqrt{5}$. **21.** Center $(-1, 1)$, radius 5.
24. a) $C_1 = -2h, C_2 = -2k, C_3 = h^2 + k^2 - r^2$ **b)** $h = -C_1/2, k = -C_2/2, r = \sqrt{(C_1^2 + C_2^2 - 4C_3)/4}$

Article 8–5, pp. 410–411

1. $x^2 = 8y; y = -2$ **2.** $y^2 = -8x; x = 2$ **3.** $(x + 2)^2 = 4(y - 3); y = 2$ **4.** $(y - 3)^2 = -4x; x = 1$
5. $(y - 1)^2 = 12(x + 3);$ $x = -6$ **6.** $(x - 1)^2 = 12(y + 3);$ $y = -6$ **7.** $y^2 = 8(x - 2);$ $F(4, 0)$ **8.** $(x - 1)^2 = -8(y + 2);$
$F(1, -4)$
9. $(y - 1)^2 = -16(x + 3); F(-7, 1)$ **10.** $(x + 2)^2 = 4(y + 2); F(-2, -1)$ **11.** $(y - 1)^2 = 4x; F(1, 1)$ **12.** $x^2 = -4(y - 1);$
$F(0, 0)$
13. $V(1, 1); x = 1; F(1, -1); y = 3$ **14.** $V(-4, -3); x = -4; F(-4, -\frac{5}{2}); y = -\frac{7}{2}$ **15.** $V(2, 0); y = 0; F(1, 0); x = 3$
16. $V(0, -\frac{1}{2}); x = 0; F(0, \frac{3}{2}); y = -\frac{5}{2}$ **17.** $V(-1, -1); x = -1; F(-1, 0); y = -2$ **18.** $V(\frac{1}{4}, -\frac{1}{2}); y = -\frac{1}{2}; F(0, -\frac{1}{2}); x = \frac{1}{2}$
19. $V(2, 1); y = 1; F(\frac{29}{16}, 1); x = \frac{35}{16}$ **20.** $V(2, -3); y = -3; F(\frac{3}{2}, -3); x = \frac{5}{2}$ **21.** $V(2, -2); x = 2; F(2, -\frac{4}{3}); y = -\frac{8}{3}$

22. $V(-3, -1)$; $y = -1$; $F(-\frac{21}{8}, -1)$; $x = -\frac{27}{8}$ **23.** Points above parabola $x^2 = 8y$ **24. b)** $\frac{5}{3}$ dollars/lb; 10 lbs/person

25. a) $x = 125 - \frac{1}{5}p^2$ **26.** $4p$ **27.** $b^2y = 4hx(b - x)$ **28. a)** $7y^2 - 3y + 6x - 16 = 0$ **b)** $7x^2 - 9x - 6y - 4 = 0$

    b) \$14.43   **30.** The points of the line $2x + y - 3 = 0$, the circle $x^2 + y^2 - 4 = 0$, and the parabola $x^2 - 8y = 0$. The product is zero if and only if at least one factor is zero.

37.   **38.** $x^2 + y^2 - 8x - 8y - 2xy + 16 = 0$

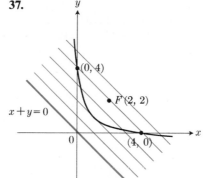

Article 8–6, pp. 417–418

1. $(x^2/12) + (y^2/16) = 1$; $e = \frac{1}{2}$ **2.** $(x^2/25) + (y^2/16) = 1$; $e = \frac{3}{5}$ **3.** $9x^2 + 5(y - 2)^2 = 45$; $e = \frac{2}{3}$ **4.** $[(x + 3)^2/12] + (y^2/16) = 1$; $e = \frac{1}{2}$ **5.** $(x - 2)^2 + 10(y - 2)^2 = 10$; $e = 3/\sqrt{10}$ **6.** $9(x - 1)^2 + 4(y - 4)^2 = 36$; $F(1, 4 \pm \sqrt{5})$ **7.** $(2, -3)$; $(2, 2)$, $(2, -8)$; $(2, 1)$, $(2, -7)$ **9.** $x^2 + 2y^2 - 4y = 0$ **10.** $e = \frac{3}{4}$; $y = \pm\frac{16}{3}$ **11.** $\frac{4}{3}\pi ab^2$ **12. a)** $\int_0^a \sqrt{a^2 - x^2}\, dx$ $(= \frac{1}{4}\pi a^2$ for $\frac{1}{4}$ of a circle)   **b)** $(b/a)\int_0^a \sqrt{a^2 - x^2}\, dx$. Area of ellipse $= \pi ab$.   **14.** $2b^2/a$ **15.** $5x^2 + 9y^2 = 180$ **16.** $A = C = 0$, $B = -4$

18. Interior of ellipse $9x^2 + 16y^2 = 144$ **19.** Graph consists of parabola $x^2 + 4y = 0$, straight line $2x - y - 3 = 0$, circle $x^2 + y^2 - 25 = 0$, ellipse $x^2 + 4y^2 - 4 = 0$.   **20.** One factor must be positive, the other negative. Graph consists of region between circle $x^2 + y^2 = 1$ and ellipse $9x^2 + 4y^2 = 36$.

21.

22.

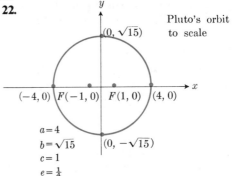

23. $e \approx 0.968$ **24. c)** $L \approx 5.8698$ by trapezoidal approximation. $L \approx 5.8700$ from tables of elliptic integrals.   **d)** Estimated $|E_T| < 0.013$ for full ellipse. Actual error ≈ 0.0002.   **25. a)** Distances to the two pegs along taut rope sum to a constant.   **b)** The height of the weight is minimized when the ring is in the symmetric position.

Article 8–7, pp. 425–426

2. $C(2, -3)$; $V(2 \pm 2, -3)$; $F(2 \pm \sqrt{13}, -3)$; $A: 3(x - 2) = \pm 2(y + 3)$ **3.** $C(2, -3)$; $V(2 \pm 3, -3)$; $F(2 \pm \sqrt{13}, -3)$; $A: 2(x - 2) = \pm 3(y + 3)$ **4.** $C(2, -3)$; $V(2, -3 \pm \frac{1}{2})$; $F(2, -3 \pm \sqrt{13}/6)$; $A: 2(y + 3) = \pm 3(x - 2)$ **5.** $C(-2, 1)$; $V(-2 \pm 2, 1)$; $F(-2 \pm 3, 1)$; $A: \sqrt{5}(x + 2) = \pm 2(y - 1)$ **6.** $C(0, 2)$; $V(\pm 1, 2)$; $F(\pm\sqrt{5}, 2)$; $A: 2x = \pm(y - 2)$ **7.** $C(2, 0)$; $V(2 \pm 2, 0)$, $F(2 \pm \sqrt{5}, 0)$; $A: x - 2 = \pm 2y$ **8.** $C(2, 1)$; $V(2, 1 \pm 2)$, $F(2, 1 \pm 3)$; $A: 2(x - 2) = \pm\sqrt{5}(y - 1)$ **10.** $\frac{4}{3}\pi(b^4/a)$ **12.** $x^2 - 3y^2 + 12y = 9$ **13.** $4x^2 - 5y^2 - 8x + 60y + 4 = 0$ **15. a)** It lies on the branch nearest A of the hyperbola with foci at A, B and with $a = 6.86 \times 10^5$ ft.

Article 8–8, pp. 429–430

1. $(x')^2 - (y')^2 = 4$ **2.** $3(x')^2 + (y')^2 = 2$ **3.** $(\frac{1}{2} - \sqrt{3})(x')^2 + (\frac{1}{2} + \sqrt{3})(y')^2 = 2$ or $-1.232(x')^2 + 2.232(y')^2 = 2$

4. $4(x')^2 + 2(y')^2 = 19$　**5.** $5(y')^2 - (x')^2 = 10$　**6.** $5(x')^2 - 3(y')^2 = 7$　**7.** $15x^2 + 13y^2 - 2\sqrt{3}\,xy - 14\sqrt{3}\,y + 18x = 33$, $\alpha = 60°$　**12.** $2(y')^2 = 1$

Article 8–9, p. 432

1. Ellipse　**2.** Hyperbola　**3.** Parabola　**4.** Circle　**5.** Hyperbola　**6.** Parabola　**7.** Hyperbola　**8.** Ellipse　**9.** Ellipse
12. If $C = -A$, then $A + C = A' + C' = 0$, and $C' = -A'$. Hence $A' = C' = 0$ if $\tan 2\alpha = -2A/B$ by Eqs. (6), Article 8–8

Article 8–10, p. 434

3. Line L and the point D do not exist.　**4.** $(1 - e^2)x^2 + y^2 - 2pe^2x - p^2e^2 = 0$.

Miscellaneous Problems Chapter 8, pp. 435–438

1. a) A. Symmetric about the x-axis　B. $0 \leq x \leq 4, -2 \leq y \leq 2$　C. $(0, 0), (4, 0)$　D. None　E. ∞ at both intercepts
　b) A. Symmetric about the x-axis　B. $x \leq 0, x \geq 4$, all y　C. $(0, 0), (4, 0)$　D. Asymptotic to $y = \pm(x - 2)$　E. ∞ at both intercepts　**c)** A. Symmetric about the x-axis　B. $0 \leq x < 4$, all y　C. $(0, 0)$　D. Asymptotic to $x = 4$　E. ∞ at $(0, 0)$
2. a) A. None　B. All $y, |x| > 0$　C. $(-1, 0)$　D. $y = x, x = 0$　E. 3　**b)** A. Symmetric about the x-axis　B. All $y; -1 \leq x < 0, x > 0$　C. $(-1, 0)$　D. $x = 0$　E. ∞　**c)** A. None　B. All $y, |x| > 0$　C. $(-1, 0)$　D. $x = 0$　E. -3
3. a) A. None　B. All y, all x　C. $(0, 0), (-1, 0), (2, 0)$　D. None　E. -2 at $(0, 0)$,　3 at $(-1, 0)$,　6 at $(2, 0)$
　b) A. Symmetric about the x-axis　B. All $y, -1 \leq x \leq 0, x \geq 2$　C. $(0, 0), (-1, 0), (2, 0)$　D. None　E. ∞ at all intercepts
4. a) A. Symmetric about the y-axis　B. All $x, 0 < y \leq 2$　C. $(0, 2)$　D. $y = 0$　E. 0
　b) A. Symmetric about the y-axis　B. $y < 0, y \geq 2; x^2 \neq 4$　C. $(0, 2)$　D. $y = 0, x = \pm 2$　E. 0
　c) A. Symmetric about the origin　B. $|y| \leq 2$, all x　C. $(0, 0)$　D. $y = 0$　E. 2
5. a) A. Symmetric about the origin　B. $|y| \geq 2, |x| > 0$　C. None　D. $y = x, x = 0$　E. ——
　b) A. About $(1, 2)$　B. $y \leq 0, y \geq 4; x \neq 1$　C. $(0, 0)$　D. $x = 1, y = x + 1$　E. 0.
　Remark. Translate axes to new origin at $(1, 2)$; becomes same as 5(a).
6. a) A. Symmetric about both axes and the origin　B. All $y, |x| \geq 1$ and $x = 0$　C. $(0, 0), (-1, 0), (1, 0)$　D. None
　E. ∞ at $(\pm 1, 0)$; no derivative exists at the isolated point $(0, 0)$　**b)** A. Symmetric about the x-axis　B. $x \leq 1, x > 2$; $y^2 \neq 1$　C. $(0, \pm\sqrt{2}/2), (1, 0)$　D. $y = \pm 1, x = 2$　E. $\mp\sqrt{2}/8$ at $(0, \pm\sqrt{2}/2)$, ∞ at $(1, 0)$
7. A. None　B. $y \leq 4 - 2\sqrt{3}, y \geq 4 + 2\sqrt{3}; x^2 \neq 1$　C. $(0, 8), (2, 0)$　D. $x = \pm 1, y = 0$　E. -4 at $(0, 8)$, $\frac{4}{3}$ at $(2, 0)$
8. A. Symmetric about the y-axis　B. $y \leq -1, y > 1; x^2 \neq 1$　C. $(0, -1)$　D. $x = \pm 1, y = 1$　E. 0　**9.** A. Symmetric about the origin　B. $|x| \leq 2, |y| \leq 2$　C. $(0, \pm\sqrt{3}), (\pm\sqrt{3}, 0)$　D. None　E. $-\frac{1}{2}$ at $(0, \pm\sqrt{3})$; -2 at $(\pm\sqrt{3}, 0)$
10. $x^2 + xy + y^2 = 3k^2$　**12.** $a = c = d = e = 1; b = f = g = 0$　**14.** $y + 2x = 6$　**16.** $y = 6x - 14; y = 6x + 18$　**18. b)** 1:1
21. $5x^2 + 5y^2 = 4x + 8y$　**23.** $x = 2pm$　**24.** $Q(4p^3/y_1^2, -4p^2/y_1)$　**25.** $(\pm\frac{8}{9}\sqrt{3}, \frac{4}{3})$　**27.** $(-2, 1), (2, -1)$
28. $27x - 3y + 56 = 0, 27x - 3y - 104 = 0$　**30.** $r = 2.56$, center $(4, 1.61)$; results are approximate and are based on 1.55 as positive root of $x^4 + 4x - 12 = 0$.　**31.** $(-\frac{16}{5}, \frac{53}{10})$
32. a) A conic passing through the points of intersection of the three lines, and tangent to the lines $L_1 + hL_3 = 0, L_2 + kL_3 = 0$, $hL_2 + kL_1 = 0$.　**b)** $3x^2 + 3y^2 - 8x - 16y + 20 = 0$　**c)** $2y = 3x^2 - 4x + 4$　**33.** 10^7 mi　**34.** $\pi/2$
35. $y^2 = 2x - 7$　**36.** $(5, 10\sqrt{10}/3)$　**38.** $3x^2 + 3y^2 - 16y + 16 = 0$, circle　**40.** Curves consist of circle $x^2 + y^2 = 9$ and hyperbola $y^2 - x^2 = 9$.　**41.** No; for points inside the circle, $x^2 + (y^2 - 9)$ is negative while $x^2 - (y^2 - 9)$ is positive, so their product cannot equal 1.　**43.** $5x^2 + 9y^2 - 30x = 0$
44. a) $F_1 P = 5, F_2 P = \sqrt{5}$　**b)** Outside, since $OF_1 + OF_2 = 8 > F_1 P + F_2 P = 5 + \sqrt{5}$　**45.** $2ab$　**47.** $x^2 + 4xy + 5y^2 = 1$
48. $(x + 3)^2/36 + (y - 1)^2/20 = 1$　**50.** $x^2 - y^2 = 4$　**51.** Center at $(\frac{1}{2}\sqrt{2}, 0), e = \sqrt{2}$
52. [*Hint.* Eliminate λ^2 and obtain the differential equation $xy(y')^2 + (x^2 - y^2 - c^2)y' - xy = 0$ for both families. The product of the roots $y' = m_1$ and $y' = m_2$ is $m_1 m_2 = -1$.]　**53.** Square, area $= 2$
55. a) Center $(2, -1)$, foci $((4 \pm 3\sqrt{3})/2, -1)$, major axis 6, minor axis 3, $e = \sqrt{3}/2$　**b)** Center $(-2, -\frac{3}{2})$, foci $(-2 \pm \sqrt{13}, -\frac{3}{2})$, major axis $= \sqrt{13}$, conjugate axis $= \sqrt{39}$, $e = 2$, asymptotes: $2y \pm 2\sqrt{3}x + (3 \pm 4\sqrt{3}) = 0$　**57. b)** Bounded; both $9x^2 + 4y^2 - 36$ and $4x^2 + 9y^2 - 36$ exceed one when $4(x^2 + y^2) > 37$
58. Foci: $(\pm\sqrt{p - q}, 0)$　**59.** $\sqrt{2}$　**60.** On a branch of a hyperbola with the rifle and target at its foci
62. Center $(1, -2)$; foci $(1, -2 \pm \sqrt{13})$; asymptotes: $2(y + 2) = \pm 3(x - 1)$　**63.** $9x^2 - y^2 = 9$　or　$9y^2 - x^2 = 9$
65. a) Center $(3, 2)$; $e = \sqrt{\frac{11}{12}}$　**b)** $(3, 0)$　**66.** $x^2 + y^2 - 6x - 15y + 9 = 0$　**67.** With $A(0, 0)$ and $B(c, 0)$, curve is left branch of hyperbola $3x^2 - y^2 - 4cx + c^2 = 0$.　**68.** $2y'^2 - 2a\sqrt{2}x' + a^2 = 0$

CHAPTER 9

Article 9–2, p. 443

	sinh u	cosh u	tanh u	coth u	sech u	csch u
6. a)	$-\frac{3}{4}$	$\frac{5}{4}$	$-\frac{3}{5}$	$-\frac{5}{3}$	$\frac{4}{5}$	$-\frac{4}{3}$
b)	$\pm\frac{8}{15}$	$\frac{17}{8}$	$\pm\frac{8}{17}$	$\pm\frac{17}{8}$	$\frac{15}{17}$	$\pm\frac{15}{8}$
c)	$-\frac{7}{24}$	$\frac{25}{24}$	$-\frac{7}{25}$	$-\frac{25}{7}$	$\frac{24}{25}$	$-\frac{24}{7}$
d)	$\frac{12}{5}$	$\frac{13}{5}$	$\frac{12}{13}$	$\frac{13}{12}$	$\frac{5}{13}$	$\frac{5}{12}$
e)	$\pm\frac{4}{3}$	$\frac{5}{3}$	$\pm\frac{4}{5}$	$\pm\frac{5}{4}$	$\frac{3}{5}$	$\pm\frac{3}{4}$
f)	$\frac{12}{5}$	$\frac{13}{5}$	$\frac{12}{13}$	$\frac{13}{12}$	$\frac{5}{13}$	$\frac{5}{12}$

Article 9–3, p. 447

2. $3 \cosh 3x$ **3.** $10 \cosh 5x \sinh 5x = 5 \sinh 10x$ **4.** 0 **5.** $2 \operatorname{sech}^2 2x$ **6.** $-\sec^2 x \operatorname{csch}^2 (\tan x)$ **7.** $-3 \operatorname{sech}^3 x \tanh x$
8. $-\operatorname{csch} (x/4) \coth (x/4)$ **9.** $\sec^2 x \operatorname{sech} y$ **10.** $\frac{1}{2} \sinh (2x + 1) + C$ **11.** $\ln \cosh x + C$ **12.** $-\frac{1}{3} \operatorname{sech}^3 x + C$
13. $\tanh x + C$ **14.** $\ln \cosh x + C$ **15.** $x - \tanh x + C$ **16.** $2 \cosh \sqrt{x} + C$ **17.** $\frac{1}{2}x + \frac{1}{12} \sinh 6x + C$
18. $2\sqrt{2} \cosh (x/2) + C$ **19.** $u/2$ **20.** $\frac{1}{2}(e - (1/e)) = \sinh 1 \approx 1.1752$ **22. a)** 115 ft **b)** 16 lb

Article 9–5, p. 454

2. $\cosh^{-1} x = \ln (x + \sqrt{x^2 - 1})$ **6.** $2/\sqrt{1 + 4x^2}$ **7.** $-\csc x$ **8.** $\sec x$ if $\tan x > 0$, $-\sec x$ if $\tan x < 0$ **9.** $-\csc x$
10. $-2 \csc 2x$ if $\cos 2x > 0$, $2 \csc 2x$ if $\cos 2x < 0$ **11.** $\frac{1}{2} \sinh^{-1} 2x + C$ **12.** $\sinh^{-1} (x/2) + C$ **13.** 0.5493
14. -0.5493 **15.** $-\frac{1}{2} \operatorname{csch}^{-1} (|x|/2) + C = -\frac{1}{2} \sinh^{-1} (2/|x|) + C$

Article 9–6, pp. 456–457

1. $a \sinh (x_1/a)$ **3.** $(\pi a/2)(2x_1 + a \sinh (2x_1/a))$ **4.** $\bar{x} = 0$, $\bar{y} = \frac{1}{2}y_1 + (x_1/2) \operatorname{csch} (x_1/a)$ **5.** $(\pi a^2/4)(2x_1 + a \sinh (2x_1/a))$
6. b) $dx/ds = a/\sqrt{s^2 + a^2}$, $dy/ds = s/\sqrt{a^2 + s^2}$ **7. c)** $a = 25$ ft, dip ≈ 4.6 ft **d)** $H = 50$ lb

Miscellaneous Problems Chapter 9, pp. 457–458

3. $\lim PQ = 0$ **4.** $\sinh x = \pm\frac{3}{4}$, $\tanh x = \pm\frac{3}{5}$ **5.** $\cosh x = \frac{41}{9}$, $\tanh x = -\frac{40}{41}$ **9.** $y = 1$ **12.** $3 \sinh 6x$
13. $\sec^2 x/(2 \tanh y \operatorname{sech}^2 y)$ **14.** $-(\cosh y \coth y)/\sqrt{1 - x^2}$ **15.** $\tanh y \tan x$ **16.** $(1 + y^2)/(1 - x^2)$
17. $x^{-1} \operatorname{sech}^2 (\ln x) = 4x(x^2 + 1)^{-2}$ **18.** $y \operatorname{csch} (\ln y)$ **19.** $3e^{3x} \cosh (\tan^{-1} e^{3x})/(1 + e^{6x})$ **20.** $|\sec x|$
21. $-(\cosh y + \sinh 2x)/(2y + x \sinh y)$ **22.** $-e^{-\theta} + C$ **23.** $(2\theta - e^{-2\theta})/4$ **24.** $(\cosh^3 x - 3 \cosh x)/3 + C$
25. $(e^{3x} + 3e^{-x})/6 + C$ **26.** $\ln (\cosh x) + C$ **27.** $\frac{1}{2} \tanh^{-1} (\frac{1}{2})$ **28.** $\frac{1}{2}(\coth^{-1} \frac{5}{2} - \coth^{-1} \frac{3}{2})$ **29.** $\sinh^{-1} (e^t) + C$
30. $-\tanh^{-1} (\cos x) + C$ **31.** $\cosh^{-1} (\tan \theta) + C$ **36. a)** $\lim v = \sqrt{mg/k}$ where $k =$ resistance proportionality factor; $m =$ mass of body; $g =$ acceleration due to gravity. **b)** $s = (m/k) \ln \cosh (t\sqrt{gk/m})$ **37.** $\ln 2$ **38.** $\ln [2/(1 + \sqrt{2})]$

CHAPTER 10

Article 10–1, pp. 463–464

1. a) $(3, (\pi/4) + 2n\pi)$, $(-3, -(3\pi/4) + 2n\pi)$, n any integer. **b)** $(-3, (\pi/4) + 2n\pi)$, $(3, -(3\pi/4) + 2n\pi)$, n any integer.
c) $(3, -(\pi/4) + 2n\pi)$, $(-3, (3\pi/4) + 2n\pi)$, n any integer. **d)** $(-3, -(\pi/4) + 2n\pi)$, $(3, (3\pi/4) + 2n\pi)$, n any integer.

2.

3.

4.

5.

6. **7.** **8.** **9.**

10. a) $(3/\sqrt{2}, 3/\sqrt{2})$ **b)** $(-3/\sqrt{2}, -3/\sqrt{2})$ **c)** $(3/\sqrt{2}, -3/\sqrt{2})$ **d)** $(-3/\sqrt{2}, 3/\sqrt{2})$ **11.** $x = 2$ **12.** $y = -1$
13. $x + y = 1$ **14.** $y = x$ **15.** $x + \sqrt{3}y = 6$ **16.** $\sqrt{2}x + \sqrt{2}y = 8$ **17.** $x - y = 2$ **18.** $\sqrt{3}x + y = 0$
19. $(2, \frac{3}{4}\pi)$ is the same as $(-2, -(\pi/4))$ and $2 \sin(-(\pi/2)) = -2$ **20.** $(\frac{1}{2}, \frac{3}{2}\pi) = (-\frac{1}{2}, (\pi/2))$ and $-\sin(\pi/6) = -\frac{1}{2}$
21. If (r_1, θ_1) satisfies $r_1 = \cos\theta_1 + 1$, then the same point has coordinates $(-r_1, \theta_1 + \pi)$ which satisfy the second equation. Also,
if (r_2, θ_2) satisfies the second equation, the coordinates $(-r_2, \theta_2 + \pi)$ of the same point satisfy the first equation.
22. $(\pm a, 15°), (\pm a, 75°)$ **23.** The origin and $(a/\sqrt{2}, 45°)$ **24.** The origin and $(a + (a/\sqrt{2}), -(\pi/4)), (a - (a/\sqrt{2}), (3\pi/4))$
25. The origin and $(\frac{8}{5}a, \sin^{-1}\frac{3}{5})$ **26.** The origin, $(a, \pm(\pi/2)), (a/2, \pm(2\pi/3)), (0.22a, \pm141.3°)$

Article 10–2, p. 467

1. $r[3\cos\theta + 4\sin\theta] = 5$ **2.** $x^2 + y^2 = 2ax$ **11. a)** $(\frac{3}{2}a, \pm60°), (0, 180°)$ **b)** $(2a, 0°), (\frac{1}{2}a, \pm120°)$ **12.** $30°$
13. Symmetry about the y-axis

Article 10–3, pp. 471–472

1. $r = a\sin2\theta$; rose of 4 leaves. **2.** $r = 2a\sin\theta\tan\theta$, $x = r\cos\theta = 2a\sin^2\theta \to 2a$ as $\theta \to \pi/2$ **3.** $r = 2a\sin\theta$
4. $r = a(1 - \cos\theta)$, $r = -a(1 + \cos\theta)$ (Both equations represent the same curve.) **5.** $r\cos(\theta - \alpha) = p$
6. $r(1 - \cos\theta) = 2a$, $r(1 + \cos\theta) = -2a$ (Both equations represent the same curve.) **7.** $r^2 = \cos2\theta$ **8.** $x^2 + y^2 = 4x$
9. $x^2 + y^2 = 6y$ **10.** $(x^2 + y^2)^3 = 4x^2y^2$ **11.** $(x^2 + y^2)^2 = 2a^2(x^2 - y^2)$ **12.** $3x^2 - y^2 + 32x + 64 = 0$
13. $x^2 + y^2 - ay = a\sqrt{x^2 + y^2}$ **15.** d **16.** e **17.** l **18.** f **19.** k **20.** h **21.** i **22.** j
23. a) $p = |c|/\sqrt{a^2 + b^2}$, $\cos\beta = a/\sqrt{a^2 + b^2}$, $\sin\beta = b/\sqrt{a^2 + b^2}$ **b)** $p = 3$, $\beta = 30°$ **24.** $r = 4/(1 - \cos\theta)$
25. $(50, 0°)$, $r = 45/(4 + 5\cos\theta)$ **26.** $(-\frac{16}{15}, 0°)$, $r = 8/(4 + \cos\theta)$ **27. a)** max $= \sqrt{a^2 + b^2}$, min $= \sqrt{|a^2 - b^2|}$
  b) max $= a\sqrt{5}$, min $= a\sqrt{3}$; max $= a\sqrt{2}$, min $= 0$; max $= a\sqrt{5}/2$, min $= a\sqrt{3}/2$
28. ±1 **29.** $(\frac{2}{3}, 0°)$ **30.** $\pm\sqrt{e^2 - 1}$

Article 10–4, p. 477

2. When $\tan\psi_2 = -1/\tan\psi_1$. **3.** $(2, \pm60°)$; $90°$ **4.** $(\frac{3}{2}a, \pm60°), (0, 180°)$ **5.** $8a$ **6.** $(\frac{4}{3}a, 0)$ **7.** $4\pi a^2(2 - \sqrt{2})$
8. $2a$. The curve is the cardioid $r = (a/2)(1 - \cos\theta)$ **9.** $(a/3)[(4 + \pi^2)^{3/2} - 8]$ **10.** $(a/8)(4\pi - 3\sqrt{3})$ **11.** $4\pi^2 a^2$

Article 10–5, p. 479

1. $\frac{3}{2}\pi a^2$ **2.** πa^2 **3.** $2a^2$ **4.** $(a^2/3)(3\sqrt{3} - \pi)$ **5.** $\frac{9}{2}\pi a^2$ **6.** $(a^2/2)(\pi - 2)$ **7.** πa^2 **9.** $(\frac{5}{6}a, 0)$ **10.** $(4a/3\pi)$ from center

Miscellaneous Problems Chapter 10, pp. 480–481

15. $\pi/3$ at $(a, \pi/6)$ and $(a, 5\pi/6)$ **16.** $\pi/4$ at $(a, 0)$ and (a, π) **17.** 0 at $(a\sqrt{2}, \pi/4)$ **18.** $\pi/2$ at $r = 0$ **19.** $\pi/4$ at $r = 0$;
$2\tan^{-1}(\sqrt{3}/6)$ at $(a/2, \theta_i)$ where $\theta_i = \pm\pi/3, \pm2\pi/3$ **20.** $\pi/3$ at $(\sqrt{2}, \pm\pi/6)$ and $(\sqrt{2}, \pm5\pi/6)$ **21.** $r = 2/(1 + \cos\theta)$
22. $r(b\cos\theta + a\sin\theta) = ab$ **23.** $r = -2a\cos\theta$ **24.** $r[1 + \cos(\theta - \pi/4)] = 2a$ **25.** $r = 8/(3 - \cos\theta)$ **26.** $r = 3/(1 + 2\sin\theta)$
27. $(0.75a, -3.44°)$, approx. **29.** $\pi/4$ **30.** $\pi/2$ **31.** -1 **32.** $\pi/2$ **33. b)** $xy = 1$ **c)** $\pi/2$ **34. a)** $(1/4)\tan\alpha$ **b)** $\sec\alpha$
35. a) $32\pi a^2/5$ **b)** $\bar{y} = 0$; $\bar{x} = 5a\int_0^\pi \sin^6(\theta/2)\cos(\theta/2)\cos\theta\,d\theta$ **c)** $\bar{x} = -50a/63$ **38.** $P = 3\pi a/2$ **39.** $2a^2$ **40.** $(3\pi - 8)a^2/2$
41. a^2 **42.** $9a^2\pi/2$ **43.** $3\pi a^2/2$ **44.** πa^2 **45.** πa^2 **46.** $4a^2$ **47.** $a^2(\pi + 2)$ **48.** $5\pi a^2/4$

CHAPTER 11

Article 11–1, p. 487

1. $\mathbf{i} - 4\mathbf{j}$ **2.** $-\mathbf{i} + \mathbf{j}$ **3.** $-2\mathbf{i} - 3\mathbf{j}$ **4.** 0 **5.** $\frac{1}{2}\sqrt{3}\,\mathbf{i} + \frac{1}{2}\mathbf{j}$ **6.** $\frac{1}{2}\sqrt{3}\,\mathbf{i} - \frac{1}{2}\mathbf{j}$ **7.** $\frac{3}{5}\mathbf{i} - \frac{4}{5}\mathbf{j}$ **8.** $(\mathbf{i} + 4\mathbf{j})/\sqrt{17}$ **9.** $(-4\mathbf{i} + \mathbf{j})/\sqrt{17}$
10. $-y\mathbf{i} + x\mathbf{j}$ or $y\mathbf{i} - x\mathbf{j}$ **11.** $\sqrt{2}$, $45°$ **12.** $\sqrt{13}$, $\tan^{-1}(-1.5) = -56.3°$ **13.** 2, $30°$
14. $\sqrt{13}$, $180° - \tan^{-1}(1.5) = 123.7°$ **15.** 13, $\tan^{-1}\frac{12}{5} = 67.4°$ **16.** 13, $180° + \tan^{-1}\frac{12}{5} = 247.4°$

Article 11–2, pp. 490–491

1. $\alpha_1 = \frac{1}{2}\sin^{-1}0.8 = 26°34'$, $\alpha_2 = 90° - \alpha_1 = 63°26'$ **5.** $x = e^t$, $y = -(7 + e^{2t})/2$ **6.** $y = (1 - t)^{-1}$, $x = -\ln|1 - t|$
7. $x = \sin t$, $y = 1 + (t - \sin t \cos t)/2$, for $0 \le t \le \pi/2$; $x = 1$, $y = t + 1 - \pi/4$, for $t > \pi/2$

Article 11–3, pp. 496–497

1. $x^2 + y^2 = 1$ **2.** $x = 1 - 2y^2$; $|y| \le 1$ **3.** $x^2 - y^2 = 1$; $x > 0$ **4.** $[(x - 2)^2/16] + [(y - 3)^2/4] = 1$ **5.** $y = x^2 - 6x$
6. $4x^2 - y^2 = 4$; $x \ge 1$, $y \ge 0$ **7.** $(x - 2)(y - 2) + 1 = 0$; $x > 2$, $y < 2$ **8.** $y = x^2 - 2x + 5$; $x \ge 1$ **9.** $2(x + y) = (x - y)^2$
10. $[(x - 3)^2/4] + [(y - 4)^2/9] = 1$; $x > 3$ **11.** $x = -at/\sqrt{t^2 + 1}$, $y = a/\sqrt{t^2 + 1}$ **12.** $x = a \tanh\theta$, $y = a \operatorname{sech}\theta$
13. $x = a\cos(s/a)$, $y = a\sin(s/a)$ **14.** $x = a\sinh^{-1}(s/a)$, $y = \sqrt{a^2 + s^2}$ **15.** $x = a\cos\phi + a\phi\sin\phi$,
    $y = a\sin\phi - a\phi\cos\phi$ **16.** $x = (a + b)\cos\theta - b\cos([(a + b)/b]\theta)$, $y = (a + b)\sin\theta - b\sin([(a + b)/b]\theta)$
17. $x = (a - b)\cos\theta + b\cos([(a - b)/b]\theta)$, $y = (a - b)\sin\theta - b\sin([(a - b)/b]\theta)$ **18.** $8a$
21. a) $x = 2a\cot\theta$, $y = 2a\sin^2\theta$ **b)** $y = 8a^3/(x^2 + 4a^2)$ **22.** 6723 ft

Article 11–4, p. 501

1. $\mathbf{i}2e^{2t} + \mathbf{j}(1 - t)e^{-t}$, $-\infty < t < \infty$ **2.** $\mathbf{i}[1/(2(1 + t))] - \mathbf{j}[t/\sqrt{1 - t^2}]$, $-1 < t < 1$
3. $\mathbf{i}(2/\sqrt{1 - 4t^2}) + \mathbf{j}(3\sec^2 3t)$, $-\frac{1}{2} < t < \frac{1}{2}$ **4.** $\mathbf{i}(1/(|x|\sqrt{9x^2 - 1})) + \mathbf{j}(2\sinh 2x)$, $|x| > \frac{1}{3}$
5. $\mathbf{i}[4/(2t + 1)^2] - \mathbf{j}(8t/(1 - 4t^2))$, $-\frac{1}{2} < t < \frac{1}{2}$

Article 11–5, p. 505

1. $\mathbf{v} = -(a\omega\sin\omega t)\mathbf{i} + (a\omega\cos\omega t)\mathbf{j}$, $\mathbf{a} = -(a\omega^2\cos\omega t)\mathbf{i} - (a\omega^2\sin\omega t)\mathbf{j} = -\omega^2\mathbf{R}$;
    when $\omega t = \pi/3$, $\mathbf{v} = a\omega(-\frac{1}{2}\sqrt{3}\,\mathbf{i} + \frac{1}{2}\mathbf{j})$,   speed $= a\omega$, $\mathbf{a} = -a\omega^2(\frac{1}{2}\mathbf{i} + \frac{1}{2}\sqrt{3}\,\mathbf{j})$
2. $\mathbf{v} = -(2\sin t)\mathbf{i} + (3\cos t)\mathbf{j}$, $\mathbf{a} = -(2\cos t)\mathbf{i} - (3\sin t)\mathbf{j}$;
    at $t = \pi/4$, $\mathbf{v} = -\sqrt{2}\,\mathbf{i} + \frac{3}{2}\sqrt{2}\,\mathbf{j}$,   speed $= \sqrt{6.5}$, $\mathbf{a} = -\sqrt{2}\,\mathbf{i} - \frac{3}{2}\sqrt{2}\,\mathbf{j}$.
3. $\mathbf{v} = \mathbf{i} + 2t\mathbf{j}$, $\mathbf{a} = 2\mathbf{j}$;   at $t = 2$, $\mathbf{v} = \mathbf{i} + 4\mathbf{j}$, $\mathbf{a} = 2\mathbf{j}$,   speed $= \sqrt{17}$.
4. $\mathbf{v} = -(2\sin 2t)\mathbf{i} + (2\cos t)\mathbf{j}$, $\mathbf{a} = -(4\cos 2t)\mathbf{i} - (2\sin t)\mathbf{j}$;   at $t = 0$, $\mathbf{v} = 2\mathbf{j}$, $\mathbf{a} = -4\mathbf{i}$,   speed $= 2$
5. $\mathbf{v} = e^t\mathbf{i} - 2e^{-2t}\mathbf{j}$, $\mathbf{a} = e^t\mathbf{i} + 4e^{-2t}\mathbf{j}$;   at $t = \ln 3$, $\mathbf{v} = 3\mathbf{i} - \frac{2}{9}\mathbf{j}$, $\mathbf{a} = 3\mathbf{i} + \frac{4}{9}\mathbf{j}$,   speed $= \frac{1}{9}\sqrt{733}$
6. $\mathbf{v} = (\sec t\tan t)\mathbf{i} + (\sec^2 t)\mathbf{j}$, $\mathbf{a} = (\sec^3 t + \sec t\tan^2 t)\mathbf{i} + (2\sec^2 t\tan t)\mathbf{j}$;
    at $t = \pi/6$, $\mathbf{v} = \frac{2}{3}\mathbf{i} + \frac{4}{3}\mathbf{j}$, $\mathbf{a} = (10\mathbf{i} + 8\mathbf{j})/(3\sqrt{3})$, speed $= \frac{1}{3}\sqrt{20}$
7. $\mathbf{v} = (3\sinh 3t)\mathbf{i} + (2\cosh t)\mathbf{j}$, $\mathbf{a} = (9\cosh 3t)\mathbf{i} + (2\sinh t)\mathbf{j}$;   at $t = 0$, $\mathbf{v} = 2\mathbf{j}$, $\mathbf{a} = 9\mathbf{i}$,   speed $= 2$
8. $\mathbf{v} = [\mathbf{i}/(t + 1)] + 2t\mathbf{j}$, $\mathbf{a} = [-\mathbf{i}/(t + 1)^2] + 2\mathbf{j}$;   at $t = 1$, $\mathbf{v} = \frac{1}{2}\mathbf{i} + 2\mathbf{j}$, $\mathbf{a} = -\frac{1}{4}\mathbf{i} + 2\mathbf{j}$,   speed $= \frac{1}{2}\sqrt{17}$
9. $\mathbf{R} = -\frac{1}{2}gt^2\mathbf{j} + \mathbf{v}_0 t = (tv_0\cos\alpha)\mathbf{i} + (tv_0\sin\alpha - \frac{1}{2}gt^2)\mathbf{j}$

Article 11–6, p. 508

1. $-\mathbf{i}\sin t + \mathbf{j}\cos t$ **2.** $(e^t\mathbf{i} + 2t\mathbf{j})/\sqrt{e^{2t} + 4t^2}$ **3.** $-\mathbf{i}\cos t + \mathbf{j}\sin t$ **4.** $(\mathbf{i} + 2x\mathbf{j})/\sqrt{1 + 4x^2}$
5. $-(2\mathbf{i}\cos t + \mathbf{j})/\sqrt{1 + 4\cos^2 t}$ **6.** $(it + \mathbf{j})/\sqrt{1 + t^2}$ **7.** $[(\cos t - \sin t)/\sqrt{2}]\mathbf{i} + [(\cos t + \sin t)/\sqrt{2}]\mathbf{j}$ **8.** $(\tanh t)\mathbf{i} + (\operatorname{sech} t)\mathbf{j}$

Article 11–7, p. 512

1. $(1/a)\operatorname{sech}^2(x/a)$ **2.** $|\cos x|$ **3.** $4e^{2x}/(1 + 4e^{4x})^{3/2}$ **4.** $1/(3a|\sin t\cos t|)$ **5.** $1/|a\theta|$ **6.** $(1/4a)|\csc(\theta/2)|$ **7.** $|\cos y|$
8. $2/[\sqrt{y^2 + 2}(y^2 + 1)^2]$ **9.** $48y^5/[(4y^6 + 1)^2]$ **10.** $1/[2(1 + t^2)^{3/2}]$ **11.** $1/[|t|(1 + t^2)^{3/2}]$ **12.** $e^{-t}/\sqrt{2}$
13. $\mathbf{N} = -\sin\theta\,\mathbf{i} + \cos\theta\,\mathbf{j}$ **14.** $\mathbf{N} = (t/\sqrt{1 + t^2})\mathbf{i} + (1/\sqrt{1 + t^2})\mathbf{j}$ **15. a)** $\mathbf{N} = (-1/\sqrt{1 + t^2})\mathbf{i} + (t/\sqrt{1 + t^2})\mathbf{j}$
    b) $\mathbf{N} = (1/\sqrt{1 + t^2})\mathbf{i} - (t/\sqrt{1 + t^2})\mathbf{j}$ **16.** $\mathbf{N} = (-(\cos t + \sin t)/\sqrt{2})\mathbf{i} + ((\cos t - \sin t)/\sqrt{2})\mathbf{j}$
17. $(x + 2)^2 + (y - 3)^2 = 8$.   For the circle: $y' = -(x + 2)/(y - 3)$, $y'' = -8/(y - 3)^3$. Both of these $= +1$ at $(0, 1)$.

Article 11–8, p. 515

2. $\mathbf{v} = 2\mathbf{i}\sinh 2t + 2\mathbf{j}\cosh 2t$, $\quad\mathbf{a} = 4\mathbf{i}\cosh 2t + 4\mathbf{j}\sinh 2t$, $\quad ds/dt = |\mathbf{v}| = 2\sqrt{\cosh 4t}$; $\quad a_T = d^2s/dt^2 = (4\sinh 4t)/\sqrt{\cosh 4t}$, $a_N = \sqrt{|\mathbf{a}|^2 - a_T^2} = 4\sqrt{\operatorname{sech} 4t}$ 3. $a_T = 2t/\sqrt{1+t^2}$, $a_N = 2/\sqrt{1+t^2}$ 4. $a_T = 0$, $a_N = \omega^2 a$ 5. $a_T = 0$, $a_N = 2/(t^2+1)$
6. $a_T = \sqrt{2}\,e^t$, $a_N = \sqrt{2}\,e^t$

Article 11–9, p. 517

2. $\mathbf{v} = 3a\sin\theta\mathbf{u_r} + 3a(1-\cos\theta)\mathbf{u_\theta}$, $\quad\mathbf{a} = 9a(2\cos\theta - 1)\mathbf{u_r} + 18a\sin\theta\mathbf{u_\theta}$. 3. $\mathbf{v} = 4at\cos 2\theta\mathbf{u_r} + 2at\sin 2\theta\mathbf{u_\theta}$,
$\mathbf{a} = (4a\cos 2\theta - 20at^2\sin 2\theta)\mathbf{u_r} + (2a\sin 2\theta + 16at^2\cos 2\theta)\mathbf{u_\theta}$. 4. $\mathbf{v} = 2ae^{a\theta}\mathbf{u_r} + 2e^{a\theta}\mathbf{u_\theta}$, $\quad\mathbf{a} = 4e^{a\theta}(a^2-1)\mathbf{u_r} + 8ae^{a\theta}\mathbf{u_\theta}$.
5. $\mathbf{v} = (a\cos t)\mathbf{u_r} + ae^{-t}(1+\sin t)\mathbf{u_\theta}$, $\quad\mathbf{a} = -a[\sin t + e^{-2t}(1+\sin t)]\mathbf{u_r} + ae^{-t}[2\cos t - 1 - \sin t]\mathbf{u_\theta}$.
6. $\mathbf{v} = -(8\sin 4t)\mathbf{u_r} + (4\cos 4t)\mathbf{u_\theta}$, $\quad\mathbf{a} = -(40\cos 4t)\mathbf{u_r} - (32\sin 4t)\mathbf{u_\theta}$

Miscellaneous Problems Chapter 11, pp. 518–520

1. $x = (1-t)^{-1}$, $\;y = 1 - \ln(1-t)$, $\;t < 1$ 2. $x = \tan^{-1}(t+1)$, $\;y = (t+1)\tan^{-1}(t+1) - \frac{1}{4}\pi - \frac{1}{2}\ln(1+t+\frac{1}{2}t^2)$
3. $x = e^t$, $\;y = e^{e^t} - e$ 4. $x = 3 - 3\cos 2t$, $\;y = 4 + 2\sin 2t$ 5. $x = t - \sin t$, $\;y = 1 - \cos t$
6. $y = e^t$, $\;x = 2\sqrt{1+e^t} - 2\sqrt{2} - 2\coth^{-1}\sqrt{1+e^t} + 2\coth^{-1}\sqrt{2}$ 7. $x = \sinh^{-1}t$, $\;y = t\sinh^{-1}t - \sqrt{1+t^2} + 1$
8. $x = 2 + 2\sinh(t/2)$, $\;y = 2t - 4 + 4\cosh(t/2)$ 9. $x = 4\sin t$, $\;y = 4\cos t$ 10. $x = 2 - e^{-t}$, $\;y = 2t + e^{-t}$
12. $x = 8t - 2\sin 2t$, $\;y = 4 - 2\cos 2t$ 13. $x = 2a\sin^2\theta\tan\theta$, $\;y = 2a\sin^2\theta$ 14. $x = \cot\theta \pm a\cos\theta$, $\;y = \pm a\sin\theta$
15. a) $3\pi a^2$ b) $8a$ c) $-4a\sin(t/2)$ d) $64\pi a^2/3$ e) πa, $(5a/6)$ 17. 0 24. a) $\mathbf{v} = 2^{-3/2}(-\mathbf{i} + \mathbf{j})$, $\quad\mathbf{a} = 2^{-5/2}(\mathbf{i} - 3\mathbf{j})$
b) $t = 0$ 25. a) $\mathbf{v} = \pi(\mathbf{i}(1 - \cos\pi t) + \mathbf{j}\sin\pi t)$, $\quad\mathbf{a} = \pi^2(\mathbf{i}\sin\pi t + \mathbf{j}\cos\pi t)$ b) Slope of $PC = \cot\pi t$,
slope of $PQ = \csc\pi t + \cot\pi t$ c) Slope of $\mathbf{v}$ = slope of PQ, slope of $\mathbf{a}$ = slope of PC 26. Speed $= a\sqrt{1+t^2}$,
$a_T = at/\sqrt{1+t^2}$, $\;a_N = a(t^2+2)/\sqrt{1+t^2}$ 28. b) $\pi/2$ 29. $|ad - bc|(a^2 + b^2)^{-3/2}$, provided $a^2 + b^2 \neq 0$
30. $x = a\theta + a\sin\theta$, $\;y = -a(1 - \cos\theta)$ 31. $(-\frac{1}{2}\ln 2, 1/\sqrt{2})$ 32. b) πab, πa^2 33. $\kappa = \pi s$
34. $y = \pm\sqrt{1-x^2} \pm \ln(1 - \sqrt{1-x^2})/x + C$. Set $C = 0$. Then $x = e^{-s}$ $[s = -\ln x$, measured from $(1, 0)]$,
$y = \pm\sqrt{1 - e^{-2s}} \pm \ln(e^s - \sqrt{e^{2s} - 1})$ 35. $s = s_0 + 2\pi p$, $\;A = A_0 + s_0 p + \pi p^2$, $\;R = R_0 + p$, where s_0, A_0, R_0
are the length of arc, area, and radius of curvature of the original curve. 36. a) $320\sqrt{10}$ b) $16[\sqrt{2} + \ln(\sqrt{2} + 1)]$
37. $\mathbf{v} = 3\cos t\mathbf{i} - 2\sin t\mathbf{j}$, $\quad\mathbf{a} = -3\sin t\mathbf{i} - 2\cos t\mathbf{j}$, $\quad$speed $= (4 + 5\cos^2 t)^{1/2}$, $\quad a_T = -5\sin t\cos t(4 + 5\cos^2 t)^{-1/2}$,
$a_N = 6(4 + 5\cos^2 t)^{-1/2}$ 38. a) $a_T = 0$, $\;a_N = 4$ b) 1 c) $r = 2\cos\theta$ 39. $\mathbf{v} = (\cos t - t\sin t)\mathbf{i} + (\sin t + t\cos t)\mathbf{j}$,
$\mathbf{a} = -(t\cos t + 2\sin t)\mathbf{i} - (t\sin t - 2\cos t)\mathbf{j}$, $\;\kappa = (t^2 + 2)/(t^2 + 1)^{3/2}$ 40. $\kappa = |f^2 + 2f'^2 - ff''|/(f^2 + f'^2)^{3/2}$
41. a) $r = e^{2\theta}$ b) $\frac{1}{2}\sqrt{5}(e^{4\pi} - 1)$ 42. $\sqrt{2}\mathbf{u_r}$ 43. $2(\omega^2 - 1)\mathbf{i}$ 44. a) $\mathbf{v} = -\mathbf{u_r} + 3\mathbf{u_\theta}$, $\quad\mathbf{a} = -9\mathbf{u_r} - 6\mathbf{u_\theta}$
b) $\sqrt{37} + \frac{1}{6}\ln(6 + \sqrt{37})$ 45. $r = a\cosh\omega t$ 46. $1/r - k = (1/k)(1 + e\cos\theta)$

CHAPTER 12

Article 12–2, pp. 530–531

1. $0, -\frac{1}{4}, -\frac{2}{9}, -\frac{3}{16}$; converges to 0 2. $\frac{1}{2}, \frac{1}{2}, \frac{3}{8}, \frac{1}{4}$; converges to 0 3. $\frac{1}{3}, \frac{1}{9}, \frac{1}{27}, \frac{1}{81}$; converges to 0 4. $1, \frac{1}{2}, \frac{1}{6}, \frac{1}{24}$; converges to 0
5. $1, -\frac{1}{3}, \frac{1}{5}, -\frac{1}{7}$; converges to 0 6. $1, 3, 1, 3$; diverges 7. $0, -1, 0, 1$; diverges 8. $8, 8^{1/2}, 8^{1/3}, 8^{1/4}$; converges to 1
9. $1, -1/\sqrt{2}, 1/\sqrt{3}, -\frac{1}{2}$; converges to 0 10. $1, 1, 1, 1$; converges to 1 11. Converges to 0 12. Diverges 13. Converges to 1
14. Converges to 0 15. Diverges 16. Diverges 17. Converges to $-\frac{2}{3}$ 18. Converges to $\frac{1}{2}$ 19. Converges to $\sqrt{2}$
20. Converges to 0 21. Diverges 22. Converges to 1 23. Diverges 24. Converges to 0 25. Converges to 1
26. Converges to 1 27. Converges to -5 28. Converges to 9 29. Converges to 1 30. Converges to 0 31. Converges to 1
32. Diverges 33. Converges to 5 34. Diverges 35. Converges to 0 36. Converges to 10 37. Converges to 0
38. Converges to 1 39. Converges to $\sqrt{2}$ 40. Converges to 2 41. Diverges 42. Converges to 0 43. Converges to 0
44. Converges to -1 45. Diverges 46. Converges to 1 47. Converges to 0 48. Converges to 1 49. Converges to $\pi/2$
50. Diverges 51. Converges to 1 52. Converges to 2 53. Converges to $\frac{1}{2}$ 54. Converges to 0 55. Use $0 < n!/n^n \leq 1/n$
56. $x_7 = 1.732050808 = x_6$ 57. Yes. No; the limit is 1 for any $x > 0$.
58. a) $x_1 = 1, x_2 = 1.54\ldots, x_3 = 1.57\ldots, x_4 = 1.570796327$ b) $x_1 = 5, \ldots, x_8 = x_9 = 7.853981634\,(\approx 5\pi/2)$ 60. 1 61. 1

Article 12–3, pp. 534–535

1. Converges; $L = 0$ 2. Converges; $L = 0$ 3. Converges; $L = 0$ 4. Converges; $L = 1$ 5. Converges; $L = 0$ 6. Diverges
7. Converges; $L = e^7$ 8. Converges; $L = e^5$ 9. Converges; $L = 0$ 10. Converges; $L = 1$ 11. Diverges
12. Converges; $L = 0$ 13. Converges; $L = 1$ 14. Converges; $L = 1$ 15. Converges; $L = 0$ 16. Converges; $L = 1$
17. Converges; $L = 1/e$ 18. Converges; $L = 1/e$ 19. Converges; $L = 0$ 20. Converges; $L = 1$ 21. Converges; $L = x$

22. Converges; $L = 1$ **23.** Converges; $L = 1$ **24.** Converges; $L = 0$ **25.** Converges; $L = 1$ **26.** Converges; $L = 4$
27. Converges; $L = 1/e$ **28.** Converges; $L = 1$ **29.** Converges; $L = 0$ **30.** Converges; $L = 1/(p - 1)$ **31.** $N \geq 693$
32. $N \geq 9124$ **33.** $N \geq 17$

Article 12–4, pp. 543–545

1. $s_n = \frac{1}{2} - (1/n + 2)$, $\lim_{n \to \infty} s_n = \frac{1}{2}$ **2.** $s_n = -\ln(n + 1)$, diverges **3.** $s_n = (1 - (1/e)^n)/(1 - (1/e))$, $\lim_{n \to \infty} s_n = e/(e - 1)$
4. $s_n = \frac{2}{3}(1 - (-1/2)^n)$, $\lim_{n \to \infty} s_n = \frac{2}{3}$ **5.** $s_n = \frac{1}{3}(1 - (-2)^n)$, diverges **6.** $s_n = 3(1 - (\frac{1}{3})^n)$, $\lim_{n \to \infty} s_n = 3$
7. $s_n = \frac{1}{11}(1 - (\frac{1}{100})^n)$, $\lim_{n \to \infty} s_n = \frac{1}{11}$ **8.** $s_n = n(n + 1)/2$, diverges
9. a) $\sum_{n=-2}^{\infty} 1/[(n + 4)(n + 5)]$ b) $\sum_{n=0}^{\infty} 1/[(n + 2)(n + 3)]$ c) $\sum_{n=5}^{\infty} 1/[(n - 3)(n - 2)]$ **10.** $28m$
11. $1 + \frac{1}{4} + \frac{1}{16} + \frac{1}{64}$; $\frac{4}{3}$ **12.** $\frac{1}{16} + \frac{1}{64} + \frac{1}{256} + \frac{1}{1024}$; $\frac{1}{12}$ **13.** $\frac{7}{4} + \frac{7}{16} + \frac{7}{64} + \frac{7}{256}$; $\frac{7}{3}$
14. $5 - \frac{5}{4} + \frac{5}{16} - \frac{5}{64}$; 4 **15.** 11.5 **16.** 8.5 **17.** 5/3 **18.** 10/3 **19.** 1 **20.** $\frac{1}{4}$ **21.** $\frac{1}{9}$ **22.** 1
23. a) 234/999 b) Yes; if $x = 0.a_1 a_2 \cdots a_n a_1 a_2 \cdots a_n$, then $(10^n - 1)x = a_1 a_2 \cdots a_n = p$ is an integer and $x = p/q$ with
$q = 10^n - 1$. **24.** 123999/99900 **25.** $2 + \sqrt{2}$ **26.** Diverges **27.** 1 **28.** Diverges **29.** Diverges **30.** 5/6 **31.** $e^2/(e^2 - 1)$
32. Diverges **33.** Diverges **34.** 2/9 **35.** 3/2 **36.** Diverges **37.** Diverges **38.** $x/(x - 1)$ **39.** $a = 1$, $r = -x$
40. $a = 1$, $r = -x^2$ **41.** 8 **42.** $s_n = (1 + (-1)^{n+1})/2$ **48.** d) $n \geq 6$ e) $n \geq 999$
49. a) $R_n = C_0 e^{-kt_0}(1 - e^{-nkt_0})/(1 - e^{-kt_0})$, $R = C_0(e^{-kt_0})/(1 - e^{-kt_0}) = C_0/(e^{kt_0} - 1)$
  b) $R_1 = 1/e \approx 0.368$, $R_{10} = R(1 - e^{-10}) \approx R(0.9999546) \approx 0.58195$; $R \approx 0.58198$; $0 < (R - R_{10})/R < 0.0001$
  c) 7 e) 20 hr f) Give initial dose that produces a concentration of 2 mg/ml, followed every $100 \ln 2 \approx 69.31$ hr by dose
  that raises concentration by 1.5 mg/ml g) $5 \ln(10/3) \approx 6$ (hr)

Article 12–5, pp. 558–560

[*Note.* The tests mentioned in Problems 1–30 may not be the only ones that apply.]
1. Converges; ratio test; geometric series, $r < 1$. **2.** Diverges; $\lim_{n \to \infty} a_n = 1$ **3.** Converges; compare with $\sum (1/2^n)$
4. Diverges; multiple of $\sum (1/n)$ **5.** Converges; ratio test **6.** Converges; ratio test **7.** Diverges; compare with $\sum (1/n)$
8. Converges; p-series, $p > 1$ **9.** Converges; ratio test **10.** Diverges; integral test; multiple of $\sum_{n=1}^{\infty} (1/n)$
11. Diverges: compare with $\sum (1/n)$ **12.** Diverges; p-series, $p < 1$; integral test **13.** Diverges; ratio test
14. Converges; compare with $\sum (\frac{1}{3})^n$; root test **15.** Converges; ratio test (or root test) **16.** Diverges; p-series, $p < 1$
17. Converges; comparison with $\sum (1/n^{3/2})$ **18.** Diverges; nth-term test **19.** Converges; ratio test **20.** Converges; compare
with $\sum (1/n^{3/2})$ **21.** Diverges; integral test **22.** Converges; ratio test (or root test) **23.** Diverges; nth-term test, $a_n \to e$
24. Converges; compare with $\sum (1/3^n)$ **25.** Converges; ratio test **26.** Diverges; integral test **27.** Converges; ratio test or
comparison with $\sum (1/n!)$ **28.** Diverges; root test
29. Converges; ratio test **30.** Converges; ratio test; comparison to $\sum (1/2^n)$ **32.** $x^2 < 2$ **33.** $x^2 \leq 1$ **34.** $|x| > 1$
35. 1.649767731 **36.** $\sum_{n=1}^{6} (1/n^2) = 1.49138$, $\sum_{n=1}^{6} [3[(n - 1)!]^2/(2n)!] = 1.644911616$
37. $n = 27$, $s_n + n^{-3}/3 = 1.082324151$; $\pi^4/90 = 1.082323234$; difference $\approx 0.9 \times 10^{-6}$
38. $40.5548555 < s_n < 41.5548555$ **39.** $\sum (1/n)$ is divergent, as is any nonzero multiple of this series.

Article 12–6, p. 562

[*Note.* In the answers provided for this article, "Yes" means that the series converges absolutely. "No" means that the series does *not* converge absolutely. The reasons given for the convergence or divergence of the series of absolute values may not be the only appropriate ones.]
1. Yes; p-series, $p = 2$ **2.** Yes; p-series, $p = 3$ **3.** No; harmonic series divergence **4.** Yes; geometric series; $r < 1$
5. Yes; comparison to p-series, $p = 2$ **6.** No; multiple of harmonic series **7.** Yes; comparison to p-series, $p = \frac{3}{2}$ **8.** No;
multiple of harmonic series **9.** Yes; comparison test **10.** Yes; comparison test **11.** No; nth-term test
12. Yes; root test or ratio test **13.** Yes; geometric series, $r < 1$ **14.** No; nth-term test **15.** Yes; ratio test
16. No; nth-term test **17.** Yes; compare with $(2 + n)/n^3$ **18.** Yes; compare with $(1/2^n) + (1/3^n)$

Article 12–7, pp. 567–568

1. Converges **2.** Converges **3.** Diverges **4.** Diverges **5.** Converges **6.** Converges **7.** Converges **8.** Diverges
9. Converges **10.** Diverges **11.** Absolutely convergent **12.** Conditionally convergent **13.** Absolutely convergent
14. Divergent **15.** Conditionally convergent **16.** Absolutely convergent **17.** Divergent **18.** Conditionally convergent
19. Conditionally convergent **20.** Absolutely convergent **21.** Absolutely convergent **22.** Divergent

23. Absolutely convergent   **24.** Conditionally convergent   **25.** Divergent   **26.** Absolutely convergent   **27.** Conditionally convergent   **28.** Absolutely convergent   **29.** $\frac{1}{5} = 0.2$ **30.** 10^{-5} **31.** $(0.01)^5/5 = 2 \times 10^{-11}$ **32.** t^4

33. 0.54030   (actual: $\cos 1 = 0.540302306$)   **34.** 0.36788   (actual: $1/e = 0.367879441$)

35. a) It is not decreasing (condition 2)   **b)** $-\frac{1}{2}$ **36.** $s_{20} + \frac{1}{2} \cdot \frac{1}{21} = 0.692580927$, $\ln 2 = 0.693147181$

39. $\sum_{n=1}^{\infty} a_n = \sum_{n=1}^{\infty} (-1)^n (1/\sqrt{n})$, $\sum_{n=1}^{\infty} b_n = \sum_{n=1}^{\infty} (-1)^n (1/\sqrt{n})$, $\sum_{n=1}^{\infty} a_n b_n = \sum_{n=1}^{\infty} (1/n)$

Article 12–8, p. 573

1. $1 - x + (x^2/2!) - (x^3/3!)$; $1 - x + (x^2/2!) - (x^3/3!) + (x^4/4!)$ **2.** $x - (x^3/3!)$; $x - (x^3/3!)$

3. $1 - (x^2/2!)$; $1 - (x^2/2!) + (x^4/4!)$ **4.** $1 - (x^2/2!)$; $1 - (x^2/2!) + (x^4/4!)$

5. $x + (x^3/3!)$; $x + (x^3/3!)$ **6.** $1 + (x^2/2!)$; $1 + (x^2/2!) + (x^4/4!)$ **7.** $-2x + 1$; $x^4 - 2x + 1$

8. $x^3 - 2x + 1$; $x^3 - 2x + 1$ **9.** $x^2 - 2x + 1$; $x^2 - 2x + 1$ **10.** $\sum_{n=0}^{\infty} (-1)^n x^n = 1 - x + x^2 - \cdots$ **11.** x^2 **12.** $x^2 + 2x + 1$

13. $1 + (3x/2) + (3/2 \cdot 4)x^2 - [3/(8 \cdot 3!)]x^3 + [9/(16 \cdot 4!)]x^4 - [45/(32 \cdot 5!)]x^5 + \cdots = \sum_{n=0}^{\infty} (3/n^2)x^n$

14. $1 + x + x^2 + x^3 + \cdots$; geometric series with $r = x$

15. $e^{10} + e^{10}(x - 10) + (e^{10}/2!)(x - 10)^2 + (e^{10}/3!)(x - 10)^3 + \cdots$ **16.** $\frac{1}{4} + (x - \frac{1}{2}) + (x - \frac{1}{2})^2$

17. $(x - 1) - [(x - 1)^2/2] + [(x - 1)^3/3] - [(x - 1)^4/4] + \cdots$

18. $2 + \frac{1}{2}(x - 4)/2 - [1/(2 \cdot 4)][(x - 4)^2/2^3] + [(1 \cdot 3)/(2 \cdot 4 \cdot 6)][(x - 4)^3/2^5] - [(1 \cdot 3 \cdot 5)/(2 \cdot 4 \cdot 6 \cdot 8)][(x - 4)^4/2^7]$

19. $-1 - (x + 1) - (x + 1)^2 - (x + 1)^3 - \cdots$ **20.** $(\sqrt{2}/2)[1 + (x + (\pi/4)) - [(x + (\pi/4))^2/2!] - [(x + (\pi/4))^3/3!] + \cdots]$

21. $1 + 2(x - (\pi/4)) + 2(x - (\pi/4))^2$ **22.** $\ln (0.5) - \sqrt{3}(x - (\pi/3)) - 2(x - (\pi/3))^2$

23. 1.0100 with error less than 0.0001   (use 2 terms)

Article 12–9, pp. 582–583

1. $1 + \frac{1}{2}x + \frac{1}{4}(x^2/2!) + \frac{1}{8}(x^3/3!) + \frac{1}{16}(x^4/4!) + \cdots$ **2.** $3x - 3^3(x^3/3!) + 3^5(x^5/5!) - 3^7(x^7/7!) + \cdots$

3. $5 - (5/\pi^2)(x^2/2!) + (5/\pi^4)(x^4/4!) - (5/\pi^6)(x^6/6!) + \cdots$ **4.** $x + (x^3/3!) + (x^5/5!) + (x^7/7!) + \cdots$

5. $(x^4/4!) - (x^6/6!) + (x^8/8!) - (x^{10}/10!) + \cdots$ **6.** $1 - x^2 + (8x^4/4!) - (32x^6/6!) + (128x^8/8!) - \cdots$

9. $1 - x + x^2 - 3\int_0^x (x - t)^2 (1 + t)^{-11} \, dt$ **10.** $x - (x^2/2) + \int_0^x (x - t)^2 (1 + t)^{-3} \, dt$

11. $1 + (x/2) - \frac{1}{8}x^2 + \frac{3}{16}\int_0^x (x - t)^2 (1 + t)^{-(5/2)} \, dt$ **12.** $e[1 + (x - 1) + [(x - 1)^2/2!] + [(x - 1)^3/3!] + \cdots]$

13. $|x| < \sqrt[5]{0.06} \approx 0.57$ **14.** $|R| < 0.00261$. Too small.   **15.** $|R| < (10^{-9}/6)$; $x < \sin x$ for $x < 0$.

16. $|R| < 1.3 \times 10^{-5}$ **17.** $|R| < e^{0.1}/6,000 \approx 1.84 \times 10^{-4}$ **18.** $1.\overline{6} \times 10^{-4}$ **19.** $R_4(x, 0) < 0.0003$

22. a) $\sin 0.1$ **b)** $\cos (\pi/4)$ **c)** $\cosh 1$

Article 12–10, pp. 589–590

1. Use $\cos x \approx (\sqrt{3}/2) - \frac{1}{2}(x - (\pi/6))$. $\cos 31° \approx 0.857\,299$.   Actual: $\cos 31° = 0.857\,167$.

2. Use $\tan x \approx 1 + 2(x - (\pi/4)) + 4[(x - (\pi/4))^2/2!]$. $\tan 46° \approx 1.035\,516$.   Actual: $\tan 46° = 1.035\,530$.

3. Use $\sin x \approx (x - 2\pi)$. $\sin (6.3) \approx 0.0168\,147$.   Actual: $\sin (6.3) = 0.0168\,139$.

4. Use $\cos x \approx 1 - [(x - 22\pi)^2/2!]$. $\cos 69 \approx 0.993\,383$.   Actual: $\cos 69 = 0.993\,390$.

5. Use $\ln x \approx (x - 1) - [(x - 1)^2/2] + [(x - 1)^3/3] - [(x - 1)^4/4]$. $\ln 1.25 \approx 0.222\,982$.   Actual: $\ln 1.25 = 0.223\,144$.

6. Use $\tan^{-1} x \approx (\pi/4) + \frac{1}{2}(x - 1)$. $\tan^{-1} 1.02 \approx 0.795\,398$.   Actual: $\tan^{-1} 1.02 = 0.795\,299$.

7. $\ln (1 + 2x) = 2x - [(2x)^2/2] + [(2x)^3/3] - [(2x)^4/4] + \cdots = \sum_{n=1}^{\infty} (-1)^{n+1}[(2x)^n/n]$; converges for $|x| < \frac{1}{2}$.

8. $|x| < 0.0197$ **9.** $\int_0^{0.1} [(\sin x)/x] \, dx \approx x - (x^3/18)]_0^{0.1} \approx 0.09994$

10. $\int_0^{0.1} e^{-x^2} \, dx \approx x - (x^3/3)]_0^{0.1} = 0.09967$ **13.** $\ln 1.5 \approx 0.405\,465$ **14.** 50 terms (through $\frac{1}{99}$)

17. $c_3 = 3.141592665$ **21. c)** 6   **d)** $1/q$ **22. a)** $E(x) = 2$ **b)** $E(x) = 6$ **c)** The series for $E(x)$ diverges.

Article 12–11, p. 593

1. 1   **2.** $\frac{1}{2}$ **3.** $-\frac{1}{24}$ **4.** 1   **5.** -2 **6.** $\frac{1}{3}$ **7.** 0   **8.** 1   **9.** $-\frac{1}{3}$ **10.** -1 **11.** $\frac{1}{120}$ **12.** 2   **13.** $\frac{1}{3}$

14. $\frac{1}{2}$ **15.** -1 **16.** 2   **17.** 3   **18.** 2   **19.** 0   **20.** $\frac{1}{12}$ **21. b)** $\frac{1}{2}$ **22.** $r = -3, s = \frac{9}{2}$ -

23. This approximation gives better results than the approximation $\sin x \approx x$. See table.

x	± 1.0	± 0.1	± 0.01
$6x/(6 + x^2)$	± 0.857142857	± 0.099833611	± 0.009999833
$\sin x$	± 0.841470985	± 0.099833417	± 0.009999833

Article 12–12, pp. 601–602

1. $|x| < 1$. Diverges at $x = \pm 1$ **2.** $|x| < 1$. Diverges at $x = \pm 1$ **3.** $|x| < 2$. Diverges at $x = \pm 2$
4. $-\infty < x < \infty$ **5.** $-\infty < x < \infty$ **6.** $0 < x < 2$. Converges at $x = 2$; diverges at 0
7. $-4 < x < 0$. Diverges at $x = 0, -4$ **8.** $|x| < 1$. Diverges at $x = \pm 1$ **9.** $|x| < 1$. Converges at $x = \pm 1$
10. $1 \le x \le 3$ **11.** $|x| < \infty$ **12.** $|x| \le \frac{1}{2}$ **13.** $|x| < (1/e)$. Converges at $x = -(1/e)$; diverges at $(1/e)$
14. $|x| < \infty$ **15.** $x = 0$ **16.** $|x| < \infty$ **17.** $\frac{1}{2} < x < \frac{3}{2}$. Diverges at $x = \frac{1}{2}, \frac{3}{2}$
18. $0 < x < 4$. Converges at $x = 4$; diverges at 0   **19.** $|x| < \sqrt{3}$. Diverges at $x = \pm\sqrt{3}$
20. $-4 < x < -2$. Converges at $x = -4$; diverges at -2 **21.** e^{3x+6} **22.** $2/(3 - x^2)$
24. $1 - 2x + 3x^2 - 4x^3 + \cdots = \sum_{n=0}^{\infty} (-1)^n (n+1)x^n$ **25.** $\sum_{n=1}^{\infty} 2nx^{2n-1}$
26. $\sin^2 x = \frac{1}{2}([(2x)^2/2!] - [(2x)^4/4!] + \cdots)$, $(d/dx)(\sin^2 x) = 2\sin x \cos x = (2x/1!) - [(2x)^3/3!] + \cdots = \sin 2x$
27. 0.002666   **28.** 0.004992   **29.** 0.000331   **30.** 0.099889   **31.** 0.363305   **32.** 0.097605   **33.** 0.099999   **34.** 0.251715
35. a) $\sinh^{-1} x = x - \frac{1}{2}(x^3/3) + [(1 \cdot 3)/(2 \cdot 4)](x^5/5) - [(1 \cdot 3 \cdot 5)/(2 \cdot 4 \cdot 6)](x^7/7) + \cdots$
   b) $\sinh^{-1} 0.25 \approx 0.247$ (Actual: $\sinh^{-1} 0.25 = \ln(0.25 + \sqrt{(0.25)^2 + 1}) \approx 0.24746646$)
36. 0.904531532   **37.** $\sum_{n=1}^{\infty} n^n x^n$ **38.** $\sum_{n=1}^{\infty} (x^n/n)$; conditional at $x = -1$; $\sum_{n=1}^{\infty} (x^n/n^2)$; absolute at $x = \pm 1$
39. By the theorem, the series converges absolutely for $|x| < d$, for all positive $d < r$. This means it converges absolutely for all $|x| < r$. [Take $d = \frac{1}{2}(r + |x|)$.]
40. $|a_{n+1}/a_n| = |x_{m-n}/n|$; $\lim_{n\to\infty} |a_{n+1}/a_n| = |x|$.   So the series converges for $|x| < 1$.

Miscellaneous Problems Chapter 12, pp. 603–604

1. $s_n = \ln[(n+1)/(2n)]$; series converges to $-\ln 2$ **2.** $s_n = \frac{1}{2}[\frac{3}{2} - 1/(n+1)]$; limit $= \frac{3}{4}$
6. a) $\sum_{n=2}^{\infty} (-1)^n x^n$ **b)** No, because it will converge in an interval symmetric about $x = 0$, and it cannot converge when $x = -1$.
7. $(1 - t^2)^{-(1/2)} = \sum_{k=0}^{\infty} 2^{-2k}(k!)^{-2}(2k)! \, t^{2k}$, $-1 < t < 1$, $\sin^{-1} x = \sum_{k=0}^{\infty} 2^{-2k}(k!)^{-2}(2k)! \, x^{2k+1}/(2k+1)$, $-1 \le x \le 1$
8. $(1 + t^2)^{-(1/2)} = \sum_{k=0}^{\infty} (-1)^k 2^{-2k}(k!)^{-2}(2k)! \, t^{2k}$, $-1 \le t \le 1$,
   $\sinh^{-1} x = \sum_{k=0}^{\infty} (-1)^k 2^{-2k}(k!)^{-2}(2k)! \, x^{2k+1}/(2k+1)$, $-1 \le x \le 1$
9. $e^{\sin x} = 1 + x + x^2/2! - 3x^4/4! - \cdots$ **11. a)** $\ln \cos x = -(x^2/2) - (x^4/12) - (x^6/45) - \cdots$ **b)** -0.00017 **12.** 0.946
13. 0.747   **14.** $\sqrt{2}[1 + (x-1)/2 + (x-1)^2/8 + \cdots]$ **15.** $\sum_{n=0}^{\infty} (-1)^{n+1}(x-2)^n$, $1 < x < 3$
16. $\tan x = x + x^3/3 + 2x^5/15 + \cdots$ **17.** $\sum_{n=0}^{\infty} [(-1)^n(x-3)^n/4^{n+1}]$
18. $\cos x = \frac{1}{2} \sum_{n=0}^{\infty} (-1)^n [1/(2n)! \, (x - (\pi/3))^{2n} + \sqrt{3}/(2n+1)! \, (x - (\pi/3))^{2n+1}]$ **19.** $\sum_{n=0}^{\infty} (-1)^n (x - \pi)^n/\pi^{n+1}$ **20.** 1.543
22. $e^{e^x} = e(1 + x + 2x^2/2! + 5x^3/3! + \cdots$ **23.** 0.0027   **24.** -0.0011 **25.** $-\infty$ **26.** $e^{-(1/6)}$
27. Converges; by integral test   **28.** Diverges, since nth term doesn't approach zero
29. Diverges   **30.** Diverges   **31.** Diverges   **32.** Converges   **33.** Diverges   **34.** Diverges   **35.** Converges   **36.** Converges
37. Diverges   **38.** Diverges   **39.** Diverges   **40.** Converges   **41.** $\frac{1}{2}$
43. b) Converges   **c)** Converges, by comparison test   **45.** $-5 \le x < 1$ **46.** $-\infty < x < \infty$ **47.** $-\infty < x < \infty$
48. $-e < x < e$ **49.** $1 < x < 5$ **50.** $-1 < x < 5$ **51.** $0 \le x \le 2$ **52.** $-1 \le x < 1$ **53.** $-\infty < x < \infty$
54. $(6n-1)\pi/6 \le x \le (6n+1)\pi/6$ ($n = 0, \pm 1, \pm 2, \ldots$)   **55.** $x \ge \frac{1}{2}$ **56. a)** $-\infty < x < \infty$ **b)** $y'' = xy$ ($a = 1, b = 0$)

CHAPTER 13

Article 13–3, p. 610

1. $(x^2 + 1)(2y - 3) = C$ **2.** $2/3\sqrt{x^3 + 1} + \frac{1}{2}\ln(y^2 + 1) = C$ **3.** $e^y = e^x + C$ **4.** $y^{3/2} = 3\sqrt{x/2} + C$
5. $\sinh 2y - 2\cos x = C$ **6.** $\frac{1}{2}(\ln|x|)^2 = \ln|y| + C$ **7.** $(y-1)e^y + (x^2/2) + \ln|x| = C$ **8.** $\sqrt{2x^2 + 3} - 2\sqrt{4 - y^2} = C$
9. $\cosh^{-1} y + \sinh^{-1} x = C$ **10.** $-y\cos y + \sin y = -x^{-1} + \ln|x| + C$ **11.** $2^{48} \approx 2.815 \times 10^{14}$ **12.** $Q = Q_0 e^{kt}$
13. $i = (E/R)(1 - e^{-Rt/L})$, E/R **15. a)** $(\ln 2)/5700 \approx 1.216 \times 10^{-4}$ **b)** 18,935 years   **c)** 6,658 years

Article 13–4, p. 612

1. $x^2(x^2 + 2y^2) = C$ **2.** $x/y = \ln|x| + C$ **3.** $\ln|x| + e^{-(y/x)} = C$ **4.** $2\tan^{-1}(y/x) + \ln(x^2 + y^2) = C$
5. $\ln|x| - \ln|\sec((y/x) - 1) + \tan((y/x) - 1)| = C$ **6.** $x\sin(y/x) = C$
7. $\ln((x+2)^2 + (y-1)^2) + 2\tan^{-1}((x+2)/(y-1)) = C, a = -2, b = 1$ **8.** $\tan^{-1}(x+y) = x + C$
9. a) $x^2 = yC$ **b)** $x^2 + 2y^2 = C$ **10. a)** $x^2 + y^2 = Cx$ **b)** $x^2 + y^2 = Cy$ **11.** $x^2 - y^2 = C$

Article 13–5, p. 615

1. $y = e^{-x} + Ce^{-2x}$ 2. $y = \frac{1}{2}(x + C)e^{x/2}$ 3. $x^3 y = C - \cos x$ 4. $xy = C - \cos x$ 5. $x = (y/2) + (C/y)$
6. $(x - 1)^4 y = (x^3/3) - x + C$ 7. $y \cosh x = C - e^x$ 8. $xe^{2y} = y^2 + C$ 9. $xy = y^2 + C$ 10. $x = (C - y)/(1 + y^2)$
11. a) $C = G/100kV + (C_0 - G/100kV)e^{-kt}$ b) $G/100kV$

Article 13–6, p. 618

1. $y = Cx^2 - x$ 2. $xy = C$ 3. $y = Cx$ 4. $(x^2/2) + xy + (y^3/3) = C$ 5. $e^x + e^y(x^2 + 1) = C$ 6. $x^2 y + xy^2 - (y^2/2) = C$
7. $x^2 + 2x\sqrt{y^2 + 1} - y^2 = C$ 8. $2y + x^3 = Cx$ 9. $y = x \tan(x + C)$ 10. $y = x(C - x - \ln|x|)$
11. $e^x + x \ln y + y \ln x - \cos y = C$ 12. $y^2 \tan^{-1} x - 2xy + \cosh y = C$ 13. $xy + \cos x = C$

Article 13–7, p. 620

1. $y = C_1 e^{-x} + C_2$ 2. $y = C$, or $y = -2a \tan(ax + C)$, or $y = 2a \tanh(ax + C)$, or $y = 2/(x + C)$
3. $y = C_1 \int e^{-x^2/2}\, dx + C_2$. Note that the integral appearing here could be evaluated as an infinite series, giving
$y = C_1[x - [x^3/(2 \cdot 3)] + [x^5/(2 \cdot 4 \cdot 5)] - [x^7/(2 \cdot 4 \cdot 6 \cdot 7)] + \cdots] + C_2$
4. $y = C_1 \ln|x| + C_2$ 5. $y = C_1 \sinh(x + C_2)$ 6. $y = C_1 \sin(\omega x + C_2)$ 7. $y = C_1 x^4 + C_2 x + C_3$
8. $y = -2 \ln|e^{-x/2} - C_1 e^{x/2}| + C_2$; or $x = \pm \ln|(u - 1)/(u + 1)| + C_2$, where $u = (1 + C_1 e^y)^{1/2}$
9. $x = A \sin(\sqrt{k/m}\, t + (\pi/2)) = A \cos(\sqrt{k/m}\, t)$
10. $s = (m^2 g/k^2)[(kt/m) + e^{-kt/m} - 1]$, where m is the man's mass, g is the acceleration due to gravity, and k is the factor of proportionality in the air resistance $-kv$ (v being velocity).

Article 13–9, p. 624

1. $y = C_1 + C_2 e^{-2x}$ 2. $y = C_1 e^{-2x} + C_2 e^{-3x}$ 3. $y = C_1 e^{-x} + C_2 e^{-5x}$ 4. $y = C_1 e^{3x} + C_2 e^{-x}$
5. $y = e^{-x/2}[C_1 \cos(x\sqrt{3}/2) + C_2 \sin(x\sqrt{3}/2)]$ 6. $y = (C_1 + C_2 x)e^{2x}$ 7. $y = (C_1 + C_2 x)e^{-3x}$
8. $y = e^{3x}(C_1 \cos x + C_2 \sin x)$ 9. $y = e^x(C_1 \cos\sqrt{3}\, x + C_2 \sin\sqrt{3}\, x)$ 10. $y = C_1 e^{2x} + C_2 e^{8x}$

Article 13–10, pp. 632–634

1. $y = (x^2/2) - x + C_1 + C_2 e^{-x}$ 2. $y = -\cos x \sinh^{-1}(\tan x) + C_1 \cos x + C_2 \sin x$
3. $y = -\frac{1}{2}x \cos x + C_1 \cos x + C_2 \sin x$
4. $y = \frac{1}{4}e^x + e^{-x}(C_1 + C_2 x)$ 5. $y = e^{-x}(C_1 + C_2 x + \frac{1}{2}x^2)$ 6. $y = C_1 e^x + C_2 e^{-x} - x$ 7. $y = C_1 e^x + C_2 e^{-x} + (x/2)e^x$
8. $y = C_1 e^x + C_2 e^{-x} - \frac{1}{2}\sin x$ 9. $y = e^{-2x}(C_1 \cos x + C_2 \sin x) + 2$ 10. $y = C_1 + C_2 x + 2^x/((\ln 2)^2 - \ln 2)$
11. $y = C_1 \cos x + C_2 \sin x + \cos x \ln(\cos x) + x \sin x$ 12. $y = C_1 + C_2 e^x + (e^x/2)(\sin x - \cos x)$
13. $y = C_1 e^{5x} + C_2 e^{-2x} + \frac{3}{10}$ 14. $y = C_1 e^{5x} + C_2 e^{-2x} - \frac{1}{5}x + \frac{9}{25}$ 15. $y = C_1 + C_2 e^x + \frac{1}{2}\cos x - \frac{1}{2}\sin x$
16. $y = C_1 e^{-x} + C_2 xe^{-x} + x^2 - 4x + 6$ 17. $y = C_1 \cos x + C_2 \sin x - \frac{1}{8}\cos 3x$ 18. $y = C_1 \cos x + C_2 \sin x + \frac{1}{5}e^{2x}$
19. $y = C_1 e^{2x} + C_2 e^{-x} - 6 \cos x - 2 \sin x$ 20. $y = C_1 \cos x + C_2 \sin x + 2x + \frac{3}{2}e^x$ 21. $y = C_1 e^x + C_2 e^{-x} - x^2 - 2 + \frac{1}{2}xe^x$
22. $y = C_1 e^{-x} + C_2 xe^{-x} - \frac{24}{25}\cos 2x - \frac{18}{25}\sin 2x$ 23. $y = C_1 e^{3x} + C_2 e^{-2x} - \frac{1}{4}e^{-x} + \frac{49}{50}\cos x + \frac{7}{50}\sin x$
24. $y = C_1 e^{-x} + C_2 e^{-2x} + xe^{-x} - xe^{-2x} - \frac{1}{2}x + \frac{3}{4}$ 25. $y = C_1 + C_2 e^{-5x} + x^3 - \frac{3}{5}x^2 + \frac{6}{25}x$
26. $y = C_1 + C_2 e^x + 4x^2 + 5x$ 27. $y = C_1 + C_2 e^{3x} + \frac{1}{3}xe^{3x} + 2x^2 + \frac{4}{3}x$ 28. $y = C_1 + C_2 e^{-7x} + 2x^3 - \frac{1}{2}x^2 + \frac{2}{7}x$
29. $y = C_1 + C_2 e^{5x} - \frac{1}{25}xe^{5x} + \frac{1}{10}x^2 e^{5x}$ 30. $y = C_1 + C_2 e^x - \sin x$ 31. $y = C_1 \cos x + C_2 \sin x - \frac{1}{2}x \cos x + x \sin x$
32. $y = C_1 e^{2x} + C_2 xe^{2x} + x^2 e^{2x}$ 33. $y = C_1 + C_2 e^x + xe^x + \frac{1}{2}e^{-x}$ 34. $y = C_1 + C_2 e^{9x} + xe^{9x}$
35. $y = C_1 e^{5x} + C_2 e^{-x} - \frac{1}{8}e^x - \frac{4}{5}$ 36. $y = C_1 \cos x + C_2 \sin x - x \cos x + \sin x \ln(\sin x)$
37. $y = C_1 \cos x + C_2 \sin x - \sin x \ln(\csc x + \operatorname{ctn} x)$ 38. $y = C_1 \cos 2x + C_2 \sin 2x + \frac{1}{3}\sin x$
39. $y = C_1 + C_2 e^{8x} + \frac{1}{8}xe^{8x}$ 40. $y = e^{-2x}(C_1 \cos x + C_2 \sin x) + \frac{1}{5}x + \frac{6}{25}$ 41. $y = C_1 + C_2 e^x - \frac{1}{4}x^4 - x^3 - 3x^2 - 6x$
42. $y = C_1 \cos 3x + C_2 \sin 3x + x - \frac{1}{8}\cos x$ 43. $y = C_1 + C_2 e^{-2x} - \frac{1}{3}e^x + \frac{1}{6}x^3 - \frac{1}{4}x^2 + \frac{1}{4}x$
44. $y = C_1 e^x + C_2 e^{2x} - xe^x - xe^{2x}$ 45. $y = C_1 \cos x + C_2 \sin x + (x - \tan x)\cos x - \sin x \ln(\cos x)$
46. $y = Ce^{-4x} + \frac{1}{4}x - \frac{1}{16}$ 47. $y = Ce^{3x} - \frac{1}{2}e^x$ 48. $y = Ce^{-x} - \frac{1}{2}\cos x + \frac{1}{2}\sin x$ 49. $y = Ce^{3x} + 5xe^{3x}$
50. $y = \frac{1}{5}e^{2x} - \frac{1}{5}\cos x$ 51. $y = 2 \cos x + \sin x - 1 + \sin x \ln(\sec x + \tan x)$ 52. $y = [x^2 + 2x + 2 + Ce^x]^{-1}$
53. $y = 1 - e^{-x}$

Article 13–11, p. 638

1. $x = x_0 \cos \omega t + (v_0/\omega) \sin \omega t = \sqrt{x_0^2 + (v_0^2/\omega^2)} \sin(\omega t + \phi)$, where $\omega = \sqrt{k/m}$, $\phi = \tan^{-1}(\omega x_0/v_0)$
2. $x = 0.288 \sin(13.9t)$; x in feet, t in sec

3. a) $I = C_1 \cos \omega t + C_2 \sin \omega t$ b) $I = C_1 \cos \omega t + C_2 \sin \omega t + (A\alpha/L(\omega^2 - \alpha^2)) \cos \alpha t$
   c) $I = C_1 \cos \omega t + C_2 \sin \omega t + (A/2L)t \sin \omega t$ d) $I = e^{-5t}(C_1 \cos 149t + C_2 \sin 149t)$
4. $\theta = \theta_0 \cos(\sqrt{g/\ell}\, t)$ 5. $\theta = \theta_0 \cos \omega t + (v_0/\omega) \sin \omega t$, where $\omega = \sqrt{2k/mr^2}$ 6. $C = 5.1$ lb sec/ft.
7. a) $x = C_1 \cos \omega t + C_2 \sin \omega t + (\omega^2 A/(\omega^2 - \alpha^2)) \sin \alpha t$, where $\omega = \sqrt{k/m}$
   b) $x = C_1 \cos \omega t + C_2 \sin \omega t - (\omega A/2)t \cos \omega t$, with $\omega = \sqrt{k/m}$

Miscellaneous Problems Chapter 13, pp. 639–640

1. $\ln(C \ln y) = -\tan^{-1} x$ 2. $y = [Cx^3 + 2(x+1)^3][(x+1)^3 - Cx^3]^{-1}$ 3. $y = \ln(C - \frac{1}{3}e^{-3x})$ 4. $ky + \sqrt{k^2 y^2 - 1} = Ce^{kx}$
5. $y^2 + \sqrt{y^4 + 1} = Ce^{2x}$ 6. $x^2 + xy - y^2 = C$ 7. $y^2 = x^2 + Cx$ 8. $y + \sqrt{x^2 + y^2} = Cx^2$ 9. $y = x \tan^{-1}(\ln Cx)$
10. $y = xe^{\sqrt{2 \ln Cx}}$ 11. $y = (x^2 + 2)/4 + Cx^{-2}$ 12. $y - x \sec y = C$ 13. $y = \cosh x \ln(C \cosh x)$
14. $y = \frac{1}{6}(2x^3 + 3x^2 + C)(x+1)^{-2}$ 15. $y^3 + 3xy^2 + 3(x+y) = C$ 16. $x^3 + 3xy + 3e^y = C$ 17. $x^3 + 3xy^2 + 3 \sinh y = C$
18. $e^x + x \ln y + y = C$ 19. $x^2 + e^y(x^2 + y^2 - 2y + 2) = C$ 20. $2x \tan^{-1}(y/x) + y \ln(x^2 + y^2) - 2 \cos x - (y+1)^2 = C$
21. $y = C$, or $y = a \tan(ax + C)$, or $y = -a \tanh(ax + C)$, or $y = -1/(x + C)$ 22. $x = C_1 \cos 2y + C_2 \sin 2y$
23. $y = -\ln|\cos(x + C)| + D$ 24. $x = \pm(y + C)$, or $x + C_2 = \ln \cosh(y + C_1)$, or $x + C_2 = \ln \sinh(y + C_1)$
25. $y = \frac{1}{2}(\ln Cx)^2 + D$ 26. $y = C_1 e^x + C_2 e^{3x}$ 27. $y = C_1 + (C_2 x + C_3)e^x$ 28. $y = C_1 \sin 2x + C_2 \cos 2x + (x/2) \sin 2x + \frac{1}{4} \cos 2x \ln \cos 2x$ 29. $y = C_1 e^{-x} + (C_2 + x/3)e^{2x}$ 30. $y = e^x(C_1 \cos 2x + C_2 \sin 2x) + \frac{1}{8}e^{-x}$ 31. $y = C_1\sqrt{x} + C_2/\sqrt{x}$
33. $\frac{3}{2}x^2 + y^2 = D$ 34. $x^2 + (y - D)^2 = D^2$ 35. $y^2 = D^2 + 2Dx$ 36. $y = 10 \cos 10t + 5 \sin 10t$
37. a) $y = C_1 \cos 4x + C_2 \sin 4x$ b) $y = \frac{5}{4} \sin 4x$ 38. a) $y = C_1 e^{4x} + C_2 e^{-4x}$ b) $y = \frac{5}{8}e^{4x} - \frac{5}{8}e^{-4x}$
39. a) $x = C_1 e^{3t} + C_2 e^{-t}$ b) $x = 2e^{-t}$ 40. a) $y = e^{-t}(C_1 \cos 2t + C_2 \sin 2t)$ b) $y = e^{-t}(3 \cos 2t + 4 \sin 2t)$
41. a) $y = C_1 e^{2x} + C_2 e^{-2x} - \frac{1}{3}e^x$ b) $y = e^{2x} - \frac{2}{3}e^{-2x} - \frac{1}{3}e^x$

INDEX